Scott, Foresman

GEOMETRY

Teacher's
Edition

CHRISTIAN R. HIRSCH

HAROLD L. SCHOEN

ANDREW J. SAMIDE

DWIGHT O. COBLENTZ

MARY ANN NORTON

◆

Scott, Foresman and Company
Editorial Offices: Glenview, Illinois

Regional Offices: Sunnyvale, California
Tucker, Georgia ▪ Glenview, Illinois
Oakland, New Jersey ▪ Dallas, Texas

ABOUT THE COVER: The *Scott, Foresman GEOMETRY* cover pictures a cluster of ordinary soap bubbles.

Authors

Christian R. Hirsch

Dr. Hirsch is a Professor of Mathematics at Western Michigan University, Kalamazoo, Michigan. He received his Ph.D. in mathematics education from The University of Iowa. He has had extensive high school and college teaching experience. Dr. Hirsch was a member of the NCTM's Commission on Standards for School Mathematics and Chairman of its Working Group on Curriculum for Grades 9-12. He is the author of numerous articles in mathematics education journals and is the editor of three NCTM publications, including *The 1985 Yearbook on The Secondary School Mathematics Curriculum.*

Harold L. Schoen

Dr. Schoen is a Professor of Mathematics and Education at The University of Iowa, Iowa City, Iowa. He received his Ph.D. in mathematics education from The Ohio State University. His 25 years as a mathematics educator includes teaching high school and university mathematics and methods courses for teachers. Dr. Schoen is active in professional organizations such as NCTM, in which he recently served on the NCTM Commission on Standards for School Mathematics as a member of the Working Group on Curriculum for Grades 9-12. He has published numerous articles on the teaching and learning of mathematics in professional journals and texts.

Andrew J. Samide

Mr. Samide is a teacher of mathematics at Wheaton North High School, Wheaton, Illinois. He received his Master of Science degree in education from Illinois State University, Normal, Illinois. Mr. Samide has had extensive teaching experience in Illinois schools. He is an active member of NCTM and of the Illinois Council of Teachers of Mathematics. Mr. Samide is a current recipient of the Illinois Council of Teachers of Mathematics T. E. Rine Aware for excellence in the teaching of mathematics.

Dwight O. Coblentz

Dr. Coblentz is the Director of Curriculum and Staff Development, San Diego County Office of Education, San Diego, California. He holds a Ph.D. in mathematics education from Northwestern University, Evanston, Illinois. Dr. Coblentz has had many years' experience as a school administrator, and is an active member of NCTM, the California Mathematics Council, and the National Council of Supervisors of Mathematics.

Mary Ann Norton

Dr. Norton is Director of Mathematics, K-12, for Spring Independent School District in Houston, Texas. She holds a Ph.D. in mathematics education from Texas A & M University. Dr. Norton has served the Educational Testing Service in various capacities. She is active in NCTM, the National Council of Supervisors of Mathematics, and the Mathematical Association of America.

Readers and Consultants

Cecilia Cooper

Ms. Cooper teaches mathematics at William Rainey Harper College in Palatine, Illinois. She holds a Master of Science degree in mathematics from the University of Notre Dame. Ms. Cooper has also taught at Mundelein College in Chicago; Kendall College in Evanston, Illinois; and Loyola Academy in Wilmette, Illinois.

Robert Hamada

Mr. Hamada is a mathematics specialist in the Los Angeles Unified School District. He holds master's degrees from Oregon State University and the University of Southern California. He has taught at the junior and senior high school levels, as well as at the college level. Mr. Hamada is an active member of NCTM, the National Council of Supervisors of Mathematics, and the California Mathematics Council.

Shirley Ross

Mrs. Ross is Mathematics Chairperson and Computer Lab Coordinator at South Shore Community Academy, Chicago. She received her Master of Science degree in education from Governor State University, Park Forest, Illinois. Mrs. Ross has had extensive teaching experience at the high school level and has served as lecturer for Chicago Citywide College. She has written mathematics curricula for the Chicago Board of Education and is active in NCTM.

ISBN: 0-673-45253-0

Copyright © 1990
Scott, Foresman and Company, Glenview, Illinois
All Rights Reserved
Printed in the United States of America

1 2 3 4 5 6 7 8 9-VHJ-99 98 97 96 95 94 93 92 91 90

Editorial development and design:
Scott, Foresman staff
Edward Hughes Design
Rusty Kane Design
Ernestine Giesecke Production

Contents

G · E · O · M

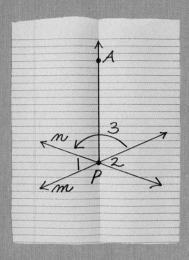

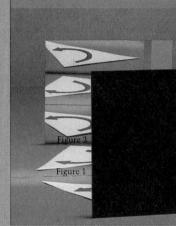

Concepts are developed carefully through a variety of methods to ensure student understanding.

Real-world applications help students see the relevance of mathematics.

Connections are made *within* geometry and *between* algebra and geometry.

Timely tools offer ongoing maintenance and assessment of skills.

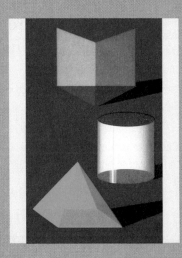

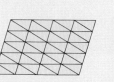

Excursion: Nonperiodic Te

The first two tessellations, or tilings, u
triangle. The one on the right uses a c
and "darts."

A tiling that fits on itself when slid is
cannot fit onto itself when slid is calle

CHAPTER 2

Reasoning

Chapter Overview

This chapter sets the stage for
opment of geometric proof thr
of inductive and deductive reas
ductive reasoning is introduced
means of discovering relations
may later be proved by deduct
Students are encouraged to lo
terns, make conjectures and th
verify with further examples or
with a counterexample.
    Parallel lines and angle relati
also introduced. Students are
to make conjectures about the
lationships.
    The "if . . . then" statement
duced as a way to express co
statements, and related forms
inverse and contrapositive) are
Students are shown how to us
only if" sentence to rewrite de
    The study of deductive reas
gun with two laws of logic: affi
hypothesis and the Transitive

Teacher's Resource File
includes five books:

1. Worksheets
2. Extensions
3. Teacher Aids
4. Computer Materials
5. Tests

Visual Aids
Solution Key

Computer material is integrated throughout as a means of exploration and discovery.

Provisions for student ability differences help all your students succeed.

The comprehensive Teacher's Edition meets *your* needs.

A wealth of components cuts your preparation time.

1-4 Segments and Rays

Using a laser beam, scientists have measured the distance to the moon to within 6 cm. A beam of light from an observatory at A is aimed at a reflecting surface at B on the moon. The time required for the light to travel to the moon and back is measured. Points A and B together with the points on the path of the beam between A and B provide a physical model of a line segment.

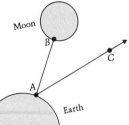

Moon

Earth

Not to scale

4-7 The Angles of a Triangle

A physical model frequently suggests relationships that can be established by proof. Trace $\triangle ABC$ and cut out your triangle. Fold it so that B lies on $\overline{AC}$ and the fold is parallel to $\overline{AC}$ as shown. Then fold it so that A and C are at B.

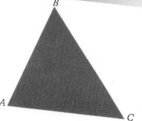

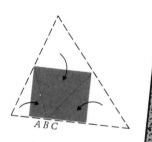

$A\ B\ C$

It appears that $m\angle A + m\angle B + m\angle C = 180$. Try this with several different triangles. Your results should suggest Theorem 4-14.

Theorem 4-14

The sum of the measures of the angles of a triangle is 180.

D B E

Checking for Understanding

How many endpoints does each figure have?

1. A segment   **2.** A ray   **3.** A line

Name the endpoint(s)

4. of $\overline{DE}$.   **5.** of $\overrightarrow{PQ}$.

6. Do $\overline{AB}$ and $\overline{BA}$ name the same segment? Explain.

7. Name the intersection of $\overline{AB}$ and $\overrightarrow{AB}$.

8. Do $\overrightarrow{ST}$ and $\overrightarrow{TS}$ name the same ray? Explain.

9. Must $\overrightarrow{QP}$ and $\overrightarrow{QR}$ be opposite rays? Explain.

10. Must $\overrightarrow{QP}$ and $\overrightarrow{QR}$ be opposite rays if Q, P, and R are collinear? Explain.

plane contain its edge?

Ideas are introduced in real-world settings to help students see the relevance of geometry and to motivate them to want to learn more.

Concrete models are shown throughout to promote hands-on learning experiences.

Checking for Understanding exercises are included in every lesson to make sure that students have mastered one level of understanding before moving on to the next.

Thinking Ahead On a sheet of lined paper, use a straightedge to darken two lines with your pencil or pen as shown in the photo. Call these lines *r* and *s*. Draw a transversal *t* to *r* and *s*, labeling ∠1, ∠2, ∠3, and ∠4 as shown.

38. Trace each angle on another sheet of paper. Can you fit ∠1 exactly over ∠2?

39. Repeat Exercise 38 with other lines and transversals. What conjecture is suggested?

40. For each set of parallel lines and transversals, find m∠1 + m∠3 and m∠4 + m∠2. What conjecture can you make?

Construction Exercises

Construction 6

Through a point not on a given line, construct a line parallel to the given line.

Given Line ℓ; point *P* not on line ℓ

Construct A line through *P* parallel to ℓ

Method Step 1: Mark any point *A* on ℓ. Draw $\overleftrightarrow{AP}$ to determine ∠1.

Step 2: Using $\overrightarrow{AP}$ as one ray, construct ∠2 on the same side of $\overrightarrow{AP}$ as ∠1 so that m∠1 = m∠2. Label as *Q* the point where the arcs meet.

Step 3: Draw $\overleftrightarrow{PQ}$. Then $\overleftrightarrow{PQ} \parallel ℓ$.

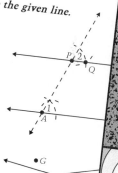

Trace the drawing at the right as needed.

1. Construct a line through *G* and parallel to *n*.

2. Construct a line through *G* and parallel to *t*.

Oboes

Computer Activities: Drawing and Measuring

1. Draw segment *AB*. Then draw $\overline{CD}$, with *C* on $\overline{AB}$ and *D* not on $\overline{AB}$. Measure the two angles formed at *C*. What is the sum of their measures?

2. Using the same drawing, choose points *E*, *F*, *G*, . . . , not on $\overline{AB}$ and draw $\overline{CE}$, $\overline{CF}$, $\overline{CG}$, . . . In each case, what is the sum of the measures of the two angles formed by the $\overline{AB}$ and the second segment?

3. What conjecture can you make regarding the measures of linear pairs of angles?

Challenge

A farmer wants to plant 9 trees in groups of 3. The trees in each group of 3 are to be collinear. Draw a diagram showing the maximum number of groups.

2-4 *Reasoning from "If . . . Then" Statements*

8-3 Special Right Triangles

An architect is going to use glass panels, many of which are shaped like equilateral triangles, to build a geodesic dome. She plans to first make a model of the dome using Plexiglas. How many equilateral triangles with sides of length 2.4 inches can she cut from one sheet of Plexiglas, 24 inches by 36 inches, if she minimizes the waste?

Rows of triangles can be arranged on the Plexiglas in two ways.

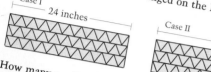

Case I
24 inches

Case II
36 inches

How many equilateral triangles are in each row? How many rows can be laid out in each case? What do you need to know about the triangular pieces in order to find the number of rows? Use Theorem 8-6 to help you. The proof is left to Exercise 29.

By Theorem 8-6, $BC = AC\sqrt{3}$. Therefore, $BC = (5\sqrt{21})\sqrt{3} = 15\sqrt{7}$.

A baseball diamond is a square with sides that are 90 feet long. The distance d from home plate to second base is the length of a diagonal of the square. Since the diagonal divides the square into two 45-45-90 triangles, d is also the hypotenuse of the triangles. Theorem 8-8 shows a way to find d. Its proof is left to Exercise 27.

"in a plane," would it be a true statement? Explain.

27. Next to the painting is a plumb line (weight hanging by a string). Is the plumb line perpendicular to the horizontal line where the wall and the floor meet?

28. Use Theorem 4-1 to explain how the plumb line can be used to straighten the painting.

29. Explain how to use a carpenter's square to get a shelf parallel to a shelf that is already on a wall. Which theorem verifies that the shelves are parallel?

Set C   30. Prove: If two parallel lines are cut by a transversal,

T8

REAL-WORLD APPLICATIONS HELP STUDENTS SEE THE RELEVANCE OF MATHEMATICS

Applications involving careers show the usefulness of geometry and encourage students to further their study of mathematics.

Frequent real-world examples help students apply what they are studying and promote a deeper understanding of the content.

Applications in all exercise sets continually show students how the content applies to their world, answering the question, "When am I going to use this?"

Example 5

a. Use the parallel lines on a sheet of notebook paper as a guide to draw two parallel lines, ℓ and m.
b. Draw a transversal t. Label $\angle 1$ and $\angle 2$ as shown.
c. Place tracing paper over your figure and trace ℓ, m, and t. Label the traced figure ℓ', m', and t'. Label $\angle 1'$ and $\angle 2'$.
d. Slide the tracing paper along t, keeping t' over t, until ℓ coincides with m.

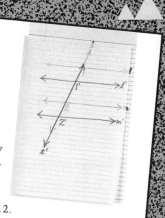

Repeat this activity with several other pairs of parallel lines. Draw the transversals so that the angles formed have different measures. What conjecture about corresponding angles is suggested?

Solution

In each case, $\angle 1'$ coincides with $\angle 2$. This suggests that $m\angle 1 = m\angle 2$. These are corresponding angles. The conjecture is: If two parallel lines are cut by a transversal, then corresponding angles are equal.

As you think about these exploratory activities, remember that they only *suggest* conjectures. Writing proofs for conjectures, including some of those in these examples, is in Chapter 3.

Example 3

Coordinates of the vertices of trapezoid QRST are Q(0, −2), R(10, −2), S(8, 3), and T(2, 3). $\overline{TS}$ is parallel to $\overline{QR}$. Is QRST an isosceles trapezoid?

Solution

Determine the length of each leg.

$$QT = \sqrt{(2-0)^2 + (3-(-2))^2}$$
$$= \sqrt{4+25}$$
$$= \sqrt{29}$$

$$RS = \sqrt{(8-10)^2 + (3-(-2))^2}$$
$$= \sqrt{4+25}$$
$$= \sqrt{29}$$

Since QT = RS, trapezoid QRST is isosceles.

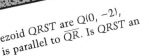

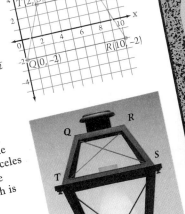

Sometimes lamps have decorative wire inserts in front of the glass panels. These wires represent the diagonals of an isosceles trapezoid. What appears to be true about $\overline{QS}$ and $\overline{TR}$? The answer to this question is verified by Theorem 6-15, which is ... cise 17.

Algebra Review: Solving Quadratic Equations

Examples

1. Solve $x^2 + 4x - 12 = 0$ by factoring.

2. Solve $x^2 + 9x - 2 = 0$ by using the quadratic formula at the right. $x = \dfrac{-b \pm \sqrt{b^2 - 4ac}}{2a}$

Solutions

1. $x^2 + 4x - 12 = 0$
   $(x + 6)(x - 2) = 0$
   $x + 6 = 0$ or $(x - 2) = 0$
   $x = -6$ or $x = 2$

2. $x = \dfrac{-9 \pm \sqrt{9^2 - (4)(1)(-2)}}{(2)(1)}$ *Here, a = 1, b = 9, and c = −2.*

   $= \dfrac{-9 \pm \sqrt{89}}{2}$

   $x = \dfrac{-9 + \sqrt{89}}{2}$ or $\dfrac{-9 - \sqrt{89}}{2}$

Solve by the method of your choice.

1. $x^2 + 4x - 21 = 0$
2. $x^2 - 10x - 39 = 0$
3. $x^2 - 3x = 3$
4. $x^2 - 16 = 0$
5. $x^2 + 4x - 2 = 0$
6. $x^2 + 5x = 0$
7. $9x^2 + 12x = -4$
8. $2x^2 - 3x - 20 = 0$
9. $x^2 = 81$

Connections are made throughout the text between synthetic, coordinate, and transformational geometric approaches to ensure that students get a complete view of mathematics.

Students also make connections between geometry and algebra through an emphasis on coordinate geometry and on frequent algebra reviews. Students see how various topics are related and strengthen their ability to formulate and analyze problems within and outside of mathematics.

At least one Algebra Review per chapter and **Algebra Review Worksheets** in the Teacher's Resource File ensure that students maintain the algebra skills they need in geometry and in future courses.

    Five review exercises in every lesson review important concepts in the previous two lessons and in earlier lessons to promote skills maintenance.

Two Progress Checks in each chapter can be used for students to check their own progress or as quizzes. Also, for each chapter there is a mid-chapter quiz in the Teacher's Resource File to help you spot problem areas before moving on.

Algebra Review: Equation for a Line in Slope-Intercept Form

Example

A line with slope $m = 6$ contains the point with coordinates $(-1, 4)$. Write the equation of the line in slope-intercept form.

Solution

The line has equation $y = mx + b$. We are given $m = 6$.

  $y = 6x + b$ *Substitute 6 for m.*

  $4 = 6(-1) + b$ *Substitute −1 for x and 4 for y.*

  $4 = -6 + b$ *Simplify.*

  $10 = b$ *Add 6 to both sides of the equation.*

  $y = 6x + 10$ *Substitute 10 for b in the original equation.*

Write the equation in slope-intercept form for the line with the given slope through the given point.

1. $m = 2$; $(3, 5)$ **2.** $m = 5$; $(1, -3)$ **3.** $m = -1$; $(0,4)$ **4.** $m = 1$; $(0, 4$

                                          $-3)$ **8.** $m = -\frac{1}{2}$; $(-$

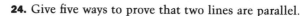

Review   **23.** Given $\ell \parallel m$, if $m\angle 1 = 4x$ and $m\angle 2 = 10x + 12$, then $x = \underline{?}$.

24. Give five ways to prove that two lines are parallel.

25. Given $\overleftrightarrow{AB} \parallel \overleftrightarrow{CD}$, $\overleftrightarrow{DE} \perp \overleftrightarrow{AB}$, and $\overleftrightarrow{BF} \perp \overleftrightarrow{CD}$, what postulate(s) or theorem(s) explain why $\overleftrightarrow{DE} \parallel \overleftrightarrow{BF}$?

26. $\angle P$ and $\angle Q$ are both supplements of $\angle R$. If $m\angle P = 38$, then $m\angle Q = \underline{?}$.

27. How many planes contain three noncollinear points?

Progress Check

Lesson 9-1, page 375

For $\odot A$, identify each of the following.

1. A radius   **2.** A diameter

3. A secant   **4.** A chord

5. Write the equation of $\odot A$.

Lesson 9-2, page 381

$\overleftrightarrow{PS}$ and $\overleftrightarrow{PT}$ are tangent to $\odot W$ at S and T.

6. $PS = \underline{?}$ **7.** $m\angle PSW = \underline{?}$

8. Draw two internally tangent circles.

Lesson 9-3, page 387

In $\odot Q$, $AB = 24$, $QA = 13$, and $QX = QY$.

9. $XB = \underline{?}$ **10.** $QX = \underline{?}$ **11.** $CD = \underline{?}$

Lesson 9-4, page 392

12. Define *incircle*.   **13.** Define *circumcenter*.

14. The $\underline{?}$ of $\triangle FGH$ is equidistant from F, G, and H.

15. The $\underline{?}$ of $\triangle FGH$ is equidistant from $\overline{FG}$, $\overline{GH}$, and $\overline{HF}$.

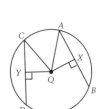

Chapter 3 Summary

Important Terms

Diagram (96)
Given (96)
Inventory of geometric facts (115)

Plan for Proof (116)
Proof (95)
Prove (96)
Theorem (95)

Two-column proof (96)
Working backward (122)
Working forward (121)
Working forward/backward (122)

Important Ideas

1. A theorem is a statement that is proved. (95)
2. A proof in two-column form consists of a diagram, the Given, the Prove, and a list of statements with reasons. (96)
3. The reasons in a proof can be definitions, postulates, properties of real numbers, previo... Given. (96)
4. The hypothesis of a conditional p... information; the conclusion indic...
5. Some important theorems are:
   a. If two lines intersect, then they one point. (101)
   b. A line and a point not on the l... and only one plane. (101)
   c. Supplements of equal angles ar...
   d. Complements of equal angles a...
   e. Vertical angles are equal. (116)
   f. If the angles of a linear pair are containing their sides are perpe...
   g. Two perpendicular lines interse... angles. (126)
6. Strategies that are helpful in plan... forward from the Given, working... and a combination of these two. (...
7. The steps of the proof-writing pr...
   1. Restate the statement in "if . .
   2. Draw and label a diagram.
   3. Write the Given and Prove in te...
   4. Develop a Plan for Proof.
   5. Write a proof in two-column fo...

132   **Chapter 3** *Proof in Geometry*

Chapter 3 Review

Lesson 3-1, page 95

1. Supply the missing parts in the proof.
   Given: $m\angle 1 + m\angle 2 + m\angle 3 = 180$
   Prove: $m\angle 1 + m\angle 2 = m\angle 4$

Statements	Reasons
1. $\perp$	1. Given
2. $\angle 4$ and $\angle 3$ are supp.	2. $\perp$
3. $m\angle 4 + m\angle 3 = 180$	3. $\perp$ $\lfloor \perp \rfloor$
4. $m\angle 1 + m\angle 2 + m\angle 3 = m\angle 4 + m\angle 3$	4. $\perp$ $\lfloor \perp \rfloor$
5. $\perp$	5. Reflexive Prop.
6. $\perp$	6. Subtraction Prop. [4, 5]

Lesson 3-2, page 101

Use a straightedge to draw a diagram for the given information.

2. $\angle 1$ and $\angle 2$ are complements of $\angle 3$.
3. $\overrightarrow{XY}$ is the perpen...
4. $\angle 4$ and $\angle 5$ are ad...
5. Draw a diagram t... following statem... linear pair.

Lesson 3-3, page 10...

6. Write the proof v...
   Given: $m\angle ABC =$
   Prove: $m\angle ABD =$

Statements
a. $m\angle ABC + m\angle$
b. $m\angle ABC = m\angle$
c. $m\angle ABD = m\angle$
d. $m\angle DBE + m\angle$
e. $m\angle ABC + m\angle$
$m\angle DBE + m\angle$
f. $m\angle CBD = m\angle$

Lesson 3-4, page 11...

Use the inventory ...

Chapter 3 Test

Is each statement *true* or *false*? If false, give a counterexample.

1. A line and a point not on the line are coplanar.
2. If $m\angle 1 = m\angle 2$, then $\angle 1$ and $\angle 2$ are vertical angles.
3. If two equal angles form a linear pair, each is a right angle.
4. Two different lines may have two different points in common.
5. If $\angle 1$ and $\angle 2$ are complementary to the same angle, then $m\angle 1 = m\angle 2$.
6. Find $m\angle QOS$, given $m\angle TOR = m\angle ROV$ and $m\angle SOT = 10$.
7. Find $m\angle VOW$, given $m\angle SOR = 110$ and $\overrightarrow{QR} \perp \overrightarrow{TV}$.

8. Find x, y, $m\angle ABE$, and $m\angle CBE$.

Cumulative Review   Chapters 1–3

Select the best answer for each item.

1. A tabletop suggests a $\perp$.
   A. Point
   B. Line
   C. Ray
   D. Plane

2. Points A, B, and C are contained in both plane $\mathcal{H}$ and plane $\mathcal{E}$. Which of these statements must be true?
   A. A, B, and C are noncoplanar.
   B. A, B, and C are collinear.
   C. B is between A and C.
   D. $\overleftrightarrow{AB}$ and $\overrightarrow{BC}$ are noncoplanar.

3. On a number line, the graph of $y \geq 2$ is a $\perp$.
   A. Line
   B. Half-plane
   C. Segment
   D. Ray

4. If B is between A and C on $\overline{AC}$ such that $AB = BC$, then B is a(n) $\perp$.
   A. Vertex
   B. Midpoint
   C. Coordinate
   D. Endpoint

5. Given half-plane $\mathcal{H}$ with edge $\overrightarrow{AB}$, there is exactly one angle, $\angle BAC$, such that $m\angle BAC = 50$. This result is guaranteed by the $\perp$ Postulate.
   A. Protractor
   B. Angle Construction
   C. Angle Addition
   D. Angle Bisector

7. If two angles form a linear pair, they are also $\perp$.
   A. Vertical and opposite
   B. Acute and complementary
   C. Equal and right
   D. Adjacent and supplementary

8. Watching from a window, you see three red cars go by in a row. If you predict that the fourth car to go by will also be red, you are using $\perp$.
   A. Inductive reasoning
   B. Deductive reasoning
   C. Mathematical models
   D. Argument by counterexample

9. If $\overleftrightarrow{AB}$ and $\overleftrightarrow{CD}$ are noncoplanar and have no points in common, they are $\perp$.
   A. Parallel
   B. Skew
   C. Perpendicular
   D. Transversals

10. Corresponding parts of congruent triangles are equal. In "if . . . then" form, this statement is:
    A. If two triangles are congruent, then their corresponding parts are equal.
    B. If two triangles have equal parts, then the parts are corresponding.
    C. If a part of one triangle is equal to the corresponding part of another triangle, then the triangles are

135

A **Chapter Summary** lists the vocabulary and summarizes the important ideas in the chapter to help students review.

A **Chapter Review** keyed to the lessons prepares students for the Chapter Test.

Chapter Tests, including one in the Student Edition and three per chapter in the Teacher's Resource File, give you options for assessing mastery.

Multiple-choice **Cumulative Reviews** prepare students for standardized testing. In addition, the Teacher's Resource File has **Cumulative Tests** in multiple-choice and free-response forms and four **Practice for Standardized Tests.**

COMPUTER MATERIAL IS INTEGRATED THROUGHOUT FOR EXPLORATION AND DISCOVERY

Computer Activities preview new content by enabling students to use the computer to discover and examine geometric properties and relationships. Additional similar activities are provided in the Teacher's Edition.

Computer Features offer either a *Using Logo* or *Using BASIC* activity that is an extension or application reinforcing the chapter topic.

Computer Activities in the Teacher's Resource File parallel the Computer Activities in the Student and Teacher's Editions and provide record-keeping charts for use with *The Geometric preSupposer* and *Supposer* or *GeoDraw*.

Computer Worksheets in the Teacher's Resource File present simple Logo or BASIC programs that are similar to the computer features in the text and are perfect for extra practice.

Calculator use is suggested throughout the Student and Teacher's Editions.

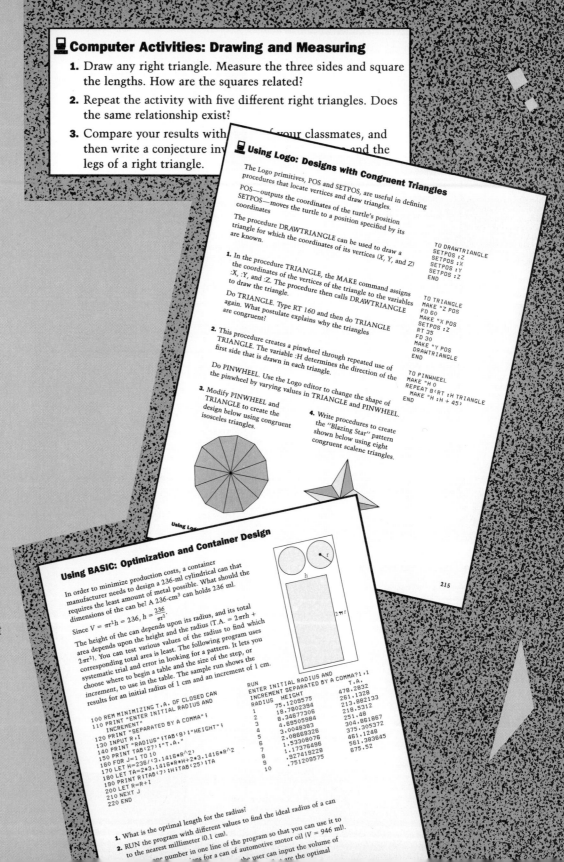

💻 Computer Activities: Drawing and Measuring

1. Draw any right triangle. Measure the three sides and square the lengths. How are the squares related?

2. Repeat the activity with five different right triangles. Does the same relationship exist?

3. Compare your results with ~~~~~ of your classmates, and then write a conjecture inv~~~~~ ~~~~~ and the legs of a right triangle.

💻 Using Logo: Designs with Congruent Triangles

The Logo primitives, POS and SETPOS, are useful in defining procedures that locate vertices and draw triangles.
POS—outputs the coordinates of the turtle's position
SETPOS—moves the turtle to a position specified by its coordinates

The procedure DRAWTRIANGLE can be used to draw a triangle for which the coordinates of its vertices (X, Y, and Z) are known.

1. In the procedure TRIANGLE, the MAKE command assigns the coordinates of the vertices of the triangle to the variables :X, :Y, and :Z. The procedure then calls DRAWTRIANGLE to draw the triangle.
Do TRIANGLE. Type RT 160 and then do TRIANGLE again. What postulate explains why the triangles are congruent?

2. This procedure creates a pinwheel through repeated use of TRIANGLE. The variable :H determines the direction of the first side that is drawn in each triangle.
Do PINWHEEL. Use the Logo editor to change the shape of the pinwheel by varying values in TRIANGLE and PINWHEEL.

3. Modify PINWHEEL and TRIANGLE to create the design below using congruent isosceles triangles.

4. Write procedures to create the "Blazing Star" pattern shown below using eight congruent scalene triangles.

```
TO DRAWTRIANGLE
SETPOS :Z
SETPOS :X
SETPOS :Y
SETPOS :Z
END

TO TRIANGLE
MAKE "Z POS
FD 60
MAKE "X POS
SETPOS :Z
RT 35
FD 30
MAKE "Y POS
DRAWTRIANGLE
END

TO PINWHEEL
MAKE "H 0
REPEAT 8[RT :H TRIANGLE
MAKE "H :H + 45]
END
```

Using Lo~~~~~

215

Using BASIC: Optimization and Container Design

In order to minimize production costs, a container manufacturer needs to design a 236-ml cylindrical can that requires the least amount of metal possible. What should the dimensions of the can be? A 236-cm³ can holds 236 ml.

Since $V = \pi r^2 h = 236$, $h = \dfrac{236}{\pi r^2}$.

The height of the can depends upon its radius, and its total area depends upon the height and the radius (T.A. $= 2\pi rh + 2\pi r^2$). You can test various values of the radius to find which corresponding total area is least. The following program uses systematic trial and error in looking for a pattern. It lets you choose where to begin a table and the size of the step, or increment, to use in the table. The sample run shows the results for an initial radius of 1 cm and an increment of 1 cm.

```
100 REM MINIMIZING T.A. OF CLOSED CAN
110 PRINT "ENTER INITIAL RADIUS AND
    INCREMENT"
120 PRINT "SEPARATED BY A COMMA";
130 INPUT R,I
140 PRINT "RADIUS"TAB(9)"HEIGHT";
150 PRINT TAB(27)"T.A."
160 FOR J=1 TO 10
170 LET H=236/(3.1416*R^2)
180 LET TA=2*3.1416*R*H+2*3.1416*R^2
190 PRINT R;TAB(7)H;TAB(25)TA
200 LET R=R+I
210 NEXT J
220 END
```

```
RUN
ENTER INITIAL RADIUS AND
INCREMENT SEPARATED BY A COMMA?1,1
RADIUS   HEIGHT              T.A.
1        75.1209575          478.2832
2        18.7802394          261.1328
3        8.34677306          213.882133
4        4.69505984          218.5312
5        3.0048383           251.48
6        2.08669326          304.861867
7        1.53308076          375.305372
8        1.17376496          461.1248
9        .927419228          561.383645
10       .751209575          675.52
```

1. What is the optimal length for the radius?

2. RUN the program with different values to find the ideal radius of a can to the nearest millimeter (0.1 cm).

~~~~~ne number in one line of the program so that you can use it to ~~~~~~s for a can of automotive motor oil (V = 946 ml).
~~~~~ the user can input the volume of
~~~~~~ are the optimal

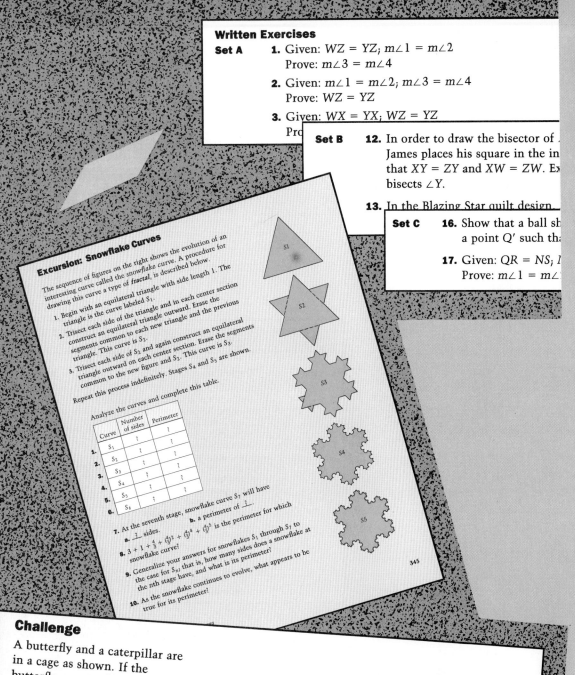

Written Exercises

Set A
1. Given: $WZ = YZ$; $m\angle 1 = m\angle 2$
   Prove: $m\angle 3 = m\angle 4$

2. Given: $m\angle 1 = m\angle 2$; $m\angle 3 = m\angle 4$
   Prove: $WZ = YZ$

3. Given: $WX = YX$; $WZ = YZ$
   Pr...

Set B
12. In order to draw the bisector of ∠... James places his square in the in... that $XY = ZY$ and $XW = ZW$. Ex... bisects ∠Y.

13. In the Blazing Star quilt design...

Set C
16. Show that a ball sh... a point Q' such tha...

17. Given: $QR = NS$; ...
    Prove: $m\angle 1 = m\angle$...

Excursion: Snowflake Curves

The sequence of figures on the right shows the evolution of an interesting curve called the *snowflake curve*. A procedure for drawing this curve a type of *fractal*, is described below.

1. Begin with an equilateral triangle with side length 1. The triangle is the curve labeled S_1.

2. Trisect each side of the triangle and in each center section construct an equilateral triangle outward. Erase the segments common to each new triangle and the previous triangle. This curve is S_2.

3. Trisect each side of S_2 and again construct an equilateral triangle outward on each center section. Erase the segments common to the new figure and S_2. This curve is S_3.

Repeat this process indefinitely. Stages S_4 and S_5 are shown.

Analyze the curves and complete this table.

Curve	Number of sides	Perimeter
1. S_1	?	?
2. S_2	?	?
3. S_3	?	?
4. S_4	?	?
5. S_5	?	?
6. S_6	?	?

7. At the seventh stage, snowflake curve S_7 will have
   a. ? sides.
   b. a perimeter of ?.

8. $3 + 1 + \frac{4}{3} + (\frac{4}{3})^2 + (\frac{4}{3})^4 + (\frac{4}{3})^5$ is the perimeter for which snowflake curve?

9. Generalize your answers for snowflakes S_1 through S_7 to the case for S_n; that is, how many sides does a snowflake at the nth stage have, and what is its perimeter?

10. As the snowflake continues to evolve, what appears to be true for its perimeter?

345

Challenge

A butterfly and a caterpillar are in a cage as shown. If the butterfly were to fly in a direct path to escape through the opening, what is the shortest path? How long is it? What is the shortest path the caterpillar could take to escape from the cage?

12 in.   8 in.
9 in.

THE COMPREHENSIVE TEACHER'S EDITION MEETS YOUR NEEDS

A **Professional Sourcebook for Teachers** offers timely information on **Levels of Geometric Learning, Reasoning and Proof,** and **Computers in the Classroom.** *See pages T17–T25.*

Before each chapter, you'll find a Chapter Overview, **which discusses background information;** Perspectives, which provide the rationale for each lesson; and a **Pacing Chart,** which provides you with plans for three ability levels.

Warm-Up Review helps students maintain skills by reviewing material from earlier in the text and by reviewing skills, such as algebra, that they need for the lesson.

Teacher Resources lists all of the worksheets, materials, computer activities, etc., that you need for the lesson.

Objective is written in terms of student understanding and application of proof.

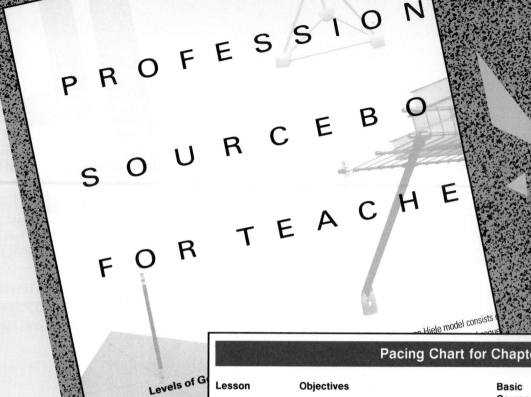

PROFESSIONAL SOURCEBOOK FOR TEACHERS

Levels of G...

... Hiele model consists

Pacing Chart for Chapter

Lesson	Objectives	Basic Course
2–1	Use inductive reasoning to discover mathematical relationships; recognize real-world applications of inductive reasoning.	1
2–2	Make conjectures based upon exploration; recognize parallel and skew lines and angles formed when two lines are cut by a transversal.	1
2–3	Write statements in "if . . . then" form; identify the hypothesis and conclusion of a conditional; use Venn diagrams.	$1\frac{1}{2}$
2–4	Use affirming-the-hypothesis arguments to draw necessary conclusions.	$1\frac{1}{2}$
2–5	Use the Transitive Property for Conditionals and affirming the hypothesis with deductive arguments; justify numerical and geometric relationships.	$1\frac{1}{2}$

CHAPTER 2

Reasoning in Geometry

Chapter Overview

This chapter sets the stage for the development of geometric proof through a study of inductive and deductive reasoning. Inductive reasoning is introduced as a means of discovering relationships that may later be proved by deductive methods. Students are encouraged to look for patterns, make conjectures and then either verify with further examples or disprove with a counterexample.

... lines and angle relationships are ... are encouraged

Three points about indu... should be emphasized: (1) ... reasoning to find patterns ... **problem-solving strategy:** ... reasoning is used in geom... conjectures about relations... then proved using deducti... and (3) conclusions that s... based on a few cases may ... all cases.

Lesson 2–2 stresses the ... reasoning when making co... important definitions, inclu... relationships created by a ... presented. Before stating ...

Warm-Up Review

1. Lines equidistant from each other are __?__. Parallel
2. Lines that form four 90° angles are __?__. Perpendicular
3. If a segment is split into two congruent parts, it is __?__. Bisected
4. What is the slope of a line parallel to the line whose equation is $y = 3x + 5$? $m = 3$

4-4 Parallels and Perpendiculars to a Line

The fastener attached to the wall is like a point through which the top of the calendar must pass. In how many positions can this calendar hang so that its top edge is parallel to the bottom edge of the wall? The answer suggests Theorem 4-7, Part I of which is to be proved in Exercise 6. Only 1

Theorem 4-7

... point not on a given line, there is exactly one line ... the given line.

... point P not on ℓ

... ough P parallel to ℓ.
... e through P parallel to ℓ.
... t P not on ℓ, choose two
... draw $\overrightarrow{PA}$ by the Line
... alf-plane with edge $\overrightarrow{PA}$ not
... $PA = m\angle PAB$. Then, $\overrightarrow{CP}$

The proof of Theorem 4–7 utilizes an auxiliary line. Emphasize that any line segment or ray can be added to a figure if it can be justified.

As a **group activity**, explore the consequences of deleting the phrase "in a plane" from Theorems 4–8, 4–9 and 4–10.

Discuss lines with zero slopes and undefined slopes.

Additional Examples

Example 1
Write an equation of the line through $(-2, 2)$ parallel to $y = x + 2$. $y = x + 4$

Example 2
Write equations of lines m and n, each passing through the point $(2, 3)$. Line m is perpendicular to $y =$

EXTENSION

Name _____ Lesson 4-4

Mod Art

Some interesting abstract designs can be created by using *modular arithmetic*, or *clock arithmetic*. Addition in modular arithmetic is similar to addition on a clock. For example, in *mod 4* addition, there are four numbers: 0, 1, 2, and 3. Think of a clock with only these four numbers on the face.

To find 1 + 2: Start at 1.
Move clockwise two spaces to 3.

To find 2 + 3: Start at 2.
Move clockwise three spaces to 1.

A complete addition table for *mod 4* arithmetic is shown.

+	0	1	2	3
0	0	1	2	3
1	1	2	3	0
2	2	3	0	1
3	3	0	1	2

To make a design, you can assign a pattern to each number in the table.

On grid paper, place the patterns according to the sums.

By flipping the designs over various borders, you can create an even more complex design.

1. Create another design for *mod 4* addition. Use these patterns.

2.
+	0	1	2	3	4
0	0	1	2	3	4
1	1	2	3	4	0
2	2	3	4	0	1
3	3	4	0	1	2
4	4	0	1	2	3

2. Make a table for addition in *mod 5*. Use this table to make your own design by assigning different patterns for 0, 1, 2, 3, and 4.

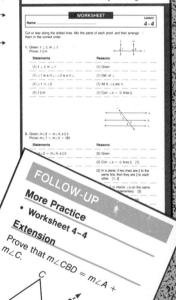

Error Analysis   Students may have the following problems with auxiliary lines:
1. When and where to draw them.
2. Justifying them.

In dealing with the first problem, use the **problem-solving strategy** of testing all possibilities.

Students must be familiar with the appropriate postulates or theorems so they can justify the drawing of any auxiliary line.

EXERCISE NOTES

Exercises 1–14 and **27–29** provide direct application of Theorem 3–8.

Exercises 15–20 are accomplished using the **proof subskill** writing conclusions from given statements.

158

ANSWERS

Written Exercises

6. Proof: 1. Line ℓ with pt. ... on ℓ (Given) 2. Choose 2 ... and B, on ℓ. (Points Post... $\overrightarrow{PA}$. (Line Post. [1, 2]) 4 ... half-plane with edge $\overrightarrow{P}$ ... taining B, draw $\overrightarrow{PC}$ so ... $= m\angle PAB$. (Angle C... $\overrightarrow{CP} \parallel \ell$ (Alt. int. $\angle s \Rightarrow \parallel$ ...

10. Align the square along AB ... shown, but so that P is on the other edge of the tool. Draw $\overrightarrow{PC}$ $\perp \overrightarrow{AB}$ at C. Then align the tool along $\overrightarrow{PC}$ so that the corner of the tool rests at P. Draw $\overrightarrow{PD} \perp \overrightarrow{PC}$ at P. Then $\overrightarrow{PD} \parallel \overrightarrow{AB}$. (In a plane, 2 lines $\perp$ the same line are $\parallel$.)

11. Proof: 1. $p \parallel r$; $m\angle 1 = m\angle 2$

LESSON 4-4

Resources

Compass
Straightedge
Worksheet 4–4
Extension 4–4
💻 Computer Worksheet 4–4

OBJECTIVE

Use theorems about parallels and perpendiculars to a given line through a given point.

TEACHING NOTES

Introduce this lesson by referring to a picture hanging on the classroom bulletin board by a single thumbtack. Challenge students to find more than one way to hang

---

WORKSHEET

Name _____ Lesson 4-4

Cut or tear along the dotted lines. Mix the parts of each proof, and then arrange them in the correct order.

1. Given: $\ell \perp t$; $m \perp t$
   Prove: $\ell \parallel m$

Statements	Reasons
(1) $\ell \perp t$; $m \perp t$	(1) Given
(1) $\angle 1$ is a rt $\angle$; $\angle 2$ is a rt $\angle$	(1) Def. of $\perp$
(1) $\angle 1 = \angle 2$	(1) All rt $\angle$s are $=$.
(1) $\ell \parallel m$	(1) Con. $\angle s = \Rightarrow$ lines $\parallel$

2. Given: $m\angle 2 = m\angle 4$; $a \parallel b$
   Prove: $m\angle 1 + m\angle 4 = 180$

Statements	Reasons
$m\angle 2 = m\angle 4$; $a \parallel b$	(2) Given
	(2) Con. $\angle s = \Rightarrow$ lines $\parallel$ [1]
	(2) In a plane, if two lines $\parallel$ to the same line, then they are $\parallel$ to each other. [1, 2]
	(2) interior $\angle s$ on the same ... omplementary [3]

FOLLOW-UP

More Practice
• **Worksheet 4-4**

Extension
Prove that $m\angle CBD = m\angle A + m\angle C$.

Draw auxiliary $\overrightarrow{BE}$ parallel to $\overrightarrow{AC}$, and show that $m\angle 1 = m\angle C$ and $m\angle 2 = m\angle A$. This previews Theorem 4–18.

• **Extension 4-4**

Computers
• **Computer Worksheet 4-4**

Teaching Notes include computer and calculator references, notes on proof subskills, problem-solving strategies, suggestions for group work and using concrete materials, and much more.

The **Worksheet** is pictured where you need it for your convenience.

Additional Examples parallel those in the text, giving you more opportunities to work with students on problem-solving strategies.

Error Analysis helps you catch student errors—before they occur.

Exercise Notes highlights **proof subskills, calculator and computer use, group activities,** and more for easy reference.

The **Extension** is pictured on the second page of each lesson.

Assignment Guide suggests which exercises to assign to average, basic, and extended ability levels.

Follow-Up includes **More Practice,** which offers **Alternate Approaches** and **Extensions** and frequently provides suggestions for group activities. Periodically, an additional **Computer Activity** gives you even more computer options.

T15

A WEALTH OF COMPONENTS CUTS YOUR PREPARATION TIME

STUDENT EDITION

TEACHER'S EDITION

TEACHER'S RESOURCE FILE is
a welcome, well-organized resource that comes complete with five books:

1. **WORKSHEETS** give you abundant practice and reteaching exercises for each lesson.

2. **EXTENSIONS** offer students a variety of opportunities for going beyond each lesson in the text.

3. **TEACHING AIDS** are Blackline Masters that parallel the Visual Aids (transparencies).

4. **COMPUTER MATERIALS** offer three types of computer help.

COMPUTER HANDBOOK discusses the differences among the available software, including their strengths and weaknesses, to help you decide what's best for you.

COMPUTER ACTIVITIES/ RECORD SHEETS help students keep track of their findings from the computer activities in the text and in the Teacher's Edition. They also help you monitor students' computer work (2 or more per chapter).

COMPUTER WORKSHEETS are easy-to-use one-page programs for both Logo and BASIC (2–3 per chapter).

5. **TESTS** have a variety of forms and functions.

READINESS TEST AND WORKSHEETS help you identify student levels of learning.

CHAPTER TESTS come in free-response forms for different ability levels and in a multiple-choice form.

CUMULATIVE TESTS, four in all, come in both free-response and multiple-choice forms.

PLUS, PRACTICE FOR STANDARDIZED TESTS, ALGEBRA REVIEWS, AND QUIZZES help students sharpen their skills.

VISUAL AIDS offer 32 transparencies that include grids, models, proof forms, charts, and much more.

SOLUTION KEY

PROFESSIONAL SOURCEBOOK FOR TEACHERS

Levels of Geometric Reasoning

A traditional goal of any geometry course is to develop students' ability to reason carefully and to write mathematical proofs within an axiomatic system. *Scott, Foresman GEOMETRY* has been written to help you more effectively achieve this ambitious and important goal. In particular, the text makes practical use of prominent models of geometric reasoning such as the one developed by two Dutch educators, Dina van Hiele-Geldorf and her husband, Pierre Marie van Hiele.

The van Hiele model consists of five levels of reasoning in geometry which proceed sequentially from concrete and visual to abstract and rigorous. The five levels are: (1) *visualization*—a student can recognize geometric shapes; (2) *analysis*—a student can analyze a figure to establish its properties; (3) *informal deduction*—a student can establish definitions and relationships; (4) *deduction*—a student can write precise mathematical proofs; and (5) *rigor*—a student can analyze different axiomatic systems. (This last level is not addressed by high school geometry.)

The levels of geometric reasoning in *Scott, Foresman GEOMETRY*, presented on the next page, designed to help students move through the first four levels of the van Hiele model. (You may wish to note that in *Scott, Foresman GEOMETRY,* levels 3 and 4 of geometric reasoning are expansions of the third level of the van Hiele model, thus allowing development of both informal deduction and applications.) An important aspect of such models of reasoning is the sequential, hierarchical nature of the levels. In particular, preceding levels are prerequisite for subsequent levels. Thus, a learner must proceed through the levels in order. Furthermore, since each level has its own language and style of reasoning, it is possible for a "mismatch" to occur between teacher and student. That is, if the student is at one level while instruction is at a different level, the desired learning and progress may not occur.

The van Hieles assert that, in fact, progress through the levels is more dependent on methods of instruction than on age or maturation. They recommend a systematic, activity-oriented method of instruction which includes exploration, problem solving, explanation, and summarizing. In all cases, direct involvement of the student is crucial.

The instructional philosophies of the van Hieles are well supported in *Scott, Foresman GEOMETRY.*

▷ The early chapters move students gradually toward comprehension of formal deduction.
▷ Attention is given to planning proofs and developing proof subskills throughout the text.
▷ Each lesson includes a Checking for Understanding section which helps to ensure that the lesson's content is understood before moving on to the exercises.
▷ Each lesson includes an exploratory Thinking Ahead section which often suggests concrete activities leading into the next lesson.
▷ Computer Activities are included throughout, providing

opportunities to use the computer as a discovery tool.
▷ The exercises are divided into three sections, progressing from more concrete, lower-level questions to more abstract, higher-level activities.
▷ Each chapter has a comprehensive Summary and Review which help to consolidate understanding.

The Teacher's Resource File includes:
▷ a series of readiness worksheets and a test which specifically target the lower levels of geometric reasoning;
▷ many exploratory and problem-solving activities;
▷ computer activities and worksheets, many of which are exploratory in nature.

For each lesson in the text, you will find in the Teacher's Edition:

▷ a quiz that reviews requisite skills and concepts for the lesson;
▷ suggestions for teaching aids which can be used to give students concrete experiences;
▷ suggestions for activities that will get students involved;
▷ identification of problem-solving strategies and proof subskills that are used in the lesson;
▷ suggestions for ways to eliminate some typical errors that can occur if, for example, a student is at the "wrong" level of geometric reasoning;
▷ suggestions for alternative approaches to a concept that might accommodate students at lower levels of geometric reasoning; and
▷ suggestions for extension topics that can stabilize a level or promote progress to the next level of geometric reasoning.

The features highlighted above should provide your students with the mathematical experiences necessary to develop higher-level geometric reasoning skills.

Scott, Foresman GEOMETRY
Levels of Geometric Reasoning

Level 1   Identifying and Drawing Figures

▷ Exercises require students to *make drawings.*
▷ Activities deal with *spatial visualization* and *3-dimensional figures.*
▷ *Real-world examples* involve geometric figures.
▷ *Concrete materials* are used.
▷ *Construction exercises* are included throughout.

Level 2   Examining Relationships and Making Conjectures

▷ *Thinking Ahead exercises* lead students to make discoveries and offer conjectures.
▷ Lesson developments include *lead-ins to theorems.*
▷ *Oral and written communication* of relationships and conjectures is encouraged.
▷ *Small-group interaction* is suggested with *exploratory* activities.
▷ Hands-on, informal experiences include:
   sketching (paper and pencil, computer);
   measuring (ruler, protractor, computer);
   moving (folding paper, tracing and moving, using a mirror);
   using coordinates (paper and pencil, computer, graphing calculator);
   constructing (compass and straightedge, computer);
   and *using concrete models* (paper, plastic, or wood manipulatives, common objects).

Level 3   Applying Theorems to Specific Problems

▷ *Real-world problems,* including *career applications,* are solved using geometric theorems.
▷ *Algebraic exercises* require frequent applications of geometric theorems.

Level 4   Making Plausible Arguments

▷ Students *give plausible arguments in writing.*
▷ Students *give plausible arguments orally.*

Level 5   Writing Proofs

▷ Gradual proof preparation develops a variety of *proof subskills.*
▷ Lesson *development includes Plans for Proof.*
▷ Students *write Plans for Proof.*
▷ *Paragraph proof* is presently early.
▷ Students have extensive practice with *easy proofs.*
▷ *Proof reasons are keyed* to previous statements.
▷ *Logic skills* include inference schemes in both mathematical and non-mathematical settings.

Reasoning and Proof

Success in writing proofs indicates competence at the highest level of geometric reasoning expected of the high school student. *Scott, Foresman GEOMETRY* uses a three-pronged approach to help students learn to reason and to write mathematical proofs.

1. *Advancement through lower levels of geometric reasoning:* Activities are provided to move students through the lower levels of geometric reasoning. This ensures that they have reached the appropriate level of understanding before they are expected to write proofs.

2. *Reasoning Activities:* Students engage in many

activities that require informal types of reasoning before and concurrent with their learning to write proofs. This places the role of formal proof in a proper perspective as one, but certainly not the only, type of reasoning that is useful in mathematics.

3. *Proof subskills:* The complex task of writing proofs is analyzed into its important subskills, and these subskills are taught in a systematic and meaningful way. This approach is meant to *teach* students to construct proofs and to *understand* what they have constructed.

Features of the textbook which focus on the first strategy above, moving students through lower levels of geometric reasoning, are described on pages T17-T19. Examples pertinent to the second and third strategies are given below.

Reasoning Activities

Inductive and deductive reasoning are required in mathematics not just to construct proofs, but also to solve problems, to recognize and generalize patterns, to follow the logic of arguments, to explain why certain methods work, to make and test conjectures, and to give counterexamples. In *Scott, Foresman GEOMETRY,* informal reasoning is both a basis for proof writing and an important goal for its own sake. The rudiments of reasoning are taught specifically in Chapter 2 and then are used throughout the text. The following activities are implemented to develop reasoning ability, and then they are used to focus directly on proof writing.

▷ *Inductive reasoning:* Students engage in explorations involving the first several instances of a situation and then generalize the pattern of results to predict the outcome in other instances. For example, by considering the first four triangular numbers, the students can generalize to a formula that would give the nth triangular number in terms of n.

▷ *Making conjectures:* In order to arrive at generalizations that appear to be true, students participate in such concrete activities as paper folding, graphing, and tracing and moving figures. Students then can test their conjectures to see if they apply in situations other than those previously explored. When appropriate, students may attempt to prove a conjecture suggested by extensive exploration.

▷ *Formulating counterexamples:* If further experimentation indicates a conjecture is false in a particular instance, the false case constitutes a counterexample which disproves the conjecture. Thus, students recognize from their own explorations that while a single counterexample disproves a statement, numerous examples for which the statement is true do not constitute a proof.

▷ *Following logical arguments:* Arguments that appear in the media or in advertisements, as well as mathematical arguments, are used to study the forms of reasoning and the exact meaning of given statements. Venn diagrams also serve as a useful tool in this regard.

▷ *Formulating valid arguments:* Queries of "why" and "explain your answer" appear frequently throughout the text. They require a reasoned argument that applies in a particular situation, but not a general, formal proof. Such reasoning is defensibly as important as formal proof in mathematics.

Proof Subskills

A solid foundation in informal reasoning activities prepares students for learning proof writing. In *Scott, Foresman GEOMETRY,* this is done by the explicit and careful teaching of (1) the component parts of a two-column proof, (2) the basic argument forms used to put the parts together, (3) a powerful strategy for proof writing, *working forward and backward,* (4) indirect proof, and (5) proofs in paragraph form, which are presented earlier than in most texts so that there is time for students to develop facility with this form of proof. In particular, the following proof subskills are introduced early and emphasized throughout the text.

▷ Write statements in "if . . . then" form.
▷ Write conclusions from given statements.
▷ Supply missing reasons.
▷ Supply missing statements.
▷ Supply both missing statements and missing reasons.
▷ Supply keying of reasons to previous statements.
▷ Write "given" and "prove" parts of a proof.
▷ Draw a diagram for a proof.
▷ Place the steps of a scrambled proof in a correct order.
▷ Identify extraneous steps in a proof.
▷ Write plans for proof.
▷ Given a hypothesis, write possible conclusions (work forward).
▷ Given a conclusion, write possible hypotheses (work backward).

As these strategies are studied and practiced, students should become skillful in writing proofs.

Computers in the Classroom

While it is premature to say that computers play a major role in most geometry classrooms, many geometry teachers do indicate a desire to do more with computers. What an individual teacher actually does is a function not only of personal philosophy and interest, but the extent to which the textbook utilizes computer instruction. The mandate for textbooks is particularly demanding because of all the variables computers present. There are different makes of computers, and there are even more differences in configurations and memory requirements. There is a great diversity among schools in the number of computers and their accessibility. There is also the matter of software and the additional expense it entails. Because of these factors, *Scott, Foresman GEOMETRY* offers computer resources that are varied, as well as individual activities that are independent of each other so that teachers may pick and choose as befits individual circumstances.

Instructional computing is often characterized in four ways: (1) drill and practice, (2) tutorials, (3) games and simulations, and (4) problem solving. The computer activities in *Scott, Foresman GEOMETRY* do not address the first two categories. Nor are there many computer activities that would qualify as games or simulations. Instead, the activities in *Scott, Foresman GEOMETRY* share the common goal of the fourth category: to expand the student's problem-solving capabilities, using the computer to discover and to create geometry in ways that are not possible without it.

The computer component of *Scott, Foresman GEOMETRY* is best viewed in three parts:

1. The computer activities themselves, their design and content.
2. The computer environments in which the activities exist.
3. The integration, both pedagogically and physically, of these activities and environments into the curriculum.

Activities

While computers are often motivational, they are no longer a novelty. Part of the reason for using computers must be to educate the student as to what the computer can make possible, or what it can do more efficiently than could otherwise be done. Inappropriate use constitutes negative learning experience. Therefore it makes sense to analyze which of the computer's attributes can make significant contributions in the study of geometry.

▷ *Graphics:* The computer graphics screen makes possible the drawing of any two-dimensional figure.

▷ *Flexibility:* A computer can be programmed to vary certain conditions while holding others constant and to provide large numbers of examples either randomly or in a prescribed sequence.

▷ *Computations:* A computer can be used to perform complex computations in a fraction of a second. It not only saves time and effort, but eliminates errors and allows real-world data to be handled with ease.

▷ *Recursion:* A computer can be programmed to repeat any computation or drawing indefinitely.

▷ *Logic:* The computer's internal structure is dictated by fundamental principles of logic.

The extent to which these attributes are utilized in the computer activities of *Scott, Foresman GEOMETRY* is determined by the objectives of the curriculum. Listed are some areas in which the various computer characteristics are adapted to enhance the curriculum.

▷ *Shapes and relationships* Since geometry is primarily the study of shapes, the most important application of computer technology is the use of its graphic capabilities. Examples are abundant. Students can write programs to draw regular polygons. They can also work with software that enables the computer not only to draw circles, tangents, and secants at a keystroke, but to measure angles precisely and to vary the location of the tangents and secants with parameters defined by the students themselves. Students can program the computer to graph lines and circles, or they can use analytic geometry techniques with graphing software to verify properties of quadrilaterals. These types of activities extend the students' ability to experience experimentation and discovery beyond the time and physical limitations of pencil, paper, and other tools.

▷ *Reasoning:* Geometry requires logical thinking. Inductive reasoning skills can be developed by using computer software that facilitates experimentation. Deductive reasoning skills can be developed through programming, an activity with the same structure as proof writing. Furthermore, the computer acts as its own judge in measuring the validity of a program: Does it work or doesn't it? If it doesn't, most programming software also allows the exact programming error to be specified.

▷ *Numerical:* The computer's computational speed and accuracy allows students to investigate the numerical aspects of geometry in a way not otherwise possible. For example, students can learn proportional relationships in triangles and circles using software that accurately computes the lengths of various segments. They can even use very simple programs to print Pythagorean triples and can modify these programs to print only relatively prime triples.

▷ *Applications:* There are many worthwhile applications of geometry which cannot be studied effectively without the computer to perform recursive computations or drawings. For example, the student can use computer programs to find the optimal design of a cylindrical container, derive pi, and even work with fractal geometry through the drawing of a snowflake.

Environments

A computer environment is that which is produced by a hardware-software combination. It can be defined in terms of input (how a user interacts with the computer-keyboard, mouse, joystick, voice) and output (how the computer provides feedback to the user-monitor, printer, sound). Environments are further defined by certain structures determined by the software, such as layout, input routines, and method of evaluation. Where possible, the software for the activities in *Scott, Foresman GEOMETRY* is not a specified title, but one of a genre of software. The selection of the software was based on three factors: (1) its suitability to the task of learning geometry, (2) the difficulty of learning how to use the software, and (3) its compatability with the computers commonly found in schools.

There are three software components of the environments in *Scott, Foresman GEOMETRY*.

▷ *Geometry and Graphing Software:* These include several product specifically designed for in mathematics or geometry, such as *The Geometric preSupposer* and *Supposer, GeoDraw,* and various graphing software packages. Each creates a nonprogramming graphics environment with its own set of interface mechanisms. Teachers and students generally find them easy to learn and may already have experience with some. Their purpose is to provide the student with an environment that facilitates exploration and discovery with geometric figures. Ordering information for specific products is located on page T25 in the Teacher's Edition.

▷ *Logo:* Logo is unique among programming languages in its suitability to geometry. While many languages can be used to draw geometric figures using coordinate graphing techniques, Logo can be used to draw them using their angle and distance characteristics. This enables students to apply what they learn to generate geometric figures by manipulating the Logo "turtle" with direct commands or

procedures. While there are many variations of Logo, all are dialects of either LCSI Logo (Apple Logo is the best known) or MIT Logo (Terrapin Logo is an example). All Logo computer activities in *Scott, Foresman GEOMETRY* are written in Apple Logo. (Product information is given on page T25.) However, translations to other versions of Logo mainly involve aspects of nomenclature. The Logo activities provide no information about editing or file management, so you may need to spend some time familiarizing the students with these features.

▷ *BASIC:* BASIC is the language built into many computers. Although it can be used for graphics, there are such significant differences among the graphics commands in the various dialects that only the text capabilities of BASIC are used in *Scott, Foresman GEOMETRY*. BASIC activities generally involve repeated "runs" of a program in order to determine an answer or reach a conclusion. As with Logo, no editing or file management instruction is given in the exercises.

Integration

The computer activities in *Scott, Foresman GEOMETRY* are in three locations.

▷ *Computer Activities: Drawing and Measuring* and *Graphing:* These activities, at the end of many sets of Written Exercises in the textbook, are designed to be used with either geometry or graphing software. They preview the subsequent lesson of the text by enabling students to use the computer to examine and test geometric properties and relationships. As students do each exercise, they should record their results using the record-keeping sheets found in the *Computer Materials* book in the *Teacher's Resource File*. It is expected that they will be able to make conjectures based on their observations.

You should place these activities high on your list of computer priorities. Additional activities of this type are included in the margin notes of the Teacher's Edition.

▷ *Using Logo and Using BASIC:* Each textbook chapter contains either a Using Logo or Using BASIC activity. These are often extensions or applications that reinforce a topic covered in the chapter. Most are based on a single program which is used and modified as required while doing the exercises. While it is hoped that many students are familiar with Logo and BASIC, no specific programming skills are prerequisite. Students are treated as novices and develop their programming competence as the year progresses. Commands, operations, and conditionals are introduced and defined only as needed. Hopefully, you are familiar with each language, but do not feel obligated to be an expert.

▷ *Computer Worksheets in the Computer Materials book in the Teacher's Resource File:* These 36 worksheets (from 2 to 4 per chapter) are similar in design to the Using Logo and Using BASIC activities in the text, although the worksheet programs tend to be slightly longer. No programming skills beyond those included in the text are required. Programs designed for advanced geometry concepts are not necessarily more complex than those designed for simpler concepts. Students are not expected to understand all the details of each program. (This is particularly true in Logo.) Some activities may refer to programs in earlier activities. You may find it useful to require students to keep their files on a disk or may even want to place all files on a master disk and distribute copies to your students.

There is no set formula for successfully integrating the various computer activities of *Scott, Foresman GEOMETRY* into the curriculum. Computer Activities: Drawing and Measuring and Computer Activities: Graphing exercises in the text are designed to preview new content and are best used upon completion of the lesson of the text in which they occur. Using Logo and Using BASIC pages in the text, as well as the worksheets in the *Computer Materials* book, can be used as needed, as: an alternative to the regular class routine, review, motivation, enrichment, remediation, and even homework.

Above all, you are encouraged to be creative in regard to computer use. The activities should be measured against the needs of the students. It is unlikely, and probably undesirable, to expect classes to do every activity. Some exercises are more suitable for better students, others for weaker ones. Some students may work better alone, others in pairs or small groups. It may not be physically possible for the whole class to work on computers at the same time. Since most activities can be completed in 10 to 20 minutes, you might want to stagger the students' class activities. Some students can be doing computer work while others are doing textbook assignments.

There is no doubt that the role of the computer as an instructional tool will continue to expand as software quality improves and hardware costs decline. You are strongly urged to make the computer resources of *Scott, Foresman GEOMETRY* an important part of your geometry instruction.

Computer Language and Software References Computer Features and Computer Worksheets

Many of the computer features in the textbook as well as many of the worksheets in the *Computer Materials* book provide listings of Logo programs for students to enter, save, and run. Please note that different versions of Logo implement different commands. Thus, certain commands used in one version may not be understood in another. The Logo programs in *Scott, Foresman GEOMETRY* are based on a version of Logo available in two products: LCSI Logo II and LogoWriter. Both are published by:

Logo Systems, Inc.
555 West 57th Street
Suite 1236
New York, NY 10019
(212) 765-4780

If you have a different version of Logo, you may be able to provide your students with instructions for adapting the programs in the computer activities for use with your version.

Computer Activities: Drawing and Measuring

The Drawing and Measuring computer activities that occur at least once per chapter, as well as the additional suggestions for these activities provided in the Teacher's Edition notes, can be completed using programs in *The Geometric Supposer* series or the *GeoDraw* program included in *Geometry Series*.

The *Geometric Supposer* series by Judah L. Schwartz and Michal Yerushalmy (Sunburst, 1988), includes the following programs: *The Geometric preSupposer: Points and Lines* and *The Geometric Supposer: Triangles; Quadrilaterals; and Circles*. Packages can be ordered directly from:

Sunburst Communications
39 Washington Avenue
Pleasantville, NY 10570-2898
(800) 431-1934 in U.S.A.
(800) 247-6756 in Canada
Ask for Micro Service Department.

Geometry Series, published by IBM (1986), includes these programs: *Geometry One: Foundations* and *Geometry Two: Proofs and Extensions.* Programs can be ordered from:

IBM Direct
PC Software Department
One Culver Road
Dayton, NJ 07645
(800) IBM-2468

Computer Activities: Graphing

The Graphing activities that occur at various points in the text can be completed using any of a number of computer graphing programs available for Apple and IBM personal computers. Most computer graphing programs are essentially similar in the capabilities they offer. Several common differences are explained below.

▷ Many programs use the notation $f(x) =$, while others, along with this text, use $y =$.

▷ Some programs automatically graph both positive and negative square roots, while others graph only positive square roots unless the negative square root is explicitly indicated.

▷ Some programs allow you to enter y and x on either side of the equation, so that any of the following could be entered and graphed:

$$y = 3 * x + 2$$
$$x = (y - 2)/3$$
$$y - 3 * x = 2$$

Other programs only allow entry of y or $f(x)$ as a function of x, so only the first form in the choices above would be accepted.

Before having students complete an activity, you should familiarize yourself with the computer graphing program you and your students will be using. Then explain to students any discrepancies that may exist between the way the material is presented to them and the manner of presentation in the program.

◆Objectives

Chapter seven

7-1 Use ratios and proportions to solve problems; use properties of equality to change the form of a proportion.

7-2 Recognize and apply the properties of similar polygons, using ratios and proportions.

7-3 Apply the AA Similarity Postulate to prove that triangles are similar.

7-4 Use similar triangles to prove that parallel lines divide certain segments proportionally; apply this property to find unknown lengths.

7-5 Apply the SAS and SSS Similarity Theorems to prove that triangles are similar.

7-6 Apply ratios to the lengths of altitudes, angle bisectors, and medians in similar triangles.

7-7 Solve real-world problems using similar figures.

Chapter eight

8-1 Apply the ideas of similarity and geometric mean to right triangles.

8-2 State and apply the Pythagorean Theorem and its converse.

8-3 Determine and apply the properties of a 30-60-90 triangle and a 45-45-90 triangle.

8-4 Use the Pythagorean Theorem to solve problems.

8-5 Identify and evaluate the tangent, sine, and cosine ratios for an acute angle of a right triangle.

8-6 Use a table of trigonometric ratios to find the measure of an angle or a ratio for a given angle.

8-7 Use the trigonometric ratios to solve indirect measurement problems.

Chapter nine

9-1 Recognize circles and spheres and lines, segments, and planes related to them.

9-2 Use theorems about tangents to circles.

9-3 Use theorems involving chords of circles.

9-4 Recognize circles and polygons that are inscribed or circumscribed; recognize points of concurrency.

9-5 Recognize central angles, arcs, and congruent arcs in circles; use postulates and theorems involving arcs of circles.

9-6 Recognize inscribed angles and other angles with vertices on circles; use theorems involving such angles.

9-7 Use theorems involving angles with vertices not on circles and segments formed by chords, secants, and tangents.

Chapter ten

10-1 State basic postulates for area of polygonal regions, and use them to find areas of squares and other rectangles.

10-2 State and apply theorems concerning the areas of regions enclosed by parallelograms and triangles.

10-3 State and apply theorems concerning the area of regions enclosed by trapezoids, rhombuses, and kites.

10-4 State and apply theorems concerning areas of similar polygons.

10-5 State and apply relationships with circumscribed and inscribed circles to find areas, perimeters, radii, and apothems of regular polygons.

10-6 State and apply theorems concerning the circumference and area of a circle.

10-7 State and apply theorems concerning arc length and areas of sectors and segments of a circle.

Chapter eleven

11-1 Define polyhedron, prism, and related terms; determine the length of diagonals.

11-2 Compute the lateral and total areas of prisms.

11-3 Compute the volume of a prism.

11-4 Compute the area and volume of cylinders.

11-5 Compute the area and volume of pyramids.

11-6 Compute the area and volume of cones.

11-7 Compute the area and volume of spheres.

Chapter twelve

12-1 Find images of points under line reflections and point reflections.

12-2 State and apply properties of isometries.

12-3 Apply properties of reflections to problem-solving situations.

12-4 State and apply properties of translations.

12-5 State and apply properties of rotations.

12-6 Examine various figures for point, line, and rotational symmetry.

12-7 Use isometries to extend the concept of congruence.

12-8 Find the images of figures under dilations.

12-9 State and apply properties of dilations.

12-10 Use similarity transformations to extend the concept of similarity.

Chapter thirteen

13-1 Plot points, and find and use distances and midpoints in both two and three dimensions.

13-2 Write an equation of a line (or circle) in standard form; graph the equation of a line (or circle).

13-3 Place coordinate axes on specific types of geometric figures; write coordinate proofs.

13-4 Name and draw vectors; find the magnitude and direction angle of a given vector.

13-5 Draw and calculate sums and differences of vectors.

13-6 Draw and compute scalar multiples of vectors.

13-7 Write proofs using vectors.

13-8 Write the proof of a theorem using synthetic, transformation, coordinate, and vector methods.

·C·O·N·S·T·R·U·C·T·I·O·N·

Scott, Foresman GEOMETRY introduces constructions near the concepts they reinforce. For teachers who prefer to concentrate only on constructions at certain times in the course, the following two units are suggested.

·E·X·E·R·C·I·S·E·S·

■ Contents

Chapter 1 *Introduction to Geometry*

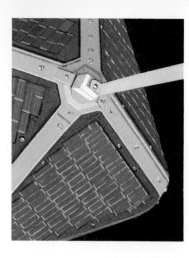

Chapter 2 *Reasoning in Geometry*

Chapter 3 *Proof in Geometry*

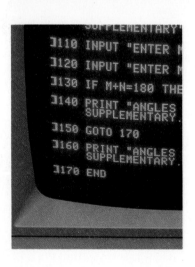

■ Contents

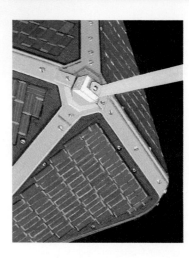

Chapter 2 *Reasoning in Geometry*

Chapter 3 *Proof in Geometry*

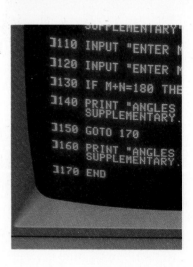

Chapter 4 *Parallel Lines and Planes*

Chapter 5 *Congruent Triangles*

Chapter 6 *Quadrilaterals*

Chapter 7 *Similarity*

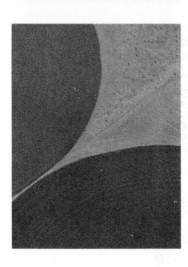

Chapter 10 *Areas of Polygons and Circles*

Chapter 11 *Solids*

Chapter 12 *Transformations*

Chapter 13 *Coordinates and Vectors*

CHAPTER

1

Introduction to Geometry

Chapter Overview

This chapter presents geometry as a mathematical model of the real world and as a mathematical system. The undefined terms "point," "line" and "plane," as well as the incidence postulates, are introduced as abstractions of real-world phenomena.

Linear measure is introduced with a series of postulates involving lengths of segments. A parallel development of angle measure follows. In both cases, constructions and the concepts they illustrate are introduced.

The final lesson of the chapter presents the coordinate plane as a mathematical model of the geometric concepts that have been introduced. We review the use of ordered pairs to represent points, equations of lines, and the Distance and Midpoint formulas.

Perspectives

Lesson 1–1 should make students aware of the pervasiveness of geometry in the real world and should help foster a positive attitude toward geometry. This lesson provides the groundwork for applying theorems to practical situations.

Lesson 1–2 introduces the undefined elements of geometry: point, line and plane. The concept of betweenness of points is treated informally.

This lesson also introduces some of the first definitions that involve the undefined terms, including the terms "collinear," "coplanar" and "between."

Lesson 1–3 states the first postulates about the basic undefined terms. These are sometimes called the incidence postulates because they express the basic positional relationships among points, lines and planes.

Lesson 1–4 expands the inventory of geometric figures by defining segments and rays in terms of the undefined terms (including betweenness). The concept of half-planes is introduced so that we can define interiors of angles and other figures in subsequent lessons.

Lesson 1–5 introduces linear measure and its properties. The postulates are presented in a manner that avoids work with distance in terms of absolute value.

Constructing one segment equal to another is introduced in this lesson. Also introduced is the concept of proving a conditional sentence false by counterexample. The sentence "If P, then Q" is proved false by finding a case in which P is true and Q is false.

Pacing Chart for Chapter 1

Lesson	Objectives	Basic Course	Average Course	Extended Course
1–1	Recognize and name geometric shapes in real-world objects.	1	1	1
1–2	Use the undefined terms "point," "line" and "plane" to define other terms.	1	1	1
1–3	State and apply postulates involving points, lines and planes.	1	1	1
1–4	Name, describe and use segments and rays.	1	1	1
1–5	Apply the basic postulates concerning linear measure; define and find midpoints and bisectors.	1	1	1
1–6	Recognize and name angles and their component parts; apply the basic postulates relating to angles and their measures.	1	1	1
1–7	Recognize and name types of angles and special pairs of angles; apply concepts relating to complements and supplements.	1	1	1
1–8	Use the coordinate plane as a mathematical model for definitions and postulates; state and apply the Distance and Midpoint formulas.	1	1	1
Review		1	1	1
Test		1	1	1
Total		10 days	10 days	10 days

Lesson 1–6 defines angles and presents the postulates necessary to begin the development of special angles and relationships. The postulates of this lesson basically parallel the postulates for linear measure.

Lesson 1–7 gives many important definitions relating to angles. Angles are classified according to measure, and pairs of angles are named according to measure or position.

Lesson 1–8 reviews graphing in the coordinate plane, in the context of a mathematical model of Euclidean geometry. Linear equations are reviewed and used as models of lines. The Distance and Midpoint formulas are introduced to allow the model to include linear measure.

Introduction to Geometry

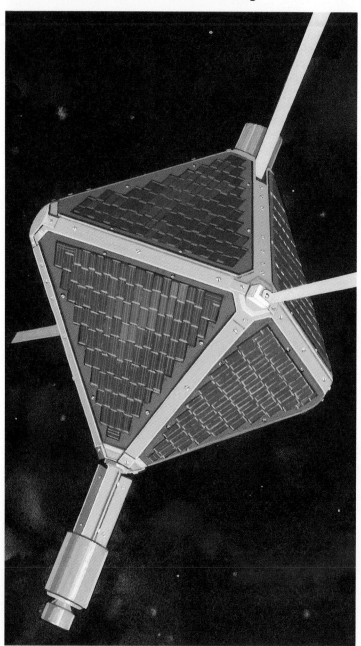

One of the world's smallest satellites, pictured here, was first launched in 1966. It had a remarkable property: no matter how it maneuvered in space, one face was always turned toward the sun to absorb energy. The other faces turned away from the sun and maintained the temperature within the capsule. All faces of the satellite were the same shape and size and contained the same number of solar panels. These satellites ranged in size from 6 to 11 inches along an edge and weighed from 5 to 9 pounds.

1. How many faces did the satellite have?

2. Draw a diagram of the face that was turned toward the sun.

3. How many edges did the satellite have?

Warm-Up Review

1. Name something in the classroom shaped like a rectangle. Chalkboard
2. Name something in your home shaped like a circle. Record
3. How many sides does a triangle have? Three
4. What shape do most doors have? Rectangle
5. True or false: The shape of a soft drink can is best described as a circle. False

1-1 Geometry and the Real World

Geometry has a long and rich history. Although geometry is used widely today in the sciences, engineering, and art, its origins can be traced back over 6,000 years to the ancient Egyptians who used geometry to measure land and construct buildings. In fact, the term **geometry** means "earth measure."

By careful experimentation and observation, the Egyptians developed methods so accurate that the sides of the Great Pyramid at Gizeh, shown here, are accurate to within 1 cm in 180 m.

In order to study the size, shape, and position of objects in the real world, you will often find it helpful to reduce them to simpler forms. A geometer concentrates only on the outline of a figure, that is, the lines, angles, planes, and intersections. The Pyramid at Gizeh might be represented as shown on the right. Describe the figures that make up the pyramid in the diagram.
4 triangles of the same size and shape and a square

In addition to giving geometric descriptions of objects, it is important to be able to make drawings of them.

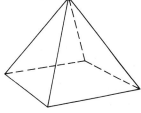

Example

Represent the object in each photograph with a drawing. Give a geometric description of the object.

a.

b.

c.

Solution

a.

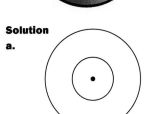

Two circles with the same center

b.

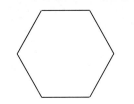

Hexagon

c.

Cylinder

LESSON 1–1

Resources

Readiness Test
Worksheet 1–1
Extension 1–1

OBJECTIVE

Recognize and name geometric shapes in real-world objects.

TEACHING NOTES

Before beginning this lesson, teachers are encouraged to give students the Readiness Test in the Teacher's Resource File and any or all of the Readiness Worksheets. More details are given on the page before the Test.

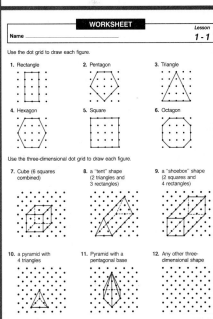

Assignment Guide

Basic: 1–8, 18–29
Average: 1–16, 18–29
Extended: 1–29

To introduce this lesson, show the class slides of geometric forms in nature (e.g., spider web, Nautilus shell, snowflake) and in the man-made environment (e.g., architecture, sports).

Discuss what this course covers. Explain the differences and similarities between algebra and geometry. Try to dispel any fears that students may have about geometry.

Show the students the list of symbols and abbreviations that appears after Chapter 13.

EXERCISE NOTES

Checking for Understanding Exercises review subskills taught in the lesson and are designed to have students refer back to the text material. The **Written Exercises** require a higher level of comprehension as you proceed

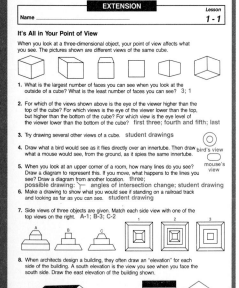

The geometry of ancient Egypt provided practical methods for solving important everyday problems. However, relying upon measurement and upon the appearance of figures sometimes led to inaccuracies and erroneous conclusions. This diagram suggests how appearances can be misleading.

To avoid such errors, Greek geometers did not rely upon drawings. They began with a few simple assumptions and used logical reasoning to reach conclusions about geometric figures. This type of mathematical reasoning is the basis of the *Elements*, a book written by Euclid in about 300 B.C. We, too, will develop geometry as a mathematical system based upon logical reasoning. We shall also emphasize the usefulness of geometry in everyday life.

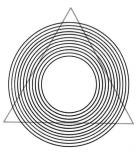

Are the sides of the blue figure straight?

Yes; however, they appear curved.

Checking for Understanding

Match each photo with one of the drawings. Use the drawing to give a geometric description of the object.

1. *d*; arc **2.** *c*; sphere
3. *a*; 5-pointed star **4.** *b*; cone

1.  **2.**  **3.**  **4.**

a.  **b.** **c.** **d.**

Written Exercises

Set A   To obtain a driver's license in some states, drivers must be able to identify certain traffic signs by their shape and color alone. Chose the appropriate sign and write a geometric description of the shape.

1. Stop   **2.** School crossing
3. Yield   **4.** Railroad crossing

1. *c*; octagon   **2.** *b*; pentagon
3. *a*; triangle   **4.** *d*; circle

a. **b.**

c.  **d.**

5. Are the three cylinders in this picture the same size? How could you be sure?
Yes; measure them

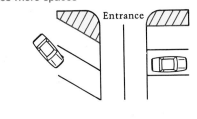

Answer these questions that a civil engineer might consider in designing a parking lot for a shopping mall. **6.** Easier to enter and exit **7.** Provides more spaces

6. What is one advantage of angle parking as on the left of the entrance?

7. What is one advantage of perpendicular parking as on the right of the entrance?

8. How can you be sure the parking lines are parallel? Measure angles at curb or distance between lines.

Entrance

Set B **9.** The illusion in Exercise 5 exists because the artist violated a geometric principle of perspective art. Study the method used at the right to locate the third pole in a proper perspective drawing of equally tall, equally spaced poles. Trace the drawing of the poles. Then draw three more poles in proper perspective.

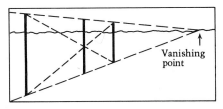
Vanishing point

Study the model of a building made from cubes.

10. a. How many cubes were used? 11

b. Draw the building as it would look if you were directly above it.

11. Assume your eyes are at the level of the model.

a. Draw the front view of the building.

b. Draw the side view of the building.

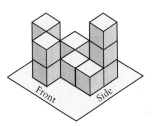
Front Side

12. Drafters make *plane perspective* drawings to show an object from the front, back, top, bottom, and sides. Dashed lines are used for edges that cannot be seen in a particular view. One side view of the given object is shown. Draw and label five other views.

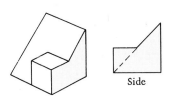
Side

13. Gestalt psychologists use geometry in their study of human perception. What is represented by these figures and their background? The word *love*

---

through the three sets. The **Review** and **Thinking Ahead Exercises** should be completed by all students.

Exercises 9–12 prepare students for the **proof subskill** of drawing a diagram.

Exercises 14–17 use the **problem-solving strategy** of finding a pattern.

ANSWERS

Answers to all Exercises will appear either a) on the reduced pupil's page; b) in the Teacher's Edition margins for that page or the page it faces; or c) in the Additional Answers section on pages 670-695.

Written Exercises

9.

10b.

11a.

11b.

The Kuba people of Zaire in Central Africa are well known for their interest in patterns. Shown at the right is a portion of a Kuba textile. For the flag patterns in Exercises 14–16, (1) describe a motion that would move the first flag to the position of the second, and (2) draw the next three flags of the pattern.

14.   **15.**   **16.**

14. Slide or translate
15. Flip or reflect
16. Turn or rotate half-way around

Set C

17. How many different ways can you label faces of a cube with *A*, *B*, *C*, *D*, *E*, and *F*, using each letter exactly once? Two labelings are the same if you can turn one cube so that it appears like the other. 30

▲ Review Compute the following.

18. $(-72) + 85$ 13   **19.** $(-18)(-16)$ 288

20. Evaluate $\dfrac{(2 + r)^2}{9}$ for $r = 4$. 4

21. What does *geometry* mean?   Earth measure

22. Rather than relying on drawings, the Greeks used __?__ to reach conclusions about geometric figures.
Logical reasoning

Thinking Ahead Draw two distinct straight lines that intersect.

23. If each line is extended in both directions, will the two lines ever intersect again? No

24. Is it possible to draw two lines that will never intersect, even if extended? Yes

25. Two lines can intersect in at most how many points? 1

Suppose that the packaging dividers shown at the right were extended upward indefinitely.

26. If each divider represents a plane, what is the intersection of the front plane with the one farthest to the left? A line

27. Is it possible that two of the planes would never intersect, no matter how far extended? Yes

28. If a *floor* plane were added to the picture, what would be in the intersection of the floor plane, the plane nearest the front, and the plane farthest left?

29. What are the possible intersections for two planes?
28. A point   **29.** A line or not at all

Warm-Up Review

Identify each of the following as an example of (a) a point (location), (b) a line or (c) a plane (flat surface).
1. A piece of paper Plane (c)
2. One edge of a piece of paper Line (b)
3. The corner of a piece of paper Point (a)

1-2 Points, Lines, and Planes

Point, *line*, and *plane* are the basic concepts of geometry. Each is an abstraction based on our experience.

A star in the night sky suggests a **point**. Points have no size. They are represented with dots and are named with capital letters.

A straight, thin wire suggests a **line**. A line extends infinitely far in both directions and has no width. A line is represented by a stroke of a pencil, with an arrowhead at each end. Lines can be named with lower-case letters. If A and B are two points on a line, the line can also be named $\overleftrightarrow{AB}$ (read "line AB"), or $\overleftrightarrow{BA}$.

A flat surface such as a hockey rink suggests a **plane**. A plane extends infinitely far in all directions and has no thickness. Planes can be represented with four-sided figures and are named with capital script letters.

A good definition gives the meaning of a word using terms that are already known. But we must start with some basic words. In geometry we begin with the basic terms *point*, *line*, and *plane*. These are **undefined terms** in this course. The following definitions use our three undefined terms.

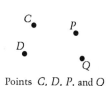

Points C, D, P, and Q

Line ℓ or $\overleftrightarrow{AB}$

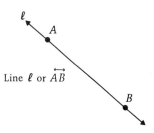

Plane $\mathcal{E}$

Definition *Space*

Space is the set of all points.

"Cubic Space Division," a lithograph by the Dutch artist Maurits C. Escher, illustrates portions of planes in space. The edges of the girders illustrate relationships among lines.

Points A, B, and C are in line ℓ. Such points are called collinear. Are points A, B, and D collinear? No

Definition *Collinear Points*

Collinear points are points that are contained in one line.

Points that are not contained in one line are said to be **noncollinear**. Unless otherwise specified, points may be assumed to be collinear if they appear that way in a diagram.

1-2 *Points, Lines, and Planes*

LESSON 1–2

Resources

Cardboard
Straightedge
Worksheet 1–2
Extension 1–2

OBJECTIVE

Use the undefined terms "point," "line" and "plane" to define other terms.

TEACHING NOTES

To emphasize the need for undefined terms, ask students to define point, line and plane. As other words are used in their proposed definitions, ask for their meanings. After several repetitions, it should

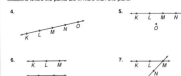
WORKSHEET

Name _____ Lesson 1-2

Name all the possible lines, segments, and rays for each set of points. Then give the maximum number of planes possible from these points.

1. A and B $\overleftrightarrow{AB}$, $\overline{AB}$, $\overrightarrow{AB}$, $\overrightarrow{BA}$; 0 planes

2. C, D, and E $\overleftrightarrow{CD}$, $\overleftrightarrow{CE}$, $\overleftrightarrow{DE}$, $\overline{CD}$, $\overline{DE}$, $\overline{CE}$, $\overrightarrow{CD}$, $\overrightarrow{DC}$, $\overrightarrow{DE}$, $\overrightarrow{ED}$, $\overrightarrow{CE}$, $\overrightarrow{EC}$; 1 plane

3. F, G, H, and I $\overleftrightarrow{FG}$, $\overleftrightarrow{GH}$, $\overleftrightarrow{HI}$, $\overleftrightarrow{FI}$, $\overleftrightarrow{FH}$, $\overleftrightarrow{GI}$, ...; 4 planes

Five points (K, L, M, N, and O) are given. For exercises 4–7, draw four different situations where the points are all in one plane. For 8–11, draw four different situations where the points are in more than one plane.

be clear that we need a base upon which to build.

Point out that points and lines may be coplanar even when the plane containing them is not drawn.

Demonstrate that betweenness of points is often determined from a diagram.

Additional Examples

Example 1

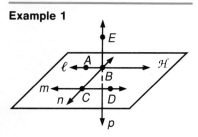

Points A, B, C and D are coplanar because they are all contained in plane $\mathcal{H}$. Lines ℓ, m and n are also coplanar.

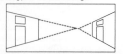

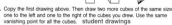

Definition *Coplanar Points or Lines*

Coplanar points (or lines) are points (or lines) that are contained in one plane.

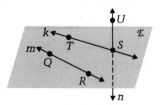

Example 1

Points Q, R, S, and T are coplanar, since each is contained in plane $\mathcal{E}$. Lines m and k are coplanar because they are both contained in plane $\mathcal{E}$.

Points or lines that are not contained in the same plane are **noncoplanar**. Points Q, R, S, and U are noncoplanar. Lines m and n are also noncoplanar.

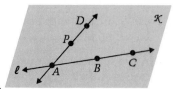

Point B is **between** points A and C. The word "between" is used to describe collinear points only. Thus P *is not* between A and C, since A, P, and C are noncollinear. However, P *is* between A and D.

The intersection of two sets is the set of elements that they have in common. Lines and planes are sets of points, so their intersections are sets of points.

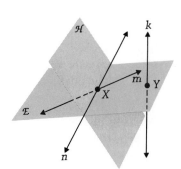

Example 2

The intersection of lines m and n is point X. Line k intersects plane $\mathcal{E}$ at point Y. Planes $\mathcal{E}$ and $\mathcal{H}$ intersect in line n.

In this text, *two lines* means *two distinct or different lines*; *four points* means *four distinct or different points*; and so on.

Checking for Understanding

1. With which undefined terms do we begin our study of geometry? **Point, line, plane**

Use the diagram at the right for Exercises 2–10.

2. Points A, C, and ___?___ are collinear. **B**

3. Points A, B, D, and ___?___ are coplanar. **C**

4. Give another name for $\overleftrightarrow{BE}$. **Line ℓ**

5. Points C, D, B, and ___?___ are noncoplanar. **E**

6. Points A, B, and ___?___ are noncollinear. **D or E**

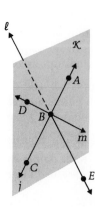

Assignment Guide

Basic: 1–21, 28–34
Average: 2–8 (even), 9–26, 28–34
Extended: 2–20 (even), 21–34

7. Give another name for line *j*. $\overleftrightarrow{AB}$, $\overleftrightarrow{AC}$, or $\overleftrightarrow{BC}$

8. List three points which are coplanar and collinear. **A, B, C**

9. List two lines which are coplanar. **j and m**

10. Name a point between *A* and *C*. **B**

Written Exercises

Set A

1. List three collinear points. **A, G, B or F, G, D**

2. List three noncollinear points. **Sample: A, G, F**

3. Name the intersection of $\overleftrightarrow{AB}$ and $\overleftrightarrow{FD}$. **G**

4. Name the intersection of *E* and *H*. $\overleftrightarrow{AB}$

5. List four coplanar points. **Sample: A, G, B, F**

6. List four noncoplanar points. **Sample: A, G, B, J**

7. Name a point between *G* and *H*. **B**

8. Name a point between *F* and *D*. **G**

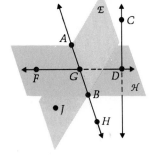

Tell whether a *point*, a *line*, or a *plane* is suggested by each object.

9. A tabletop **Plane**   **10.** A parking lot **Plane**

11. A grain of sand **Point**   **12.** The sharp end of a pin **Point**

13. A telephone wire **Line**

Use a straightedge or ruler to draw and label a diagram to illustrate each description.

14. Point *P* is contained in two lines.

15. Points *A*, *Q*, and *S* are coplanar.

16. Point *M* is not contained in line *ℓ*.

17. Line *t* contains *Q* and *R*, but not *P* and *S*.

18. Plane *H* contains *A*, *B*, and *C* but not *D*.

19. Points *Q* and *R* are in the intersection of *H* and *E*.

20. Point *X* is between *A* and *B* and *A* is between *X* and *Y*.

21. Line *m* intersects $\overleftrightarrow{DE}$ at *F* with *E* between *D* and *F*.

14.

15.

16.

17.

18.

19.

20.

21.

Example 2

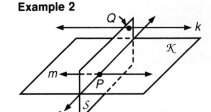

The intersection of lines *ℓ* and *m* is point *P*. Line *k* intersects plane *S* at *Q*. Planes *K* and *S* intersect in line *ℓ*.

Error Analysis   Students may have difficulty "reading" diagrams of figures in space. Models made of rectangular pieces of cardboard may help them see what is being illustrated.

ANSWERS

Written Exercises

23.

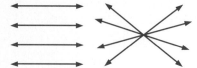

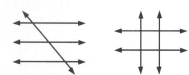

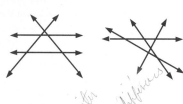

3 - 3) 3
4 - 6) 4
5 - 10) 5
6 - 15) 5
7 - 21) 6
8 - 28) 7

Set B   **22.** Three coplanar lines may have 0, 1, 2, or 3 points of intersection. Using a straightedge or ruler, draw a diagram to illustrate each case.

23. What are the possible numbers of points of intersection for four coplanar lines? Draw a diagram for each case. **0, 1, 3, 4, 5, or 6**

24. a. Draw four coplanar lines that have the maximum number of points of intersection.

   b. Suppose a fifth line is drawn that intersects each of the four lines at distinct points. How many new points of intersection are there? **4**

   c. What is the maximum number of points of intersection for five coplanar lines? **10**

25. Using the reasoning suggested in Exercise 24, determine the maximum number of points of intersection for

   a. 6 coplanar lines. **15**   **b.** 7 coplanar lines. **21**

   c. 8 coplanar lines. **28**   **d.** 12 coplanar lines. **66**

26. Think about a cardboard box and the planes and points suggested by the sides and corners. Using a straightedge, draw a single diagram that illustrates all of these descriptions.

   a. Point A is in the intersection of planes $\mathcal{E}$, $\mathcal{F}$, and $\mathcal{H}$.

   b. Points B and C are in the intersection of planes $\mathcal{E}$ and $\mathcal{F}$.

   c. Points P and Q are in the intersection of planes $\mathcal{F}$ and $\mathcal{H}$.

   d. Points S and T are in the intersection of planes $\mathcal{E}$ and $\mathcal{H}$.

Set C   **27.** If the maximum number of points of intersection for $n - 1$ lines is x, what is the maximum number of points of intersection for n lines? $x + n - 1$

22.

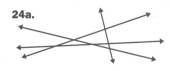

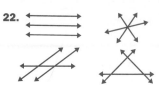

24a.

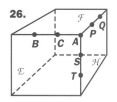

one more for each one

26.

◀ CHALLENGES

▲ Review Represent each object with a geometric drawing.

28. Tabletop   **29.** Megaphone

30. The Pentagon building

Name three real-world objects that might be represented by each geometric figure.

31. A circle Ring, plate, wheel   **32.** A rectangle Flag, door, stamp

Samples: **28.**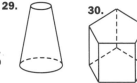

29.

30.

Thinking Ahead **33. a.** Mark points P and Q on a sheet of paper.

b. Use a straightedge to draw a line which contains them.

c. Can you draw another line containing P and Q? No

d. What can you conclude about the number of lines that contain two given points?
There is only one such line.

33a,b.

34. Use a sheet of paper to represent a plane and the tips of three sharpened pencils to represent points.

a. If the points are collinear, how many planes can contain all three points? Infinitely many

b. If the points are noncollinear, how many planes can contain all three points? One

c. What can you conclude about the number of planes that contain three given noncollinear points? There is only one such plane

Challenge

Suppose a **row** is defined to be four collinear points. How can ten lights be fixed to the wall of a teen center so that each light is in exactly two rows?

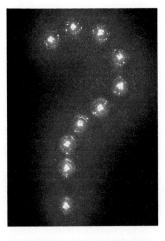

This Challenge is the first of many features in this book. Challenges usually involve solving nonroutine problems or use **problem-solving strategies** to find a solution.

FOLLOW-UP

More Practice

To reinforce the need for the undefined terms "point," "line" and "plane," discuss Euclid's definitions of these terms:
1. A point is that which has no part.
2. A line is length without breadth.
3. A surface is that which has only length and breadth.
Discuss the problem that arises when trying to define terms such as "length" and "breadth."
• **Worksheet 1–2**

Extension

• **Extension 1–2**

Warm-Up Review

1. What is the intersection of lines *m* and *n*? P
2. True or false: *P*, *Q* and *R* are collinear. False
3. True or false: *P*, *Q* and *R* are coplanar. True
4. What is the intersection of planes *H* and *K*? Line ℓ
5. Name two points on line ℓ. Q, R

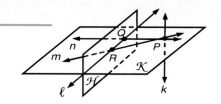

LESSON 1–3

Resources

Cardboard
Wire
Worksheet 1–3
Extension 1–3

OBJECTIVE

State and apply postulates involving points, lines and planes.

TEACHING NOTES

Use the **Thinking Ahead Exercises** in the previous lesson to motivate Postulates 2 and 3. **Concrete materials** may be used to clarify Postulates 3–5. Use rectangular pieces of cardboard to represent planes and stiff wire to represent lines.

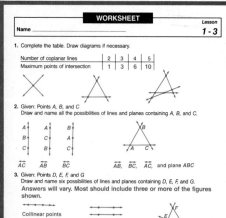

1-3 Basic Postulates

In Lesson 1-2, we introduced three undefined terms—point, line, and plane. We give meaning to these terms by assuming certain facts about them. The statements we assume are **postulates**. The postulates lead to other facts involving points, lines, and planes. Our first postulate simply ensures that some points exist.

Postulate 1 *Points Postulate*

A line contains at least two points. A plane contains at least three noncollinear points. Space contains at least four noncoplanar, noncollinear points.

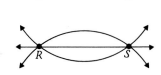

Intuition suggests that a line can be drawn through any two points. If some lines were not straight, more than one line could contain the two points. Since lines are straight, there is only one such line. Postulate 2 guarantees this in our geometry.

Postulate 2 *Line Postulate*

Two points are contained in one and only one line.

The model at the right suggests that three noncollinear points are contained in a plane. Do you think a second plane could also contain these three points? The next postulate ensures that there is only one such plane. No

Postulate 3 *Plane Postulate*

Three noncollinear points are contained in one and only one plane.

The phrases "exactly one" and "unique" have the same meaning as "one and only one." The word "determine" means "are contained in one and only one." Postulates 2 and 3 can be restated as follows: Postulate 2: Two points determine a line; Postulate 3: Three noncollinear points determine a plane.

Example

a. Name two points that determine line ℓ.

b. Name three points that determine plane *H*.

Solution

a. Points *Q* and *S* determine line ℓ. Line ℓ is also determined by *Q* and *V* and by *S* and *V*.

b. Points *T*, *Q*, and *S* determine plane *H*. Plane *H* is also determined by *T*, *Q*, and *V* and by *T*, *S*, and *V*.

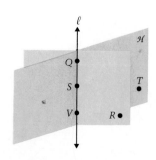

Assignment Guide

Basic: 1–14, 28–34
Average: 1–24, 28–34
Extended: 1–34

There are many physical examples of the next two postulates. After you read Postulates 4 and 5, find examples in your classroom.

Postulate 4   *Flat Plane Postulate*

If two points are contained in a plane, then the line through them is contained in the same plane.

Postulate 5   *Plane Intersection Postulate*

If two planes intersect, then they intersect in a line.

Checking for Understanding

For each exercise, state the postulate that justifies your answer. 1. Exactly one; Line Post.

1. How many lines contain points A and B? 2. Sample: A, B, C;
Plane Post.

2. List three points that determine plane $\mathcal{K}$.

3. Is $\overleftrightarrow{AC}$ contained in plane $\mathcal{K}$? Yes; Flat Plane Post.

4. Is there a point in plane $\mathcal{E}$ not $\overleftrightarrow{AB}$? Yes; Points Post.

5. Name the intersection of planes $\mathcal{E}$ and $\mathcal{K}$. $\overleftrightarrow{AB}$; Plane Intersection Post.

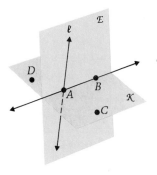

Written Exercises

Set A   Complete each statement.

1. Two points determine a _?_. line

2. If two planes intersect, the intersection is a _?_. line

3. Three noncollinear points determine a _?_. plane

4. In space there are at least four _?_, noncollinear points. noncoplanar

5. If P and Q are coplanar, then _?_ is in the same plane. $\overleftrightarrow{PQ}$

6. A _?_ contains at least two points. line

State the postulate that applies to each situation.

7. A camera tripod has three legs instead of four.

8. Two endposts determine the position of a fence.

9. Each edge of a shoebox represents a line.

10. To check the flatness of a board, a carpenter places a ruler across it in several directions and looks for any space between the ruler and the board.

7. Plane Post. 8. Line Post.
9. Plane Intersection Post.
10. Flat Plane Post.

Students may tend to visualize planes as rectangles with definite boundaries. Have students think of a plane as a "slice of air" or a similar model.

Error Analysis   When using the phrase "contained in a line" or "contained in a plane," point out that the line or plane does not have to be drawn for it to be true.

EXERCISE NOTES

Exercises 7–10   involve geometric relationships in real-world situations.
Exercises 15–20   foreshadow the **proof subskill** of supplying missing reasons.

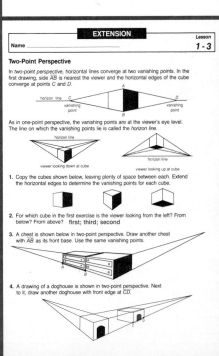

ANSWERS

Written Exercises

25. *Post. 1* A pair of blocks contains at least two blocks. A triple of blocks contains at least three blocks. Space contains at least four blocks. [true]

Post. 2 If two blocks are contained in a triple of blocks, then a pair of blocks is contained in a triple of blocks. [true]

Post. 3 Three noncollinear blocks determine a triple of blocks. [true]

Post. 4 If two blocks are contained in a triple of blocks, then a pair of blocks is contained in a triple of blocks. [true]

Post. 5 If two triples of blocks intersect, then they intersect in a pair of blocks. [true]

Complete each statement with *always*, *sometimes*, or *never*.

11. Two points are _?_ collinear. always

12. Three points _?_ determine a plane. sometimes

13. Four points are _?_ coplanar. sometimes

14. A line and a point not on the line are _?_ coplanar. always

Set B The information in the first column is given. State the postulate(s) that support each conclusion.

Given information	Conclusion	
15. P and Q are points.	Exactly one line contains P and Q.	**15.** Line Post.
16. A and B are in $\mathcal{E}$.	$\overleftrightarrow{AB}$ is in $\mathcal{E}$.	**16.** Flat Plane Post.
17. D, E, and F are noncollinear.	Exactly one plane contains D, E, and F.	**17.** Plane Post.
18. S and T are each in $\mathcal{H}$ and $\mathcal{E}$.	The intersection of $\mathcal{H}$ and $\mathcal{E}$ is $\overleftrightarrow{ST}$.	**18.** Flat Plane Post. and Plane Intersection Post.
19. ℓ is a line.	ℓ contains at least two points.	**19.** Points Post.
20. $\overleftrightarrow{XY}$ is on $\mathcal{E}$.	$\mathcal{E}$ contains a point Z not on $\overleftrightarrow{XY}$.	**20.** Points Post.

Given: A and B are on ℓ; A and B are on m.

21. What must be true about ℓ and m? **21.** They are the same line.

22. Which postulate supports your answer to Exercise 21? **22.** Line Post.

Given: A and B are on ℓ. A and B are each on $\mathcal{E}$ and $\mathcal{H}$.

23. What must be true about ℓ, $\mathcal{E}$, and $\mathcal{H}$? **23.** Planes $\mathcal{E}$ and $\mathcal{H}$ intersect in line ℓ.

24. Which postulate(s) support your answer to Exercise 23? **24.** Line Post., Flat Plane Post. and Plane Intersection Post.

Set C **25.** Study the model formed by the blocks and sticks. Suppose our undefined terms are interpreted as follows: point ↔ block; line ↔ pair of blocks (a stick is *not* part of a line); plane ↔ triple of blocks. Verify that Postulates 1−5 are true for this interpretation.

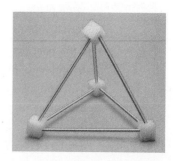

26. Find the maximum number of planes determined by four points, no three of which are collinear. 4

27. Find the maximum number of planes determined by five points, no three of which are collinear. 10

▲ **Review**

28. Name the undefined terms in this course.

29. Draw and label $\overleftrightarrow{JK}$.

30. Draw collinear points P, X, and G, with G between P and X.

31. What are *coplanar lines?* Lines contained in one plane.

32. Draw a geometric figure to represent a nickel.

≡ **Thinking** Two special subsets of a line are shown.
Ahead

33. Using our undefined terms and the idea of *between*, write a definition for segment AB.

34. Write a definition for ray AB using the words *segment* and *between*.

28. Point, line, plane

29.

30.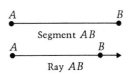

32.

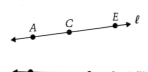

Segment AB

Ray AB

Challenge

Copy the figure at the right. Label the intersection of $\overleftrightarrow{CF}$ and $\overleftrightarrow{DE}$ point P; the intersection of $\overleftrightarrow{AF}$ and $\overleftrightarrow{BE}$ point Q; and the intersection of $\overleftrightarrow{AD}$ and $\overleftrightarrow{BC}$ point R. What appears to be true about points P, Q, and R? They appear collinear.

Repeat this activity with a different pair of lines. Is your conclusion the same? Yes

Your observation was first recorded around A.D. 300 by Pappus of Alexandria. Pappus was the author of *Mathematical Collections*, eight books that consolidated earlier writings in geometry.

Algebra Review: Solving Linear Equations

Examples

1. Solve $7x - 6 = 4x + 18$.

2. Solve $\frac{4}{5}(x + 9) = 16$.

Solutions

1. $7x - 6 = 4x + 18$

$3x - 6 = 18$ *Subtract 4x from both sides.*

$3x = 24$ *Add 6 to both sides.*

$x = 8$ *Divide both sides by 3.*

2. $\frac{4}{5}(x + 9) = 16$

$4(x + 9) = 80$ *Multiply both sides by 5.*

$4x + 36 = 80$ *Remove parentheses.*

$4x = 44$ *Subtract 36 from both sides.*

$x = 11$ *Divide both sides by 4.*

Solve each equation.

1. $3x + 5 = 26$ $x = 7$ **2.** $29 = 7x - 6$ $x = 5$ **3.** $3.2 = 5x + 0.7$ $x = 0.5$

4. $135 - 83a = 882$ $a = -9$ **5.** $8x + 2 = 5x + 44$ $x = 14$ **6.** $9 + \frac{1}{2}w = 14$ $w = 10$

7. $\frac{x + 15}{6} = 10$ $x = 45$ **8.** $6b - 12 = -4(b + 2)$ $b = 0.4$ **9.** $\frac{2}{3}(x + 4) = 6 - x$ $x = 2$?

~5¦5

Thinking Ahead

33. Segment AB is the set of points A, B and all points on line AB between A and B.

34. Ray AB is the set of segment AB and all points on line AB such that B is between A and that point.

FOLLOW-UP

More Practice

- Worksheet 1–3

Extension

Ask students to find the maximum number of lines determined by 5 points. 10

- Extension 1–3

◀ **ALGEBRA REVIEWS**

Algebra Review Exercises are another feature of this book that appear periodically. These exercises review an algebraic skill that will usually be used in a later lesson. These sets of exercises are designed to better prepare students for advanced algebra.

LESSON 1-4

Resources

Teaching Aid 4, number lines
Visual Aid 4, number lines
Worksheet 1-4
Extension 1-4
Computer Activities 1-4
Computer Worksheet 1-4
Quiz 1

OBJECTIVE

Name, describe and use segments and rays.

TEACHING NOTES

Use the following **activity** to strengthen students' ability to reason with geometric concepts.
1. Ask students to propose a def-

WORKSHEET

Name _____ Lesson **1-4**

Use the diagram to name each of the following.

A B   C   D   E   F   G   H   I   J

1. Three pairs of opposite rays $\overrightarrow{BA}$ and 2. All collinear points A, B, C, D,
   $\overrightarrow{BD}$; $\overrightarrow{CB}$ and $\overrightarrow{CE}$; $\overrightarrow{DA}$ and $\overrightarrow{DG}$; etc.   E, F, G, H, I, and J
3. All noncollinear points none   4. Intersection of $\overline{CD}$ and $\overline{DG}$ $\overline{EC}$
5. Combination of $\overline{DC}$ and $\overline{DH}$ $\overline{AJ}$ 6. Intersection of $\overline{EB}$ and $\overline{EH}$ E
   (or any two letters)
7. Intersection of $\overline{DF}$ and $\overline{GH}$ $\overline{GH}$ 8. Combination of $\overline{BE}$ and $\overline{DI}$ $\overline{BI}$

Draw a diagram to illustrate the information given.

9. Opposite half-planes X_1 containing D
   and X_2 containing E separated by t
10. $\overline{EF}$ and $\overline{FG}$ whose intersection is $\overline{EF}$
11. Opposite rays with endpoint T
12. Combination of two rays that form a line
13. $\overline{AB}$ and $\overline{CD}$ that intersect at E
14. $\overline{GH}$ and $\overline{IJ}$ whose intersection is $\overline{HI}$

Graph each of the following on a separate number line and then describe geometrically.

15. $x \geq 8$ 16. $x \leq 0$
17. $5 \geq x \geq -1$ 18. $x \geq -5$ or $x > 2$
19. $x \geq -4$ or $x < 3$ 20. $6 \leq x \leq 10$

1-4 Segments and Rays

Using a laser beam, scientists have measured the distance to the moon to within 6 cm. A beam of light from an observatory at A is aimed at a reflecting surface at B on the moon. The time required for the light to travel to the moon and back is measured. Points A and B together with the points on the path of the beam between A and B provide a physical model of a line segment.

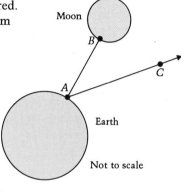

Moon
Earth
Not to scale

Definition *Segment*

A segment $\overline{RT}$ is the set of points containing R, T, and all the points between R and T.

The symbol $\overline{RT}$ is read "segment RT." The **endpoints** of the segment are R and T. This segment may also be called $\overline{TR}$.

If a laser beam is aimed away from the moon, it can be used to measure distances to objects farther out in space. The set of points on the path starting at A and extending without end through C is an example of a ray.

Definition *Ray*

A ray $\overrightarrow{RT}$ is the set of points containing $\overline{RT}$ and all points S such that T lies between R and S.

The symbol $\overrightarrow{RT}$ is read "ray RT." The endpoint of the ray is R.

Each point on a line determines two rays with the same endpoint. At the right, point B determines $\overrightarrow{BA}$ and $\overrightarrow{BC}$.

Definition *Opposite Rays*

$\overrightarrow{BA}$ and $\overrightarrow{BC}$ are opposite rays if and only if A, B, and C are collinear and B is between A and C.

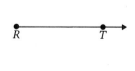

Example 1
Name the intersection of $\overrightarrow{PQ}$ and $\overrightarrow{SR}$.

Solution
$\overrightarrow{PQ}$ includes $\overline{PQ}$ and all the points on ℓ to the right of Q. $\overrightarrow{SR}$ includes $\overline{SR}$ and all the points on ℓ to the left of R. Therefore, the intersection of $\overrightarrow{PQ}$ and $\overrightarrow{SR}$ is $\overline{PS}$.

Example 2
Describe the graph of $x \geq 4$ geometrically.

Solution
Graph $x \geq 4$ on a number line.

The graph of $x \geq 4$ is a ray.

Each line in a plane separates the plane into two **half-planes**, or *sides* of the line. At right, ℓ separates the plane into half-planes $\mathcal{H}_1$ and $\mathcal{H}_2$. $\mathcal{H}_1$ contains A and all points X such that $\overline{AX}$ does not intersect ℓ.

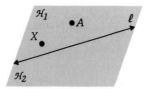

Line ℓ is the *edge* of each half-plane, but is not contained in either one. Two points A and B are in **opposite half-planes** if neither point is on the edge, and $\overline{AB}$ intersects the edge.

Checking for Understanding
How many endpoints does each figure have?
1. A segment 2
2. A ray 1
3. A line 0

Name the endpoint(s)
4. of $\overline{DE}$. D and E
5. of $\overrightarrow{PQ}$. P

6. Do $\overline{AB}$ and $\overline{BA}$ name the same segment? Explain. **6.** Yes, same set of points
7. Name the intersection of $\overline{AB}$ and $\overrightarrow{AB}$. $\overline{AB}$
8. Do $\overrightarrow{ST}$ and $\overrightarrow{TS}$ name the same ray? Explain. **8.** No; different endpoints
9. Must $\overrightarrow{QP}$ and $\overrightarrow{QR}$ be opposite rays? Explain. **9.** No; only if Q is between P and R
10. Must $\overrightarrow{QP}$ and $\overrightarrow{QR}$ be opposite rays if Q, P, and R are collinear? Explain. No; only if Q is between P and R
11. Does a half-plane contain its edge? No

---

inition for $\overline{AB}$. They will probably say something like "all points from A to B."
2. Ask them to clarify terms in their definition that are not accepted undefined terms. "From . . . to"
3. Revise the definition until it uses just the undefined terms. Use the same procedure to introduce the definition of ray.

Additional Examples

Example 1
Name the intersection of $\overline{CT}$ and $\overrightarrow{AC}$. $\overline{CA}$

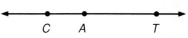

Example 2
Describe the graph of $x \leq 2$ geometrically. a ray

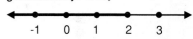

EXTENSION

Name _____   *Lesson* **1-4**

Perspective Grids

Designers, artists, and architects often use a *perspective grid* when drawing the interior of a room. A grid represents the inside surface of a huge box, with each square representing a square foot. The squares are shown in perspective. That is, various lines converge in a single point. In the grid shown, the room is fourteen feet wide, eight feet deep, and eight feet high.

This drawing shows how a perspective grid can be used to draw various objects inside a room.

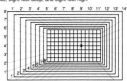

1. What are the dimensions of the door? What are the dimensions of the table? The stove? The refrigerator? 3 ft. wide × 7 ft. high; 5 ft. wide × 4 ft. deep × 3 ft. high; 4 ft. wide × 3 ft. deep × 3 ft. high; 3 ft. wide × 3 ft. deep
2. On the back wall draw a window above the table. Make the window three × 6 ft. high feet high and four feet wide. student drawing
3. Draw another window on the left wall. Make the window five feet wide and three feet high. student drawing
4. Trace the grid at the top of the page. Use it to make a simple design of a room interior. student drawing

Assignment Guide

Basic: 1–22, 36–43
Average: 2–22 (even), 23–34, 36–43
Extended: 1–21 (odd), 23–43

Error Analysis   Students may not realize that $\overline{AB}$ is the same as $\overline{BA}$, but that $\overrightarrow{AB}$ is a different set of points from $\overrightarrow{BA}$. Use diagrams to illustrate.

EXERCISE NOTES

Exercises 15–22   involve drawing a diagram, which foreshadows the **proof subskill** of supplying a diagram for a proof.
Exercises 29–34   use the **problem-solving strategy** of finding a pattern.

ANSWERS

Written Exercises

15.

16.

17.

18.

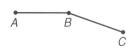

19.

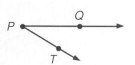

Written Exercises   **2.** Sample: $\overrightarrow{CA}$ and $\overrightarrow{BE}$
Set A   **1.** Name two segments. Sample: $\overline{AC}$ and $\overline{DE}$

2. Name two rays that are not opposite rays.

3. List two other ways of naming $\overrightarrow{BE}$. $\overrightarrow{BC}$ and $\overrightarrow{BD}$

Name the intersection of
4. $\overrightarrow{DB}$ and $\overrightarrow{CA}$. $\overrightarrow{BC}$ **5.** $\overrightarrow{BD}$ and $\overrightarrow{CE}$. $\overrightarrow{CE}$ **6.** $\overrightarrow{DC}$ and $\overrightarrow{BC}$. $\overrightarrow{BD}$

7. Name two different rays with endpoint D.

8. Name a pair of rays with endpoint C.

9. Give another name for $\overrightarrow{CB}$. $\overrightarrow{CA}$

10. Name the intersection of $\overrightarrow{DA}$ and $\overrightarrow{BC}$. $\overline{BC}$

11. Name two half-planes. $\mathcal{H}_1$ and $\mathcal{H}_2$

12. Name two points in the same half-plane.

13. Name the edge of one of the half-planes. $\overleftrightarrow{BC}$

14. Name two points in opposite half-planes.

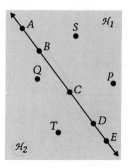

7. $\overrightarrow{DE}$ and $\overrightarrow{DC}$ (or $\overrightarrow{DB}$ or $\overrightarrow{DA}$)
8. $\overrightarrow{CD}$ (or $\overrightarrow{CE}$) and $\overrightarrow{CB}$ (or $\overrightarrow{CA}$)
12. P and S or Q and T
14. P and Q, P and T, S and Q, or S and T

Draw a diagram to illustrate the information given.

15. Point Q is on $\overleftrightarrow{DE}$, but Q is not on $\overline{DE}$.

16. $\overrightarrow{AB}$ and $\overrightarrow{AX}$ are opposite rays.

17. $\overrightarrow{RS}$ and $\overrightarrow{RT}$ are the same ray.

18. $\overline{AB}$ and $\overline{BC}$ are noncollinear.

19. $\overrightarrow{PQ}$ and $\overrightarrow{PT}$ are noncollinear.

20. Points X, Y, Q, and Z are collinear, and $\overrightarrow{XY}$ and $\overrightarrow{QZ}$ do not intersect.

21. The intersection of two rays $\overrightarrow{BC}$ and $\overrightarrow{AC}$ is $\overline{AB}$.

22. $\overline{XY}$ is in plane $\mathcal{E}$, and X and Y are in opposite half-planes with edge m.

Set B   Describe geometrically the number-line graph of each inequality.

23. $x \leq 2$ Ray   **24.** $-3 \leq x \leq 9$ Segment
25. $x > 8$ or $x \leq 8$ Line   **26.** $x \leq 1$ or $x \geq -1$ Line

27. In plane $\mathcal{E}$, P and Q are on opposite sides of line m, and Q and T are on opposite sides of line m. Are P and T on the same or opposite sides of line m?
Same

28. In plane s, A and B are on opposite sides of line ℓ, and B and C are on the same side of line ℓ. Are A and C on the same or opposite sides of line ℓ?
Opposite

Suppose points are arranged in a plane so that no three of them are collinear.

29. Find the number of rays, each containing two of the given points, that can be drawn using the specified number of points as endpoints. Record your results in a table like the one below.

Number of points	2	3	4	5	6
Number of rays	2	? 6	12	? 20	? 30

30. Look for a pattern in the table for Exercise 29. Predict the number of rays that can be drawn using 10 points.   90

31. Which expression gives the number of rays that can be drawn using n points?   d
   a. n **b.** $2n$ **c.** $n^2 - 4$ **d.** $n(n - 1)$

32. Find the number of segments that can be drawn using the given number of points as endpoints. Record answers in a table like the one below.

Number of points	2	3	4	5	6
Number of segments	? 1	? 3	? 6	? 10	? 15

33. How many segments can be drawn using 8 points?   28

34. Write an expression that gives the number of segments that can be drawn using n points. $\frac{1}{2}n(n - 1)$

Set C   **35.** There are 28 teams in the National Football League. For the annual player draft, the home office of each team must have direct telephone lines to the offices of each of the other teams. How many direct lines are required?   378

20.

21.

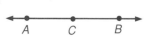

FOLLOW-UP

More Practice

• **Worksheet 1–4**

Extension

The graph of the solution set of an absolute value inequality can yield a segment or a pair of rays. For example:
1. $|x + 2| \leq 5$
$-5 \leq x + 2 \leq 5$
$-7 \leq x \leq 3$ segment
2. $|x + 2| \geq 5$
$x + 2 \geq 5$ or $x + 2 \leq -5$
$x \geq 3$ or $x \leq -7$ two rays
Have students graph various absolute value inequalities and test several values on the graph.
• **Extension 1–4**

Computers

This section includes references to either a computer activity that appears in the pupil's book, a computer activity that only appears in the teacher's book, or an activity or worksheet page from the Teacher's Resource File. See Teacher's Resource File on Computer Materials pages i-iv for further information.
    This computer activity can be completed using **The Geometric preSupposer** or **GeoDraw**. To pro-

vide a basis for understanding the Segment Addition Postulate, introduced in the next lesson, have students do the following. This and all subsequent computer activities: Drawing and measuring can be completed using one or more programs from **The Geometric Supposer** series (Sunburst, 1986) or using **GeoDraw**, a program included in each of two packages that make up the Geometry Series (IBM, 1987). Ordering information on these products is given on page i in the Computer Teacher's Resource File.

Using the computer drawing tool, draw a segment of any length and then label any point on that segment. Assuming that the endpoints of the first segment are A and B and that the point on the segment is C, have students measure $\overline{AB}$, $\overline{AC}$ and $\overline{CB}$ and then compare the sum of $AC + CB$ with AB. Repeat the activity several times. Have students make a generalization about the lengths of the three segments formed by any three collinear points.

You may complete computer drawing and measuring activities in this book in the form of a class demonstration and discussion if you have one computer available for use in your classroom, or if resources permit, you may have the students do these activities individually or in pairs.
• **Computer Activities 1–4**
• **Computer Worksheet 1–4**

◀ **PROGRESS CHECKS**

The Progress Checks that appear after every few lessons are designed to help the students review the chapter lessons studied up to that point.

▲ **Review**
36. Statements we assume are called __?__.

37. How many lines are determined by two points? 1

38. Give three names for this line. $\overleftrightarrow{XY}$, $\overleftrightarrow{YX}$, m

39. Points or lines not contained in the same plane are __?__. noncoplanar

40. Explain why our study of geometry does not depend solely on the appearance of figures.

Thinking Ahead
41. Draw a ray, $\overrightarrow{PQ}$. Is there a point S on $\overrightarrow{PQ}$ that is 5 cm from P? How many such points are there?

42. Draw a segment, $\overline{XY}$. Is there a point T on $\overline{XY}$ that is the same distance from X and Y? How many such points are there? Yes; 1

43. A rope ties Fido to a post in the yard. If he walks all around the post, keeping the rope taut, what shape is his path? Circle

36. Postulates
40. Appearances of figures can be misleading
41. Yes, 1
42.

Progress Check

Lesson 1-1, page 1 Accept any answers students can justify.
Describe each shape geometrically.
1. A record album Circle **2.** A roll of paper towels Cylinder
3. A tennis ball Sphere **4.** The top of a shoebox Rectangle

Lesson 1-2, page 5
5. Points A, B, and C are __?__ points. collinear
6. Points E, F, D, and G are __?__ points. noncoplanar
7. The intersection of $\overleftrightarrow{AC}$ and $\mathcal{K}$ is __?__. B

Lesson 1-3, page 10
8. Name points that determine line ℓ. E, F
9. Name points that determine plane $\mathcal{H}$. E, F, G
10. The intersection of $\mathcal{H}$ and $\mathcal{K}$ is __?__. line ℓ

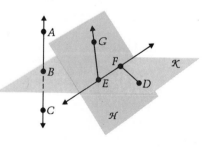

Lesson 1-4, page 14
11. Name two segments with endpoint F. $\overline{EF}$, $\overline{DF}$
12. Name two rays with endpoint E. $\overrightarrow{EF}$, $\overrightarrow{EG}$
13. Name a pair of opposite rays. $\overrightarrow{BA}$, $\overrightarrow{BC}$

1. A figure consisting of two points and all the points between them is a(n) __?__. **Segment**
2. True or false: A ray has two endpoints. **False**
3. True or false: $\overline{TV}$ is the same as $\overline{VT}$. **True**
4. True or false: $\overrightarrow{TV}$ is the same as $\overrightarrow{VT}$. **False**

1-5 Linear Measure

A ruler can be used to measure the distance between two points. For example, the distance between A and B is 6 cm. What is the distance between B and C? **3 cm**

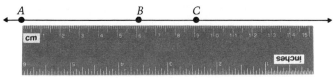

If we slide the ruler to the left, so that A is above the 2, B would be above the 8. The distance between A and B would not be changed. This concept is formalized in Postulate 6.

Postulate 6   *Ruler Postulate*

For every pair of points, there is a unique positive real number called the distance between the two points.

The distance between points A and B is denoted AB. In the diagram above, $AB = 6$ and $BC = 3$.

The *length*, or *linear measure*, of a segment is the distance between its endpoints. Note that $\overline{AB}$ represents a segment, which is a set of points, while AB represents the length of the segment, which is a real number.

When a unit is not specified in this book, you can assume it to be centimeters, meters, feet, or any convenient unit of measure. Unless otherwise specified, the same unit is used for all the measurements in a diagram.

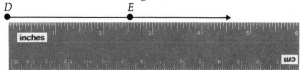

How many points F can you find on $\overrightarrow{DE}$ such that $DF = 4$ inches? **One**
Postulate 7 generalizes this property.

Postulate 7   *Segment Construction Postulate*

On any ray, there is exactly one point at a given distance from the endpoint of the ray.

This postulate justifies the method used to cut a 4-ft. length from a longer board: From R, measure along the edge of the board to locate the unique point Q, such that $RQ = 4$ ft.

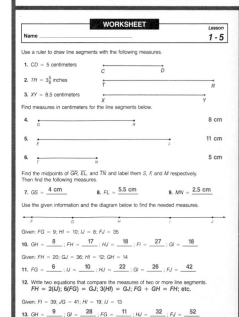

LESSON 1–5

Resources

Compass
Meter stick
Straightedge
Worksheet 1–5
Extension 1–5
💻 Computer Activities 1–5

OBJECTIVES

Apply the basic postulates concerning linear measure; define and find midpoints and bisectors.

TEACHING NOTES

Begin this lesson with an **activity** to clarify the Ruler Postulate. Draw several segments and have students use a meter stick with the first few centimeters broken

WORKSHEET — Lesson **1-5**

Name _____

Use a ruler to draw line segments with the following measures.

1. CD = 5 centimeters
2. $TR = 3\frac{5}{8}$ inches
3. XY = 8.5 centimeters

Find measures in centimeters for the line segments below.

4. 8 cm
5. 11 cm
6. 5 cm

Find the midpoints of $\overline{GR}$, $\overline{EL}$, and $\overline{TN}$ and label them S, F, and M respectively. Then find the following measures.

7. $GS = $ **4 cm**   8. $FL = $ **5.5 cm**   9. $MN = $ **2.5 cm**

Use the given information and the diagram below to find the needed measures.

Given: FG = 9; HI = 10; IJ = 8; FJ = 35

10. $GH = $ **8** ; $FH = $ **17** ; $HJ = $ **18** ; $FI = $ **27** ; $GI = $ **18**

Given: FH = 20; GJ = 36; HI = 12; GH = 14

11. $FG = $ **6** ; $IJ = $ **10** ; $HJ = $ **22** ; $GI = $ **26** ; $FJ = $ **42**

12. Write two equations that compare the measures of two or more line segments.
$FH = 2(IJ)$; $6(FG) = GJ$; $3(HI) = GJ$; $FG + GH = FH$; etc.

Given: FI = 39; JG = 41; HI = 19; IJ = 13

13. $GH = $ **9** ; $GI = $ **28** ; $FG = $ **11** ; $HJ = $ **32** ; $FJ = $ **52**

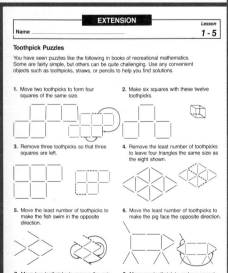
Example 1
How might a contractor measure a 20-foot section of gutter using a 16-foot tape measure?

Solution
Since P is between A and B, $AP + PB = AB$. Thus, $AB = 20$. Postulate 8 formalizes this idea.

Postulate 8 *Segment Addition Postulate*

If point P is between points A and B, then $AP + PB = AB$.

Note that in the equation $AP + PB = AB$, we are adding lengths, which are real numbers.

Definition *Midpoint of a Segment*

A midpoint of a segment $\overline{RT}$ is a point S between R and T such that $RS = ST$.

This definition means that if S is a midpoint of $\overline{RT}$, then S is between R and T and $RS = ST$. It also means that if S is between R and T and $RS = ST$, then S is a midpoint of $\overline{RT}$.

If the lengths of two segments are equal, we will also say that the segments are equal. Thus, a midpoint separates a segment into two equal segments. In the next postulate, *exactly one* means *one and only one*.

Postulate 9 *Midpoint Postulate*

A segment has exactly one midpoint.

Plane $\mathcal{K}$ intersects $\overline{AB}$ at C, the midpoint of $\overline{AB}$. We say that $\mathcal{K}$ bisects $\overline{AB}$. A plane, a line, a ray, a segment, or even a single point can bisect a segment.

Definition *Bisector of a Segment*

A bisector of a segment is a set of points whose intersection with the segment is the midpoint of the segment.

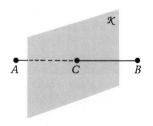

Assignment Guide

Basic: 1–14, 27–32
Average: 1–20, 27–32
Extended: 1–32

We can now describe a circle in terms you have just learned. A *circle* is the set of points in a plane at a fixed distance—the *radius*—from a fixed point—the *center*. Name the center of the circle at the right. Name two radii. C; any two of $\overline{CS}$, $\overline{CT}$, $\overline{CP}$

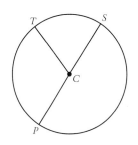

Some geometric statements are always true, some are never true, and some are true only in certain cases. To show that a given statement is not always true, we need just one case in which the statement is false. That one case is called a *counterexample*.

Example 2
Show that the following statement is not always true: If a line intersects a segment, it bisects the segment.

Solution
The diagram at the right shows a counterexample. In this case, ℓ intersects $\overline{FG}$ but does not bisect $\overline{FG}$.

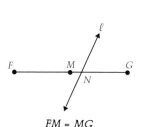

FM = MG

Checking for Understanding   2. Seg. Addition Post.
State the postulate or definition that supports each statement.

1. For two points P and Q, PQ ≠ −7. Ruler Post.

2. If R is between S and T, SR = 6, and RT = 8, then ST = 14.

3. If X is on $\overrightarrow{AB}$ and AX = 7, then there is not another point Y on $\overrightarrow{AB}$ such that AY = 7. Seg. Construction Post.

4. If B is between A and C, and AB = BC, then B is the midpoint of $\overline{AC}$. Def. of midpt.

5. If $\overleftrightarrow{CD}$ bisects $\overline{AB}$ at M, then M is the midpoint of $\overline{AB}$. Def. of bisector

Written Exercises
Set A   **1.** If BD = 6, then DB = _?_. 6

2. If AD = 10 and AD = BE, then BE = _?_. 10

3. If AC = 7 and CE = 5, then AE = _?_. 12

4. If BD = 8 and C is the midpoint of $\overline{BD}$, then BC = _?_. 4

5. If BE = 12 and DE = 3, then BD = _?_. 9

6. If AC = CE then C is the _?_ of $\overline{AE}$. midpoint

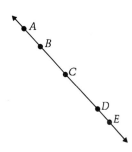

Because S is between P and Q, PS + SQ = PQ, so PQ = $8\frac{1}{2}$.

Example 2
Show that the following statement is not always true: If a point is between A and B, then it is the midpoint of $\overline{AB}$.

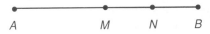

If M is the midpoint of $\overline{AB}$, let N be the midpoint of $\overline{MB}$. N is between A and B, but it is not the midpoint of $\overline{AB}$.

Error Analysis   The notation of $\overline{AB}$ representing a segment and AB representing its length is often confusing to students. Point out the distinction between the two notations.

EXERCISE NOTES

Exercises 11–14   develop the **proof subskill** of supplying missing reasons.
Exercises 15–20   involve the concept of proof by contradiction.

7. Explain how a plumber applies the Segment Construction Postulate to cut a length of pipe.

8. The distance of a flight between Chicago and New York can be determined by using a map. Which postulate explains why it makes no difference in which direction you measure?

9. A third-down football play involved a 20-yard forward pass from the line of scrimmage followed by a 15-yard run.

   a. How many yards were gained on the play?

   b. Upon which postulate is your conclusion based?

10. To cut a 36-cm rod in half, you can measure 18 cm from one end of the rod. Which postulate guarantees that it makes no difference from which end you measure?

The information in the first column is given. State the postulate or definition that supports each conclusion.

	Given information	**Conclusion**
11.	Points A and B	AB is a positive real number.
12.	Plane $\mathcal{F}$ bisects $\overline{CD}$ at point P.	P is the midpoint of $\overline{CD}$.
13.	$\overline{XY}$	$\overline{XY}$ has only one midpoint.
14.	Point Q is the midpoint of $\overline{MN}$.	$MQ = QN$

Set B Sketch a counterexample for each statement.

15. If points P, Q, and R are collinear, then $PQ + QR = PR$.

16. If $AM = MB$, then M is the midpoint of $\overline{AB}$.

17. If point P is on line m, there is only one point on m at a given distance from P.

18. If $RS = AB$, and $\overline{RS}$ bisects $\overline{AB}$ at M, then M is the midpoint of $\overline{RS}$.

19. Point B is between A and C and $AC = 24$. If BC is 3 times AB, find AB. 6

20. Point Q is between P and R and $PR = 41$. If PQ is 8 more than twice QR, find PQ. 30

7. Starting at one end of the pipe, measure the length desired. There is only one place on the pipe the given distance from the end.
8. Ruler Post.
9. a. 35 yd.
   b. Seg. Addition Post.
10. Midpt. Post.
11. Ruler Post.
12. Def. of bisector
13. Midpt. Post.
14. Def. of midpt.

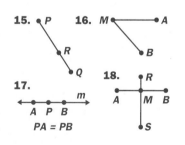

15. P   16. M   A
              R   B
           Q   18.   R
17.   A M B
        m
    A P B
    PA = PB   S

Set C Which postulate in this lesson ensures

21. that any ray contains infinitely many points?

22. that any line contains infinitely many points?

23. Where along the line should a supply depot be located so that the sum of the distances traveled by the two robots to the depot is as small as possible? Any pt. on $\overline{X_1X_2}$

Repeat Exercise 23 for the case of

24. a robot at each of 3 collinear stations. X_2

25. a robot at each of 4 collinear stations.

26. a robot at each of n collinear stations.
     25. Any pt. on $\overline{X_2X_3}$

♦ **Review** **27.** Draw and label $\overline{MN}$, $\overrightarrow{TW}$, and opposite rays JK and JD.

28. Describe geometrically the number-line graph of $-6 \le x \le -1$. Segment

29. How many planes are determined by three noncollinear points? 1

30. Name a real-world object that can be represented by this figure. Sample: piece of floor tile

31. Draw and label a diagram to show $\overleftrightarrow{MN}$ and $\overleftrightarrow{ST}$ intersecting at G.

≡ **Thinking Ahead** **32.** Sketch two noncollinear rays that have a common endpoint P. Locate point A on one of the rays and point B on the other. Draw $\overline{AB}$ and label its midpoint M. Then draw $\overrightarrow{PM}$.

  a. $\overrightarrow{PM}$ is a ___?___ of $\overline{AB}$. bisector

  b. Name your other pairs of rays, each pair with a common endpoint. $\overrightarrow{PA}$ and $\overrightarrow{PM}$; $\overrightarrow{PB}$ and $\overrightarrow{PM}$

💻 **Computer Activities: Drawing and Measuring**

1. Draw noncollinear rays AB and AC with common endpoint A. Draw segment BC. Mark point D on $\overline{BC}$, and draw $\overrightarrow{AD}$. Ray AD is ___?___ rays AB and AC. between

2. Draw noncollinear rays AB and AC with common endpoint A and with $AB = AC$. Draw segment BC and label its midpoint D. Draw $\overline{AD}$. Segment $\overline{AD}$ is a ___?___ of $\overline{BC}$. bisector

21. Seg. Construction Post.
22. Seg. Construction Post.

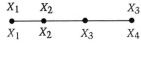

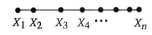

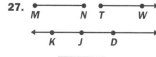

27.

31.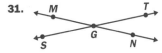

32.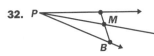

1. 2.

FOLLOW-UP

More Practice

• **Worksheet 1–5**

Extension

Given the sentence "If P, then Q," we need to know that hypothesis P is true in order to conclude Q. Use the following problems to give students some informal experience with this type of reasoning.
1. What information do you need to use the Segment Addition Postulate to show that $XY + YZ = XZ$? Y is between X and Z.
2. What information do you need to show that M is the midpoint of $\overline{AB}$? M is between A and B, and $AM = MB$.

• **Extension 1–5**

Computers

The computer activity in the pupil's book can be completed using **The Geometric preSupposer: Points and Lines** or **GeoDraw**. If you are using the **Geometric preSupposer:** The program does not directly offer the option to draw a ray. The best way for the student to begin this activity is to draw an angle of any measure.

  If you are using **GeoDraw:** To create segments of of equal length on rays $\overrightarrow{AB}$ and $\overrightarrow{AC}$, students use the "aRc" command.
• **Computer Activities 1–5**

⚙ Construction Exercises

The Greeks used only two instruments when constructing
geometric figures. The **straightedge**, an unmarked ruler, was
used to draw lines. The **compass** was used to draw circles
and parts of circles called **arcs**. We also use only those
instruments. The following construction applies the Segment
Construction Postulate.

Construction 1

Construct a segment equal to a given segment.

Given $\overline{AB}$

Construct A segment equal to $\overline{AB}$

Method **Step 1:** Draw a line ℓ with a straightedge.
Mark any point X on ℓ.

Step 2: Put the compass point on A and the
compass pencil on B. The *compass radius*
is now AB.

Step 3: Using X as the center and AB as
the compass radius, draw an arc that
intersects ℓ. Label the point of intersection Y.
Then $XY = AB$.

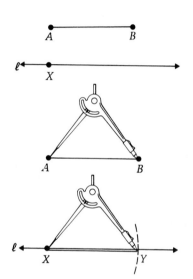

Construct a segment equal to the given segment.

1. P ——————— Q **2.** E ——————— F

3. G ——————— H **4.** R ——————— S

Given: $\overline{AB}$ and $\overline{CD}$. Construct a segment of the required length.

5. $AB + CD$ **6.** $2AB$ **7.** $CD - AB$

8. $AB + 2CD$ **9.** $4AB - CD$ **10.** $2(DC - AB)$

11. Given $AB = 6$ and $CD = 10$, construct $\overline{XY}$ so $XY = 2$.

Warm-Up Review

1. Points *B*, *D* and *A* are __?__. Noncollinear or coplanar
2. __?__ rays form a line. Opposite
3. What do we call the set of all points on the same side of $\overleftrightarrow{AB}$ as *C*? A half-plane
4. If *RS* = *ST*, then *S* is the __?__ of $\overline{RT}$. Midpoint

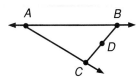

1-6 Angles and Angle Measure

The angle formed by the face of a golf club determines the angle at which a hit ball leaves the ground. This lesson gives a formal definition of angle and discusses the way angles are measured. As you will see, the properties of angle measure are similar to those of linear measure, though the units are different.

Definition *Angle*

An angle is the union of two noncollinear rays which have the same endpoint.

The rays are called the *sides* of the angle and their common endpoint is the *vertex*.

The sides of the angle at the right are $\overrightarrow{PA}$ and $\overrightarrow{PB}$; the vertex is *P*. The angle can be denoted by ∠*APB*, ∠*BPA*, ∠*P*, or ∠1. When three letters are used, the letter of the vertex is in the middle.

When two or more angles have the same vertex, using a single-letter name causes confusion. In the figure at the right, no angle should be named ∠*S*. Why? Instead, three letters are used: ∠*RST*, ∠*TSV*, or ∠*VSR*. There are 3 ∠s with vertex S.

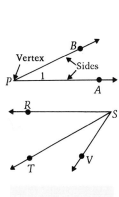

An angle determines three sets of points in a plane: the points on the angle, those in its interior, and those in its exterior.

Definition *Interior of an Angle*

The interior of ∠APB is the intersection of two half-planes: the side of $\overleftrightarrow{PA}$ containing B and the side of $\overleftrightarrow{PB}$ containing A.

Definition *Exterior of an Angle*

The exterior of an angle is the set of points in the plane which do not belong to the interior of the angle or to the angle itself.

Unless otherwise specified, points may be assumed to be in the interior (or exterior) of an angle when a diagram shows them in that position.

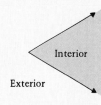

1-6 *Angles and Angle Measure*

LESSON 1-6

Resources

Compass
Straightedge
Teaching Aid 1, protractor
Visual Aid 1, protractor
Worksheet 1–6
Extension 1–6
Computer Worksheet 1–6

OBJECTIVES

Recognize and name angles and their component parts; apply the basic postulates relating to angles and their measures.

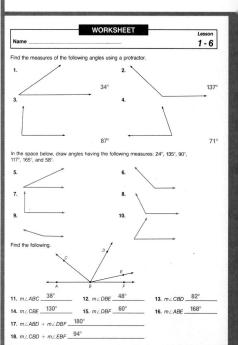

TEACHING NOTES

Begin this lesson with the definition of angle, stressing that the sides are *noncollinear* rays with the *same* endpoint.

As postulates are introduced, ask students to name the corresponding postulate for linear measure when applicable.

Before introducing the Protractor Postulate, review how to measure angles using a protractor.

Additional Example

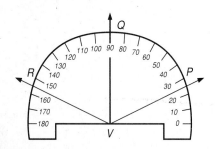

A protractor can be used to measure an angle in *degrees*. Each placement of the protractor shown at the right yields the same measure for ∠SQR. Postulate 10 confirms this for all angles.

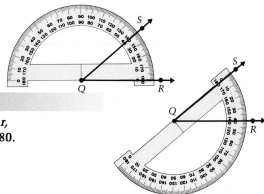

Postulate 10 *Protractor Postulate*

For every angle there is a unique real number r, called its degree measure, such that $0 < r < 180$.

If the degree measure of ∠SQR is 40, we write $m\angle SQR = 40$. Or we say that ∠SQR is an angle of 40° (read "40 degrees").

A protractor can also be used to draw an angle with a given measure. In the diagram at the right, $\overrightarrow{PB}$ was drawn so that $m\angle APB = 60$. Can you draw another 60° angle, ∠APD, with D in $\mathcal{H}_1$? **No**

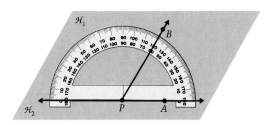

Postulate 11 *Angle Construction Postulate*

Let $\mathcal{H}_1$ be a half-plane with edge $\overleftrightarrow{PA}$. There is exactly one ray $\overrightarrow{PB}$ with B in $\mathcal{H}_1$ such that ∠APB has a given measure.

Example

Using the diagram at the right, find $m\angle APB$, $m\angle BPC$, and $m\angle APC$. How are these measures related?

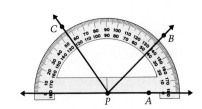

Solution

$m\angle APB = 45$, $m\angle BPC = 80$, and $m\angle APC = 125$.
So $m\angle APB + m\angle BPC = m\angle APC$.

The next postulate, similar to the Segment Addition Postulate, generalizes this result.

Postulate 12 *Angle Addition Postulate*

If B is in the interior of ∠APC, then $m\angle APB + m\angle BPC = m\angle APC$.

Since angle measures are real numbers, algebra may be used to rewrite $m\angle APB + m\angle BPC = m\angle APC$ as $m\angle BPC = m\angle APC - m\angle APB$.

Assignment Guide

Basic: 1–19, 38–48
Average: 1–19 (odd), 20–34, 38–48
Extended: 2–18 (even), 20–48

Just as segments have midpoints, angles have bisectors.

Definition   *Angle Bisector*

A bisector of an angle APC is a ray $\overrightarrow{PB}$ such that B is in the interior of $\angle APC$ and $m\angle APB = m\angle BPC$.

If two angles have the same measure, we will say they are equal. Thus an angle bisector separates an angle into two equal angles.

Postulate 13   *Angle Bisector Postulate*

An angle has exactly one bisector.

If you compare Postulates 10–13 with Postulates 6–9, you will notice many similarities.

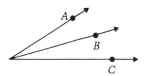

Checking for Understanding

1. Name a point in the interior of $\angle EPG$.   F
2. Name a point in the exterior of $\angle BPD$.   A, E, F, G, or H
3. Name the vertex of $\angle HPF$.   P   4. $\angle APG, \angle BPG, \angle CPG,$
4. Name seven angles that have $\overrightarrow{PG}$ as a side. $\angle DPG, \angle EPG,$ $\angle FPG, \angle HPG$

Give the measure of each angle.

5. $\angle APC$ 40   6. $\angle APE$ 100   7. $\angle APG$ 165   8. $\angle FPB$ 140
9. $\angle BPD$ 60   10. $\angle EPD$ 30   11. $\angle CPD$ 30   12. $\angle GPD$ 95

Give the bisector of each angle.

13. $\angle DPB$ $\overrightarrow{PC}$ 14. $\angle HPF$ $\overrightarrow{PG}$

15. Name an angle equal to $\angle EPC$. $\angle BPD$

Written Exercises

$\angle DEG, \angle GED$

Set A
1. Name $\angle 1$ in two other ways. $\angle 3, \angle GEF$
2. Name all the angles shown which have $\overrightarrow{EF}$ as a side.
3. Name all the angles shown. $\angle 1, \angle 2, \angle 3, \angle DEH, \angle GEF$
4. Name a point in the interior of $\angle GEF$.   H
5. Name a point in the exterior of $\angle 2$.   D or F
6. Is the union of $\overrightarrow{ED}$ and $\overrightarrow{EG}$ an angle? Explain.
7. Is the union of $\overrightarrow{ED}$ and $\overrightarrow{EF}$ an angle? Explain.
8. If $\overrightarrow{EH}$ is the bisector of $\angle GEF$, what can you conclude about $\angle 2$ and $\angle 3$? $m\angle 2 = m\angle 3$
9. What information is needed to conclude that $\overrightarrow{EG}$ is the bisector of $\angle DEH$? $m\angle 1 = m\angle 2$

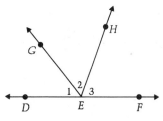

6. Yes; rays are noncollinear with same endpoint.
7. No; rays are collinear.

(a) Using the diagram, find $m\angle$ PVQ   50; $m\angle QVR$ 65; and $m\angle$ PVR   115.
(b) How are these angles related? $m\angle PVQ + m\angle QVR =$ $m\angle PVR$

Error Analysis   Students often incorrectly name angles. Stress the following points:
1. An angle may be named by its vertex if there is only *one* angle in the diagram with that vertex.
2. When using a three-letter name for an angle, the middle letter must be the vertex.
3. $\angle ABC$ is an angle, but $m\angle ABC$ is a real number.

EXERCISE NOTES

Exercise 9   uses the affirming-the-hypothesis technique.
Exercises 20–25   foreshadow the **proof subskill** of drawing a diagram.
Exercise 28   could be done on a **computer**.
Exercise 34   could be completed as a **group activity**.
Exercise 37   involves the **problem-solving strategy** finding a pattern.

10. Using $\overrightarrow{PD}$ as a side, can you draw another angle with the same measure as that of $\angle DPC$? Explain.

10. Yes; use half-plane with edge $\overleftrightarrow{PD}$ not containing C.

11. $m\angle APB + m\angle BPC = m\angle \underline{\quad?\quad}$ **APC**

12. $m\angle DPB + m\angle BPA = m\angle \underline{\quad?\quad}$ **DPA**

13. $m\angle BPD - m\angle CPD = m\angle \underline{\quad?\quad}$ **BPC**

14. $m\angle BPD - m\angle BPC = m\angle \underline{\quad?\quad}$ **CPD**

15. If $\overrightarrow{PC}$ is the bisector of $\angle DPB$ and $m\angle CPD = 28$, then $m\angle BPC = \underline{\quad?\quad}$. **28**

16. If $\overrightarrow{PC}$ is the bisector of $\angle DPB$ and $m\angle DPB = 62$, then $m\angle DPC = \underline{\quad?\quad}$. **31**

17. If $m\angle APC = x + 10$ and $m\angle CPD = x - 10$, find $m\angle APD$. **2x**

18. If $m\angle BPD = 2x$ and $m\angle CPD = x - 1$, find $m\angle BPC$. **x + 1**

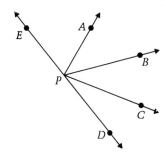

19. A drafting student drew $\angle PQR$. What is $m\angle PQR$? Which postulate is used to get this measure?
150; Angle Addition Post.

Set B   Draw a sketch, if possible, to illustrate each situation. Otherwise, write *not possible*.

20. Two angles whose intersection is a point

21. Two angles whose intersection is a segment

22. Two angles whose intersection is a ray

23. Two angles whose intersection is a line **Not possible**

24. The vertex of $\angle 1$ is in the interior of $\angle 2$ and vice versa.

25. $\angle 3$ and $\angle 4$ have the same vertex, and the interior of $\angle 3$ is contained in the interior of $\angle 4$.

A point X is in the interior of $\angle PQR$.

26. If $m\angle PQX = 40$ and $m\angle PQR = 110$, find $m\angle XQR$. **70**

27. If $m\angle PQX$ is 30 more than $m\angle RQX$ and $m\angle PQR = 90$, find $m\angle PQX$ and $m\angle RQX$. **60; 30**

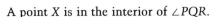

28. The list of instructions at the right is in a computer language called Logo. A pointer *A* is at the center of the screen. "RIGHT 30" means "rotate the pointer 30° to the right." Sketch the design that would be produced by this list of Logo instructions.

```
RIGHT 30
FORWARD 50
RIGHT 120
FORWARD 50
RIGHT 120
FORWARD 50
```

Point *P* is between *A* and *B*. Points *C*, *E*, and *D* are in the same half-plane with edge $\overleftrightarrow{AB}$. Point *C* is in the interior of ∠*APE*. $\overrightarrow{PE}$ bisects ∠*DPC*.

29. Draw a diagram to illustrate the situation.

30. If *m*∠*APC* = 72 and *m*∠*CPD* = 70, find *m*∠*APE*. **107**

The U.S. Army Artillery Corps uses a semicircular protractor divided into 3,200 units. This unit of angle measure is called a *mil*.

31. Modify the postulates of this lesson so that they would be useful to the Artillery Corps.

32. Would the changes in angle measure from degrees to mils require changes in any definitions in this lesson? **No**

33. Give the mil measure of a 90° angle; of a 135° angle. **1,600; 2,400**

34. A hot-air balloon is directly over a line between two observers who are 1 km apart. The observers, at *A* and *B*, find that the balloon's *angles of elevation* are 30° and 15°. Make a scale drawing and estimate the height of the balloon and its distance from each observer.

Set C A creative geometry student suggested that the measure of an angle *ABC* be determined as follows:

a. Choose *X* on $\overrightarrow{BA}$ such that *BX* = 1 unit.

b. Choose *Y* on $\overrightarrow{BC}$ such that *BY* = 1 unit.

c. The measure of ∠*ABC* is the length of $\overline{XY}$.

35. Draw angles with degree measures of 30, 60, and 90. Find their measures as defined above.

36. Are Postulates 10, 11, and 12 still satisfied when angles are measured in this new way? Explain.

29.

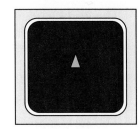

30. ...

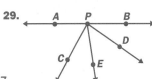

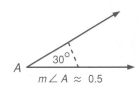

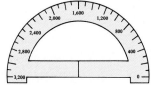

31. In Post. 10, change "degree" to "mil" and "0<*r*<180" to 0<*r*<3,200. Post. 11-13 remains the same.

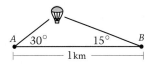

34. ...1 km scale drawing

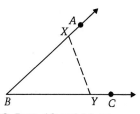

36. Post. 10 and 11 are satisfied; Post. 12 is not.

Written Exercises

28. (equilateral △)

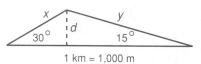

34. *d* ≈ 180 m; *x* ≈ 360 m; *y* ≈ 700 m

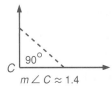

1 km = 1,000 m

35.

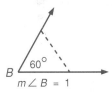

m∠*A* ≈ 0.5

m∠*B* = 1

90°
m∠*C* ≈ 1.4

Thinking Ahead

46. c. 70 **d.** $\overrightarrow{PA}$ **e.** opposite **f.** 180

FOLLOW-UP

More Practice

• **Worksheet 1–6**

Extension

Airport runways are numbered from 0 through 35, where the number is one-tenth the degree measure of the clockwise rotation from due north. Work through an example and have students try the following problems:

1. Sketch the positions of runways 17 and 30.

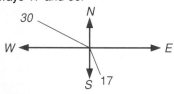

2. What runways would be opposite runways 17 and 30? 35; 12
3. If a plane is cleared for landing on runway 27, in what direction is it heading? due east

• **Extension 1–6**

Computers

• **Computer Worksheet 1–6**

37. Determine the maximum number of angles formed by 20 coplanar, noncollinear rays that have a common endpoint. **190**

▲ **Review 38.** If ℓ contains the midpoint of $\overline{JK}$, then ℓ is a __?__ of $\overline{JK}$. **bisector**

39. State the Segment Construction Postulate.

40. Can $\overrightarrow{MO}$ and $\overrightarrow{OC}$ be opposite rays? Explain.

39. On any ray, there is exactly one point at a given distance from the endpoint of the ray.

Is each statement *always*, *sometimes*, or *never* true?

41. A plane is determined by three points. **Sometimes**
42. Space is the set of all points. **Always**

40. No; different endpoints

≛ **Thinking 43.** Give a pair of angle measures whose sum
▼ **Ahead**
  a. is less than 90.   **b.** is 90.
  c. is between 90 and 180. **d.** is 180.
  e. is greater than 180.

**43. Samples: a. 35 and 40
b. 25 and 65 c. 100 and 50
d. 120 and 60 e. 150 and 75**

44. Use a protractor to draw two angles with a common side, but no common interior points, and whose sum
  a. is 90.   **b.** is 180.

45. Mark points P and A on a line, m. Let $\mathcal{H}_1$ and $\mathcal{H}_2$ be the half-planes with edge m.
  a. Use a protractor to locate a point B in $\mathcal{H}_1$ so that $m\angle APB = 45$.
  b. Choose a point C in $\mathcal{H}_2$ on $\overrightarrow{PB}$.
  c. Measure $\angle APC$. **135**
  d. What is common to $\angle APB$ and $\angle APC$? $\overrightarrow{PA}$
  e. What kind of rays are $\overrightarrow{PB}$ and $\overrightarrow{PC}$? **Opposite**
  f. What is the sum of $m\angle APB$ and $m\angle APC$? **180**

46. Repeat Exercise 45 with $m\angle APB = 110$.

47. $m\angle A + m\angle B = 90$. Find $m\angle B$ if $m\angle A$ is
  a. 30. **60**   **b.** 42. **48**   **c.** 2x. **90 − 2x** **d.** x − 1. **91 − x**

48. $m\angle C + m\angle D = 180$. Find $m\angle D$ if $m\angle C$ is
  a. 86. **94**   **b.** 29. **151**   **c.** 90. **90**   **d.** 5 − 2x. **175 + 2x**

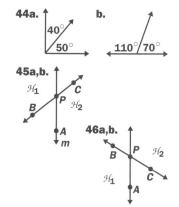

Construction Exercises

Construction 2

Construct an angle equal to a given angle.

Given   ∠*FGH*

Construct   An angle equal to ∠*FGH*

Method   **Step 1:** Draw ray $\overrightarrow{QR}$.

Step 2: With *G* as center, construct an arc which intersects $\overrightarrow{GF}$ and $\overrightarrow{GH}$. Label the points of intersection *V* and *W*, respectively.

Step 3: With center *Q* and radius *GV*, construct an arc which intersects $\overrightarrow{QR}$ at *S*.

Step 4: With center *S* and radius *VW*, construct an arc which intersects the arc in Step 3 at *P*.

Step 5: Draw $\overrightarrow{QP}$. Then *m*∠*PQR* = *m*∠*FGH*, so ∠*PQR* and ∠*FGH* are equal angles.

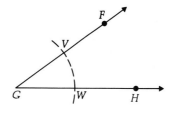

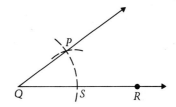

Construction 3

Construct the bisector of a given angle.

Given   ∠*ABC*

Construct $\overrightarrow{BD}$, the bisector of ∠*ABC*

Method   **Step 1:** With *B* as center, construct an arc that intersects $\overrightarrow{BA}$ and $\overrightarrow{BC}$ at *X* and *Y*, respectively.

Step 2: With *X* and *Y* as centers, and a radius greater than $\frac{1}{2}XY$, construct two arcs that intersect in the interior of ∠*ABC*. Label the point of intersection *D*.

Step 3: Draw $\overrightarrow{BD}$. Then $\overrightarrow{BD}$ bisects ∠*ABC*.

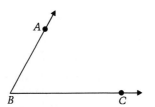

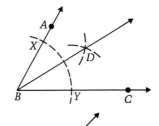

Trace each angle at the right.

1. Construct an angle equal to ∠M.

2. Construct an angle equal to ∠N.

3. Construct an angle ∠*T* so that *m*∠*F* = *m*∠*M* + *m*∠*N*.

Trace the angles at the right again.

4. Bisect ∠M.   **5.** Bisect ∠N.

6. Construct an angle ∠*V* so that *m*∠*V* = $\frac{1}{2}$(*m*∠*M* + *m*∠*N*).

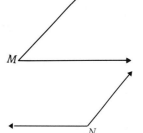

Warm-Up Review

1. Name a pair of opposite rays. $\overrightarrow{VA}$ and $\overrightarrow{VD}$
2. Name a point in the interior of ∠AVC. B
3. According to the __?__ Postulate, $m\angle CVB + m\angle BVA = m\angle CVA$. Angle Addition
4. V is the __?__ of ∠AVB. Vertex

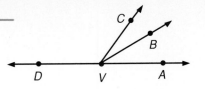

LESSON 1-7

Resources

Carpenter's square
Compass
Straightedge
Teaching Aid 1, protractor
Visual Aid 1, protractor
Worksheet 1-7
Extension 1-7
Computer Activities 1-7

OBJECTIVES

Recognize and name types of angles and special pairs of angles; apply concepts relating to complements and supplements.

WORKSHEET   Lesson **1-7**

Name _____

Use the diagram to name each of the following.

1. Two pairs of vertical angles Answers to exercises 1, 2, 4, and 5 will vary.
2. Two linear pairs
3. Two pairs of complementary angles ∠CBD and ∠DBE; ∠ABG and ∠GBF
4. Two pairs of adjacent angles
5. Two acute angles

Find the following.

6. $m\angle ABC =$ __53__
7. $m\angle CBD =$ __37__
8. $m\angle JKL =$ __80__
9. $m\angle LKM =$ __100__

Given: The complement of ∠A has a measure of 58.

10. measure of ∠A = __32__
11. measure of the supplement of ∠A = __148__

Given: ∠S and ∠R are supplementary; $m\angle S = 7(m\angle R)$

12. $m\angle S = $ __$157\frac{1}{2}$__
13. $m\angle R = $ __$22\frac{1}{2}$__

Given: ∠CAB ≅ ∠BAD; $m\angle CAD = 105$

14. $m\angle CAB = $ __$52\frac{1}{2}$__
15. $m\angle BAD = $ __$52\frac{1}{2}$__

Given: ∠EDG and ∠GDF form a right angle; $m\angle EDG = 4(m\angle GDF)$

16. $m\angle EDG = $ __72__
17. $m\angle GDF = $ __18__

Given: $\overrightarrow{QR}$ bisects ∠SQT; $m\angle SQR = 4x - 10$; $m\angle RQT = 3x + 5$

18. $x = $ __15__
19. $m\angle SQR = $ __50__

Given: ∠KML and ∠KMN are a linear pair; $m\angle KML = 3(m\angle KMN)$

20. $m\angle KML = $ __135__
21. $m\angle KMN = $ __45__

1-7 Special Angles and Pairs of Angles

Artisans and designers are among those who find a knowledge of special angles and pairs of angles very useful.

Angles can be classified according to their measures.

Definition   *Right, Acute, Obtuse Angles*

A right angle is an angle whose measure is 90.
An acute angle is an angle whose measure is less than 90.
An obtuse angle is an angle whose measure is greater than 90.

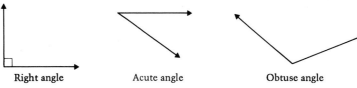

Right angle   Acute angle   Obtuse angle

The mark ⌐ is used to indicate a right angle.

Special terms are also used to classify pairs of angles related by their measures.

Definition   *Complementary Angles*

Complementary angles are two angles whose measures have a sum of 90. Each angle is called a complement of the other.

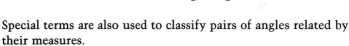

∠A and ∠B are complementary angles.   ∠3 is a complement of ∠4.

Definition   *Supplementary Angles*

Supplementary angles are two angles whose measures have a sum of 180. Each angle is called a supplement of the other.

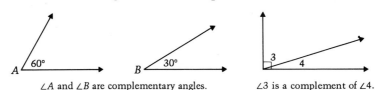

∠P and ∠Q are supplementary angles.   ∠ABC is a supplement of ∠CBD.

32   Chapter 1 *Introduction to Geometry*

Example 1

a. Classify each labeled angle in the stained glass on page 32.

b. Which angles are complementary? supplementary?

Solution

a. $m\angle 2 < 90$ and $m\angle 5 < 90$, so $\angle 2$ and $\angle 5$ are acute angles.
$m\angle 4 = 90$ and $m\angle 6 = 90$, so $\angle 4$ and $\angle 6$ are right angles.
$m\angle 1 > 90$ and $m\angle 3 > 90$, so $\angle 1$ and $\angle 3$ are obtuse angles.

b. $m\angle 2 + m\angle 5 = 90$, so $\angle 2$ and $\angle 5$ are complementary angles.
$m\angle 2 + m\angle 3 = 180$ and $m\angle 4 + m\angle 6 = 180$, so $\angle 2$ and $\angle 3$
are supplementary angles and so are $\angle 4$ and $\angle 6$.

Angles can also be related by position.

Definition *Adjacent Angles*

Adjacent angles are two coplanar angles with a common side and no common interior points.

$\angle APB$ and $\angle BPC$ are adjacent angles with $\overrightarrow{PB}$ as their common side. $\angle BPD$ and $\angle BPC$ also have $\overrightarrow{PB}$ as a common side. However, they have interior points in common, so they are not adjacent.

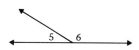

Adjacent angles such as $\angle APB$ and $\angle BPD$, whose noncommon sides form a line, are given a special name.

Definition *Linear Pair of Angles*

A linear pair of angles is a pair of adjacent angles whose noncommon sides are opposite rays.

Angles in a linear pair are related by measure as well as position.

Postulate 14 *Supplement Postulate*

The angles in a linear pair are supplementary.

Since $\angle 5$ and $\angle 6$ are a linear pair, they are supplementary, and
$m\angle 5 + m\angle 6 = 180$.

Example 2

$\angle T$ and $\angle S$ form a linear pair, $\angle V$ is a complement of $\angle T$, and
$m\angle S = 145$. Find $m\angle V$.

Solution

Since they are a linear pair, $\angle T$ and $\angle S$ are supplementary and
$m\angle T + m\angle S = 180$. So $m\angle T = 35$. Then, since $\angle V$ and $\angle T$
are complementary, $m\angle V + m\angle T = 90$, and $m\angle V = 55$.

1-7 *Special Angles and Pairs of Angles*

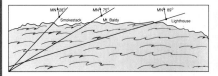

34

Additional Examples

Example 1

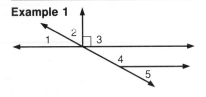

(a) Classify each numbered angle in the diagram.
∠1, ∠2 and ∠5 are acute; ∠3 is right; ∠4 is obtuse.

(b) Which angles are complementary? Supplementary? ∠1 and ∠2; ∠4 and ∠5

Example 2
In the diagram, ∠7 and ∠8 are complements, and ∠6 and ∠7 form a linear pair. If $m∠8 = 32$, find $m∠7$ and $m∠6$. 58; 122

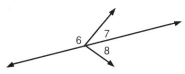

EXERCISE NOTES

Exercises 35–40 provide an opportunity to use **concrete materials.**

When two lines intersect, they form four linear pairs of angles. The pairs are ∠1 and ∠2, ∠2 and ∠3, ∠3 and ∠4, and ∠4 and ∠1. The two lines also form two pairs of "opposite angles," such as ∠1 and ∠3. These are called vertical angles.

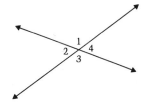

Definition

Vertical angles are two angles whose sides form two pairs of opposite rays.

In the physical world, two lines are often constructed so they intersect to form a 90° angle. This relationship occurs so frequently that such lines are given a special name.

Definition *Perpendicular Lines*

Perpendicular lines are lines that intersect to form a right angle.

If $\overleftrightarrow{AC}$ and $\overleftrightarrow{DF}$ are perpendicular, we write $\overleftrightarrow{AC} \perp \overleftrightarrow{DF}$ (read "$\overleftrightarrow{AC}$ is perpendicular to $\overleftrightarrow{DF}$"). Rays and segments are said to be perpendicular if the lines containing them are perpendicular. Thus $\overrightarrow{AC} \perp \overrightarrow{DF}$, $\overline{FD} \perp \overline{BC}$, and so on.

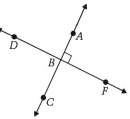

Definition *Perpendicular Bisector of a Segment*

A perpendicular bisector of a segment is a line which is perpendicular to the segment and contains its midpoint.

In the figure above, $\overleftrightarrow{AC} \perp \overleftrightarrow{DF}$. If, in addition, $DB = BF$, then $\overleftrightarrow{AC}$ is a perpendicular bisector of $\overline{DF}$.

Checking for Understanding 1. ∠APB, ∠APD, ∠DPC, or ∠CPB
Name each item. 2. ∠APE, ∠EPD, ∠CPF, ∠FPB

1. A right angle
2. Four acute angles
3. Four obtuse angles
4. Eight pairs of adjacent angles
5. Two supplements of ∠BPE
6. Six linear pairs of angles
7. A pair of complementary angles
8. Six pairs of vertical angles
9. A pair of perpendicular rays Samples: $\overrightarrow{PA}, \overrightarrow{PD}; \overrightarrow{BD}, \overrightarrow{AC}$
10. Explain why ∠BPC is a right angle. $\overleftrightarrow{AC}; \overline{BD}$
11. If $BP = PD$, then _?_ is the perpendicular bisector of _?_.
12. ∠R and ∠S are complementary and $m∠R = 50$. Find $m∠S$. 40

10. ∠APB and ∠BPC form a linear pair, so they are supplementary.

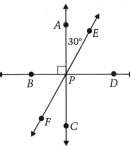

3. ∠BPE, ∠EPC, ∠DPF, ∠FPA
4. Samples: ∠BPA, ∠APE, ∠APD, ∠DPC; ∠EPD, ∠DPC, ∠EPD, ∠DPF; ∠DPC, ∠CPF; ∠CPB, ∠BPA; ∠FPB, ∠BPA; ∠FPA, ∠APE
5. ∠EPD, ∠BPF
6. Samples: ∠BPA, ∠APD; ∠BPE, ∠EPD; ∠APE, ∠EPC; ∠APD, ∠DPC; ∠EPC, ∠CPF; ∠CPF, ∠FPA

7. ∠APE, ∠EPD or ∠CPF, ∠FPB
8. ∠BPA, ∠DPC; ∠BPE, ∠DPF; ∠APE, ∠CPF; ∠APD, ∠CPB; ∠EPD, ∠FPB; ∠EPC, ∠FPA

34 Chapter 1 *Introduction to Geometry*

Assignment Guide

Basic: 1–34, 45–51
Average: 2–20 (even), 21–42, 45–51
Extended: 2–34 (even), 35–51

Written Exercises

Set A   Name each item.

1. Two right angles **2.** Three obtuse angles

3. Ten acute angles **4.** Four linear pairs of angles

5. Eight pairs of adjacent angles

6. Two pairs of complementary angles

7. Five pairs of supplementary angles

8. Two pairs of perpendicular lines

Find the measure of a complement of $\angle A$. **14.** $105 - r$

9. $m\angle A = 5$ 85 **10.** $m\angle A = 45$ 45 **11.** $m\angle A = 38$ 52

12. $m\angle A = 72$ 18 **13.** $m\angle A = x$ $90-x$ **14.** $m\angle A = r - 15$

Find the measure of a supplement of $\angle P$. **19.** $180 - 2x$

15. $m\angle P = 31$ 149 **16.** $m\angle P = 43$ 137 **17.** $m\angle P = 75$ 105

18. $m\angle P = 152$ 28 **19.** $m\angle P = 2x$ **20.** $m\angle P = 40 - x$ $140 + x$

State whether the numbered angles are adjacent. If they are not adjacent, explain why not.

21. **22.** **23.** **24.**

21. No **22.** Yes **23.** No **24.** No

25. $m\angle AED = \underline{}$ 140 **26.** $m\angle BEF = \underline{}$ 50

27. $m\angle FED = \underline{}$ 90 **28.** $m\angle AEF = \underline{}$ 130

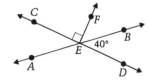

29. What kind of angle is $\angle 2$? Right

30. Is $\ell \perp m$? Explain. Yes; they form a rt. $\angle$.

31. What kind of angle is $\angle 1$? Explain. Right

32. What kind of angle is $\angle 3$? Explain. Right

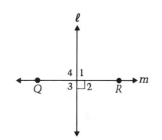

---

33. How many right angles are formed by two perpendicular lines? **4**

34. Line ℓ intersects $\overline{QR}$ at Y and is a perpendicular bisector of $\overline{QR}$. Name a pair of equal segments. **QY, YR**

Set B   Shown is part of a square-cornered picture frame of uniform width. **35. Acute or complemetary**

35. What kind of angles are $\angle 1$ and $\angle 2$?

36. At what angles should the pieces be cut, or *mitered*, to form a right-angled corner? **45°**

37. $\angle A$ and $\angle B$ are complementary angles. $m\angle A$ is 4 times $m\angle B$. Find $m\angle A$ and $m\angle B$. **$m\angle A = 72$; $m\angle B = 18$**

38. $\angle C$ and $\angle D$ are supplementary angles. $m\angle C$ is 30 more than 5 times $m\angle D$. Find $m\angle C$ and $m\angle D$.   **38. $m\angle c = 155$; $m\angle D = 25$**

A *goniometer* is used by geologists to measure the angle between the faces of mineral crystals.

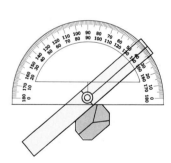

39. What is the measure of the angle between the two faces of the crystal shown? **140**

40. How is this method of measurement related to Postulate 14 and the definitions in this lesson?

41. Suppose that $\angle 1$ and $\angle 2$ are a linear pair, and that $\angle 2$ is a right angle. What can you conclude about $\angle 1$? Why?

42. Suppose that $\angle 1$ and $\angle 2$ are a linear pair, and that $m\angle 1 = m\angle 2$. What can you conclude about $\angle 1$ and $\angle 2$? Why?

40. The $\angle$ between the crystal faces and the $\angle$ formed by the edge of the protractor and the edge of the pointer are a linear pair. Hence, they are supp. $\angle$s.
41. $\angle 1$ is a rt. $\angle$. $m\angle 1 + m\angle 2 = 180$. Since $m\angle 2 = 90$, $m\angle 1 = 90$.
42. They are rt. $\angle$s. $m\angle 1 + m\angle 2 = 180$, so $2(m\angle 1) = 180$.

Set C   **43.** The measure of a supplement of an angle is 40 more than 3 times the measure of its complement. Find the measure of the angle. **65**

44. If $\angle A$ is acute, $\angle B$ is a supplement of $\angle A$, and $\angle C$ is a complement of $\angle A$, find $m\angle B - m\angle C$. **90**

⬥ Review   **45.** Can opposite rays be the sides of an angle? Explain. **No; rays must be noncollinear.**

46. If $\overrightarrow{AH}$ is the bisector of $\angle DAC$, then $m\angle DAC = (\underline{\;?\;})(m\angle DAH)$. **2**

FOLLOW-UP

More Practice

• Worksheet 1–7

Extension

Challenge students to devise an informal argument to prove that perpendicular lines form four right angles. Definition guarantees one; angle adjacent to it forms a linear pair with it, and so is right; other two for the same reason.

• Extension 1–7

Computers

• Computer Activities 1–7

47. If $DX = 9$ and $XE = 9$, is X the midpoint of $\overline{DE}$?
Explain. No; only if D, X, and E are collinear

48. Line m separates the plane into half-planes $\mathcal{H}_1$ and
$\mathcal{H}_2$. In which half-plane is m contained? Neither

49. The intersection of two planes is __?__. Line

 Thinking Ahead Mr. Arnold's seating chart is shown at the right. He uses pairs of numbers to designate the students. For example, the pair (5, 2) designates the student in row 5, seat 2, which is Les. An X in the chart denotes a vacant place.

50. Which student does each of these pairs designate?

a. (2, 4) Marta **b.** (1, 5) Lee

c. (3, 3) Vacant **d.** (6, 1) Kenji

51. What pair of numbers designates each student?

a. Pat (5, 3) **b.** Bob (3, 5)

c. Diane (6, 5) **d.** Amy (4, 1)

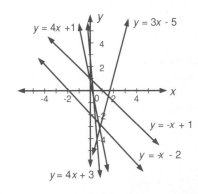

💻 **Computer Activities: Graphing**

For each exercise, first graph the five equations on the same axes. Then give a geometric description for each graph in terms of the given question.

1. Is each graph a point, a line, a segment, or a ray?

a. $2y = x + 7$ **b.** $y = x$ **c.** $2x = y + 3$ **d.** $x - y = 4$ **e.** $x - 2 = 0$

2. How is each graph related to either the horizontal or the vertical axis?

a. $y = 7$ **b.** $x = -3$ **c.** $y = 4$ **d.** $y = -1$ **e.** $x = 5$

3. How is the constant (last) term in each equation related to the vertical axis?

a. $y = 4x + 3$ **b.** $y = 4x + 1$ **c.** $y = -x - 2$ **d.** $y = -x + 1$ **e.** $y = 3x - 5$

ANSWERS

Computer Activities

1.

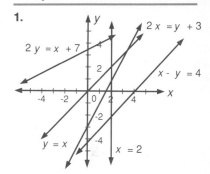

a–e. All are lines.

2.

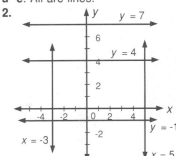

a, c, d. Lines are ∥ to horizontal axis.
b, e. Lines are ∥ to vertical axis.

3.

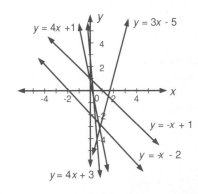

a–e. Last term is y-intercept (coordinate on vertical axis at point where line crosses axis).

⚊ Construction Exercises

Construction 4

Through a point on a given line, construct a line perpendicular to the given line.

Given   Point P on line m

Construct $\overleftrightarrow{PQ} \perp m$

Method   **Step 1:** With P as center and a convenient radius, construct arcs intersecting m at two points, A and B.

            Step 2: With A and B as centers and a radius greater than AP, construct two intersecting arcs. Label the point of intersection Q.

            Step 3: Draw $\overleftrightarrow{PQ}$. Then $\overleftrightarrow{PQ} \perp m$ at P.

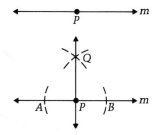

Construction 5

Construct the perpendicular bisector of a given segment.

Given $\overline{AB}$

Construct   The perpendicular bisector of $\overline{AB}$

Method   **Step 1:** With A and B as centers and radius greater than $\frac{1}{2}AB$, construct two pairs of intersecting arcs. Label the points of intersection of the arcs P and Q.

            Step 2: Draw $\overleftrightarrow{PQ}$. Then $\overleftrightarrow{PQ}$ is the perpendicular bisector of $\overline{AB}$.

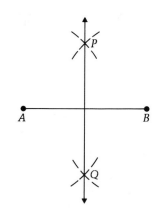

For each of Exercises 1–4, make a new tracing of $\overleftrightarrow{CD}$.

1. Construct a line perpendicular to $\overleftrightarrow{CD}$ through C.

2. Construct the perpendicular bisector of $\overline{CD}$.

3. Find the midpoint of $\overline{CD}$ by construction.

4. Construct a segment whose length is $\frac{1}{2}CD$.

5. On one drawing, construct $\overline{XZ} \perp \overline{ZT}$, then $\overline{XY} \perp \overline{ZX}$, then $\overline{TV} \perp \overline{TZ}$, with $\overleftrightarrow{TV}$ intersecting $\overleftrightarrow{XY}$ at W.

6. Trace $\overline{RS}$. Construct t, the perpendicular bisector of $\overline{RS}$, intersecting $\overline{RS}$ at V. On t, mark points X and Y so that VX = VY = RV. Draw $\overline{RX}$, $\overline{XS}$, $\overline{SY}$, and $\overline{RY}$. Use a protractor to find the number of right angles and angle bisectors in the figure.

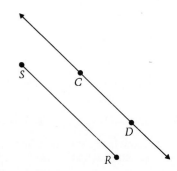

◀EXCURSIONS

An Excursion feature appears in every chapter. These pages deal with applications of mathematical topics in the real world and often involve a project.

Excursion: Dihedral Kaleidoscope

A *dihedral angle* is the union of two noncoplanar half-planes with a common edge, together with the common edge. A two-mirror kaleidoscope is a physical example of a dihedral angle. Designers use kaleidoscopes to design patterns for wallpaper, floor coverings, and fabrics.

Make a kaleidoscope using two mirrors hinged with tape. Draw a line segment 10 cm long on a sheet of paper. Position the mirrors as shown. Adjust the mirrors so that you can see a figure with 5 equal sides.

a. Carefully trace the angle formed by the mirrors.

b. Remove the mirrors and use a protractor to measure the angle you drew. This is the measure of the dihedral angle formed by the mirrors.

1. Complete the table below by adjusting the mirrors until you see a figure with the indicated number of sides.

Number of sides	3	4	5	6	7	8
Measure of dihedral angle	120 ?	90 ?	72	60 ?	$51\frac{3}{7}$?	45 ?

2. What measure would the angle have if the figure had 10 sides? 36

3. Write a formula relating the measure m of the dihedral angle and n, the number of sides in the figure. $m = \frac{360}{n}$

In additon to computer activities and worksheets, this book includes short computer programs in BASIC or Logo that are designed for students to run and test by answering questions about or revising the program. These features were designed so that even students who do not have access to a computer may learn about programming. See Teacher's Resource File on Computer Materials pages i–iv for further information.

Have students name the postulate or definition in the numbered statements. Relate all the postulates and definitions for segments to the corresponding ones for angles.

Using BASIC: Complements and Supplements

The computer program below is written in the language called BASIC. The program can be used to compute and print the measures of the complements and supplements of six acute angles.

```
100 PRINT "ANGLE", "COMP.", "SUPP."
110 PRINT "MEAS.", "MEAS.", "MEAS."
120 PRINT
130 FOR I = 1 TO 6
140 READ A            A is the measure of a given angle.
150 LET C = 90 - A    C is the measure of a complement.
160 LET S = 180 - A   S is the measure of a supplement.
170 PRINT A, C, S
180 NEXT I
190 DATA 20, 45, 50, 75, 80, 89
200 END
```

3. This program would give negative or zero measures for the complements. Obtuse and right ∠s have no complements.

1. RUN the program and use its output to discover a relationship between the complement and supplement of an acute angle. $c + 90 = s$

2. Test your conjecture for Exercise 1 by using a different set of measures of acute angles in line 190.

3. Explain why the program cannot be used with measures of obtuse or right angles.

4. Revise the program so that it can be used with measures of any angle by adding the following lines:

   ```
   145 IF A > = 90 THEN 175
   172 GOTO 180
   175 PRINT A, "NONE", 180 - A
   ```

   RUN the modified program with these measures as data:
   30, 110, 70, 90, 1, 150

5. How might the original program be modified so that it would handle ten angle measures as input data?

6. Write a program to identify whole-number angle measures from 1 to 90 where the measure A of the angle is equal to the difference between the measure S of its supplement and twice the measure C of its complement.

```
100 PRINT "ANGLE
MEASURES:"
110 FOR A =1 TO 90
120 LET C = 90 - A
130 LET S = 180 - A
140 IF A ≠ S - 2*C
THEN GO TO 170
150 PRINT A
160 NEXT A
170 END
```

5. Line 130 becomes for I = 1 to 10; line 190 will need 10 data items.
6. This relationship holds for all the angle measures

1-8 A Coordinate Model

Scientists use models to illustrate what is known about a structure. In the computer graphic at the right, atoms are represented by colored balls and the atomic bonds by connecting rods. Study of a model often leads to new discoveries. This is also the case in mathematics.

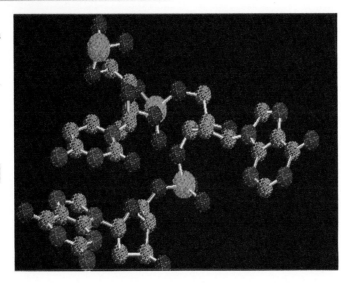

Definition *Mathematical Model*

A mathematical model is an interpretation of the terms of a mathematical system in which the postulates and the results that follow from them are true statements.

We will borrow from your experience in algebra to build a *coordinate model* for geometry. Recall that the undefined terms in geometry are point, line, and plane. In our coordinate model for a plane, the plane will be interpreted as the set of all *ordered pairs* (x, y) of real numbers.

This **coordinate plane** contains two perpendicular number lines, the **x-axis** and the **y-axis**, that intersect at the **origin**, a point corresponding to 0 on both lines.

In our model, a point will be interpreted as an ordered pair (x, y) of real numbers. Point *A* corresponds to the ordered pair (−2, 3). The **x-coordinate**, −2, indicates that *A* is two units to the left of the y-axis. The **y-coordinate**, 3, indicates that *A* is three units above the x-axis. Point *B* corresponds to (4, −5). To what ordered pair does point *C* correspond? **(5, 0)**

Note that for each of the points marked on $\overleftrightarrow{PQ}$ the y-coordinate is one more than twice the x-coordinate. This pattern can be expressed by the equation $y = 2x + 1$. In our coordinate model, a line will be interpreted as a set of all the ordered pairs (x, y) that satisfy *either* $y = mx + b$ or $x = c$, where *m*, *b*, and *c* are specific real numbers.

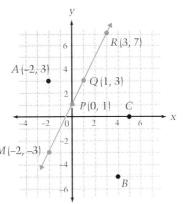

LESSON 1–8

Resources

Teaching Aid 3, grid paper
Visual Aid 3, grid paper
Teaching Aid 5, graphs
Visual Aid 5, graphs
Teaching Aid 18, square root table
Visual Aid 18, square root table
Worksheet 1–8
Extension 1–8

Computer Worksheet 1–8
Algebra Review 1
Chapter 1 Test, Form I
Chapter 1 Test, Form II
Chapter 1 Test, Form III

OBJECTIVES

Use the coordinate plane as a mathematical model for definitions and postulates; state and apply the Distance and Midpoint formulas.

WORKSHEET   *Lesson* **1-8**

Name _____

Graph the following points.

1. A(5, 0)   2. B(−4, 2)   3. C(2, −5)
4. D(−1, −5)   5. E(0, −2)   6. F(−4, −3)

Give a coordinate description for each geometric figure.

7. $\overline{DC}$ y = −5 with −1 ≤ x ≤ 2   8. $\overline{BE}$ y = −1x + (−2)
9. $\overline{BF}$ x = −4 with −3 ≤ y ≤ 2   10. $\overline{AE}$ y = $\frac{2}{5}$x − 2

Find the length of each segment to the nearest tenth.

11. $\overline{DC}$ __3__   12. $\overline{BF}$ __5__   13. $\overline{BE}$ __5.7__   14. $\overline{AE}$ __5.4__   15. $\overline{EC}$ __3.6__

Find the coordinates of the midpoint of each segment.

16. $\overline{BF}$ ($\frac{-4}{}$, $-\frac{1}{2}$)   17. $\overline{CA}$ ($3\frac{1}{2}$, $-2\frac{1}{2}$)   18. $\overline{DE}$ ($-\frac{1}{2}$, $-3\frac{1}{2}$)   19. $\overline{BC}$ (-1, $-1\frac{1}{2}$)

Graph the following lines and then name two ordered pairs from each line. Ordered pairs will vary. Samples are given.

20. x = −1   21. y = 4x + −5   22. y = x + 2

(−1, 0); (−1, 2)   (0, −5); (2, 3)   (0, 2); (1, 3)

23. y = 3   24. y = $\frac{3}{4}$x   25. 2y = 8x − 6

(0, 3); (2, 3)   (4, 3); (0, 0)   (1, 1); (0, −3)

Example 1

Graph the set of ordered pairs satisfying each of the following conditions and describe the geometric figure.

a. $y = 4$ **b.** $x = -5$ **c.** $y = -x + 2$

Solution

a. The equation $y = 4$ asserts that for every value of x, the y-value is 4. Thus the graph contains such points as $(3, 4)$, $(-2, 4)$, and $(0, 4)$. Since $y = 4$ can also be written as $y = 0(x) + 4$, the graph is a line in our model. Note that the line is horizontal and crosses the y-axis at 4. We say that the **y-intercept** is 4.

b. The equation $x = -5$ states that the value of x is always -5 for any value of y. Such points as $(-5, 3)$, $(-5, -1)$, and $(-5, 0)$ are on the graph. We see that this graph is a vertical line with an **x-intercept** of -5.

c. Since the graph of $y = -x + 2$ is a line, and a line is determined by two points, it is sufficient to find two ordered pairs satisfying the equation.

When $x = 0$, $y = 0 + 2 = 2$, so graph $(0, 2)$.

When $x = 3$, $y = -3 + 2 = -1$, so graph $(3, -1)$.

The graph can now be drawn. As a check, note that when $x = 5$, $y = -5 + 2 = -3$, so that the ordered pair $(5, -3)$ is on the graph. What is the y-intercept for the line $y = -x + 2$? **2**

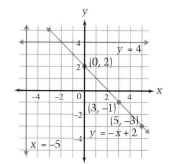

Example 2

Give a coordinate description for each geometric figure.
a. $\overline{AB}$ **b.** $\overline{PQ}$ **c.** $\overleftrightarrow{ST}$

Solution

a. All points on $\overline{AB}$ have x-coordinate -2. The y-values are between 2 and 6, inclusively. Thus, $\overline{AB}$ can be described by the equation $x = -2$ with the restriction $2 \le y \le 6$.

b. All points on $\overline{PQ}$ have y-coordinate -5. The x-values are between 3 and 6, inclusively. So $\overline{PQ}$ can be described by the equation $y = -5$ with the restriction $3 \le x \le 6$.

c. $\overleftrightarrow{ST}$ can be described by an equation of the form $y = mx + b$. To find b, use the coordinates of S: $-4 = m(0) + b$ so $b = -4$. Thus, the equation must be of the form $y = mx - 4$. To find m, use the coordinates of T: $2 = m(2) - 4$ or $2m = 6$, so $m = 3$. Hence $\overleftrightarrow{ST}$ can be described by the equation $y = 3x - 4$.

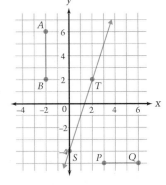

Examples 1 and 2 suggest several generalizations:

- The equation $y = h$ describes a *horizontal line* whose points each have y-coordinate h.
- The equation $x = k$ describes a *vertical line* whose points each have x-coordinate k.
- The equation $y = mx + b$, where $m \neq 0$, describes an *oblique line* with y-intercept b.

The Ruler Postulate asserts that between any two points there is a unique distance. We can now interpret distance within our coordinate model.

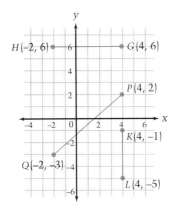

To find GH, you can simply count the units between the endpoints, or find the absolute value of the difference of the x-coordinates: $GH = |-2 - 4| = 6$.

To find KL, just find the absolute value of the difference of the y-coordinates: $KL = |-5 - (-1)| = 4$.

To find PQ, we will use the Distance Formula you studied in algebra: $PQ = \sqrt{(-2 - 4)^2 + (-3 - 2)^2} = \sqrt{36 + 25} = \sqrt{61} \approx 7.8$

Distance Formula

If the coordinates of points P and Q are (x_1, y_1) and (x_2, y_2) respectively, then the distance d between P and Q is
$$d = \sqrt{(x_2 - x_1)^2 + (y_2 - y_1)^2}.$$

Verify that the general formula for distance in the coordinate plane gives the same values for GH and KL as obtained above.

$GH = \sqrt{(-2 - 4)^2 + (6 - 6)^2} = 6$
$KL = \sqrt{(4 - 4)^2 + (-5 - (-1))^2}$
$\qquad = 4$

The Midpoint Postulate guarantees that a segment has a unique midpoint. Our interpretation of distance in the coordinate model permits us to develop a coordinate interpretation of midpoint.

Using the definition of midpoint, it follows that the midpoint of $\overline{RS}$ is $M(-4, 1)$, since $RM = MS$.

Similarly, the midpoint of $\overline{TU}$ is $N(2.5, -3)$, and the midpoint of $\overline{VW}$ is $P(5, 5)$.

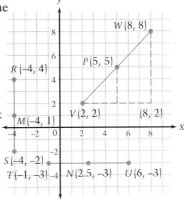

In each case, the coordinates of the midpoint are simply the average of the coordinates of the endpoints of the segments.

(a) $x = -3$ vertical line
(b) $y = 2x - 1$ line with slope of 2, y-intercept of -1
(c) $y = 0$ horizontal line (the x-axis)

Example 2
Give a coordinate description for each geometric figure.

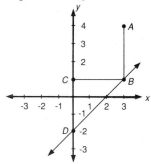

(a) $\overline{CB}$ $y = 1, 0 \leq x \leq 3$
(b) $\overline{AB}$ $x = 3, 1 \leq y \leq 4$
(c) $\overleftrightarrow{BD}$ $y = x - 2$

Example 3
(a) Find LM for $L(4, 1)$ and $M(-8, 6)$. 13
(b) Find the coordinates of the midpoint I of $\overline{RN}$ whose endpoints are $R(2, 1)$ and $N(-4, 6)$. $(-1, 3.5)$

Error Analysis In dealing with equations of lines, students usually have the most difficulty with horizontal and vertical lines. Two problems are common:
1. Students do not recognize $x = c$ and $y = c$ as equations of lines.
2. They confuse one with the other. Stress $y = 7$, for example, as the set of *all* points with a y-coordinate of 7. By plotting some of these, students will see that it is a horizontal line.

Midpoint Formula

If the coordinates of points P and Q are (x_1, y_1) and (x_2, y_2) respectively, then the midpoint M of $\overline{PQ}$ has coordinates $\left(\dfrac{x_1 + x_2}{2}, \dfrac{y_1 + y_2}{2}\right)$.

Example 3

a. Find AB for $A(-5, 4)$ and $B(3, -2)$.

b. Find the coordinates of the midpoint M of $\overline{GH}$ whose endpoints are $G(-7, 5)$ and $H(4, 11)$.

Solution

a. $AB = \sqrt{(x_1 - x_2)^2 + (y_1 - y_2)^2}$

$= \sqrt{(-5 - 3)^2 + (4 - (-2))^2}$

$= \sqrt{64 + 36}$

$= \sqrt{100}$

$= 10$

b. The coordinates of the midpoint are:

$\left(\dfrac{x_1 + x_2}{2}, \dfrac{y_1 + y_2}{2}\right)$

$\left(\dfrac{-7 + 4}{2}, \dfrac{5 + 11}{2}\right)$

$(-1.5, 8)$

In your study of geometry, you will find the coordinate model to be a useful tool to better understand and to gain new insights into geometric relationships. A summary of key features follows.

Summary Key Features of the Coordinate Model

Geometry	Coordinate Model
Point	Ordered pair (x, y) of real numbers
Line	All ordered pairs (x, y) satisfying either $y = mx + b$ or $x = c$
Plane	All possible ordered pairs (x, y) of real numbers
Distance PQ	$\sqrt{(x_2 - x_1)^2 + (y_2 - y_1)^2}$, where (x_1, y_1) and (x_2, y_2) are the coordinates corresponding to P and Q, respectively
Midpoint of $\overline{PQ}$	$\left(\dfrac{x_1 + x_2}{2}, \dfrac{y_1 + y_2}{2}\right)$ where (x_1, y_1) and (x_2, y_2) are the coordinates corresponding to P and Q, respectively

Assignment Guide

Basic: 1–27, 47–51
Average: 2–20 (even), 22–44, 47–51
Extended: 2–26 (even), 28–51

Checking for Understanding

Give the coordinates corresponding to each point.

1. A (2.5, 2)   **2.** D (−2, 1.5)   **3.** O (0, 0)   **4.** E (0, −1.5)

Name the point that corresponds to each ordered pair.

5. (−2, −1) F **6.** (1.5, 1.5) C **7.** (−1.5, 0) L **8.** (1.5, −0.5) K

Give a coordinate description for each figure.

9. $\overleftrightarrow{CD}$ **10.** $\overline{OE}$ **11.** $\overrightarrow{OA}$ **12.** $\overrightarrow{BH}$

Find the length of each segment to the nearest tenth.

13. $\overline{HE}$ 2.0   **14.** $\overline{DF}$ 2.5   **15.** $\overline{KH}$ 1.1   **16.** $\overline{AF}$ 5.4

Find the coordinates of the midpoint of each segment.

17. $\overline{LO}$ **18.** $\overline{CK}$ **19.** $\overline{AE}$ **20.** $\overline{CH}$
(−0.75, 0)   (1.5, 0.5)   (1.25, 0.25)   (1.75, 0)

Written Exercises

Set A   Give the coordinates corresponding to each point.

1. H (2, 1)   **2.** L (−4, 2)   **3.** G (2, 0)   **4.** P (−2, −3)

Name the point that corresponds to each ordered pair.

5. (−4, −2) M **6.** (0, 3) K **7.** (5, −1) Q

Give a coordinate description for each figure.

8. $\overrightarrow{HN}$ $x = 2$ **9.** $\overleftrightarrow{LJ}$ $y = 2$ **10.** $\overline{OG}$ $y = 0$ for $0 \le x \le z$
11. $\overleftrightarrow{LM}$ $x = -4$ **12.** $\overrightarrow{OR}$ $y = -x$ **13.** $\overline{OL}$ $y = -\frac{1}{2}x$
for $-2 \le y \le 2$

Find the length of each segment to the nearest tenth.

14. $\overline{MK}$ 6.4   **15.** $\overline{PR}$ 4.1   **16.** $\overline{LN}$ 8.5   **17.** $\overline{HO}$ 2.2

Find the coordinates of the midpoint of each segment.

18. $\overline{KG}$ **19.** $\overline{MQ}$ **20.** $\overline{LG}$ **21.** $\overline{KR}$ **18.** (1.5, 1.5) **19.** (0.5, −1.5)
20. (−0.5, 1) **21.** (1, 0.5)

Graph the set of ordered pairs satisfying the given condition(s) and describe the geometric figure.

22. $x = 6$ **23.** $y = -2$ **24.** $y = 4$ and $-3 \le x \le 5$
25. $y = x$ **26.** $y = -3x + 2$ **27.** $y = -2x$ and $y = -3$

Set B   Give a coordinate description for each figure.

28. $\overline{AB}$ **29.** $\overline{BD}$ **30.** $\angle ABC$ **31.** $\angle CBD$

Give a coordinate description for

32. a half-plane with edge $\overleftrightarrow{AB}$ containing point D.
33. a half-plane with edge $\overleftrightarrow{BC}$ containing point A.
34. the interior of $\angle ABC$.

EXERCISE NOTES

Exercises 14–17 could be done with the use of a **calculator.**
Exercises 30–31 involve the union of two rays.
Exercises 35–38 should be solved algebraically.

ANSWERS

Checking for Understanding

9. $y = 1.5$ and $-2 \le x \le 1.5$
10. $x = 0$ and $-1.5 \le y \le 0$
11. $y = 0.8x$
12. $x = 2$ and $-1.5 \le y \le 0$

Written Exercises

22–27.

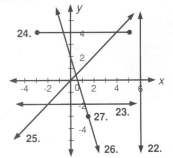

22. line
23. line
24. segment
25. line
26. line
27. point
28. $y = -2x + 1$ and $-2 \le x \le 0$
29. $y = -\frac{1}{3}x + 1$ and $0 \le x \le 3$
30. $(y = -2x + 1$ and $x \le 0)$ or $(y = x + 1$ and $x \ge 0)$
31. $(y = x + 1$ and $x \ge 0)$ or $(y = -\frac{1}{3}x + 1$ and $x \ge 0)$
32. $y > -2x + 1$
33. $y > x + 1$
34. $y > -2x + 1$ and $y > x + 1$

FOLLOW-UP

More Practice

• Worksheet 1-8

Extension

Demonstrate that the Midpoint Formula produces the unique midpoint of the segment. There are two parts to be shown: (1) *M* is between *P* and *Q* and (2) *PM* = *MQ*.

To do this, choose two specific points. Show that the first part is true by writing the equation for $\overline{PQ}$ and by showing that *M* satisfies it. The second part is done by using the Distance Formula.

• Extension 1-8

Computers

• Computer Worksheet 1-8

Find point *S* so that *T* is the midpoint of $\overline{RS}$.

35. *R*(3, −6); *T*(0, −3) (−3, 0) **36.** *R*(−4, 7); *T*(−2, 0) (0, −7)
37. *R*(4, −5); *T*(6, 1) (8, 7) **38.** *R*(−2, 6); *T*(2, 2) (6, −2)

The x-and y-axes separate the points of the coordinate plane not on the axes into four regions, called *quadrants*. Which quadrant contains the point (*s, t*) for the given restrictions on *s* and *t*?

39. *s* < 0, *t* < 0 III **40.** *s* < 0, *t* > 0 II
41. *s* > 0, *t* < 0 IV **42.** *s* > 0, *t* > 0 I

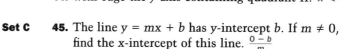

Give a coordinate description for a half-plane
43. with edge the x-axis containing quadrant II. *y* > 0
44. with edge the y-axis containing quadrant II. *x* < 0

Set C **45.** The line *y* = *mx* + *b* has y-intercept *b*. If *m* ≠ 0, find the x-intercept of this line. $\frac{0-b}{m}$

46. Tell why the following interpretations would not constitute a mathematical model for our system of geometry: Point corresponds to an ordered pair (*m, n*) of integers; line to all ordered pairs of integers satisfying the equation *y* = *mx* + *b*; and plane to all possible ordered pairs of integers.

46. Lines and planes could not be continuous. Sets of points

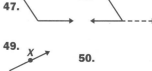

▲ **Review** **47.** Draw an obtuse angle.
48. Draw a supplement of your angle in Exercise 47.
49. Draw a counterexample to show that the following statement is not always true. If *m*∠*RPX* = *m*∠*SPX*, then $\overrightarrow{PX}$ bisects ∠*RPS*.
50. Draw and label collinear points *Y, T,* and *J,* such that *TJ* − *TY* = *JY*.
51. If *m*∠*BND* = 80, then *m*∠*CND* = __?__. 46

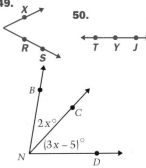

Progress Check

Lesson 1-5, page 19
State the postulate or definition that supports each statement.
1. If *I* is between *J* and *K*, then *JI* + *IK* = *JK*. Seg. Addition Post.
2. If *T* is the midpoint of $\overline{VN}$, then *VT* = *TN*. Def. of midpt.
3. There is exactly one point *R* on $\overrightarrow{MG}$ such that *MR* = 12. Seg. Construction Post.

Lesson 1-6, page 25 4. ∠*RPS* or ∠*SPR*   5. *m*∠1 = *m*∠2

4. Name ∠2 with 3 letters.   5. If $\overrightarrow{PS}$ bisects ∠*TPR*, then __?__.

6. Name a point in the exterior of ∠*SPT*. **R**

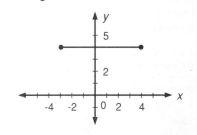

Lesson 1-7, page 32

7. If ∠*C* is a supplement of ∠*D*, and ∠*C* is a right angle, then *m*∠*D* = __?__. **90**

8. If ∠*H* is a complement of ∠*E*, and *m*∠*E* = 47, then *m*∠*H* = __?__. **43**

9. If ∠*A* and ∠*B* form a linear pair, the sum of their measures is __?__. **180**

Lesson 1-8, page 41

10. Find, to the nearest tenth, the distance between (4, −3) and (−1, −4). **5.1**

11. Find the coordinates of the midpoint of $\overline{AB}$, for *A*(8, 11) and *B*(−5, 3). **(1.5, 7)**

12. Graph the set of ordered pairs (x, y) satisfying y = 4 and −3 ≤ x ≤ 4, and identify the geometric figure.

Chapter 1 Summary

Important Terms

Acute angle (32)	Exterior of an angle (25)	Points Postulate (10)
Adjacent angles (33)	Flat Plane Postulate (11)	Postulate (10)
Angle (25)	Geometry (1)	Protractor Postulate (26)
Angle Addition Postulate (26)	Half-plane (15)	Quadrant (46)
Angle bisector (27)	Interior of an angle (25)	Radius (21)
Angle Bisector Postulate (27)	Length, linear measure (19)	Ray (14)
Angle Construction	Line (5, 41)	Right angle (32)
Postulate (26)	Linear pair of angles (33)	Ruler Postulate (19)
Arc of a circle (24)	Line Postulate (10)	Segment (14)
Between (6)	Mathematical model (41)	Segment Addition
Bisector of a segment (20)	Midpoint (20)	Postulate (20)
Center of a circle (21)	Midpoint Formula (44)	Segment Construction
Circle (21)	Midpoint Postulate (20)	Postulate (19)
Collinear (5)	Obtuse angle (32)	Sides of an angle (25)
Compass (24)	Opposite rays (14)	Space (5)
Complement (32)	Ordered pair (41)	Straightedge (24)
Construction (24)	Origin (41)	Supplement (32)
Coordinate plane (41)	Perpendicular bisector (34)	Supplement Postulate (33)
Coplanar (6)	Perpendicular lines (34)	Vertex of an angle (25)
Counterexample (21)	Plane (5, 41)	Vertical angles (34)
Distance Formula (43)	Plane Intersection Postulate (11)	x-and y-axes (41)
Equal angles (27)	Plane Postulate (10)	x-and y-coordinates (41)
Equal segments (20)	Point (5, 41)	x-and y-intercepts (42)

Progress Check

12. segment

◀CHAPTER SUMMARY

Important Terms

At the end of every chapter important terms are listed with page references so that students may find information quickly.

Important Ideas

Important ideas are summarized at the end of each chapter with page references, again so that students may find further information on a given topic quickly.

Important Ideas

1. *Point, line,* and *plane* are undefined terms in our geometry. (5)

2. Two points determine a line, and three noncollinear points determine a plane. (5)

3. Postulates are statements which are accepted without proof. (10)

4. If A and B are in $\mathcal{R}$, then $\overleftrightarrow{AB}$ is in $\mathcal{R}$. (11)

5. If two planes intersect, then they intersect in a line. (11)

6. The distance between two given points is a unique real number. (19)

7. There is exactly one point on a ray at a given distance from the endpoint of the ray. (19)

8. If P is between A and B, then $AP + PB = AB$. (20)

9. If $AB = BC$, then B is the midpoint of $\overline{AC}$, and vice versa. (20)

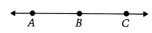

10. Equal segments have the same length. (20)

11. The measure of an angle is a unique real number. (26)

12. In each of the half-planes determined by $\overleftrightarrow{AB}$, there is exactly one ray AC such that $\angle BAC$ has a given measure. (26)

13. If P is in the interior of $\angle ABC$, then $m\angle ABP + m\angle PBC = m\angle ABC$. (26)

14. If $m\angle 1 = m\angle 2$, then $\overrightarrow{BP}$ is the bisector of $\angle ABC$, and vice versa. (27)

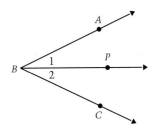

15. Equal angles have the same measure. (27)

16. Angles can be classified as acute, right, or obtuse; and pairs of angles can be classified as complementary, supplementary, adjacent, a linear pair, or vertical. (32–33)

17. The angles in a linear pair are supplementary. (33)

18. Perpendicular lines form a right angle. (34)

19. If $\ell \perp \overline{AB}$ at its midpoint, then ℓ is a perpendicular bisector of $\overline{AB}$. (34)

20. In the coordinate plane, the distance d between $P(x_1, y_1)$ and $Q(x_2, y_2)$ is given by $d = \sqrt{(x_2 - x_1)^2 + (y_2 - y_1)^2}$. (43)

21. In the coordinate plane, given $A(x_1, y_1)$ and $B(x_2, y_2)$, the midpoint of $\overline{AB}$ has coordinates $\left(\dfrac{x_1 + x_2}{2}, \dfrac{y_1 + y_2}{2} \right)$ (44)

Chapter 1 Review

◀ CHAPTER REVIEWS

Each chapter includes review exercises separated by lessons that cover the main objectives of the chapter.

Lesson 1-1, Page 1

Name two real world objects that might be represented by each drawing.

1. **Samples: Box, book**
2. **Samples: doorstop, ramp**

1. 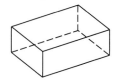   **2.**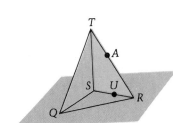

For the stairway shown at the right,

3. sketch a side view.

4. sketch a top view.

Lesson 1-2, Page 5

Use the diagram at the right.

5. Name three collinear points. *T, A, R,* or *S, U, R*

6. Name four coplanar points. Sample: *S, U, R, Q*

7. Name three noncollinear points. Sample: *T, A, S*

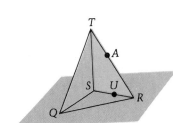

Lesson 1-3, Page 10

Tell whether each statement is *true* or *false*. Explain each answer.

8. Three given points are contained in exactly one plane.

9. If *P* and *Q* are in plane *E*, then $\overleftrightarrow{PQ}$ is in *E*.

10. The intersection of two planes *H* and *K* is a point *A*.

8. False; only if noncollinear
9. True; by Flat Plane Post.
10. False; a line

Lesson 1-4, Page 14

11. Name the endpoints of $\overline{DE}$. *D, E*

12. Point *P* is between *S* and *T*. Name a pair of opposite rays. $\overrightarrow{PS}, \overrightarrow{PT}$

13. Into how many half-planes does a line separate a plane? **2**

Lesson 1-5, Page 19

14. Point *D* is between *A* and *G* such that *AG* = 18 and *DG* = 7. Find *AD*. **11**

15. Point *R* is the midpoint of $\overline{QS}$ and *QR* = 11. Find *QS*. **22**

16. Give a counterexample for the statement: If $\overline{BD}$ bisects $\overline{AC}$, then $\overline{AC}$ bisects $\overline{BD}$.

ANSWERS

Chapter Review

3.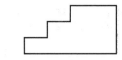

4.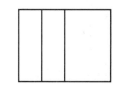

16.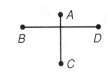

Lesson 1-6, Page 25

At the right, $m\angle RYT = 90$. $\angle SYT$, $\angle SYV$, $\angle TYV$

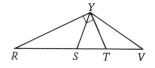

17. Name all the angles with vertex Y. $\angle RYS$, $\angle RYT$, $\angle RYV$

18. Name a point in the interior of $\angle SYV$. T

19. Name a point in the exterior of $\angle RYT$. V

20. If $m\angle SYV = 75$ and $m\angle RYS = 42$, find $m\angle RYV$. 117

21. If $\overrightarrow{YS}$ is the bisector of $\angle RYT$, find $m\angle SYT$. 45

Lesson 1-7, Page 32

At the right, $m\angle DEB = 90$.

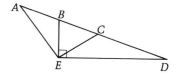

22. Name a right angle. $\angle DEB$

23. Name an obtuse angle. $\angle DEA$, $\angle ABE$, or $\angle ECD$

24. Name an acute angle. Samples: $\angle A$, $\angle D$, $\angle CED$

25. Name a pair of complementary angles. Sample: $\angle BEC$, $\angle CED$

26. Name a pair of supplementary angles. Sample: $\angle ABE$, $\angle CBE$

27. Name two pairs of adjacent angles with vertex E.

27. Sample: $\angle AEB$, $\angle BED$; $\angle AEC$, $\angle CED$

28. Name two linear pairs of angles. $\angle ABE$, $\angle EBC$; $\angle BCE$, $\angle ECD$

29. If $\angle A = \angle B$ and $\angle A$ is a complement of $\angle B$, find $m\angle B$. 45

30. If $\angle X = \angle Y$ and $\angle Y$ is a supplement of $\angle X$, find $m\angle Y$. 90

31. Two perpendicular lines form ___?___ pairs of vertical angles. 2

Lesson 1-8, Page 41

32. Given $A(7, -6)$ and $B(-4, -1)$, find AB to the nearest tenth. 12.1

33. Find the coordinates of the midpoint of $\overline{AB}$ in Item 32. (1.5, −3.5)

34. Give a coordinate description for $\overleftrightarrow{CD}$. $y = x$

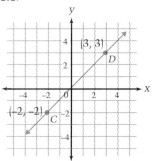

Chapter 1 Test

CHAPTER TESTS

Each chapter concludes with a free response test that covers the main objectives of the chapter. The Teacher's Resource File also includes three different forms of tests for each chapter. Form I is a free response test that is slightly less difficult than the test that appears in the pupil's book. Form II is a free response test that parallels the test in the pupil's book. Form III is a multiple choice test that is about the same level of difficulty as Form II and the test in the pupil's book.

1. Give two other names for line ℓ. Two of $\overleftrightarrow{AB}$, $\overleftrightarrow{AG}$ or $\overleftrightarrow{BG}$

2. Give another name for $\overrightarrow{DC}$. $\overrightarrow{DG}$

3. Name a pair of opposite rays. $\overrightarrow{GA}$, $\overrightarrow{GB}$ or $\overrightarrow{GC}$, $\overrightarrow{GD}$

4. $AG + GB = \underline{?}$ AB

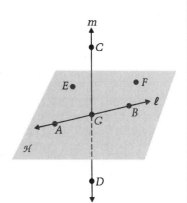

Answer the question, and then state a postulate or definition to support your answer.

5. How many lines contain points A and F? 1; Line Post.

6. How many planes contain points A, C, and F? 1; Plane Post.

7. Is $\overleftrightarrow{BE}$ contained in plane $\mathcal{H}$? Yes, Flat Plane Post.

8. If $\underline{?}$, then $AE = EC$. E is the midpt. of $\overline{AC}$; Def. of midpt.

9. If $\underline{?}$, then m is perpendicular to $\overline{AB}$. M intersects $\overline{AB}$ to form a rt. $\angle$; Def. of $\perp$ lines

10. Points E and F are in the same half-plane with edge $\underline{?}$. $\overleftrightarrow{AB}$

11. $m\angle PTQ = \underline{?}$ 80

12. $m\angle QPT + m\angle TPR = m\angle \underline{?}$ QPR

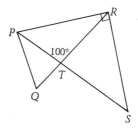

13. A particular case which shows that a given statement is not always true is called a $\underline{?}$. counterexample

14. Name an obtuse angle. $\angle PTR$ or $\angle QTS$

15. Name a right angle. $\angle PRS$

16. $\angle QPT$ and $\angle \underline{?}$ are adjacent angles. TPR

17. Name a pair of complementary angles. $\angle PRT$, $\angle SRT$ or $\angle TPR$, $\angle TSR$

18. Name two pairs of vertical angles. $\angle PTQ$, $\angle RTS$; $\angle PTR$, $\angle QTS$

19. Name two points in the interior of $\angle QPR$. T, S

20. Name two supplements of $\angle PTR$. $\angle PTQ$, $\angle RTS$

21. The measure of $\angle V$ is five times the measure of its supplement, $\angle W$. Find $m\angle V$ and $m\angle W$. 150, 30

22. If $m\angle ABC = 84$ and $\overrightarrow{BK}$ bisects $\angle ABC$, then $m\angle ABK = \underline{?}$. 42

Given $P(-5, 1)$ and $Q(7, -4)$,

23. Find PQ. 13

24. Find the coordinates of the midpoint of $\overline{PQ}$. $(1, -1.5)$

25. Identify the geometric figure satisfying $y = x + 3$ and $x \geq 0$. Ray

CHAPTER 2

Reasoning in Geometry

Chapter Overview

This chapter sets the stage for the development of geometric proof through a study of inductive and deductive reasoning. Inductive reasoning is introduced as a means of discovering relationships that may later be proved by deductive methods. Students are encouraged to look for patterns, make conjectures and then either verify with further examples or disprove with a counterexample.

Parallel lines and angle relationships are also introduced. Students are encouraged to make conjectures about these angle relationships.

The "if . . . then" statement is introduced as a way to express conditional statements, and related forms (converse, inverse and contrapositive) are studied. Students are shown how to use an "if and only if" sentence to rewrite definitions.

The study of deductive reasoning is begun with two laws of logic: affirming the hypothesis and the Transitive Property for Conditionals. Students write deductive arguments to draw specific conclusions and to justify processes that previously were simply assumed to be valid.

This chapter begins the development of many **proof subskills**. Much time is spent developing the ability to supply missing reasons and statements, to write "if . . . then" statements and to write possible conclusions from a given hypothesis.

Perspectives

Lesson 2-1 introduces inductive reasoning with examples from the real world and pure mathematics. Inductive reasoning is used to discover patterns and relationships.

Three points about inductive reasoning should be emphasized: (1) using inductive reasoning to find patterns is a useful **problem-solving strategy**; (2) inductive reasoning is used in geometry to make conjectures about relationships, which are then proved using deductive reasoning; and (3) conclusions that seem reasonable based on a few cases may not be true for all cases.

Lesson 2-2 stresses the use of inductive reasoning when making conjectures. Some important definitions, including the angle relationships created by a transversal, are presented. Before stating a theorem to be proved, encourage students to make conjectures based on the given hypotheses. Making conjectures is also an aspect of the guess-and-check **problem-solving strategy**.

Lesson 2-3 studies deductive reasoning. Conditional statements provide the basis for drawing conclusions from previously established statements.

Students will learn to identify hypotheses and conclusions by rewriting given statements in "if . . . then" form and by using Venn diagrams to represent relationships in conditional statements. This lesson also develops the **proof subskill** of writing "if . . . then" statements.

Lesson 2-4 continues the study of deductive reasoning. "If . . . then" statements are now used in logical arguments to draw conclusions using the law of logic called "affirming the hypothesis."

Students begin to write informal proofs, and several **proof subskills** are developed (e.g., writing conclusions from given statements and supplying missing statements and reasons).

Pacing Chart for Chapter 2

Lesson	Objectives	Basic Course	Average Course	Extended Course
2–1	Use inductive reasoning to discover mathematical relationships; recognize real-world applications of inductive reasoning.	1	1	1
2–2	Make conjectures based upon exploration; recognize parallel lines and angles formed when two lines are cut by a transversal.	1	1	1
2–3	Write statements in "if . . . then" form; identify the hypothesis and conclusion of a conditional; use Venn diagrams.	$1\frac{1}{2}$	1	1
2–4	Use affirming-the-hypothesis arguments to draw necessary conclusions.	$1\frac{1}{2}$	1	1
2–5	Use the Transitive Property for Conditionals and affirming the hypothesis with deductive arguments; justify numerical and geometric relationships.	$1\frac{1}{2}$	1	1
2–6	Write the converse, the inverse and the contrapositive of a conditional; write an "if and only if" statement as two "if . . . then" statements.	$1\frac{1}{2}$	1	1
Review		1	1	1
Test		1	1	1
Total		10 days	8 days	8 days

Lesson 2–5 continues the development of deductive reasoning by introducing a second rule of logic—the Transitive Property for Conditionals.

This lesson also develops the ability to organize conditionals, rules of logic, definitions, postulates and properties of real numbers to form a chain of deductive reasoning. In particular, students should be able to follow and complete the details of a chain of reasoning.

Lesson 2–6 presents statements that are related to a given conditional—its converse, inverse and contrapositive. The "if and only if" statement is also introduced here.

The most important points to keep in mind during this lesson are (1) a conditional and its contrapositive are equivalent, (2) the converse and the inverse are equivalent to each other but not to the original conditional and (3) an "if and only if" statement means that both the conditional and its converse are true.

52

Reasoning in Geometry

Chapter 2

Galileo, an Italian astronomer and physicist, was a professor at the University of Pisa nearly four hundred years ago. One of his famous experiments involved dropping weights from the top of the Leaning Tower of Pisa. His findings, represented below, helped Galileo develop an important law of motion.

Time (seconds)	Speed of weight (feet per second)
0	0
1	32
2	64
3	96
4	?

Galileo studied his findings and noticed a pattern. For each second the weight fell, the speed of the weight increased by the same amount.

1. Consider the first 3 seconds the weight was falling. By how much did the speed of the weight increase during each second?

2. Predict the speed of the weight after 4 seconds.

3. Predict the speed of the weight after t seconds.

52   **Chapter 2** *Reasoning in Geometry*

1. True or false: A linear pair is two adjacent and supplementary angles. True
2. A ray that forms two congruent angles from a larger angle is a(n) __?__. Angle bisector
3. A five-sided polygon is a(n) __?__. Pentagon
4. What is the measure of a right angle? 90

LESSON 2–1

Resources

Small ball
String with attached weight
Worksheet 2–1
Extension 2–1
💻 Computer Activities 2–1

2-1 Inductive Reasoning

In 1584, Galileo conducted experiments with pendulums which led to a number of important discoveries. He observed that the amount of time it takes the pendulum to complete one full swing depends upon the length of the pendulum. The data he collected are represented in the table below.

Time of swing (seconds)	1	2	3	4	5
Pendulum length (units)	1	4	9	16	_?_ 25

Do you see a pattern in the table? What is the length of a pendulum that takes 5 seconds to complete one swing? The correct answer can be verified experimentally. In general, the data suggest that if it takes n seconds to complete one swing, the length of the pendulum is n^2.

The process of forming a conclusion based upon examination of several specific cases is called *inductive reasoning*. It is one of the methods used for discovering geometric relationships.

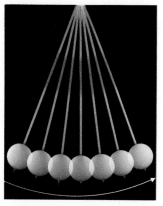

Path of one full swing

OBJECTIVES

Use inductive reasoning to discover mathematical relationships; recognize real-world applications of inductive reasoning.

TEACHING NOTES

Introduce this lesson by using **concrete materials** to demonstrate the relationship between

Example 1
Drawing a line through the center of a circle separates the circular region into 2 parts. Two lines through the center yield 4 parts, and three lines give 6 parts. Predict the number of parts if four lines are drawn. How many parts result from n lines?

Solution
Counting the parts in the diagrams provides the following data.

Number of lines	1	2	3	4
Number of parts	2	4	6	_?_ 8

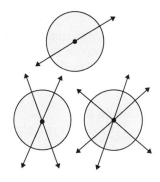

The pattern in the data suggests that for four lines there are 8 parts and, in general, for n lines there are $2n$ parts.

The diagram at the right verifies that four lines give 8 parts.

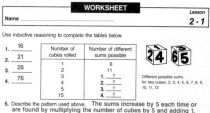

WORKSHEET

Name _____   Lesson 2-1

Use inductive reasoning to complete the tables below.

1. __16__
2. __21__
3. __26__
4. __76__

Number of cubes rolled	Number of different sums possible
1	6
2	11
3	1. _?_
4	2. _?_
5	3. _?_
15	4. _?_

Different possible sums for two cubes: 2, 3, 4, 5, 6, 7, 8, 9, 10, 11, 12

5. Describe the pattern used above. The sums increase by 5 each time or are found by multiplying the number of cubes by 5 and adding 1.

6. __4__
7. __8__
8. __16__
9. __512__

Row Number	Sum of numbers in this row
1	1
2	2
3	6. _?_
4	7. _?_
5	8. _?_
10	9. _?_

Pascal's Triangle
Row 1   1
Row 2   1   1
Row 3   1   2   1
Row 4   1   3   3   1
Row 5   1   4   6   4   1

10. Describe the pattern used above. Each sum is doubled, or the sums are powers of 2 with the exponent one less than the row number.

11. __9__
12. __14__
13. __20__

Number of dots on each side of the square	Number of segments having different lengths
2	2
3	5
4	11. _?_
5	12. _?_
6	13. _?_

14. Describe the pattern used above. Each answer is the sum of the number of dots and the previous answer.

15. __24__
16. __120__
17. __720__

Number of letters	Number of possible arrangements
2	2
3	6
4	15. _?_
5	16. _?_
6	17. _?_

Possible arrangements for three letters:
ABC   CAB
ACB   CBA
BAC
BCA

18. Describe the pattern used above. Each answer is the product of the number of letters and the previous answer.

pendulum length and time of swing. Use a string with a weight tied to one end.

Use **concrete materials** to demonstrate Heron's discovery about angles of incidence and reflection. Point out that a conclusion based on inductive reasoning can be false.

Additional Examples

Example 1

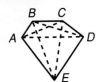

Diagonals:
$\overline{AC}, \overline{AD}, \overline{BD},$
$\overline{BE}, \overline{CE}$

A diagonal of a polygon is a line segment drawn from one corner to another nonadjacent corner. Fill in the following table for other polygons.

Heron, a Greek mathematician, used inductive reasoning to discover that the angle at which a ball strikes a flat surface has the same measure as the angle at which it rebounds.

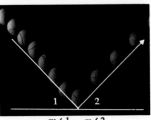

$m\angle 1 = m\angle 2$

In these diagrams of game tables, a ball is shot from corner A at a 45° angle. On each table, Heron's discovery is used to draw the path of the ball. The numbers indicate where and in what order the ball strikes the sides. In what corner does the ball always end up? Corner D

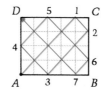
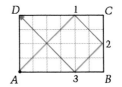
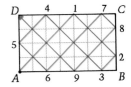

Using inductive reasoning, you might conclude that for any table with $AD = 4$, a ball shot from A will always end up in corner D.

However, the diagram at the right of a 4-by-8 table shows that this conclusion is not correct. The ball ends up in corner B.

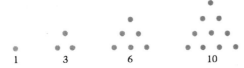

This raises an important question about inductive reasoning. Do conclusions that seem reasonable for some cases necessarily apply to all cases? What advice would you give to someone using inductive reasoning? No, one must be cautious when using inductive reasoning.

Example 2
Predict the next two *triangular* numbers.

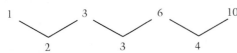

1   3   6   10

Solution
The triangular numbers above form this sequence: 1, 3, 6, 10. The differences between successive terms suggest this pattern:

1   3   6   10

2   3   4

Thus, the next two triangular numbers should be $10 + 5$, or 15, and $15 + 6$, or 21.

Number of sides	3	4	5	6	7	8	9
Number of diagonals	0	2	5	9	14	20	27

Checking for Understanding

1. A pendulum takes 7 seconds to complete a full swing. What is the length of the pendulum? 49 units

2. How many seconds would it take a pendulum 36 units in length to complete a full swing? 6 sec

3. Draw triangular arrays of dots to verify that 15 and 21 are the correct numbers in Example 2.

4. A gardener experimented with a new fertilizer, using it on alternate rows of the garden. The rows with the new fertilizer gave the better yield. What conclusion might the gardener make? The new fertilizer produces better yields

5. A farmer tried a new pesticide this year. The crops were damaged much less this year from pests than they were last year. What conclusion might the farmer make?

6. Who is more likely to make an incorrect conclusion, the gardener in Exercise 4 or the farmer in Exercise 5? Explain.

Written Exercises

Set A   Give an example of how inductive reasoning might be used by

1. an automobile driver.   **2.** a medical researcher.

3. Draw a linear pair of angles. Then draw the bisector of each angle. Measure the angle formed by the bisectors. Repeat the procedure with different linear pairs. What did you discover?

4. Trace the semicircle shown at the right.

   a. Choose a point P on the semicircle and draw $\angle APB$. What is the measure of $\angle APB$? 90

   b. Choose another point Q on the semicircle and find $m\angle AQB$. 90   Each $\angle$ is a rt. $\angle$

   c. What conclusion is suggested in each case?

   d. Check your answer in Exercise c with several more points on the semicircle.

5. Draw a large triangle and the perpendicular bisector of each side. Repeat the procedure with several triangles of different shapes. What appears to be true in each case?

6. Draw a large triangle. Then draw its three angle bisectors. Repeat with several different triangles. What seems to be true of the bisectors?

3.

5. The new pesticide is more effective.

3. The bisectors of a lin. pr. of $\angle$s are $\perp$.

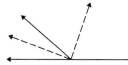

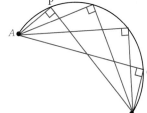

5. The $\perp$ bisectors intersect in a single pt.

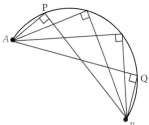

6. The $\angle$ bisectors intersect in a single pt.

Example 2

The sum of the first n odd numbers forms an interesting pattern.

$$1 \quad\quad\quad\quad\; = 1 \;\; = 1^2$$
$$1 + 3 \quad\quad\quad = 4 \;\; = 2^2$$
$$1 + 3 + 5 \quad\;\; = 9 \;\; = 3^2$$
$$1 + 3 + 5 + 7 = 16 = 4^2$$

(a) What is the sum of the first five odd numbers? $5^2 = 25$

(b) What is the sum of the first nine odd numbers? $9^2 = 81$

(c) What is the sum of the first n odd numbers? n^2

Error Analysis   Students often conclude that consideration of one or more examples constitutes proof of the conclusion. Stress that even performing many trials may lead to a wrong conclusion.

ANSWERS

Checking for Understanding

6. The farmer in Exercise 5; all rows in Exercise 4 have probably been influenced by the same factors, such as temperature, precipitation and soil conditions. The crops in Exercise 5 have probably *not* been influenced by the same factors.

Written Exercises

1. Sample: Upon entering a street which experience has shown to be heavily used by children on bicycles, a driver will decrease the speed of his car.

12. When reduced to lowest terms, if the ratio is of the form even : odd, the ball will end up in corner *D*. If the ratio is of the form even : even, the ball will end up in corner *B*.

13. To determine the number of times the ball will hit the sides of a 4-by-*n* table, find the reduced form of the ratio 4 : *n*. If *a* : *b* is the reduced form, the ball will hit the sides (*a* + *b* − 2) times.

14. 22, 35, 61

16. Each pentagonal number is the sum of the corresponding triangular and square numbers minus the position of the number in the sequence.

FOLLOW-UP

More Practice

- **Worksheet 2–1**

Extension

Have students use inductive reasoning to guess the next few terms in a sequence of numbers such as 2, 5, 11, 23, ... 47, 95, 191. Discuss the pattern. Computer software that draws a figure and asks the student to predict a geometric relationship would be ideal for this lesson.

- **Extension 2–1**

Computers

- **Computer Activities 2–1**

Set B When three points on a circle are connected, four nonoverlapping regions are enclosed.

7. Copy and complete the table below. Draw a new circle for each case. Mark points on the circle. Then draw *all* the segments determined by the points. Count the regions.

Number of points	1	2	3	4	5
Number of regions	? 1	? 2	4	? 8	? 16

8. Predict the number of regions enclosed when six points are connected. Check your prediction.

8. 32 regions; a diagram shows at most 31 regions

By placing segments end to end, you can create a figure that encloses nonoverlapping regions as shown at the right. Figure **a** has one region and figure **b** has three.

9. Copy and complete the table below. For each figure, count the number of segments *S*, points *P*, and regions *R*.

Figure	a	b	c	d
Segments	? 3	? 7	? 12	? 9
Points	? 3	? 5	? 8	? 8
Regions	1	3	? 5	? 2

10. Write a formula relating the number of segments *S*, points *P*, and regions *R*. S + 1 = P + R

11. How many regions are formed by a figure with 8 segments and 6 points? Check with a drawing.

Sample:

3 regions

Refer to the game tables on page 54.

12. Study the ratios, in reduced form, of *AD* to *AB*. Predict in which corner a ball will end up for any 4-by-*n* table, where *n* is any positive integer.

13. Predict the number of times the ball will hit the sides of a 4-by-*n* table before landing in a corner.

14. Illustrated at the right are the first three *pentagonal* numbers. Use inductive reasoning to predict the next three pentagonal numbers.
22, 35, 51; *n*th pentagonal number =
$$\left(\frac{n}{2}\right)(3n - 1)$$

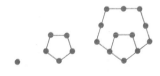

Set C Consider the triangular and pentagonal numbers.

15. Draw the first three *square* numbers. Then predict the next three square numbers. **16, 25, 36**

1   4   9

16. Study the triangular numbers, the square numbers, and the pentagonal numbers. Describe the relationship that exists among the three sets of numbers.

17. Draw the first three *hexagonal* numbers. Then predict the next three hexagonal numbers. **28, 45, 66**

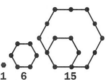
1   6   15

▲ Review Given points $A(6, 1)$ and point $B(-2, 7)$,   **(2, 4)**

18. find AB. **10**   **19.** find the midpoint of $\overline{AB}$.

20. $x = 7$; $m\angle Q = 47$; $m\angle R = 43$ 21. Collinear pts. are pts. contained in one line. 23. The measures of the vert. ∠s in each pair are =.

20. $\angle Q$ and $\angle R$ are complementary: $m\angle Q = 6x + 5$ and $m\angle R = 4x + 15$. Find x, $m\angle Q$, and $m\angle R$.

21. What are collinear points?

22. Point M is the midpoint of $\overline{TS}$ and $TM = 13$. Find TS. **26** **Sample:**

 Thinking Ahead

23. Draw a pair of intersecting lines. Measure each angle in a pair of vertical angles. Repeat the procedure with three different sets of lines. How do the measures of vertical angles appear to be related?

150° 30°
30° 150°

🖳 Computer Activities: Graphing

1. Graph these equations on the same axes. What do you notice? **All graphs contain (0, 5)**
   a. $y = 3x + 5$ **b.** $y = 5$ **c.** $y = -x + 5$ **d.** $y = x + 5$ **e.** $y = -2x + 5$

2. Now graph these equations on the same axes. What do you notice? **Lines are not concurrent; no graph contains (0, 5).**
   a. $2y = 3x + 5$ **b.** $5y = 5$ **c.** $3y = x + 5$ **d.** $-y = x + 5$ **e.** $2y = -3x + 5$

3. How are the two groups of equations alike? How are they different? What conjecture can you make?

Algebra Review: Equations in the Form $y = mx + b$

Example

Write $x + 2y = 6$ in the form $y = mx + b$.

Solution

$x + 2y = 6$

$\quad 2y = -x + 6$ *Add $-x$ to both sides of the equation.*

$\quad\quad y = -\frac{1}{2}x + 3$ *Multiply both sides of the equations by $\frac{1}{2}$.*

Write each equation in the form $y = mx + b$.

1. $2x + y = 3$ $y = -2x + 3$ **2.** $3x + 4y = 8$ $y = -\frac{3}{4}x + 2$ **3.** $x - y = 7$ $y = 1x - 7$

4. $x + y = 0$ $y = -1x$ **5.** $5y - 3x = 10$ $y = \frac{3}{5}x + 2$ **6.** $5x + 2y + 8 = 0$ $y = -\frac{5}{2}x - 4$

Computer Activities

1.

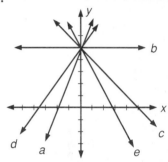

2.

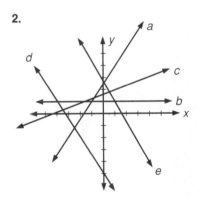

3. The constant term in each equation is 5. In the first set of equations, the coefficient of $y = 1$; In the second set, the coefficient of $y \neq 1$. If an equation is in the form $y = mx + b$, then the graph of the equation contains the point $(0, b)$

Excursion

1. $n^2 + 3$
2. $7n + 1$
3. $3n^2 - 1$
4. $\frac{1}{2}n^2$
5. $\frac{3}{2}n^2 - \frac{1}{2}n$
6.

a.

n	s	1st diff.	2nd diff.	3rd diff.
1	1			
		7		
2	8		12	
		19		6
3	27		18	
		37		6
4	64		24	
		61		
5	125			

Excursion: Finite Differences

In Lesson 2-1, we examined several situations involving number patterns, such as those at the right. In **a**, s is the length of a pendulum that takes n seconds to complete one full swing. In **b**, s is the number of regions into which a circle is divided by n lines. In **c**, s is the nth triangular number.

a.

n	1	2	3	4	5
s	1	4	9	16	25

b.

n	1	2	3	4	5
s	2	4	6	8	10

c.

n	1	2	3	4	5
s	1	3	6	10	15

Example 1
Make a conjecture about the general rule that gives s in terms of n in patterns **a**, **b**, **c**.

Solution
In **a** each value of s is the square of n, so $s = n^2$. In **b**, each value of s is twice the corresponding n, so $s = 2n$. In **c**, to find s, look at the corresponding n and at $n + 1$—the next value in the n column.

Multiply n by $(n + 1)$ and then divide by 2 to get s.
The rule is $s = \dfrac{n(n + 1)}{2} = \dfrac{1}{2}n^2 + \dfrac{1}{2}n$.

An approach that can help you discover general patterns is called the method of *finite differences*. This method consists of subtracting consecutive values of s, next subtracting the consecutive differences you found, and then repeating this process until the differences are constant. Applying this method to pattern **b** at the right gives a common difference of 2 as the first difference.

n	s	1st difference
1	2	2
2	4	2
3	6	2
4	8	2
5	10	
n	$2n$	

Example 2
Apply the method of finite differences to number patterns **a** and **c**.

Solution

a.

n	s	1st diff.	2nd diff.
1	1	3	2
2	4	5	2
3	9	7	2
4	16	9	
5	25		

c.

n	s	1st diff.	2nd diff.
1	1	2	1
2	3	3	1
3	6	4	1
4	10	5	
5	15		

For pattern **b**, the *first* differences are constant; while for patterns **a** and **c**, it is the *second* differences that are constant. Notice that the rule for patterns **a** and **c** has an n^2 term, but the rule for pattern **b** does *not*.

The next patterns also show this connection between the rule and the point at which the differences become constant.

d.

n	s	1st diff.
1	7	3
2	10	3
3	13	3
4	16	3
5	19	
n	$3n + 4$	

e.

n	s	1st diff.	2nd diff.
1	6	3	2
2	9	5	2
3	14	7	2
4	21	9	
5	30		
n	$n^2 + 5$		

f.

n	s	1st diff.	2nd diff.
1	3	8	6
2	11	14	6
3	25	20	6
4	45	26	
5	71		
n	$3n^2 - n + 1$		

The following table summarizes our finding so far.

Rule	Difference that is constant	Constant difference
$2n$	First	2
$3n + 4$	First	3
n^2	Second	2
$\frac{1}{2}n^2 + \frac{1}{2}n$	Second	1
$n^2 + 5$	Second	2
$3n^2 - n + 1$	Second	6

This summary suggests the following generalization:
A number pattern with a rule of the form $an + b$ has a constant first difference a. A number pattern with a rule of the form $an^2 + bn + c$ has a constant second difference $2a$.

Use this generalization to find the rule for each number pattern.

1. 4, 7, 12, 19, 28, . . . $n^2 + 3$ **2.** 8, 15, 22, 29, 36, . . . $7n + 1$

3. 2, 11, 26, 47, 74, . . . $3n^2 - 1$ **4.** $\frac{1}{2}, 2, \frac{9}{2}, 8, \frac{25}{2}, \ldots \frac{n^2}{2}$

5. In Exercise 14 of Lesson 2-1, you examined a pattern of numbers called the pentagonal numbers which arise from a pentagon as shown at the right. Use the method of finite differences to find a general rule for this pattern.

6. Write the first five terms of the number patterns that have these general rules. Apply the method of finite differences until the differences are constant. Make a conjecture about which difference is constant and what the constant difference is.

a. n^3 **b.** $2n^3$ **c.** $n^3 - n$ **d.** $2n^3 - n^2$ **e.** $\frac{1}{2}(n^3 - n)$

The third difference is constant; the constant difference is 6a.

$\frac{3n^2 - n}{2}$

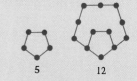

1   5   12

a. 1, 8, 27, 64, 125
b. 2, 16, 54, 128, 250
c. 0, 6, 24, 60, 120
d. 1, 12, 45, 112, 225
e. 0, 3, 12, 30, 60

b.

n	s	1st diff.	2nd diff.	3rd diff.
1	2			
		14		
2	16		24	
		38		12
3	54		36	
		74		12
4	128		48	
		122		
5	250			

c.

n	s	1st diff.	2nd diff.	3rd diff.
1	0			
		6		
2	6		12	
		18		6
3	24		18	
		36		6
4	60		24	
		60		
5	120			

d.

n	s	1st diff.	2nd diff.	3rd diff.
1	1			
		11		
2	12		22	
		33		12
3	45		34	
		67		12
4	112		46	
		113		
5	225			

e.

n	s	1st diff.	2nd diff.	3rd diff.
1	0			
		3		
2	3		6	
		9		3
3	12		9	
		18		3
4	30		12	
		30		
5	60			

A number pattern involving n^3 has a constant third difference 6a.

LESSON 2–2

Resources

Compass
Shoebox
Teaching Aid 1, protractor
Visual Aid 1, protractor
Teaching Aid 5, graphs
Visual Aid 5, graphs
Worksheet 2–2
Extension 2–2
Computer Worksheet 2–2

OBJECTIVES

Make conjectures based upon exploration; recognize parallel and skew lines and angles formed when two lines are cut by a transversal.

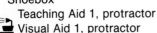
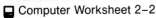

WORKSHEET

Name _____ Lesson **2-2**

1. Draw all possible triangles that can be formed by connecting the given points to the corners of each figure.

2. What conjecture about sides of figures and triangles is suggested? **The number of triangles formed will be 2 less than the number of sides.**

Joy decided to buy some blouses and skirts so that she could mix and match outfits. How many different outfits can she wear given the following selections?

3. A pink blouse; a white blouse; a gray skirt; a navy blue skirt; a black skirt **6 outfits**
4. A red blouse; a white blouse; a navy blue blouse; a red skirt; a white skirt; a black skirt **9 outfits**
5. A red blouse; a white blouse; a navy blue blouse; a black blouse; a red skirt; a white skirt; a navy blue skirt; a black skirt; a gray skirt **20 outfits**

6. How did you determine the number of outfits in each case above? **Answers may vary. A possible answer is to list the combinations.**
7. What conjecture about the number of outfits is suggested? **The number of outfits equals the number of blouses times the number of skirts.**
8. A number cube is marked with the numbers 1, 2, 3, 4, 5, and 6. If the number cube is rolled twice, list the possible sums. **2, 3, 4, 5, 6, 7, 8, 9, 10, 11, and 12**
9. List the possible sums if a number cube is rolled three times. **3, 4, 5, 6, 7, 8, 9, 10, 11, 12, 13, 14, 15, 16, 17, and 18**
10. What conjecture about the number of rolls and the possible sums is suggested? **The possible sums are the numbers starting with the number of rolls through that number times 6.**
11. If two number cubes (each marked 1–6) are rolled 100 times, which sum (or sums) would you expect to appear most often? Why? Which sum (or sums) would you expect to appear least often? Why? **6 and 7; more ways to roll a 6 or a 7 than the others; 2, 3, 11, and 12; less ways to roll these numbers**
12. Determine the smallest number of colors needed to color any map so that each state or region is colored, but two states or regions with a common boundary are colored with different colors. **4 colors**
13. How did you determine the answer you got in exercise 12? **Answers will vary. A possible answer is to color an outline map with complicated borders using two, three, and four colors.**

2-2 Making Conjectures

A *conjecture* is a statement that seems to be true. It often results from exploratory activities such as drawing and measuring. Making conjectures is an important way to discover new mathematics.

In Example 1, paper folding is used to help make a conjecture.

Example 1

Draw lines n and m intersecting in point P. Label vertical angles $\angle 1$ and $\angle 2$. Draw $\overrightarrow{PA}$, the bisector of $\angle 3$, and fold your paper along $\overrightarrow{PA}$. Repeat this activity with two more pairs of vertical angles with measures different from $m\angle 1$. Make a conjecture about $\angle 1$ and $\angle 2$.

Solution

In each case, $\angle 1$ and $\angle 2$ coincide. A possible conjecture is: Vertical angles are equal.

Algebra is used to make a conjecture in the next example.

Example 2

Graph the following equations on the same axes.

a. $y = x$
b. $y = 2x$
c. $y = 4x$
d. $y = 2x - 3$
e. $y = 0.5x$
f. $y = x + 2$

What possible conjectures are suggested by these graphs?

Solution

The graphs shown at the right suggest this conjecture: The coefficient of x determines the steepness of the graph of the equation. In particular, for the equation $y = mx + b$ where $m > 0$, as m gets larger, the graph of the corresponding equation gets steeper. Another possible conjecture is: The constant term in the equation determines where the graph crosses the y-axis.

In our coordinate model, a nonvertical line with equation $y = mx + b$ will be said to have slope m and y-intercept b.

What do you think would be an equation of a line whose graph lies between the graphs of $y = 0.5x$ and $y = x$? **Sample: $y = 0.75x$**

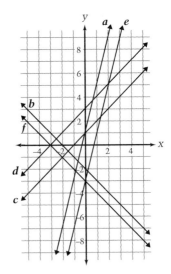

Definition *Parallel Lines*

Parallel lines are lines that are coplanar and do not intersect.

$\overleftrightarrow{AB}$ and $\overleftrightarrow{CD}$ are parallel lines, and we write $\overleftrightarrow{AB} \parallel \overleftrightarrow{CD}$. Special arrows are used to indicate parallel lines. Name another pair of parallel lines. $\overleftrightarrow{AC} \parallel \overleftrightarrow{BD}$

Segments and rays are parallel if the lines containing them are parallel. For example, $\overline{AC} \parallel \overline{BD}$. Name a pair of parallel rays.
Samples: $\overrightarrow{AB} \parallel \overrightarrow{CD}$; $\overrightarrow{BE} \parallel \overrightarrow{CF}$; $\overrightarrow{CA} \parallel \overrightarrow{BD}$

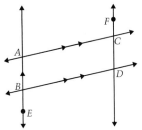

Example 3
Consider again the equations in Example 2. Make a conjecture about two lines that have the same slope.

Solution
The lines for equations **a** and **f** have the same slope and are parallel. The same appears to be true for the lines for equations **b** and **d**. A possible conjecture is: Two lines with the same slope are parallel.

In our coordinate model, parallel lines are lines with the same slope and different y-intercepts.

What would be an equation of a line parallel to the line with equation **c**? $y = 4x + b$, *b* is a real number

Definition *Transversal*

A transversal is a line that intersects two or more coplanar lines in distinct points.

At the right, lines *m* and *n* are "cut" by transversal *t*. Groups of the eight angles formed have special names.

Interior angles: $\angle 3, \angle 4, \angle 5, \angle 6$

Exterior angles: $\angle 1, \angle 2, \angle 7, \angle 8$

Corresponding angles: $\angle 1$ and $\angle 5$, $\angle 2$ and $\angle 6$, $\angle 3$ and $\angle 7$, $\angle 4$ and $\angle 8$

Alternate interior angles: $\angle 3$ and $\angle 5$, $\angle 4$ and $\angle 6$

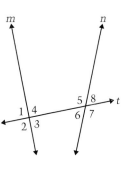

Corresponding angles, such as $\angle 1$ and $\angle 5$, are on the same side of the transversal and are in "corresponding" positions (above or below, or left or right) relative to the two lines.

Alternate interior angles, such as $\angle 3$ and $\angle 5$, have different vertices, are on opposite sides of the transversal, and lie "between" the two lines.

TEACHING NOTES

Introduce this lesson by using **concrete materials** so students can readily make a connection between real experiences and conjectures.

When discussing parallel and skew lines, try having students discover the criterion for coplanarity by using **concrete materials** such as a shoebox. Ask students to find two lines that do not intersect but are not parallel. It should then be easy to establish that the two edges are not sides of the same face and that there is no plane that contains both.

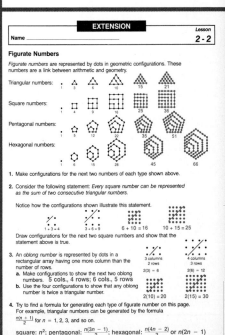

Additional Examples

Example 1

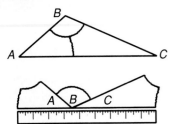

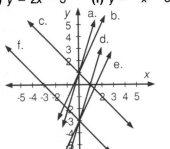

Tear off the corners of any triangle. Fit these corners together as shown above.

(a) Do the angles of the triangle together form a straight line? **yes** Try this with several different triangles.

(b) Make a conjecture from your examples. **The sum of the angles of any triangle equals a straight angle.**

Example 2

Graph the following equations on the same set of axes.

(a) $y = 3x + 1$ **(b)** $y = 2x + 1$
(c) $y = -x + 1$ **(d)** $y = 3x - 3$
(e) $y = 2x - 3$ **(f)** $y = -x - 3$

What conjecture is suggested? **If an equation is in the form $y = mx + b$, then the b value indicates the y-intercept of the graph of that equation.**

The next two examples ask for conjectures that relate some of these special angles and parallel lines.

Example 4

Draw $\overleftrightarrow{AB}$ and $\overleftrightarrow{AC}$ with $m\angle BAC = 50$. Now draw $\overleftrightarrow{DC}$ so that D and B are on opposite sides of $\overleftrightarrow{AC}$ and with $m\angle ACD = 50$. Do this again with angles of 30°, 100°, and 85°. What conjecture is suggested?

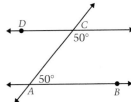

Solution
In the figure $\overleftrightarrow{AB}$ and $\overleftrightarrow{CD}$ appear to be parallel. $\angle BAC$ and $\angle ACD$ are equal alternate interior angles. The conjecture is: If two coplanar lines are cut by a transversal form a pair of equal alternate interior angles, then the lines are parallel.

Example 5

a. Use the parallel lines on a sheet of notebook paper as a guide to draw two parallel lines, ℓ and m
b. Draw a transversal t. Label $\angle 1$ and $\angle 2$ as shown.
c. Place tracing paper over your figure and trace ℓ, m, and t. Label the traced figure ℓ', m', and t'. Label $\angle 1'$ and $\angle 2'$.
d. Slide the tracing paper along t, keeping t' over t, until ℓ coincides with m.

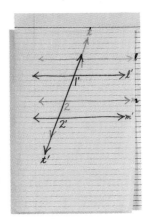

Repeat this activity with several other pairs of parallel lines. Draw the transversals so that the angles formed have different measures. What conjecture about corresponding angles is suggested?

Solution
In each case, $\angle 1'$ coincides with $\angle 2$. This suggests that $m\angle 1 = m\angle 2$. These are corresponding angles. The conjecture is: If two parallel lines are cut by a transversal, then corresponding angles are equal.

As you think about these exploratory activities, remember that they only *suggest* conjectures. Writing proofs for conjectures, including some of those in these examples, is in Chapter 3.

Checking for Understanding

1. In Examples 1–5, what type of reasoning is used to help make a conjecture? **Inductive reasoning**

2. How many interior angles are formed when a transversal cuts two lines? How many pairs of corresponding angles? **4;4**

3. In the diagram at the right, which angles do you think might be called *alternate exterior angles*? **∠1 and ∠7; ∠2 and ∠8**

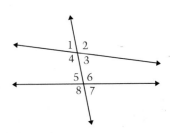

Assignment Guide

Basic: 1–11, 22–27
Average: 1–4, 8–19, 22–27
Extended: 1–27

If the lines containing the segments of each letter are shown, which letters contain each item? **4. A, E, F, H, M, N, W, Z**

4. Transversals   **5.** Corresponding angles **E, F**

6. Parallel segments **7.** Alternate interior angles
E, F, H, M, N, W, Z   A, H, M, N, W, Z

A E F H M N
T V W X Y Z

Written Exercises

Set A

1. Draw line AB. Fold your paper so that A and B coincide. How is the line along the crease related to $\overleftrightarrow{AB}$? It is the ⊥ bisector of $\overline{AB}$.

2. Draw $\angle MNP$. Fold your paper so that N is on the crease and $\overrightarrow{NP}$ coincides with $\overrightarrow{NM}$. What does the part of the crease in the interior of $\angle MNP$ represent? It represents the bisector of $\angle MNP$

3. Draw $\overline{ST}$. Find its midpoint using paper folding. How can you verify that this is the midpoint?

Classify each pair of angles as alternate interior angles or corresponding angles.

4. $\angle 4$ and $\angle 6$ alt. int. ∠s **5.** $\angle 3$ and $\angle 7$ corr. ∠s

6. $\angle 2$ and $\angle 16$ **7.** $\angle 2$ and $\angle 14$ corr. ∠s
alt. int. ∠s

8. Consider lines r and s and transversal t. Clearly, r and s are not parallel. $\angle 1$ and $\angle 2$ are alternate interior angles. How do their measures compare?

9. Repeat Exercise 8 with two other pairs of $m\angle 2 > m\angle 1$ nonparallel lines cut by a transversal. A conjecture you could make based on these activities is: If two nonparallel lines are cut by a transversal, then alternate interior angles are __?__. not =

Refer to the figure at the right. Identify

10. three pairs of lines that appear to be parallel.

11. three pairs of lines that appear to be perpendicular.

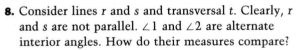

Set B   Graph all three equations on the same axes.

12. a. $y = x$ **b.** $y = 2x - 4$ **c.** $y = 5x + 2$

13. a. $y = -x + 1$ **b.** $y = -4x$ **c.** $y = -3x + 4$

14. A conjecture you could make based on the graphs in Exercises 12 and 13 is: The graph of $y = mx + b$ slants upward to the right if m is __?__ and slants downward to the right if m is __?__. positive; negative

Example 3

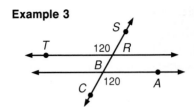

Draw $\overrightarrow{BA}$ and $\overrightarrow{BC}$ so that $m\angle ABC$ = 120. Draw $\overrightarrow{RT}$ so that T and A are on opposite sides of $\overleftrightarrow{CB}$ with $m\angle SRT = 120$. Repeat this with angles of 150, 70 and 45. What conjecture is suggested? If two coplanar lines cut by a transversal form a pair of equal alternate exterior angles, then the lines are parallel.

Example 4

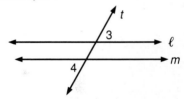

Repeat the tracing paper exercises described in **Example 5** in the student text, using $\angle 3$ and $\angle 4$. What conjecture about alternate exterior angles is suggested? If two parallel lines are cut by a transversal, then alternate exterior angles are equal.

ANSWERS

Written Exercises

3. by measuring the two segments into which this point divdes $\overline{ST}$

10. Sample: $\overleftrightarrow{RS} \parallel \overleftrightarrow{TU}$; $\overleftrightarrow{XW} \parallel \overleftrightarrow{RU}$; $\overleftrightarrow{TW} \parallel \overleftrightarrow{UV}$

11. Sample: $\overleftrightarrow{SR} \perp \overleftrightarrow{RU}$; $\overleftrightarrow{SX} \perp \overleftrightarrow{ST}$; $\overleftrightarrow{TW} \perp \overleftrightarrow{TU}$

Review

22. the process of forming a conclusion based upon examination of several specific cases

23. to develop laws of motion based upon conclusions from several pendulum experiments

25. A bisector of a segment is a set of points whose intersection with the segment is the midpoint of the segment.

26. A bisector of an angle is a ray in the interior that forms two equal angles.

15. Graph all three equations on the same axes.

   a. $y = 5$ **b.** $y = 3$ **c.** $y = -2$

A conjecture you could make based on these graphs is: The graph of $y = mx + b$ is parallel to the x-axis when m is ___?___; the graph intersects the y-axis at ___?___. (0, b)

    0

Do you think each statement is true for *all*, *some*, or *no* lines? You may want to refer to Exercises 10–11.

16. Two lines parallel to the same line are parallel. **All**

17. Two lines perpendicular to the same line are parallel. **Some**

18. In a plane, two lines perpendicular to the same line are parallel. **All**

19. a. Draw parallel lines ℓ and m along the parallel lines on a sheet of notebook paper.
   b. Draw a transversal t. Label $\angle 1$ and $\angle 2$ as shown.
   c. Locate and label M, the midpoint of the segment on t cut off by ℓ and m.
   d. Trace your figure. Label ℓ', m', t', $\angle 1'$, $\angle 2'$, and M'.
   e. Keeping M' on top of M, rotate the tracing paper until ℓ' coincides with m.

Repeat steps a–e with several other pairs of parallel lines and transversals. What conjecture about alternate interior angles is suggested? If two ‖ lines are cut by a transversal, then the alt. int. ∠s formed are =.

Set C Describe two kinds of activities that might help convince someone of these conjectures.

20. The sum of the angle measures in a triangle is 180.

21. If two parallel lines are cut by a transversal, the interior angles on the same side of the transversal are supplementary.

◆ **Review** **22.** What is inductive reasoning?

23. How might Galileo have used inductive reasoning?

24. Write an equation for $\overline{AB}$ given $A(3, -1)$ and $B(-2, -1)$. $y = -1$

Define each of the following.

25. Bisector of a segment   **26.** Bisector of an angle

20. 1)Measure ∠s 2)Use tracing paper
21. 1)Measure ∠s 2)Use tracing paper

 Thinking Ahead **27.** Does "A Wanderer gets good mileage" mean (a) "If a car is a Wanderer, then it gets good mileage" or (b) "If a car gets good mileage, then it is a Wanderer"? a

2-3 "If . . . Then" Statements

Everyday statement often have the form "**If** some event occurs, **then** something else will happen." The advertisement at the right is an example.

The exact meaning of some *"if . . . then" statements* is very important, especially in mathematics.

WANDERER

If you own a Wanderer, then driving is an adventure.

Consider the following statement.

If you get an A in geometry, **then** you will receive a math award.

The statement has two parts which we call p and q.

p: You get an A in geometry.

q: You will receive a math award.

Any statement in the form "If p, then q" is called a *conditional statement* or just a *conditional*. It is often written "$p \Rightarrow q$," which is read "p implies q."

The clause following "if" and corresponding to p is called the **hypothesis** and the clause following "then" and corresponding to q is called the **conclusion**. The statement about the math award is a conditional. What is the hypothesis? the conclusion? **You get an A in geometry; you will receive a math award.**

Venn diagrams are sometimes used to illustrate a conditional. In the diagram at the right, imagine that all students who get an A in geometry are inside the inner circle, and all students who receive a math award are inside the outer circle. Since any point inside the inner circle is also inside the outer circle, the meaning of the diagram is: Anyone who gets an A in geometry receives a math award. This is equivalent to the conditional above. **If** you get an A in geometry, **then** you will receive a math award. Notice in the Venn diagram that the hypothesis p is represented by points inside the inner circle.

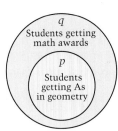

q
Students getting math awards

p
Students getting As in geometry

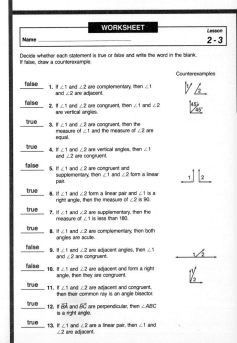

hypothesis and the outer circle representing the conclusion and (3) identifying hypotheses and conclusions.

Another important point in this lesson is the truth or falsity of a conditional. Explain that the conclusion must be true for every case in which the hypothesis is true.

Additional Examples

Example 1
Write a conditional whose conclusion is "$\angle ABM = \angle CBM$" and whose hypothesis is "$\overline{BM}$ bisects $\angle ABC$." If $\overline{BM}$ bisects $\angle ABC$, then $\angle ABM = \angle CBM$.

Example 2
(a) Explain why the following conditional is true: If $m\angle B = 35$, then $\angle B$ is acute. By definition, every angle whose measure is less than 90 is acute.

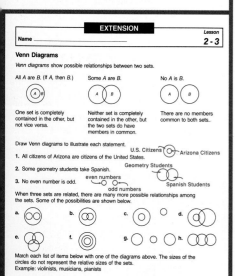

Example 1
Write a conditional whose conclusion is "$AM = MB$" and whose hypothesis is "M is the midpoint of $\overline{AB}$."

Solution
The conditional is, "**If** M is the midpoint of $\overline{AB}$ **then** $AM = MB$."

A conditional $p \Rightarrow q$ **is true** provided that for *every* case in which p is true, q is also true.

Example 2
Explain why the following conditional is true: If $m\angle S = 105$, then $\angle S$ is obtuse. Then illustrate the statement with a Venn diagram.

Solution
By definition, *every* angle with measure greater than 90 is obtuse. Since $m\angle S = 105$, and $105 > 90$, $\angle S$ is obtuse. In the Venn diagram, the hypothesis, $m\angle S = 105$, is represented by the inner circle. The conclusion, $\angle S$ is obtuse, is represented by the outer circle.

A conditional $p \Rightarrow q$ **is false** if there is a *counterexample*, that is, an instance for which the hypothesis p is true but the conclusion q is false.

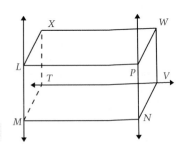

q
Obtuse angles

p

105°
angles

Example 3
Show with a counterexample that this conditional is false: If two lines do not intersect, then they are parallel.

Solution
In the diagram at the right, $\overleftrightarrow{LM}$ and $\overleftrightarrow{TV}$ do not intersect, but they are not parallel. Why? This counterexample shows that the conditional is false. Because $\overleftrightarrow{LM}$ and $\overleftrightarrow{TV}$ are noncoplanar; ‖ lines must be coplanar.

Definition   *Skew Lines*

Skew lines are lines that are not coplanar.

Are lines LM and PN skew lines? Why? No; because they are coplanar

Remember, for a conditional statement to be true, it must be true in every case. A conditional statement is considered to be false if it fails to be true in *just one case*.

Assignment Guide

Basic: 1–13, 32–38
Average: 1–13 (odd), 14–27, 32–38
Extended: 1–13 (odd), 14–38

The exact meaning of a statement can often be made clearer if it is written in "if . . . then" form.

Example 4

Write each statement in "if . . . then" form.

a. A hard worker is a good employee.

b. Vertical angles are equal.

c. The last digit in a whole number is 2 only if the number is even.

Solution

a. If you are a hard worker, **then** you are a good employee.

b. If two angles are vertical angles, **then** they are equal.

c. If the last digit of a whole number is 2, **then** the number is even.

Checking for Understanding

Hypothesis underlined once; conclusion underlined twice.

Identify the hypothesis and the conclusion of each statement.

1. If there is a good wind today, then I'll go sailing.

2. If you are a good driver, then you are alert when you drive.

3. If two angles are right angles, then they are equal.

4. Write "p only if q" in "if . . . then" form. If p then q.

5. Tell if each conditional in Example 4 is *true* or *false*. If false, give a counterexample. They are all true.

Written Exercises

Set A   Write each statement in "if . . . then" form, and identify the hypothesis and the conclusion.

1. Students who pass the exam will graduate.

2. All children in the United States have a right to a quality education.

3. Two intersecting line segments lie in a plane.

4. Supplements of the same angle are equal.

5. A geometric figure is a triangle only if it has three sides.

6. When two planes intersect, they intersect in a line.

7. Two angles have a common side if they are adjacent.

8. Rover is a collie only if he is a dog.

Draw a Venn diagram for

9. Exercise 1.   **10.** Exercise 8.

(b) Illustrate the statement with a Venn diagram.

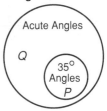

Example 3

Show with a counterexample that the following conditional is false: If all four sides of polygon *RSTW* are equal, then *RSTW* is a square. Use a rhombus as a counterexample.

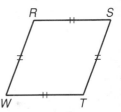

Example 4

Write each statement in "if . . . then" form.

(a) A thing of beauty is a joy forever. If a thing is a thing of beauty, then it is a joy forever.

(b) Right angles are equal. If two angles are right angles, then they are equal.

(c) A whole number whose last digit is 0 is divisible by 5. If the last digit of a whole number is 0, then that number is divisible by 5.

Error Analysis   The most common error in this lesson will probably be writing a conditional with the clauses reversed. Give several counterexamples to convince students that the order is wrong.

Remind students that the words "if" and "then" are not part of the hypothesis and conclusion.

ANSWERS

Written Exercises

11. If a figure is a square, then it is a four-sided figure.

12. If a point is the midpoint of a segment, then it is equidistant from the endpoints of the segment.

13. If one is a resident of Texas, then one is a resident of the United States.

14. If a tile is an Outdoor Tile, then its hardness ensures its easy maintenance and long wear.

15. false;

16. false;

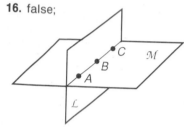

18. false;

19. false;

20. false; $0 < x < 180$
21. false;

25. If 3 points are noncollinear, then they are contained in 1 and only 1 plane.

26. If A and B are 2 distinct points, then there is a unique positive real number called the distance between A and B.

Give an "if . . . then" statement for each Venn diagram.

11.

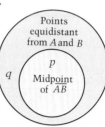

q
Four-sided figures

p
Squares

12.

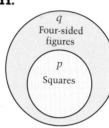

Points equidistant from A and B

q

p
Midpoint of $\overline{AB}$

13.

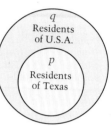

q
Residents of U.S.A.

p
Residents of Texas

Set B   **14.** Study the advertisement shown at the right. Rewrite the statement in "if . . . then" form, and discuss its meaning with another student.

Indicate whether each conditional is *true* or *false*. If false, give a counterexample. If true, cite the definition or postulate in Chapter 1 that supports the statement.

15. If points A, B, and C are collinear, then $AB = BC$.

16. If points A, B, and C are distinct points, then they are contained in one and only one plane. **False: P = A or P = B**

17. If P is on $\overline{AB}$, then P is between A and B.

18. If M is between A and B, then $AM = MB$.

19. If $XY = YZ$, then Y is the midpoint of $\overline{XZ}$.

20. If $0 < x < 360$, then x is the degree measure of an angle.

21. If B is in the interior of $\angle APC$, then $m\angle APB = m\angle BPC$.

22. If $m\angle A = 98$, then there is no angle that is complementary to $\angle A$. **True: Def. comp. ∠s**

23. If two intersecting lines form equal vertical angles, then the lines are perpendicular.

24. The vertex of an angle is contained in both of its sides. **True: Def. of ∠.**

Write each postulate in "if . . . then" form.

25. Postulate 3   **26.** Postulate 6   **27.** Postulate 14

Set C   **28.** Show with a counterexample that this conditional is false: If $\angle A$ and $\angle B$ are supplementary, then they are a linear pair.

29. Draw a Venn diagram showing the correct relationship between linear pairs and supplementary angles.

The hardness of Outdoor Tiles ensures their easy maintenance and long wear.

23. **False:** ⟨image⟩

28. **Sample:**
55°   125°

29.
Supp. ∠s
Linear pairs

30. Draw a Venn diagram illustrating the "if...then" statement in Exercise 28.

31. Compare and discuss with another student your work in Exercises 28–30.

◆ **Review** **32.** If two parallel lines are cut by a transversal, how are alternate interior angles related? corresponding angles? They are =; they are =.

33. Draw a triangle. Find the sum of the lengths of two sides; find the length of the third side. Repeat this activity with three more triangles. Make a conjecture about how the sum of the lengths of two sides compares to the length of the third side.

34. How might a doctor use inductive reasoning?

35. Name the endpoint of $\overrightarrow{CD}$. C

36. If $m\angle A = m\angle B$ and $m\angle A$ and $\angle B$ are supplementary, find $m\angle B$. 90

≡ **Thinking Ahead** Consider that part of Postulate 1 that states: A line contains at least two points. In "if... then" form, this statement is: If a geometric figure is a line, then it contains at least two points.

37. Draw a Venn diagram illustrating this conditional.

38. Suppose you are given line ℓ at the right. What can you conclude about line ℓ? Explain how your Venn diagram in Exercise 37 verifies your conclusion.

30.

33. The sum of the lengths of the two sides of a triangle is greater than the length of the third side.

37.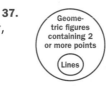

38. Line ℓ contains at least two pts.; line ℓ is contained in the inner circle, and therefore in the outer circle, of the diagram.

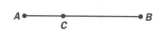

Progress Check

Lesson 2-1, page 53

1. Draw $\overline{AB}$ with point C between A and B. Into how many parts does C separate $\overline{AB}$? Into how many parts do 2 points C and D separate $\overline{AB}$? Into how many parts would n points separate $\overline{AB}$? 2; 3; $n + 1$

2. What is inductive reasoning? Describe how you used it in Exercise 1.

3. Two points determine just one segment. What is the maximum number of segments determined by 3 points? 4 points? 5 points? Predict the number of segments for 6 points. 3; 6; 10; 15

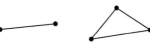

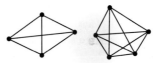

FOLLOW-UP

More Practice

• **Worksheet 2–3**

Extension

Have students use the **problem-solving strategy** of drawing a diagram to solve the following problem. All the members of the Computer Club are sophomores. Of these students, 22 take geometry, 24 take biology, 10 take both geometry and biology, and 4 take neither course. How many members are in the club? 40 members

• **Extension 2–3**

Computers

This computer activity can be completed using *The Geometric preSupposer* or *GeoDraw*. To prepare students for work with reasoning from "if . . . then" statements, have students use the computer drawing tool to do the following.

Draw two segments that lie on parallel lines. Draw a transversal through the two segments. The transversal should not be perpendicular to the parallel segments. Draw another transversal parallel to the first. Put all the resulting angles into two lists such that all the angles in each list are equal. Describe the reasoning that led you to make up each set. Then check your conclusions by measuring all the angles in your two lists.

• **Computer Activities 2–3**

ANSWERS

Progress Check

2. the process of forming a conclusion based upon examination of several specific cases; examined cases of 1 point and 2 points and generalized conclusion for n points

7–9. Hypothesis underlined once; conclusion underlined twice.

7. If <u>the crop is good</u>, then <u><u>profits will be up</u></u>.

Reasons for increased profits

Good crop

8. If <u>two angles are complements of the same angle</u>, then <u><u>they are equal</u></u>.

9. If <u>a plane contains points A and B</u>, then <u><u>$\overleftrightarrow{AB}$ lies in that plane</u></u>.

Challenge

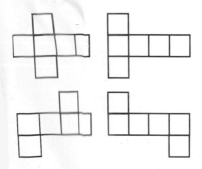

Lesson 2-2, page 60

Is each statement *always*, *sometimes*, or *never* true?

4. Coplanar lines r and s intersect. **Sometimes**

5. A transversal intersects two coplanar lines in two distinct points. **Always**

6. Parallel lines h and k are not coplanar. **Never**

Lesson 2-3, page 65

Restate in "if...then" form and identify the hypothesis and conclusion. Also draw a Venn diagram for Exercise 7.

7. A good crop imples that profits will be up.

8. Complements of the same angle are equal.

9. Line AB lies in any plane that contains points A and B.

Increased profits

Good crop

Algebra Review: Simplifying Monomials

Examples

1. Simplify $\dfrac{7a^2b}{ab^3}$.

2. Simplify $\left(\dfrac{-2a}{3b}\right)\left(\dfrac{6b}{a^2}\right)$.

Solutions

1. $\dfrac{7a^2b}{ab^3} = \dfrac{7 \cdot a \cdot a \cdot b}{a \cdot b \cdot b^2}$

$= \dfrac{ab(7a)}{ab(b^2)}$

$= \dfrac{7a}{b^2}$

2. $\left(\dfrac{-2a}{3b}\right)\left(\dfrac{6b}{a^2}\right) = \dfrac{-2a \cdot 6b}{3b \cdot a^2}$

$= \dfrac{-2 \cdot a \cdot 2 \cdot 3 \cdot b}{3 \cdot b \cdot a \cdot a}$

$= \dfrac{3ab \cdot -2 \cdot 2}{3ab \cdot a}$

$= -\dfrac{4}{a}$

Simplify.

1. $\dfrac{2bc}{b}$ $2c$

2. $\dfrac{12x^3y}{16x^4y}$ $\dfrac{3}{4x}$

3. $(7mn^2)(2mn^3)$ $14m^2n^5$

4. $\left(\dfrac{5ax}{2y}\right)\left(\dfrac{6y}{a}\right)$ $15x$

5. $\left(\dfrac{9a^2b^2c}{2a}\right)\left(\dfrac{2a^3b}{9c}\right)$ a^4b^3

6. $\dfrac{r}{s}\left(\dfrac{2s}{5r}\right)\left(\dfrac{3r}{10s}\right)$ $\dfrac{3r}{25s}$

7. $-6x^5yz^2(2xyz^4)$ $-12x^6y^2z^6$

8. $\left(\dfrac{4x^2y}{3y^3}\right)^2$ $\dfrac{16x^4}{9y^4}$

Challenge

The first figure at the right shows six connected squares. Copy it on your paper, cut it out, and fold it along the dashed edges to form a closed box. Can the second figure be folded into a box? **No**

Draw all ways for six squares to be connected along an edge so that they can form a box.

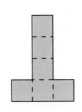

2-4 Reasoning from "If . . . Then" Statements

Consider this statement: Butterflies are insects. It can be written in "if . . . then" form as follows: If a creature is a butterfly, then it is an insect. It is an insect; since the anglewing is contained in the inner circle, it is also contained in the outer circle

An anglewing is a butterfly. What can you conclude about the anglewing? How does the Venn diagram verify your conclusion?

The logical reasoning, or **argument**, leading to your conclusion uses **affirming the hypothesis**, or establishing that the hypothesis is true in a particular case.

	Symbols	Words	Example
Known fact	$p \Rightarrow q$	**If $p \Rightarrow q$ is true** in every case,	If a creature is a butterfly (p), then it is an insect (q).
Given	p	**and p is true in** a particular case,	An anglewing is a butterfly
Conclusion	q	**then q is true** in that case.	An anglewing is an insect.

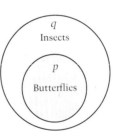

The examples in this lesson involve affirming-the-hypothesis arguments.

Example 1
The Supplement Postulate states: The angles of a linear pair are supplementary.

a. Write the Supplement Postulate in "if . . . then" form.

b. Draw a Venn Diagram representing this statement.

c. Give a case in which p is true. What conclusion can you make?

Solution
a. In "if . . . then" form, the Supplement Postulate is: If two angles form a linear pair, then the angles are supplementary.

b. The Venn diagram for this conditional is at the right.

c. There are many cases in which p is true. In the diagram at the right, for example, we see that $\angle 1$ and $\angle 2$ form a linear pair. We conclude that $\angle 1$ and $\angle 2$ are supplementary.

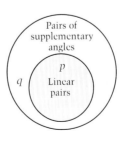

LESSON 2-4

Resources

Worksheet 2–4
Extension 2–4
Computer Activities 2–4

OBJECTIVE

Use affirming-the-hypothesis arguments to draw necessary conclusions.

TEACHING NOTES

Begin by reviewing drawing Venn diagrams.

Examples 1 and **2** involve the **proof subskill** of writing conclusions from given statements. **Example 2** shows an example of when the affirming-the-hypothesis

WORKSHEET   *Lesson* **2-4**

Name _____

Complete each affirming-the-hypothesis argument.

1. $p \Rightarrow q$: If two angles are complementary, then the sum of their measures is 90.
    p: ∠3 and ∠4 are complementary angles.
    q: m∠3 + m∠4 = 90

2. $p \Rightarrow q$: If two angles are congruent, then the measure of one angle is equal to the measure of the second angle.
    p: ∠HIJ ≅ ∠XYZ
    q: m∠HIJ = m∠XYZ

3. $p \Rightarrow q$: If an angle is acute, its supplement is an obtuse angle.
    p: ∠MNO is an acute angle.
    q: The supplement of ∠MNO is an obtuse angle.

4. $p \Rightarrow q$: If two lines are perpendicular, four right angles are formed.
    p: $\overline{AB} \perp \overline{CD}$ at point O
    q: ∠AOC, ∠COB, ∠BOD, and ∠DOA are right angles.

5. $p \Rightarrow q$: If two angles are a linear pair, the sum of their measures is 180.
    p: ∠6 and ∠7 are a linear pair.
    q: m∠6 + m∠7 = 180

6. $p \Rightarrow q$: If two angles are vertical, the angles are congruent (or their measures are equal).
    p: ∠1 and ∠2 are vertical angles.
    q: ∠1 ≅ ∠2 (or m∠1 = m∠2)

Complete each statement with +, −, =, >, or <.

7. If ∠RST and ∠GFE are supplementary, then the sum of their measures is __=__ 180.

8. If ∠DEF is a right angle, then m∠DEF __=__ 90.

9. If m∠MNO __+__ m∠QRS = 90, then ∠MNO and ∠QRS are complementary.

10. If X, Y, and Z are collinear and X is between Y and Z, then YX + XZ __=__ YZ.

11. If ∠RST is adjacent to ∠TSV, then m∠RST __+__ m∠TSV = m∠RSV.

rule cannot be used to make a conclusion.

Additional Examples

Example 1
Any student who scored at least 90 on the last test is excused from tonight's homework.
(a) Write this statement in "if . . . then" form. If a student scored at least 90 on the last test, then that student is excused from tonight's homework.
(b) Julio scored 94 on the last test. What conclusion can we draw? Julio is excused from tonight's homework.
(c) Draw a Venn diagram representing the above information.

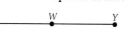
The affirming-the-hypothesis argument used in Example 1 is summarized below.

Known fact $p \Rightarrow q$: If two angles form a linear pair (*p*), then they are supplementary (*q*).
Given p: $\angle 1$ and $\angle 2$ form a linear pair.
Conclusion q: $\angle 1$ and $\angle 2$ are supplementary.

Example 2
Use this statement: If M is the midpoint of $\overline{AB}$, then $AM = MB$. Indicate what, if anything, can be concluded in each case.
a. W is the midpoint of $\overline{XY}$. **b.** $FG = GH$

Solution
To conclude anything we must have a case in which the hypothesis p is true; that is, we must be given the midpoint of a segment.

a. We are given that p is true; namely, W is the midpoint of $\overline{XY}$. Therefore, we *can* use affirming the hypothesis to conclude that q is true in this case; that is, $XW = WY$.

b. We are *not* given that p is true, so we *cannot* use affirming the hypothesis to make a conclusion.

Example 3
By definition, if two lines intersect to from a right angle, then the lines are perpendicular. To use this definition to conclude that $r \perp s$, what must be true?

Solution
The form of this argument is:
$p \Rightarrow q$: If two lines intersect to form a right angle (*p*), then the lines are perpendicular (*q*).
p: $\underline{\quad ? \quad}$
q: $r \perp s$

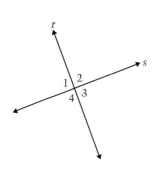

To conclude that $r \perp s$, we must establish that p is true in this case. That means $\angle 1$, $\angle 2$, $\angle 3$, or $\angle 4$ must be a right angle.

Example 4
Find a definition or postulate in Chapter 1 that would be a reason to conclude that $m\angle A$ is between 0 and 180. Explain how the definition or postulate justifies this conclusion.

Solution

The Protractor Postulate states that the measure of any angle is between 0 and 180. This can be restated as follows: If a geometric figure is an angle, then its measure is between 0 and 180. Since p is true in this particular case, that is, the figure on page 72 is an angle, we can conclude q, that $0 < m\angle A < 180$.

Checking for Understanding

1. Jim's father said to Jim, "If you get an A on your math test tomorrow, we will go to the ball game on Saturday." The next day Jim reported, "I got an A on my math test." What can you conclude?

   1. Jim and his father will go to the ball game on Saturday.

2. Identify p, q, and $p \Rightarrow q$ that are used in Exercise 1.

Complete the conclusions you can draw from these statements.

3. All sophomores take physical education. Jane is a sophomore, so __?__. Jane takes physical education

4. Anyone who practices every day will learn to play better. I practice every day, so __?__. I will learn to play better.

5. If a and b are any numbers, $a + b = b + a$. 7 and 12 are numbers, so __?__. 7 + 12 = 12 + 7

Written Exercises

Set A

1. Everyone in geometry class is a sophomore. Rosa is a sophomore. Can you conclude from these statements that Rosa is in geometry class? Explain with a Venn diagram. **No**

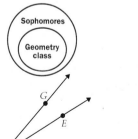

2. Which definition or postulate justifies the conclusion that $m\angle GHE + m\angle EHF = m\angle GHF$? **Add. angle Post.**

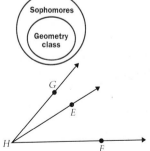

For each conditional $p \Rightarrow q$ in Exercises 3–7, indicate whether the sentence that follows it is a case in which p is true. If so, state the conclusion that can be made.

3. If one angle is a complement of another, the sum of their measures is 90. $\angle 1$ is a complement of $\angle 2$.

   3. Yes: $m\angle 1 + m\angle 2 = 90$

4. If points are on a circle, then they are coplanar points. Points A, B, and C are coplanar. **No**

5. If $a = b$ and $c = d$, then $ac = bd$. $8 = 3 + 5$ and $2 = 2$.

   5. Yes: $(8)(2) = (3 + 5)2$

Example 2

Examine the following statement: If two angles are vertical angles, then they are equal. Indicate what, if anything, can be concluded in each case.

(a)

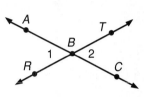

$\angle 1$ and $\angle 2$ are vertical angles.
$m\angle 1 = m\angle 2$

(b)

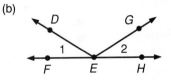

$m\angle 1 = m\angle 2$. **no conclusion**

Example 3

By definition, if the measures of three sides of a triangle are equal, then the triangle is an equilateral triangle. To use this definition to conclude that $\triangle ONE$ is equilateral, what must be true? $ON = NE = EO$

Example 4 involves the **proof subskill** of supplying missing reasons.

Example 4

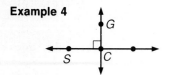

In the diagram, $\overleftrightarrow{SC} \perp \overleftrightarrow{CG}$.
(a) Find a definition or postulate in Chapter 1 to conclude that $m\angle C = 90$. If two lines are $\perp$, then they intersect to form at least one right angle.
(b) Explain how the definition or postulate justifies this conclusion. If an angle is a right angle, then its measure is 90.

Error Analysis The most common mistakes students are likely to make will be to use a statement that affirms the conclusion or one that affirms the negation of the hypothesis. Venn diagrams are useful in correcting these errors.

ANSWERS

Checking for Understanding

2. $p \Rightarrow q$: If you get an A on your math test tomorrow, we will go to the ball game on Saturday.
p: you get an A on your math test tomorrow
q: we will go to the ball game on Saturday

6. If a point P is between A and B, then P is on $\overleftrightarrow{AB}$. Point T is on $\overleftrightarrow{RS}$. No

7. If $\overrightarrow{GH}$ is the bisector of $\angle XGY$, then $m\angle XGH = m\angle HGY$. $m\angle XGH = m\angle HGY$ No

Refer to the figure at the right. State the conclusion, if any, that can be drawn from only the given conditional and the information in each exercise.

Given conditional: If two lines are perpendicular, then they intersect to form a right angle.

8. $\angle 1$ is right angle.   **9.** $\angle 1$ and $\angle 2$ form a linear pair.
10. $m \perp n$ **11.** $\angle 3$ and $\angle 4$ are supplementary.

Given conditional: If two angles form a linear pair, then the angles are supplementary.

12. $\angle 1$ is right angle.   **13.** $\angle 1$ and $\angle 2$ form a linear pair
14. $m \perp n$ **15.** $\angle 3$ and $\angle 4$ are supplementary.

Set B   Complete each affirming-the-hypothesis argument.

16. $p \Rightarrow q$: If any three points are noncollinear, then those points are contained in one and only one plane.
    p: _?_ Pts. x, y, and z are noncollinear
    q: Points X, Y, and Z are contained in one and only one plane.

17. $p \Rightarrow q$: If $a = b$, then $a + c = b + c$.
    p: _?_ $x - 5 = 32$
    q: $(x - 5) + 5 = 32 + 5$

18. $p \Rightarrow q$: If two points are on a circle with center O, the points are the same distance from O.
    p: _?_ x and y are pts. on circle O
    q: $OX = OY$

19. $p \Rightarrow q$: The sides of an angle are noncollinear rays.
    p: $\angle BAC$ is an angle.
    q: _?_ $\overrightarrow{AB}$ and $\overrightarrow{AC}$ are noncollinear rays

20. $p \Rightarrow q$: _?_
    p: $\angle A$ and $\angle B$ are complementary.
    q: $m\angle A + m\angle B = 90$

21. $p \Rightarrow q$: _?_
    p: X is in the interior of $\angle QRS$.
    q: $m\angle QRX + m\angle XRS = m\angle QRS$

8. No conclusion
9. No conclusion
10. Sample: $\angle 1$ is a rt. $\angle$ ($\angle 2$, $\angle 3$, $\angle 4$ = rt. $\angle$s.)
11. No conclusion
12. No conclusion
13. $\angle 1$ is supp. to $\angle 2$.
14. No conslusion
15. No conclusion

20. If $\angle$s are comp., then the sum of their measures is 90
21. If B is in the interior of $\angle APC$, then $m\angle APB + m\angle BPC = m\angle APC$

Thinking Ahead

27. If an instrument is an oboe, then it is a woodwind.

28. If an object is a woodwind, then it is a musical instrument.

Review

22. Write this statement in "if . . . then" form: An angle is a plane figure.

22. If a figure is an ∠, then it is a plane figure

23. Draw a Venn diagram for the statement in Exercise 22.

24. What is a transversal?

25. State the Flat Plane Postulate.

26. Given X(3, 7) and Y(8, −5), find XY. 13

24. A line which intersects 2 coplanar lines in 2 distinct pts.
25. If 2 pts. are contained on a plane, then the line through them is continued in the same plane.
29. If an object is an oboe, then it is a musical instrument.

Thinking Ahead

Write each statement in "if . . . then" form. Then draw a Venn diagram illustrating the conditional.

27. An oboe is a woodwind.

28. A woodwind is a musical instrument.

29. Now suppose the conditionals in Exercises 27 and 28 are both true. The Venn diagram at the right shows the relationship between oboes, woodwinds, and musical instruments. A third conditonal impled by this diagram is: ___?___.

Computer Activities: Drawing and Measuring

1. Draw segment AB. Then draw $\overrightarrow{CD}$, with C on $\overrightarrow{AB}$ and D not on $\overrightarrow{AB}$. Measure the two angles formed at C. What is the sum of their measures? 180

2. Using the same drawing, choose points E, F, G, . . . , not on $\overrightarrow{AB}$ and draw $\overrightarrow{CE}$, $\overrightarrow{CF}$, $\overrightarrow{CG}$, . . . In each case, what is the sum of the measures of the two angles formed by the $\overrightarrow{AB}$ and the second segment? 180

3. What conjecture can you make regarding the measures of linear pairs of angles? The sum of the measures of a lin. pr. of ∠s is 180.

Challenge

A farmer wants to plant 9 trees in groups of 3. The trees in each group of 3 are to be collinear. Draw a diagram showing the maximum number of groups. 10 groups

FOLLOW-UP

More Practice

• **Worksheet 2–4**

Extension

This example requires students to apply the affirming-the-hypothesis rule twice. The following statements are given: (1) a 70 is a passing grade and (2) any student who passes geometry may study trigonometry. Write an affirming-the-hypothesis argument to explain why Larry, who received a 70 in geometry, may study trigonometry.

• **Extension 2–4**

Computers

The computer activity in the pupil's book can be completed using *The Geometric preSupposer: Points and Lines* or *GeoDraw*.

• **Computer Activities 2–4**

Warm-Up Review

1. In the "if . . . then" form, the phrase after the "then" is its ___?___ . Conclusion
2. The numbers -2, 0, $\frac{1}{2}$ and $\sqrt{3}$ are all ___?___ numbers. Real
3. Solve for x: $4x - 5 = 7$. $x = 3$
4. The ___?___ Property for Conditionals says that if $p \Rightarrow q$ and
   $q \Rightarrow r$, then $p \Rightarrow r$. Transitive

LESSON 2–5

Resources

Worksheet 2–5
Extension 2–5
💻 Computer Worksheet 2–5

OBJECTIVES

Use the Transitive Property for Conditionals and affirming the hypothesis with deductive arguments; justify numerical and geometric relationships.

TEACHING NOTES

In this lesson stress that a proof is just logical reasoning and that logical reasoning is something we all use in everyday life.

WORKSHEET

Name _____

Lesson 2 - 5

In the blank, complete the statement by applying the given property or by writing the name of the property illustrated.

1. If $AB = BC$ and $BC + CD = BD$, then ___$AB + CD = BD$___ .
   Substitution Property

2. If $AB > QR$, then $2(AB) > 2(QR)$. ___Multiplication Property___

3. If $m\angle 2 + m\angle 6 = m\angle ABC$ and $m\angle ABC = m\angle K$, then
   ___$m\angle 2 + m\angle 6 = m\angle K$___ .   Transitive Property

4. If $2(m\angle QRS) = 2(m\angle 3)$, then $m\angle QRS = m\angle 3$. ___Division Property___

5. If $m\angle 2 + m\angle 6 > m\angle 3$ and $m\angle DEF = m\angle 3$, then
   ___$m\angle 2 + m\angle 6 > m\angle DEF$___   Substitution Property

6. If $x = y$, then $x - 9 = y - 9$. ___Subtraction Property___

7. If ___$a = b$___ , then ___$b = a$___ .
   Symmetric Property

Use deductive reasoning to write a conclusion to each set of statements below.

8. $p \Rightarrow q$: If Monica crosses the finish line first, then she wins the event.
   $q \Rightarrow r$: If Monica wins the event, she qualifies for the state meet.
   Conclusion: **If Monica crosses the finish line first, she qualifies for the state meet.**

9. $p \Rightarrow q$: If D lies in the interior of $\angle ABC$, then $\angle ABD$ and $\angle DBC$ share a common ray.
   $q \Rightarrow r$: If $\angle ABD$ and $\angle DBC$ share a common ray, then $\angle ABD$ and $\angle DBC$ are adjacent.
   Conclusion: **If D lies in the interior of $\angle ABC$, then $\angle ABD$ and $\angle DBC$ are adjacent.**

10. $p \Rightarrow q$: If Mark sits in the front row, then he can see the examples on the blackboard.
    $q \Rightarrow r$: If Mark can see the examples on the blackboard, then his grade improves.
    Conclusion: **If Mark sits in the front row, then his grade improves.**

2-5 Deductive Reasoning

We all use logical thinking in everyday life. Consider the following situation.

> Jack asked a clerk at the music store where he could find a compact disc by the Hangups.
>
> The clerk said, "Discs by the Hangups are on the GX label. All our GX discs are in Aisle 3."
>
> Jack walked over to Aisle 3 and found the disc he wanted.

We can analyze the simple reasoning Jack used in this example to help understand how we reason in geometric arguments. Let's think of what the clerk said as conditionals.

$p \Rightarrow q$: If the disc is by the Hangups, then it's on the GX label.

$q \Rightarrow r$: If a disc has the GX label, then it's in Aisle 3.

As Jack reasoned, it follows from these two conditionals that **if** the disc is by the Hangups, **then** it's in Aisle 3.

Jack's reasoning is verified by the Venn diagram. Since p is inside q, and q is inside r, then p is inside r. This illustrates the **Transitive Property for Conditionals**: If $p \Rightarrow q$ and $q \Rightarrow r$, then $p \Rightarrow r$.

Example 1 uses this chain of reasoning in a geometric situation.

Example 1

Apply the Transitive Property for Conditionals to these statements.

$p \Rightarrow q$: If two angles form a linear pair, then they are supplementary.

$q \Rightarrow r$: If two angles are supplementary, then the sum of their measures is 180.

Solution

By the Transitive Property for Conditionals, we reason that if $p \Rightarrow q$ and $q \Rightarrow r$, then $p \Rightarrow r$.

$p \Rightarrow r$: If two angles form a linear pair, then the sum of their measures is 180.

The following example shows how the Transitive Property for Conditionals can be extended to any number of statements. That is, if $p \Rightarrow q$, $q \Rightarrow r$, $r \Rightarrow s$, and $s \Rightarrow t$, then $p \Rightarrow t$.

Example 2
Assume the following conditionals are true.

a. If Mr. and Mrs. Hogan have to attend a meeting, then Janie will visit Grandma tonight.

b. If TV sets are on sale, then Mrs. Hogan will buy one today.

c. If Janie visits a relative tonight, then she will watch TV.

d. If Mr. and Mrs. Hogan have to attend a meeting, then they will take a taxi.

e. If Janie watches TV tonight, then she will practice piano tomorrow morning.

f. If Janie practices piano in the morning, then her sister will pack the lunches.

Give an argument showing that if Mr. and Mrs. Hogan attend a meeting, then tomorrow Janie's sister will pack the lunches.

Solution
1. $p \Rightarrow q$: If Mr. and Mrs. Hogan have to attend a meeting, then Janie will visit Grandma tonight.
2. $q \Rightarrow r$: If Janie visits a relative (Grandma) tonight, then she will watch TV.
3. $r \Rightarrow s$: If Janie watches TV tonight, then she will pratice piano tomorrow morning.
4. $s \Rightarrow t$: If Janie practices piano in the morning, then her sister will pack the lunches.

By applying the Transitive Property several times, we reason that
$p \Rightarrow t$: If Mr. and Mrs. Hogan have to attend a meeting, then Janie's sister will pack the lunches.

Rules of logic such as the Transitive Property for Conditionals and affirming the hypothesis are used to reach conclusions from assumed or previously established statements. This is called **deductive reasoning**. The set of steps which describe how the conclusion was reached is called a **deductive argument**.

2-5 *Deductive Reasoning*

Additional Examples

Example 1
Apply the Transitive Property for Conditionals to the following conditionals.

$p \Rightarrow q$: If two angles in a triangle are equal, then the sides opposite those angles are equal.

$q \Rightarrow r$: If two sides of a triangle are equal, then the triangle is isosceles.

$p \Rightarrow r$: If two angles of a triangle are equal, then the triangle is isosceles.

Point out the extraneous information in **Example 2**, and mention that eliminating extraneous information is often a useful **problem-solving strategy**. This example also leads into the **proof subskill** of identifying extraneous steps in proofs.

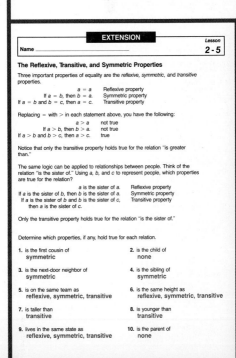

EXTENSION

Lesson 2-5

Name _____

The Reflexive, Transitive, and Symmetric Properties

Three important properties of equality are the *reflexive, symmetric,* and *transitive* properties.

$a = a$	Reflexive property
If $a = b$, then $b = a$.	Symmetric property
If $a = b$ and $b = c$, then $a = c$.	Transitive property

Replacing = with > in each statement above, you have the following:

$a > a$	not true
If $a > b$, then $b > a$.	not true
If $a > b$ and $b > c$, then $a > c$.	true

Notice that only the transitive property holds true for the relation "is greater than."

The same logic can be applied to relationships between people. Think of the relation "is the sister of." Using a, b, and c to represent people, which properties are true for the relation?

a is the sister of a.	Reflexive property
If a is the sister of b, then b is the sister of a.	Symmetric property
If a is the sister of b and b is the sister of c, then a is the sister of c.	Transitive property

Only the transitive property holds true for the relation "is the sister of."

Determine which properties, if any, hold true for each relation.

1. is the first cousin of
   symmetric
2. is the child of
   none
3. is the next-door neighbor of
   symmetric
4. is the sibling of
   symmetric
5. is on the same team as
   reflexive, symmetric, transitive
6. is the same height as
   reflexive, symmetric, transitive
7. is taller than
   transitive
8. is younger than
   transitive
9. lives in the same state as
   reflexive, symmetric, transitive
10. is the parent of
    none

Example 2

Assume the following conditionals are true.

(a) If Mike studies for his physics exam, then he will do well.

(b) If Mike does well on his physics exam, then he will get the car Friday night.

(c) If Joyce goes out with Mike Friday night, then she will have to baby-sit for Jason Saturday night.

(d) If Mike gets the car Friday night, then he will go out with Joyce.

By applying the Transitive Property several times, what conditional can be deduced? If Mike studies for his physics exam, Joyce will have to baby-sit for Jason Saturday night.

Example 3

Write a deductive argument to show that for all real numbers, if $4x - 7 = 13$, then $x = 5$.

1. Reflexive Property: $7 = 7$
2. Addition Property: $4x - 7 + 7 = 13 + 7$, or $4x = 20$
3. Reflexive Property: $4 = 4$
4. Division Property: $4x/4 = 20/4$, or $x = 5$

Deductive arguments in geometry are based upon definitions, postulates that we assume to be true, and any statements that have been proved previously. Since geometric arguments involve segment and angle measures, which are real numbers, we also use properties of real numbers, including those that follow.

Summary **Properties of Equality and Inequality for Real Numbers**

Reflexive Property	$a = a$
Trichotomy Property	$a = b$, $a > b$, or $a < b$
Symmetric Property	If $a = b$, then $b = a$.
Transitive Properties	If $a = b$ and $b = c$, then $a = c$.
	If $a > b$ and $b > c$, then $a > c$.
Addition Properties	If $a = b$ and $c = d$, then $a + c = b + d$.
	If $a > b$, then $a + c > b + c$.
Subtraction Properties	If $a = b$ and $c = d$, then $a - c = b - d$.
	If $a > b$, then $a - c > b - c$.
Multiplication Properties	If $a = b$ and $c = d$, then $ac = bd$.
	If $a > b$ and $c > 0$, then $ac > bc$.
	If $a > b$ and $c < 0$, then $ac < bc$.
Division Properties	If $a = b$ and $c = d$, then $\frac{a}{c} = \frac{b}{d}$ for $c \neq 0$ and $d \neq 0$.
	If $a > b$ and $c > 0$, then $\frac{a}{c} > \frac{b}{c}$.
	If $a > b$ and $c < 0$, then $\frac{a}{c} < \frac{b}{c}$.
Substitution Property	If $a = b$, then a or b may be replaced by the other in any equation or inequality.

If each step in a deductive argument follows by one of the rules of logic, the argument is said to be **valid**. Notice how each step in the following argument uses affirming the hypothesis.

Example 3

Write a deductive argument to show that for all real numbers, if $3x + 5 = 11$, then $x = 2$.

Solution

1. Since we are using real numbers, by the Reflexive Property $5 = 5$.

2. Since $3x + 5 = 11$ and $5 = 5$, by the Subtraction Property $3x + 5 - 5 = 11 - 5$, or $3x = 6$.

3. Since we are using real numbers, by the Reflexive Property $3 = 3$.

4. Since $3x = 6$ and $3 = 3$, by the Division Property $\frac{3x}{3} = \frac{6}{3}$, or $x = 2$.

Example 4

Write a deductive argument to show that if R is between Q and S, then $QR = QS - RS$.

Solution

1. Since R is between Q and S, by the Segment Additon Postulate $QR + RS = QS$.

2. Since Q, R, and S are points, by the Ruler Postulate QR, RS, and QS are real numbers.

3. Since RS is a real number, by the Reflexive Property $RS = RS$.

4. Since $QR + RS = QS$ and $RS = RS$, by the Subtraction Property $QR + RS - RS = QS - RS$, or $QR = QS - RS$.

Checking for Understanding

Suppose the clerk is mistaken about the label and that discs by the Hangups are really on the HQ label.

1. When Jack looked in Aisle 3, would he find the disc he wanted? Explain your thinking.

2. Do you still feel that Jack's reasoning is valid? **Yes**

3. Do you think an argument based upon false conditionals can be valid? Why or why not?

4. If a valid argument is based upon postulates from Chapter 1, is its conclusion true? Why do you think so?

5. If $a < b$ and $b < c$, is it true that $a < c$? Why?

Give several examples to show that if $a < b$,

6. $a + c < b + c$.   **7.** $a - c < b - c$.

State the property of real numbers that justifies each statement.

8. If $AB = RS$ and $RS = CD$, then $AB = CD$. **Transitive Prop.**

9. If $2AM > 12$, then $AM > 6$. **Div. Prop.**

10. If $m\angle RST + 90 = m\angle XYZ$, then $m\angle XYZ = m\angle RST + 90$.

11. If $LM + MN > LN$ and $MN = QS$, then $LM + QS > LN$.

Written Exercises

Set A Use the warranty at the right to tell what the company will do in each case.

1. The hour hand was missing when the clock was purchased.

2. The clock was left out in the rain one month after it was purchased, and it does not work.

1. Possibly (if HQ label is in Aisle 3)
3. Yes: the validity of the reasoning is independent of the validity of the conclusion
4. Yes, postulates are assumed to be true as a basis for deductive reasoning.
5. Yes; Transitive Prop. of Inequality
6. Sample: $a = 5$, $b = 6$, $c = 7$; $5 < 6$ and $5 + 7 < 6 + 7$
7. Sample: $a = 5$, $b = 6$, $c = 1$; $5 < 6$ and $5 - 1 < 6 - 1$
10. Symmetric Prop.
11. Substitution Prop.

This clock is warranted for one year from date of purchase against defects in materials and workmanship. During this period such defects will be repaired or the product will be replaced at the company's option without charge. This warranty does not cover damage caused by misuse or negligence.

Example 4

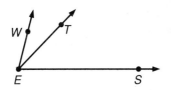

Write a deductive argument to show that if $\overrightarrow{ET}$ lies in the interior of $\angle WES$, then $m\angle WET = m\angle WES - m\angle TES$.

1. Angle Addition Postulate: $m\angle WET + m\angle TES = m\angle WES$
2. Protractor Postulate: $m\angle WET$, $m\angle WES$ and $m\angle TES$ are real numbers.
3. Reflexive Property: $m\angle TES = m\angle TES$
4. Subtraction Property: $m\angle WET + m\angle TES - m\angle TES = m\angle WES - m\angle TES$, or $m\angle WET = m\angle WES - m\angle TES$.

Error Analysis Students are not accustomed to justifying steps in a process that they consider "obvious," so they often leave out steps and justifications. This may be remedied by breaking the process into smaller steps.

ANSWERS

Written Exercises

1. repair or replace the clock
2. Nothing; warranty does not cover damage caused by negligence.

3. If $\overleftrightarrow{AM}$ bisects $\overline{CD}$ at point M, then $CM = MD$.

4. If B is in the interior of $\angle XYZ$, then $m\angle BYZ = m\angle XYZ - m\angle XYB$.

5. If it rains, then I will be grounded.

6. If $\overrightarrow{ED}$ and $\overrightarrow{EH}$ are opposite rays, then $DE = DH - EH$.

7. If a student is 16 years old before September 1, then he or she will have extra money.

10. 1. Since we are using real numbers, it follows from the Reflexive Prop. that $1 = 1$. **2.** Since $4x - 1 = 19$ and $1 = 1$, by the Addition Prop. $4x - 1 + 1 = 19 + 1$, or $4x = 20$. **3.** Since we are using real numbers, by the Reflexive Prop. $4 = 4$. **4.** Since $4x = 20$ and $4 = 4$, by the Division Prop. $4x/4 = 20/4$, or $x = 5$.

Apply the Transitive Property for Conditionals to determine the conditional that follows from each set of statements.

3. $p \Rightarrow q$: If $\overleftrightarrow{AM}$ bisects $\overline{CD}$ at point M, then M is the midpoint of $\overline{CD}$.

   $q \Rightarrow r$: If M is the midpoint of $\overleftrightarrow{CD}$, then $CM = MD$.

4. $p \Rightarrow q$: If B is in the interior of $\angle XYZ$, then $m\angle XYB + m\angle BYZ = m\angle XYZ$.

   $q \Rightarrow r$: If $m\angle XYB + m\angle BYZ = m\angle XYZ$, then $m\angle BYZ = m\angle XYZ - m\angle XYB$.

5. $p \Rightarrow q$: If it rains, then I will take an umbrella to school.

   $q \Rightarrow r$: If I take an umbrella, then I will lose it.

   $r \Rightarrow s$: If I lose my umbrella, then I will be grounded.

6. $p \Rightarrow q$: If $\overrightarrow{ED}$ and $\overrightarrow{EH}$ are opposite rays, then E is between D and H.

   $q \Rightarrow r$: If E is between D and H, then $DE + EH = DH$.

   $r \Rightarrow s$: If $DE + EH = DH$, then $DE = DH - EH$.

7. $p \Rightarrow q$: If a student is 16 years old before September 1, then the student will take driver education this year.

   $q \Rightarrow r$: If a student takes driver education, then the student will receive lower insurance rates.

   $r \Rightarrow s$: If a person has lower insurance rates, then he or she will have extra money.

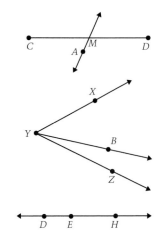

Complete each deductive argument given below.

8. Suppose F is the midpoint of $\overline{GK}$. Show that $GF + GF = GK$.

   1. Since F is the midpoint of $\overline{GK}$, it follows from definition of ___?___ that F is between G and K and $GF = FK$. the midpt. of a seg.

   2. Since F is between G and K, it follows from the ___?___ Postulate that $GF + FK = GK$. Seg. Add.

   3. Since G, F, and K are points, it follows from the ___?___ Postulate that GF, FK, and GK are real numbers.

   4. Since $GF + FK = GK$ and $GF = FK$, it follows from the Substitution Property that ___?___.
   $GF + GF = GK$ or $FK + FK = GK$

   Ruler

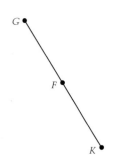

9. Show that if ∠Q and ∠R are right angles, then
m∠Q + m∠R = 180. **∠Q and ∠R are rt. ∠s; 90; 90**

1. Since __?__, it follows from the definition of right
angles that m∠Q = __?__ and m∠R = __?__.

2. Since ∠Q and ∠R are angles, it follows from
the __?__ Postulate that m∠Q and m∠R are real
numbers. **Protractor**

3. Since m∠Q = 90 and m∠R = 90, it follows
from the __?__ Property that m∠Q + m∠R = 90 + 90,
or m∠Q + m∠R = 180. **Add.**

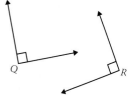

Set B Write a deductive argument like the one in Example 3.

10. For all real numbers, if 4x − 1 = 19, then x = 5.

11. For all real numbers, if −3x + 2 > 14, then x < −4.

Write a deductive argument like the one in Example 4.

12. If m∠APB = 90, then $\overleftrightarrow{AP} \perp \overleftrightarrow{PB}$.

13. If QM = RM, then $\overleftrightarrow{HM}$ bisects $\overline{QR}$ at M.

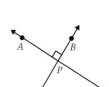

Use conditionals a–f in Example 2 along with
conditionals g–i below.

g. If Mrs. Hogan buys a TV set today, then Janie will
watch TV tonight.

h. If Mr. Hogan gets home by 4:00 P.M., then he and
Mrs. Hogan will attend a school meeting tonight.

i. If the storm ends, Mr. Hogan will get home by 4:00 P.M.

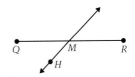

14. Give a deductive argument to show that if TV
sets go on sale, then Janie will practice piano
tomorrow morning.

15. Give a deductive argument to show that if the storm
ends, then Mr. and Mrs. Hogan will take a taxi.

▲ Review **16.** Give the conclusion: The degree measure of an
angle is between 0 and 180. m∠Q = x, so __?__.
0 < x < 180

17. Which definition or postulate justifies the
conclusion that ∠ABC and ∠FGH are complementary?
Def. comp. ∠s

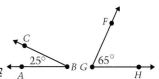

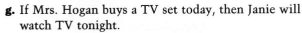

11. 1. Since we are using real numbers, by the Reflexive Prop. 2 = 2. 2. Since −3x + 2 > 14 and 2 = 2, by the Subtraction Prop. −3x + 2 − 2 > 14 − 2, or −3x > 12. 3. Since we are using real numbers, by the Reflexive Prop. −3 = −3. 4. Since −3x > 12 and −3 = −3, by the Division Prop. −3x/−3 < 12/−3, or x < −4.
12. 1. Since m∠APB = 90, by the definition of a rt. ∠ ∠APB is a rt. ∠. 2. Since ∠APB is a rt. ∠, by the def. of ⊥ lines $\overleftrightarrow{AP} \perp \overleftrightarrow{PB}$.
13. 1. Since QM = RM, and assuming Q, R and M are collinear and distinct, by the def. of the midpt. of a seg. M is the midpt. of $\overline{QR}$. Assuming H is not on $\overleftrightarrow{QR}$, and M is the intersection of $\overleftrightarrow{HM}$ and $\overleftrightarrow{QR}$, by the def. of a seg. bisector $\overleftrightarrow{HM}$ bisects $\overline{QR}$.
14. If TV sets are on sale, then Mrs. Hogan will buy one today (b). If Mrs. Hogan buys a TV set today, then Janie will watch TV tonight (g). If Janie watches TV tonight, then she will practice piano tomorrow morning (e).
15. If the storm ends, then Mr. Hogan will get home by 4:00 P.M. (i). If Mr. Hogan gets home by 4:00 P.M., then he and Mrs. Hogan will attend a school meet, tonight (h). If Mr. and Mrs. Hogan have to attend a meeting, then they will take a taxi (d).

Review

18.

19. point; line; plane

Thinking Ahead

21. If I mean something, then I say it.

22. (1) If I eat something, then I see it; (2) If I see something, then I eat it.

23.

FOLLOW-UP

More Practice

• Worksheet 2–5

Extension

The Transitive Property for Conditionals may be combined with affirming-the-hypothesis arguments to produce interesting results. In **Exercise 5**, for example, ask students to draw a conclusion if they are also given the fact that it is raining today. I will be grounded.

• Extension 2–5

Computers

• Computer Worksheet 2–5

---

18. Draw a Venn diagram for this conditional: If a number is divisible by 8, then it is divisible by 2.

19. Which three terms are undefined in this course?

20. Find y and the measure of each angle.
$y = 45$; 45 and 135

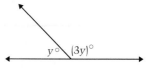

Thinking Ahead Mathematician Charles Dodgson, alias Lewis Carroll, authored several famous children's books including *Alice's Adventures in Wonderland*, the source of the following excerpt.

"Then you should say what you mean," the March Hare went on. "I do," Alice hastily replied; "at least—at least I mean what I say— that's the same thing, you know." "Not the same thing a bit!" said the Hatter. "Why, you might just as well say that 'I see what I eat' is the same thing as 'I eat what I see'!" "You might just as well say," added the March Hare, "That 'I like what I get' is the same thing as 'I get what I like'!" "You might just as well say," added the Dormouse, who seemed to be talking in his sleep, "That 'I breathe when I sleep' is the same thing as 'I sleep when I breathe'!" "It *is* the same thing with you," said the Hatter, and here the conversation dropped, and the party sat silent for a minute.

Alice is confusing two statements which appear to be similar, but which have very different meanings. In "if . . . then" form, "I mean what I say" is "If I say something, then I mean it."

21. Write the statement "I say what I mean" in "if . . . then" form.

22. Write the two statements of the Hatter in "if . . . then" form.

23. Draw Venn diagrams to show that the Hatter's two statements have different meanings.

2-6 Related "If . . . Then" Statements

Suppose you use Vita-Green. Can you validly conclude from this ad that you will get better crop yields?

The first Venn diagram represents the statement in the ad. If you use Vita-Green, you are among the points inside the outer circle, but you might not be inside the inner circle. So you do not necessarily get better yields.

In order to imply that you will get better crop yields, the statement would have to be: If you're a Vita-Green gardener, then you get better yields.

This statement is represented by the second Venn diagram. Vita-Green gardeners are among the points inside the inner circle, so they are automatically inside the outer circle. Thus, they get better yields.

The meaning of the second statement is very different from the one in the ad. The second statement is said to be the ***converse*** of the one in the ad. The converse of a conditional is the statement formed by interchanging the hypothesis and the conclusion.

$p \Rightarrow q$: If you get better yields, then you're a Vita-Green gardener.

$q \Rightarrow p$: If you're a Vita-Green gardener, then you get better yields.

*If you get better yields, you're a **Vita-Green** gardener.*

Ad

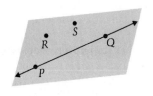

Converse

Example 1

Write the converse of each true conditional. Tell whether each converse is *true* or *false*.

a. If two lines are perpendicular, then they intersect to form four right angles.

b. If four points are collinear, then they are coplanar.

Solution

a. The converse is: If two lines intersect to form four right angles, then they are perpendicular. The definition of perpendicular lines ensures that this statement is true.

b. The converse is: If four points are coplanar, then they are collinear. Since the diagram at the right shows a counterexample, the converse is false.

The converse of a true statement may be either true or false.

LESSON 2–6

Resources

Worksheet 2–6
Extension 2–6
Algebra Review 2
Chapter 2 Test, Form I
Chapter 2 Test, Form II
Chapter 2 Test, Form III

OBJECTIVES

Write the converse, the inverse and the contrapositive of a conditional; write an "if and only if" statement as two "if . . . then" statements.

TEACHING NOTES

Introduce this lesson by using Venn diagrams to clarify the difference between conditionals and

---

WORKSHEET

Lesson **2 - 6**

Name _____

Write the following for each Given.

Given: You are going to school today.
1. Negation: You are not going to school today.

Given: If I get an *A* in mathematics, then my father will reward me.
2. Converse: If my father will reward me, then I will get an *A* in mathematics.
3. Inverse: If I do not get an *A* in mathematics, then my father will not reward me.
4. Contrapositive: If my father will not reward me, then I will not get an *A* in mathematics.

Given: Julie did not vote in the primary.
5. Negation: Julie did vote in the primary.

Write *negation*, *converse*, *inverse*, or *contrapositive* after each statement. Use the conditional to decide if the statement is *true* or *false*, and underline the appropriate word.

$p \Rightarrow q$: If ∠1 and ∠2 are a linear pair, then m∠1 + m∠2 = 180.
6. If m∠1 + m∠2 ≠ 180, then ∠1 and ∠2 are not a linear pair. — contrapositive — True — False
7. If m∠1 + m∠2 = 180, then ∠1 and ∠2 are a linear pair. — converse — True — False
8. If ∠1 and ∠2 are not a linear pair, then m∠1 + m∠2 ≠ 180. — inverse — True — False

p: ∠1 and ∠2 are a linear pair.
9. ∠1 and ∠2 are not a linear pair. — negation — True — False

$p \Rightarrow q$: If an angle is acute, then its supplement is obtuse.
10. If an angle is not acute, then its supplement is not obtuse. — inverse — True — False
11. If the supplement to an angle is not obtuse, then the angle is not acute. — contrapositive — True — False
12. If the supplement to an angle is obtuse, then the angle is acute. — converse — True — False

$p \Rightarrow q$: If two lines are parallel, then they are coplanar.
13. If two lines are coplanar, then they are parallel. — converse — True — False
14. If two lines are not coplanar, then they are not parallel. — contrapositive — True — False
15. If two lines are not parallel, then they are not coplanar. — inverse — True — False

converses. **Example 1** shows that the converse of a true statement may or may not be true.

Additional Examples

Example 1

Write the converse of each true conditional and state whether each converse is *true* or *false*.

(a) If two rectangles have the same lengths and widths, then they have the same perimeters. If two rectangles have the same perimeters, then they have the same lengths and widths. [false]

(b) If two lines never intersect, then they are parallel. If two lines are parallel, then they never intersect. [true]

Consider the case where both the conditional and its converse are true, and introduce "if and only if" statements. Stress that "*p* if and only if *q*" means "if *p*, then *q*, and if *q*, then *p*."

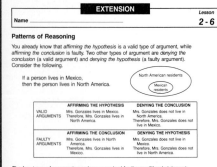

The first statement in Example 1 is true and so is its converse. If a conditional and its converse are both true, we may combine the two statements in one *"if and only if" statement*.

When we write "*p* if and only if *q*" we mean both "if *q*, then *p*" (*p if q*) and "if *p*, then *q*" (*p only if q*).

Two lines are perpendicular **if and only if** they intersect to form four right angles

If two lines are perpendicular, **then** they intersect to form four right angles, (if *p*, then *q*)

and

If two lines intersect to form four right angles, **then** they are perpendicular. (if *q*, then *p*)

Example 2

Try to write the definition of each term in "if and only if" form.

a. Vertical angles **b.** Complementary angles

Solution

First write the "if . . . then" statement impled by each definition.

a. If two angles are vertical angles, then their sides form two pairs of opposite rays.

b. If two angles are complementary angles, then the sum of their measures is 90.

Then write the converse of each "if . . . then" statement.

If the sides of two angles form two paris of opposite rays, then they are vertical angles.

If the sum of the measures of two angles is 90, then they are complementary angles.

In each case, the "if . . . then" statement and its converse are true, so you can write these "if and only if" statements.

Two angles are vertical angles if and only if their sides form two pairs of opposite rays.

Two angles are complementary angles if and only if the sum of their measures is 90.

Definitions are always understood to be "if and only if" statements, even when they are not written in this form.

Other important related forms of a conditional statement $p \Rightarrow q$, require the negations of *p* and *q*. The **negation** of a statement *p* is "*not p.*" When *p* is true, *not p* is false. When *p* is false, *not p* is true.

Example 3
Write the negation of each statement.

a. p: $\angle X$ is obtuse.   **b.** r: M is between A and B.

Solution

a. *not* p: $\angle X$ is not obtuse. This means that $\angle X$ is right
or acute.

b. *not* r: M is not between A and B.

Two other conditionals related to the statement $p{\Rightarrow}q$ are the
inverse and the contrapositive. The ***inverse*** of $p{\Rightarrow}q$ is the
conditional *not* $p{\Rightarrow}$*not* q. The ***contrapositive*** of $p{\Rightarrow}q$ is the
conditional *not* $q{\Rightarrow}$*not* p.

Example 4
Write the converse, the inverse, and the contrapositive of: If $\angle 1$
and $\angle 2$ are vertical angles, then $\angle 1$ and $\angle 2$ are equal.

Solution

Converse: If $\angle 1$ and $\angle 2$ are equal, then $\angle 1$ and $\angle 2$ are
         vertical angles.
Inverse: If $\angle 1$ and $\angle 2$ are not vertical angles, then they
         are not equal.
Contrapositive: If $\angle 1$ and $\angle 2$ are not equal, then they are
         not vertical angles.

Recall from Lesson 2-2 that the original statement in Example 4
above appears to be true. The Venn diagram can help you determine
which of the other statements are true and which are false.

For the converse, if $\angle 1$ and $\angle 2$ are equal, then they are inside the
outer circle. But they may not be inside the inner circle, so they
are not necessarily vertical angles. There is a counterexample,
such as $\angle 1$ and $\angle 2$ at the right, so the converse is false.

Similarly, for the inverse, if $\angle 1$ and $\angle 2$ are not vertical angles,
then they are not inside the inner circle. But they may or may
not be inside the outer circle, so they are not necessarily
unequal. So, here also, there is a counterexample, such as $\angle 1$
and $\angle 2$ at the right. The inverse is false.

Finally, for the contrapositive, if $\angle 1$ and $\angle 2$ are not equal, then
they are not inside the outer circle. Therefore, they cannot be
inside the inner circle, so they cannot be vertical angles. Since
there is no counterexample, the contrapositive is true.

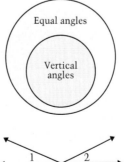

Example 2
Write the definition of each term in
"if and only if" form.
(a) **Right triangle** A triangle is a
    right triangle if and only if one
    of its angles is a right angle.
(b) **Angle bisector** A ray is an an-
    gle bisector if and only if it di-
    vides the angle into two equal
    halves.

Example 3
Write the negation of each statement.
(a) q: $\overline{ST} \perp \overline{AB}$ *not* q: $\overline{ST}$ is not
    $\perp$ to $\overline{AB}$.
(b) s: Point P lies on line k *not* s:
    Point P does not lie on line k.

Example 4
Write the converse, inverse and
contrapositive: If $5x + 2 = 37$,
then $x = 7$. Converse: If $x = 7$,
then $5x + 2 = 37$. Inverse: If
$5x + 2 \neq 37$, then $x \neq 7$. Contrapositive: If $x \neq 7$, then $5x + 2 \neq$
37.

Example 5
Write the contrapositive of each
true statement and determine if it
is *true* or *false*.
(a) If today is Sunday, then I don't
    go to school. If I go to school,
    then today is not Sunday.
    [true]
(b) If you don't study, you won't
    pass this course. If you pass
    this course, then you did
    study. [true]

Error Analysis   Students often
incorrectly interpret the negation.
Point out that the negation of "*not*
p" is p. Make sure they do not
assume that a conditional and its
converse have the same truth
value.

ANSWERS

Checking for Understanding

5. Converse: If $m\angle 1 = m\angle 2$, then $\angle 1$ and $\angle 2$ are rt. $\angle$s. [false]
Inverse: If $\angle 1$ and $\angle 2$ are not rt. $\angle$s, then $m\angle 1 \neq m\angle 2$. [false]
Contrapositive: If $m\angle 1 \neq m\angle 2$, then $\angle 1$ and $\angle 2$ are not rt. $\angle$s. [true]
6a. Converse: If an animal is a mammal, then it is a zebra. [false]
Inverse: If an animal is not a zebra, then it is not a mammal. [false] **b.** Converse: If $2x = 12$, then $x = 6$. [true] Inverse: If $x \neq 6$, then $2x \neq 12$. [true]
7. If an $\angle$ is obtuse, then its measure is greater than 90. If the measure of an $\angle$ is greater than 90, then the $\angle$ is obtuse.

Written Exercises

7. Converse: If I swim in salt water, then I swim in the Atlantic. [false]
Inverse: If I do not swim in the Atlantic, then I do not swim in salt water. [false]
Contrapositive: If I do not swim in salt water, then I do not swim in the Atlantic. [true]
8. Converse: If 2 $\angle$s are supp. $\angle$s, then they form a lin. pr. [false]
Inverse: If 2 $\angle$s do not form a lin. pr., then they are not supp. $\angle$s. [false]
Contrapositive: If 2 $\angle$s are not supp. $\angle$s, then they do not form a lin. pr. [true]
9. Converse: If 2 $\angle$s do not have a common side, then they are not adj. $\angle$s. [true]
Inverse: If 2 $\angle$s are adj. $\angle$s, then they have a common side. [true]
Contrapositive: If 2 $\angle$s have a

Example 5

Write the contrapositive of each true statement and determine if it is *true* or *false*.

a. If an animal is a zebra, then it is a mammal.

b. If x = 6, then 2x = 12.

Solution

a. If an animal is not a mammal, then it is not a zebra.

b. If $2x \neq 12$, then $x \neq 6$.

Both contrapositives are true as there are no counterexamples.

In general, the converse and inverse of a true statement may or may not be true. The contrapositive of a true statement is always true.

Checking for Understanding

1. What is the converse of $q \Rightarrow p$? $p \Rightarrow q$

Give the negation of each statement.

2. $\angle A$ and $\angle B$ are complements.   **3.** Lines ℓ and m are parallel.

4. Give the converse, the inverse, and the contrapositive of $r \Rightarrow s$.

5. Give the converse, the inverse and the contrapositive of this true conditional: If $\angle 1$ and $\angle 2$ are right angles, then $m\angle 1 = m\angle 2$. Which of the conditionals you gave are true?

6. Give the converse and the inverse of each statement in Example 3. Which of these conditionals are true?

7. Give the two "if . . . then" statements that can be combined to make the following statement: An angle is obtuse if and only if its measure is greater than 90.

2. $\angle A$ and $\angle B$ are not complements.
3. Lines ℓ and m are not parallel
4. Converse: $s \Rightarrow r$; inverse not $r \Rightarrow$ not s; contrapositive: not $s \Rightarrow$ not r

Written Exercises

Set A   Is each statement *always, sometimes,* or *never* true?

1. The converse of a true conditional is true. Sometimes

2. Postulates are "if and only if" statements although they are not always written in that form. Sometimes

3. Definitions are "if and only if" statements although they are not always written in that form. Always

4. The contrapositive of a true conditional is false. Never

5. The negation of a false statement is true. Always

6. The inverse of a true conditional is false. Sometimes

Write the converse, the inverse, and the contrapositive of each conditional, and tell whether each is *true* or *false*.

7. If I swim in the Atlantic, then I swim in salt water.

8. A linear pair of angles are supplementary.

9. If two angles are not adjacent, then they do not have a common side.

10. If x + 2 = 10, then x ≠ 3.

11. Raul drinks Sunbright juice. Can he validly conclude from the ad at the right that his day will sparkle? No

If your day sparkles, then it started with SUNBRIGHT JUICE.

Set B The twins' father told them, "If you two don't stop arguing, we won't go to the movie tonight."

12. The twins stopped arguing. Can they validly conclude from their father's statement that they will go to the movie tonight? Explain.

13. If the twins go to the movie tonight, can you validly conclude that they had stopped arguing? Explain.

14. Suppose *not t⇒not s* is the converse of a conditional. Write the inverse and contrapositive of that conditional.

15. Suppose *not r⇒p* is the contrapositive of a conditional. Write the converse and inverse of that conditional.

Write two conditionals from each statement.

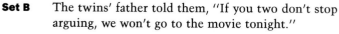

16. $\overrightarrow{OA}$ bisects ∠XOY if and only if m∠XOA = m∠AOY.

17. Two angles are supplementary if and only if the sum of their measures is 180.

Write a definition of each term using "if and only if."

18. Perpendicular lines   **19.** Right angle

20. Midpoint   **21.** Complementary angles

Set C **22.** Show that this argument from Lewis Carroll is valid: Babies are illogical; nobody is despised who can manage a crocodile; illogical persons are despised. Hence, babies cannot manage crocodiles. Discuss your thinking with another student.

common side, then they are adj. ∠s. [true]

10. Converse: If x ≠ 3, then x + 2 = 10. [false]
Inverse: If x + 2 ≠ 10, then x = 3. [false]
Contrapositive: If x = 3, then x + 2 ≠ 10. [true]

12. No; given p ⇒ q and *not p*, there is no valid conclusion. (The inverse is not necessarily true.)

13. Yes; given p ⇒ q and *not q*, it follows that *not p* is true. (The contrapositive of a true conditional is true: *not q ⇒ not p*.)

14. Inverse: s ⇒ t
Contrapositive: t ⇒ s

15. Converse: r ⇒ not p
Inverse: p ⇒ not r

16. If $\overrightarrow{OA}$ bisects ∠XOY, then m∠XOA = m∠AOY. If m∠XOA = m∠AOY, then $\overrightarrow{OA}$ bisects ∠XOY.

17. If 2 ∠s are supp. ∠s, then the sum of their measures is 180. If the sum of the measures of 2 ∠s is 180, then the ∠s are supp. ∠s.

18. Two lines are ⊥ if and only if they intersect to form a rt. ∠.

19. An ∠ is a rt. ∠ if and only if its measure is 90.

20. A pt. is the midpt. of a seg. if and only if it divides the seg. into 2 = segs.

21. Two ∠s are comp. ∠s if and only if the sum of their measures is 90.

22. If a person is a baby, then the person is illogical: p ⇒ q. If a person can manage a crocodile, then the person is not despised: r ⇒ s, which is equivalent to *not s ⇒ not r*. If a person is despised: q ⇒ not s. Using the Transitive Property for Conditionals gives the following argument: If p ⇒ q, q ⇒ not s, and *not s ⇒ not r*, then p ⇒ not r. Therefore, if a person is a baby, then the person is not despised.

Review

23. If $p \Rightarrow q$ and $q \Rightarrow r$, then $p \Rightarrow r$.

24. If $a = b$, then a or b may be replaced by the other in any equation or inequality.

FOLLOW-UP

More Practice

• Worksheet 2–6

Extension

Ask students to illustrate the sentence "A if and only if B" with a Venn diagram. The inner and outer circles must be the same.

• **Extension 2–6**

ANSWERS

Progress Check

6. If the measure of a supplement of ∠A is 95, then ∠A is not a rt. ∠.

7. Converse: If the supplement of an ∠ is obtuse, then the ∠ is acute. [true]
Inverse: If an ∠ is not acute, then its supplement is not obtuse. [true]
Contrapositive: If the supplement of an ∠ is not obtuse, then the ∠ is not acute. [true]

8. Converse: If I am studying mathematics, then I am studying trigonometry. [false]
Inverse: If I am not studying trigonometry, then I am not studying mathematics. [false]
Contrapositive: If I am not studying mathematics, then I am not studying trigonometry. [true]

▲ **Review** **23.** State the Transitive Property for Conditionals.

24. State the Substitution Property.

25. If $p \Rightarrow q$ is true in every case, and p is true in a particular case, then ___?___. *q is true*

26. Name an obtuse angle. ∠GHE

27. Name an acute angle. ∠EHD

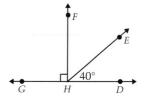

Progress Check

Lesson 2-4, page 71

State the conclusion, if any, that can be drawn from only the following conditional and the information in each exercise:
If two angles are right angles, then their measures are equal.

1. $m\angle 1 = m\angle 2$ **2.** ∠1 and ∠2 are right angles.
No conclusion $m\angle 1 = m\angle 2$

3. Complete this affirming-the-hypothesis argument.

$p \Rightarrow q$: If two angles are supplementary, then the sum of their measures is 180.

   p: __?__ ∠A and ∠B are supp. ∠s
   p: $m\angle A + m\angle B = 180$.

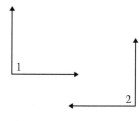

Lesson 2-5, page 76   **Subtraction Prop.**

4. State the property of real numbers that justifies this statement: If $AB + 16 = 20$, then $AB = 20 - 16$.

Apply the Transitive Property for Conditionals to determine the conditional that follows from each set of statements.

5. $p \Rightarrow q$: If x is positive, then $x > 0$.   **If x is positive,**
   $q \Rightarrow r$: If $x > 0$, then $-x < 0$.   **then $-x < 0$**

6. $p \Rightarrow q$: If the measure of a supplement of ∠A is 95, then the $m\angle A = 85$.
   $q \Rightarrow r$: If $m\angle A = 85$, the ∠A is acute.
   $r \Rightarrow s$: If ∠A is acute, then ∠A is not a right angle.

Lesson 2-6, page 83

Write the converse, the inverse, and the contrapositive of each true conditional, and tell whether each is *true* or *false*.

7. If an angle is acute, then its supplement is obtuse.

8. If I am studying trigonometry, then I am studying mathematics.

9. What is an "if and only if" statement? **A combination of two "if . . . then" statements which are both true and which are converses of each other.**

Using Logo: Teaching the Turtle Geometry

The Logo turtle obeys commands called procedures. Some procedures are built into Logo and are known as "primitives." These include turtle graphics commands such as:

CLEARSCREEN or CS   FORWARD or FD   RIGHT or RT   PENUP or PU
                     BACK or BK   LEFT or LT   PENDOWN or PD

Other procedures can be defined to teach the turtle new commands. To make the turtle respond to any command, simply type its full name or short form, and press RETURN.

1. Logo procedures are defined using the command TO. Type the following procedure to teach the turtle a command LINE.

   Type CS to clear the screen and then type LINE.

   ```
   TO LINE
   PD
   FD 70
   BK 140
   FD 70
   PU
   END
   ```

2. Type CS. Now change the turtle's heading by typing the command RT 90. Type LINE. What kind of line is drawn? Could you also draw an oblique line?

3. A previously defined procedure can be employed in another procedure. The procedure INTERSECTING calls the procedure LINE twice. Clear the screen and type INTERSECTING.

   ```
   TO INTERSECTING
   LINE
   LT 65
   LINE
   END
   ```

4. Clear the screen. Type the command LT 25 and then type INTERSECTING. Is either line horizontal? What other commands using numbers between 0 and 360 could also be used before INTERSECTING to make one of the lines horizontal?

5. Use the Logo editor to revise INTERSECTING so that the lines will be perpendicular.

6. Use the Logo editor to revise LINE so that the turtle starts and ends at an endpoint of the line segment. Define a procedure LINPR that draws a linear pair in which the measure of one of the angles is 70.

7. Define a procedure PARALLEL that draws a pair of parallel lines without a transversal. Modify PARALLEL so that it draws the lines with a transversal.

8. Write a procedure GRID to draw a 6-by-6 grid in which each cell is 10-by-10. How could GRID be modified to draw an 8-by-8 grid?

Using Logo

2. Horizontal; an oblique line could be drawn using RT or LT with any value except multiples of 90.

4. Yes; LT 90, RT 90, LT 270, RT 270, RT 155, RT 335 and LT 205 are the others.

5. Change LT 65 to LT 90 or RT 90.

6.
```
TO LINE        TO LINPR
   PD             LINE
   FD 140 ←       RT 70
   BK 140 ←       LINE
   PU             RT 110
   END            LINE
                  END
```
(Numbers may vary.)

7.
```
TO PARALLEL
   LINE
   RT 90 ←
   FD 20 ← (can vary)
   LT 90 ← (could be
   LINE        any combination
   END         of RT 90, LT 90)
```
To draw a transversal insert a PD command between LINE and FD 20 (before or after RT 90).

8. *Many* ways to do it. One way is shown below. (Change the FD command in PARALLEL to FD 10.)
```
TO GRID
REPEAT 6 [PARALLEL] ←
LT 90
REPEAT 6 [PARALLEL] ←
END
```
(Note: student may list (PARALLEL six times if he/she is not aware of the REPEAT command.)

Chapter 2 Summary

Important Terms

Affirming the hypothesis (71)
Alternate interior angles (61)
Argument (71)
Conclusion (65)
Conditional (65)
Conjecture (60)
Contrapositive (85)
Converse (83)
Corresponding angles (61)
Deductive argument (77)

Deductive reasoning (77)
Exterior angles (61)
Hypothesis (65)
"If and only if" statement (84)
"If . . . then" statement (65)
Inductive reasoning (53)
Interior angles (61)
Inverse (85)
Negation (84)
Parallel lines (61)

$p \Rightarrow q$ is false (66)
$p \Rightarrow q$ is true (66)
Properties of Equality and
    Inequality (78)
Skew lines (66)
Transitive Property for
    Conditionals (76)
Transversal (61)
Valid argument (78)
Venn diagram (65)

Important Ideas

1. Inductive reasoning is the process of reaching a general conclusion by observing several specific cases. (53)

2. A conjecture is a statement that seems to be true and is often a result of exploratory activities. (60)

3. Coplanar lines that do not intersect are parallel. (61)

4. A transversal (t at the right) is a line that intersects two or more coplanar lines (r and s) in distinct points. (61)

5. "If p, then q" is a conditional statement. The hypothesis is p, and the conclusion is q. (65)

6. If $p \Rightarrow q$ is true in every case, and p is true in a particular case, then q is true in that case. This reasoning uses affirming the hypothesis. (75)

7. The Transitive Property for Conditionals is: If $p \Rightarrow q$ and $q \Rightarrow r$, then $p \Rightarrow r$. (76)

8. Deductive reasoning uses rules of logic to reach conclusions from assumed or previously proved statements. (77)

9. The Properties of Equality and Inequality for Real Numbers are sometimes used in deductive arguments. (78)

10. The converse of $p \Rightarrow q$ is $q \Rightarrow p$; the inverse is *not $p \Rightarrow$ not q*; and the contrapositive is *not $q \Rightarrow$ not p*. (83, 85)

11. All definitions can be written as "if and only if" statements. (84)

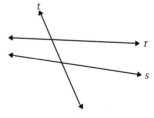

Chapter 2 Review

Lesson 2-1, Page 53

1. A 1-by-1 grid is just one square, but a 2-by-2 grid contains five squares: four 1-by-1 and one 2-by-2. A 3-by-3 grid will contain squares of three sizes. Complete this table.

1-by-1

2-by-2

Size of grid	1-by-1	2-by-2	3-by-3	4-by-4
Number of squares	1	5	_?_ 14	_?_ 30

2. Predict the number of squares in an *n*-by-*n* grid. What type of reasoning did you use? $n^2 + (n-1)^2 + \ldots + 1^2$; inductive

Lesson 2-2, page 58

3. Draw a triangle. Label the vertices of the angles *A*, *B*, and *C*. Find midpoint *M* of $\overline{AB}$ and midpoint *N* of $\overline{AC}$. Draw $\overline{MN}$. Measure $\overline{MN}$ and $\overline{BC}$. Repeat this activity with three other triangles. Write a conjecture about the relationship between one side of a triangle and the segment joining the midpoints of the other two sides.

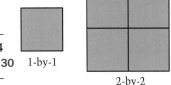

The segment joining the midpt. of two sides of a triangle is ∥ to and half as long as the third side.

4. $\overleftrightarrow{RS}$ and $\overleftrightarrow{TV}$ have no common points, but they are not parallel. $\overleftrightarrow{RS}$ and $\overleftrightarrow{TV}$ are _?_ lines. skew

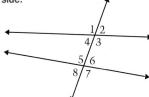

Identify a pair of

∠1 and ∠5; ∠2 and ∠6; ∠4 and ∠8; ∠3 and ∠7

5. alternate interior angles.
∠4 and ∠6; ∠3 and ∠5

6. corresponding angles.

Lesson 2-3, page 65 Hypothesis underlined once, conclusion twice.
Identify the <u>hypothesis</u> and <u>conclusion</u> of each statement.

7. If <u>3*AB* = 90</u>, then <u>*AB* = 30</u>.

8. If <u>your dog eats Barko,</u> <u>he'll stay happy and healthy.</u>

9. <u>Two angles are equal</u> if <u>they are vertical angles.</u>

Write each statement in "if . . . then" form. Draw a Venn diagram for Exercise 10.

10. Everyone who is in senior mathematics is also in physics.

11. The angles in a linear pair are supplementary.

12. Two circles intersect in at most two points.

13. The principal is in a bad mood when it rains.

ANSWERS

Chapter Review

10. If a student is in senior mathematics, then he is also in physics.

11. If 2 ∠s form a lin. pr., then they are supp. ∠s.
12. If 2 circles intersect, then they intersect in at most 2 pts.
13. If it rains, then the principal is in a bad mood.

24. Converse: If $\overset{\leftrightarrow}{KB}$ bisects $\overline{JH}$, then $JK = KH$.
Inverse: If $JK \neq KH$, then $\overset{\leftrightarrow}{KB}$ does not bisect $\overline{JH}$.
Contrapositive: If $\overset{\leftrightarrow}{KB}$ does not bisect $\overline{JH}$, then $JK \neq KH$.

25. Converse: If it is not summer, then it snows.
Inverse: If it does not snow, then it is summer.
Contrapositive: If it is summer, then it does not snow.

26. Converse: If $m\angle 1 = m\angle 2$, then $\angle 1$ and $\angle 2$ are complements of the same $\angle$.
Inverse: If $\angle 1$ and $\angle 2$ are not complements of the same $\angle$, then $m\angle 1 \neq m\angle 2$.
Contrapositive: If $m\angle 1 \neq m\angle 2$, then $\angle 1$ and $\angle 2$ are not complements of the same $\angle$.

27. If an $\angle$ is acute, then its measure is less than 90. If the measure of an $\angle$ is less than 90, then the $\angle$ is acute.

Lesson 2-4, page 71
Complete each affirming-the-hypothesis argument.

14. $p \Rightarrow q$: If two angles are obtuse, then the sum of their measures is greater than 180.
  $\underline{p:}$ $\angle 1$ and $\angle 2$ are obtuse angles.
  $q:$ $\underline{\ ?\ }$ $m\angle 1 + m\angle 2 > 180$

15. $r \Rightarrow s$: All right angles have equal measure.
  $\underline{r:}$ $\underline{\ ?\ }$ $\angle x$ and $\angle y$ are rt. $\angle$s
  $s:$ $m\angle X = m\angle Y$

State the conclusion, if any, that can be drawn from only the information in each exercise and this conditional: If two lines cut by a transversal form a pair of equal corresponding angles, then the lines are parallel. **16. No conclusion 18. No conclusion**

16. $m\angle 1 = m\angle 2$ **17.** $m\angle 2 = m\angle 3$ $r \parallel s$ **18.** $s \parallel r$

19. Which definition or postulate justifies the conclusion that, for the figure at the right, $AX + XB = AB$? **Seg. Add. Post.**

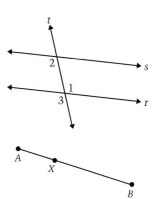

Lesson 2-5, page 76
State the property of real numbers that justifies each statement.

20. If $m\angle G = m\angle H$, then $m\angle H = m\angle G$. **Symmetric Prop.**

21. If $2AX = 2BY$, then $AX = BY$. **Division Prop.**

22. If $AB + 5 > AC$, then $AB > AC - 5$. **Subtraction Prop.**

23. State the conditional that follows from these statements: If the noncommon sides of two adjacent angles are perpendicular, then the angles are complementary. If two angles are complementary, then the sum of their measures is 90. **If the noncommon sides of two adjacent $\angle$s are $\perp$, then the sum of the measures of the $\angle$s is 90.**

Lesson, 2-6, page 83
Write the converse, the inverse, and the contrapositive of each conditional.

24. If $JK = KH$, then $\overset{\leftrightarrow}{KB}$ bisects $\overline{JH}$.

25. If it snows, then it is not summer.

26. If $\angle 1$ and $\angle 2$ are complements of the same angle, then $m\angle 1 = m\angle 2$.

27. Write this statement as two conditionals: An angle is acute if and only if its measure is less than 90.

Chapter 2 Test

Is each statement *true* or *false*? If false, give a counterexample.

1. Inductive reasoning is the process of reaching necessary conclusions from assumed or previously proven statements. **False**

2. Lines that do not intersect are parallel lines. **False**

3. A conditional is always a true statement. **False**

4. A conjecture is a valid deductive argument. **False**

5. For real numbers a, b, and c, if $a > b$, then $a + c > b + c$. **True**

6. $\angle 1$ and $\angle 2$ at the right are alternate interior angles. **False**

Use this statement: If $m\angle A = 20$, then $\angle A$ is acute.

7. Identify the hypothesis and the conclusion of the statement. **Hypothesis underlined once, conclusion twice.**

8. Draw a Venn diagram illustrating the statement.

9. Write the converse of the statement.

10. Write the contrapositive of the statement.

11. Write as two conditionals: Two angles are complementary if and only if the sum of their measures is 90.

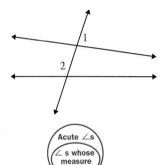

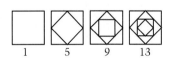

Beneath each of these designs is the number of nonoverlapping regions formed. Suppose the pattern continues. Use inductive reasoning to predict the number of nonoverlapping regions enclosed in

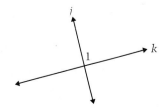

1	5	9	13

12. the fifth design. **17**   13. the nth design. **4n − 3**

14. Give the conclusion. All band members play at the pep rallies. Rosana is in the band, so __?__.
   Rosana plays at the pep rallies

15. Complete this affirming-the-hypothesis argument.
   $p \Rightarrow q$: If a line bisects a segment, then it contains the midpoint of the segment.

   __p: ?__   line ℓ bisects seg. $\overline{ST}$
   q: ℓ contains the midpoint of $\overline{ST}$.

16. Give the conditional that follows from these statements.
   $p \Rightarrow q$: If $j \perp k$, then $\angle 1$ is a right angle.
   $q \Rightarrow r$: If $\angle 1$ is a right angle, then $m\angle 1 = 90$.
   $r \Rightarrow s$: If $m\angle 1 = 90$, then $2(m\angle 1) = 180$.
   $p \Rightarrow s$: If $j \perp k$, then $2(m\angle 1) = 180$

Chapter Test

9. If $\angle A$ is acute, then $m\angle A = 20$.
10. If $\angle A$ is not acute, then $m\angle A \neq 20$.
11. (1) If 2 $\angle$s are comp. $\angle$s, then the sum of their measures is 90. (2) If the sum of the measures of 2 $\angle$s is 90, then the $\angle$s are comp. $\angle$s.

CHAPTER 3

Proof in Geometry

Chapter Overview

This chapter is an extension of the concepts of inductive and deductive reasoning. In a step-by-step process, students are led to develop all **proof subskills** necessary for writing a complete two-column proof. After a presentation of the form as a whole, the first three parts (diagram, Given and Prove) are studied. Previous work with the structure of conditional statements is applied here.

Next, students apply their understanding of deductive arguments to place the steps of a given proof in the correct order. Inductive methods are then used to develop strategies for writing a plan for a proof, and the **problem-solving strategies** of working forward and working backward are applied to this task. Finally, students are asked to write complete proofs.

As vehicles for the development of these subskills, some important theorems are presented and proved. They deal primarily with perpendicular lines and right angles, complements and supplements, and vertical angles.

Perspectives

Lesson 3–1 introduces the two-column form as one way to present a deductive argument. It is a shorthand method for presenting the affirming-the-hypothesis arguments that constitute most proofs. This approach emphasizes the connection between proofs written in two-column form and the deductive arguments using $p \Rightarrow q$ statements and affirming-the-hypothesis arguments.

This lesson completes the introduction of the **proof subskills** of supplying missing statements and reasons.

Lesson 3–2 considers the first three parts of a proof: the Given, the Prove and the diagram. Establishing the conventions for what may and may not be assumed from the diagram is an important part of this lesson.

The first three theorems involve the initial parts of the proof process.

Lesson 3–3 requires students to unscramble steps of a proof in preparation for constructing complete proofs. Better students are also expected to identify and eliminate extraneous steps from a given set. Students should try to understand the logical flow of the steps in a proof. This lesson carefully examines the statements and reasons.

As a vehicle for this work, four theorems dealing with supplementary and complementary angles are stated and proved.

Lesson 3–4 provides guidelines for writing an entire proof. The Euclidean geometry system is viewed as an ever-growing inventory of geometric facts consisting of definitions, postulates, real number properties and theorems that have been proved.

Pacing Chart for Chapter 3

Lesson	Objectives	Basic Course	Average Course	Extended Course
3–1	Supply missing statements and reasons for a given proof.	2	1	1
3–2	Draw and label a diagram; write the Given and the Prove in terms of the diagram.	2	1	1
3–3	Order the steps of a proof.	2	2	$1\frac{1}{2}$
3–4	Write a plan for a proof.	2	2	$1\frac{1}{2}$
3–5	Use a strategy to write a proof.	2	2	$1\frac{1}{2}$
3–6	Write a two-column proof.	2	2	$1\frac{1}{2}$
Review		2	1	1
Test		1	1	1
Cumulative Review and Test		1	1	1
Practice for Standardized Tests 1		1	1	1
Total		17 days	14 days	12 days

Any reason in a proof other than the Given must be drawn from this inventory. As the inventory grows, we are provided with more power to prove succeeding theorems.

The **proof subskill** of writing plans for proofs is presented in this lesson. Practice is provided in the context of Theorem 3–8, which involves the equality of vertical angles.

Lesson 3–5 emphasizes the planning and writing of a proof. This is a complex problem-solving task, but some **problem-solving strategies** may be helpful. The basic ideas for these strategies were introduced earlier when students were asked to find what is implied by a given statement and what hypotheses would allow us to draw a particular conclusion. The **proof subskills** of working forward and working backward involve asking these questions repeatedly.

Theorem 3–10 allows us to conclude that lines are perpendicular if the angles in a linear pair are equal.

Lesson 3–6 combines the parts of a two-column proof with **proof subskills** so that students can write entire proofs in two-column form. The approach is to consider entire proofs, but the option exists to analyze them in terms of parts and subskills.

Theorem 3–11, which allows us to conclude that all four angles formed by perpendicular lines are right angles, is proved as an example of complete proof-writing.

Proof in Geometry

Chapter 3

```
]
]
]100 REM "TESTS WHETHER ANGLES ARE
        SUPPLEMENTARY"
]110 INPUT "ENTER MEASURE OF ANGLE M";M
]120 INPUT "ENTER MEASURE OF ANGLE N";N
]130 IF M+N=180 THEN 160
]140 PRINT "ANGLES M AND N ARE NOT
        SUPPLEMENTARY."
]150 GOTO 170
]160 PRINT "ANGLES M AND N ARE
        SUPPLEMENTARY."
]170 END
```

A computer processes the steps of a BASIC program in order unless a statement like the "if . . . then" statement in line 130 changes the sequence. For example, suppose $m\angle M = 78$ and $m\angle N = 102$. Since $78 + 102 = 180$, the computer will skip from line 130 to line 160. What will the output be in this case?

Now suppose $m\angle M = 134$ and $m\angle N = 53$. Give the order in which the computer will process the steps. What is the output?

In this chapter, you will learn that the steps in a mathematical argument, like those in a BASIC program, must be carefully organized. "If . . . then" statements play an important role in both proofs and programs.

Warm-Up Review

1. State the hypothesis: If $a = b$ and $c = d$, then $a + c = b + d$. $a = b$ and $c = d$
2. If $x = 6$ and $y = 3$, then $x + y = $ ___?___ .   9
3. If the measure of an angle is 90, it is a(n) ___?___ angle.   Right
4. If the sum of the measures of two angles is 180, they are ___?___ angles.   Supplementary

3-1 Two-Column Proofs

Just as a computer programmer needs to order the lines of a program, you need to order and explain the steps of a geometric argument. For example, suppose $\angle 1$ is a right angle, and $\angle 2$ and $\angle 1$ are supplementary. What is $m\angle 2$? Think about how you would explain your answer. You might argue as follows: Since $\angle 1$ is a right angle, I know its measure is 90 ($m\angle 1 = 90$). Since $\angle 1$ and $\angle 2$ are supplementary, I know that $m\angle 1 + m\angle 2 = 180$. By the Subtraction Property, $m\angle 2 = 180 - m\angle 1$. Substituting 90 for $m\angle 1$ gives $m\angle 2 = 90$.

A deductive argument in which each step follows from the previous one(s) by affirming the hypothesis is called a **proof**. One way to present a proof is to write out each use of affirming the hypothesis as shown in Example 1.

Example 1
Prove that if $\angle A$ and $\angle B$ are right angles, then $\angle A$ and $\angle B$ are supplementary.

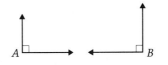

Solution
1. By hypothesis, $\angle A$ and $\angle B$ are right angles.

2. $p \Rightarrow q$: If an angle is a right angle, then its measure is 90. (Definition of right angle)

   p: $\angle A$ and $\angle B$ are right angles.
   q: $m\angle A = 90$ and $m\angle B = 90$

3. $q \Rightarrow r$: If $a = b$ and $c = d$, then $a + c = b + d$. (Addition Property)

   q: $m\angle A = 90$ and $m\angle B = 90$
   r: $m\angle A + m\angle B = 90 + 90$, or $m\angle A + m\angle B = 180$

4. $r \Rightarrow s$: If the sum of the measures of two angles is 180, then the angles are supplementary. (Definition of supplementary angles)

   r: $m\angle A + m\angle B = 180$
   s: $\angle A$ and $\angle B$ are supplementary angles.

This proves the conditional in Example 1, using only the definitions, postulates, and properties of real numbers from Chapters 1 and 2. Later you will also use **theorems**, or statements which have been proved, as reasons in the proofs of conditionals.

3-1 *Two-Column Proofs*

Additional Examples

Example 1

Write out each use of affirming the hypothesis in a proof of the following statement: If ∠1 and ∠3 are both complementary to ∠2, then $m\angle 1 = m\angle 3$. (See Additional Answers.)

Introduce the two-column form as a shorthand method for the longer deductive argument. Point out the connection between a **computer** program and a two–column proof.

Example 2

Write a two-column proof of the statement in **Example 1.**
Given: ∠1 is complementary to ∠2; ∠3 is complementary to ∠2.
Prove: $m\angle 1 = m\angle 3$

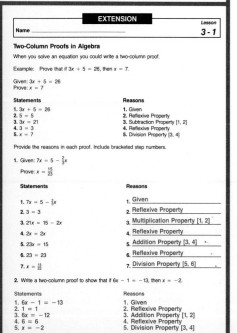

Whenever you are asked to prove a conditional, assume the hypothesis of the statement is true. Therefore, in Example 1, "∠A and ∠B are right angles" is true.

One way to avoid some of the repetition and to shorten the proof given in Example 1 is to use the **two-column form** shown in Example 2. Compare each step in Example 1 with the corresponding step in Example 2.

Example 2

If ∠A and ∠B are right angles,
then ∠A and ∠B are supplementary angles.

Given ∠A and ∠B are right angles.

Prove ∠A and ∠B are supplementary angles.

Proof

Statements	Reasons
1. ∠A and ∠B are right angles.	1. Given
2. $m\angle A = 90$ and $m\angle B = 90$	2. Def. of rt. ∠ [1]
3. $m\angle A + m\angle B = 90 + 90 = 180$	3. Addition Prop. [2]
4. ∠A and ∠B are supp. ∠s.	4. Def. of supp. ∠s [3]

Notice the brackets [ ] in the Reasons column. The numbers written in the brackets refer to the statements in the Statements column. Each reference number shows where the hypothesis of the reason has been affirmed. For example, consider Step 4. Statement 3 affirms the hypothesis in the definition of supplementary angles: If the sum of the measures of two angles is 180, then the angles are supplementary.

Summary Parts of a Two-Column Proof

1. A *diagram* that illustrates the hypothesis of the conditional that you want to prove
2. *Given*, the hypothesis written in terms of the diagram
3. *Prove*, the conclusion written in terms of the diagram
4. The *proof*, with steps presented in two columns headed *Statements* and *Reasons*. Usually the first statement is what is given, and the last step is what is to be proved. A reason for a statement can be Given, a definition, a postulate, a property of real numbers, or a theorem.

In all proofs in this text we assume, without stating explicitly, that angle measures and lengths of segments are real numbers.

Example 3

Supply the reasons and the bracketed reference numbers in the two-column proof below.

Given R is between P and O.

Prove $PR = PO - RO$

P   R   O

Proof

Statements	Reasons
1. R is between P and O.	1. $\underline{\ ?\ }$
2. $PR + RO = PO$	2. $\underline{\ ?\ }$ [$\underline{\ ?\ }$]
3. $RO = RO$	3. $\underline{\ ?\ }$
4. $PR = PO - RO$	4. $\underline{\ ?\ }$ [$\underline{\ ?\ }$]

Solution

As in most proofs, the first reason is *Given*. Abbreviated for convenience, the other reasons and reference numbers are:
2. Seg. Add. Post. [1]; *3. Reflexive Prop.;* and *4. Subtraction Prop.* [2, 3]. Notice that Step 4 uses Statements 2 and 3 for reference. Both are necessary. Why?

Also notice that the last statement is what you are asked to prove. Our logical argument ensures that "If Statement 1, then Statement 4."

The Subtraction Prop. states that if $a = b$ and $c = d$, then $a - c = b - d$. There are two equations in the hypothesis. Statement 2 corresponds to $a = b$ and statement 3 corresponds to $c = d$.

Checking for Understanding

Suppose you are asked to prove the following conditional:
If an angle is a right angle, then the lines that contain its sides are perpendicular.

1. Hypothesis: an $\angle$ is a right $\angle$; conclusion: the lines that contain its sides are $\perp$.

1. What is the hypothesis? the conclusion?

2. Draw a right angle and label it $\angle ABC$. Write the Given and the Prove in terms of your diagram.

2. Given: $\angle ABC$ is a rt. $\angle$.
Prove: $\overleftrightarrow{AB} \perp \overleftrightarrow{BC}$

3. What will be the last statement in your proof? $\overleftrightarrow{AB} \perp \overleftrightarrow{BC}$

4. What are usually the first statement and the first reason in a proof? The Given; Given

5. In general, what may be used as reasons in a proof?

5. Given a def., a post., a prop. of real numbers, or a thm.

6. Could [2, 5] be written after the reason in Step 4 of a proof? Explain your answer.

7. Yes, a proof is begun with a hypothesis that is written in terms of the diagram. Then a conclusion follows and it is written in terms of the diagram. The conclusion becomes a new hypothesis and so on.

7. Mary Lee studied Examples 2 and 3 and then made the following generalization: The Statements column contains hypotheses and conclusions in terms of the diagram. Do you agree with her? Why or why not?

Proof:
Statements

1. $\angle 1$ is complementary to $\angle 2$; $\angle 3$ is complementary to $\angle 2$.
2. $m\angle 1 + m\angle 2 = 90$; $m\angle 3 + m\angle 2 = 90$
3. $m\angle 1 + m\angle 2 = m\angle 3 + m\angle 2$
4. $m\angle 2 = m\angle 2$
5. $m\angle 1 = m\angle 3$

Reasons

1. Given
2. Def. of comp. $\angle$s [1]
3. Subst. Prop. [2]
4. Reflex. Prop.
5. Subtr. Prop. [3, 4]

Example 3

Supply the reasons and the bracketed reference numbers in the two-column proof below.

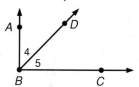

Given: $\angle 4$ and $\angle 5$ are complements. Prove: $\overrightarrow{BA} \perp \overrightarrow{BC}$

Proof:
Statements

1. $\angle 4$ and $\angle 5$ are complements.
2. $m\angle 4 + m\angle 5 = 90$
3. $m\angle 4 + m\angle 5 = m\angle ABC$
4. $m\angle ABC = 90$
5. $\angle ABC$ is a rt. $\angle$.
6. $\overrightarrow{BA} \perp \overrightarrow{BC}$

Reasons

1. $\underline{\ ?\ }$ Given
2. $\underline{\ ?\ }$ [$\underline{\ ?\ }$] Def. of comp. $\angle$s, [1]
3. $\underline{\ ?\ }$ $\angle$ Add. Post.
4. $\underline{\ ?\ }$ [$\underline{\ ?\ }$] Substitution Prop. [2, 3]
5. $\underline{\ ?\ }$ [$\underline{\ ?\ }$] Def. of rt. $\angle$ [4]
6. $\underline{\ ?\ }$ [$\underline{\ ?\ }$] Def. of $\perp$ lines [5]

Assignment Guide

Basic: 1, 2, 8–15
Average: 1–5, 8–15
Extended: 1–15

EXERCISE NOTES

Exercise 1   makes use of the **proof subskill** of supplying missing reasons.

Exercises 2–4   ask students to supply missing statements and reasons, another **proof subskill**.

Exercise 7   asks for a complete proof. This will probably be difficult at this stage, even for the best students.

ANSWERS

Written Exercises

5. 1. By hypothesis, R is between P and O. 2. $p \Rightarrow q$: If P is between A and B, then $AP + PB = AB$. (Seg. Add. Post.) p: R is between P and O. q: $PR + RO = PO$ 3. $q \Rightarrow r$: For all real numbers a, $a = a$. (Reflexive Prop.) q: RO is a real number. r: $RO = RO$ 4. $r \Rightarrow s$: For all real numbers a, b, c and d, if $a = b$ and $c = d$, then $a - c = b - d$. (Subtraction Prop.) r: $PR + RO = PO$ and $RO = RO$ s: $PR = PO - RO$

6. 1. By hypothesis, N is in the interior of $\angle AOB$. 2. $p \Rightarrow q$: If B is in the interior of $\angle APC$, then $m\angle APB + m\angle BPC = m\angle APC$. ($\angle$ Add. Post.) p: N is in the interior of $\angle AOB$. q: $m\angle AON + m\angle NOB$

Written Exercises

Set A   Supply the missing parts in each proof.

1. Given: $RY = RO$; R is between O and P.
Prove: $PR + RY = PO$

Statements	Reasons
1. $RY = RO$	1. ? Given
2. R is between O and P.	2. ? Given
3. $PR + RO = PO$	3. Seg. Add. Post. [2]
4. $PR + RY = PO$	4. ? [?] Substitution Prop.[1, 3]

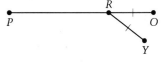

2. Given: N is in the interior of $\angle AOB$;
$m\angle AON + m\angle NOB = 90$
Prove: $\overleftrightarrow{AO} \perp \overleftrightarrow{OB}$

Statements	Reasons
1. ?	1. Given
2. ?	2. Angle Add. Post. [1]
3. $m\angle AON + m\angle NOB = 90$	3. ? Given
4. $m\angle AOB = 90$	4. ? [2, 3]
5. $\angle AOB$ is a rt. $\angle$.	5. Def. of rt. $\angle$ [?] [4]
6. $\overleftrightarrow{AO} \perp \overleftrightarrow{OB}$	6. ? [?]

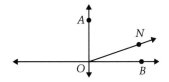

1. N is in the int. of $\angle AOB$.
2. $m\angle AON + m\angle NOB = m\angle AOB$
4. Substitution Prop.

6. Def. of $\perp$ lines [5]

Set B   **3.** Given: $\angle A$ is a right $\angle$; $m\angle A = m\angle B$
Prove: $\angle B$ is a right angle.

Statements	Reasons
1. ?	1. Given $\angle A$ is a rt.$\angle$.
2. $m\angle A = m\angle B$	2. ? Given
3. ?	3. Def. of rt. $\angle$ [1] $m\angle A = 90$
4. $m\angle B = 90$	4. ? [2, 3] Substitution Prop.
5. ?	5. ? [?]

4. Given: D is in the interior of $\angle FEW$;
$\angle FED$ is complementary to $\angle DEW$.
Prove: $\angle FEW$ is a right angle.

Statements	Reasons
1. $\angle FED$ is comp. to $\angle DEW$.	1. ? Given
2. ? $m\angle FED + m\angle DEW = 90$	2. Def. of comp. $\angle$s [1]
3. ?	3. Given
4. $m\angle FED + m\angle DEW = m\angle FEW$	4. ? [3]
5. ? $m\angle FEW = 90$	5. Substitution Prop. [2, 4]
6. ? $\angle FEW$ is a rt. $\angle$.	6. ? [?]
3. D is in the int. of $\angle FEW$.	4. Angle Addition Post.
	6. Def. of rt. $\angle$ [5]

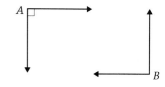

5. $\angle B$ is a rt. $\angle$; def. of a rt. $\angle$ [4]

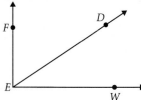

5. Write a proof of Example 3 in the form used in Example 1.

6. Write a proof of Exercise 2 in the form used in Example 1.

7. Write a two-column proof.
Given: ∠A is right angle; ∠B is an obtuse angle.
Prove: m∠A < m∠B

8. If it is November, then it is Thanksgiving Day; false.
9. If it is not November, then it is not Thanksgiving Day; true.

▲ **Review** Consider this statement: If it is Thanksgiving Day, then it is November.

8. Write the converse and tell if it is true.

9. Write the contrapositive and tell if it is true.

10. State the Reflexive Property for real numbers.

11. __?__ and __?__ are opposite rays. $\overrightarrow{YW}$, $\overrightarrow{YZ}$

12. Point __?__ is in the exterior of ∠XYZ. U

10. For any real number a, a = a.

≡ **Thinking**
▼ **Ahead** For Exercises 13-15, discuss your ideas with other students in class.

You know how to mark a diagram to show parallel lines and right angles. Think of some ways to mark

13. equal angles.   **14.** equal segments.

15. Copy the diagram at the right and mark it to show that AB = BC, m∠A = m∠ACB, ∠Q is a right angle, and $\overleftrightarrow{AC} \parallel \overleftrightarrow{BQ}$.

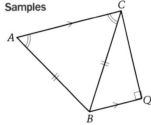

Samples

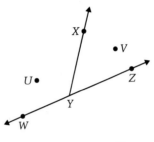

Challenge
Which of these arguments, posed by Lewis Carroll, are valid?

1. All lions are fierce; some lions do not drink coffee. Hence, some creatures that drink coffee are not fierce. **Not valid**

2. Gold is heavy; nothing but gold will silence him. Hence, nothing light will silence him. **Valid**

3. Some pillows are soft; no pokers are soft. Hence, some pokers are not pillows. **Not valid**

= m∠AOB 3. By hypothesis, m∠ AON + m∠NOB = 90. 4. q ⇒ r: For all real numbers a, b and c, if a = b and b = c, then a = c. (Transitive Prop.) q: m∠AOB = m∠AON + m∠NOB and m∠AON + m∠NOB = 90 r: m∠AOB = 90 5. r ⇒ s: If the measure of an ∠ is 90, then it is a rt. ∠. (Def. of rt. ∠) r: m∠AOB = 90 s: ∠AOB is a rt. ∠. 6. s ⇒ t: If lines intersect to form a rt. ∠, then they are ⊥. (Def. of ⊥ lines) s: ∠AOB is a rt. ∠. t: $\overrightarrow{AO} \perp \overrightarrow{OB}$.
7. 1. ∠A is a rt. ∠. (Given) 2. m∠A = 90 (Def. of rt. ∠ [1]) 3. ∠B is obtuse. (Given) 4. m∠B > 90 (Def. of obtuse ∠ [3]) 5. m∠B > m∠A (Substitution Prop. [2, 4])

FOLLOW-UP

More Practice

Another way to introduce the **proof subskills** of supplying missing statements or reasons is to look at just one or two steps at a time. For example,
2. __?__
3. PR + RO = PO Seg. Add. Post. [2] (/)
What is the missing statement in step 2? the hypothesis of the Segment Addition Postulate, or R is between O and P
• **Worksheet 3-1**

Extension

• **Extension 3-1**

ANSWERS

Excursion

1. *p*: Wade plays third base for the Red Sox.
q: The third baseman bats first for the Red Sox.
not p: Wade does not play third base for the Red Sox.
not q: The third baseman does not bat first for the Red Sox.
p ⇒ *q*: If Wade plays third base for the Red Sox, then the third baseman bats first for the Red Sox.
q ⇒ *p*: If the third baseman bats first for the Red Sox, then Wade plays third base for the Red Sox.
p ⇔ *q*: Wade plays third base for the Red Sox if and only if the third baseman bats first for the Red Sox.
not q ⇒ *not p*: If the third baseman does not bat first for the Red Sox, then Wade does not play third base for the Red Sox.
not p ⇒ *not q*: If Wade does not play third base for the Red Sox, then the third baseman does not bat first for the Red Sox.
2. converse; "if and only if" statement; contrapositive; inverse
3. *p*⇒*q* and *not q*⇒*not p*; *q*⇒*p* and *not p*⇒*not q*
4. The concept of affirming the hypothesis refers to the assumption that a hypothesis is true in a particular case. Specifically, if *p* ⓒ*q* is true in every case, and *p* is true in a particular case, then *q* is true in that case. This conclusion is supported by the truth table.

Excursion: Logic and Truth Tables

Many of the rules of mathematical logic can be represented symbolically. Consider these statements:

p: Wade plays third base for the Red Sox.
q: The third baseman bats first for the Red Sox.

Closely related to *p* is the statement *not p*. Furthermore, statements *p* and *q* may be combined or connected in various ways to form conditionals such as *p*⇒*q*, *q*⇒*p*, or *not p*⇒*not q*. If we know whether *p* and *q* are true or false, we can determine whether each of these related and connected statements is true or false.

This is illustrated in a table, called a *truth table*. Here T means the statement is true, and F means it is false.

p	*q*	*not p*	*not q*	*p*⇒*q*	*q*⇒*p*	*p*⇔*q*	*not q*⇒*not p*	*not p*⇒*not q*
T	T	F	F	T	T	T	T	T
T	F	F	T	F	T	F	F	T
F	T	T	F	T	F	F	T	F
F	F	T	T	T	T	T	T	T

Notice that *p*⇒*q* is considered to be true *except* when *p* is true and *q* is false. Thus, if *p* is false—that is, "Wade does not play third base for the Red Sox"—then *p*⇒*q* is true whether or not *q* is true.

1. Translate the headings in the truth table using the above statements for *p* and *q*. For example, *not q*⇒*not p* means "If the third baseman does not bat first for the Red Sox, then Wade does not play third base for the Red Sox." Convince yourself that the lines of the truth table are correct for these statements.

2. Many of the statements in the headings of the truth tables were named in previous lessons. For example, *not p* is the negation of *p* and *p*⇒*q* is a conditional statement. What are the names of the last four statements as they are related to *p*⇒*q*? See Lesson 2-6.

3. Statements that have exactly the same truth values are said to be *logically equivalent*. Which statements in this truth table are logically equivalent?

4. Use the truth table to explain affirming the hypothesis.

3-2 Beginning a Proof

The first three parts of a two-column proof—the diagram, the Given, and the Prove—provide the starting and ending points, as well as the language of the proof. The *diagram* contains the information in the hypothesis of the conditional that is to be proved. The *Given* is the hypothesis stated in terms of the diagram. The *Prove* is the conclusion stated in terms of the diagram.

Example 1

Draw a diagram and write the Given and the Prove for this conditional: If two lines intersect, then they intersect in one and only one point.

Solution

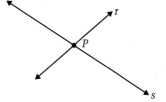

Since the hypothesis is "two lines intersect," draw two lines, r and s, that intersect at point P. Then use the labels on the diagram to write the Given and the Prove.

Given: Lines r and s intersect.
Prove: r and s intersect at P and only at P.

Recall that a theorem is a statement that is proved. The theorems in this lesson can be proved using only the definitions, postulates, and properties of real numbers that you have studied so far. But, since the object of this lesson is to draw and label diagrams and to write the Given and the Prove, the proofs of these theorems are presented in later lessons or left to exercises.

Theorem 3-1

If two lines intersect, then they intersect in one and only one point.

Theorem 3-2

A line and a point not on the line are contained in one and only one plane.

Theorem 3-3

Two intersecting lines lie in one and only one plane.

Theorem 3-1 which is the conditional in Example 1 will be proved in Lesson 4-3. The diagram, the Given, and the Prove for Theorems 3-2 and 3-3 are required in Exercises 18 and 19. Their proofs are requested in the exercises of Lessons 3-6 and 4-3.

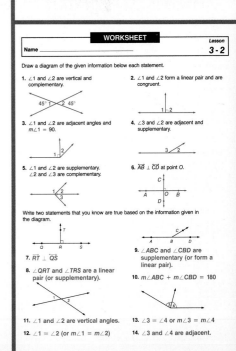

for practice in writing the Given and Prove and drawing the diagram before going on to other aspects of this lesson. Have students practice just the first three parts of the proof process.

Additional Examples

Example 1
Draw a diagram and write the Given and the Prove for the following conditional: If two angles are vertical angles, then they are equal.

Given: ∠1 and ∠2 are vertical.
Prove: m∠1 = m∠2

Be sure that students understand what they can and cannot assume from a given diagram. Students must choose the best diagram from several that are given in **Example 2**. The role of dia-

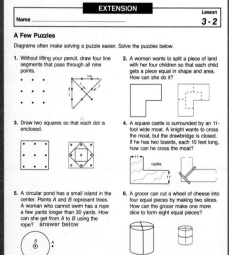

After you have stated the Given and the Prove in terms of the diagram, mark the Given on the diagram. Only the information in the Given may be marked. For example, given that ∠HGK is a right angle, $\overline{FG} \parallel \overline{IH}$, HJ = IJ, m∠FJI = m∠GJH, and m∠HIJ = m∠IHJ, you may mark the diagram at the right as indicated. How could you mark the diagram to show $\overleftrightarrow{IF} \parallel \overleftrightarrow{HG}$? JF = JG?

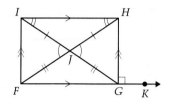

When a diagram is provided, use these guidelines.

Given a diagram,
  you may assume, from its appearance only, that:
    points and lines are coplanar;
    rays and points on lines are collinear;
    angles are adjacent, vertical, or a linear pair;
    a point is between two others or in the interior of an angle;

  you may not assume that:
    lines are parallel or perpendicular;
    segments or angles have specific lengths or measures.

The diagram at the right is a plane figure that shows two lines intersecting a ray at its endpoint.

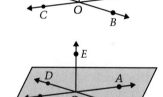

The second diagram shows $\overrightarrow{OE}$ intersecting the plane at point O. $\overleftrightarrow{CA}$ and $\overleftrightarrow{DB}$ are in plane $\mathcal{K}$ and intersect at O.

To avoid confusion, all diagrams in this book are plane figures unless otherwise stated or drawn to show three dimensions.

After you mark the Given on the diagram, and note the facts that you can assume from the diagram and use in your proof, you are ready to begin writing your proof.

Example 2
Select the best diagram for the following proof.
Given: AN = NB; BO = OC; CP = PD; DM = MA
Prove: MN = OP

a. 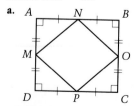   b. 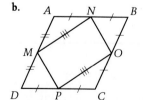   c.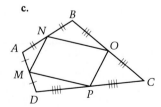

Solution
Diagrams a and b both have markings which are not given. The Given and *no more* is marked on diagram c, so c is the best choice.

In addition to their use in proofs, diagrams can provide counterexamples to show that statements are false.

Example 3

Sketch a counterexample of the following statement: The lines containing the sides of a linear pair are perpendicular.

2. Sample: *A*, *E*, and *C* are collinear; ∠*AEB* and ∠1 form a linear pair.

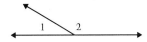

Solution

A linear pair in which neither angle is a right angle, such as ∠1 and ∠2 in the diagram at the right, is a counterexample.

Checking for Understanding

1. Draw a diagram and then write the Given and the Prove for the following conditional: If the angles of a linear pair are equal, then the lines containing their sides are perpendicular.

2. Name at least two facts that can be assumed from the diagram at the right.

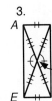

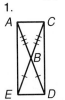

What information is indicated by the marks on each diagram?

3.

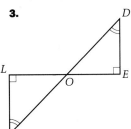

4.

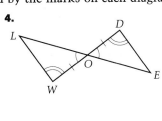

5.

D

L

O

W

E

3. *m∠W = m∠D*; ∠*L*, ∠*E* are rt. ∠s
4. *m∠LOW = m∠DOE*; *DO = OW*; *m∠D = m∠W*
5. *m∠W = m∠W = m∠D*
6. Exercise 5's diagram

6. Which diagram from Exercises 3-5 shows the correct marks for the following given facts?

Given: Vertical angles ∠*DOE* and ∠*LOW*; *m∠ODE* = *m∠OWL*

Tell whether each statement is *true* or *false*.

7. Two intersecting lines lie in a plane. **True**

8. A line and a point lie in one and only one plane. **False**

9. If two lines look perpendicular in a diagram, you should mark the diagram with the symbol for a right angle. **False**

10. Draw a counterexample for the following statement: If *R* is between *P* and *Q*, then *R* is the midpoint of $\overline{PQ}$.

grams as counterexamples, as in **Example 3**, is often overlooked.

Example 2
Select the best diagram for the following proof. 2

1.　　　　2.　　　　3.

Given: *AB = BD*; *EB = BC*
Prove: *AD = CE*

Example 3
Sketch a counterexample of the following statement: If a line passes through two points on a circle, then that line divides the circle into two equal halves.

Error Analysis　Most students have difficulty understanding that the diagram in a proof represents the Given and cannot provide any information other than the Given. Stress the connection among the first three parts of a proof.

ANSWERS

Checking for Understanding

1.

Given: *m∠1 = m∠2*
Prove: ℓ ⊥ n

Assignment Guide

Basic: 1–13, 28–35
Average: 2–26 (even), 28–35
Extended: 2–12 (even), 14–35

Written Exercises

3.

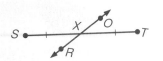

4.

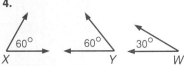

5. Sample:

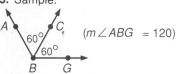 $(m\angle ABG = 120)$

or

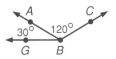

6. Impossible; if segs. bisect each other, then they intersect at their common midpt.; $\overline{AB}$ and $\overline{AQ}$ intersect at their common endpt., A.

7.

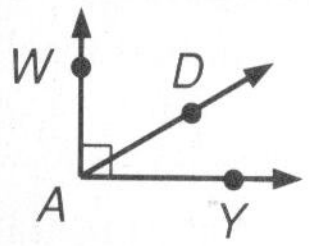

8. Impossible; the endpt. of the $\angle$ bisector must be the vertex of the bisected $\angle$.

14.

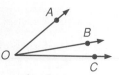

15.

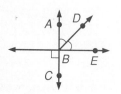

Written Exercises

Set A   **1.** Select the best diagram, given $\overline{JX} \parallel \overline{NY}$, $m\angle N = 90$, and $JK = NM$. **c**

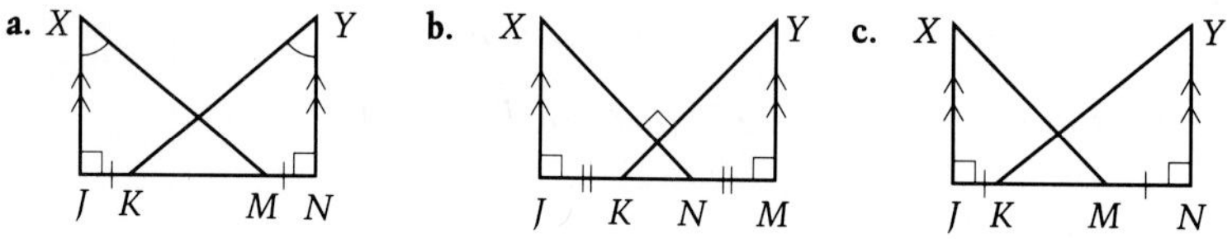

    a.   **b.**   **c.**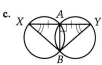

2. Select the best diagram, given $AY = BX$ and $m\angle X = m\angle Y$. **a**

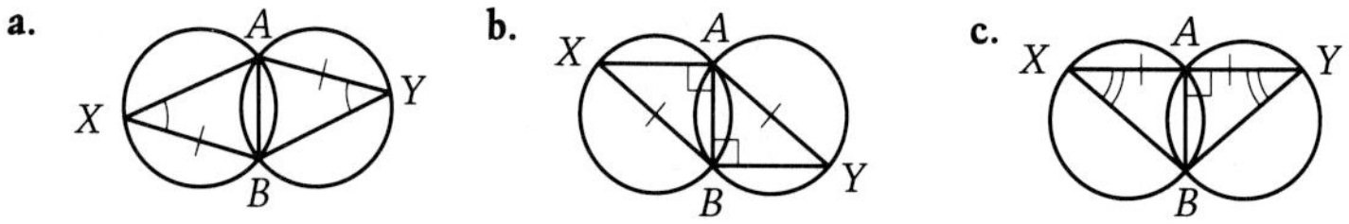

    a.   **b.**   **c.**

Use a straightedge to draw a diagram; then label it. If the diagram cannot be drawn, explain why.

3. Given: $\overleftrightarrow{OR}$ bisects $\overline{ST}$ at point X.

4. Given: $\angle X$ and $\angle Y$ are complements of $\angle W$.

5. Given: $\angle ABG$ and $\angle CBG$ are supplementary.

6. Given: $\overline{AB}$ and $\overline{AQ}$ bisect each other.

7. Given: $\angle WAD$ and $\angle DAY$ are complementary and adjacent.

8. Given: $\overrightarrow{AB}$ bisects $\angle CDA$.

Which theorem in this lesson explains

9. why the skeleton of the kite at the right can be covered by a flat surface? Thm. 3-3

10. why the point of a skier's pole and his uphill ski determine a plane? Thm. 3-2

11. why identifying a row and a column located just one desk in a classroom? Thm. 3-1

Sketch a counterexample for each statement. **12.** Sample:

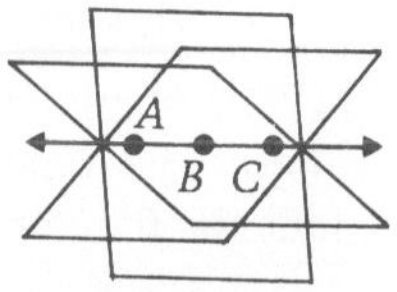

12. Three points are contained in one and only one plane.

13. If $\angle 1$ and $\angle 2$ are supplementary, then one of the angles is acute.

13. Sample:

Set B Draw and label a diagram for each statement.

14.–15. Samples:

14. In a plane, $\overrightarrow{OA}$, $\overrightarrow{OB}$, and $\overrightarrow{OC}$ are such that $m\angle AOC - m\angle BOC = m\angle AOB$.

15. In a plane, $\overleftrightarrow{BE} \perp \overleftrightarrow{AC}$ at B; $\overrightarrow{BD}$ bisects $\angle ABE$.

16. $\angle ROW$ and $\angle WON$ are a linear pair; $\overrightarrow{OC}$ bisects $\angle ROW$; $\overrightarrow{OA}$ bisects $\angle WON$.

17. $\overleftrightarrow{AD}$ bisects $\overline{QR}$ at point M; $\overleftrightarrow{AD} \perp \overline{QR}$

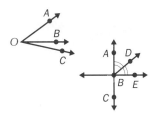

Draw and label diagrams and state the Given and the Prove for each theorem.

18. Theorem 3-2   **19.** Theorem 3-3

Tell whether the statement is *true* or *false*, given $\angle AOC$ is a right angle and $\overrightarrow{OD}$ bisects $\angle EOC$.

20. $\angle 1$ and $\angle 2$ are complementary. **True**

21. $\angle 5$ and $\angle BOE$ are supplementary. **True**

22. $\angle 2$ and $\angle 3$ are complementary. **False**

23. $m\angle 3 = m\angle 4$ **True**

24. $m\angle 3 = m\angle 2$ **False**

25. $\angle 6$ is acute. **True**

26. $\angle 1$ and $\angle 6$ are complementary. **True**

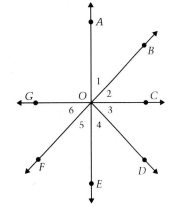

Set C **27.** Draw and label a diagram and state the Given and the Prove needed to prove: Complements of equal angles are equal.

▲Review **28.** List the parts of a two-column proof.

29. In most proofs the first reason is __?__. **Given**

30. Write the definition of *bisector of an angle* using "if and only if."

31. Define *space*.   **32.** Find $m\angle A$. **40**

28. Diagram, Given, Prove, proof: statements and reasons
31. The set of all pts.

30. Ray $\overrightarrow{PB}$ is the bisector of $\angle APC$ if and only if B is in the interior of $\angle APC$ and $m\angle APB = m\angle BPC$.

16.

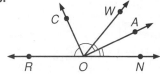

17.

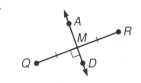

18.

Given: line m and pt. P not on m
Prove: m and P are contained in one, and only one, plane.

19.

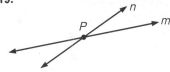

Given: lines m and n intersecting at P Prove: m and n are contained in one, and only one, plane.

27.

Given: $\angle 1$ is complementary to $\angle 2$; $\angle 3$ is complementary to $\angle 4$; $m\angle 2 = m\angle 3$ Prove: $m\angle 1 = m\angle 4$

Thinking Ahead **33.** Draw $\angle ABC$ and $\angle DEF$ so that $m\angle ABC = m\angle DEF = 38$. Draw the rays opposite $\overrightarrow{BA}$ and $\overrightarrow{ED}$ as in the diagram at the right to form $\angle GBC$ and $\angle HEF$. How are $\angle ABC$ and $\angle GBC$ related? How are $\angle DEF$ and $\angle HEF$ related?

34. Measure $\angle GBC$ and $\angle HEF$. How are these angles related? Their measures are 142.

35. Repeat Exercises 33 and 34 with angles that measure 56, 88, and 134. Complete this conjecture: Supplements of $\underline{\ ?\ }$ angles are $\underline{\ ?\ }$. equal, equal

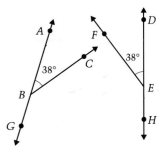

💻 Computer Activities: Drawing and Measuring

1. Draw $\angle ABC$ with measure 90. Choose point D in the interior of $\angle ABC$. Draw $\angle DBE$ with measure 90. Measure $\angle ABD$, $\angle DBC$, and $\angle CBE$. Sample: 30, 60, 90

2. Repeat the activity using different points D in the interior of $\angle ABC$. How are $\angle ABD$ and $\angle CBE$ related to $\angle DBC$?

3. What conjecture is suggested by your angle measures?

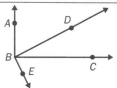

2. Both ∠s are comp. to ∠DBC.

3. If 2∠s are comp. to the same ∠, then they are =.

Algebra Review: Working with Formulas

Example

Use the formula $d = rt$ to find the time t in hours required to drive a distance d of 330 miles when traveling at a speed r of 55 miles per hour.

Solution
$d = rt$
$330 = 55t$
$6 = t$
The drive will take 6 hours.

1. $d = rt$
$d = 70(8\frac{1}{2})$
$d = 595$ mi.

3. $F = \frac{9}{5}C + 32$
$F = \frac{9}{5}(35) + 32$
$F = 63 + 32$
$F = 95$

4. $F = \frac{9}{5}C + 32$
$14 = \frac{9}{5}C + 32$
$-18 = \frac{9}{5}C$
$C = \frac{5}{9}(-18)$
$C = -10$

Use the formula above to solve each problem.

1. How far can a train travel in $8\frac{1}{2}$ hours if its speed is 70 miles per hour?

2. Doris drove 240 kilometers in 4 hours. What was her average speed? $d = rt$ $240 = r(4)$ $r = 60$ mph

The formula $F = \frac{9}{5}C + 32$ relates a temperature in degrees Celsius to the equivalent temperature in degrees Fahrenheit.

3. Give 35°C in degrees Fahrenheit.

4. Give 14°F in degrees Celsius.

Warm-Up Review

1. The sum of the measures of two __?__ angles is 90. Complementary
2. The __?__ Property says "If $a = b$, then $a - x = b - x$. Subtraction
3. From what part of a conditional to be proved do we get the Given? Hypothesis
4. True or false: Parallel lines form a plane. True

3-3 Ordering Steps in a Proof

A carpenter measures an angle on a board and marks it $\angle 1$. Then
he measures and marks $\angle 2$ on another board so that $m\angle 2 = m\angle 1$.
He marks the supplements of $\angle 1$ and $\angle 2$ as $\angle 3$ and $\angle 4$,
respectively. Theorem 3-4 ensures that $m\angle 3 = m\angle 4$.

Theorem 3-4

Supplements of equal angles are equal.

Before you try to write the proof of Theorem 3-4, you should
have a good understanding of the structure and meaning of
two-column proofs. One way to start to develop this
understanding is to consider the order of the steps. In Example 1,
we consider only two steps of a proof.

Example 1

What is Statement 3 of Step 3?

Statements	Reasons
·	·
·	·
·	·
3. __?__	
4. $m\angle ABC = 90$	4. Def. of rt. $\angle$ [3]
·	·
·	·
·	·

Solution

Reason 4 is "If an angle is a right angle, then its measure is
90," and [3] tells you that the hypothesis is affirmed in
Statement 3. Therefore, Statement 3 must be "$\angle ABC$ is a
right angle."

Remember that after a given fact or a true statement p is stated
in a proof, the next statement in an affirming-the-hypothesis
argument is q. Then q becomes a true statement which allows
you to conclude r, and so on. Sometimes you need two
statements to affirm the hypothesis as shown in Example 2.

LESSON 3-3

Resources

- Teaching Aid 8, proof form
- Visual Aid 8, proof form
- Worksheet 3-3
- Extension 3-3
- Computer Activity 3-3
- Computer Worksheet 3-3
- Quiz 3

OBJECTIVE

Order the steps of a proof.

TEACHING NOTES

The **proof subskill** of ordering
steps makes an excellent **group
activity**. Have students discuss
and share their **problem-solving
strategies** for finding a correct
order. **Examples 1** and **2** focus on

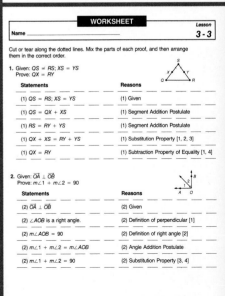

isolated steps from a proof and emphasize the role of the bracketed number in the reason.

Additional Examples

Example 1
What is Statement 3 of Step 3?

Proof:

Statements	Reasons
⋮	
3. ?	
4. $m\angle R + m\angle S = 90$	4. Def. of complementary $\angle$s 1 [/]

$\angle R$ and $\angle S$ are complementary.

Example 2
What are Statements 3 and 4?

Proof:

Statements	Reasons
⋮	
3. ?	
4. ?	
5. $AB + BC =$ $RS + ST$	5. Add. Prop. [3, 4]

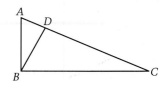

Example 2
What are Statements 4 and 5?

Statements	Reasons
·	·
·	·
·	·
4. ?	
5. ?	
6. $m\angle ABC - m\angle ABD = 90 - 30$	6. Subtraction Prop. [4, 5]
·	·
·	·
·	·

Solution
Since Reason 6 is "If $a = b$ and $c = d$, then $a - c = b - d$," *two* statements are needed to affirm the hypothesis. One of the statements must be "$m\angle ABC = 90$" and the other must be "$m\angle ABD = 30$." Notice that the bracketed numbers refer only to the statements that affirm the hypothesis and not necessarily to the order in which they are used.

In Example 3, we will consider the order of all the steps in a two-column proof.

Example 3
Here is a proof of Theorem 3-4 with the steps in scrambled order. Write the proof with the steps in a correct order.

Restated in "if . . . then" form, Theorem 3-4 is: If two angles are supplements of equal angles, then the two angles are equal.

Given $\angle 1$ and $\angle 3$ are supplementary; $\angle 2$ and $\angle 4$ are supplementary; $m\angle 1 = m\angle 2$

Prove $m\angle 3 = m\angle 4$

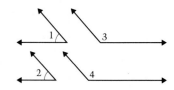

Proof

Statements	Reasons
a. $m\angle 1 + m\angle 3 = m\angle 2 + m\angle 4$	a. Substitution Prop. [3]
b. $\angle 1$ and $\angle 3$ are supp.; $\angle 2$ and $\angle 4$ are supp.	b. Given
c. $m\angle 1 = m\angle 2$	c. Given
d. $m\angle 3 = m\angle 4$	d. Subtraction Prop. [2, 4]
e. $m\angle 1 + m\angle 3 = 180;$ $m\angle 2 + m\angle 4 = 180$	e. Def. of supp. $\angle$s. [1]

Solution

Step 1 is either *b* or *c*. Since *e* shows the reason as the definition of supplementary angles [1], Step 1 must be *b*. Step 5 is the Prove *d*. Since Step 3 precedes *a*, *a* must be Step 4. Notice that Reason *d* has Statements 2 and 4 affirming the hypothesis. Step 2 must be *c*, leaving *e* as Step 3. This reordering results in the following proof of Theorem 3-4.

Proof

Statements	Reasons
1. $\angle 1$ and $\angle 3$ are supp.; $\angle 2$ and $\angle 4$ are supp.	1. Given
2. $m\angle 1 = m\angle 2$	2. Given
3. $m\angle 1 + m\angle 3 = 180$; $m\angle 2 + m\angle 4 = 180$	3. Def. of supp. $\angle$s. [1]
4. $m\angle 1 + m\angle 3 = m\angle 2 + m\angle 4$	4. Substitution Prop. [3]
5. $m\angle 3 = m\angle 4$	5. Subtraction Prop. [2, 4]

Example 4

Place the steps of the scrambled proof in a correct order.

Given B is between A and C; $BC = XB$

Prove $AB = AC - XB$

Proof

Statements	Reasons
a. $AB = AC - XB$	a. Subtraction Prop. [2, 3]
b. $AB + BC = AC$	b. Segment Add. Post. [1]
c. B is between A and C.	c. Given
d. $BC = XB$	d. Given

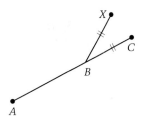

Solution

Step 4 is *a*, the Prove. Step 1 is *c* because Statement *c* affirms the hypothesis for the Segment Addition Postulate in Reason *b*. Steps 2 and 3 are *b* and *d*, or *d* and *b* (See Example 2).

The next theorem follows directly from Theorem 3-4. Its proof is left to Exercise 10.

Theorem 3-5

Supplements of the same angle are equal.

$AB = RS$ and $BC = ST$

The strategy for dealing with one or two isolated steps is next used repeatedly to find a correct order for a larger set of steps, as **Examples 3** and **4** show. Various **problem-solving strategies** may be useful here. Students working in small groups could also try to explain why various orders are not correct—a guess-and-check strategy.

Example 3

Place the steps of this scrambled proof in correct order.

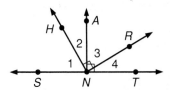

Given: $\overrightarrow{NA} \perp \overleftrightarrow{SI}$; $\overrightarrow{NH} \perp \overrightarrow{NR}$

Prove: $\angle 1 = \angle 3$

Proof:

Statements

a. $m\angle SNA = 90$; $m\angle HNR = 90$
b. $m\angle 2 = m\angle 2$
c. $\overrightarrow{NA} \perp \overleftrightarrow{SI}$; $\overrightarrow{NH} \perp \overrightarrow{NR}$
d. $\angle SNA$ is a rt. $\angle$; $\angle HNR$ is a rt. $\angle$.
e. $m\angle 1 = m\angle 3$
f. $m\angle 1 = 90 - m\angle 2$; $m\angle 3 = 90 - m\angle 2$
g. $m\angle 1 + m\angle 2 = 90$; $m\angle 3 + m\angle 2 = 90$

Reasons

a. Def. of a rt. $\angle$ [2]
b. Reflexive Prop.
c. Given
d. Def. of $\perp$ lines [1]
e. Substitution [6]
f. Subtraction Prop. [4, 5]
g. Substitution Prop. [3]

c, d, a, g, b, f, e

Assignment Guide

Basic: 1–10, 17–25
Average: 1–13, 17–25
Extended: 2–12 (even), 14–25

Error Analysis   This lesson involves some complex problem-solving, and students may become confused. If this occurs, ask students to consider smaller sub-problems.

EXERCISE NOTES

The exercises are organized in increasing order of problem-solving complexity. All use **proof sub-skills**.
   Exercises 1–9   deal with supplying missing statements.
   Exercises 10–11   ask students to order the steps in a complete proof when the statements and reasons are in matching pairs.
   Exercise 12   has the statements and reasons scrambled separately.
   Exercise 13   asks students to supply keying of reasons.
   Exercise 14   calls for a two-column proof.
   Exercise 15   introduces extraneous steps.

ANSWERS

Checking for Understanding

7.

Given: B is between A and C; $BC = XB$ Prove: $AB = AC - XB$; 1. B is between A and C. (Given) 2. $AB + BC = AC$ (Seg. Add. Post. [1]) 3. $BC = XB$ (Given) 4. $AB = AC - XB$ (Subtraction Prop. [2, 3])

Two similar theorems exist for complementary angles.

Theorem 3-6
Complements of equal angles are equal.

Theorem 3-7
Complements of the same angle are equal.

Theorems 3-6 and 3-7 are to be proved in Exercises 13 and 14.

Sometimes a conditional statement has two parts in its conclusion. When this occurs, the last statement of the proof will usually be only one part of the conclusion because the other part has been proved earlier in the proof.

Checking for Understanding

Is each statement about two-column proofs *true* or *false*? If the answer is false, explain why.

1. The given information is from the hypothesis of the conditional to be proved. True

2. No step except the first one can have Given as the reason.

3. There is only one correct way to prove a conditional statement.

4. The information in the Prove is from the conclusion of the conditional statement to be proved. True

5. The statement in the last step is all or some part of the Prove. True

6. The numbers in brackets in the Reasons column are the numbers of previous statements in the proof. True

7. Write the complete proof of the conditional in Example 4.

2. False; The given information may be used anywhere in the proof. 3. False; There is often more than one way to prove a conditional statement.

Written Exercises

Set A   Each of the following is Step 5 in a proof. What is Statement 4 in each proof?

1. 5. $AC = CB$ 5. Def. of midpt. [4]

2. 5. $\angle 5$ is supp. to $\angle 6$.   5. Supp. Post. [4]

3. 5. $m\angle 1 + m\angle 2 = 180$ 5. Def. of supp. $\angle$s [4]

4. 5. $\angle 1$ and $\angle 2$ are comp.   5. Def. of comp. $\angle$s [4]

5. 5. $m\angle ABD = m\angle CBD$ 5. Def. of $\angle$ bisector [4]

1. C is the midpt. of $\overline{AB}$.
2. $\angle 5$ and $\angle 6$ form a lin. pr.
3. $\angle 1$ and $\angle 2$ are supp.
4. $m\angle 1 + m\angle 2 = 90$
5. $\overrightarrow{BD}$ bisects $\angle ABC$.

A statement in a proof is "$m\angle A = m\angle B$." Which reasons given below might correspond to this statement? Explain each answer.

6. Given   **7.** Comp. of = $\angle$s are =.

8. Supp. of = $\angle$s are =. **9.** Supplement Postulate

10. Write this proof of Theorem 3-5 with the steps in a correct order.
Given: $\angle 1$ and $\angle 2$ are supp.; $\angle 2$ and $\angle 3$ are supp.
Prove: $m\angle 1 = m\angle 3$ **c, a, b**

Statements	Reasons
a. $m\angle 2 = m\angle 2$	a. Reflexive Prop.
b. $m\angle 1 = m\angle 3$	b. Supp. of = $\angle$s are =. [1, 2]
c. $\angle 1$ and $\angle 2$ are supp.;	c. Given
$\angle 2$ and $\angle 3$ are supp.	

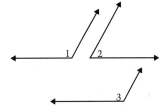

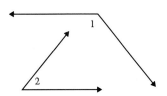

Set B   **11.** Write this proof with steps in a correct order.
Given: $\angle 1$ and $\angle 2$ form a lin. pr.; $\angle 2$ and $\angle 3$ form a lin. pr.
Prove: $m\angle 1 = m\angle 3$ **e, a, b, d, c**

Statements	Reasons
a. $\angle 1$ is supp. to $\angle 2$.	a. Supp. Post. [1]
b. $\angle 2$ and $\angle 3$ form a lin. pr.	b. Given
c. $m\angle 1 = m\angle 3$	c. Supp. of same $\angle$ are =. [2, 4]
d. $\angle 3$ is supp. to $\angle 2$.	d. Supp. Post. [3]
e. $\angle 1$ and $\angle 2$ form a lin. pr.	e. Given

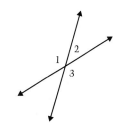

For Exercises 12–13, *both* statements and reasons are scrambled. Write the proof with steps in a correct order.

12. Given: $\angle 1$ is obtuse; $\angle 1$ and $\angle 2$ are supplementary.
Prove: $\angle 2$ is acute.

Statements	Reasons
a. $\angle 2$ is acute.	m. Given
b. $\angle 1$ is supp. to $\angle 2$.	n. Multiplication Prop. [7, 8]
c. $m\angle 1 > 90$	o. Def. of acute $\angle$ [11]
d. $m\angle 2 < 90$	p. Addition Prop. [9, 10]
e. $\angle 1$ is obtuse.	q. Reflexive Prop.
f. $m\angle 1 + m\angle 2 = 180$	r. Def. of supp. $\angle$s [3]
g. $m\angle 1 = 180 - m\angle 2$	s. Given
h. $-180 + m\angle 2 < -90$	t. Substitution Prop. [2, 6]
i. $m\angle 2 = m\angle 2$	u. Def. of obtuse $\angle$ [1]
j. $180 - m\angle 2 > 90$	v. Subtraction Prop. [4, 5]
k. $180 = 180$	w. Reflexive Prop.
l. $-1 = -1$	x. Reflexive Prop.

Written Exercises

6. Yes; any information may be given.
7. Yes; the conclusion from this reason is that 2 $\angle$s are =.
8. Yes; the conclusion from this reason is that 2 $\angle$s are =.
9. No; the conclusion from this reason is that 2 $\angle$s are supp.

12. Statements: e, c, b, f, i, g, j, l, h, m, d, a Reasons: m or s, u, m or s, r, q or w or x, v, t, q, or w or x, n, q or w or x, p, o

14.

Given: ∠1 and ∠2 are comp; ∠2 and ∠3 are comp. Prove: $m∠1 = m∠3$ 1. ∠1 and ∠2 are comp. (Given) 2. ∠2 and ∠3 are comp. (Given) 3. $m∠2 = m∠2$ (Reflexive Prop.) 4. $m∠1 = m∠3$ (If 2 ∠s are comp. to = ∠s, then they are =. [1, 2, 3])

16. It would be valid to begin with the given information that ∠ABC and ∠ABD form a lin. pr.; then the sequence of statements would be h, b, f, g, e, d, i.

Review

17. Sample:

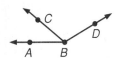

18. Sample:

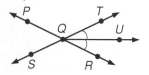

Thinking Ahead

24. Sample

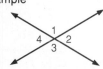

$m∠1 = 120$
$m∠2 = 60$
$m∠3 = 120$
$m∠4 = 60$

---

13. As you write the proof of Theorem 3-6 with steps in a correct order, insert the bracketed reference numbers.

Given: ∠1 and ∠3 are complementary; ∠2 and ∠4 are complementary; $m∠1 = m∠2$
Prove: $m∠3 = m∠4$

Statements	Reasons
a. ∠1 and ∠3 are comp.; ∠2 and ∠4 are comp.	f. Def. of comp. ∠s
	g. Substitution Prop.
b. $m∠1 + m∠3 = m∠2 + m∠4$	h. Subtraction Prop.
c. $m∠3 = m∠4$	i. Given
d. $m∠1 + m∠3 = 90$; $m∠2 + m∠4 = 90$	j. Given
e. $m∠1 = m∠2$	

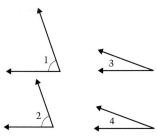

13. Statements: a, d, b, e, c; reasons: i or j, f[1], g [2], i or j, h [3, 4]

Set C   **14.** Write a two-column proof of Theorem 3-7. Use the proof of Theorem 3-5 in Exercise 10 as a model.

15. Both the statements and reasons are scrambled, and two of the statements and reasons are *not* needed in the proof. Write the proof with steps in a correct order, and insert bracketed statement numbers.

Given: ∠ABC is a right angle; ∠ABC and ∠ABD form a linear pair.
Prove: ∠ABD is a right angle.

Statements	Reasons
a. $m∠ABC = m∠ABC$	j. Subtraction Prop.
b. ∠ABC and ∠ABD are supp.	k. Def. of rt. ∠
c. $m∠ABC = m∠ABD$	l. Def. of rt. ∠
d. $m∠ABD = 90$	m. Given
e. $m∠ABC = 90$	n. Supp. Post.
f. $m∠ABC + m∠ABD = 180$	o. Reflexive Prop.
g. ∠ABC is a rt. ∠.	p. Given
h. ∠ABC and ∠ABD form a lin. pr.	q. Def. of Supp. ∠s
i. ∠ABD is a rt. ∠.	r. Rt. ∠s are =.

15. Statements; g, e, h, b, f, d, i; reasons: m or p, l [1], m or p, n [3], q [4], j [2, 5], k or l [6]

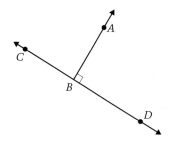

16. Is there another order for some of the statements and reasons in Exercise 15 that also gives a valid proof? Explain your answer.

▲ Review Draw and label a diagram for each statement.

17. ∠*ABC* and ∠*CBD* are adjacent.

18. ∠*PQS* and ∠*TQR* are vertical angles; $\overrightarrow{QU}$ bisects ∠*TQR*.

19. What may be used as reasons in a proof?

20. What is inductive reasoning?

21. Give an "if . . . then" statement for the Venn diagram at the right. **If one is a 15-year-old, then one is a teenager. 22.** $m\angle 1 = m\angle 2$

≡ Thinking ▽ Ahead

22. What seems to be true about $m\angle 1$ and $m\angle 2$?

23. Find the measures of ∠1 and ∠2. **20; 20**

24. Draw two intersecting lines and measure all of the angles.

25. Complete this conjecture: Vertical angles are __?__. **equal**

19. Definitions; postulates, properties, of real numbers, theorems, and Given

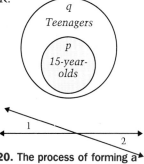

20. The process of forming a conclusion based upon examination of several specific cases

---

Progress Check

Lesson 3-1, page 95

1. Supply the reasons and the bracketed reference numbers.

Given: *O* is the midpoint of $\overline{NW}$; *OM* = *OW*

Prove: *OM* = *ON*

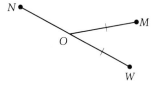

Statements	Reasons
1. *O* is the midpoint of $\overline{NW}$.	1. __?__ **Given**
2. *OM* = *OW*	2. __?__ **Given**
3. *OW* = *ON*	3. __?__ [__?__] **Def of midpt.** [1]
4. *OM* = *ON*	4. __?__ [__?__]
	4. Transitive prop. [2, 3]

Lesson 3-2, page 101

Sketch a diagram and state the Given and the Prove needed in a proof for each conditional statement.

2. If a ray bisects a right angle, then two 45° angles are formed.

3. If two segments have equal lengths, then two segments each with twice this length are also equal.

4. If two complementary angles are adjacent, then the sides that are not common form a right angle.

5. Mark the diagram for a proof using this Given and Prove.

Given: ∠*A* and ∠*B* are right angles; $\overline{BC} \parallel \overline{EF}$ and $\overline{GH} \parallel \overline{AD}$; *BE* = *EG* = *GA*

Prove: *CF* = *FH* = *HD* and $\overline{EF} \parallel \overline{GH}$

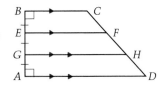

ANSWERS

Algebra Review

Solution check for Example: 1) 9 + 3(3) = 18; 9 + 9 = 18; 18 = 18; 2) 3(9) − 5(3) = 12; 27 − 15 = 12; 12 = 12

Lesson 3-3, page 107

6. Write this proof with steps in a correct order. d, a, c, b

Given: D is in the interior of $\angle ABC$.
Prove: $m\angle 1 = m\angle ABC - m\angle 2$

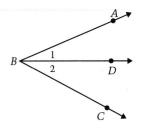

Statements	Reasons
a. $m\angle 1 + m\angle 2 = m\angle ABC$	a. Angle Add. Post. [1]
b. $m\angle 1 = m\angle ABC - m\angle 2$	b. Subtraction Prop. [2, 3]
c. $m\angle 2 = m\angle 2$	c. Reflexive Prop.
d. D is in the interior of $\angle ABC$.	d. Given

Algebra Review: Solving Systems of Linear Equations

Example
Solve for x and y: $x + 3y = 18$ (1)
$\qquad\qquad\qquad 3x - 5y = 12$ (2)

Solution

Addition Method
Multiply equation (1) by −3.
Add the equations.
$$-3x - 9y = -54$$
$$3x - 5y = 12$$
$$-14y = -42$$
$$y = 3$$
Then solve for x.
$$x + 3(3) = 18$$
$$x = 9$$

Substitution Method
Solve equation (1) for x.
Substitute into equation (2).
$$x + 3y = 18$$
$$x = 18 - 3y$$
$$3(18 - 3y) - 5y = 12$$
$$54 - 9y - 5y = 12$$
$$-14y = -42$$
$$y = 3$$
Then solve for x.
$$x + 3(3) = 18$$
$$x = 9$$

The solution (9, 3) checks in both equations.

1. $m = 2; n = 2$
2. $x = \frac{5}{2}; y = \frac{-3}{2}$
3. $x = 4; y = 3$
4. $x = 3; y = 9$
5. $a = \frac{19}{5}; b = \frac{24}{5}$
6. $x = 7; y = -1$
7. $r = -3; s = 2$
8. $x = -2; y = -2$

Solve and check.

1. $m + n = 4$
$\quad\ 5m - 3n = 4$

2. $5x + 7y = 2$
$\quad\ x = y + 4$

3. $5x + 5y = 35$
$\quad\ 3x + 2y = 18$

4. $y = 3x$
$\quad\ x + 2y = 21$

5. $2a + 3b = 22$
$\quad\ a = b - 1$

6. $x + y = 6$
$\quad\ x - y = 8$

7. $3r + 4s = -1$
$\quad\ 5r - 3s = -21$

8. $7x - 3y + 8 = 0$
$\quad\ 4x + 6y + 20 = 0$

3-4 Planning Proofs

We began our study of geometry with three undefined terms—
point, *line*, and *plane*. Then these undefined terms were
used to write *definitions* of other geometric terms, such as
segment and ray. *Postulates* stated certain relationships among
these geometric terms. Using these definitions, postulates, and
properties of real numbers, we proved a few *theorems*.

The definitions, postulates, properties of real numbers, and
theorems make up our *inventory of geometric facts*. Only these
items from our inventory may be used as reasons in a proof.

You can think of this inventory as a file of index cards. The cards
contain all of the definitions, postulates, properties of real
numbers, and theorems that you have learned in previous lessons.
The inventory will become larger as you add a card for each new
definition, postulate, or theorem.

Linear Pair
A linear pair of angles is a pair of
adjacent angles whose noncommo
sides are opposite rays.

Supplement Postulate
The angles in a linear pair
are supplementary.

Theorem 3-5
Supplements of the same angle
are equal.

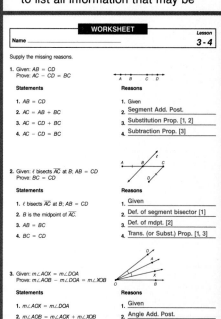

directly assumed. Collinearity, adjacent angles and opposite rays This should lead into the plan for the proof. Point out that the written plan for a proof is essentially a proof in paragraph form.

Have students work on some plans for proofs (see Additional Example) as a **group activity**. They will profit from seeing the **problem-solving strategies** of others.

Additional Example

Write plans of proofs for the following:
(a) Given: $\overrightarrow{CD}$ bisects right $\angle ACB$.
Prove: $m\angle ACD = 45$

The following discussion shows how you might use the inventory to prove the next theorem.

Theorem 3-8

Vertical angles are equal.

In order to draw a diagram and to write the Given and the Prove, restate the theorem in "if . . . then" form: If two angles are vertical angles, then they are equal.

Given $\angle 1$ and $\angle 2$ are vertical angles.

Prove $m\angle 1 = m\angle 2$

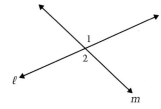

Keep in mind what is to be proved while you study the diagram and the Given. Since vertical angles are given, look through your inventory for statements about vertical angles. So far, there is only one card in the inventory—the definition of vertical angles. It tells you that vertical angles are formed by two pairs of opposite rays.

Now check the inventory for items related to opposite rays. The definition of a linear pair of angles mentions opposite rays. In the diagram, $\angle 1$ and an adjacent angle, call it $\angle 3$, form a linear pair, and $\angle 2$ and $\angle 3$ also form a linear pair.

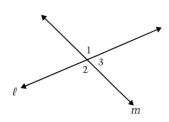

What else in the inventory mentions a linear pair of angles? The Supplement Postulate tells you that the angles in a linear pair are supplementary. So $\angle 1$ and $\angle 3$ are supplementary, and $\angle 2$ and $\angle 3$ are also supplementary.

Now you have two angles, $\angle 1$ and $\angle 2$, each supplementary to $\angle 3$. Look through your inventory to find statements that mention supplementary angles in the hypothesis. Theorem 3-5 says that two angles supplementary to the same angle are equal. Therefore, it follows that $m\angle 1 = m\angle 2$.

This thinking is summarized below in a *Plan for Proof*.

Plan for Proof $\angle 1$ and $\angle 3$ are a linear pair; so are $\angle 2$ and $\angle 3$. Use the Supplement Postulate and Theorem 3-5 to show that $m\angle 1 = m\angle 2$.

We then write the proof using the Given and the Prove, with the diagram and Plan for Proof as guides.

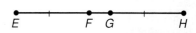

Theorem 3-8

Vertical angles are equal.

Restatement: If two angles are vertical angles, then they are equal.

Given $\angle 1$ and $\angle 2$ are vertical angles.

Prove $m\angle 1 = m\angle 2$

Plan for $\angle 1$ and $\angle 3$ are a linear pair; so are $\angle 2$ and $\angle 3$. Use
Proof   the Supplement Postulate and Theorem 3-5 to show
that $m\angle 1 = m\angle 2$.

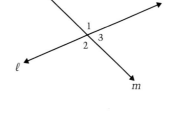

Proof

Statements	Reasons
1. $\angle 1$ and $\angle 2$ are vert. $\angle$s.	1. Given
2. $\angle 1$ and $\angle 3$ form a lin. pr.;	2. Def. of lin. pr.
$\angle 2$ and $\angle 3$ form a lin. pr.	
3. $\angle 1$ and $\angle 3$ are supp.;	3. Supp. Post. [2]
$\angle 2$ and $\angle 3$ are supp.	
4. $m\angle 1 = m\angle 2$	4. Supp. of the same $\angle$ are =.

Now you may add Theorem 3-8 and Theorem 3-9, which you
are asked to prove in Exercise 31, to your inventory.

Theorem 3-9

*If one angle of a linear pair is a right angle, then the other
angle is also a right angle.*

Checking for Understanding

1. List four types of statements in the inventory of
geometric facts.

Make a list of all the items in the inventory that have each of
the following facts in the conclusion.

2. Two angles are equal.   **3.** Two segments are equal.

4. Two angles are supplementary.   **5.** An angle is a right angle.

Make a list of all the items in the inventory that mention

6. perpendicular lines.   **7.** a linear pair of angles.

8. What is a plan for proof?

1. Defs., posts. props. of real
numbers, thms.
2. Thms. 3-4, 3-5, 3-6, 3-7,
3-8
3. Def. of midpt. of a seg.
4. Supplement Post.
5. Def. $\perp$ lines; Thm 3-9
6. Def. of $\perp$ lines
7. Def. of lin. pr. of $\angle$s;
Supplement Post.; Thm. 3-9
8. A summary of the chain of
reasoning to be used in a
proof; a guide for writing a
proof

If $\overrightarrow{CD}$ is an angle bisector,
then by definition $m\angle ACD =$
$m\angle DCB$. Since $\angle ACB$ is a right
$\angle$, $m\angle ACB = 90$ and both $m\angle$
ACD and $m\angle ACB$ must equal
45.

(b) Given: $EF = GH$
Prove: $EG = FH$

From the Reflexive Property
$FG = FG$. From the Addition
Property $EF + FG = GH + FG$.
From the Segment Addition
Postulate $EF + FG = EG$ and
$FG + GH = FH$, so by sub-
stitution $EG = FH$.

(c) Given: $\angle 1$ and $\angle 2$ are adjacent
and complementary.
Prove: $m\angle JKL = 90$

Because $\angle 1$ and $\angle 2$ are complementary, $m\angle 1 + m\angle 2 =$
90. From the $\angle$ Add. Post.
$m\angle 1 + m\angle 2 = m\angle JKL$, so by
substitution $m\angle JKL = 90$.

Error Analysis As proofs become more complex and the inventory of geometric facts grows,
students tend to create their own
reasons in a proof. Emphasize
that the only acceptable entries
for reasons (other than the Given)
are taken from the inventory.
   Have students keep an actual
written inventory on index cards
or in a special notebook to be
maintained throughout the course.

Assignment Guide

Basic: 1–22, 33–40
Average: 2–20 (even), 21–30, 33–40
Extended: 2–22 (even), 23–40

EXERCISE NOTES

Exercises 1–14 and **27–29** provide direct application of Theorem 3–8.

Exercises 15–20 are accomplished using the **proof subskill** writing conclusions from given statements.

Exercises 21–22 combine the two **proof subskills** of writing a Plan for Proof and ordering steps in a proof.

Exercises 23–25 and **30** call for writing a Plan for Proof, a **proof subskill**.

Exercises 27–29 may require a review of algebraic skills.

Exercises 31–32 require the writing of two-column proofs.

ANSWERS

Written Exercises

15–20. Accept any answers that students can justify. Samples are given.
15. $m\angle FOD = 90$;
$m\angle DOP = m\angle POF$;
$m\angle DOP = 45$;
$m\angle POF = 45$
16. $m\angle DOP + m\angle FOP = 90$;
$m\angle DOP + m\angle FOP = m\angle DOF$;
$m\angle DOF = 90$;
$\angle DOF$ is a rt. $\angle$
17. $m\angle DOF > 90$;
$m\angle DOP = m\angle POF$;
$m\angle DOP + m\angle POF = m\angle DOF$;
$m\angle DOP + m\angle POF > 90$
18. O is the midpt. of $\overline{WY}$;
O is the midpt. of $\overline{XZ}$;
$WO = OY$;
$XO = OZ$

Written Exercises

Set A   If $m\angle 3 = 110$, find

1. $m\angle 1$. **70**   2. $m\angle 2$. **70**   3. $m\angle 4$. **70**

If $m\angle 1 + m\angle 2 = 150$, find

4. $m\angle 1$. **75**   5. $m\angle 3$. **105**   6. $m\angle 4$. **105**

7. Suppose $\angle 1$ and $\angle 2$ are supplementary angles. What can you conclude about k and ℓ?
   $k \perp \ell$

Suppose $m\angle 1$ is increased by 10. What effect does this have on **8. Increased by 10**   **9. Decreased by 10**

8. $m\angle 2$?   9. $m\angle 3$?   10. $m\angle 4$?

10. Decreased by 10

Find the measure of each labeled angle.

11.
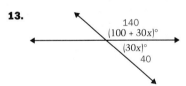
78
$(2x)°$
$(x + 39)°$
78

12.
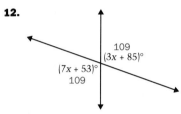
109
$(3x + 85)°$
$(7x + 53)°$
109

13.
140
$(100 + 30x)°$
$(30x)°$
40

14.
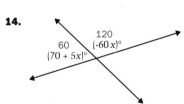
120
$(-60x)°$
60
$(70 + 5x)°$

Make a list of at least four conclusions that follow from each Given and its diagram.

15. Given: $\angle FOD$ is a right angle; $\overrightarrow{OP}$ bisects $\angle DOF$.

16. Given: $\angle DOP$ is complementary to $\angle FOP$.

17. Given: $\angle DOF$ is an obtuse angle; $\overrightarrow{OP}$ bisects $\angle DOF$.

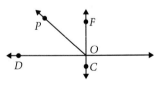

18. Given: $\overline{WY}$ and $\overline{XZ}$ bisect each other.

19. Given: $\overline{WY} \perp \overline{XZ}$

20. Given: $\overrightarrow{ZX}$ bisects $\angle WZY$.

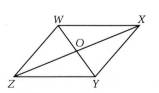

The steps for each Plan for Proof are scrambled.
Arrange the steps in a correct order. **a, c, b**

21. Given: Y is between X and Z; Z is between X and W.
Prove: $XY + YZ + ZW = XW$

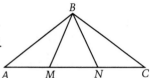

a. Since Y is between X and Z, use the Segment Addition Postulate to get $XY + YZ = XZ$.

b. Then substitute to show $XY + YZ + ZW = XW$.

c. Since Z is between X and W, use the Segment Addition Postulate to get $XZ + ZW = XW$.

22. Given: $AM = MN$; $MN = NC$
Prove: $AC = 3MN$ **c, a, b, d**

a. Substitute for AN to show $AC = AM + MN + NC$.

b. Substitute again using the given information.

c. Use the Segment Addition Postulate to show $AC = AN + NC$ and $AN = AM + MN$.

d. Add to show $AC = 3MN$.

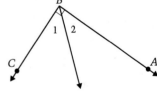

Set B   Write a Plan for Proof.

23. Given: $\angle ABC$ is a right angle.
Prove: $\angle 1$ and $\angle 2$ are complementary.

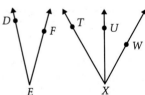

24. Given: $m\angle DEF = m\angle TXU$; $\overrightarrow{XU}$ bisects $\angle TXW$.
Prove: $m\angle DEF = m\angle UXW$

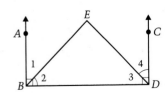

25. Given: $\angle ABD$ and $\angle CDB$ are right angles;
$m\angle 2 = m\angle 4$
Prove: $m\angle 1 = m\angle 3$

19. $\angle WOX$ is a rt. $\angle$;
$m\angle WOX = 90$;
$m\angle ZOY = m\angle WOX$;
$m\angle ZOY = 90$
20. $m\angle WZX = m\angle XZY$;
$m\angle WZX + m\angle XZY = m\angle WZY$;
$2(m\angle WZX) = m\angle WZY$;
$m\angle WZX = \frac{1}{2}(m\angle WZY)$
23–26. Answers will vary. Samples are given.
23. Use the def. of a rt. $\angle$ to show that $m\angle ABC = 90$. Then use the $\angle$ Add. Post. to show that $m\angle 1 + m\angle 2 = m\angle ABC$. Use the Transitive Prop. to show that $m\angle 1 + m\angle 2 = 90$ and the def. of complementary $\angle$s to show that $\angle 1$ is complementary to $\angle 2$.
24. Use the def. of an $\angle$ bisector to show that $m\angle TXU = m\angle UXW$. Then use the Transitive Prop. to show that $m\angle DEF = m\angle UXW$.
25. Use the reasoning from #23 above to show that $\angle 1$ is complementary to $\angle 2$ and $\angle 3$ is complementary to $\angle 4$. Then use Thm. 3–6 to show that $m\angle 1 = m\angle 3$.

26. Use the Add. Prop. to show that $PQ + QR > RS + QR$. Then use the Seg. Add. Post. to show that $PQ + QR = PR$ and $RS + QR = QS$. Finally, use the Substitution Prop. to show that $PR > QS$.

27. $x = 94$; $y = 8$; $m\angle 1 = 118$; $m\angle 2 = 62$; $m\angle 3 = 118$

28. $x = 29$; $y = 170$; $m\angle 1 = 54$; $m\angle 2 = 126$; $m\angle 3 = 54$

29. $x = 5$; $y = -6$; $m\angle 1 = 47$; $m\angle 2 = 133$; $m\angle 3 = 47$

30.

Given: $\angle 1$ is a rt. $\angle$. Prove: $\angle 2$ is a rt. $\angle$. Plan for Proof: $\angle 1$ is a rt. $\angle$. From the def. of a rt. $\angle$, $m\angle 1 = 90$. $\angle 1$ and $\angle 2$ form a linear pair so $\angle 1$ and $\angle 2$ are supplementary. From the def. of supplementary $\angle$s, $m\angle 1 + m\angle 2 = 180$. Use the Substitution Prop. to show that $90 + m\angle 2 = 180$ and the Subtraction Prop. to show that $m\angle 2 = 180 - 90$, or $m\angle 2 = 90$. From the def. of a rt. $\angle$, $\angle 2$ is a rt. $\angle$.

FOLLOW-UP

More Practice

• Worksheet 3–4

Extension

Although the instruction has not yet focused on putting all of the subskills together to write a complete proof, students should now have all the tools necessary to do so. Challenge students to write complete two-column proofs for **Exercises 21** and **22**. Discuss the connection between the plan and the parts of the two-column proof.
• Extension 3–4

---

26. Given: $PQ > RS$
Prove: $PR > QS$

Given these angle measures, solve for x and y. Then find $m\angle 1$, $m\angle 2$, and $m\angle 3$.

27. $m\angle 1 = x + 3y$; $m\angle 2 = x - 4y$; $m\angle 3 = y + 110$

28. $m\angle 1 = x + 25$; $m\angle 2 = y - 44$; $m\angle 3 = y - 4x$

29. $m\angle 1 = x - 7y$; $m\angle 2 = 5x - 3y + 90$; $m\angle 3 = 8x + 7$

30. Write a Plan for Proof for Theorem 3-9.

Set C **31.** Write a two-column proof for Theorem 3-9.

32. Prove that the bisectors of a linear pair of angles are perpendicular.

▲ **Review** A statement in a proof is "$m\angle ABC = 90$." Tell if the reasons below might correspond to this step.

33. Subtraction Prop. **Yes** **34.** Def. of comp. $\angle$s **No**

35. List three facts that can be assumed from the diagram at the right.

36. Given A on $\overline{MN}$, $AM = AN$, and $m\angle PAN = 90$, $\overrightarrow{PA}$ is the ? of $\overline{MN}$. **⊥ bisector**

37. If two planes intersect, they intersect in a ?. **line**

Thinking Ahead **38.** Draw two intersecting lines and label one linear pair of angles $\angle 1$ and $\angle 2$. Measure $\angle 1$ and $\angle 2$. Is $\angle 1$ obtuse or acute? What about $\angle 2$?

39. Repeat Exercise 38 with two other pairs of intersecting lines. Complete this conjecture: If one angle of a linear pair is acute, then the other is ?. **obtuse**

40. Consider this statement: In every linear pair of angles, one angle must be acute. Is the statement *true* or *false*? If it is true, explain why. If it is false, sketch a counterexample. **False**

35. $\angle UVT$ and $\angle SVW$ are vert. $\angle$s; T, V, and S are collinear; V is between U and W.

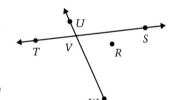

Sample:
$m\angle 1 = 35 \rightarrow \angle 1$ is acute;
$m\angle 2 = 145 \rightarrow \angle 2$ is obtuse.

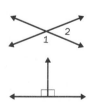

1. State a conclusion that follows from the hypothesis "∠A and ∠B are complementary angles." $m∠A + m∠B = 90$
2. State a hypothesis that allows you to conclude that ∠XYZ is a right angle. $\overleftrightarrow{XY} ⊥ \overleftrightarrow{YZ}$
3. True or false: Opposite rays form a linear pair. False
4. True or false: The rays of a right angle are perpendicular. True

3-5 Strategies for Writing Proofs

There is no set of rules that will tell you how to develop a plan and write a proof of every statement. However, there are some strategies that might help. One strategy is called **working forward from the Given**.

To work forward from the Given:
a. Search the inventory of geometric facts to *find conclusions* that follow from each fact in the Given. Then state each conclusion in terms of the diagram.

b. Next search the inventory to find all conclusions that follow from each of the conclusions that you found in **a**. (A conclusion in **a** becomes a new hypothesis from which another conclusion can be drawn.)

Example 1
What are some conclusions you can make, given a linear pair?

Solution
Draw a diagram and state the Given in terms of the diagram.
Given: ∠ABC and ∠CBD form a linear pair.

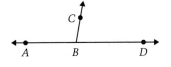

Working forward from the Given:
a. Search the inventory for "linear pair." Look for conclusions that follow when you have a linear pair in the "if" part of a statement in the inventory. You might begin by using the definition of a linear pair. It allows you to conclude that $\overrightarrow{BA}$ and $\overrightarrow{BD}$ are opposite rays. Continue to look for "linear pair" in the inventory. Linear pair is also mentioned in the Supplement Postulate. Therefore, you can also conclude that ∠ABC and ∠CBD are supplementary.

b. In **a**, the conclusion that "$\overrightarrow{BA}$ and $\overrightarrow{BD}$ are opposite rays" is a fact from which another conclusion can be drawn. The definition of opposite rays allows you to conclude that A, B, and D are collinear and B is between A and D. The conclusion that "∠ABC and ∠CBD are supplementary" is a fact from which another conclusion can be drawn. By the definition of supplementary angles, you know that $m∠ABC + m∠CBD = 180$.

You could continue the working-forward process by searching the inventory using "$m∠ABC + m∠CBD = 180$" as a new hypothesis.

LESSON 3–5

Resources

Teaching Aid 8, proof form
Visual Aid 8, proof form
Worksheet 3–5
Extension 3–5
Computer Activity 3–5
Computer Worksheet 3–5

OBJECTIVE

Use a strategy to write a proof.

TEACHING NOTES

Write the diagram, Given and Prove for Theorem 3–10 on the board, and ask for some conclusions. Also ask for some hypotheses that allow you to conclude the

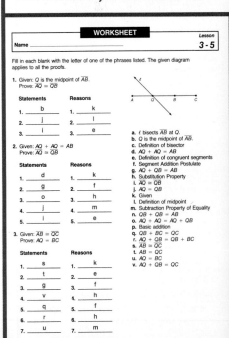

Prove. Point out when you are working forward and when you are working backward.

Additional Examples

Example 1
What are some conclusions you can make if you are given perpendicular lines?

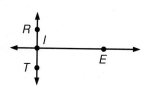

∠RIE and ∠TIE are right, supplementary and equal angles.

Sometimes you might work forward to a certain statement and not know where to go next in the inventory. When this happens, a second strategy for writing proofs, called **working backward from the Prove**, can be used.

To work backward from the Prove:

a. Search the inventory to *find hypotheses* that allow you to conclude what you want to prove. Then state each hypothesis in terms of the diagram.

b. Search the inventory for hypotheses that allow you to conclude each of the hypotheses you found in **a**. (The hypothesis in **a** becomes a new conclusion that you use to find another hypothesis.)

Example 2
What are some hypotheses that will allow you to prove that two lines are perpendicular?

Solution
Draw a diagram and state the Prove in terms of the diagram.
Prove: $\overleftrightarrow{AD} \perp \overleftrightarrow{CE}$

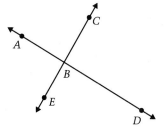

Working backward from the Prove:

a. Search the inventory for "perpendicular lines." When you find perpendicular lines in the "then" part of a statement, look at the hypothesis. From the definition of perpendicular lines, you can conclude that $\overleftrightarrow{AD} \perp \overleftrightarrow{CE}$ if at least one of the angles, ∠ABC, ∠CBD, ∠ABE, or ∠DBE, is a right angle.

b. The fact that one of the angles is a right angle becomes a new conclusion. By definition of right angle, you can conclude that one of the angles, say ∠ABC, is a right angle *if* m∠ABC = 90.

When you work backward from the Prove and arrive at the facts in the Given, you can complete the proof by writing the statements in reverse order with their corresponding reasons.

To write a proof of Theorem 3-10, we will use a combination of these strategies, called **working forward and backward**. When we use this strategy, we find a statement that we can conclude by working forward from the Given and that appears also when we work backward from the Prove.

Theorem 3-10

If the angles in a linear pair are equal, then the lines containing their sides are perpendicular.

Given ∠ABC and ∠CBD form a linear pair;
m∠ABC = m∠CBD

Prove $\overleftrightarrow{AD} \perp \overleftrightarrow{CE}$

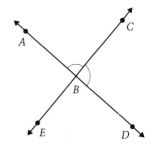

In Example 2, you could prove $\overleftrightarrow{AD} \perp \overleftrightarrow{CE}$ if you could show that m∠ABC = 90. In Example 1, the Given led to the statement m∠ABC + m∠CBD = 180. We will continue with the working-forward strategy and use the other given fact. Since m∠ABC = m∠CBD and m∠ABC + m∠CBD = 180, we can conclude by the Substitution Property that m∠ABC + m∠ABC = 180. Simplifying, 2(m∠ABC) = 180. The Division Property allows us to conclude that m∠ABC = 90. We have worked forward to m∠ABC = 90 and worked backward to m∠ABC = 90. We can now use this thinking to write a Plan for Proof and then the proof of Theorem 3-10.

Plan for Proof Use the Supplement Postulate and the definition of supplementary angles to show that m∠ABC + m∠CBD = 180. Substituting m∠ABC for m∠CBD and using the Division Property gives m∠ABC = 90. ∠ABC is a right angle and $\overleftrightarrow{AD} \perp \overleftrightarrow{CE}$.

Proof

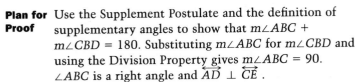

Statements	Reasons
1. ∠ABC and ∠CBD form a lin. pr.	1. Given
2. ∠ABC and ∠CBD are supp.	2. Supp. Post. [1]
3. m∠ABC + m∠CBD = 180	3. Def. of Supp. ∠s [2]
4. m∠ABC = m∠CBD	4. Given
5. m∠ABC + m∠ABC = 180, or 2(m∠ABC) = 180	5. Substitution Prop. [3, 4]
6. 2 = 2	6. Reflexive Prop.
7. m∠ABC = 90	7. Division Prop. [5, 6]
8. ∠ABC is a rt. ∠.	8. Def. of rt. ∠ [7]
9. $\overleftrightarrow{AD} \perp \overleftrightarrow{CE}$	9. Def. of ⊥ lines [8]

Statements like "2 = 2" will be omitted in later proofs because these statements are considered trivial or obvious. The proofs are still valid. Knowing which statements can be omitted in proofs comes with practice.

Example 2
What are some hypotheses that will allow you to prove that m∠1 = m∠2?

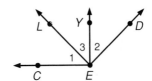

Samples: (a) m∠1 = m∠3 and m∠2 = m∠3. ∠1 and ∠2 are both complementary to ∠3. (b) ∠CEY and ∠LED are right angles. (c) $\overrightarrow{EC} \perp \overrightarrow{EY}$ and $\overrightarrow{EL} \perp \overrightarrow{ED}$.

Point out when **proof subskills**, such as writing the Given and the Prove, drawing diagrams and writing conclusions from given statements are used in this lesson.

Error Analysis Problems encountered in the use of these strategies usually result from the complexity of the problem-solving situation. Have students focus on single steps only. Have students write down the conclusions they can draw and the hypotheses they need. This should help them organize their thoughts as they work forward and backward.

Assignment Guide

Basic: 1–8, 16–22
Average: 2–8 (even), 9–14, 16–22
Extended: 2–8 (even), 9–22

ANSWERS

Checking for Understanding

2. To "work forward" from the Given, search the inventory of geometric facts to find conclusions that follow from each fact in the Given. Next search the inventory to find all conclusions that follow from each of the conclusions that you have found. (Each conclusion becomes a new hypothesis from which another conclusion may be drawn.) To "work backward" from the Prove, search the inventory to find all hypotheses that allow you to conclude what you want to prove. Then search the inventory for hypotheses that allow you to conclude each of the hypotheses that you have found. (Each hypothesis becomes a new conclusion that you use to find another hypothesis.)

Written Exercises

7. $m\angle ABD = m\angle CBF$; $m\angle ABD = 120$ and $m\angle CBF = 120$

8. $m\angle ABD + m\angle DBE = 90$; $m\angle ABD + m\angle DBE = m\angle ABE$ and $m\angle ABE = 90$

9. Since $\angle GPK$ is a rt. $\angle$, $\angle 3$ is a rt. $\angle$, by Thm. 3-9. Since $\angle 3$ is a rt. $\angle$, $\angle 4$ is a rt. $\angle$ by Thm. 3-9. Since $\angle 3$ and $\angle 4$ are rt. $\angle$s, their measures are 90. Then by the Substitution Prop., $m\angle 3 = m\angle 4$.

10. Use Thm. 3-10 to show that $\overleftrightarrow{GH} \perp \overleftrightarrow{JK}$. Then use the def. of $\perp$ lines to show that $\angle GPK$ is a rt. $\angle$.

Checking for Understanding **4.** Sample: $\angle 1$ is a rt. $\angle$; $m\angle 1 = 90$

1. What can you add to the inventory of geometric facts? Thm. 3-10

2. Describe "working forward" and "working backward."

3. If $m\angle 1 = m\angle 2$, find $m\angle 3$. How is ℓ related to n? 90; $\ell \perp n$

4. Given that $\ell \perp n$, search the inventory to find a conclusion. Then find a second conclusion that follows from the first.

5. Given the diagram, search the inventory to find a hypothesis that allows you to conclude that $\angle 1$ and $\angle 2$ are complementary. Then find a second hypothesis that allows you to conclude the first. The second hypothesis has two parts. $m\angle 1 + m\angle 2 = 90$; $m\angle 1 + m\angle 2 = m\angle ABC$ and $m\angle ABC = 90$
1-8: Accept any answers that students can justify.

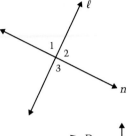

Written Exercises Sample answers are given.

Set A Work forward to find a conclusion that follows from each Given and its diagram. Then find a second conclusion that follows from the first. **1.** $\angle 3$ is a rt. $\angle$. $\angle 4$ is a rt. $\angle$.

1. Given: $\angle GPK$ is a right angle.

2. Given: $m\angle 3 = m\angle 4$ $\overleftrightarrow{JK} \perp \overleftrightarrow{GH}$; $\angle 3$ is a rt.$\angle$.

3. Given: $\angle EBC$ is a right angle; $\overrightarrow{BE}$ bisects $\angle DBF$.

4. Given: $m\angle ABE = m\angle CBE$ $\overleftrightarrow{AB} \perp \overrightarrow{BE}$; $\angle ABE$ is a rt.$\angle$.

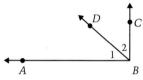

Work backward from each Prove and its diagram to find a hypothesis that allows you to conclude the Prove. Then find a second hypothesis that allows you to conclude the first hypothesis. A hypothesis may have two parts. **Sample answers are given.**

5. Prove: $m\angle 3 = m\angle 4$ $m\angle 3 = 90$; $\angle 3$ is a rt.$\angle$.

6. Prove: $\angle GPK$ is a right angle. $m\angle GPK = 90$; $m\angle 4 = 90$

7. Prove: $m\angle ABD = m\angle CBF$

8. Prove: $\angle ABD$ and $\angle DBE$ are complementary.
3. $\angle EBA$ is a rt.$\angle$; $m\angle DBE = m\angle EBF$

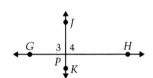

Set B Use "working forward and backward" to write a Plan for Proof for each exercise.

9. Given: $\angle GPK$ is a right angle.   Prove: $m\angle 3 = m\angle 4$
(HINT: See Exercises 1 and 5.)

10. Given: $m\angle 3 = m\angle 4$ Prove: $\angle GPK$ is a right angle.
(HINT: See Exercises 2 and 6.)

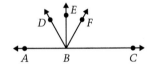

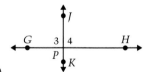

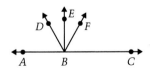

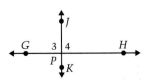

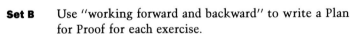

11. Given: ∠EBC is a right angle; $\overrightarrow{BE}$ bisects ∠DBF.
Prove: m∠ABD = m∠CBF (HINT: See Exercises 3 and 7.)

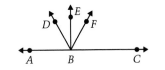

12. Given: m∠ABE = m∠CBE
Prove: ∠ABD and ∠DBE are complementary.
(HINT: See Exercises 4 and 8.)

Write a two-column proof for each exercise.

13. Given: m∠1 = m∠4   Prove: m∠2 = m∠5

14. Given: m∠2 = m∠3 = m∠4   Prove: r ⊥ s

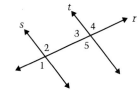

Set C   **15.** Write a complete two-column proof for this statement: A line and a point not on the line lie in a plane. (HINT: Use Postulates 1, 2, and 3.)

▲ **Review**   **16.** If m∠1 = 72, then m∠2 = $\underset{72}{\underline{\ ?\ }}$ and m∠3 = $\underset{108}{\underline{\ ?\ }}$.

17. If m∠1 = 2x + 9 and m∠2 = 5x − 45, then m∠4 = $\underline{\ ?\ }$. 135

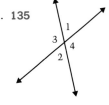

18. In a two-column proof, what do the numbers in the brackets represent?

19. State the Segment Addition Postulate.

20. All mammals have backbones. Jay's pet has a backbone. Is Jay's pet a mammal? Explain.

≣ **Thinking Ahead**   **21.** Fold a sheet of lined notebook paper so that one of the horizontal lines is perpendicular to the fold. What is the measure of each of the four angles that the fold makes with the rule? 90

22. Does your fold line appear to be perpendicular to the other parallel rules on the paper? Measure some of the angles to check your answer. Then complete this conjecture: Two perpendicular lines intersect to form four $\underline{\ ?\ }$ angles. Yes; right

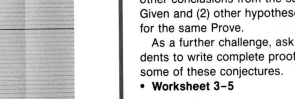

⎚ **Computer Activities: Drawing and Measuring**

1. Draw line AB. Then draw line CD with C between A and B and D not on $\overleftrightarrow{AB}$. Measure ∠ACD and ∠BCD. How does the measure of each angle compare with 90?

2. Repeat the activity several times, forming angles of different sizes.

3. Complete these conjectures: If one angle in a linear pair is acute, then the other is $\underline{\ ?\ }$. If one angle in a linear pair is obtuse, then the other is $\underline{\ ?\ }$.

1. m∠1 <90 and m∠2 > 90, or both ∠s are 90 **3.** obtuse; acute

11. From the def. of an ∠ bisector m∠DBE = m∠EBF. ∠EBC and ∠EBA form a lin. pr. Use Thm. 3–9 to show that ∠EBA is a rt. ∠, so m∠EBC = 90 and m∠EBA = 90. Then use the Transitive Prop. to show that m∠EBC = m∠EBA. Use the Subtraction Prop. to show that m∠EBC − m∠EBF = m∠EBA − m∠DBE. From the ∠ Add. Post. m∠ABD + m∠DBE = m∠EBA and m∠EBF + m∠CBF = m∠EBC. Then use the Subtraction Prop. to show that m∠ABD = m∠EBA − m∠DBE and m∠CBF = m∠EBC − m∠EBF. Then use the Substitution Prop. to show that m∠ABD = m∠ CBF.

FOLLOW-UP

More Practice

Have students work on the plans for proof in **Exercises 9–12** as **group activities**. Challenge them to make some conjectures for (1) other conclusions from the same Given and (2) other hypotheses for the same Prove.
  As a further challenge, ask students to write complete proofs for some of these conjectures.
• **Worksheet 3–5**

Extension

• **Extension 3–5**

Computers

The computer activity in the pupil's book can be completed using *The Geometric preSupposer: Points and Lines* or *GeoDraw*.
• **Computer Activity 3-5**
• **Computer Worksheet 3-5**

Warm-Up Review

1. State a conclusion that can be made from the hypothesis "$\overline{AB}$ is perpendicular to $\overline{BC}$." $m\angle ABC = 90$ or $\angle ABC$ is a right $\angle$
2. State a hypothesis that allows us to conclude "$\angle PQR$ is obtuse." $m\angle PQR > 90$
3. How is a right angle marked in a diagram? A "box" (└)
4. Explain why an obtuse angle cannot have a complement. It already has a measure > 90.

LESSON 3–6

Resources

Teaching Aid 8, proof form
Visual Aid 8, proof form
Worksheet 3–6
Extension 3–6
Computer Worksheet 3–6
Algebra Review 3
Chapter 3 Test, Form I
Chapter 3 Test, Form II
Chapter 3 Test, Form III
Cumulative Test, Form I
Cumulative Test, Form II
Practice for Standardized Tests 1

OBJECTIVE

Write a two-column proof.

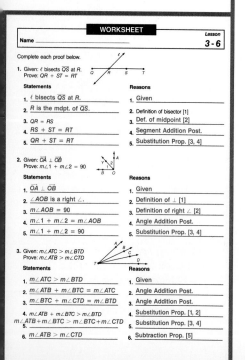

3-6 Writing Two-Column Proofs

You have studied the various parts of a two-column geometric proof. In this lesson, you will put those parts together to write complete proofs.

Summary The Proof-Writing Process

①.If necessary, write the statement to be proved in "*if . . . then*" form.

②.Draw and label an appropriate *diagram*.

③.State the *Given* and the *Prove* in terms of the diagram.

④.Develop a *Plan for Proof*.

⑤.Write a *proof* in two-column form.

Here is a proof of Theorem 3-11 with each part shown.

Theorem 3-11

Two perpendicular lines intersect to form four right angles.

If two lines are perpendicular, then they form four right angles. ①

Given $\ell \perp m$

Prove $\angle 1, \angle 2, \angle 3,$ and $\angle 4$ are right angles. ③

Plan for Proof Use the definition if $\perp$ lines to get one right angle, say $\angle 1$. Use Theorem 3-8 to show $\angle 3$ is a right angle. Then ④ use Theorem 3-9 to show $\angle 2$ and $\angle 4$ are right angles.

Proof

Statements	Reasons
1. $\ell \perp m$	1. Given
2. One $\angle$, say $\angle 1$, is a rt. $\angle$.	2. Def. of $\perp$ lines [1]
3. $m\angle 1 = 90$	3. Def. of rt. $\angle$ [2]
4. $m\angle 1 = m\angle 3$	4. Vert. $\angle$s are =.
5. $m\angle 3 = 90$	5. Substitution Prop. [3, 4]
6. $\angle 3$ is a right angle.	6. Def. of rt. $\angle$ [5] ⑤
7. $\angle 2$ is a right angle; $\angle 4$ is a right angle.	7. If one $\angle$ in lin. pr. is a rt. $\angle$, then the other is also a rt. $\angle$. [6]

Another useful theorem dealing with right angles is Theorem 3-12. Its proof is requested in Exercise 27.

Theorem 3-12

All right angles are equal.

Study the steps of the proof-writing process shown in the next two examples.

Example 1

Prove the following statement: If two lines cut by a transversal ① form a pair of equal alternate interior angles, then the other pair of alternate interior angles are equal.

Solution

Given   Lines r and s cut by transversal t; $m\angle 1 = m\angle 4$ ③

Prove $m\angle 2 = m\angle 3$

Plan for Proof $\angle 1$ and $\angle 2$ are supplementary. $\angle 3$ and $\angle 4$ are supplementary. Use the theorem that states two ④ angles supplementary to equal angles are equal.

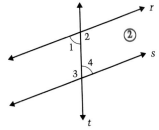

Proof

Statements	Reasons
1. $m\angle 1 = m\angle 4$	1. Given
2. $\angle 1$ and $\angle 2$ are supp.; $\angle 3$ and $\angle 4$ are supp.	2. Supp. Post. ⑤
3. $m\angle 2 = m\angle 3$	3. Supp. of $=\angle$s are $=$. [1, 2]

Example 2

Prove that a supplement of an acute angle is an obtuse angle.

Solution

If two angles are supplementary and one of the angles is acute, ① then the other angle is obtuse.

Given $\angle 1$ and $\angle 2$ are supplementary; $\angle 1$ is acute. ③

Prove $\angle 2$ is obtuse.

Plan for Proof   Use the definition of supplementary angles, and then show that $m\angle 1 = 180 - m\angle 2$. By the definition of ④ acute angle, $m\angle 1 < 90$. Substitute and simplify to show $m\angle 2 > 90$.

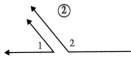

Proof

Statements	Reasons
1. $\angle 1$ and $\angle 2$ are supp.	1. Given
2. $m\angle 1 + m\angle 2 = 180$	2. Def. of supp. $\angle$s [1]
3. $\angle 1$ is acute.	3. Given
4. $m\angle 1 < 90$	4. Def. of acute $\angle$ [3]
5. $m\angle 1 = 180 - m\angle 2$	5. Subtraction Prop. [2] ⑤
6. $180 - m\angle 2 < 90$	6. Substitution Prop. [4, 5]
7. $-m\angle 2 < -90$	7. Subtraction Prop. [6]
8. $m\angle 2 > 90$	8. Multiplication Prop. [7]
9. $\angle 2$ is obtuse.	9. Def. of obtuse $\angle$ [8]

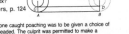

Additional Examples

Example 1

Prove the following statement: If two lines cut by a transversal form a pair of equal alternate exterior angles, then a pair of alternate interior angles are also equal.

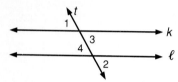

Given: $m\angle 1 = m\angle 2$
Prove: $m\angle 3 = m\angle 4$
Plan for Proof: Because $\angle 1$ and $\angle 3$ are vertical $\angle$s, they are equal. Similarly, $\angle 2$ and $\angle 4$ are also equal. Use the Substitution Prop.

Statements	Reasons
1. $m\angle 1 = m\angle 2$	1. Given
2. $m\angle 1 = m\angle 3$;	2. Vertical
$m\angle 4 = m\angle 2$	$\angle$s are =.
3. $m\angle 3 = m\angle 4$	3. Subst. [1, 2]

Example 2

Prove that the supplement of a right angle is also a right angle.

If two angles are supplementary, and one angle is a right angle, then the other angle is right.
Given: $\angle 1$ and $\angle 2$ are supplementary; $\angle 1$ is a right angle.
Prove: $\angle 2$ is a right angle.
Plan for Proof: Use the definitions of supplementary and right angles and the Substitution Property to show $90 + m\angle 2 = 180$. Apply the Subtraction Property to get a right angle.

Perpendicular lines occur throughout our study of geometry. In Theorem 3-11, we proved that perpendicular lines intersect to form four right angles. From now on, we will use a right-angle symbol to indicate perpendicular lines as well as right angles. Since the symbol ⌐ on a diagram can have two meanings, you must be careful in writing your proof.

Given: $\angle 1$ is a right angle. After you write the Given in your proof, the next step might be that $m\angle 1 = 90$ by definition of right angle, or that $\ell \perp n$ by definition of perpendicular lines.

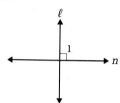

Given: ℓ is perpendicular to n. After you write the Given in your proof, the next step might be that $\angle 1$ is a right angle by definition of perpendicular lines. The third step might then be $m\angle 1 = 90$.

Checking for Understanding

Discuss these exercises with another student.

1. What are the five steps of the proof-writing process?

2. What can you add to the inventory of geometric facts?

3. Write in "if . . . then" form: An angle equal to a right angle is a right angle. If an $\angle$ is = to a rt. $\angle$, then it is a rt. $\angle$.

Use the markings on the diagrams to tell what is given.

4.
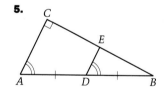

5.
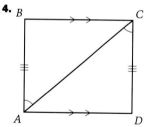

2. Thm. 3–11 and Thm. 3–12
4. $BC \parallel AD$; $AB = CD$; $m\angle BAC = m\angle ACD$
5. $\angle C$ is a rt. $\angle$; $m\angle A = m\angle EDB$; $AD = DB$

Written Exercises

Set A   Write each statement in "if . . . then" form.

1. Two angles that are equal and supplementary are both right angles.

2. The midpoint M of $\overline{AB}$ divides $\overline{AB}$ into two segments $\overline{AM}$ and $\overline{MB}$ such that $AM = \frac{1}{2}AB$.

3. The measure of any obtuse angle is greater than the measure of any acute angle.

1. If 2 $\angle$s are = and supp., then they are both rt. $\angle$s.
2. If M is the midpt. of $\overline{AB}$, then $AM = \frac{1}{2} AB$.
3. If an $\angle$ is obtuse, then its measure is greater than the measure of any acute $\angle$.

4. Two complementary angles are both acute.

5. The measure of a complement of an acute angle is less than the measure of its supplement.

6. Two lines that intersect to form one acute angle also form a second acute angle and two obtuse angles.

Draw a diagram, and state the Given and the Prove needed for a proof of the statement in

7. Exercise 1. **8.** Exercise 2. **9.** Exercise 3.

10. Exercise 4. **11.** Exercise 5. **12.** Exercise 6.

Write a Plan for Proof of the statement in

13. Exercise 1. **14.** Exercise 2. **15.** Exercise 3.

16. Exercise 4. **17.** Exercise 5. **18.** Exercise 6.

Write a two-column proof of the statement in

19. Exercise 1. **20.** Exercise 2. **21.** Exercise 3.

22. Exercise 4. **23.** Exercise 5. **24.** Exercise 6.

Set B Write a two-column proof for each statement.

25. If two lines cut by a transversal form a pair of equal corresponding angles, then the other pairs of corresponding angles are equal.

26. If two lines cut by a transversal form a pair of interior angles on the same side of the transversal that are supplementary, then the other pair of interior angles on the same side of the transversal are supplementary.

27. Theorem 3-12

Set C **28.** If one of two lines cut by a transversal is perpendicular to the transversal and a pair of alternate interior angles are equal, then the other line is also perpendicular to the transversal.

29. A line and a point not on the line lie in a plane. (Theorem 3-2, Part I)

30. Two intersecting lines lie in a plane. (Theorem 3-3, Part I)

4. If 2∠s are comp., then they are both acute.
5. If ∠A is an acute angle, then the measure of any complement of ∠A is less than the measure of any supplement of ∠A.
6. If 2 lines intersect to form 1 acute ∠, then they also form a second acute ∠ and 2 obtuse ∠s.

Statements
1. ∠1 and ∠2 are supp.
2. $m\angle 1 + m\angle 2 = 180$
3. ∠1 is a rt. ∠.
4. $m\angle 1 = 90$
5. $90 + m\angle 2 = 180$
6. $m\angle 2 = 90$
7. ∠2 is a rt. ∠.

Reasons
1. Given
2. Def. of supp. ∠s [1]
3. Given
4. Def. of rt. ∠ [3]
5. Substitution [2, 4]
6. Subtraction Prop. [5]
7. Def. of rt. ∠ [6]

Error Analysis Students usually have difficulty drawing and labeling a diagram and developing a plan. The diagram should reflect nothing more than the Given. Review the strategies of working forward and working backward.

ANSWERS

Written Exercises

7.

Given: $m\angle 1 = m\angle 2$; ∠1 and ∠2 are supplementary. Prove: ∠1 and ∠2 are rt. ∠s.

8.

Given: M is the midpt. of $\overline{AB}$.
Prove: $AM = \frac{1}{2}(AB)$

Review

32. 1. $\overrightarrow{XZ}$ bisects $\angle WXU$. (Given)
2. $m\angle 1 = m\angle 2$ (Def. of $\angle$ bisector
[1]) 3. $\overrightarrow{XT}$ bisects $\angle VXY$. (Given) 4.
$m\angle 3 = m\angle 4$ (Def. of $\angle$ bisector
[3]) 5. $m\angle 1 = m\angle 3$ (Given) 6.
$m\angle 2 = m\angle 4$ (Substitution Prop.
[2, 4, 5])

ANSWERS

Progress Check

1. Use the def. of an $\angle$ bisector
to show that $m\angle 1 = m\angle 2$. Since
the diagram shows that $\angle 1$ and
$\angle 3$ are vert. $\angle$s, use Thm. 3–8 to
show that $m\angle 1 = m\angle 3$. Then use
the Transitive Prop. to show that
$m\angle 2 = m\angle 3$.

---

31. Given that $\overleftrightarrow{AC}$ bisects $\overline{JK}$, search the inventory to
find a conclusion that follows from the Given.
Then find a second conclusion that follows from
the first.

32. Write a two-column proof.
Given: $\overrightarrow{XZ}$ bisects $\angle WXU$; $\overrightarrow{XT}$ bisects $\angle VXY$;
$m\angle 1 = m\angle 3$ **34.** Defs., posts., props.
Prove: $m\angle 2 = m\angle 4$ of real numbers, thms

33. What is the inventory of geometric facts?

34. Define *parallel lines*.   **35.** Define *obtuse angle*.

31. B is the midpt. of $\overline{JK}$;
JB = BK

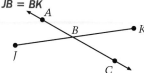

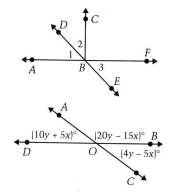

Progress Check

Lesson 3-4, page 115

1. Write a Plan for Proof.
Given: $\overleftrightarrow{AF}$ and $\overleftrightarrow{DE}$ intersect at point B; $\overrightarrow{BD}$ bisects $\angle ABC$.
Prove: $m\angle 2 = m\angle 3$

2. Find x, y, $m\angle AOB$, and $m\angle BOC$.   −3; 5; 145; 35

3. Sample: $m\angle VXJ = m\angle YXJ$ and
$m\angle WXK = m\angle ZXK$; $m\angle VXJ = m\angle YXJ = m\angle WXK = m\angle ZXK$

4. Sample: $m\angle YXJ = m\angle JXY$ and $m\angle WXK = m\angle JXY$;
$\overrightarrow{XJ}$ bisects $\angle VXY$.

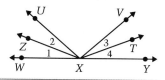

Lesson 3-5, page 121

3. Work forward to find a conclusion that follows from the
Given and its diagram. Then find a second conclusion that
follows from the first conclusion.
Given: $\overrightarrow{XJ}$ bisects $\angle VXY$; $\overrightarrow{XK}$ bisects $\angle WXZ$.

4. Work backward from the Prove and its diagram to find a
hypothesis that allows you to conclude the Prove. Then find
a second hypothesis that allows you to conclude the first
hypothesis.
Prove: $m\angle VXJ = m\angle WXK$

5. Write a two-column proof.
Given: $\overrightarrow{XJ}$ bisects $\angle VXY$; $\overrightarrow{XK}$ bisects $\angle WXZ$.
Prove: $m\angle VXJ = m\angle WXK$

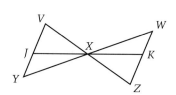

Lesson 3-6, page 126

6. Write a two-column proof.
Given: M and N are midpoints; $QM = RN$
Prove: $PM = PN$

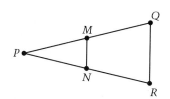

Using BASIC: Writing a Program to Classify Angles

Below is an incomplete BASIC program to classify an angle.

```
100 REM CLASSIFYING ANGLES
110 INPUT "ENTER MEASURE OF <A"; A
120
130
140
150 PRINT "<A IS A RIGHT ANGLE."
160 GOTO 200
170 PRINT "<A IS AN ACUTE ANGLE."
180 GOTO 200
190 PRINT "<A IS AN OBTUSE ANGLE."
200 END
```

1. Type the program and add this line to classify ∠A as acute:
   120 IF (A>0) and (A<90) THEN 170
   RUN the program and type 60 as the input. What happens?   Output: ∠A IS AN ACUTE ANGLE

2. Add lines 130 and 140 to classify ∠A as right or obtuse. RUN the 130 IF A = 90 THEN 150
program with input 90, then with input 120 to test the program. 140 IF (A>90) AND (A<180)
                                                                      THEN 190

3. When you RUN the program does it work if you enter either a
negative number or a number greater than 180? No, computer prints ∠A IS A RIGHT ANGLE

4. Rearrange the lines of this
program by filling in numbers
to make a program that selects
the smallest of the measures
of three different angles. Verify
that the program works by
entering three different
measures separated by
commas. Example: 40, 32, 65.

```
180 PRINT "<B HAS THE LEAST MEASURE."
120 IF (A>B) AND (A>C) THEN 160
190 END
150 GOTO 190
160 PRINT "<A HAS THE LEAST MEASURE."
130 IF (B>C) THEN 180
140 PRINT "<C HAS THE LEAST MEASURE."
110 INPUT "MEASURES OF <A, <B, AND <C:";
    A,B,C
170 GOTO 190
```

5. Points A, B, and C are collinear. Write a program that
requires inputs, AB, AC, and BC, and determines which
point is between the other two. Be sure to include a PRINT
statement to handle incorrect input values.

Using BASIC

```
5. 100   REM DETERMINING
         BETWEENNESS
   110   PRINT"ENTER
         POSITIVE VALUES
         FOR EACH DIS-
         TANCE."
   115   IF (A < = 0) OR (A
         > = 180) THEN
         PRINT "NO SUCH
         ANGLE": GOTO 200
   120   INPUT "ENTER THE
         DISTANCE AB:";AB
   130   IF AB <= 0 THEN 120
   140   INPUT "ENTER THE
         DISTANCE AC:";AC
   150   IF AC <= 0 THEN 140
   160   INPUT "ENTER THE
         DISTANCE BC:";BC
   170   IF BC <= 0 THEN 160
   180   IF AB + BC = AC THEN
         GOTO 240
   190   IF AC + BC = AB THEN
         GOTO 260
   200   IF AB + AC = BC THEN
         GOTO 280
   210   PRINT :PRINT "A,
         B, AND C ARE
         NONCOLLINEAR."
   220   PRINT "TRY AGAIN!"
         :PRINT
   230   GOTO 110
   240   PRINT "B IS
         BETWEEN A AND C."
   250   GOTO 999
   260   PRINT "C IS
         BETWEEN A AND B."
   270   GOTO 999
   280   PRINT "A IS
         BETWEEN B AND C."
   999   END
```

Chapter 3 Summary

Important Terms

Diagram (96)
Given (96)
Inventory of geometric facts (115)

Plan for Proof (116)
Proof (95)
Prove (96)
Theorem (95)

Two-column proof (96)
Working backward (122)
Working forward (121)
Working forward/backward (122)

Important Ideas

1. A theorem is a statement that is proved. (95)

2. A proof in two-column form consists of a diagram, the Given, the Prove, and a list of statements with reasons. (96)

3. The reasons in a proof can be definitions, postulates, properties of real numbers, previously proved theorems, and Given. (96)

4. The hypothesis of a conditional provides the given information; the conclusion indicates what is to be proved. (96)

5. Some important theorems are:
   a. If two lines intersect, then they intersect in one and only one point. (101)
   b. A line and a point not on the line are contained in one and only one plane. (101)
   c. Supplements of equal angles are equal. (107)
   d. Complements of equal angles are equal. (109)
   e. Vertical angles are equal. (116)
   f. If the angles of a linear pair are equal, then the lines containing their sides are perpendicular. (123)
   g. Two perpendicular lines intersect to form four right angles. (126)

6. Strategies that are helpful in planning a proof are working forward from the Given, working backward from the Prove, and a combination of these two. (121-122)

7. The steps of the proof-writing process are:
   1. Restate the statement in "if . . . then" form, if necessary.
   2. Draw and label a diagram.
   3. Write the Given and Prove in terms of the diagram.
   4. Develop a Plan for Proof.
   5. Write a proof in two-column form. (126)

Chapter 3 Review

Lesson 3-1, page 95

1. Supply the missing parts in the proof.
Given: $m\angle1 + m\angle2 + m\angle3 = 180$
Prove: $m\angle1 + m\angle2 = m\angle4$

Statements	Reasons
1. _?_	1. Given
2. $\angle4$ and $\angle3$ are supp.	2. _?_
3. $m\angle4 + m\angle3 = 180$	3. _?_ [_?_]
4. $m\angle1 + m\angle2 + m\angle3 = m\angle4 + m\angle3$	4. _?_ [_?_]
5. _?_	5. Reflexive Prop.
6. _?_	6. Subtraction Prop. [4, 5]

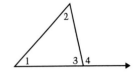

1. $m\angle1 + m\angle2 + m\angle3 = 180$
2. Supplement Post.
3. Def of supp. $\angle$s [2]
4. Substitution Prop. [1, 3]
5. $m\angle3 = m\angle3$
6. $m\angle1 + m\angle2 = m\angle4$

Lesson 3-2, page 101

Use a straightedge to draw a diagram for the given information.

2. $\angle1$ and $\angle2$ are complements of $\angle3$.

3. $\overleftrightarrow{XY}$ is the perpendicular bisector of $\overline{PR}$.

4. $\angle4$ and $\angle5$ are adjacent and equal.

5. Draw a diagram that shows a counterexample for the following statement: Two supplementary angles form a linear pair.

Lesson 3-3, page 107

6. Write the proof with steps in a correct order. b, f, e, a, d, c
Given: $m\angle ABC = m\angle DBE$
Prove: $m\angle ABD = m\angle CBE$

Statements	Reasons
a. $m\angle ABC + m\angle CBD = m\angle ABD$	a. Angle Add. Post.
b. $m\angle ABC = m\angle DBE$	b. Given
c. $m\angle ABD = m\angle CBE$	c. Substitution Prop. [3, 4, 5]
d. $m\angle DBE + m\angle CBD = m\angle CBE$	d. Angle Add. Post.
e. $m\angle ABC + m\angle CBD = m\angle DBE + m\angle CBD$	e. Addition Prop. [1, 2]
f. $m\angle CBD = m\angle CBD$	f. Reflexive Prop.

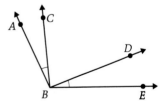

Lesson 3-4, page 115

Use the inventory of geometric facts to make a list of all the items that mention

7. perpendicular lines.

8. linear pairs of angles.

7. Def. of $\perp$ lines; Thms. 3-10, 3-11
8. Def. of lin. pr. of $\angle$s; Supplement Post.; Thms 3-9, 3-10.

ANSWERS

Chapter Review

2. Samples:

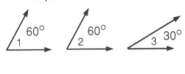

or

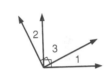

3. Sample:

4. Sample:

5. Sample:

9. Sample: $m\angle 3 = m\angle 4$;
M is the midpt. of $\overline{GN}$;
$GM = NI$

10. Sample: $GM = MN$;
$MN = NI$, $GM = NI$

13. Since $\angle ABC$ is a rt. $\angle$, $\angle 1$ and $\angle 2$ are complementary. By the def. of comp. $\angle$s, $m\angle 1 + m\angle 2 = 90$. Use Thm. 3–8 to show that $m\angle 1 = m\angle 3$. Then use the Substitution Prop. to state $m\angle 3 + m\angle 2 = 90$. By the def. of comp. $\angle$s, $\angle 3$ and $\angle 2$ are comp.

21.

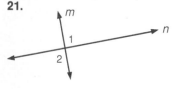

22. Given: $\angle 1$ and $\angle 2$ are supplementary. Prove: $m \perp n$

23. From the def. of supp. $\angle$s, $m\angle 1 + m\angle 2 = 180$. $\angle 1$ and $\angle 2$ are vert. $\angle$s, so by Thm. 3–8 $m\angle 1 = m\angle 2$. Then use the Substitution Prop. to show that $2(m\angle 1) = 180$. Use the Div. Prop. to show that $m\angle 1 = 90$, so $\angle 1$ is a rt. $\angle$. From the def. of $\perp$ lines, $m \perp n$.

24. 1. $\angle 1$ and $\angle 2$ are supplementary. (Given) 2. $m\angle 1 + m\angle 2 = 180$ (Def. of supp. $\angle$s [1]) 3. $m\angle 1 = m\angle 2$ (Vert. $\angle$s are =.) 4. $m\angle 1 + m\angle 1 = 180$, or $2(m\angle 1) = 180$ (Substitution Prop. [2, 3]) 5. $2 = 2$ (Reflexive Prop.) 6. $m\angle 1 = 90$ (Div. Prop. [4, 5]) 7. $\angle 1$ is a rt. $\angle$ (Def. of rt. $\angle$ [6]) 8. $m \perp n$ (Def. $\perp$ lines [7])

Use the inventory and the diagram to make a list of at least three conclusions that follow from the Given.

9. Given: $m\angle 1 = m\angle 2$; $GM = MN$; $MN = NI$

10. Given: M is the midpoint of $\overline{GN}$; N is the midpoint of $\overline{MI}$; $m\angle 1 + m\angle 2 = 240$; $m\angle 3 = m\angle 4$

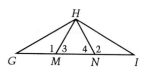

Use the inventory and the diagram to make a list of at least two hypotheses that imply the Prove.

11. Prove: $s \perp r$
$m\angle 1 = 90$; $\angle 2$ is a rt. $\angle$.

12. Prove: $\angle 1$ is a right angle.
$m\angle 1 = m\angle 2$; $\angle 1$ is a rt. $\angle$

13. Write a Plan for Proof.
Given: $\angle ABC$ is a right angle.
Prove: $\angle 3$ is complementary to $\angle 2$.

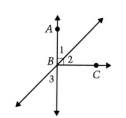

Lesson 3-5, page 121
Work forward from each Given and the diagram to find a conclusion that follows from the Given. Then find a second conclusion that follows from the first. Sample answers:

14. Given: $m\angle 1 = m\angle 4$ $m\angle 2 = m\angle 3$, $m\angle 2 = m\angle 5$

15. Given: $\angle 2$ and $\angle 4$ are supplementary.

16. Given: $m\angle 1 = m\angle 6$ $m\angle 2 = m\angle 5$; $m\angle 1 = m\angle 4$

17. Given: $\angle 6$ and $\angle 2$ are supplementary.

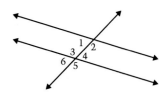

Work backward from each Prove and the diagram to find a hypothesis that implies the Prove. Then find a second hypothesis that implies the first.

18. Prove: $\overline{RD}$ bisects $\overline{SQ}$.

19. Prove: $AQ = AS$

Lesson 3-6, page 126
Exercises 20-24 refer to proving this statement: The sides of two supplementary vertical angles are perpendicular.

20. Restate in "if . . . then" form.

21. Draw a diagram and label it.

22. Write the Given and the Prove.

23. Write a Plan for Proof.

24. Write a two-column proof.

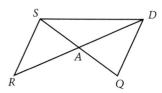

15. $m\angle 2 + m\angle 4 = 180$; $m\angle 1 = m\angle 4$
17. $m\angle 2 + m\angle 6 = 180$; $m\angle 2 = m\angle 5$

18. $AS = AQ$; A is the midpt. + $\overline{SQ}$.
19. A is the midpt. of $\overline{SQ}$; $\overline{RD}$ bisects $\overline{SQ}$.
20. If $2\angle$s are supp. and vert. $\angle$s, then their sides are $\perp$.

Chapter 3 Test

Is each statement *true* or *false?* If false, give a counterexample.

1. A line and a point not on the line are coplanar. **True**

2. If $m\angle 1 = m\angle 2$, then $\angle 1$ and $\angle 2$ are vertical angles. **False**

3. If two equal angles form a linear pair, each is a right angle.

4. Two different lines may have two different points in common. **3. True 4. False: 2 pts. determine 1 line.**

5. If $\angle 1$ and $\angle 2$ are complementary to the same angle, then $m\angle 1 = m\angle 2$. **True**

6. Find $m\angle QOS$, given $m\angle TOR = m\angle ROV$ and $m\angle SOT = 10$. **80**

7. Find $m\angle VOW$, given $m\angle SOR = 110$ and $\overleftrightarrow{QR} \perp \overleftrightarrow{TV}$. **20**

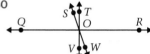

8. Find x, y, $m\angle ABE$, and $m\angle CBE$. **5; 50; 70; 110**

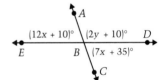

9. Supply the missing reasons.

Given: $m\angle 4 = m\angle 3$
Prove: $\angle 3$ and $\angle 5$ are supplementary.

Statements	Reasons
1. $m\angle 4 = m\angle 3$	1. __?__ Given
2. $\angle 4$ and $\angle 5$ are supp.	2. __?__ Supplement Post.
3. $m\angle 4 + m\angle 5 = 180$	3. __?__ [__?__] Def. of Supp. $\angle$s [2]
4. $m\angle 3 + m\angle 5 = 180$	4. __?__ [__?__] Substitution Prop. [1, 3]
5. $\angle 3$ and $\angle 5$ are supp.	5. __?__ [__?__] Def. of Supp. $\angle$s [4]

10. Write the proof with the steps in a correct order.

d, c, b, e, a

Given: $BC = XB$
Prove: $AB = AC - XB$

Statements	Reasons
a. $AB = AC - XB$	a. Substitution Prop. [3, 4]
b. $AB = AC - BC$	b. Subtraction Prop. [1, 2]
c. $BC = BC$	c. Reflexive Prop.
d. $AB + BC = AC$	d. Seg. Add. Post.
e. $BC = XB$	e. Given

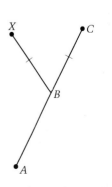

11. Write a two-column proof of this statement: The two angles formed by an angle and its bisector are acute angles.

2. false; sample:

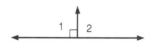

11.

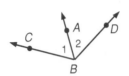

Given: $\overrightarrow{BA}$ bisects $\angle CBD$.
Prove: $\angle 1$ and $\angle 2$ are acute.
1. $\overrightarrow{BA}$ bisects $\angle CBD$. (Given) 2. $m\angle 1 = m\angle 2$ (Def. of $\angle$ bisector [1]) 3. $m\angle 1 + m\angle 2 = m\angle CBD$ ($\angle$ Add. Post.) 4. $2(m\angle 1) = m\angle CBD$; $2(m\angle 2) = m\angle CBD$ (Substitution Prop. [2, 3]) 5. $0 < m\angle CBD < 180$ (Protractor Post.) 6. $0 < 2(m\angle 1) < 180$; $0 < 2(m\angle 2) < 180$ (Substitution Prop. [4, 5]) 7. $2 = 2$ (Reflexive Prop.) 8. $0 < m\angle 1 < 90$; $0 < m\angle 2 < 90$ (Div. Prop. [7]) 9. $\angle 1$ and $\angle 2$ are acute. (Def. of acute $\angle$ [8])

Cumulative Review   Chapters 1–3

Select the best answer for each item.

1. A tabletop suggests a ___?___ .

  A. Point   **B.** Line

  C. Ray   **(D.)** Plane

2. Points A, B, and C are contained in both plane $\mathcal{H}$ and plane $\mathcal{E}$. Which of these statements must be true?

  A. A, B, and C are noncoplanar.

  (B.) A, B, and C are collinear.

  C. B is between A and C.

  D. $\overleftrightarrow{AB}$ and $\overleftrightarrow{BC}$ are noncoplanar.

3. On a number line, the graph of $y \geq 2$ is a ___?___ .

  A. Line   **B.** Half-plane

  C. Segment   **(D.)** Ray

4. If B is between A and C on $\overline{AC}$ such that $AB = BC$, then B is a(n) ___?___ .

  A. Vertex   **(B.)** Midpoint

  C. Coordinate   **D.** Endpoint

5. Given half-plane $\mathcal{H}$ with edge $\overleftrightarrow{AB}$, there is exactly one angle, $\angle BAC$, such that $m\angle BAC = 50$. This result is guaranteed by the ___?___ Postulate.

  A. Protractor

  (B.) Angle Construction

  C. Angle Addition

  D. Angle Bisector

6. The coordinates of A and B are $(-2, 6)$, and $(-8, -4)$, respectively. The midpoint of $\overline{AB}$ has coordinates ___?___ .

  A. $(-10, 2)$ **(B.)** $(-5, 1)$

  C. $(6, 10)$ **D.** $(3, 5)$

7. If two angles form a linear pair, they are also ___?___ .

  A. Vertical and opposite

  B. Acute and complementary

  C. Equal and right

  (D.) Adjacent and supplementary

8. Watching from a window, you see three red cars go by in a row. If you predict that the fourth car to go by will also be red, you are using ___?___ .

  (A.) Inductive reasoning

  B. Deductive reasoning

  C. Mathematical models

  D. Argument by counterexample

9. If $\overline{AB}$ and $\overline{CD}$ are noncoplanar and have no points in common, they are ___?___ .

  A. Parallel   **(B.)** Skew

  C. Perpendicular   **D.** Transversals

10. Corresponding parts of congruent triangles are equal. In "if . . . then" form, this statement is:

  (A.) If two triangles are congruent, then their corresponding parts are equal.

  B. If two triangles have equal parts, then the parts are corresponding.

  C. If a part of one triangle is equal to the corresponding part of another triangle, then the triangles are congruent.

  D. If two triangles have corresponding parts, then the triangles are congruent.

11. This diagram shows a counterexample for the statement: Complementary angles form a right angle.

A.

B.

C.

D. (circled)

60°   30°

12. Complete this argument.

$p \Rightarrow q$: If two angles are vertical, then they are equal.

$\underline{\quad p: \underline{?} \quad}$
$q: m\angle A$ and $m\angle B$

A. $\angle A$ and $\angle B$ are equal angles.

B. Two angles are vertical.

C. Two angles are equal.

D. (circled) $\angle A$ and $\angle B$ are vertical angles.

13. If $x < y$, then $\underline{?}$.

A. $x + 5 > y + 5$ **B.** (circled) $x + 5 < y + 5$

C. $x + 5 = y + 5$ **D.** $x + 5 \geq y + 5$

14. The $\underline{?}$ of $p \Rightarrow q$ is not $p \Rightarrow q$.

A. Negation   **B.** Converse

C. (circled) Inverse   **D.** Contrapositive

15. Given: $m\angle 1 = 130$
Prove: $m\angle 2 = 50$

Statements

1. $m\angle 1 = 130$
2. $\angle 1$ and $\angle 2$ form a linear pair.
3. $\angle 1$ and $\angle 2$ are supplementary.
4. $m\angle 1 + m\angle 2 = 180$
5. $m\angle 2 = 50$

The reason for Step 5 is $\underline{?}$.

A. Definition of supplementary angles

B. Addition Property

C. (circled) Subtraction Property

D. Substitution Property

16. In a proof using this diagram, you can assume that $\underline{?}$.

A. $m\angle DAB = 90$

B. $\overleftrightarrow{CB} \perp \overleftrightarrow{DE}$

C. (circled) C, A, and B are collinear

D. $AC = AB$

17. In the diagram $y = \underline{?}$.

A. 5   **B.** 15

C. (circled) 35   **D.** 105

18. Prove: $\ell_1 \parallel \ell_2$
Tell which hypothesis allows you to conclude the Prove.

A. $m\angle 1 = m\angle 4$

B. (circled) $m\angle 1 = m\angle 5$

C. $m\angle 1 + m\angle 3 = 180$

D. $m\angle 1 + m\angle 2 = 180$

19. If $m\angle 1 = m\angle 2$, you can conclude that $\underline{?}$.

A. $m\angle 3 = m\angle 5$

B. (circled) ℓ_1 and ℓ_2 are parallel

C. $\angle 1$ and $\angle 2$ form a linear pair

D. $\angle 1$ and $\angle 4$ are vertical

20. If $m\angle 1 = m\angle 2$, then $\underline{?}$.

A. $\angle 1$ and $\angle 2$ are complementary

B. $\angle 1$ and $\angle 2$ are obtuse

C. (circled) Lines m and ℓ are perpendicular

D. Lines m and ℓ are skew

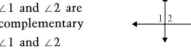

CHAPTER
4

Parallel Lines and Planes

Chapter Overview

A postulate that relates parallelism of two lines to congruence of corresponding angles is introduced. Theorems specifying other conditions that guarantee parallelism follow.

A lesson devoted to indirect proof builds upon experiences with indirect reasoning outside of mathematics.

Theorems and constructions regarding parallel lines and lines perpendicular to a given line through a given point are also presented. Analogous results are applied to a plane.

Theorems involving the sum of the measures of the angles of a triangle and of any convex polygon are derived in the last lessons.

Perspectives

Lesson 4–1 connects parallelism with the angles formed when lines are cut by a transversal.

The theorems use the postulate concerning corresponding angles to prove that two lines are parallel if and only if they are perpendicular to the same line. The criterion of equal slopes for parallel lines in the coordinate model is also stated and applied.

Lesson 4–2 completes the main Euclidean results dealing with parallel lines cut by a transversal. Two theorems deal with alternate interior angles, and two deal with interior angles on the same side of the transversal.

Lesson 4–3 approaches indirect reasoning as a natural thought process. By seeing indirect proof developed in connection to real situations, students are able to grasp its application in geometry.

Proof by contrapositive is treated as indirect proof.

Lesson 4–4 includes Theorem 4–7, which establishes the existence and the uniqueness of a line parallel to a given line through a point not on the line. The "Parallel Postulate" states that there is not more than one such line.

Other theorems concerning parallel and perpendicular lines and the slope criteria for both parallelism and perpendicularity are also studied in this lesson.

Lesson 4–5 states and proves some three-dimensional counterparts of earlier theorems. Encourage students to provide other three-dimensional analogs to earlier theorems.

The idea of a dihedral angle (an angle formed by two intersecting planes) is applied informally.

Lesson 4–6 concentrates on triangles which are basic to Euclid's approach to geometry. This lesson gives the definitions and classifications relating to triangles that form the foundation for theorems proved in later chapters.

Triangles are important in construction because they are the only rigid polygons; that is, an angle cannot be changed without changing the length of a side.

Pacing Chart for Chapter 4

Lesson	Objectives	Basic Course	Average Course	Extended Course
4–1	Use the postulate concerning corresponding angles and theorems about parallel lines with perpendicular transversals.	1	1	1
4–2	Use theorems about parallel lines and alternate interior angles or interior angles on the same side of the transversal.	1	1	1
4–3	Write indirect proofs.	1	1	2
4–4	Use theorems about parallels and perpendiculars to a given line through a given point.	$1\frac{1}{2}$	1	1
4–5	Use theorems about parallel planes and about lines perpendicular to planes.	$1\frac{1}{2}$	1	1
4–6	Identify triangles according to sides and according to angles.	$1\frac{1}{2}$	1	1
4–7	Use theorems about the sum of the measures of the angles of a triangle.	$1\frac{1}{2}$	1	1
4–8	Name and classify polygons by their number of sides and the characteristics of sides and angles.	$1\frac{1}{2}$	1	1
4–9	Find the sum of the measures of the interior as well as the exterior angles of a convex polygon.	$1\frac{1}{2}$	1	1
Review		1	1	1
Test		1	1	1
Total		14 days	11 days	12 days

Lesson 4-7 introduces Theorem 4–14, which involves the sum of the measures of the angles of a triangle. This is an important statement in Euclidean geometry. In non-Euclidean geometries, this sum could be more or less than 180.

Lesson 4-8 provides the necessary vocabulary to study polygons. Polygons are classified using many of the same criteria and terms as for triangles.

Lesson 4-9 shows how the study of geometry contributes to the development of the following **problem-solving strategies**:
1. Organizing data.
2. Searching for patterns.
3. Making conjectures.
4. Testing conjectures.

Inductive techniques are used to develop the concepts that are proved in Theorems 4–20 and 4–21 concerning interior and exterior angles of a convex polygon.

CHAPTER OPENER

The bases of each set of hurdles are an example of parallel lines, lines that do not meet even when extended and that are equidistant from each other throughout their entire length. Each participant jumps hurdles that are positioned in parallel planes along the track before the race begins.

ANSWERS

The edge of the track is perpendicular to the line; the lines are parallel to each other.

Parallel Lines and Planes

Chapter 4

Think about the lines containing the bases of each set of hurdles. How is the edge of the track related to these lines? How are these lines related to each other?

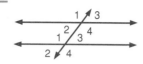

4-1 Parallel Lines and Corresponding Angles

On the track shown on the facing page, either edge forms equal corresponding angles—in this case, right angles—with the lines containing the sets of hurdles. You can see that the sets of hurdles are parallel.

In the diagram at the right, corresponding angles 1 and 2 are equal. Use a tracing of lines p and ℓ to check if ℓ can be slid **Yes** along p to coincide with m. Are lines ℓ and m parallel? Recall that in Lesson 2-2 you conjectured that if two parallel lines are cut by a transversal, the corresponding angles formed are equal. Together, these conjectures suggest Postulate 15.

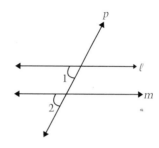

Postulate 15

Two coplanar lines cut by a transversal are parallel if and only if a pair of corresponding angles are equal.

Postulate 15 consists of these two "if . . . then" statements:

If two parallel lines are cut by a transversal, then a pair of corresponding angles are equal. (Lines ∥ ⇒ corr. ∠s =.)

If two lines are cut by a transversal so that a pair of corresponding angles are equal, then the lines are parallel. (Corr. ∠s = ⇒ lines ∥.)

When two coplanar lines are cut by a transversal, *four* pairs of corresponding angles are formed. We proved in Exercise 25 of Lesson 3-6 that if there is one pair of equal corresponding angles, then there are four pairs. In the figure at the right, if any of the following is true then they are all true: $m\angle 1 = m\angle 5$, $m\angle 2 = m\angle 6$, $m\angle 3 = m\angle 7$, and $m\angle 4 = m\angle 8$.

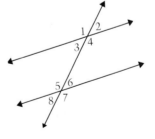

If two lines are parallel, you can use Postulate 15, as below, to show that any pair of corresponding angles are equal.

Example 1
Suppose $\ell \parallel m$. Find the measures of $\angle 1$ and $\angle 2$.

Solution

$m\angle 1 = m\angle 2$ *Postulate 15 implies that $m\angle 1 = m\angle 2$.*

$2x + 7 = x + 21$ *Substitution Property*

$x = 14$ *Subtraction Property*

$m\angle 1 = 2(14) + 7 = 35$, and $m\angle 2 = m\angle 1 = 35$.

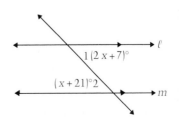

LESSON 4-1

Resources

Carpenter's square
Compass
Plumb line
Straightedge
   Teaching Aid 9, models of
     parallel lines
Visual Aid 9, models of
     parallel lines
Worksheet 4-1
Extension 4-1
Computer Activities 4-1

OBJECTIVE

Use the postulate concerning corresponding angles and theorems about parallel lines with perpendicular transversals.

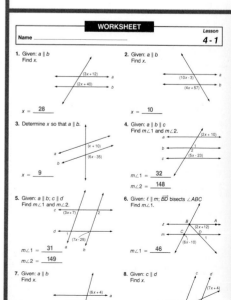

TEACHING NOTES

Students may be able to generate a conjecture about Theorem 4–1 by using **concrete materials** such as a carpenter's square.

As a **group activity**, have students make a conjecture about lines on a football field that are perpendicular to the same line. This leads into Theorem 4–2. Discuss the need for the phrase "in a plane" in Theorem 4–2.

In **Example 3**, any two vertical lines (equations of the form $x = k$) are parallel even though the slopes are undefined.

Steps such as $2 = 2$ gradually will be omitted from the proofs when not necessary. The placement of the given facts in proofs will also vary.

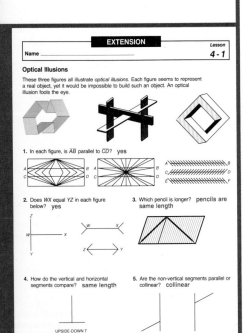

EXTENSION

Name _____

Lesson **4-1**

Optical Illusions

These three figures all illustrate *optical illusions*. Each figure seems to represent a real object, yet it would be impossible to build such an object. An optical illusion fools the eye.

1. In each figure, is $\overline{AB}$ parallel to $\overline{CD}$? yes

2. Does *WX* equal *YZ* in each figure below? yes

3. Which pencil is longer? pencils are same length

4. How do the vertical and horizontal segments compare? same length

UPSIDE-DOWN T

5. Are the non-vertical segments parallel or collinear? collinear

POGGENDORF

The hurdles on the track also suggest Theorems 4-1 and 4-2.

Theorem 4-1

If a transversal is perpendicular to one of two parallel lines, then it is perpendicular to the other.

Given   Lines ℓ and m cut by transversal t; $\ell \parallel m$; $t \perp \ell$

Prove $t \perp m$

Plan for Proof   Label corresponding angles, $\angle 1$ and $\angle 2$. Show $m\angle 1 = m\angle 2$ by Postulate 15. Show $\angle 2$ is a right angle.

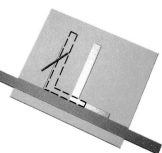

You are asked to prove Theorem 4-1 in Exercise 24. Theorem 4-2, to be proved in Exercise 25, is a direct result of Postulate 15.

Theorem 4-2

In a plane, if two lines are perpendicular to the same line, then they are parallel.

Given   Coplanar lines n, m, and t; $n \perp t$; $m \perp t$

Prove $n \parallel m$

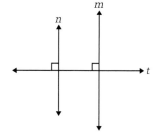

Example 2

Draftsman Ron Jenks used a carpenter's square and a straightedge to draw these segments. How do you know they are parallel?

Solution

The straightedge is a transversal perpendicular to each of the two segments. By Theorem 4-2, the segments are parallel.

In Lesson 2-2, you saw that two lines are parallel if and only if they have the same slope. In Exercise 32, you are to give an argument showing that if (x_1, y_1) and (x_2, y_2) are any two points in a nonvertical line with the equation $y = mx + b$, then the slope $m = \dfrac{y_2 - y_1}{x_2 - x_1}$.

Example 3

Give the slope of a line parallel to $\overleftrightarrow{AB}$ if A and B have coordinates $(7, 12)$ and $(-1, -4)$, respectively.

Solution

The slope m of $\overleftrightarrow{AB}$ is $\dfrac{y_2 - y_1}{x_2 - x_1} = \dfrac{-4 - 12}{-1 - 7} = \dfrac{-16}{-8} = 2$.

Any line parallel to $\overleftrightarrow{AB}$ must have the same slope, 2.

Assignment Guide

Basic: 1–15, 33–40
Average: 2–14 (even), 16–29, 33–40
Extended: 2–22 (even), 24–40

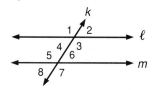

Checking for Understanding 5. Post. 15, Thm. 4–1, Thm. 4–2
Which postulate or theorem supports each statement?

1. If $n \parallel m$, then $m\angle 1 = m\angle 5$. Post. 15

2. If $\ell \perp n$ and $n \parallel m$, then $\ell \perp m$. Thm. 4–1

3. If $m\angle 3 = m\angle 7$, then $n \parallel m$. Post. 15

4. If $n \perp \ell$ and $m \perp \ell$, then $n \parallel m$. Thm. 4–2

5. What can you add to your inventory of geometric facts?

6. Give an equation of a line parallel to $y = -6x$. Sample: $y = -6x + 1$

7. Find the slope of a line through $A(4, -5)$ and $B(-2, 8)$. $\dfrac{-13}{6}$

Written Exercises

Set A Find each measure, given $m\angle 3 = 102$, $j \parallel k$, and $m \parallel n$.

1. $m\angle 11$ 102   **2.** $m\angle 7$ 102   **3.** $m\angle 10$ 78

Tell which pair of lines must be parallel, given each pair of equal angles. **4.** $j \parallel k$ **5.** $m \parallel n$ **6.** $m \parallel n$

4. $m\angle 1 = m\angle 5$ **5.** $m\angle 4 = m\angle 12$ **6.** $m\angle 8 = m\angle 16$

7. The crossarms of a telephone pole are perpendicular to the pole. Give the theorem that explains why the crossarms are parallel. Thm. 4–2

8. Is there any danger of collision if oil tankers A and B continue on the same course? Why or why not?

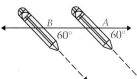

Find the slope of the line containing each set of points.

9. $(-3, 7)$, $(5, 2)$ $-\dfrac{5}{8}$ **10.** $(4, -2)$, $(0, 3)$ $-\dfrac{5}{4}$

11. Sketch the graphs of these equations on the same set of axes. Which ones appear to be parallel?

  a. $y = 4x + 1$ **b.** $y - 4x = 3$ **c.** $2y = 8x + 6$

12. Given: $m\angle 1 = m\angle 3$
   Prove: $m\angle 2 = m\angle 4$

13. Given: $\overleftrightarrow{BC} \parallel \overleftrightarrow{DE}$; $m\angle 1 = m\angle 2$
   Prove: $m\angle 2 = m\angle 3$

14. Given: $m\angle 1 = m\angle 3$; $m\angle 1 = m\angle 2$
   Prove: $m\angle 3 = m\angle 4$

15. The opposite sides of each street are parallel. What are the measures of the angles formed at the other three corners? 120; 60; 120

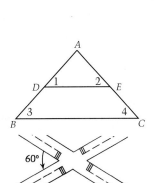

Additional Examples

Example 1

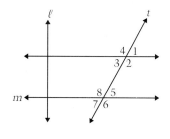

Given: $\ell \parallel m$;
   $m\angle 1 = 10x - 26$;
   $m\angle 6 = 3x + 11$
Find $m\angle 1$ and $m\angle 6$. 124; 56

Example 2
The rows of seats in a classroom are all perpendicular to the line where the back wall meets the floor. Explain how you know they are parallel.
Theorem 4–2

Example 3
Give the slope of a line parallel to $\overleftrightarrow{PQ}$ if P and Q have coordinates $(-3, 6)$ and $(4, -15)$, respectively.
$m = \dfrac{-15 - 6}{4 - -3} = \dfrac{-21}{7} = -3$

Error Analysis Some students think that lines cut by a transversal are parallel. Therefore, they conclude that corresponding angles are always equal. Emphasize that any two coplanar lines can be cut by a transversal, and use drawings of obviously nonparallel lines cut by a transversal whenever possible.

ANSWERS

Written Exercises

8. No; by Post. 15, the paths of the tankers are $\parallel$, and by the def. of $\parallel$ lines, the paths will never intersect.

19a. $y = 3x - 5$; **b.** $y = -5x + 3$; **c.** $y = 3x + 6$; **a** ∥ **c**; slopes are =.

20. Yes; $\frac{1}{2}$ is the slope of both lines.

24. Proof: 1. Lines ℓ and m cut by transversal t; $\ell \parallel m$; $t \perp \ell$ (Given) 2. ∠1 is a rt. ∠. (2 ⊥ lines form 4 rt. ∠s. [1]) 3. $m\angle 1 = 90$ (Def. of rt. ∠ [2]) 4. $m\angle 1 = m\angle 2$ (Lines ∥ ⇒ corres. ∠s =. [1]) 5. $m\angle 2 = 90$ (Substitution Prop. [3, 4]) 6. ∠2 is a rt. ∠. (Def. of rt. ∠ [5]) 7. $t \perp m$ (Def. of ⊥ lines [6])

25. Proof: 1. Coplanar lines n, m and t; $n \perp t$; $m \perp t$ (Given) 2. ∠1 and ∠2 are rt. ∠s. (2 ⊥ lines form 4 rt. ∠s. [1]) 3. $m\angle 1 = m\angle 2$ (All rt. ∠s are =. [2]) 4. $n \parallel m$ (Corres. ∠s = ⇒ lines ∥. [3])

26. No; if the two lines were noncoplanar, then they would be skew lines, not ∥ lines.

28. If the vert. sides of the painting are aligned so that they are ∥ to the plumb line, then the horizontal sides of the painting will be ⊥ to the plumb line and ∥ to the horizontal line where the wall and the floor meet.

29. Align the carpenter's square so that one edge is ∥ to the level shelf. Then the vertical edge is ⊥ to the level shelf. Align the new shelf so that it is ⊥ to the vertical edge of the carpenter's square. It will be ∥ to the first shelf by Thm. 4–2.

FOLLOW-UP

More Practice

• Worksheet 4–1

Extension

Have students draw a triangle. Construct a line through each vertex (corner point) parallel to the opposite side (side across from it).

Set B If $\overleftrightarrow{AC} \parallel \overleftrightarrow{DB}$, find x and the measures of ∠1 and ∠2.

16. $m\angle 1 = 25(x - 104)$; $m\angle 2 = 3(x - 82)$

17. $m\angle 1 = x + 27$; $m\angle 2 = 2x - 36$

18. $m\angle 1 = 3x - 10$; $m\angle 2 = x + 70$

16. $x = 107$; $m\angle 1 = m\angle 2 = 75$

17. $x = 63$; $m\angle 1 = m\angle 2 = 90$

18. $x = 40$; $m\angle 1 = m\angle 2 = 110$

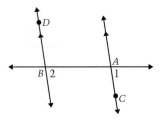

19. Write each equation in the form $y = mx + b$ and indicate which, if any, are equations of parallel lines. Explain.
  a. $3x - y = 5$ **b.** $5x + y = 3$ **c.** $6x - 2y + 12 = 0$

20. Points $A(-5, 4)$ and $B(5, 9)$ are in ℓ and $C(-1, -2)$ and $D(7, 2)$ are in k. Are ℓ and k parallel? Explain.

21. What is the slope of any horizontal line? 0

Give the slope of a line parallel to ℓ if ℓ contains

22. $C(8, 3)$ and $D(-2, 7)$. $-\frac{2}{5}$ **23.** $E(-6, 2)$ and $F(0, 0)$. $-\frac{1}{3}$

24. Prove Theorem 4-1.   **25.** Prove Theorem 4-2.

26. If Theorem 4-2 did not specify that the lines were "in a plane," would it be a true statement? Explain.

27. Next to the painting is a plumb line (weight hanging by a string). Is the plumb line perpendicular to the horizontal line where the wall and the floor meet? Yes

28. Use Theorem 4-1 to explain how the plumb line can be used to straighten the painting.

29. Explain how to use a carpenter's square to get a shelf parallel to a shelf that is already on a wall. Which theorem verifies that the shelves are parallel?

Set C **30.** Prove: If two parallel lines are cut by a transversal, then bisectors of corresponding angles are parallel.

31. Prove the converse of the statement in Exercise 30.

32. Show that if (x_1, y_1) and (x_2, y_2) are any two points on the graph of $y = mx + b$, then the slope $m = \frac{y_2 - y_1}{x_2 - x_1}$.

▲ **Review** Use this statement: The bisectors of the angles of a linear pair are perpendicular.

33. Draw a diagram; write the Given and the Prove needed for a proof.

34. Write a two-column proof.

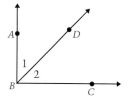

35. Given that ∠1 and ∠2 are complementary, search the inventory to find a conclusion. Then find a second conclusion that follows from the first.

36. What is a *postulate*?   **37.** What is a *theorem*?

≡ **Thinking**
▽ **Ahead** On a sheet of lined paper, use a straightedge to darken two lines with your pencil or pen as shown in the photo. Call these lines *r* and *s*. Draw a transversal *t* to *r* and *s*, labeling ∠1, ∠2, ∠3, and ∠4 as shown.

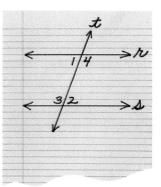

38. Trace each angle on another sheet of paper. Can you fit ∠1 exactly over ∠2? **Yes**

39. Repeat Exercise 38 with other lines and transversals. What conjecture is suggested?

40. For each set of parallel lines and transversals, find m∠1 + m∠3 and m∠4 + m∠2. What conjecture can you make?

⚲ Construction Exercises

Construction 6

Through a point not on a given line, construct a line parallel to the given line.

Given   Line ℓ; point *P* not on line ℓ

Construct A line through *P* parallel to ℓ

Method   Step 1: Mark any point *A* on ℓ. Draw $\overrightarrow{AP}$ to determine ∠1.

Step 2: Using $\overrightarrow{AP}$ as one ray, construct ∠2 on the same side of $\overrightarrow{AP}$ as ∠1 so that m∠1 = m∠2. Label as *Q* the point where the arcs meet.

Step 3: Draw $\overleftrightarrow{PQ}$. Then $\overleftrightarrow{PQ} \parallel \ell$.

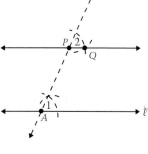

Trace the drawing at the right as needed.

1. Construct a line through *G* and parallel to *n*.

2. Construct a line through *G* and parallel to *t*.

3. Which postulate or theorem justifies these constructions?
Post. 15

---

1. What figures are formed by the constructed lines? triangles

2. Discuss any other observations.

• **Extension 4–1**

Computers

This computer activity can be completed using *The Geometric preSupposer: Points and Lines* or *GeoDraw*.

To introduce concepts covered in the next section, have students use the drawing tool to draw two parallel lines (or segments on parallel lines) and a transversal. Ask students to identify two pairs of alternate interior angles and two pairs of interior angles on the same side. Have students measure the angles in a pair of alternate interior angles and then find the sum of one of those angles with the interior angle on the same side of the transversal.

Guide students to notice the relationship between the measures of the two angles in a pair of alternate interior angles. They are equal. Then ask students if they can see a relationship between the measures of the two interior angles on the same side of the transversal. They are supplementary. Have students erase the transversal, draw a new transversal and repeat the measurements of interior angles as described above. Ask students to make a generalization about alternate interior angles formed by a transversal through two parallel lines and a generalization about interior angles on the same side of a transversal through two parallel lines.

• **Computer Activities 4–1**

LESSON 4-2

Resources

Teaching Aid 9, models of
   parallel lines
Visual Aid 9, models of parallel
   lines
Worksheet 4-2
Extension 4-2

OBJECTIVE

Use theorems about parallel lines
and alternate interior angles or interior angles on the same side of
the transversal.

4-2 Parallel Lines and Interior Angles

Postulate 15 states that if two parallel lines are cut by a
transversal, corresponding angles are equal. This postulate can
be used to prove that alternate interior angles are also equal.

Theorem 4-3

*If two parallel lines are cut by a transversal, then alternate
interior angles are equal. (Lines ∥ ⇒ alt. int. ∠s =.)*

Given   Lines ℓ and m cut by a transversal t; $\ell \parallel m$

Prove $m\angle 1 = m\angle 3$; $m\angle 2 = m\angle 4$

Plan for   Proof   Show vertical angles $\angle 1$ and $\angle 5$ are equal. Show
corresponding angles $\angle 5$ and $\angle 3$ are equal. Thus,
$m\angle 1 = m\angle 3$. Use a similar argument for $\angle 2$ and $\angle 4$.

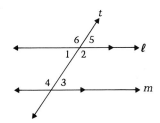

Proof

Statements	Reasons
1. ℓ and m cut by t; $\ell \parallel m$	1. Given
2. $m\angle 1 = m\angle 5$	2. Vert. ∠s are =.
3. $m\angle 5 = m\angle 3$	3. Lines ∥ ⇒ corr. ∠s =. [1]
4. $m\angle 1 = m\angle 3$	4. Transitive Prop. [2, 3]
5. $m\angle 2 = m\angle 6$	5. Vert. ∠s are =.
6. $m\angle 6 = m\angle 4$	6. Lines ∥ ⇒ __?__. [1] Corr. ∠s are =
7. $m\angle 2 = m\angle 4$	7. __?__ Transitive Prop. [5, 6]

Theorem 4-4 is the converse of Theorem 4-3. The proof of
Theorem 4-4 is left to Exercise 20.

Theorem 4-4

*If two lines are cut by a transversal so that a pair of alternate
interior angles are equal, then the lines are parallel. (Alt. int.
∠s = ⇒ lines ∥.)*

Parallel rulers at the right show how angles are related when
two parallel lines are cut by a transversal. Examine the interior
angles on the same side of the transversal. In the upper set of
rulers, $m\angle 1 = m\angle 2 = 90$, so the sum of the measures is 180.

In the lower set of rulers, $m\angle 1$ has increased while $m\angle 2$ has
decreased. The angles are no longer equal. What appears to be
the sum of their measures now? The answer is in Theorem 4-5.
180

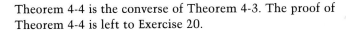

WORKSHEET   Lesson **4-2**

Name _____

Find the unknown angle measures.

1. Given: $k \parallel j$; $m\angle 4 = (3x + 8)$;
   $m\angle 6 = (2x + 12)$

   $m\angle 1 = \underline{104}$ $m\angle 2 = \underline{76}$
   $m\angle 3 = \underline{76}$ $m\angle 4 = \underline{104}$
   $m\angle 5 = \underline{104}$ $m\angle 6 = \underline{76}$
   $m\angle 7 = \underline{76}$ $m\angle 8 = \underline{104}$

2. Given: $k \parallel j$; $m\angle 3 = (5x + 3)$;
   $m\angle 5 = (5x + 7)$

   $m\angle 1 = \underline{92}$ $m\angle 2 = \underline{88}$
   $m\angle 3 = \underline{88}$ $m\angle 4 = \underline{92}$
   $m\angle 5 = \underline{92}$ $m\angle 6 = \underline{88}$
   $m\angle 7 = \underline{88}$ $m\angle 8 = \underline{92}$

3. Given: $k \parallel j$; $m\angle 2 = (3x - 2)$;
   $m\angle 7 = (7x - 10)$

   $m\angle 1 = \underline{176}$ $m\angle 2 = \underline{4}$
   $m\angle 3 = \underline{4}$ $m\angle 4 = \underline{176}$
   $m\angle 5 = \underline{176}$ $m\angle 6 = \underline{4}$
   $m\angle 7 = \underline{4}$ $m\angle 8 = \underline{176}$

Complete the following proof.

4. Given: $a \parallel b$ and is cut by t.
   Prove: $\angle 7$ and $\angle 1$ are supplementary.

Statements	Reasons
1. $a \parallel b$ and is cut by t.	1. Given
2. $\angle 3$ and $\angle 1$ form a linear pair.	2. Opp. rays form a linear pair.
3. $\angle 3$ and $\angle 1$ are supp.	3. Def. of linear pair [2]
4. $m\angle 3 + m\angle 1 = 180$	4. Def. of supp. ∠s [3]
5. $m\angle 3 = m\angle 7$	5. Lines ∥ ⇒ corr. ∠s = . [1]
6. $m\angle 7 + m\angle 1 = 180$	6. Substitution Prop. [4, 5]
7. $\angle 7$ and $\angle 1$ are supp.	7. Def. of supp. ∠s [6]

Theorem 4-5

If two parallel lines are cut by a transversal, then interior angles on the same side of the transversal are supplementary. (Lines ∥ ⇒ int. ∠s on the same side supp.)

Theorem 4-6 also relates to interior angles on the same side of the transversal.

Theorem 4-6

If two lines are cut by a transversal so that a pair of interior angles on the same side of the transversal are supplementary, then the lines are parallel. (Int. ∠s on the same side supp. ⇒ lines ∥.)

Theorems 4-5 and 4-6 are to be proved in Exercises 21 and 22.

Summary Parallel Lines

Properties of Parallel Lines

Corresponding angles are equal.
Alternate interior angles are equal.
Interior angles on the same side of a transversal are supplementary.
A line perpendicular to one line is perpendicular to another.

To Prove Lines Parallel, Show that:

The lines are coplanar and do not intersect.
Two corresponding angles are equal.
Two alternate interior angles are equal.
Two interior angles on the same side of a transversal are supplementary.
A transversal is perpendicular to each of two given lines.

Example 1

If $\ell \parallel m$, $m\angle 1 = 5y + 16$, and $m\angle 2 = y + 44$, find y, $m\angle 1$, and $m\angle 2$.

Solution

By Theorem 4-5, $\angle 1$ and $\angle 2$ are supplementary.

$$
\begin{aligned}
m\angle 1 + m\angle 2 &= 180 && \textit{Definition of supplementary } \angle s \\
(5y + 16) + (y + 44) &= 180 && \textit{Substitution Property} \\
6y + 60 &= 180 \\
6y &= 120 && \textit{Subtraction Property} \\
y &= 20 && \textit{Division Property}
\end{aligned}
$$

$m\angle 1 = 5(20) + 16 = 116$, and $m\angle 2 = 20 + 44 = 64$.

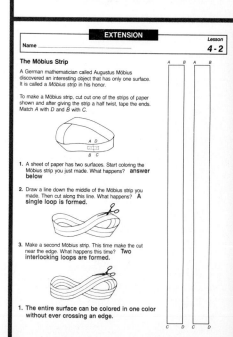

Assignment Guide

Basic: 1–19, 35–44
Average: 2–20 (even), 21–32, 35–44
Extended: 2–24 (even), 26–44

Additional Example

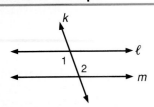

Given: $\ell \parallel m$;
  $m\angle 1 = 5x - 5$;
  $m\angle 2 = 3x + 41$
Find $m\angle 1$ and $m\angle 2$. both 110

Error Analysis In using Theorems 4–3 to 4–6 as reasons in a proof, students may be confused between using a particular statement and using its converse. Review ideas from Chapter 2 concerning affirming-the-hypothesis arguments.

ANSWERS

Written Exercises

4. $k \parallel \ell$ (Thm. 4–4)
5. $k \parallel \ell$ (Thm. 4–4)
6. none
7. none
8. $k \parallel \ell$ (Thm. 4–6)
9. $m \parallel n$ (Thm. 3–8, Thm. 4–6)
10. none
11. none
13. $\angle 1$ and $\angle 3$ are corr. $\angle$s; by Post. 15, corr. $\angle$s = $\Rightarrow$ $\parallel$ lines
17. Proof: 1. $\ell \parallel m$ (Given) 2. $m\angle 1$ = $m\angle 4$ ($\parallel$ lines $\Rightarrow$ corres. $\angle$s =. [1]) 3. $m\angle 1 = m\angle 2$ (Given) 4. $m\angle 2 = m\angle 4$ (Substitution Prop. [2, 3])
18. Proof: 1. $m\angle 1 = m\angle 2$ (Given) 2. $m\angle 2 = m\angle 4$ (Given) 3. $m\angle 1 = m\angle 4$ (Transitive Prop. [1, 2]) 4. $\ell \parallel m$ (Corres. $\angle$s = $\Rightarrow$ lines $\parallel$. [3])
19. Proof: 1. $\angle 1$ and $\angle 5$ are supp.

Checking for Understanding

1. What statements in this lesson can be added to your inventory? Thm. 4–3, Thm. 4–4, Thm. 4–5, Thm. 4–6

If $\ell \parallel m$, find $m\angle 5$ given each measure.

2. $m\angle 1 = 74$ 74   **3.** $m\angle 3 = 66$ 66   **4.** $m\angle 4 = 112$ 68

If $m\angle 3 = 75$, what must be the measure of each angle in order for ℓ and m to be parallel?

5. $\angle 1$ 75   **6.** $\angle 2$ 105   **7.** $\angle 6$ 105

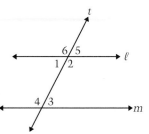

Written Exercises

Set A   If $m \parallel n$ and $k \parallel \ell$, give the measure of $\angle 12$ in each case.

1. $m\angle 2 = 75$ 75   **2.** $m\angle 8 = 80$ 80   **3.** $m\angle 1 = 110$ 70

For each equation, tell which lines are parallel. If none are parallel, write *none*. Give the postulate(s) or theorem(s) that justify each set of parallel lines.

4. $m\angle 5 = m\angle 15$ **5.** $m\angle 6 = m\angle 16$
6. $m\angle 14 + m\angle 8 = 180$ **7.** $m\angle 3 = m\angle 10$
8. $m\angle 2 + m\angle 11 = 180$ **9.** $m\angle 9 + m\angle 16 = 180$
10. $m\angle 12 = m\angle 5$ **11.** $m\angle 10 = m\angle 8$

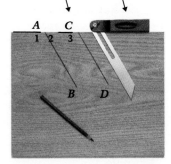

The photo shows a carpenter's *bevel*, a tool used to draw parallel line segments.

12. How are $m\angle 1$ and $m\angle 3$ related? =
13. How does Postulate 15 assure that $\overleftrightarrow{AB} \parallel \overleftrightarrow{CD}$?
14. What is $m\angle 2 + m\angle 3$? Why? 180; Thm. 4–5

In a certain ladder, the rungs are perpendicular to the sides.

15. Give three theorems that explain why the rungs are parallel to one another. Thm. 4–2, Thm. 4–4, Thm. 4–6
16. Are the sides of the ladder necessarily parallel? Yes

17. Given: $\ell \parallel m$; $m\angle 1 = m\angle 2$
    Prove: $m\angle 2 = m\angle 4$
18. Given: $m\angle 1 = m\angle 2$; $m\angle 2 = m\angle 4$
    Prove: $\ell \parallel m$
19. Given: $\angle 1$ and $\angle 5$ are supplementary.
    Prove: $\ell \parallel m$

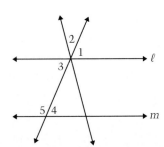

Set B **20.** Prove Theorem 4-4.   **21.** Prove Theorem 4-5.

22. Prove Theorem 4-6.

23. Given: $\overleftrightarrow{BC} \parallel \overleftrightarrow{EF}$; $m\angle 1 + m\angle 4 = 180$
Prove: $\overleftrightarrow{BA} \parallel \overleftrightarrow{ED}$

24. Given: $\overleftrightarrow{BC} \parallel \overleftrightarrow{EF}$; $\overleftrightarrow{BA} \parallel \overleftrightarrow{ED}$
Prove: $\angle 1$ and $\angle 4$ are supplementary.

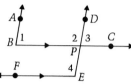

25. Given: $\overleftrightarrow{HJ} \parallel \overleftrightarrow{ML}$; $\overleftrightarrow{HG} \parallel \overleftrightarrow{KL}$
Prove: $m\angle 5 = m\angle 8$

26. Refer to Exercises 24 and 25 to complete the following conjecture: "If the sides of two coplanar angles lie in parallel lines, then the angles are either __?__ or __?__." **equal; supp.**

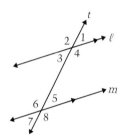

Given $\ell \parallel m$, find x and the measures of the angles in each exercise.

27. $m\angle 3 = 2x + 16$; $m\angle 5 = 7x - 4$

28. $m\angle 4 = 8x - 80$; $m\angle 5 = -2x + 116$

29. $m\angle 3 = x^2 - 2x$; $m\angle 6 = 2x + 131$

30. Use the fact that supplements of equal angles are equal to prove that if $m\angle 3 = m\angle 5$, then $m\angle 4 = m\angle 6$.

31. $\angle 1$ and $\angle 7$ are *alternate exterior angles*, as are $\angle 2$ and $\angle 8$. Make and prove two conjectures similar to Theorems 4-3 and 4-4 involving alternate exterior angles.

32. Give a counterexample for this statement: If two lines are perpendicular to the same line, then they are parallel.

Set C **33.** Prove: If two parallel lines are cut by a transversal, then the bisectors of alternate interior angles are parallel.

34. Prove the converse of the statement in Exercise 33.

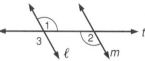

Thinking Ahead

40a.

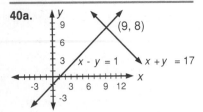

b.

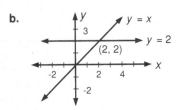

c.

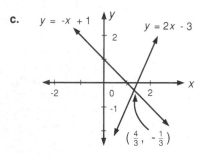

More Practice

• Worksheet 4–2

Extension

As a **group activity**, have students explore the connection between parallel lines and alternate exterior angles and between parallel lines and exterior angles on the same side of the transversal. Students should be able to generate and prove some conjectures.

• Extension 4–2

◆ **Review** **35.** If $\ell \parallel m$, find $m\angle 1$. 130

36. Give the slope of a line parallel to $\overleftrightarrow{XY}$ if X and Y have coordinates $(3, 5)$ and $(-2, -5)$, respectively. 2

37. What information is given by the markings on the diagram at the right? $m\angle A = m\angle E$; $\angle D$ and $\angle B$ are rt. $\angle$s; $AC = CE$

38. If $p \Rightarrow q$ and $q \Rightarrow r$, then $\underline{\ ?\ }$. $p \Rightarrow r$

39. The $\underline{\ ?\ }$ in the proof of a conditional is the hypothesis stated in terms of the diagram. Given

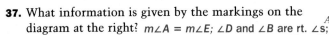
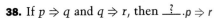
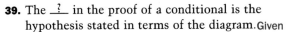
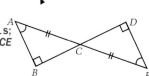

≡ **Thinking** **40.** Solve each pair of equations simultaneously.
▼ **Ahead** Graph the equations and label your solutions.

　a. $x - y = 1$　　**b.** $y = x$　　**c.** $y = 2x - 3$
　　　$x + y = 17$　　　$y = 2$　　　$y = -x + 1$

41. What does Theorem 3-1 mean in the coordinate model?

42. Sally's favorite vase was broken Tuesday afternoon. She assumed that her dog Sparky—not her cat Mittens—was responsible. Tuesday evening Sally's brother said he and Sparky had been at the park all afternoon. How does this affect Sally's conclusion about Sparky and the vase? What other conclusion can Sally draw?

43. Write the contrapositive of Theorem 4-5. Is the statement you wrote true?

44. What is the contrapositive property? (HINT: See Lesson 2-6.) What does this suggest about the answer to Exercise 43?

Challenge

Mrs. Garcia, a geometry teacher, has three sons. When Mr. Edwards, the algebra teacher, asked how old they were, Mrs. Garcia said, "The product of their ages is 72. The sum of their ages is the number I wrote on the chalkboard."

Intrigued, Mr. Edwards rushed to Mrs. Garcia's classroom. When he returned, he said, "I still don't have enough information to tell their ages."

"That's right, but the oldest boy plays the violin," said Mrs. Garcia.

How old are the boys? How do you know? 3, 3, and 8; of the possible number triples, only 6, 6, and 2 and 3, 3, and 8 have the same sum, 14; there is only one *oldest* boy.

Warm-Up Review

1. "Line *r* is parallel to line *s*" is the ___?___ of the statement "Line *r* is not parallel to line *s*." Negation
2. A model drawn to show that a statement is false is a(n) ___?___. Counterexample
3. The hypothesis of "If it rains, then the baseball game will be cancelled" is ___?___. It rains

4-3 Indirect Proof

This lithograph by Escher is entitled "Ascending and Descending." Could a stairway such as the one being traveled by the monks exist in the real world? The following example of *indirect reasoning* shows that this stairway could not exist.

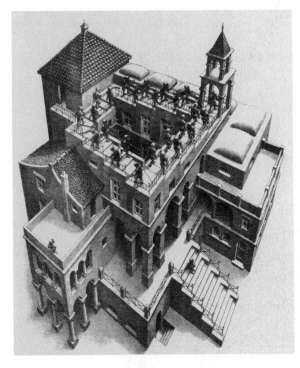

Either (1) the stairway could exist in the real world, *or* (2) the stairway could not exist in the real world.

Suppose the stairway could exist in the real world.

Then each stair would be at a level higher than that of the previous stair. So after completing a circuit, a monk would be at a higher level than that at which he began.

But this contradicts the lithograph which shows each monk on the same level at the end of a circuit as he was at the beginning.

Therefore, the assumption that the stairway could exist in the real world *is false*.

We conclude that the stairway could not exist in the real world.

LESSON 4–3

Resources

Teaching Aid 9, models of parallel lines
Visual Aid 9, models of parallel lines
Worksheet 4–3
Extension 4–3

OBJECTIVE

Write indirect proofs.

TEACHING NOTES

Use the Escher lithograph as a **group activity** to introduce the topic of indirect reasoning. Ask students to comment on the possible existence of such a stairway.

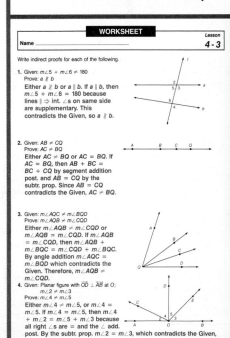

WORKSHEET

Name _____   Lesson **4 - 3**

Write indirect proofs for each of the following.

1. Given: $m\angle 5 + m\angle 6 \neq 180$
   Prove: $a \nparallel b$
   Either $a \nparallel b$ or $a \parallel b$. If $a \parallel b$, then $m\angle 5 + m\angle 6 = 180$ because lines $\parallel \Rightarrow$ int. $\angle$s on same side are supplementary. This contradicts the Given, so $a \nparallel b$.

2. Given: $AB \neq CQ$
   Prove: $AC \neq BQ$
   Either $AC \neq BQ$ or $AC = BQ$. If $AC = BQ$, then $AB + BC = BC + CQ$ by segment addition post. and $AB = CQ$ by the subtr. prop. Since $AB = CQ$ contradicts the Given, $AC \neq BQ$.

3. Given: $m\angle AQC \neq m\angle BQD$
   Prove: $m\angle AQB \neq m\angle CQD$
   Either $m\angle AQB \neq m\angle CQD$ or $m\angle AQB = m\angle CQD$. If $m\angle AQB = m\angle CQD$, then $m\angle AQB + m\angle BQC = m\angle CQD + m\angle BQC$. By angle addition $m\angle AQC = m\angle BQD$ which contradicts the Given. Therefore, $m\angle AQB \neq m\angle CQD$.

4. Given: Planar figure with $\overline{OD} \perp \overline{AB}$ at O; $m\angle 2 \neq m\angle 3$
   Prove: $m\angle 4 \neq m\angle 5$
   Either $m\angle 4 \neq m\angle 5$, or $m\angle 4 = m\angle 5$. If $m\angle 4 = m\angle 5$, then $m\angle 4 + m\angle 2 = m\angle 5 + m\angle 3$ because all right $\angle$s are = and the $\angle$ add. post. By the subtr. prop. $m\angle 2 = m\angle 3$, which contradicts the Given, so $m\angle 4 \neq m\angle 5$.

Focus on the process of concluding that the original assumption is false when a contradiction of a known fact is encountered.

Review the concept of negation. In **Example 2**, the "alternatives" are the statement of the desired conclusion and its negation.

Emphasize that an indirect proof is a proof, even though it is not in two-column form.

Additional Examples

Example 1
To indirectly prove the statement "If $n \perp \ell$ and $m\angle 1 \neq m\angle 2$, then ℓ is not parallel to t," what would you assume?
ℓ is parallel to t

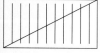
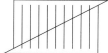

EXTENSION

Name _____

Lesson **4-3**

The Disappearing Line Segment

Trace the first rectangle, then cut out the rectangle and cut it into two pieces by cutting along the diagonal. In the original rectangle there are ten parallel line segments. When the two pieces are arranged as shown in the second figure, there are only nine line segments. What happened to the other segment?

The trick above is based on the *principle of concealed distribution.* If you examine the puzzle closely, you see that eight segments in the original rectangle are cut into two, and the sixteen parts have been redistributed with the two outer segments to form nine segments.

Copy the figure below. Then cut the figure into two strips and slide the bottom half to obtain a figure with only five faces. **student activity**

Example 1
Use indirect reasoning to justify the conclusion in this article from a company's newsletter.

Jennifer Gibson is our new Sales Representative. During her first 6 months on the job, she added 20 new accounts. That's quite an accomplishment– 4 or more new accounts in one month.

Solution

ALTERNATIVES: *Either* (1) she added 4 or more new accounts during at least one of the months, *or* (2) she added fewer than 4 new accounts each month.

ASSUMPTION: *Suppose* she opened fewer than 4 accounts each month.

ARGUMENT: *Then* she added 3 or fewer new accounts each month. If so, the total number of added accounts would be 6 times this number—18 or fewer new accounts.

CONTRADICTION: *But this contradicts* the fact that she added 20 new accounts.

FALSE ASSUMPTION: *Therefore, the assumption* that she added fewer than 4 new accounts each month *is false*.

CONCLUSION: *We conclude* that she added 4 or more new accounts during at least one of the months.

We often use this type of reasoning in geometry proofs.

Summary **Steps in an Indirect Proof**

1. List the alternatives, including the desired conclusion.
2. Assume that the alternative(s) to the conclusion are true.
3. Argue to a contradiction of a known fact—a definition, a postulate, a theorem, a real-number property, or a given fact.
4. Indicate that the assumption is false.
5. Conclude that the statement to be proved is true.

Indirect proofs are written in paragraphs, rather than in two columns. Later we will write other proofs in paragraph form as well.

In the next example, our assumption leads to a contradiction of the Given.

Example 2

Given: $\ell \parallel m$; t and ℓ are not $\perp$.

Prove: $m\angle 1 \neq 90$

Solution

ALTERNATIVES: *Either* (1) $m\angle 1 \neq 90$, *or* (2) $m\angle 1 = 90$.

ASSUMPTION: *Suppose* that $m\angle 1 = 90$.

ARGUMENT: *Then* by the definition of perpendicular, $t \perp m$. Since $\ell \parallel m$, and $t \perp m$, it follows that $t \perp \ell$.

CONTRADICTION: *But this contradicts* the given.

FALSE ASSUMPTION: *Therefore, the assumption* that $m\angle 1 = 90$ *is false.*

CONCLUSION: *We conclude* that $m\angle 1 \neq 90$.

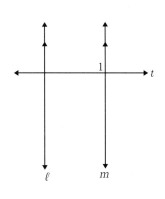

The proof of Theorem 3-1 was postponed because its second part required indirect reasoning. We now prove this theorem.

Theorem 3-1

If two lines intersect, then they intersect in one and only one point.

Given Two intersecting lines, ℓ and m

Prove *Part I* Lines ℓ and m intersect in at least one point.

Part II Lines ℓ and m intersect in only one point.

Proof *Part I* We know that the intersection of ℓ and m contains at least one point because it is given that the lines intersect.

Part II

ALTERNATIVES: *Either* (1) ℓ and m intersect in only one point, *or* (2) ℓ and m intersect in two or more points.

ASSUMPTION: *Suppose* ℓ and m intersect in two or more points. Call two of the points P and Q.

ARGUMENT: *Then* the two points, P and Q, would be contained in two lines, ℓ and m.

CONTRADICTION: *But this contradicts* the fact that, by the Line Postulate, two points are contained in one and only one line.

FALSE ASSUMPTION: *Therefore, the assumption* that ℓ and m intersect in two or more points *is false.*

CONCLUSION: *We conclude* that ℓ and m intersect in only one point.

Example 2

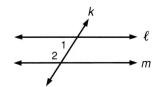

Given: $\ell \parallel m$; $\angle 1$ is acute.

Prove: $\angle 2$ is not acute.

Assume $\angle 2$ is acute. Because $\ell \parallel m$, $\angle 1$ and $\angle 2$ are supplementary. If both angles are acute, it contradicts the fact that they are supplementary. Therefore, $\angle 2$ is not acute.

Error Analysis Indirect proof is challenging for most students. Expect difficulties with the following:

1. Not knowing where to begin.

2. Not realizing a contradiction has been reached.

3. Not knowing what the contradiction implies.

4. Not being able to negate some statements.

ANSWERS

Written Exercises

4. Yes; if P lies on both ℓ and m then the lines intersect.

5. No; an acute $\angle$ is an $\angle$ whose measure is between 0 and 90, and $0 < 63 < 90$.

6. Yes; if B is between A and C, then $AB + BC = AC$ and AC must be greater than BC.

8. Assuming any days of the week, only one ends in "rsday": Thursday. Assuming any months of the year, only two end in "ary": Jan. and Feb. Since there are at most 29 days in Feb., it must be Jan.

15. Proof: *Either* $m\angle 1 = m\angle 4$ or $m\angle 1 \neq m\angle 4$. *Suppose that* $m\angle 1 = m\angle 4$. *Then* since $\angle 1$ and $\angle 4$ are = corres. $\angle$s, $\ell \parallel m$. *But this contradicts* the given fact that $\ell \not\parallel m$. *Therefore, the assumption* that $m\angle 1 = m\angle 4$ is false. *We conclude that* $m\angle 1 \neq m\angle 4$.

16. Proof: *Either* $\ell \parallel m$ or $\ell \not\parallel m$. *Suppose that* $\ell \parallel m$. *Then* since $\angle 2$ and $\angle 4$ are int. $\angle$s on the same side of the trans., $\angle 2$ and $\angle 4$ are supp. and by the def. of supp. $\angle$s $m\angle 2 + m\angle 4 = 180$. *But this contradicts* the Given. *Therefore, the assumption* that $\ell \parallel m$ is false. *We conclude that* $\ell \not\parallel m$.

17. Proof: *Either* the waterfall exists in the real world, *or* the waterfall cannot exist in the real world. *Suppose* the waterfall does exist in the real world. *Then* an object in the top of the waterfall would float down the falls and up the course to the top of the falls. Thus, the water flows uphill. This defies the law of gravity. *Therefore, the assumption* that the waterfall exists in the real world *is false*, and *we conclude* the waterfall cannot exist in the real world.

19. Proof: *Either* she did 20 or more sit-ups during at least one 30-second interval, *or* she did less than 20 sit-ups during every 30-second interval. *Suppose* Pat did

---

Assignment Guide

Basic: 1–16, 23–31
Average: 2–8 (even), 9–21, 23–31
Extended: 2–8 (even), 9–31

Recall that the proofs previous to this lesson were *direct* proofs; that is, they began with the hypothesis of the conditional to be proved and argued deductively to its conclusion.

An *indirect* proof begins with assuming the alternative(s) to the conclusion of the conditional to be proved and argues deductively to a contradiction of a known fact. This leads us to accept the conclusion as true.

Checking for Understanding

1. What is the meaning of the symbol $\neq$? the symbol $\not\parallel$? **Not =; not ∥**

2. In the Given of Example 2, would it be correct to write "$t \not\perp \ell$"? Why? **Yes; $\not\perp$ means not $\perp$.**

To prove each statement indirectly, what would you assume?

3. If $\angle A$ and $\angle B$ are complementary to $\angle C$, then $m\angle A = m\angle B$.

4. If $m\angle 1 + m\angle 2 = 180$ and $m\angle 1 = m\angle 2$, then $\ell \parallel n$. $\ell \not\parallel n$
   3. $m\angle A \neq m\angle B$

Written Exercises

Set A Give the definition, postulate, or theorem contradicted by each statement.

   1. Lines m and n intersect in points A and B. **Thm. 3–1**

   2. Right $\angle PXQ$ and acute $\angle QXR$ are a linear pair.

   3. Planes $\mathcal{H}$ and $\mathcal{E}$ contain intersecting lines m and t.
       2. Thm. 3–9 or Supp. Post.   **3.** Thm. 3–3

Are these pairs of statements contradictory? Explain.

   4. $\ell \parallel m$; point P lies on ℓ and m.

   5. $\angle D$ is acute; $m\angle D = 63$

   6. Point B is between A and C; $BC > AC$

   7. The announcement is faded. What day and date are the tryouts? **Thursday, January 30**

   8. Explain how you used indirect reasoning in Exercise 7.

In exercises 9–14, complete this proof of the second part of Theorem 3-2: A line and a point not on the line are contained in only one plane.
Given: Point P not on line ℓ
Prove: P and ℓ lie in only one plane.

   9. *Either* (1) __?__, or (2) P and ℓ lie in two or more planes. **P and ℓ lie in only 1 plane**

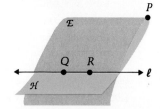

Sophomore Class
Play Tryouts
The Little Theater
...rsday at 7:00
...uary 30

10. *Suppose* __?__. *Call two of these planes E and H.*

11. *Then* line ℓ lies in both __?__. *By the* __?__ *Postulate,* ℓ contains at least two points, Q and R. *It is given that P does not lie in* $\overrightarrow{RQ}$ *(that is, line ℓ), so three noncollinear points,* __?__, __?__, *and* __?__, *all lie in E and also all lie in H.* **and E; Pts.; P; Q; R**

12. *But this contradicts the fact that, by the Plane Postulate, three noncollinear points* __?__.

13. *Therefore, the assumption that* __?__ *is* __?__.

14. *We conclude that* __?__. **P and ℓ lie in only 1 plane**

Write an indirect proof for each exercise.

15. Given: ℓ ∦ m
Prove: $m\angle 1 \neq m\angle 4$

16. Given: $m\angle 4 + m\angle 2 \neq 180$
Prove: ℓ ∦ m

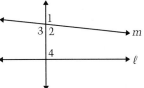

Set B **17.** Write an indirect argument to explain why this waterfall cannot exist in the real world.

18. Elena, Rick, and Dan are different heights. Who is tallest and who is shortest if only one of these statements is true? (1) Dan is tallest; (2) Rick is not tallest; and (3) Elena is not shortest.
18. Tallest: Rick; shortest: Dan

19. Write an indirect argument to support the following reasoning: Pat did 90 sit-ups in 2 minutes. This means she must have 20 or more sit-ups during at least one 30-second interval.

Write an indirect proof for each exercise.

20. Given: Points D and E are in the interior of ∠ABC; B, D, and E are not collinear.
Prove: $\overrightarrow{BD}$ and $\overrightarrow{BE}$ are not both bisectors of ∠ABC.

21. Two intersecting lines lie in only one plane. (Theorem 3-3, Part II)

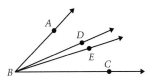

Set C **22.** Given: $\overleftrightarrow{RS}$ and $\overleftrightarrow{TW}$ are skew lines.
Prove: $\overleftrightarrow{RS}$ and $\overleftrightarrow{SW}$ are skew lines.

less than 20 sit-ups during each interval. *Then* she did less than 80 sit-ups in 2 minutes. *But this contradicts* the fact that she did 90 sit-ups in 2 minutes. *Therefore, the assumption* that she did less than 20 sit-ups during each 30-second interval *is false. We conclude* she did 20 or more sit-ups during at least one 30-second interval.

20. Proof: *Either* $\overrightarrow{BD}$ and $\overrightarrow{BE}$ are both bisectors of ∠ABC, *or* they are not both bisectors of ∠ABC. *Suppose* $\overrightarrow{BD}$ and $\overrightarrow{BE}$ are both bisectors of ∠ABC. *Then* ∠ABC has 2 ∠ bisectors. *This contradicts* the Angle Bisector Post. *Therefore, the assumption* that $\overrightarrow{BD}$ and $\overrightarrow{BE}$ are both bis. of ∠ABC *is false. We conclude* that $\overrightarrow{BD}$ and $\overrightarrow{BE}$ are not both bisectors of ∠ABC.

21. Given: ℓ and m intersect at pt. P. Prove: ℓ and m lie in only one plane. Proof: *Either* ℓ and m lie in only one plane, *or* ℓ and m lie in two or more planes. *Suppose* ℓ and m lie in two or more planes. *Then* by the Points Post., there is a pt. other than P, say A, on ℓ, and a pt. other than P, say B, on m. Since ℓ and m intersect at P, we know that A, B and P are noncollinear. Then there are 3 noncollinear points in two or more planes. *But this contradicts* the Plane Post. *Therefore, the assumption* that ℓ and m lie in two or more planes *is false. We conclude* ℓ and m lie in only 1 plane.

22. Proof: *Either* $\overleftrightarrow{RT}$ and $\overleftrightarrow{SW}$ are skew lines or $\overleftrightarrow{RT}$ and $\overleftrightarrow{SW}$ are not skew lines. *Suppose* that $\overleftrightarrow{RT}$ and $\overleftrightarrow{SW}$ are not skew lines. *Then* $\overleftrightarrow{RT}$ and $\overleftrightarrow{SW}$ are coplanar lines, and all pts. on $\overleftrightarrow{RT}$ and $\overleftrightarrow{SW}$ lie in the same plane. Since pts. R, T, S and W are coplanar, lines $\overleftrightarrow{RS}$ and $\overleftrightarrow{TW}$ are coplanar by the Flat Plane Post. *But this contradicts* the Given, which states that lines $\overleftrightarrow{RS}$ and $\overleftrightarrow{TW}$ are skew lines. *Therefore, the assumption* that $\overleftrightarrow{RT}$ and $\overleftrightarrow{SW}$ are not skew lines *is false. We conclude* that $\overleftrightarrow{RT}$ and $\overleftrightarrow{SW}$ are skew lines.

Review

24. Show two corr. ∠s =; two alt. int. ∠s =; two int. ∠s on the same side of a trans. supp.; a trans. is ⊥ to each of two given lines; the lines are coplanar and do not intersect.

Thinking Ahead

28. Sample:

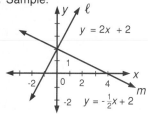

29. Sample:

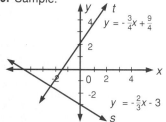

FOLLOW-UP

More Practice

• Worksheet 4–3

Extension

Prove: If the sides of two coplanar angles lie in parallel lines, then the angles are either equal or supplementary.

If we try to prove this indirectly, what is the assumption? The angles are not equal, and they are not supplementary. Discuss other examples of indirect proofs of statements with "and" or "or" in the conclusion.

• Extension 4–3

▲ Review   **23.** Given ℓ ∥ m, if $m\angle 1 = 4x$ and $m\angle 2 = 10x + 12$, then x = _?_. **12**

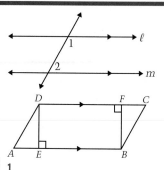

24. Give five ways to prove that two lines are parallel.

25. Given $\overleftrightarrow{AB} \parallel \overleftrightarrow{CD}$, $\overleftrightarrow{DE} \perp \overleftrightarrow{AB}$, and $\overleftrightarrow{BF} \perp \overleftrightarrow{CD}$, what postulate(s) or theorem(s) explain why $\overleftrightarrow{DE} \parallel \overleftrightarrow{BF}$? **Thm. 4–1 and Thm. 4–2**

26. ∠P and ∠Q are both supplements of ∠R. If $m\angle P = 38$, then $m\angle Q = $ _?_. **38**

27. How many planes contain three noncollinear points? **1**

≡ Thinking Ahead   On separate sets of axes, draw

28. a line ℓ with slope 2 and a line m with slope $-\frac{1}{2}$. How do lines ℓ and m appear to be related? What is the product of their slopes? **ℓ ⊥ m; −1**

29. a lines s with slope $-\frac{2}{3}$ and a line t with slope $\frac{3}{2}$. How do lines s and t appear to be related? What is the product of their slopes? **s ⊥ t; −1**

30. Without drawing a figure, find the slope of a line p if p is perpendicular to q and q has slope $-\frac{5}{6}$. **$\frac{6}{5}$**

31. Write a conjecture about the slope of perpendicular lines in our coordinate model.

31. If two lines are ⊥, then the product of their slopes is −1.

Algebra Review: Equation for a Line in Slope-Intercept Form

Example

A line with slope $m = 6$ contains the point with coordinates $(-1, 4)$. Write the equation of the line in slope-intercept form.

Solution

The line has equation $y = mx + b$. We are given $m = 6$.

$y = 6x + b$ Substitute 6 for m.

$4 = 6(-1) + b$ Substitute −1 for x and 4 for y.

$4 = -6 + b$ Simplify.

$10 = b$ Add 6 to both sides of the equation.

$y = 6x + 10$ Substitute 10 for b in the original equation.

Write the equation in slope-intercept form for the line with the given slope through the given point.

1. $m = 2$; $(3, 5)$ **2.** $m = 5$; $(1, -3)$ **3.** $m = -1$; $(0, 4)$ **4.** $m = 1$; $(0, 4)$

5. $m = -3$; $(0, 2)$ **6.** $m = 0$; $(3, -1)$ **7.** $m = \frac{2}{3}$; $(-1, -3)$ **8.** $m = -\frac{1}{2}$; $(-6, 0)$

1. $y = 2x - 1$ **2.** $y = 5x - 8$
3. $y = -1x + 4$ **4.** $y = 1x + 4$
5. $y = -3x + 2$ **6.** $y = 0x - 1$
7. $y = \frac{2}{3}x - \frac{7}{3}$ **8.** $y = -\frac{1}{2}x - 3$

Warm-Up Review

Warm-Up Review

1. Lines equidistant from each other are ___?___.   Parallel
2. Lines that form four 90° angles are ___?___.   Perpendicular
3. If a segment is split into two congruent parts, it is ___?___.   Bisected
4. What is the slope of a line parallel to the line whose equation is $y = 3x + 5$? $m = 3$

4-4 Parallels and Perpendiculars to a Line

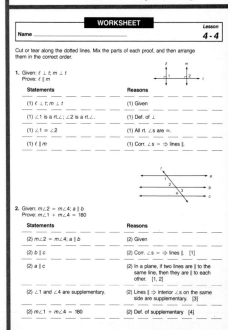

The fastener attached to the wall is like a point through which the top of the calendar must pass. In how many positions can this calendar hang so that its top edge is parallel to the bottom edge of the wall? The answer suggests Theorem 4-7, Part I of which is to be proved in Exercise 6.   Only 1

Theorem 4-7

Through a point not on a given line, there is exactly one line parallel to the given line.

Given   Line ℓ; point P not on ℓ

Prove   *Part I*   There is *one* line through P parallel to ℓ.

   Part II   There is *only one* line through P parallel to ℓ.

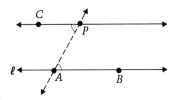

Plan for Proof   *Part I*   Given line ℓ and point P not on ℓ, choose two points A and B on ℓ and then draw $\overleftrightarrow{PA}$ by the Line Postulate. Draw $\overleftrightarrow{PC}$ in the half-plane with edge $\overleftrightarrow{PA}$ not containing B such that $m\angle CPA = m\angle PAB$. Then, $\overleftrightarrow{CP}$ is parallel to ℓ.

Proof   *Part II*

   ALTERNATIVES: *Either* (1) there is only one line through P parallel to ℓ *or* (2) there are two or more lines through P parallel to ℓ.

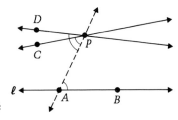

   ASSUMPTION: *Suppose* there are two or more lines through P parallel to ℓ. Call two of them $\overleftrightarrow{PC}$ and $\overleftrightarrow{PD}$.

   ARGUMENT: *Then* $m\angle DPA = m\angle PAB$ because parallel lines imply alternate interior angles are equal. For the same reason, $m\angle CPA = m\angle PAB$. By the Substitution Property, then, $m\angle DPA = m\angle CPA$.

   CONTRADICTION: *But this contradicts* the fact that, by the Angle Construction Postulate, there is exactly one angle with a given side and a given measure.

   FALSE ASSUMPTION: *Therefore, the assumption* that there are two or more lines through P parallel to ℓ *is false*.

   CONCLUSION: *We conclude* that there is only one line through P parallel to ℓ.

Notice that $\overleftrightarrow{PA}$ was added to the diagram to help prove Theorem 4-7. Such a line is called an **auxiliary line**, and its addition must be justified with a reason.

LESSON 4-4

Resources

Compass
Straightedge
Worksheet 4-4
Extension 4-4
💻 Computer Worksheet 4-4

OBJECTIVE

Use theorems about parallels and perpendiculars to a given line through a given point.

TEACHING NOTES

Introduce this lesson by referring to a picture hanging on the classroom bulletin board by a single thumbtack. Challenge students to find more than one way to hang

---

WORKSHEET   Lesson 4-4

Name _____

Cut or tear along the dotted lines. Mix the parts of each proof, and then arrange them in the correct order.

1. Given: $\ell \perp t$; $m \perp t$
   Prove: $\ell \parallel m$

Statements	Reasons
(1) $\ell \perp t$; $m \perp t$	(1) Given
(1) $\angle 1$ is a rt.$\angle$; $\angle 2$ is a rt.$\angle$.	(1) Def. of $\perp$
(1) $\angle 1 \cong \angle 2$	(1) All rt. $\angle$s are $\cong$.
(1) $\ell \parallel m$	(1) Corr. $\angle$s = $\Rightarrow$ lines $\parallel$.

2. Given: $m\angle 2 = m\angle 4$; $a \parallel b$
   Prove: $m\angle 1 + m\angle 4 = 180$

Statements	Reasons
(2) $m\angle 2 = m\angle 4$; $a \parallel b$	(2) Given
(2) $b \parallel c$	(2) Corr. $\angle$s = $\Rightarrow$ lines $\parallel$. [1]
(2) $a \parallel c$	(2) In a plane, if two lines are $\parallel$ to the same line, then they are $\parallel$ to each other. [1, 2]
(2) $\angle 1$ and $\angle 4$ are supplementary.	(2) Lines $\parallel \Rightarrow$ interior $\angle$s on the same side are supplementary. [3]
(2) $m\angle 1 + m\angle 4 = 180$	(2) Def. of supplementary [4]

the picture with the top edge parallel to the floor. The conjectures should lead to Theorem 4-7.

The proof of Theorem 4-7 utilizes an auxiliary line. Emphasize that any line segment or ray can be added to a figure if it can be justified.

As a **group activity**, explore the consequences of deleting the phrase "in a plane" from Theorems 4-8, 4-9 and 4-10.

Discuss lines with zero slopes and undefined slopes.

Additional Examples

Example 1
Write an equation of the line through $(-2, 2)$ parallel to $y = x + 2$. $y = x + 4$

Example 2
Write equations of lines m and n, each passing through the point $(2, 3)$. Line m is perpendicular to $y =$

Example 1 shows how we can apply Theorem 4-7 in the coordinate model.

Example 1
Find an equation of a line through $(1, 3)$ parallel to $y = 2x - 5$.

Solution
Theorem 4-7 tells us that there is exactly one line through $(1, 3)$ parallel to the line whose equation is $y = 2x - 5$. Because the lines are parallel, they have the same slope, 2.

$y = 2x + b$ *Substitute 2 for m in $y = mx + b$.*

$3 = 2(1) + b$ *Then, substitute 1 for x and 3 for y, and solve for b.*

$1 = b$

$y = 2x + 1$ *Substitute 1 for b in the original equation.*

Theorem 4-8 follows directly from Theorem 4-7. The indirect proof of Theorem 4-8 is left to Exercise 24.

Theorem 4-8

In a plane, if two lines are parallel to the same line, then they are parallel to each other.

Exercises 28–31 in Lesson 4-3 suggest the following property of perpendicular lines in the coordinate model. You may recall this fact from your work in algebra. *Two nonvertical and nonhorizontal lines $y = mx + b$ and $y = nx + c$ are perpendicular whenever the slopes are negative reciprocals of each other; that is, $m = -\dfrac{1}{n}$ or $n = -\dfrac{1}{m}$.*

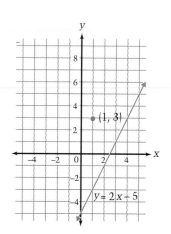

Example 2
Find the equations of two lines, s and t, each perpendicular to $y = -3x + 8$. Line s contains the point $(0, 8)$ which is on the given line. Line t contains $(1, 1)$, not on the given line.

Solution
The two lines will each have slope $m = \frac{1}{3}$ and be in the form $y = \frac{1}{3}x + b$. The coordinates of the given points satisfy the equation for each line, $(0, 8)$ in s and $(1, 1)$ in t.

Line s: $8 = \frac{1}{3}(0) + b$ Line t: $1 = \frac{1}{3}(1) + b$

$\qquad\quad 8 = 0 + b$ $\qquad\quad 1 = \frac{1}{3} + b$

$\qquad\quad 8 = b$ $\qquad\quad \frac{2}{3} = b$

$\qquad\quad y = \frac{1}{3}x + 8$ $\qquad\quad y = \frac{1}{3}x + \frac{2}{3}$

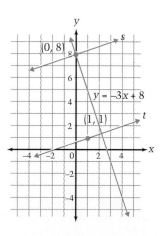

The following theorems involve perpendicular lines. The proof of Theorem 4-9 is left to Exercises 1–5 and 13–18. Theorem 4-10, which follows directly from Theorem 4-9, is to be proved in Exercise 22 and Theorem 4-11 in Exercise 23.

Theorem 4-9

In a plane, through a point on a given line, there is exactly one line perpendicular to the given line.

Theorem 4-10

In a plane, a segment has exactly one perpendicular bisector.

Example 3
Find an equation of the perpendicular bisector of a segment whose endpoints have coordinates $A(-3, -7)$ and $B(13, -9)$.

Solution
The slope of $\overleftrightarrow{AB}$ is $\frac{-9 - (-7)}{13 - (-3)}$, or $-\frac{1}{8}$, so the slope of the desired line is 8. The midpoint of $\overline{AB}$ has coordinates $\left(\frac{-3 + 13}{2}, \frac{-7 + (-9)}{2}\right)$ or $(5, -8)$. An equation of the line with slope 8 passing through the point $(5, -8)$ is $y = 8x - 48$.

Theorem 4-11

Through a point not on a given line, there is exactly one line perpendicular to the given line.

Given Line ℓ and point P not on ℓ

Prove **Part I**   There is *one* line through P perpendicular to ℓ.

   Part II   There is *only one* line through P perpendicular to ℓ.

Plan for Proof   **Part I**   Choose a point A on ℓ and draw $m \perp \ell$ at A. Then, draw n through P parallel to m. Use Theorem 4-1 to show $n \perp \ell$.

   Part II   Suppose there are two lines, j and k through P and perpendicular to ℓ. Use Theorem 4-2 to argue to a contradiction.

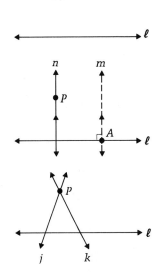

$x + 1$, and line n is perpendicular to $y = -2x$.
$y = -x + 5$; $y = \frac{1}{2}x + 2$

Example 3
Find an equation of the perpendicular bisector of a segment whose endpoints have coordinates $R(2, 3)$ and $S(-12, -4)$. slope of $\overline{RS} = \frac{-4 - 3}{-12 - 2} = \frac{-7}{-14} = \frac{1}{2}$; desired slope is -2; midpoint of $\overline{RS}$ is $\left(\frac{2 + -12}{2}, \frac{3 + -4}{2}\right)$, or $\left(-5, \frac{-1}{2}\right)$; equation desired is $y = -2x + \frac{-21}{2}$, or $2y = -4x + -21$

Example 4
State the postulate or theorem that justifies drawing each of the following.

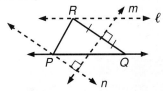

(a) ℓ through R, parallel to $\overleftrightarrow{PQ}$ Theorem 4–7
(b) m, the perpendicular bisector of $\overline{RQ}$ Theorem 4–10
(c) n through P, perpendicular to m Theorem 4–11

Error Analysis   Students may have the following problems with auxiliary lines:
1. When and where to draw them.
2. Justifying them.
   In dealing with the first problem, use the **problem-solving strategy** of testing all possibilities.
   Students must be familiar with the appropriate postulates or theorems so they can justify the drawing of any auxiliary line.

ANSWERS

Written Exercises

6. Proof: 1. Line ℓ with pt. P not on ℓ (Given) 2. Choose 2 pts., A and B, on ℓ. (Points Post.) 3. Draw $\overleftrightarrow{PA}$. (Line Post. [1, 2]) 4. In the half-plane with edge $\overleftrightarrow{PA}$ not containing B, draw $\overrightarrow{PC}$ so that $m\angle CPA = m\angle PAB$. (Angle Const. Post.) 5. $\overleftrightarrow{CP} \parallel \ell$ (Alt. int. $\angle$s $=$ $\Rightarrow$ lines $\parallel$. [4])

10. Align the square along $\overleftrightarrow{AB}$ as shown, but so that P is on the other edge of the tool. Draw $\overrightarrow{PC} \perp \overleftrightarrow{AB}$ at C. Then align the tool along $\overrightarrow{PC}$ so that the corner of the tool rests at P. Draw $\overleftrightarrow{PD} \perp \overleftrightarrow{PC}$ at P. Then $\overleftrightarrow{PD} \parallel \overleftrightarrow{AB}$. (In a plane, 2 lines $\perp$ the same line are $\parallel$.)

11. Proof: 1. $p \parallel r$; $m\angle 1 = m\angle 2$ (Given) 2. $p \parallel q$ (Alt. int. $\angle$s $=$ $\Rightarrow$ lines $\parallel$. [1]) 3. $q \parallel r$ (In a plane, 2 lines $\parallel$ to same line are $\parallel$ to each other. [1, 2])

12. Proof: 1. $m\angle 1 = m\angle 3$; $q \parallel r$ (Given) 2. $p \parallel q$ (Corres. $\angle$s $=$ $\Rightarrow$ lines $\parallel$. [1]) 3. $p \parallel r$ (In a plane, 2 lines $\parallel$ to same line are $\parallel$ to each other. [1, 2]) 4. $\angle 1$ is supp. to $\angle 4$. (Lines $\parallel$ $\Rightarrow$ int. $\angle$s on same side supp. [3])

14. there are two or more lines in $\mathcal{H}$ through $P \perp$ to ℓ

16. if $\mathcal{H}_1$ is a half-plane with edge $\overleftrightarrow{PA}$, then there is exactly one ray $\overrightarrow{PB}$, with B in $\mathcal{H}_1$, such that $\angle APB$ has a given measure

17. two or more lines in $\mathcal{H}$ through $P \perp$ to ℓ

22.

Given: $\overline{AB}$ in plane $\mathcal{K}$ Prove: In $\mathcal{K}$, $\overline{AB}$ has exactly one $\perp$ bisector. Proof: 1. $\overline{AB}$ lies in plane $\mathcal{K}$. (Given) 2. Let C be the midpt. of $\overline{AB}$. (Midpt. Post.) 3. In $\mathcal{K}$, let ℓ be $\perp$ to $\overline{AB}$ at C. (In a plane, through a pt. on a given line, there is exactly 1 line $\perp$ to the given line.) 4. In $\mathcal{K}$, ℓ is the one and only $\perp$ bisector of $\overline{AB}$. (Def. of $\perp$ bis. [2, 3])

Assignment Guide

Basic: 1–18, 41–46
Average: 2–18 (even), 19–37, 41–46
Extended: 2–30 (even), 32–46

Example 4

State the postulate or theorem that justifies each drawing.

a. Draw line s through D perpendicular to $\overleftrightarrow{BC}$.

b. Draw line t, the perpendicular bisector of $\overline{AB}$.

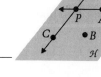

Solution

a. Theorem 4-9 ensures that through any point on a line there is a line perpendicular to the given line.

b. Theorem 4-10 ensures that $\overline{AB}$ has a perpendicular bisector.

Checking for Understanding Thms. 4–7, 4–8, 4–9, 4–10, 4–11

1. What can be added to the inventory of geometric facts?

2. In the Plan for Proof of Theorem 4-7, Part I, how do you know $\overleftrightarrow{CP}$ is parallel to ℓ? Alt. int. $\angle$s $=$ $\Rightarrow$ lines $\parallel$.

In the Plan for Proof of Theorem 4-11, Part I,

3. why can you draw $m \perp \ell$ at point A? Thm. 4–9

4. why can you draw n through P parallel to m? Thm. 4–7

Tell whether each statement is *true* or *false*. Use a theorem or example in this lesson to explain your answer.

5. $\overleftrightarrow{QT}$ and $\overleftrightarrow{QU}$ can both be parallel to $\overleftrightarrow{SR}$. False; Thm. 4–7

6. There is exactly one line perpendicular to $\overleftrightarrow{RT}$ through T.

7. The equations $y = 4x + 3$ and $y - \frac{1}{2}x = 5$ are equations of perpendicular lines. False; coordinate geometry model and Example 2

6. True; Thm. 4–9

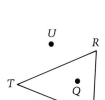

Written Exercises

Set A Complete this proof of Theorem 4-9, Part I.

Given: Line ℓ in plane $\mathcal{H}$; point P on ℓ
Prove: One line in $\mathcal{H}$ through P is perpendicular to ℓ.

Statements	Reasons
1. Line ℓ in $\mathcal{H}$; P on ℓ	1. $\underline{\ ?\ }$ Given
2. Let A be another point on ℓ and let B be another point in $\mathcal{H}$, not on ℓ.	2. $\underline{\ ?\ }$ Pts. Post.
3. In the half-plane with edge ℓ containing B, there is exactly one ray $\overrightarrow{PC}$ such that $m\angle APC = 90$.	3. $\underline{\ ?\ }$ $\angle$ Construction Post.
4. $\underline{\ ?\ }$ $\angle APC$ is a rt. $\angle$	4. Def. of rt. $\angle$ [3]
5. $\overleftrightarrow{PC} \perp \ell$	5. $\underline{\ ?\ }$ Def. of $\perp$ lines [4]

6. Prove Theorem 4-7, Part I.

Which postulate or theorem justifies each statement? **7. Thm. 4–11**

7. Draw line *m* through *A* not on *m* perpendicular to $\overleftrightarrow{BC}$.

8. Choose *P* on $\overrightarrow{BA}$ such that *BP* = *CD*. **Seg. Construction Post.**

9. Draw *t* parallel to ℓ through *P* not on ℓ. **Thm. 4–7**

10. Explain how a carpenter's square can be used to draw a line through a point *P* parallel to $\overleftrightarrow{AB}$.

11. Given *p* ∥ *r* and; *m*∠1 = *m*∠2, prove *q* ∥ *r*.

12. Given: *m*∠1 = *m*∠3; *q* ∥ *r*
Prove: ∠1 and ∠4 are supplementary.

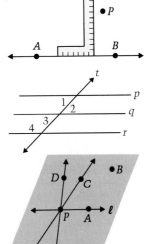

Complete this indirect proof of Theorem 4-9, Part II.
Given: Line ℓ in plane $\mathcal{H}$ and point *P* on ℓ.
Prove: In $\mathcal{H}$, there is only one line through *P* perpendicular to ℓ. **13. lines in $\mathcal{H}$ through P ⊥ ℓ**

13. *Either* (1) there is only one line in $\mathcal{H}$ through *P* perpendicular to ℓ or (2) there are two or more ⸮.

14. *Suppose* ⸮. Call two of these lines $\overleftrightarrow{PC}$ and $\overleftrightarrow{PD}$.

15. *Then m*∠*DPA* = ⸮ *and m*∠*CPA* = ⸮. **90; 90**

16. *But this contradicts* the Angle Construction Postulate, which says ⸮.

17. *Therefore, the assumption* that there are ⸮ *is false.*

18. *We conclude that* ⸮. **18. there is only 1 line in $\mathcal{H}$ through P ⊥ ℓ**

Set B Can each auxiliary line be drawn? If *yes*, justify your answer with a postulate or theorem.

19. The perpendicular bisector of $\overline{AB}$ through *C*. **No**

20. The bisector of ∠*C* **Yes; ∠ Bisector Post.**

21. The bisector of ∠*C* perpendicular to $\overline{AB}$ **No**

22. Prove Theorem 4-10.   **23.** Prove Theorem 4-11.

24. Write an indirect proof of Theorem 4-8.

25. Prove indirectly: If a line intersects one of two parallel lines, then it also intersects the other.

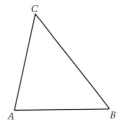

Use these equations and points for Exercises 26–31.
a. *y* = 3*x* + 5   **b.** *y* = −*x* + 4   **c.** 2*x* − *y* = 5
(3, −1)   (0, 7)   (0, 0)

Write an equation of a line parallel to the line and passing through the given point

26. in a.   **27.** in b.   **28.** in c.

Samples:
26. *y* = 3*x* − 10
27. *y* = −*x* + 7
28. *y* = 2*x*

23. Part I Proof: 1. Line ℓ does not contain point *P*. (Given) 2. Let *A* be a pt. on ℓ. (A line contains at least two pts.) 3. Through *A*, draw *m* ⊥ ℓ. (In a plane, through a pt. on a given line, there is exactly one line ⊥ to the given line.) 4. Through *P*, draw *n* ∥ *m*. (Through a pt. not on a given line, there is exactly one line ∥ to the given line.) 5. *n* ⊥ ℓ (If a transversal is ⊥ to one of two ∥ lines, it is ⊥ to the other. [3, 4])

Part II Proof: *Either* there is only 1 line through *P* perpendicular to ℓ, *or* there are 2 or more such lines. *Suppose* there are two or more lines through *P* ⊥ to ℓ. Call two of them *j* and *k*. Then *j* and *k* intersect at *P*. *This contradicts* the fact that in a plane, if two lines are ⊥ to the same line, they are ∥. Thus, *the assumption* that there are 2 or more lines through *P* ⊥ to ℓ is false. *We conclude that* there is only one line through *P* perpendicular to ℓ.

24. Proof: *Either* ℓ ∥ *n* or ℓ ∦ *n*. *Suppose* ℓ ∦ *n*. Then ℓ and *n* intersect at some point *P*. Thus, ℓ and *n* both contain *P* and are both ∥ to *m*. *This contradicts* the fact that through a pt. not on a given line, there is exactly one line parallel to the given line. Thus *the assumption* that ℓ ∦ *n* is false. *We conclude that* ℓ ∥ *n*.

25.

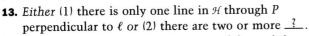

Given: *t*, ℓ and *m* are coplanar; *t* intersects ℓ at *A*; ℓ ∥ *m* Prove: *t* intersects *m* Proof: Since *t* and *m* are coplanar, *either t* ∥ *m* or *t* intersects *m*. *Suppose t* ∥ *m. Then t* and ℓ both contain *A* and *t* and ℓ are both parallel to *m. This contradicts* the fact that through a pt. not on a given line, there is one and only one line ∥ to the given line. So *the assumption* that *t* ∥ *m* is false. *We conclude that* *t* and *m* intersect.

37.

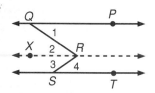

Proof: 1. $\overleftrightarrow{PQ} \parallel \overleftrightarrow{ST}$ (Given) 2. Draw $\overleftrightarrow{RX} \parallel \overleftrightarrow{ST}$ (Through a pt. not on a given line, there is exactly 1 line $\parallel$ to the given line.) 3. $\overleftrightarrow{RX} \parallel \overleftrightarrow{PQ}$ (In a plane, if 2 lines are $\parallel$ to same line, they are $\parallel$ to each other. [1, 2]) 4. $m\angle QRS = m\angle 2 + m\angle 3$ (Angle Add. Post.) 5. $m\angle 1 = m\angle 2; m\angle 3 = m\angle 4$ (2 lines $\parallel \Rightarrow$ alt. int. $\angle$s =. [2, 3]) 6. $m\angle QRS = m\angle 1 + m\angle 4$ (Substitution [4, 5])

38. If $\overleftrightarrow{PQ} \parallel \overleftrightarrow{ST}$, then $m\angle QRS = m\angle 1 + m\angle 4$.

FOLLOW-UP

More Practice

• Worksheet 4–4

Extension

Prove that $m\angle CBD = m\angle A + m\angle C$.

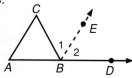

Draw auxiliary $\overrightarrow{BE}$ parallel to $\overline{AC}$, and show that $m\angle 1 = m\angle C$ and $m\angle 2 = m\angle A$. This previews Theorem 4–18.

• Extension 4–4

Computers

• Computer Worksheet 4–4

Write an equation of a line perpendicular to the line and passing through the given point

29. in a. **30.** in b. **31.** in c.

Write an equation for the perpendicular bisector of the segment having endpoints with the given coordinates.

32. $A(0, 0)$, $B(6, 10)$ **33.** $E(7, -4)$, $F(-7, 6)$

42; Thms. 4–4, 4–8, 4–3
34. $m\angle 1 = m\angle 2; m\angle 4 = 42; m\angle 3 = \underline{?}$. What theorems justify your answer?

35. $m\angle 1 = 40; m\angle 2 = 40; m\angle 4 = 50; m\angle BCD = \underline{?}$. 90

36. $\overrightarrow{CF} \parallel \overrightarrow{DE}; m\angle 1 = 30; m\angle 4 = 45; m\angle BCD = \underline{?}$. 75

37. Prove: $m\angle QRS = m\angle 1 + m\angle 4$ (HINT: Draw an auxiliary line.)

Set C **38.** Write the conditional proved in Exercise 37.

39. Write the converse of the conditional in Exercise 38. If true, prove it. If false, give a counterexample.

40. If "in a plane" were not in Theorems 4-8, 4-9, and 4-10, would the theorems still be true? Explain.

◆ **Review** **41.** Are the following two statements contradictory? $\angle A$ and $\angle B$ are complementary. $\angle B$ is obtuse. Yes

42. Given P and Q on $\overrightarrow{SP}$, prove indirectly that $SP \neq SQ$.

43. $\ell \parallel m; j \parallel k; m\angle 1 = 105; m\angle 3 = \underline{?}$ 75

44. Write the contrapositive of: Vertical angles are equal. Is the statement you wrote *true* or *false*?

45. Given $\overleftrightarrow{CB} \perp \overleftrightarrow{BE}, \overrightarrow{BA} \perp \overrightarrow{BD}, m\angle 1 = 3x + 20$, and $m\angle 3 = 5x$, find x, $m\angle 2$, and $m\angle ABF$. 10; 40; 40

≡ **Thinking** **46.** In the picture, line n is the intersection of wall 1
▽ **Ahead**   and wall 2, line t is the intersection of wall 1 and the floor 3, and line s is the intersection of wall 2 and the floor. As in most rooms, line n "goes straight up" from the floor. How are lines n and t related? lines n and s? lines s and t?
$n \perp t; n \perp s; s$ and t may be $\perp$

Samples:
29. $y = -\frac{1}{3}x$
30. $y = x + 7$
31. $y = -\frac{1}{2}x$
32. $y = -\frac{3}{5}x + \frac{34}{5}$
33. $y = \frac{7}{5}x + 1$

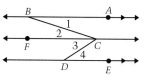

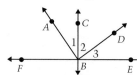

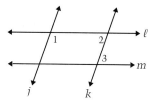

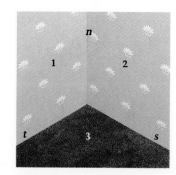

Construction Exercises

Construction 7

Through a point not on a given line, construct a line perpendicular to the given line.

Given   Point C not on line m

Construct   A line through C perpendicular to m

Method   Step 1: With C as center, draw an arc that intersects m at two points E and F.

          Step 2: Using the same radius with E and F as centers, construct two arcs that intersect at a point D, different from C.

          Step 3: Draw $\overleftrightarrow{CD}$. Then $\overleftrightarrow{CD} \perp m$.

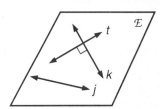

1. Draw two intersecting lines, n and t, and point H not on either line. Construct a line perpendicular to n through H.

2. Construct a line perpendicular to t through H.

Progress Check

Lesson 4-1, page 139

Given: $j \parallel k$; $m \parallel n$; $m\angle 3 = 110$. Find each measure.

1. $m\angle 7$ 110   **2.** $m\angle 2$ 70   **3.** $m\angle 15$ 110

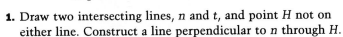

Lesson 4-2, page 144

For each pair of equal angles, tell which pair of lines you can conclude are parallel.

4. $m\angle 2 = m\angle 8$ **5.** $m\angle 6 = m\angle 1$ **6.** $m\angle 6 = m\angle 11$

    $p \parallel q$ $r \parallel s$ $p \parallel q$

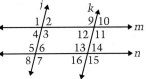

Lesson 4-3, page 149

7. What would you assume to begin an indirect proof that $j \parallel k$? $j \not\parallel k$

8. Given: In plane $\mathcal{E}$, transversal $t \perp k$; $t \not\perp j$
     Prove: $j \not\parallel k$

Lesson 4-4, page 155   Line Post.

9. What postulate or theorem justifies the statement, "Draw $\overleftrightarrow{PR}$"?

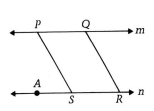

10. Write an equation of a line parallel to the line with equation $y = 5x + 5$ through the point $(1, 3)$. $y = 5x - 2$

11. Given: $m \parallel n$
     Prove: There is at least one line y through A perpendicular to both m and n.

ANSWERS

Progress Check

8.

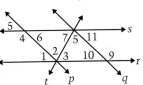

Proof: *Either $j \parallel k$ or $j \not\parallel k$. Suppose $j \parallel k$. Then since $t \perp k$, $t \perp j$ (If a trans. is $\perp$ to one of two $\parallel$ lines, it is $\perp$ to the other.) This contradicts the fact that $t \not\perp j$. Thus, the assumption that $j \parallel k$ is false. We conclude that $j \not\parallel k$.*

11.

Proof: 1. $m \parallel n$ (Given) 2. Draw a line t through $A \perp$ to n. (In a plane, through a pt. on a given line, there is exactly 1 line $\perp$ to the given line.) 3. $t \perp m$ (In a plane, if a trans. is $\perp$ to one of 2 $\parallel$ lines, it is $\perp$ to the other. [1, 2])

LESSON 4–5

Resources

Index cards
Plumb line
Protractor
  Teaching Aid 9, models of parallel lines
Visual Aid 9, models of parallel lines
Readiness Worksheet 1
Worksheet 4–5
Extension 4–5
Quiz 4

OBJECTIVE

Use theorems about parallel planes and about lines perpendicular to planes.

WORKSHEET Lesson 4-5

Name _____

1. Draw plane L parallel to plane K.
2. Draw planes K and J intersecting plane H so that $K \parallel J$.

Write A if the statement is *always* true, S if the statement is *sometimes* true, or N if the statement is *never* true.

3. Two planes parallel to the same line are parallel.   3. __S__
4. Two lines parallel to the same plane are skew.   4. __S__
5. Two lines perpendicular to the same plane are parallel.   5. __A__
6. Two lines perpendicular to the same line are parallel.   6. __S__
7. Two planes parallel to the same plane are parallel.   7. __A__
8. Two lines parallel to the same plane are parallel.   8. __S__
9. Two lines perpendicular to the same plane intersect.   9. __N__
10. Two lines perpendicular to the same line are perpendicular.   10. __S__

Make a sketch of the following.

11. Three lines perpendicular to two other lines
12. Two lines perpendicular to the same plane

4-5 Parallels and Perpendiculars to a Plane

In this pedestal table, the leg is perpendicular to the tabletop. It illustrates a perpendicular line and plane.

Definition *Perpendicular Line and Plane*

A line and a plane that intersect are perpendicular if and only if the given line is perpendicular to every line in the given plane that passes through the point of intersection.

In the photo, $k \perp H$ at P means that k is perpendicular to ℓ, m, n, and any other line in H through P.

For the tabletop to be level, it must be parallel to the plane of the ground, assuming that the ground is level.

Definition *Parallel Planes, Line and Plane*

Two planes, or a line and a plane, are parallel if and only if they do not intersect.

What must be the relationship of the table leg to the ground in order for the table top to be parallel to the ground? Your answer suggests Theorem 4-12. It must be ⊥ to the ground.

Theorem 4-12

If two planes are perpendicular to the same line, then the planes are parallel.

Given $H \perp \ell$ at P; $E \perp \ell$ at R

Prove $H \parallel E$

Proof *Either* (1) $H \parallel E$ *or* (2) H and E intersect.

  Suppose H and E intersect.

  Then by the Plane Intersection Postulate, the intersection H and E is a line m. Choose a point Q on m and use the Line Postulate to draw $\overleftrightarrow{PQ}$ and $\overleftrightarrow{RQ}$. By the Flat Plane Postulate, $\overleftrightarrow{PQ}$ lies in H and $\overleftrightarrow{RQ}$ lies in E. By the definition of a line perpendicular to a plane, $\ell \perp \overleftrightarrow{PQ}$ and $\ell \perp \overleftrightarrow{RQ}$. Then there are two lines through Q perpendicular to ℓ.

  But this contradicts Theorem 4-11.

  Therefore, the assumption that H and E intersect is false. We conclude that $H \parallel E$.

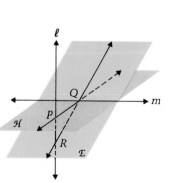

Theorem 4-13 gives another property of parallel planes. It is to be proved in Exercise 8.

Theorem 4-13

If two parallel planes are cut by a third plane, then the lines of intersection are parallel.

Given   Plane R ∥ plane S; plane T cuts R and S in lines m and n, respectively.

Prove m ∥ n

Plan for Proof   Use the definition of coplanar to show lines m and n are coplanar. Use the fact that plane R is parallel to plane S to show that m and n do not intersect. Thus, m is parallel to n.

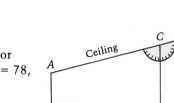
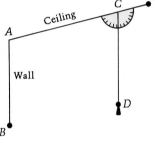

Example

To find the measure of $\angle ABC$, a contractor used a protractor and a plumb line. If the protractor indicates that $m\angle BCD = 78$, what is $m\angle ABC$?

Solution

$\overleftrightarrow{BC}$ is a transversal cutting $\overleftrightarrow{AB}$ and $\overleftrightarrow{CD}$. Since the wall $\overline{AB}$ and the plumb line $\overline{CD}$ are both vertical, they are considered parallel. By Theorem 4-5, interior angles on the same side of the transversal, $\angle ABC$ and $\angle BCD$, are supplementary angles. So, $m\angle ABC + 78 = 180$ and $m\angle ABC = 102$.

Checking for Understanding

1. Can each of three lines be perpendicular to the other two?

2. Find examples in your classroom of plane R and lines r, s, and t where $r \perp R$, r ∥ s, and r ∥ t. How are s and t related to each other? to R?
  s ∥ t; $s \perp R$; $t \perp R$

3. Find examples in your classroom of planes H, E, and R and line p where $H \perp p$, R ∥ H, and E ∥ H. How are R and E related to each other? to p?
  R ∥ E; $R \perp p$; $E \perp p$

1. Yes; corner of classroom where ceiling meets adjacent wall.

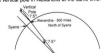

TEACHING NOTES

Discuss the effect of replacing "lines" with "planes" in Theorems 4–2 and 4–4. Note that other changes have to be made (e.g., "transversal" becomes "third plane").

Concrete materials such as index cards with slots make handy models of intersecting planes.

The proof of Theorem 4–12 presumes that the line intersects the plane at distinct points.

Example 1 provides an opportunity for a **group activity** using a blackboard protractor and a plumb line.

Additional Example

The entrance to a school is ramped. If the ramp forms an angle of 20 degrees with the sidewalk, find the measure of the angle formed by the planes of the

Assignment Guide

Basic: 1–8, 23–35
Average: 2–8 (even), 9–20, 23–35
Extended: 2–8 (even), 9–35

ramp and the landing at the
top. 160

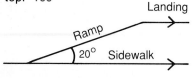

Landing

Ramp

20°   Sidewalk

ANSWERS

Written Exercises

5. $\mathcal{E} \parallel \mathcal{F}$; $j \parallel k$; $n \perp m$; $n \perp j$; $n \perp k$; $n \perp \ell$

8. Proof: 1. m lies in planes $\mathcal{R}$ and $\mathcal{T}$; n lies in planes $\mathcal{S}$ and $\mathcal{T}$. (Given) 2. m and n are coplanar in $\mathcal{T}$. (Def. of coplanar [1]) 3. Plane $\mathcal{R} \parallel$ plane $\mathcal{S}$ (Given) 4. m and n do not intersect. (Def. of $\parallel$ planes [1, 3] 5. $m \parallel n$ (Def. of $\parallel$ lines [2, 4])

21. Proof: 1. $n \perp \mathcal{H}$ at P; $\mathcal{H} \parallel \mathcal{K}$ (Given) 2. Let A be a point on n different from P. (A line contains at least two points.) 3. Let Q be any point of $\mathcal{K}$. (A plane contains at least 3 noncollinear points.) 4. Let $\mathcal{E}$ be the plane determined by A, P and Q. (3 noncollinear pts. lie in exactly one plane.) 5. Plane $\mathcal{E}$ intersects plane $\mathcal{H}$ in a line through P; call it ℓ. Plane $\mathcal{E}$ intersects plane $\mathcal{K}$ in a line through Q; call it M. (Plane Intersection Post.) 6. Plane $\mathcal{E}$ contains $\overleftrightarrow{AP}$ (line m). (Flat Plane Post.) 7. m is in $\mathcal{E}$; ℓ is in $\mathcal{E}$. (Def. of intersection [5, 6]) 8. $\overleftrightarrow{AP} \perp \ell$ (Def. of line $\perp$ to plane [1]) 9. $\ell \parallel m$ (If two $\parallel$ planes are cut by a third plane, the lines of intersection are $\parallel$. [1, 5]) 10. $\overleftrightarrow{AP}$ intersects m. (In a plane, if a line intersects one of two $\parallel$ lines, it intersects the other. [6, 7, 8, 9]) 11. $\overleftrightarrow{AP}$ (line n) intersects $\mathcal{K}$. (Def. of intersection [5, 6])

Written Exercises

Set A   Given: Lines j, k, and n in plane $\mathcal{H}$; lines j and m in plane $\mathcal{E}$; lines k and ℓ in plane $\mathcal{F}$

1. If $\mathcal{E} \parallel \mathcal{F}$, how are j and k related? $j \parallel k$

2. If $\mathcal{E} \parallel \mathcal{F}$, is ℓ necessarily parallel to m? No

3. If $j \perp n$ and $k \perp n$, what conclusion, if any, can you draw about $\mathcal{E}$ and $\mathcal{F}$? None

4. If $\mathcal{E} \parallel \mathcal{F}$ and $\mathcal{E} \perp n$, what are four conclusions that you can draw about the lines shown? $n \perp j$; $n \perp m$; $n \perp k$; $n \perp \ell$

5. If $n \perp \mathcal{E}$ and $n \perp \mathcal{F}$, what are six conclusions that you can draw about the lines and planes shown?

6. Through a point not in a plane, how many planes are there that are parallel to the given plane? 1

7. Through a point not in a plane, how many lines are there that are parallel to a given plane? Infinitely many

8. Prove Theorem 4–13.

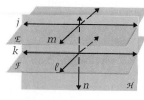

Set B   Contractor Jim Washington was hired to convert an old warehouse into a dinner theater. He built a short, open staircase up to the stage.

9. What angle should the top of each step make with the crossbar so it is parallel to the floor? 30

10. What should be the measure of $\angle A$ for the handrail to be parallel to the crossbar? 60

What postulate or theorem justifies your answer

11. in Exercise 9? Thm. 4–4 **12.** in Exercise 10? Thm. 4–6

13. The height of the stage is 108 cm. What is the "drop" from one step to the next? 18 cm

Tell whether each statement is *always*, *sometimes*, or *never* true.

14. Two lines perpendicular to the same line are perpendicular. Sometimes

15. Lines perpendicular to the same line are parallel. Sometimes

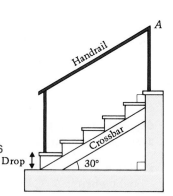

16. Two lines perpendicular to the same plane intersect. **Never**

17. Two lines perpendicular to the same plane are parallel. **Always**

18. Two lines parallel to the same plane are parallel. **Sometimes**

19. Two lines parallel to the same plane are skew.

20. Two planes parallel to the same line are parallel.
19. Sometimes **Sometimes**

Set C **21.** Given: $n \perp \mathcal{H}$ at P; $\mathcal{H} \parallel \mathcal{E}$
Prove: n intersects $\mathcal{E}$.

22. Given: R is a point on $\mathcal{E}$; $n \perp \mathcal{H}$ at P; n intersects $\mathcal{E}$ at Q; $\mathcal{H} \parallel \mathcal{E}$
Prove: $\overleftrightarrow{RQ} \perp n$

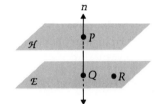

▲ Review **23.** Given $\overleftrightarrow{AB} \parallel \overleftrightarrow{CD}$, is $\overleftrightarrow{BE} \parallel \overleftrightarrow{CD}$? Why? **No; Thm. 4–7**

24. In a plane, how many lines can be drawn perpendicular to $\overleftrightarrow{CD}$ at C? **1**

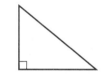

∠Y is acute or rt.

25. What should be assumed in an indirect proof of this statement? If $m\angle Y = 113$, then $\angle Y$ is obtuse.

26. $\angle 1$ and $\angle 2$ are vertical angles, $m\angle 1 = 5x - 17$, and $m\angle 2 = 3x + 21$. Find x, $m\angle 1$, and $m\angle 2$. **19; 78; 78**

27. If the angles in a linear pair are equal, then the lines containing their sides are __?__. **⊥**

 Thinking Ahead Draw a triangle that satisfies the given conditions. Write *impossible* if no triangle can be drawn.

28. One right angle   **29.** One obtuse angle

30. Two right angles   **31.** Three acute angles

32. Three equal angles   **33.** Two equal sides

34. No equal sides   **35.** No equal angles

Algebra Review: Finding the Distance Between Two Points

Find the distance between the given pairs of points.
You might want to refer back to page 43.

1. $A(6, 2)$; $B(3, -2)$ **5**   **2.** $C(8, 1)$; $D(4, 7)$ $2\sqrt{13}$ **3.** $E(0, 0)$; $F(-4, -5)$ $\sqrt{41}$

4. $G(1, 1)$; $H(-5, -5)$ $6\sqrt{2}$ **5.** $J(0, 3)$; $K(3, 3)$ **3**   **6.** $L(-2, 1)$; $M(4, 5)$ $2\sqrt{13}$

---

22. Proof: 1. n intersects $\mathcal{K}$ at Q; R is a pt. on $\mathcal{K}$. (Given) 2. Let $\mathcal{M}$ be the plane containing n and R. (A line and a pt. not on the line determine a plane.) 3. $n \perp \mathcal{H}$ at P (Given) 4. $\mathcal{M}$ and $\mathcal{H}$ intersect in a line; call it ℓ. (Plane Intersection Post. [2, 3]) 5. $\mathcal{M}$ and $\mathcal{K}$ intersect in a line. (Plane Intersection Post. [1, 2]) 6. The line of intersection of $\mathcal{M}$ and $\mathcal{K}$ is $\overleftrightarrow{RQ}$. (Flat Plane Post. [1, 2, 5]) 7. $\mathcal{H} \parallel \mathcal{K}$ (Given) 8. $\ell \parallel \overleftrightarrow{RQ}$ (If 2 $\parallel$ planes are cut by a third plane, the lines of intersection are $\parallel$. [4, 6, 7]) 9. $n \perp \ell$ (Def. of line $\perp$ to plane [3, 4]) 10. $\overleftrightarrow{RQ} \perp n$ (If a trans. is $\perp$ to one of 2 $\parallel$ lines, it is $\perp$ to the other. [8, 9])

Thinking Ahead

28–35. Samples are given.
28.

29.

30. impossible

FOLLOW-UP

More Practice

• Worksheet 4–5

Extension

As a **group activity**, ask students to define perpendicular planes in relation to dihedral angles (angles formed from two planes).
• **Extension 4–5**

Warm-Up Review

1. The measure of a(n) __?__ angle is 90. Right
2. Points on two different lines are __?__. Noncollinear
3. An angle whose measure is less than 90 is __?__. Acute
4. Two lines are __?__ if four equal angles are formed. Perpendicular
5. An obtuse angle has a measure between __?__ and __?__. 90; 180

LESSON 4–6

Resources

Fasteners
Tagboard
Readiness Worksheet 2
Worksheet 4–6
Extension 4–6
 Computer Activities 4–6

OBJECTIVE

Identify triangles according to sides and according to angles.

4-6 Triangles

Engineers and architects use triangular components to enhance the beauty and stability of their designs. *Spaceship Earth* at the right, a structure at Walt Disney World® Epcot Center in Florida, illustrates the use of triangular shapes in construction.

Definition *Triangle*

A triangle is the union of three segments determined by three noncollinear points.

If A, B, and C are noncollinear, the union of $\overline{AB}$, $\overline{BC}$, and $\overline{AC}$ is triangle ABC, denoted by $\triangle ABC$.

A, B, and C are the **vertices** of $\triangle ABC$; $\overline{AB}$, $\overline{BC}$, and $\overline{AC}$ are its **sides**; and $\angle A$, $\angle B$, and $\angle C$ are its **angles**.

A side of a triangle is **opposite** an angle if the side does not contain the vertex of the angle. (The angle is opposite the side as well.) In $\triangle ABC$, $\overline{AB}$ is opposite $\angle C$, $\overline{AC}$ is opposite $\angle B$, and $\angle A$ is opposite $\overline{BC}$.

Triangles may be classified in terms of their angles.

Definition *Acute, Right, Obtuse Triangles*

An acute triangle is a triangle with three acute angles.
A right triangle is a triangle with a right angle.
An obtuse triangle is a triangle with an obtuse angle.

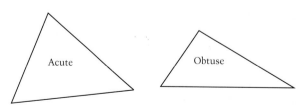
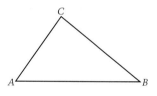

In a right triangle, the side opposite the right angle is called the **hypotenuse**. The other two sides are the **legs**.

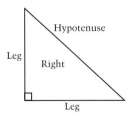

WORKSHEET

Name _____   Lesson **4-6**

Write *true* or *false* for exercises 1–10.

1. A triangle can be acute and scalene. 1. __true__
2. A triangle can be acute and isosceles. 2. __true__
3. A triangle can be acute and equilateral. 3. __true__
4. A triangle can be right and equilateral. 4. __false__
5. A triangle can be right and isosceles. 5. __true__
6. A triangle can be obtuse and equilateral. 6. __false__
7. A triangle can be obtuse and isosceles. 7. __true__
8. A triangle can be right and obtuse. 8. __false__
9. A triangle can be scalene and right. 9. __true__
10. A triangle can be scalene and obtuse. 10. __true__
11. $\triangle ABC$ is isosceles with $\overline{AC}$ as its base. Name its legs. 11. __$\overline{AB}$; $\overline{CB}$__
12. $\triangle QRS$ has a right angle at S. Name its hypotenuse. 12. __$\overline{QR}$__
13. $\triangle XYZ$ is isosceles with $\angle Y$ as its vertex angle. If $XY = 4x + 2$, $YZ = 3x + 6$, and the perimeter of $\triangle XYZ$ is 51, what is the length of its base? 13. __15__
14. The hypotenuse of isosceles right triangle DEF is $\overline{DE}$. $DF = 6x - 5$ and $EF = 4x + 7$. What is the value of x? 14. __6__
15. If $Y(-15, 5)$, $X(-5, 15)$, and $Z(5, 5)$ are the vertices of a triangle, classify the triangle according to side. 15. __isosceles__
16. If $A(-4, -6)$, $B(2, 2)$, and $C(-4, 2)$ are the vertices of a triangle, find AC and BC. 16. __8; 6__
17. $A(2, 7)$ and $B(15, 7)$ are two vertices of isosceles right triangle ABC. If $\angle A$ is the right angle, what are the possible ordered pairs for vertex C? 17. __(2, 20)__
__(2, −6)__

Example 1

Classify each triangle by its appearance as **acute, obtuse,** or **right.** Identify the hypotenuse and legs of each right triangle. What angle is opposite $\overline{AC}$? What side is opposite $\angle G$?

Solution

$\triangle ABC$ is acute because $\angle A$, $\angle B$, and $\angle C$ are acute angles. $\triangle GHK$ is obtuse because $\angle H$ is obtuse. $\triangle DEF$ is right because $\angle E$ is a right angle. The hypotenuse of $\triangle DEF$ is $\overline{DF}$, the side opposite $\angle E$. Its legs are $\overline{DE}$ and $\overline{EF}$. $\angle B$ is opposite $\overline{AC}$, while $\overline{HK}$ is opposite $\angle G$.

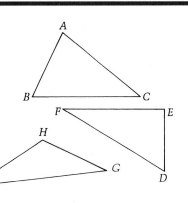

Definition *Equiangular Triangle*

An equiangular triangle is a triangle with three equal angles.

Triangles can also be classified in terms of their sides.

Definition *Scalene, Isosceles, Equilateral Triangles*

A scalene triangle is a triangle with no two sides equal.
An isosceles triangle is one with at least two equal sides.
An equilateral triangle is a triangle with three equal sides.

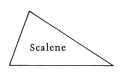

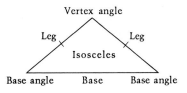

In an isosceles triangle, the equal sides are called **legs**; the third side is the **base**. The angle opposite the base is the **vertex angle**. The angles opposite the equal sides are the **base angles**.

Example 2

Classify each triangle by its appearance as **scalene, isosceles, equilateral, equiangular,** or more than one of these. Identify the legs, base, base angles, and vertex angle of any isosceles triangle.

Solution

$\triangle QRS$ is scalene because no two sides are equal. $\triangle XYZ$ is both equilateral and equiangular because $XZ = ZY = YX$ and $m\angle X = \angle Y = m\angle Z$. $\triangle UVW$ is isosceles because $VU = UW$. Its legs are $\overline{VU}$ and $\overline{UW}$. The base is $\overline{VW}$; $\angle U$, opposite the base, is the vertex angle. $\angle V$ and $\angle W$ are opposite the equal sides and are the base angles.

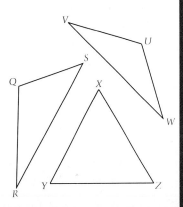

Additional Example

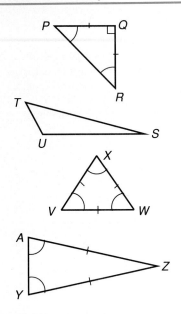

(a) Classify each triangle according to its angles. right; obtuse; acute or equiangular; acute

(b) Classify each triangle according to its sides. isosceles; scalene; equilateral; isosceles

(c) Identify the base, legs, base angles and vertex angle for △AZY. $\overline{AY}$; $\overline{AZ}$, $\overline{YZ}$; ∠A, ∠Y; ∠Z

(d) For each right triangle, identify the legs and hypotenuse. $\overline{PQ}$, $\overline{QR}$; $\overline{PR}$

(e) Name the side opposite S. $\overline{TU}$

(f) Name the angle opposite $\overline{PQ}$. ∠R

Error Analysis Students often make the following assumptions:
1. The base of an isosceles triangle must be on the bottom.
2. The legs of a right triangle must be horizontal and vertical.
  Have students draw counter-examples.

Checking for Understanding

1. Name all of the triangles in the diagram at the right.

2. Name all the vertices, sides, and angles of △ABC.

Name the triangles at the right that are

3. acute.   **4.** obtuse.   **5.** equiangular.

6. right.   **7.** scalene.   **8.** equilateral.

9. Identify the hypotenuse and legs of any right triangle named.
△ABC; hypotenuse: $\overline{BC}$; legs: $\overline{AB}$ and $\overline{AC}$

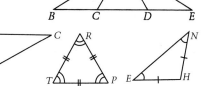

Written Exercises

Set A Draw a triangle that satisfies the given conditions. If there is no such triangle, write *none*.

1. Scalene and acute   **2.** Scalene and right

3. Scalene and obtuse   **4.** Isosceles and obtuse

5. Isosceles and acute   **6.** Equilateral and right

7. Draw a large triangle. Through each vertex draw a line perpendicular to the line containing the opposite side.

8. Draw the perpendicular bisector of each side of the triangle in Exercise 7.

What appears to be true of the three lines

9. in Exercise 7?   **10.** in Exercise 8?

11. Given: $\overleftrightarrow{AB} \parallel \overleftrightarrow{CD}$; $\overrightarrow{AC} \perp \overleftrightarrow{CD}$
Prove: △ABC is a right triangle.
9-10. They intersect in a single point.

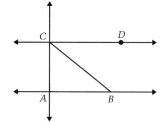

Set B **12.** Given: $\overleftrightarrow{AB} \parallel \overleftrightarrow{CD}$; ∠ACD is an acute angle.
Prove: △BAC is an obtuse triangle.

In a large triangle XYZ with m∠X = 60, m∠Y = 90, and m∠Z = 30, draw the trisectors of each angle of the triangle. (Trisectors divide an angle into three equal angles.) Label the points where adjacent trisectors of different angles intersect A, B, and C. Then draw △ABC.

13. What kind of triangle does △ABC appear to be? Check your guess. Equilateral

14. Repeat the procedure above with a triangle whose angles measure 75, 60, and 45. Is the result the same? Yes

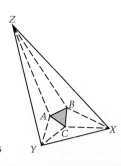

15. Prove indirectly: A triangle cannot have two right angles.

Tell whether each statement is *always*, *sometimes*, or *never* true.

16. An equilateral triangle is isosceles.

17. An isosceles triangle is equilateral.

18. An equilateral triangle is equiangular.

19. $AB = \sqrt{(4-1)^2 + (1-4)^2} = 3\sqrt{2}$
$BC = \sqrt{(5-4)^2 + (5-1)^2} = \sqrt{17}$
$AC = \sqrt{(5-1)^2 + (5-4)^2} = \sqrt{17}$;
Since $BC = AC$, $\triangle ABC$ is isosceles.

19. Use the Distance Formula to show that $\triangle ABC$, with $A(1, 4)$, $B(4, 1)$, and $C(5, 5)$, is isosceles.

Set C   **20.** Work with a classmate to decide how many triangles are determined by 4 coplanar points, no 3 of which are collinear; by 5 such points; by n such points. $4;\ 10;\ \dfrac{n(n-1)(n-2)}{6}$

Line m is $\perp$ to every line in $\mathcal{T}$ which passes through the point of intersection of m and $\mathcal{T}$.

▲ Review   **21.** What does "line m is perpendicular to plane $\mathcal{T}$" mean?

22. Plane $\mathcal{E}$ intersects parallel planes $\mathcal{R}$ and $\mathcal{S}$ in lines j and k. How are j and k related? $j \parallel k$

23. Find an equation of a line through the point $A(2, 3)$ and parallel to line ℓ whose equation is $y = -4x + 1$. $y = -4x + 11$

24. When are two lines that are perpendicular to the same line also parallel?   When they are coplanar

25. Find the coordinates of the midpoint of the segment determined by $E(3, -2)$ and $F(0, 5)$. $\left(\dfrac{3}{2}, \dfrac{3}{2}\right)$

Thinking Ahead   **26.** Draw $\triangle XYZ$ with $XY = AB$, $XZ = 2AB$, and $m\angle X = 60$. Find $m\angle Y$ and $m\angle Z$.   90; 30

A B

27. Repeat Exercise 26 with $XY = CD$ and $XZ = 2CD$.   45; 45

28. What conjecture is suggested by Exercises 26 and 27?

C D

29. Draw $\triangle RST$ with $RS = RT = AB$ and $m\angle R = 90$. Find $m\angle S$ and $m\angle T$.

30. Repeat Exercise 29 with $RS = RT = CD$.

31. What conjecture is suggested by Exercises 29 and 30?

🖥 Computer Activities: Drawing and Measuring

1. Draw any triangle ABC. Measure $\angle A$, $\angle B$, and $\angle C$, and then find the sum of the measures.   180

2. Repeat the activity in Exercise 1 with nine more triangles.

3. What conjecture can you make?   The sum of the measures of the $\angle$s of a $\triangle$ is 180.

Sample:

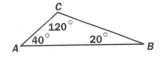

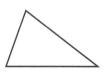

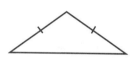

Warm-Up Review

1. The side opposite a right angle of a triangle is the __?__.   Hypotenuse
2. The sides of a(n) __?__ triangle have different lengths. Scalene
3. The sum of the measures of two adjacent angles is 180. The angles are a(n) __?__. Linear pair

---

LESSON 4–7

Resources

Construction paper
Teaching Aid 10, polygons
Visual Aid 10, polygons
Worksheet 4–7
Extension 4–7

OBJECTIVE

Use theorems about the sum of the measures of the angles of a triangle.

TEACHING NOTES

Use **concrete materials** to introduce this lesson. As a **group activity** have students fold triangles of various shapes cut from construction paper. Use the method

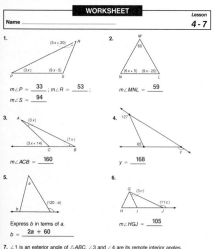

WORKSHEET   Lesson 4-7

Name _____

1. $m\angle P = \underline{33}$; $m\angle R = \underline{53}$;
    $m\angle S = \underline{94}$

2. $m\angle MNL = \underline{59}$

3. $m\angle ACB = \underline{160}$

4. $y = \underline{168}$

5. Express b in terms of a.
    $b = \underline{2a + 60}$

6. $m\angle HGJ = \underline{105}$

7. $\angle 1$ is an exterior angle of $\triangle ABC$. $\angle 3$ and $\angle 4$ are its remote interior angles. If $m\angle 4 = 37$ and $m\angle 1 = 115$, find $m\angle 3$.   **78**

8. The measures of interior angles of a triangle are 3x, 5x, and 10x. Classify the triangle according to side and angle.   **scalene, obtuse**

9. $\triangle XYZ$ is a right triangle. The measures of its acute angles are 6y and 9y. Find the measure of the smaller angle.   **36**

4-7 The Angles of a Triangle

A physical model frequently suggests relationships that can be established by proof. Trace $\triangle ABC$ and cut out your triangle. Fold it so that B lies on $\overline{AC}$ and the fold is parallel to $\overline{AC}$ as shown. Then fold it so that A and C are at B.

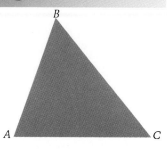

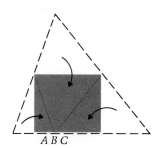

It appears that $m\angle A + m\angle B + m\angle C = 180$. Try this with several different triangles. Your results should suggest Theorem 4-14.

Theorem 4-14

The sum of the measures of the angles of a triangle is 180.

Given $\triangle ABC$

Prove $m\angle A + m\angle B + m\angle C = 180$

Plan for Proof   Draw $\overleftrightarrow{DE} \parallel \overleftrightarrow{AC}$ through B. Show $m\angle 1 + m\angle 2 + m\angle 3 = 180$. Use alternate interior angles and substitution.

Proof

Statements	Reasons
1. Through B draw $\overleftrightarrow{DE} \parallel \overleftrightarrow{AC}$.	1. Through a pt. not on a given line __?__.
2. $\angle 1$ and $\angle ABE$ are supp.	2. Supp. Post. [1]
3. $m\angle 1 + m\angle ABE = 180$	3. __?__ [2]
4. $m\angle 2 + m\angle 3 = m\angle ABE$	4. Angle Addition Post.
5. $m\angle 1 + m\angle 2 + m\angle 3 = 180$	5. Substitution Prop. [3, 4]
6. $m\angle 1 = m\angle A; m\angle 3 = m\angle C$	6. Lines $\parallel \Rightarrow$ __?__. [1]
7. $m\angle A + m\angle ABC + m\angle C = 180$	7. Substitution Prop. [5, 6]

1. there is exactly one line $\parallel$ to the given line.
3. Def. supp. $\angle$s
6. alt. int. $\angle$s. =

The following theorems follow directly from Theorem 4-14. Their proofs are left to Exercises 8–10.

Theorem 4-15

If two angles of one triangle are equal to two angles of another triangle, then the remaining angles are equal.

Theorem 4-16

The acute angles of a right triangle are complementary.

Theorem 4-17

Each angle of an equiangular triangle has measure 60.

Example 1

Find the measure of each angle in △ABC if m∠A = 40 and ∠B is a right angle.

Solution

∠B is a right angle, so m∠B = 90. By Theorem 4-16, acute angles ∠A and ∠C are complementary, so 40 + m∠C = 90 and m∠C = 50.

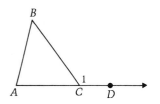

In the triangle at the right, side $\overline{AC}$ has been extended. ∠1 is called an **exterior angle** of △ABC. It forms a linear pair with ∠BCA, one of the angles of the triangle. ∠A and ∠B are called **remote interior angles** with respect to ∠1.

Notice that in △ABC, m∠A + m∠B + m∠BCA = $\underset{\text{180}}{?}$, and m∠1 + m∠BCA = $\underset{\text{180}}{?}$.

How are m∠1, m∠A, and m∠B related? Your answer should suggest Theorem 4-18. m∠1 = m∠A + m∠B

Theorem 4-18

The measure of an exterior angle of a triangle is equal to the sum of the measures of its remote interior angles.

Theorem 4-19 follows directly from Theorem 4-18.

Theorem 4-19

The measure of an exterior angle of a triangle is greater than the measure of either of its remote interior angles.

Theorems 4-18 and 4-19 are to be proved in Exercises 21 and 22.

Notice that when all sides of a triangle are extended, there are two exterior angles at each vertex. In △XYZ, ∠1 and ∠2 are both exterior angles at vertex Z. What are the exterior angles at vertex Y? vertex X? ∠3 and ∠4; ∠5 and ∠6

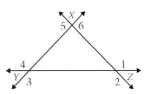

Example 2

In △ABC, m∠A = 70 and the measure of an exterior angle at C is 106. Find m∠B and m∠BCA.

Solution

By Theorem 4-18, m∠A + m∠B = 106, so 70 + m∠B = 106 and m∠B = 36.

By Theorem 4-14, m∠A + m∠B + m∠BCA = 180, so 70 + 36 + m∠BCA = 180 and m∠BCA = 74.

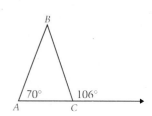

4-7 *The Angles of a Triangle*

---

described at the beginning of this lesson.

Reinforce the **proof subskill** of supplying missing reasons by having students complete the proof of Theorem 4–14.

Have students draw a triangle and two exterior angles at each vertex.

1. How are the exterior angles at each vertex related? equal

2. Why? vertical angles

Theorem 4–19 will be useful in proofs with inequalities.

Additional Examples

Example 1

In right triangle ABC, m∠A = 36 and $\overline{AB}$ is the hypotenuse. Find m∠B and m∠C. 54; 90

Example 2

In △PQR, m∠P = 37 and the measure of an exterior angle at Q is 85. Find m∠R. 48

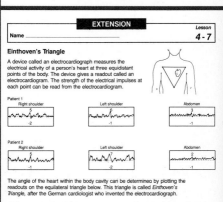

Example 3
Find the measure of an exterior angle at a vertex of an equiangular triangle. 120

Error Analysis Students often think there are three exterior angles at a vertex of a triangle. Stress that by definition an exterior angle is formed by extending only *one* side of a triangle, not both. The third angle and the interior angle are simply vertical angles.

ANSWERS

Written Exercises

1. $m\angle QRP = 30$
2. $m\angle QRP = 50$; $m\angle Q = 70$; $m\angle QRP = 60$
3. $m\angle QRP = 90$; $m\angle QRP = 37$
4. $m\angle Q = 55$; $m\angle QRP = 30$; $m\angle QRP = 95$
5. $m\angle QRP = 80$; $m\angle Q = 70$; $m\angle QRP = 30$
8.

Given: $m\angle A = m\angle D$; $m\angle B = m\angle E$
Prove: $m\angle C = m\angle F$ Proof: 1. $m\angle A = m\angle D$; $m\angle B = m\angle E$ (Given) 2. $m\angle A + m\angle B + m\angle C = 180$; $m\angle D + m\angle E + m\angle F = 180$ (Sum of meas. of $\angle$s of a $\triangle = 180$.) 3. $m\angle A + m\angle B + m\angle C = m\angle D + m\angle E + m\angle F$ (Substitution Prop. [2]) 4. $m\angle C = m\angle F$ (Subtraction Prop. [1, 3])

9.

Checking for Understanding   1. $m\angle A + m\angle B + m\angle C = 40 + 90 + m\angle C = 180$;
1. In Example 1, use Theorem 4-14 to show $m\angle C = 50$. $m\angle C = 180 - 130 = 50$

Find $m\angle 1$ in each triangle.

2. 45

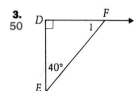

3. 50

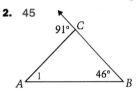

4. 35

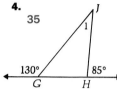

5. Are the exterior angles at a vertex equal? Explain. Yes; they are vertical $\angle$s.

6. What can you add to your inventory?
Thms. 4–14, 4–15, 4–16, 4–17, 4–18, 4–19

Written Exercises
Set A   Find the measure of each angle of $\triangle PQR$.

1. $m\angle QPR = 87$; $m\angle Q = 63$
2. $m\angle QPR = 5x$; $m\angle Q = 7x$; $m\angle QRP = 8x - 20$
3. $\angle QPR$ is a right angle; $m\angle Q = 53$
4. $m\angle Q = 4x + 7$; $m\angle QRP = 3(x - 2)$; $m\angle 1 = 85$
5. $m\angle QPR = 8x$; $m\angle Q = 7x$; $m\angle 2 = 2(x + 65)$

Given $m\angle B = m\angle DEF$ and $m\angle C = m\angle F$, explain why each statement is true.

6. $m\angle A = m\angle D$ Thm. 4–15
7. $m\angle D < m\angle EGF$ Thm. 4–19

8. Prove Theorem 4-15.   **9.** Prove Theorem 4-16.
10. Prove Theorem 4-17.

Given: $\triangle HGJ$ and $\triangle MJK$ are right triangles.
11. Prove: $m\angle H < 90$; $m\angle M < 90$ (Recall from algebra that "$a > b$" means that $a = b + c$ for some positive number c.)
12. Prove: $m\angle H = m\angle M$

Given: $\triangle ABC$ with right angle at B
13. Prove: $\angle CAD$ is obtuse
14. Prove: $m\angle DAC - 90 = m\angle ACB$
15. If $m\angle CAB = m\angle C$, prove $m\angle CAB = 45$.
16. If $m\angle CAB = 45$, prove $m\angle CAB = m\angle C$.

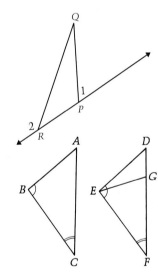

17. How are the conditionals in Exercises 15 and 16 related? They are converses of each other.

18. A support brace stands so that it makes an angle of 140° as shown. What is the measure of the exterior angle the brace makes with the wall? 130

19. The *pitch* ($m\angle 1$) of the roof at the right is 35. What is $m\angle 2$, the angle that the roof makes with the outside wall of the house? 125

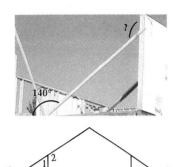

20. Sue Nakai, a surveyor, locates points on a land area by using a "triangulation method." Find the remaining angle measures in this survey.

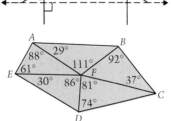

Set B **21.** Prove Theorem 4-18. **22.** Prove Theorem 4-19.

23. Given: $\overline{CD} \perp \overline{AB}$; $m\angle A = m\angle B$
Prove: $\overline{CD}$ bisects $\angle ACB$.

24. Given: $\overline{CD} \perp \overline{AB}$; $\overline{CD}$ bisects $\angle ACB$.
Prove: $m\angle A = m\angle B$.

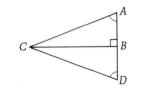

25. Prove: The measure of any exterior angle of an equiangular triangle is 120.

26. Prove: The sum of the measures of the exterior angles of a triangle, one at each vertex, is 360.

27. Prove: A triangle cannot have two obtuse angles.

To measure $\angle SPU$, a machinist places *angle gauge blocks* as shown. They indicate that $m\angle SRT = 30$ and $m\angle TQU = 25$.

28. Prove that $m\angle SPU = 55$.

29. Which theorem justifies that $m\angle TQU = 15$ in the second arrangement of blocks?

Thm. 4–18

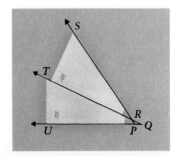

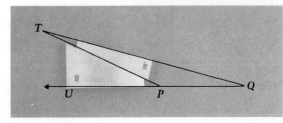

Given: $\triangle ABC$ is a rt. triangle; $\angle C$ is a rt. $\angle$. Prove: $\angle A$ and $\angle B$ are comp. Proof: 1. $\triangle ABC$ is a rt. triangle; $\angle C$ is a rt. $\angle$. (Given) 2. $m\angle C = 90$ (Def. of rt. $\angle$ [1]) 3. $m\angle A + m\angle B + m\angle C = 180$ (Sum of meas. of $\angle$s of a $\triangle$ = 180. [1]) 4. $m\angle A + m\angle B + 90 = 180$ (Substitution Prop. [2, 3]) 5. $90 = 90$ (Reflexive Prop.) 6. $m\angle A + m\angle B = 90$ (Subtraction Prop. [4, 5]) 7. $\angle A$ and $\angle B$ are comp. (Def. of comp. $\angle$s [6])

10.

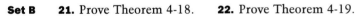

Given: $\triangle ABC$ is equiangular. Prove: $m\angle A = 60$; $m\angle B = 60$; $m\angle C = 60$ Proof: 1. $\triangle ABC$ is equiangular. (Given) 2. $m\angle A = m\angle B = m\angle C$ (Def. of equiangular $\triangle$ [1]) 3. $m\angle A + m\angle B + m\angle C = 180$ (Sum of meas. of $\angle$s of a $\triangle$ = 180.) 4. $m\angle A + m\angle A + m\angle A = 3(m\angle A) = 180$ (Substitution Prop. [2, 3]) 5. $3 = 3$ (Reflexive Prop.) 6. $m\angle A = 60$ (Div. Prop. [4, 5]) 7. $m\angle A = m\angle B = m\angle C = 60$ (Substitution Prop. [2, 6])

11. Proof: 1. $\triangle HGJ$ is a rt. triangle with rt. $\angle$ at G; $\triangle MJK$ is a rt. triangle with rt. $\angle$ at K. (Given) 2. $\angle H$ and $\angle GJH$ are comp.; $\angle M$ and $\angle KJM$ are comp. (The acute $\angle$s of a rt. $\triangle$ are comp. [1]) 3. $m\angle H + m\angle GJH = 90$; $m\angle M + m\angle KJM = 90$ (Def. of comp. $\angle$s [2]) 4. $m\angle GJH > 0$; $m\angle KJM > 0$ (Protractor Post.) 5. $m\angle H < 90$; $m\angle M < 90$ (Def. of $a > b$ [3, 4])

12. Proof: 1. $\triangle HGJ$ is a rt. triangle with rt. $\angle$ at G; $\triangle MJK$ is a rt. triangle with rt. $\angle$ at K. (Given) 2. $m\angle G = m\angle K$ (All rt. $\angle$s are =.) 3. $m\angle GJH = m\angle KJM$ (Vert. $\angle$s are =.) 4. $m\angle H = m\angle M$ (If 2 $\angle$s of a $\triangle$ are = to 2 $\angle$s of another $\triangle$, the third $\angle$s are =.)

30. Given: $m\angle 1 = m\angle 3$; $m\angle 4 = m\angle 6$; $m\angle B = 90$ Prove: $\overline{FD} \parallel \overline{GE}$
Proof: 1. $m\angle B = 90$; $m\angle 1 = m\angle 3$; $m\angle 4 = m\angle 6$ (Given) 2. $\angle B$ is a rt. $\angle$. (Def. of rt. $\angle$ [1]) 3. $\triangle BDE$ is a rt. $\triangle$. (Def. of rt. $\triangle$ [2]) 4. $\angle 4$ and $\angle 3$ are comp. $\angle$s. (The 2 acute $\angle$s of a rt. $\triangle$ are comp. [3]) 5. $m\angle 4 + m\angle 3 = 90$ (Def. of comp. $\angle$s [4]) 6. $m\angle 6 + m\angle 1 = 90$ (Substitution Prop. [1, 5]) 7. $\angle 1$ and $\angle FDB$ are supp. $\angle$s; $\angle 6$ and $\angle GEB$ are supp. $\angle$s. (Supp. Post.) 8. $m\angle 1 + m\angle FDB = 180$; $m\angle 6 + m\angle GEB = 180$ (Def. of supp. $\angle$s [7]) 9. $m\angle FDB = m\angle 2 + m\angle 3$; $m\angle GEB = m\angle 4 + m\angle 5$ (Angle Add. Post.) 10. $m\angle 1 + m\angle 2 + m\angle 3 = 180$; $m\angle 6 + m\angle 4 + m\angle 5 = 180$ (Substitution Prop. [8, 9]) 11. $m\angle 1 + m\angle 2 + m\angle 3 + m\angle 6 + m\angle 4 + m\angle 5 = 360$ (Add. Prop. [10]) 12. $90 + 90 + m\angle 2 + m\angle 5 = 360$ (Substitution Prop. [5, 6, 11]) 13. $m\angle 2 + m\angle 5 = 180$ (Subtraction Prop. [12]) 14. $\angle 2$ and $\angle 5$ are supp. $\angle$s. (Def. of supp. $\angle$s [13]) 15. $\overline{FD} \parallel \overline{GE}$ (Int. $\angle$s on the same side supp. $\Rightarrow$ 2 lines $\parallel$. [14])

FOLLOW-UP

More Practice

- Worksheet 4–7

Extension

Prove that through a point not on a given line, there is at most one line parallel to the given line. Use an indirect proof, assuming that there are two such lines. This will lead to a contradiction of Theorem 4–14.

- Extension 4–7

Set C

30. The angle at which a light ray strikes a facet of a jewel is equal to the angle at which the ray leaves the facet. A diamond sparkles because the light is reflected from facet to facet and back through its top. The sparkle is greatest if the rays entering and leaving the diamond are parallel. In the cross sections of the diamonds shown here, the first gem has been cut too deeply—$\angle Y$ is too small. Use the second figure to prove that if $\angle B$ at the base of the diamond is cut at 90°, then the entering and exiting rays will be parallel.

31. Prove: If two parallel lines are cut by a transversal, then the bisectors of the interior angles on the same side of the transversal are perpendicular.

32. Prove the converse of the statement in Exercise 31.

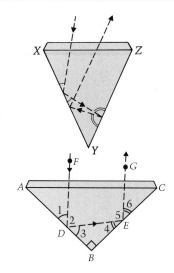
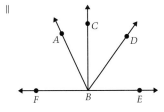

▲ Review

33. In $\triangle DEF$, which angle is opposite $\overline{EF}$? $\angle$D

34. A triangle with no two sides equal is called _?_. scalene

35. Two planes perpendicular to the same line are _?_. $\parallel$

36. In the figure at the right, identify three pairs of angles that form linear pairs.

37. Write the following statement in "if . . . then" form, and identify the hypothesis and the conclusion. All moons revolve around a planet.

≋ Thinking Ahead If a statement below accurately describes all the figures at the right, write *yes*. If the description does *not* apply to all the figures, tell which figures do not match the description.

38. Each figure is formed by line segments. C

39. Each segment intersects no more than two other segments. D

40. The segments intersect only at endpoints. D

41. Each figure has an inside and an outside. F

42. Each segment intersects at least two other segments. C, F

Warm-Up Review

1. The set of points between two points forms a(n) __?__. Line segment
2. Points on the same line are __?__. Collinear
3. A triangle with three congruent angles is __?__, __?__, __?__
   and __?__. Equiangular; equilateral; isosceles; acute

4-8 Polygons

The faces of a crystal, such as the sulphur crystals shown here, are surfaces whose edges are line segments. The figures formed by these line segments are called polygons.

Definition *Polygon*

A polygon is the union of three or more coplanar segments such that each segment intersects exactly two other segments, one at each endpoint, and no two intersecting segments are collinear.

The first two figures below are polygons; the last one is not.

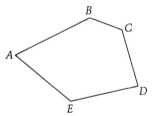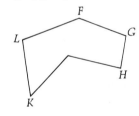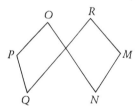

Sides of the first polygon are $\overline{AB}$, $\overline{BC}$, $\overline{CD}$, $\overline{DE}$, and $\overline{EA}$. Name the sides of the second polygon. Angles such as $\angle BCD$ and $\angle GFL$ are **angles** of the polygons; and $A, B, C, \ldots, L$ are **vertices** of the polygons. In the first polygon, $\overline{AB}$ and $\overline{BC}$ are **consecutive sides** since they intersect. $\angle AED$ and $\angle EDC$ are **consecutive angles** since they share side $\overline{ED}$. A polygon is named by listing its vertices in **consecutive order**, so this polygon might be named *ABCDE* or *CBAED*.

The **interior** of a polygon is the intersection of the interiors of its angles. The **exterior** of a polygon is the set of points in the plane which do not belong to the polygon or its interior. If each line that contains a side of the polygon contains no points in the interior of the polygon, the polygon is **convex**.

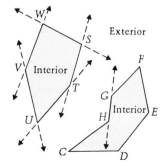

A polygon that is *not* convex is **nonconvex**. *STUVW* is convex. *CDEFGH* is nonconvex. We are interested primarily in convex polygons.

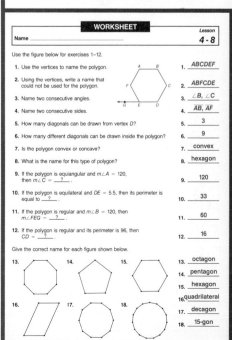

In **Example 1**, the diagonals shown divide the interior of the hexagon into triangular regions.

Have students draw a concave hexagon and its diagonals. Stress that some of the diagonals of a nonconvex polygon are not in the interior.

Discuss the value of devising a geometric model to solve a nongeometric problem.

Additional Examples

Example 1
A polygon has 20 diagonals. How many sides does it have? **8**

Example 2
The perimeter of a regular hexagon is 72 cm. How long is one side? **12 cm**

Error Analysis   Students often confuse the terms "equilateral" and "equiangular." Unlike trian-

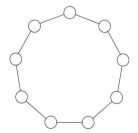
Polygons are named by the number of sides they have.

Number of sides	Name of polygon	Number of sides	Name of polygon	Number of sides	Name of polygon
3	Triangle	7	Heptagon	12	Dodecagon
4	Quadrilateral	8	Octagon	15	15-gon
5	Pentagon	9	Nonagon	n	n-gon
6	Hexagon	10	Decagon		

A segment joining two nonconsecutive vertices is a ***diagonal*** of the polygon. $\overline{XV}$ is one diagonal of $VWXYZ$. How many diagonals can be drawn from vertex X? **2**

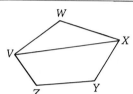

Example 1
How many diagonals does a hexagon have?

Solution

From each vertex there is a diagonal to each of the 3 nonconsecutive vertices. There are 6 vertices, so that suggests 18 diagonals. But that counts each diagonal twice. For example, $\overline{AE}$ is counted once from A and once from E. So a hexagon has 9 diagonals.

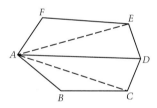

Like triangles, polygons can be classified in terms of their sides and angles.

Definition   *Equiangular, Equilateral, Regular Polygons*

An equiangular polygon is a polygon whose angles are equal.
An equilateral polygon is a polygon whose sides are equal.
A regular polygon is a polygon that is both equiangular and equilateral.

Which quadrilaterals below are equiangular? equilateral? regular?   Equiangular: rectangle, square; equilateral: rhombus, square; regular: square

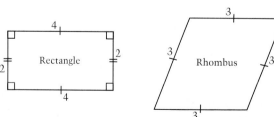

The ***perimeter*** of a polygon is the sum of the lengths of its sides. Each polygon above has perimeter 12.

Assignment Guide

Basic: 1–15, 24–34
Average: 1–21, 24–34
Extended: 1–34

Example 2

Find the perimeter of the regular pentagon at the right.

Solution

The sides of a regular polygon are equal, and the perimeter is the sum of the lengths of its sides. Hence, the perimeter is 26 + 26 + 26 + 26 + 26 = 5(26) = 130.

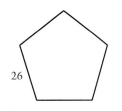

26

Checking for Understanding

If a figure is *not* a polygon, explain why not. If the figure *is* a polygon, tell whether it is *convex* or *nonconvex*, and then classify it by the number of sides.

1.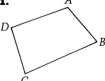

2.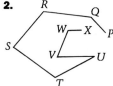

3.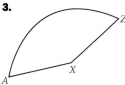

4.

Use polygon *CBFEGAD*.

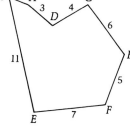

5. Tell whether the polygon is *convex* or *nonconvex*, and classify it by the number of sides. Nonconvex heptagon

6. Name the sides.　　**7.** Name a pair of consecutive angles.

8. Name a pair of nonconsecutive sides. Sample: $\overline{EF}$ and $\overline{BC}$

9. Find its perimeter. 38　**10.** Name all diagonals through *C*.
$\overline{CG}$, $\overline{CA}$, $\overline{CE}$, $\overline{CF}$

Written Exercises

Set A　Name the specified parts of polygon *ABCDEF*.

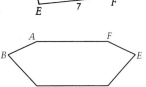

1. The vertices　　　2. Two consecutive sides
3. The sides　　　　4. Two consecutive angles
5. The angles　　　　6. Two nonconsecutive sides

7. What is the perimeter of a regular nonagon if each side measures 15? 135

8. What is the length of each side of an equilateral hexagon with perimeter 96? 16

9. A quadrilateral has sides of lengths 2x, 2x + 1, 2x − 1, and 3x. Find the perimeter in terms of x. 9x

10. If the perimeter of the quadrilateral in Exercise 9 is 18, find x and the length of each side.
x = 2, 2x = 4, 2x + 1 = 5, 2x − 1 = 3, 3x = 6

6. $\overline{AG}$, $\overline{AD}$, $\overline{CD}$, $\overline{BC}$, $\overline{EF}$, $\overline{EG}$
7. Sample ∠E and ∠E

gles, polygons with more than three sides may be one and not the other. A regular polygon is both. Some familiar examples are
1. Rectangles: equiangular but not generally equilateral.
2. Rhombuses: equilateral but not generally equiangular.
3. Squares: both equilateral and equiangular (regular).

EXERCISE NOTES

Exercises 15–17　develop the formula $n(n-3)/2$ for the number of diagonals in an *n*-gon.
Exercise 19　could be solved by representing each student as the vertex of a polygon and segments as the handshakes.
Exercises 19, 20 and **29–34** could be **group activities**.

ANSWERS

Checking for Understanding

1. convex quadrilateral
2. Not a polygon; each line seg. must intersect exactly two other segs. at their endpoints.
3. Not a polygon; a polygon is made up of segs. (not arcs).
4. nonconvex decagon

Written Exercises

1. *A, B, C, D, E, F*
2. Sample: $\overline{AB}$ and $\overline{BC}$
3. $\overline{AB}$, $\overline{BC}$, $\overline{CD}$, $\overline{DE}$, $\overline{EF}$, $\overline{AF}$
4. Sample: ∠A and ∠B
5. ∠A, ∠B, ∠C, ∠D, ∠E, ∠F
6. Sample: $\overline{AB}$ and $\overline{CD}$

22. Sample:

Review

24. Proof: *Either m∠B < 90 or
m∠B > 90 or m∠B = 90. Suppose
m∠B > 90. Then since m∠C > 90
and m∠A > 0, m∠A + m∠B +
m∠C > 90 + 90 + 0 by the Add.
Prop. Thus, m∠A + m∠B + m∠C
> 180. This contradicts the fact
that the sum of the meas. of the
∠s of a △ = 180. The assumption
that m∠B > 90 is false. Next suppose that m∠B = 90. Then since
m∠C > 90 and m∠A > 0, m∠A +
m∠B + m∠C > 180 by the Add.
Post. Again this contradicts the
fact that the sum of the meas. of
the ∠s of a △ = 180. Thus, it is
false that m∠C = 90. Since m∠B
≯ 90 and m∠B ≠ 90, we conclude
that m∠B < 90.*

Thinking Ahead

Samples are given for Exercises
29–33.

29.

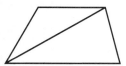

30.

31.

32.

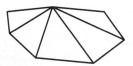

Tell whether each polygon is *convex* or *nonconvex*;
then tell if it is *equiangular, equilateral,* or *regular.*

11.   **12.**   **13.**

14. Angela wants a fence around her garden which is
in the shape of a regular pentagon with sides
16 ft. long. How many feet of fence will she need? **80 ft.**

15. Copy and complete the table. Draw the polygons.

Number of sides	3	4	5	6	7	8	10
Diagonals from each vertex	_?_ 0	_?_ 1	2	_?_ 3	_?_ 4	_?_ 5	_?_ 7
Total number of diagonals	_?_ 0	_?_ 2	5	_?_ 9	_?_ 14	_?_ 20	_?_ 35

Set B Use Exercise 15 to write expressions for

16. the number of diagonals from each vertex of an *n*-gon. $n - 3$

17. the total number of diagonals of an *n*-gon. $\dfrac{n(n-3)}{2}$

18. A regular decagon and a regular 13-gon have the
same perimeter. The length of one side of the 13-
gon is 5.4. How long is each side of the decagon? **7.02**

19. If every student in your geometry class shook
hands once with each other student, how many
handshakes would be involved?

19. $n \dfrac{(n-1)}{2}$

20. A volleyball league has seven teams, and each
team is to play each other team twice. How many
games are played? How many weeks will it take if
three league games are played each week?

20. 42 matches; 14 weeks

21. Each angle of a regular triangle measures $2x + 10$
and the length of a side is $x + 9$. Find x and the
perimeter of the triangle. **x = 25; perimeter = 102**

Set C **22.** Draw a large regular hexagon. (Each angle measure
is 120.) Draw the angle trisectors. Connect the points
of intersection of adjacent trisectors consecutively.
What kind of figure is formed? Is it regular? **Hexagon; Yes**

23. Repeat Exercise 22 with a regular pentagon. (Each
angle measure is 108.) **A regular pentagon is formed.**

33.

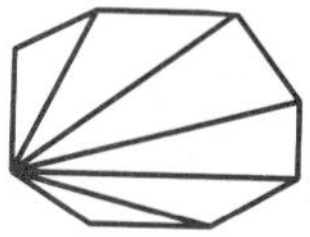

Samples are given for Exercises 1–5 and 7–11.

1.

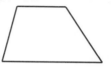

▲ **Review** **24.** Given $\triangle ABC$ with $m\angle C > 90$, prove indirectly: $m\angle B < 90$.

25. In the figure at the right, x = __?__. 12

26. Is the triangle with vertices $P(1, 3)$, $Q(0, -2)$, and $R(4, -1)$ isosceles? No

The Prove

$36°$

$(2x)°$ $(5x)°$

27. In a two-column proof, what is the last statement?

28. All Geplinks eat oofmas. 004 is a Geplink, so __?__. 004 eats oofmas

≋ **Thinking Ahead** Draw a convex polygon with the number of sides specified. Choose any vertex and draw all of the diagonals from it. Find the number of triangles formed and the measure of the angles in each triangle. Then compute the sum of the measures.

29. 4   **30.** 5   **31.** 6   **32.** 7   **33.** 8

34. Generalize your results to find the sum of the angle measures of a convex n-gon. $(n-2)180$

29. 2△s; 360
30. 3△s; 540
31. 4△s; 720
32. 5△s; 900
33. 6△s; 1,080

2.

3.

💻 **Computer Activities: Drawing and Measuring**

Draw convex polygons with the given number of sides. Then find the sum of the angle measures for each polygon.

1. 4 sides 360   **2.** 5 sides 540   **3.** 6 sides 720   **4.** 8 sides 1,080   **5.** 10 sides 1,440

6. What conjecture can you make regarding the sum of the angle measures of a polygon? The sum of the ∠ measures of a polygon is 180 (number of sides −2).

Draw *regular* polygons with the given number of sides. Then find the measure of one angle in each polygon.

7. 4 sides   **8.** 5 sides   **9.** 6 sides·   **10.** 8 sides   **11.** 10 sides

12. Write an expression for the measure of each angle of a regular polygon with n sides. $\frac{(n-2)180}{n}$

Challenge

Play this game several times with a friend. Each player should use a different colored pen or pencil.

a. Mark six points on paper in about the positions shown.

b. Take turns connecting pairs of points with line segments.

The first player who is forced to form a triangle of his or her own color is the loser. Only triangles whose vertices are among the six starting points count. See the diagram for a partially completed game. Is there always a winner? Which player has the better chance? Yes; the first player

More Practice

• Worksheet 4–8

Extension

Given a specific number of sides, challenge students to draw the following.
1. A concave equilateral polygon
2. A concave equiangular polygon.
3. A concave regular polygon
   The latter two are impossible.
• Extension 4–8

Computers

The computer activity in the pupil's book can be completed using *The Geometric preSupposer: Points and Lines* or *GeoDraw*.
• Computer Activities 4–8

Warm-Up Review

1. True or false: The diagonals of a convex polygon are always in the interior. True
2. A(n) __?__ polygon has congruent sides and angles. Regular
3. How many diagonals can be drawn from one vertex of an octagon? 5
4. A(n) __?__ angle is formed by extending a side of a polygon. Exterior
5. What is the sum of the measures of the angles of a triangle? 180

LESSON 4–9

Resources

Teaching Aid 10, polygons
Visual Aid 10, polygons
Teaching Aid 11, tessellations
Visual Aid 11, tessellations
Worksheet 4–9
Extension 4–9
Computer Worksheet 4–9
Algebra Review 4
Chapter 4 Test, Form I
Chapter 4 Test, Form II
Chapter 4 Test, Form III

OBJECTIVE

Find the sum of the measures of the interior as well as the exterior angles of a convex polygon.

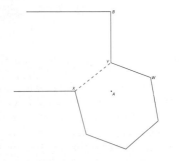

4-9 The Angles of a Polygon

Snowflakes are fascinating examples of geometry in nature. Every snowflake is shaped like a regular hexagon or could be framed by one.

In a *regular* hexagon, all angles have the same measure. This is not true for all hexagons, but perhaps it is true that the *sum* of the measures of the angles is the same for all hexagons.

In each polygon at the right, all possible diagonals from one vertex have been drawn. The sum of the angle measures of each polygon is the sum of the angle measures of the triangles. The table below shows the results of Exercises 29–34 in Lesson 4-8. The general case is stated in Theorem 4-20.

Polygon	Number of sides	Number of triangles	Sum of angle measures
Quadrilateral	4	2	(2)180 = 360
Pentagon	5	3	(3)180 = 540
Hexagon	6	4	(4)180 = 720
Heptagon	7	5	(5)180 = 900
Octagon	8	6	(6)180 = 1,080
n-gon	*n*	*n* − 2	(*n* − 2)180

Quadrilateral

Pentagon

Hexagon

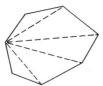
Heptagon

Theorem 4-20

The sum of the measures of the angles of a convex polygon of n sides is (n − 2)180.

Example 1

Find the sum of the angle measures of a convex dodecagon.

Solution

Use Theorem 4-20 with $n = 12$.
$(n - 2)180 = (12 - 2)180 = 1,800$

Example 2

Find the measure of an angle of a regular polygon with 20 sides.

Solution

Sum of angle measures $= (n - 2)180 = (20 - 2)180 = 3,240$

Measure of one angle $= 3,240 \div 20 = 162$

In this pentagon, the sides have been extended in succession to form one exterior angle at each vertex.

The table below describes this pentagon, an octagon, and any convex n-gon.

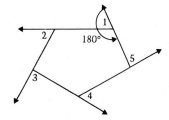

Number of vertices	Interior/exterior angle sum at *one* vertex	Interior/exterior angle sum at *all* vertices	Interior angle sum	Exterior angle sum
5	180	$180(5) = 900$	$180(5 - 2) = 540$	$900 - 540 = 360$
8	180	$180(8) = 1,440$	$180(8 - 2) = 1,080$	$1,440 - 1,080 = 360$
n	180	$180(n)$	$180(n - 2)$	$180n - 180(n - 2) = 360$

Theorem 4-21

The sum of the measures of the exterior angles of a convex polygon, one angle at each vertex, is 360.

The proofs of Theorems 4-20 and 4-21 are omitted.

Example 3

The measure of an angle of a regular polygon is 135. Find the measure m of each exterior angle and n, the number of sides.

Solution

$m = 180 -$ (measure of an angle of the polygon)

$\quad = 180 - 135 = 45$

$n =$ number of sides = number of vertices

$\quad =$ (sum of measures of exterior angles) $\div 45$

$\quad = 360 \div 45 = 8$

Checking for Understanding

1. Show that Theorem 4-20 is true for triangles. Sum $= (n - 2)180 = (3 - 2)180 = 180$

2. Verify the last expression in the table above. $180n - 180(n - 2) = 180n - 180n + 360 = 360$

TEACHING NOTES

Begin this lesson by having students do the following **group activity**.

1. Have students draw polygons of various numbers of sides.

2. Partition each polygon into triangles by drawing all possible diagonals from one vertex.

3. Calculate the angle sum by multiplying 180 by the number of triangles.

Theorem 4–20 is not applicable to concave polygons.

To help students understand Theorem 4–21 choose one vertex and draw rays from this vertex that are parallel to each side of the polygon. Point out that (1) the angles formed can be paired with equal exterior angles and (2) their sum is 360 degrees.

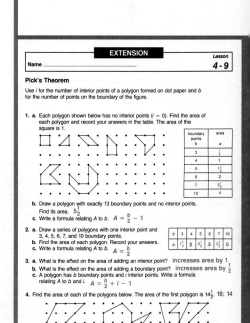

Assignment Guide

Basic: 1–18, 26–30
Average: 1–24, 26–30
Extended: 1–30

Additional Examples

Example 1
In a regular pentagon, find
(a) the sum of the measures of
the interior angles. 540
(b) the measure of one interior
angle. 108

Example 2
The measure of one interior angle
of a regular polygon is 144. Find
(a) the measure of one exterior
angle. 36
(b) the number of sides. 10

Error Analysis   If students forget the formula for the sum of the
measures of the interior angles,
have them draw the figure and
count the triangles. Some students may draw all the diagonals
and form too many triangles.
Stress that triangles should only
be formed from one vertex.

ANSWERS

Written Exercises

5. Since the measures of the ∠s
of a regular polygon are =, the
measure of each ∠ = (the sum of
the measures of the ∠s of the
polygon) ÷ (the number of ∠s).
25. Given: Any convex hexagon
ABCDEF Prove: At least one angle
of *ABCDEF* has a measure of 120
or more. Proof: *Either* a convex
hexagon has at least one angle
with measure greater than or
equal to 120 *or* it has no angles
with measures greater than or
equal to 120. *Suppose* every angle
of *ABCDEF* has a measure less
than 120. *Then* m∠A < 120, m∠B

Draw a convex nonagon. Tell whether each statement about the
nonagon is *true* or *false*. If false, explain why.

3. Six diagonals can be drawn from each vertex. True

4. The sum of the measures of its angles is 1,260. True

5. If the nonagon is regular, each exterior angle has measure 40. True

Written Exercises

Set A   Find the sum of the measures of the angles of a
convex polygon with the given number of sides.

1. 4 360   **2.** 6 720   **3.** 8 1,080   **4.** 16 2,520

5. Explain why the measure of each angle of a
regular *n*-gon is $(n - 2)180 \div n$.

The number of sides of a regular polygon is given.
Find the measure of each angle.

6. 4 90   **7.** 7 $128\frac{4}{7}$ **8.** 10 144   **9.** s $\frac{(s - 2)180}{s}$

The measure of an exterior angle of a regular polygon
is given. Find the number of sides.

10. 45 8   **11.** 60 6   **12.** 72 5   **13.** r $\frac{360}{r}$

The sum of the measures of the angles of a convex
polygon is given. Find the number of sides.

14. 900 7   **15.** 720 6   **16.** 1,260 9   **17.** 2,340 15

18. Find the measure of each angle of *ABCD*.
m∠A = 90; m∠B = 90; m∠C = 45; m∠D = 135

Set B   The measure of one angle of a regular polygon is
given. Find the number of sides.

19. 140 9   **20.** 144 10   **21.** 150 12   **22.** 165 24

23. The sides of a regular pentagon are extended to form
a star. Find the measure of the angle at each point. 36

24. How could you draw a 6-pointed star with equal
angles at the points? Find each angle's measure.

Set C   **25.** Prove indirectly: A convex hexagon must have at
least one angle whose measure is 120 or greater.

◆ **Review**   **26.** Find the perimeter of an equilateral octagon if
each side is 32 units long. 256

27. A polygon with seven sides has __?__ diagonals. 14

28. In a right triangle, the measure of one acute angle
is 22. Find the measure of the other acute angle. 68

24. Extend sides of a regular
hexagon; 60

29. Is the following inequality represented in geometry as a *ray*, a *segment*, or a *line*?
$-4 \le x \le 2$ **Segment**

30. Prove indirectly: Two skew lines do not intersect.

Construction Exercises

1. Construct: Right $\triangle PQR$ with legs $PQ = AB$ and $PR = CD$

2. Construct: Equilateral $\triangle XYZ$ with $XY = AB$

3. Construct: Square $EFGH$ with $EF = CD$

4. Construct: Rhombus $JKLM$ with $m\angle JKL = 45$ and $JK = AB$

5. Construct: Regular octagon $OPQRSTUV$ with $OP = CD$

Progress Check

Lesson 4-5, page 162
Given: Lines j, k, and n in plane $\mathcal{H}$; j and m in plane $\mathcal{E}$; k and ℓ in plane $\mathcal{F}$; plane $\mathcal{E}$ is parallel to plane $\mathcal{F}$.

1. If $n \perp \mathcal{F}$, is $n \perp \mathcal{E}$? **Yes**   **2.** How are j and k related? $j \parallel k$

3. If $j \perp m$ and $k \perp \ell$, how are m and ℓ related? $m \parallel \ell$

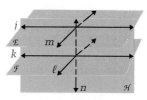

Lesson 4-6, page 166
Draw a triangle that satisfies the given conditions. If there is no such triangle, write *none*.

4. Isosceles and right   **5.** Equilateral and obtuse **None**

6. Equilateral and acute

Lesson 4-7, page 170
7. The measure of the vertex angle of an isosceles triangle is three times the measure of either base angle. Find the three measures. **108; 36; 36**

Given $\triangle ABC$ with $m\angle C = 90$. Find $m\angle A$ and $m\angle B$.

8. $m\angle A = 2x$; $m\angle B = 3x + 10$ **9.** $m\angle B = 2(m\angle A)$
$m\angle A = 32$; $m\angle B = 58$ $m\angle A = 30$; $m\angle B = 60$

Lesson 4-8, page 175
Given quadrilateral $ABCD$, with $\overline{AB} \parallel \overline{DC}$

10. Prove that the sum of the measures of the angles of $ABCD$ is 360.

11. The perimeter of $ABCD$ is 31. Find the length of each side.
$AB = 8$; $BC = 6$; $CD = 12$; $DA = 5$

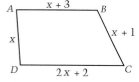

Lesson 4-9, page 180
12. The measure of an exterior angle of an equilateral triangle is ___?___. **120**

13. The measure of each angle of a regular decagon is ___?___. **144**

Review

30. Given: Lines ℓ and m are skew lines. Prove: ℓ and m do not intersect. Proof: *Either* ℓ and m intersect *or* ℓ and m do not intersect. *Suppose* ℓ and m intersect. *Then* ℓ and m are coplanar since two intersecting lines determine a plane. *This contradicts* the definition of skew lines, which states that skew lines are noncoplanar. Therefore, *the assumption* that ℓ and m intersect *is false. We conclude* that ℓ and m do not intersect.

FOLLOW-UP

More Practice

• **Worksheet 4–9**

Extension

Have advanced computer students in the class construct polygons of increasingly large numbers of sides. Ask students what conjectures can be made as the number of sides approaches infinity.

• **Extension 4–9**

Computers

• **Computer Worksheet 4–9**

EXCURSION

A *regular tessellation* is a tessellation constructed from regular polygons of a single size and shape so that vertices of the polygons always coincide with other vertices. There are only three possible regular tessellations.

Students may benefit from creating tessellations out of cut shapes.

The tessellation in **Exercise 4** is called a *semi-regular* tessellation. A semi-regular tessellation is one constructed from regular polygons of two or more types such that at each vertex the arrangement of shapes is the same.

The film "Dihedral Kaleidoscopes" presents an interesting way of generating tessellations by the use of a three-mirror kaleidoscope.

ANSWERS

Excursion

1. polygons which tessellate: equilateral triangle, square, regular hexagon

4. Since the octagons are regular, all sides are =; the measure of each interior ∠ is 135, which leaves an ∠ with a measure of 90 at each vertex. Thus a square with each side = to a side of the regular octagon will fit. The sum of the measures of the three ∠s at each vertex is 135 + 135 + 90 = 360.

5. Sample:

Excursion: Tessellations with Polygons

A tessellation, or tiling, is an arrangement of shapes that completely cover a plane surface without overlapping and without leaving gaps.

Tessellation patterns are commonly found on wallpaper, tiled floors and walls, and fabrics. The floor and ceiling of your classroom might be tessellated with squares.

1. For each regular polygon at the right, mark a point *P* on a sheet of plain paper, and see if repeated tracings of the polygon, each with one vertex at *P*, will cover the region around the point with no overlaps or gaps.

2. Use Exercise 1 to complete the table below.

Number of sides	3	4	5	6	7	8
Does the polygon tessellate?	? Yes	Yes	? No	? Yes	? No	? No
Measure *m* of one angle	? 60	90	? 108	? 120	? 128$\frac{4}{7}$	? 135
Is *m* a factor of 360?	? Yes	Yes	? No	? Yes	? No	? No

3. If a regular polygon can be used to create a tessellation, what is true of the measure of each angle?
It is a factor of 360.

4. Some tessellations use several regular polygons. In the figure at the right, explain why the shapes fit together.

5. Draw a tessellation using only squares and equilateral triangles.

Tell whether each figure tessellates. If so, draw a tessellation using the figure. Compare drawings with those of your classmates.

6. A scalene triangle

7. A quadrilateral with no two sides parallel

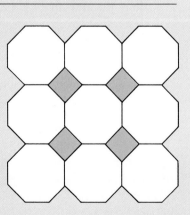

💻 Using Logo: Regular Polygons

The Logo turtle can be taught to draw regular polygons.

1. The procedure at the right causes the turtle to draw an equilateral triangle. Copy the program and then try it by typing TRIANGLE.

2. Will the turtle draw an equilateral triangle if:
   a. each "FD 30" is replaced by "FD 40"? Explain.
   b. each "RT 120" is replaced by "RT 100"? Explain.

3. The turtle can be instructed to repeat a sequence of commands. This procedure also draws an equilateral triangle.

   Use the REPEAT command to define a procedure SQUARE that can be used to draw a square of side length 60.

4. Use the REPEAT command to define a procedure PENTAGON that can be used to draw a pentagon of side length 50.

5. In Logo, a variable is identified by a colon preceding its name. The procedure OCTAGON uses the variable :SIDE to represent the side length of a regular octagon.

   Try OCTAGON 40 and OCTAGON 20 to test this procedure.

6. As you have previously seen, a Logo procedure can call another Logo procedure. At the right is a procedure for drawing a regular polygon that calls itself. Procedures that call themselves are known as recursive procedures.

   Try POLYGON 30 60 to test the procedure. Then use POLYGON to draw a decagon with side length 20.

7. Use the Logo editor to revise POLYGON so that the second input is :N representing the number of sides in the polygon. What other changes must also be made? Use POLYGON 20 9 to test your procedure. Does the turtle draw a nine–sided polygon with side length 20?

8. Define a procedure that uses the REPEAT command to draw any regular n-sided polygon. Use :N as the variable for the number of sides and :SIDE as the variable for the side length.

```
TO TRIANGLE
FD 30
RT 120
FD 30
RT 120
FD 30
RT 120
END
```

```
TO TRIANGLE
REPEAT 3 [FD 30 RT 120]
END
```

```
TO OCTAGON :SIDE
REPEAT 8[FD :SIDE RT 45]
END
```

```
TO POLYGON :SIDE :ANGLE
FD :SIDE
RT :ANGLE
IF HEADING = 0 [STOP]
POLYGON :SIDE :ANGLE
END
```

6. Sample:

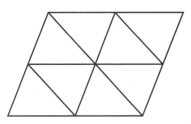

7. does not tessellate

Using Logo

2a. Yes; the equilateral triangles will have longer sides.
b. No; the measures of the int. ∠s would not equal 60, so the triangles would not be equilateral.

3.
```
TO SQUARE
    REPEAT 4[FD 60 RT 90]
END
```
4.
```
TO PENTAGON
    REPEAT 5[FD 50 RT 72]
END
```
7.
```
TO POLYGON :SIDE :N
    FD :SIDE
    RT 360 /:N
    IF HEADING = 0 [STOP]
    POLYGON :SIDE :N
END
```
8.
```
TO POLYGON :SIDE :N
    REPEAT :N[FD :SIDE
    RT 360 /:N]
END
```

Chapter 4 Summary

Important Terms

Acute triangle (166)
Angle of a polygon (166, 175)
Auxiliary line (155)
Base of an isosceles
   triangle (167)
Base angles (167)
Convex polygon (175)
Diagonal of a polygon (176)
Equiangular polygon (176)
Equiangular triangle (167)
Equilateral polygon (176)
Equilateral triangle (167)

Exterior angle of a
   triangle (171)
Exterior of a polygon (175)
Hypotenuse (166)
Indirect reasoning (149)
Interior of a polygon (175)
Isosceles triangle (167)
Legs of a right triangle (166)
Legs of an isosceles
   triangle (167)
Line and plane parallel (162)
Line and plane
   perpendicular (162)

Nonconvex polygon (175)
Obtuse triangle (166)
Parallel planes (162)
Perimeter of a polygon (176)
Polygon (175)
Regular polygon (176)
Remote interior angle (171)
Right triangle (166)
Scalene triangle (167)
Side of a polygon (166, 175)
Triangle (166)
Vertex angle (167)
Vertex of a polygon (166, 175)

Important Ideas

1. Two lines cut by a transversal are parallel if and only if a pair of
   a. corresponding angles are equal. (139)
   b. alternate interior angles are equal. (144)
   c. interior angles on the same side of the transversal are supplementary. (145)

2. If a transversal is perpendicular to one of two parallel lines,
   then it is perpendicular to the other. (140)

3. In a plane, if two lines are perpendicular to the same line,
   then they are parallel. (140)

4. Through a point not on a given line, there is exactly one line parallel to the
   given line and exactly one line perpendicular to the given line. (155, 157)

5. In a plane, through a point on a line, there is exactly one line perpendicular
   to the given line. (157)

6. Two planes that are perpendicular to the same line are parallel. (162)

7. If two parallel planes are cut by a third plane, then the lines
   of intersection are parallel. (163)

8. The sum of the measures of the angles of a triangle is 180. (170)

9. The measure of an exterior angle of a triangle equals the sum of the
   measures of the remote interior angles. (171)

10. The sum of the measures of the interior angles of a convex n-gon is
    $(n - 2)180$. (180)

11. The sum of the measures of the exterior angles of a convex polygon, one
    angle at each vertex, is 360. (181)

Chapter 4 Review

Lesson 4-1, Page 139

Given: $\ell \parallel m$ and $n \perp \ell$

1. If $m\angle 4 = 80$, then $m\angle 8 = \underline{\ ?\ }$. **80**   2. $m\angle 2 = \underline{\ ?\ }$ **90**

3. If $m\angle 9 = 90$, then n and t are $\underline{\ ?\ }$. **∥**

Lesson 4-2, Page 144

Given: $\ell \parallel m$

4. If $m\angle 7 = 120$, then $m\angle 5 = \underline{\ ?\ }$. **120**   5. $m\angle 5 + m\angle 8 = \underline{\ ?\ }$ **180**

6. A board is cut in half to be used as two rafters in constructing a roof. What theorem explains why $m\angle 1 = m\angle 2$? **Thm. 4–3**

Lesson 4-3, Page 149

7. State the definition, postulate, or theorem that this statement contradicts: Point A lies in both of the parallel lines m and n. **Def. of ∥ lines**

8. If Wayne scored a total of five goals in two hockey games, then he scored at least three goals in one of the games. Write an indirect argument to prove this statement.

Lesson 4-4, Page 155

Given: Plane $\mathcal{K}$ with noncollinear points P, Q, and R.

9. Which postulate or theorem justifies auxiliary line $\overleftrightarrow{QR}$? **Line Post.**

10. How many lines in plane $\mathcal{K}$ are perpendicular to $\overleftrightarrow{QR}$ through Q? **1**

11. How many lines are parallel to $\overleftrightarrow{QR}$ through P? **1**

12. Find an equation of a line perpendicular to $y = -3x + 4$ through $(0, 0)$. **Sample: $y = \frac{1}{3}x$**

Lesson 4-5, Page 162

Given: Lines j, k, and n in plane $\mathcal{T}$; ℓ and j in $\mathcal{R}$; m and k in $\mathcal{S}$; lines intersect in points P and Q as shown. Classify each statement as *always*, *sometimes*, or *never* true.

13. If $\mathcal{R} \parallel \mathcal{S}$, then $j \parallel k$.   14. If $n \perp \mathcal{R}$, then $\ell \perp j$.

15. If $j \parallel k$, then $j \parallel m$.   16. If $n \perp \mathcal{R}$, and $n \perp \mathcal{S}$, then $\mathcal{R} \perp \mathcal{S}$.

13. **Always**   14. **Sometimes**
15. **Never**   16. **Never**

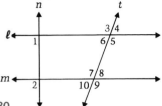

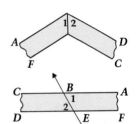

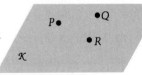

Chapter Review

8. *Either* Wayne scored at least three goals in one of the two hockey games, *or* he scored less than three goals in each game. *Suppose* he scored less than three goals in each game. *Then* he scored two or fewer goals in each game. Therefore, in two games, Wayne scored four or fewer goals. *But this contradicts* the given information that Wayne scored five goals in two hockey games. *Therefore*, *the assumption* that he scored less than three goals in each game *is false*, and *we conclude* that Wayne scored at least three goals in one of the two hockey games.

17. Sample:

legs: $\overline{AB}$, $\overline{AC}$
vertex ∠: ∠A
base ∠s: ∠B and ∠C
base: $\overline{BC}$

18. Sample:

legs: $\overline{AC}$ and $\overline{BC}$
hypotenuse: $\overline{AB}$

19.

legs: $\overline{AC}$ and $\overline{BC}$

Lesson 4-6, Page 166

17. Draw an acute isosceles triangle and name its legs, vertex angle, base angles, and base.

18. Draw a scalene right triangle and name its legs and its hypotenuse.

19. Draw an isosceles right triangle. Name its legs.

20. Use the Distance Formula to show that the triangle with vertices at (1, 1), (−1, −1), and (−3, 3) is isosceles.

20. $\sqrt{(-1-1)^2 + (-1-1)^2} = 2\sqrt{2}$
$\sqrt{(-3-(-1))^2 + (3-(-1))^2} = 2\sqrt{5}$
$\sqrt{(-3-1)^2 + (3-1)^2} = 2\sqrt{5}$

Lesson 4-7, Page 170
Given: $m\angle D = m\angle H$ and $m\angle F = m\angle K$

21. If $m\angle D = 55$ and $m\angle F = 20$, then $m\angle E = \underline{\ ?\ }$. 105

22. If the measure of an exterior angle at J is 70, then $m\angle HJK = \underline{\ ?\ }$. 110

23. If $m\angle K = 20$ and $m\angle HJL = 80$, then $m\angle H = \underline{\ ?\ }$. 60

24. Explain why it is not possible for a right triangle to be equiangular. A △ can have at most one rt. ∠, or the sum of ∠ measures > 180.

Lesson 48, Page 175
Draw a convex polygon $ABCD$.

25. Name all the diagonals of $ABCD$. $\overline{AC}$, $\overline{BD}$

26. What additional information is necessary in order to conclude that $ABCD$ is a regular polygon?

26. $AB = BC = CD = DA$;
$m\angle A = m\angle B = m\angle C = m\angle D$
27. $AB + BC + CD + AD$

27. Write an expression for the perimeter of $ABCD$.

28. Draw a quadrilateral that is equilateral, but not equiangular.

29. Draw a quadrilateral that is equiangular, but not equilateral.

Samples:
28. **29.**

Rhombus   Rectangle

Lesson 4-9, Page 180

30. The sum of the measures of the angles of a convex polygon of n sides is $\underline{\ ?\ }$. $(n-2)180$

31. The measure of an exterior angle of a regular hexagon is $\underline{\ ?\ }$. 60

32. The measure of each angle of a regular pentagon is $\underline{\ ?\ }$. 108

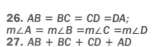

Chapter 4 Test

Is each statement *always*, *sometimes*, or *never* true? Explain.

1. Two planes that have no points in common are parallel. Always

2. If two parallel lines are cut by a transversal, then interior angles on the same side of the transversal are supplementary. Always

3. Two lines perpendicular to the same line are parallel. Sometimes; if lines are coplanar

4. Each exterior angle of a triangle measures 120. Sometimes; if △ is equiangular

5. Equilateral △DEF is isosceles. Always

6. Right △PQR is isosceles. Sometimes; if legs are =

Given: $j \parallel k$; $\ell \parallel t$

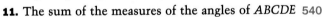

7. $m\angle 2 = m\angle\underline{\,?\,} = m\angle\underline{\,?\,} = m\angle\underline{\,?\,}$ 4; 6; 8

8. If $m\angle 5 = 40$, then $m\angle 3 = \underline{\,?\,}$. 40

9. If $m\angle 2 = 95$, then $m\angle 5 = \underline{\,?\,}$. 85

10. $m\angle 3 + m\angle 8 + m\angle 9 + m\angle 4 = \underline{\,?\,}$ 360

For regular pentagon *ABCDE*, find each of the following.

11. The sum of the measures of the angles of *ABCDE* 540

12. The sum of the measures of the exterior angles of *ABCDE* 360

13. The measure of one exterior angle of *ABCDE* 72

14. If $m\angle 4 = 80$ and $m\angle 1 = 20$, then $m\angle 2 = \underline{\,?\,}$. 60

15. Tell whether this statement can be used in a proof with the figure at the right: Draw $\overleftrightarrow{CE}$ so that $\overrightarrow{CE}$ bisects $\angle KCP$ and $\overleftrightarrow{CE} \parallel \overleftrightarrow{AP}$. No

16. Find an equation for the line that contains (1, 3) and is parallel to $y = 3x + 4$. Sample: $y = 3x$

17. Find an equation for the line that contains (−1, 0) and is perpendicular to $y = 2x + 2$. Sample: $y = -\frac{1}{2}x - \frac{1}{2}$

18. Given: Parallel planes $\mathcal{E}$ and $\mathcal{H}$ cut by plane $\mathcal{T}$. Prove indirectly that $\overleftrightarrow{AB} \parallel \overleftrightarrow{CD}$.

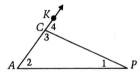

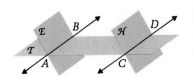

Chapter Test

18. Proof: Since $\overleftrightarrow{AB}$ and $\overleftrightarrow{CD}$ are coplanar in $\mathcal{T}$, either $\overleftrightarrow{AB} \parallel \overleftrightarrow{CD}$ or $\overleftrightarrow{AB} \not{\parallel} \overleftrightarrow{CD}$. *Suppose that* $\overleftrightarrow{AB} \not{\parallel} \overleftrightarrow{CD}$. *Then* $\overleftrightarrow{AB}$ *and* $\overleftrightarrow{CD}$ *intersect in some point P. Since* $\overleftrightarrow{AB}$ *is contained in plane* $\mathcal{E}$ *and* $\overleftrightarrow{CD}$ *is contained in plane* $\mathcal{K}$, *P lies in both planes* $\mathcal{E}$ *and* $\mathcal{K}$. *But this contradicts the fact that* $\mathcal{E} \parallel \mathcal{K}$, *which means that* $\mathcal{E}$ *and* $\mathcal{K}$ *have no points in common. Therefore, the assumption that* $\overleftrightarrow{AB} \not{\parallel} \overleftrightarrow{CD}$ *is false, and we conclude that* $\overleftrightarrow{AB} \parallel \overleftrightarrow{CD}$.

CHAPTER 5

Congruent Triangles

Chapter Overview

This chapter defines triangle congruence and states the SSS, ASA and SAS postulates. Two congruence criteria are presented as theorems—the AAS and HL theorems.

Much of this chapter concentrates on using all five criteria to prove triangles congruent, including the use of corresponding parts and proofs involving overlapping triangles.

Compass and straightedge constructions are justified using congruent triangles. Inequalities in triangles and the introduction of paragraph form for direct proof are also presented.

In the examples and exercises, various **proof subskills** are developed.

Perspectives

Lesson 5-1 defines congruent triangles in terms of equal sides and angles. Keep in mind that different correspondences between the vertices may yield different results.

Lesson 5-2 illustrates the fact that as few as three pairs of equal corresponding parts are often sufficient for congruent triangles. The SSS, SAS and ASA postulates cover three of the cases in which this is true. It is necessary to postulate only one of these three statements; the other two could then be proved as theorems.

Lesson 5-3 uses the three postulates in the last lesson to prove a fourth method of showing that two triangles are congruent. The AAS Theorem is derived from ASA and the fact that if two angles of one triangle are equal to two angles of another, the third pair of angles must be equal.

Lesson 5-4 asks students to prove all six pairs of corresponding parts are equal after they prove that the triangles are congruent. These results may also be used to show that lines are parallel or perpendicular.

Lesson 5-5 develops a strategy for proving overlapping triangles congruent. These are often encountered in real-world situations.

Lesson 5-6 justifies straightedge and compass constructions. Three special segments in a triangle are defined: angle bisector, altitude and median. These are constructed using constructions from earlier lessons.

Lesson 5-7 explores the special properties of isosceles triangles. As a result, we can show that a triangle is equilateral if and only if it is equiangular. Another result of the Isosceles Triangle Theorem and its converse is the HL Theorem, a useful method to show that two right triangles are congruent.

Pacing Chart for Chapter 5

Lesson	Objectives	Basic Course	Average Course	Extended Course
5-1	Recognize congruent triangles; identify the corresponding parts of congruent triangles.	$1\frac{1}{2}$	1	1
5-2	Use the SSS, SAS and ASA congruence postulates to prove triangles congruent.	2	$1\frac{1}{2}$	$1\frac{1}{2}$
5-3	Use the AAS Congruence Theorem to prove triangles congruent; use the AAS Theorem, the SAS Postulate and the ASA Postulate to prove right triangles congruent.	2	$1\frac{1}{2}$	$1\frac{1}{2}$
5-4	Use congruent triangles to prove segments or angles equal and to prove lines parallel or perpendicular.	$1\frac{1}{2}$	1	1
5-5	Identify the corresponding parts of overlapping congruent triangles; prove overlapping triangles congruent.	2	$1\frac{1}{2}$	$1\frac{1}{2}$
5-6	Justify constructions using congruent triangles.	2	$1\frac{1}{2}$	$1\frac{1}{2}$
5-7	Use the Isosceles Triangle Theorem and its converse; use the HL Theorem to prove right triangles congruent.	$1\frac{1}{2}$	1	1
5-8	Recognize and apply inequalities in one triangle or a pair of triangles.	$1\frac{1}{2}$	1	1
5-9	Apply the Triangle Inequality Theorem.	$1\frac{1}{2}$	1	1
Review		$1\frac{1}{2}$	1	1
Test		1	1	1
Total		18 days	13 days	13 days

Lesson 5-8 introduces the theorems that are needed for dealing with inequalities in triangles. Theorems 5-8, 5-9 and 5-10 involve inequality relationships within one triangle, and Theorems 5-11 and 5-12 involve relationships between a pair of triangles.

Lesson 5-9 provides application for the Triangle Inequality Theorem and introduces direct proof written in paragraph form.

Theorems 5-14 and 5-15 are crucial in terms of the definitions given for distance from a point to a line or plane.

The relationship among the various figures in these quilt designs is made clearer by thinking about how one might go about making a quilt. Cutting figures from the same pattern results in figures identical not only in shape—like the right triangles in the lower quilt block—but in size as well—like the hexagons in the upper quilt block.

1. hexagonal; hexagonal
2. Only one; the hexagons are all the same shape and the same size.
3. five; isosceles right triangles in two sizes; squares; quadrilaterals (trapezoids); pentagons

Congruent Triangles

Chapter 5

The designs in these two quilt blocks incorporate various polygonal shapes. The questions below do not refer to the borders of the two quilt blocks.

1. What shape are the red-print figures in the top quilt block? the solid-blue and blue-print figures?

2. How many patterns are needed to cut the quilt pieces for the figures described in Exercise 1? Explain why.

3. How many different patterns are needed for the lower quilt block? Describe the pieces that can be cut from each pattern.

Warm-Up Review

Warm-Up Review

1. Which property allows us to state that $a = a$? Reflexive
2. Which property allows us to state that if $a = b$, then $b = a$? Symmetric
3. Which property allows us to state that if $a = b$ and $b = c$, then $a = c$? Transitive
4. What kind of triangle has no pairs of equal sides? Scalene
5. What kind of triangle has one pair of equal sides? Isosceles

5-1 Congruence of Triangles

Like the polygonal shapes in the quilt blocks on page 190, figures that are cut from a single pattern are identical in size and shape. The mathematical term for this relationship is *congruence*.

The triangles at the right are identical in size and shape. You can place one of them over the other so it fits exactly. It will fit only if the corresponding vertices are matched as shown, giving the following correspondences:

Corresponding vertices: $D \leftrightarrow R, E \leftrightarrow S, F \leftrightarrow T$
Corresponding angles: $\angle D \leftrightarrow \angle R, \angle E \leftrightarrow \angle S, \angle F \leftrightarrow \angle T$
Corresponding sides: $\overline{DE} \leftrightarrow \overline{RS}, \overline{EF} \leftrightarrow \overline{ST}, \overline{DF} \leftrightarrow \overline{RT}$

$\leftrightarrow$ means "corresponds to."

Compare the angles in each pair. How is $\angle D$ related to $\angle R$? **Equal**
Are the other pairs of corresponding angles related in the same way? How are the sides in each pair related? Your answers should suggest this definition. **Yes, equal**

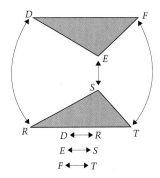
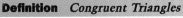

Definition *Congruent Triangles*

Two triangles are congruent if and only if there is a correspondence between the vertices such that each pair of corresponding sides and each pair of corresponding angles are equal.

Congruent polygons are defined in a similar manner.

In the diagram at the right, each pair of equal parts are marked.

$m\angle A = m\angle X, m\angle B = m\angle Y, m\angle C = m\angle Z$
$AB = XY, BC = YZ, AC = XZ$

You can conclude that $\triangle ABC$ is congruent to $\triangle XYZ$. This is written $\triangle ABC \cong \triangle XYZ$. The order of the letters tells how the vertices are paired. For example, $\triangle ABC \not\cong \triangle XZY$ since $m\angle B \neq m\angle Z$.

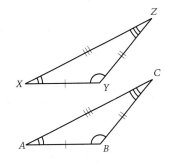

If we know that two triangles are congruent, we can conclude that pairs of corresponding sides and angles are equal. This conclusion may be justified with the following statement: "Corresponding parts of congruent triangles are equal," abbreviated as "Corr. parts of $\cong$ $\triangle$s are =." This statement is simply a rephrasing of the definition of congruent triangles.

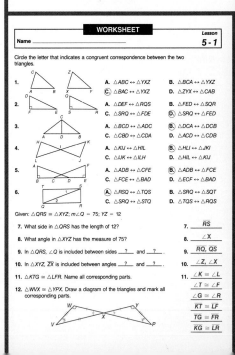

1. Congruent triangles. Show how congruent triangles "fit" one another.
2. Corresponding parts. Label the vertices and explain that not every correspondence yields congruent triangles.
3. Included sides and angles. Emphasize the properties stated in Theorem 5–1. Relations having these properties are called "equivalence relations."

Proofs may be completed using either the paragraph or two-column method; because two-column form translates more easily into paragraph form than vice versa, answers are given in two-column form.

Additional Examples

Example 1
Given $\triangle RON \cong \triangle KTS$, name the six pairs of corresponding parts that are equal. ($RO = KT$; $ON = TS$;

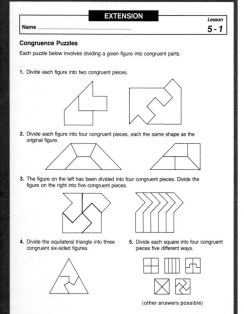

Example 1
Given $\triangle OLD \cong \triangle NEW$, name the six pairs of equal corresponding parts.

Solution
$OL = NE$, $LD = EW$, $OD = NW$, $m\angle O = m\angle N$, $m\angle L = m\angle E$, and $m\angle D = m\angle W$, because corr. parts of $\cong \triangle$s are $=$.

An **included angle** for two sides of a triangle is the angle whose sides contain the two sides of the triangle. Which angle is $\angle O$ included between $\overline{DO}$ and $\overline{TO}$? An **included side** for two angles of a triangle is a side whose endpoints are the vertices of the angles. Which side is included between $\angle D$ and $\angle T$? $\overline{DT}$

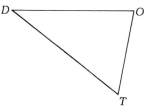

Example 2
a. In $\triangle ACD$, what angle is included between $\overline{AC}$ and $\overline{AD}$? What side is included between $\angle ADC$ and $\angle ACD$?

b. In $\triangle BCD$, what angle is included between $\overline{BC}$ and $\overline{CD}$? What side is included between $\angle CBD$ and $\angle CDB$?

c. In $\triangle ABC$, what angle is included between $\overline{AC}$ and $\overline{BC}$? What side is included between $\angle BAC$ and $\angle ABC$?

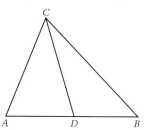

Solution
a. In $\triangle ACD$, $\angle CAD$ is included between $\overline{AC}$ and $\overline{AD}$, and $\overline{CD}$ is included between $\angle ADC$ and $\angle ACD$.

b. In $\triangle BCD$, $\angle BCD$ is included between $\overline{BC}$ and $\overline{CD}$, and $\overline{BD}$ is included between $\angle CBD$ and $\angle CDB$.

c. In $\triangle ABC$, $\angle ACB$ is included between $\overline{AC}$ and $\overline{BC}$, and $\overline{AB}$ is included between $\angle BAC$ and $\angle ABC$.

Since measures of segments and angles are real numbers, the Reflexive, Symmetric, and Transitive Properties apply to them. Hence, these properties are true for congruence of triangles as well. The proof of Theorem 5-1 is left to Exercises 17–19.

Theorem 5-1

Congruence of triangles is reflexive, symmetric, and transitive.

Checking for Understanding
Given $\triangle XYZ \cong \triangle RTS$, how would you mark each part of $\triangle RTS$?
1. $\overline{RS}$ 2 marks **2.** $\angle R$ 3 marks **3.** $\overline{TS}$ 3 marks **4.** $\angle S$ 1 mark
$\triangle RST$
5. If $\triangle XYZ \cong \triangle RTS$, then $\triangle XZY \cong \underline{\ ?\ }$, $\triangle YXZ \cong \underline{\ ?\ }$, $\triangle TRS$
$\triangle YZX \cong \underline{\ ?\ }$, $\triangle ZXY \cong \underline{\ ?\ }$, and $\triangle ZYX \cong \underline{\ ?\ }$. $\triangle STR$
$\triangle TSR$ $\qquad$ $\triangle SRT$

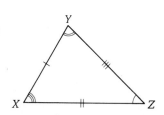

NR = SK; m∠R = m∠K; m∠O
= m∠T; m∠N = m∠S)

Example 2

(a) Name the side of △HIS included between ∠IHS and ∠S. $\overline{HS}$

(b) Name the angle of △FSH included between $\overline{FS}$ and
$\overline{HS}$. ∠S

(c) Name the side of △FIH included between ∠F and ∠FIH. $\overline{FI}$

Tell whether each statement appears to be *true* or *false*.

6. △ABC ≅ △DEF F   **7.** AB = EF F   **8.** △DEF ≅ △MNP T
9. m∠F = m∠P T   **10.** △DEF ≅ △NMP F   **11.** △ABC ≅ △BAC T

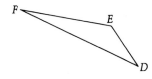
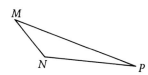

Written Exercises **1.** PA = TE; PS = TL; AS = EL
Set A   Given: △PAS ≅ △TEL **2.** m∠P = m∠T; m∠A =m∠E
                                    m∠S = m∠L

   1. List three pairs of equal sides.

   2. List three pairs of equal angles.

   3. Which side is included between ∠P and ∠S? $\overline{PS}$

   4. Which angle is included between $\overline{TL}$ and $\overline{ET}$? ∠T

Given △XYZ ≅ △JKL, is each statement always true?

   5. △YZX ≅ △KLJ Yes   **6.** △XZY ≅ △JLK Yes

   7. △XYZ ≅ △LJK No   **8.** △YXZ ≅ △KJL Yes

Tell whether each statement appears to be *true*
or *false*.

   9. △MNP ≅ △RST T   **10.** △MNP ≅ △STR F

  11. △MNP ≅ △SRT T   **12.** △MNP ≅ △RTS F

List the six pairs of equal corresponding parts, given

  13. △ABE ≅ △CBD.   **14.** △EBD ≅ △DBE.

  15. △ABD ≅ △CBE.   **16.** △ABC ≅ △CBA.

Set B   **17.** Prove that congruence of triangles is reflexive.

  18. Prove that congruence of triangles is symmetric.

  19. Prove that congruence of triangles is transitive.

Ed found that the shadows of a tree and a pole were
the same length. He assumed m∠A and m∠C were
equal, as both were formed by the sun's rays and
the ground.

  20. The pole and the tree are vertical. Is m∠D =
       m∠B? Why? Yes, both are rt. ∠s.

  21. Do △ABT and △CDP appear to be congruent? Yes

  22. How do you think the heights of the tree and the
       pole compare? They are equal.

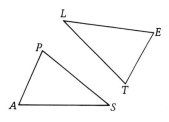
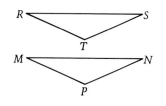
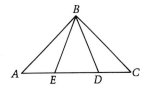
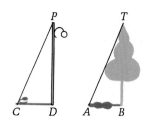

Error Analysis Students are
often careless about writing congruence statements so that corresponding vertices are in matching
positions. Point out that if we
write △ABC ≅ △DEF, the correspondences are A↔D, B↔E and
C↔F.

ANSWERS

Written Exercises

13. AB = CB; AE = CD; BE = BD;
m∠A = m∠C; m∠ABE = m∠CBD;
m∠AEB = m∠CDB
14. EB = DB; ED = DE; BD = BE;
m∠BED = m∠BDE; m∠EBD = m∠
DBE; m∠BDE = m∠BED
15. AB = CB; AD = CE; BD = BE;
m∠A = m∠C; m∠ABD = m∠CBE;
m∠ADB = m∠CEB
16. AB = CB; AC = CA; BC = BA;
m∠A = m∠C; m∠ABC = m∠CBA;
m∠C = m∠A

23. Proof: 1. $\triangle ABC \cong \triangle CBA$ (Given) 2. $AB = CB$ (Corr. parts of $\cong$ $\triangle$s are =. [1]) 3. $\triangle ABC$ is isos. (Def. of isos. $\triangle$ [2])

24. Proof: 1. $\triangle ABC \cong \triangle CBA$ (Given) 2. $CB = AB$ (Corr. parts of $\cong$ $\triangle$s are =. [1]) 3. $\triangle ABC \cong \triangle ACB$ (Given) 4. $AB = AC$ (Corr. parts of $\cong$ $\triangle$s are =. [3]) 5. $CB = AC$ (Transitive Prop. [2, 4]) 6. $\triangle ABC$ is equilateral. (Def. of equilateral $\triangle$. [2, 4, 5])

FOLLOW-UP

More Practice

• **Worksheet 5–1**

Extension

As a **group activity**, explore the number of correspondences that yield equal corresponding parts between the following triangles:
1. Congruent scalene triangles. one
2. Congruent isosceles triangles. two
3. Congruent equilateral triangles. three
• **Extension 5–1**

Computers

The computer activity in the pupil's book can be completed using *GeoDraw*. Note: Students must use the "aRc" command to draw segments of given lengths.
• **Computer Activities 5–1**
• **Computer Worksheet 5–1**

Set C **23.** Given: $\triangle ABC \cong \triangle CBA$
Prove: $\triangle ABC$ is isosceles.

24. Given: $\triangle ABC \cong \triangle CBA$; $\triangle ABC \cong \triangle ACB$
Prove: $\triangle ABC$ is equilateral and equiangular.

25. Prove indirectly: If two triangles are congruent and one of them is scalene, then the other is scalene.

▲ Review **26.** The measure of an interior angle of a regular hexagon is ___?___. 120

27. In a polygon with ___?___ sides, the sum of the measures of the angles is 540. 5

28. The perimeter of an equilateral decagon is 120. Find the length of a side. 12

29. Write the following statement in "if . . . then" form: Two angles that are equal and complementary each have a measure of 45.

30. Write a two-column proof of the statement in Exercise 29.

32. $MN = PQ = \sqrt{10}$; $LN = QR = 2\sqrt{2}$; yes

≡ Thinking Ahead **31.** Since they are both right angles, $m\angle AOB = m\angle DOC$. $AO = DO = 2$, and $B = CO = 3$. Do $\triangle AOB$ and $\triangle DOC$ appear to be congruent? Yes

32. Use the Distance Formula to show that $MN = PQ$, $LM = PR$, and $LN = QR$. Does $\triangle LMN$ appear to be congruent to $\triangle RPQ$?

29. If $2\angle$s are = and complementary, then each has a measure of 45.

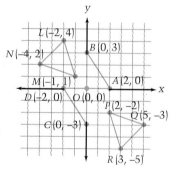

💻 Computer Activities: Drawing and Measuring

1. Draw two triangles, each with side lengths 30, 70, and 50. Do the triangles appear to be congruent? Yes

2. Repeat this activity with four more pairs of triangles having side lengths different from those in Exercise 1. Do the triangles in each pair appear to be congruent? Yes

3. Draw two triangles, each with an angle of 45° included between sides of lengths 70 and 60. Do the triangles appear to be congruent? Yes

4. Repeat this activity with four more pairs of triangles having angle measures and side lengths different from those in Exercise 3. Do the triangles in each pair appear to be congruent? Yes

5. What two conjectures can you make regarding congruence of two triangles? 2 $\triangle$s with = corr. sides are $\cong$ .2 $\triangle$s with 2 prs. of corr. sides and = included $\angle$s are $\cong$.

5-2 The SSS, SAS, and ASA Congruence Postulates

To repair a hole in the wall, plasterer Eric Jackson cut a triangular opening in the wallboard around the damaged region. The opening has sides measuring 12 in., 15 in., and 20 in. He then cut a new triangular piece of wallboard with sides of the same three lengths. Will the new piece fit? To answer this question, you need to know whether two triangles with three equal sides are necessarily congruent. Postulate 16 provides the answer.

Postulate 16   SSS Congruence Postulate

If three sides of one triangle are equal to the corresponding parts of another triangle, then the triangles are congruent.

If AB = XY, BC = YZ, and CA = ZX, then △ABC ≅ △XYZ by the SSS Congruence Postulate.

By definition, two triangles are congruent if all six pairs of corresponding parts are equal. The SSS (side-side-side) Congruence Postulate allows you to prove that two triangles are congruent using only three pairs of equal corresponding parts.

Example 1

Given: AB = DB; AC = DC
Prove: △ABC ≅ △DBC

Solution
The proof uses the SSS Congruence Postulate.

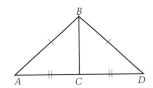

Statements	Reasons
1. AB = DB; AC = DC	1. Given
2. BC = BC	2. Reflexive Prop.
3. △ABC ≅ △DBC	3. SSS Post. [1, 2]

The next two postulates also allow you to prove triangles congruent using only three pairs of corresponding parts.

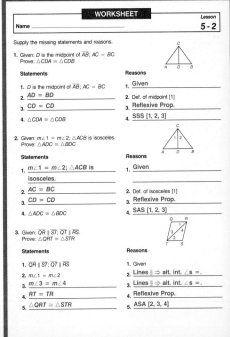

TEACHING NOTES

Introduce the postulates with the following **group activity** involving constructions.
1. Draw three line segments of given lengths.
2. Using one of the three lengths as a base, draw an arc with radius equal to a second length, using one endpoint of the base as center.
3. Draw an arc with radius equal to the third length, using the other endpoint as center.
4. Join the endpoints with the intersection of the arcs.
What is true of the resulting triangles? All have the three given lengths as sides; all are congruent.

Similar **activities** could be used to introduce the SAS and ASA postulates.

Postulate 17 *SAS Congruence Postulate*

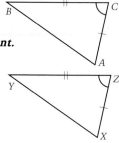

If two sides and the included angle of one triangle are equal to the corresponding parts of another triangle, then the triangles are congruent.

If $AC = XZ$, $m\angle C = m\angle Z$, and $CB = ZY$, then $\triangle ABC \cong \triangle XYZ$ by the SAS Congruence Postulate.

In the name "SAS (side-angle-side) Congruence Postulate," the A is in the middle because the angle must be the *included* angle.

Example 2

To measure the width of a pond, Ron and Leah place a marker at point P and stand at the two ends of the pond. Leah paces off the distance from L to P, and then continues walking straight ahead for the same number of paces, stopping at L' (read "L prime"). Ron locates R' in the same way. Ron then walks 17 paces from R' to L'. How wide is the pond?

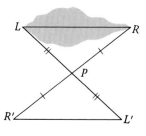

Solution   Corr. parts of $\cong$ $\triangle$s are =.

If $\triangle LRP \cong \triangle L'R'P'$, then $LR = 17$ paces. Why? It is given that $PL = PL'$ and $RP = R'P$. The angle included by $\overline{PL}$ and $\overline{RP}$ in $\triangle LRP$ is $\angle LPR$, and $\angle L'PR'$ is included by $\overline{PL'}$ and $\overline{R'P}$ in $\triangle L'R'P$. These are vertical angles, so $m\angle LPR = m\angle L'PR'$, and $\triangle LRP \cong \triangle L'R'P$ by the SAS Postulate. Thus the pond is 17 paces wide.

Postulate 18 *ASA Congruence Postulate*

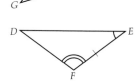
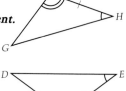

If two angles and the included side of one triangle are equal to the corresponding parts of another triangle, then the triangles are congruent.

If $m\angle H = m\angle E$, $HI = EF$, and $m\angle I = m\angle F$, then $\triangle GHI \cong \triangle DEF$ by the ASA Congruence Postulate.

In the name "ASA (angle-side-angle) Congruence Postulate," the S is in the middle because the side must be the *included* side.

Checking for Understanding

1. In $\triangle ABC$ and $\triangle XYZ$ above, if $m\angle A = m\angle X$ rather than $m\angle C = m\angle Z$, would the triangles be congruent by Postulate 17? Explain. No; $\angle$s A and X are not the included $\angle$s.

2. In $\triangle GHI$ and $\triangle DEF$ above, if $m\angle G = m\angle D$ rather than $m\angle H = m\angle E$, would the triangles be congruent by Postulate 18? Explain. No; $\overline{IH}$ and $\overline{EF}$ are not the included sides.

Assignment Guide

Basic: 1–16, 29–39
Average: 2–8 (even), 9–26, 29–39
Extended: 2–16 (even), 17–39

Which postulate justifies $\triangle ABC \cong \triangle DEF$?

3. Given: $AC = DF$; $AB = DE$; $BC = EF$ **SSS Post.**

4. Given: $EF = BC$; $AB = DE$; $m\angle B = m\angle E$ **SAS Post.**

5. Given: $m\angle C = m\angle F$; $m\angle E = m\angle B$; $BC = EF$ **ASA Post.**

6. Given: $DF = AC$; $DE = AB$; $m\angle D = m\angle A$ **SAS Post.**

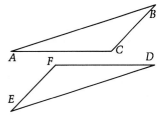

Written Exercises

Set A   The goal is to prove $\triangle NOW \cong \triangle ART$.

1. To use the SSS Postulate, show $NO = \underline{\;?\;}$, AR
$OW = \underline{\;?\;}$, and $NW = \underline{\;?\;}$. **RT; AT;**

2. Given $m\angle W = m\angle T$, to use the SAS Postulate
show $AT = \underline{\;?\;}$ and $RT = \underline{\;?\;}$. **NW; OW**

3. Given $OW = RT$, to use the ASA Postulate show
$\underline{\;?\;}$ and $\underline{\;?\;}$. **$m\angle O = m\angle R$; $m\angle W = m\angle T$**

The goal is to prove $\triangle TAR \cong \triangle WON$.

4. To use the SSS Postulate, show $NW = \underline{\;?\;}$,
$OW = \underline{\;?\;}$, and $NO = \underline{\;?\;}$. **RT; AT; RA**

5. Given $OW = AT$, to use the ASA Postulate show
$\underline{\;?\;}$ and $\underline{\;?\;}$. **$m\angle O = m\angle A$; $m\angle W = m\angle T$**

6. Use the Distance Formula to show that AB, CB,
AD, and CD are all equal. **$AB = CB = AD = CD = 5$**

7. Explain why $\triangle AOB$, $\triangle COB$, $\triangle AOD$, and $\triangle COD$ are
all congruent to one another.

8. Name the pairs of equal angles at A, B, C, and D.
7. By SSS Post. ($AB = CB = AD = CD$;
$OA = OC$; $OB = OD$
8. $\angle OAB$, $\angle OAD$; $\angle OBA$, $\angle OBC$;
$\angle OCB$, $\angle OCD$; $\angle ODC$, $\angle ODA$

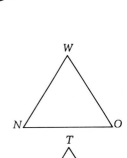

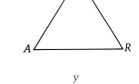

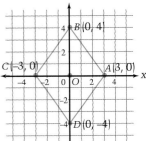

Supply the missing statements and reasons.

9. Given: $CD = CB$; $m\angle ACD = m\angle ACB$
Prove: $\triangle ACD \cong \triangle ACB$

Statements	Reasons
1. $CD = CB$	1. $\underline{\;?\;}$ Given
2. $m\angle ACD = m\angle ACB$	2. $\underline{\;?\;}$ Given
3. $\underline{\;?\;}$ $AC = AC$	3. Reflexive Prop.
4. $\triangle ACD \cong \triangle ACB$	4. $\underline{\;?\;}$ SAS Post.

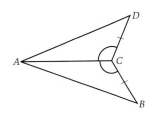

Additional Examples

Example 1
Given: $JU = MR$; $JR = UM$
Prove: $\triangle JUR \cong \triangle MRU$ $RU = RU$
by Reflexive

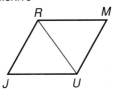

Example 2

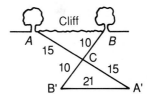

Ranger Dave wants to measure
the distance between two trees
along the edge of a cliff. He
makes a mark at 15 feet along a
30-foot rope and attaches the
rope to tree A. He also marks the
midpoint of a 20-foot rope and attaches that rope to tree B. With
the help of Ranger Shari he
stretches out the two ropes so
that the midpoint marks coincide.
They measure the distance between the ends of the ropes as 21
ft. What is the distance between
the two trees? 21 ft. How do
they know for certain? Using the
given sides and vertical angles,
the two triangles are congruent by
SAS.

Error Analysis   Caution students that when SAS is used, the
angle used must be included between the two sides. Many students are careless about this.

ANSWERS

Written Exercises

11. Proof: 1. $AD = CB$; $AB = CD$ (Given) 2. $AC = CA$ (Reflexive Prop.) 3. $\triangle ABC \cong \triangle CDA$ (SSS Post. [1, 2])

12. Proof: 1. $\overline{AB} \parallel \overline{CD}$; $AB = CD$ (Given) 2. $m\angle BAC = m\angle DCA$ (2 lines $\parallel \Rightarrow$ alt. int. $\angle$s =. [1]) 3. $AC = CA$ (Reflexive Prop.) 4. $\triangle ABC \cong \triangle CDA$ (SAS Post. [1, 2, 3])

13. Proof: 1. $\overline{BC} \parallel \overline{AD}$; $AD = CB$ (Given) 2. $m\angle BCA = m\angle DAC$ (2 lines $\parallel \Rightarrow$ alt. int. $\angle$s =. [1]) 3. $AC = CA$ (Reflexive Prop.) 4. $\triangle ABC \cong \triangle CDA$ (SAS Post. [1, 2, 3])

14. Proof: 1. $\overline{AB} \parallel \overline{CD}$; $\overline{AD} \parallel \overline{BC}$ (Given) 2. $m\angle BAC = m\angle DCA$; $m\angle BCA = m\angle DAC$ (2 lines $\parallel \Rightarrow$ alt. int. $\angle$s =. [1]) 3. $AC = CA$ (Reflexive Prop.) 4. $\triangle ABC \cong \triangle CDA$ (ASA Post. [2, 3])

16. No; $\triangle$s are same shape, but not necessarily same size.

17. Proof: 1. $m\angle A = m\angle D$; B is midpt. of $\overline{AD}$. (Given) 2. $AB = DB$ (Def. of midpt. [1]) 3. $m\angle ABC = m\angle DBE$ (Vert. $\angle$s are =.) 4. $\triangle ABC \cong \triangle DBE$ (ASA Post. [1, 2, 3])

18. Proof: 1. B is midpt. of $\overline{AD}$ and $\overline{CE}$. (Given) 2. $AB = DB$; $CB = EB$ (Def. of midpt. [1]) 3. $m\angle ABC = m\angle DBE$ (Vert. $\angle$s are =.) 4. $\triangle ABC \cong \triangle DBE$ (SAS Post. [2, 3])

19. Proof: 1. $\overline{AC} \parallel \overline{DE}$; $AC = DE$ (Given) 2. $m\angle BAC = m\angle BDE$; $m\angle BCA = m\angle BED$ (2 lines $\parallel \Rightarrow$ alt. int. $\angle$s =. [1]) 3. $\triangle ABC \cong \triangle DBE$ (ASA Post. [1, 2])

20. Proof: 1. $\overline{AC} \parallel \overline{DE}$; B is midpt. of $\overline{CE}$. (Given) 2. $m\angle BCA = m\angle BED$ (2 lines $\parallel \Rightarrow$ alt. int. $\angle$s =. [1]) 3. $CB = EB$ (Def. of midpt. [1]) 4. $m\angle ABC = m\angle DBE$ (Vert. $\angle$s are =.) 5. $\triangle ABC \cong \triangle DBE$ (ASA Post. [2, 3, 4])

21. Proof: 1. $RS = RP$; $m\angle FRO = m\angle PRO$ (Given) 2. $OR = OR$ (Reflexive Prop.) 3. $\triangle PRO \cong \triangle SRO$ (SAS Post. [1, 2])

22. $AB = DF = 5$; $AC = DE = 3$; $BC = FE = 4$; $\triangle ABO \cong \triangle DFE$ by

---

10. Given $m\angle XZY = m\angle WZV$, Z is the midpoint of $\overline{YV}$, and $\angle Y$ and $\angle V$ are right angles, prove $\triangle XYZ \cong \triangle WVZ$.

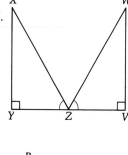

Statements	Reasons
1. $m\angle XZY = m\angle WZV$	1. $\underline{\ ?\ }$ Given
2. Z is the midpt. of $\overline{YV}$.	2. $\underline{\ ?\ }$ Given
3. $\underline{\ ?\ }$ $ZY = ZV$	3. Def. of midpt. [2]
4. $\angle Y$ and $\angle V$ are rt. $\angle$s.	4. $\underline{\ ?\ }$ Given
5. $\underline{\ ?\ }$ $m\angle Y = m\angle V$	5. All rt. $\angle$s are =. [4]
6. $\triangle XYZ \cong \triangle WVZ$	6. $\underline{\ ?\ }$ ASA Post.

Prove: $\triangle ABC \cong \triangle CDA$

11. Given: $AD = CB$; $AB = CD$

12. Given: $\overline{AB} \parallel \overline{CD}$; $AB = CD$

13. Given: $\overline{BC} \parallel \overline{AD}$; $AD = CB$ **15.** $\angle M$, $\angle F$; $\angle N$, $\angle G$; $\angle P$, $\angle H$

14. Given: $\overline{AB} \parallel \overline{CD}$; $\overline{AD} \parallel \overline{BC}$

15. List the pairs of equal parts in $\triangle MNP$ and $\triangle FGH$.

16. Is $\triangle MNP$ congruent to $\triangle FGH$? Do you think there is an AAA Congruence Postulate? Explain.

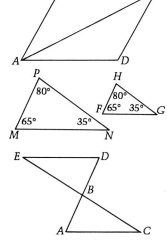

Set B Prove: $\triangle ABC \cong \triangle DBE$

17. Given: B is the midpoint of $\overline{AD}$; $m\angle A = m\angle D$.

18. Given: B is the midpoint of $\overline{AD}$ and $\overline{CE}$.

19. Given: $\overline{AC} \parallel \overline{DE}$; $AC = DE$

20. Given: $\overline{AC} \parallel \overline{DE}$; B is the midpoint of $\overline{CE}$.

21. To measure the distance OP across a lake, a surveyor marked off $\overline{PR}$ and $\overline{OR}$. Then she used a transit to mark off $\overline{RF}$ so that $m\angle FRO = m\angle PRO$. She chose S on $\overline{RF}$ so that $RS = RP$ and drew $\overline{OS}$. Prove $\triangle PRO \cong \triangle SRO$. Why does $OP = OS$?

22. Given $\triangle ABO$ with vertices $A(0, 3)$, $B(-4, 0)$, and $C(0, 0)$ and $\triangle DFE$ with vertices $D(2, 5)$, $F(5, 1)$, and $E(5, 5)$, use the Distance Formula and the SSS Postulate to show that $\triangle ABO \cong \triangle DFE$.

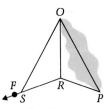

21. Corr. parts of $\cong \triangle$s are =.

Prove: $\triangle MRP \cong \triangle NRP$

23. Given: $PM = PN$; $m\angle MPR = m\angle NPR$

24. Given: $\overline{PR} \perp \overline{MN}$; R is the midpoint of $\overline{MN}$.

25. Given: $PM = PN$; R is the midpoint of $\overline{MN}$.

26. Given: $\overline{PR} \perp \overline{MN}$; $m\angle MPR = m\angle NPR$

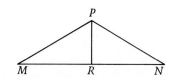

Set C   Prove: △ACD ≅ △BCD

27. Given: $\overline{DC} \perp \mathcal{H}$; △ABC is equilateral.

28. Given: $\overline{DC} \perp \mathcal{H}$; m∠ADC = m∠BDC

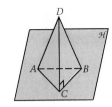

◆ Review   **29.** Given: △ABD ≅ △CBA. List the six pairs of equal corresponding parts.

30. In △MNP, the angle included between $\overline{MP}$ and $\overline{NP}$ is __?__. ∠N

31. The sum of the measures of the exterior angles of a convex polygon, one at each vertex, is __?__. 360

$\ell \parallel m$; $a \parallel b$

32. Solve for x. x = 8   **33.** m∠1 = __?__ 134

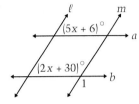

 Thinking Ahead   **34.** Draw △DEF with DF = 8 in., m∠D = 25, and EF = 5 in. Is your triangle congruent to those of your classmates?

35. Is it possible to draw two noncongruent triangles with the measures given in Exercise 34?

36. If two sides and a nonincluded angle of one triangle are equal to the corresponding parts of another triangle, are the triangles congruent? Explain.

37. Draw △ABC with AB = 6 in., m∠B = 45, and m∠C = 30. Is your triangle congruent to those of your classmates?

38. Is it possible to draw two noncongruent triangles with the measures given in Exercise 37? No

39. If two angles and a nonincluded side of one triangle are equal to the corresponding parts of another triangle, are the triangles congruent? Explain.

34. (Not actual size)

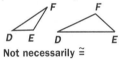

Not necessarily ≅

36. No, the 2 △s in Exer. 35 are the counterexample.

37. (Not actual size)

39. Yes; if 2 prs. of ∠s are =, then the third pr. must also be =; and the △s are ≅ by ASA Post.

🖥 Computer Activities: Drawing and Measuring

1. On the same screen, draw two right triangles, each with a side whose measure is 50 included between the right angle Yes and an angle of 25°. Do the triangles appear to be congruent?

2. Repeat the activity with five other pairs of right triangles. For each pair of triangles, choose a different angle size and a different length for the included side. What is true of the triangles in each pair?

SSS Post.

23. Proof: 1. PM = PN; m∠MPR = m∠NPR (Given) 2. PR = PR (Reflexive Prop.) 3. △MRP ≅ △NRP (SAS Post. [1, 2])

24. Proof: 1. $\overline{PR} \perp \overline{MN}$; R is midpt. of $\overline{MN}$. (Given) 2. MR = NR (Def. of midpt. [1]) 3. ∠MRP and ∠NRP are rt. ∠s. (2 ⊥ lines form 4 rt. ∠s. [1]) 4. m∠MRP = m∠NRP (All rt. ∠s are =. [3]) 5. PR = PR (Reflexive Prop.) 6. △MRP ≅ △NRP (SAS Post. [2, 4, 5])

25. Proof: 1. PM = PN; R is midpt. of $\overline{MN}$. (Given) 2. MR = NR (Def. of midpt. [1]) 3. PR = PR (Reflexive Prop.) 4. △MRP ≅ △NRP (SSS Post. [1, 2, 3])

26. Proof: 1. $\overline{PR} \perp \overline{MN}$; m∠MPR = m∠NPR (Given) 2. ∠MRP and ∠NRP are rt. ∠s. (2 ⊥ lines form 4 rt. ∠s. [1]) 3. m∠MRP = m∠NRP (All rt. ∠s are =. [2]) 4. PR = PR (Reflexive Prop.) 5. △MRP ≅ △NRP (ASA Post. [1, 3, 4])

FOLLOW-UP

More Practice

• Worksheet 5-2

Extension

We know that three equal pairs of corresponding parts do not guarantee triangle congruence. Challenge your better students to explore the following.

1. Do four equal pairs of corresponding parts guarantee congruence? no

2. Can we have noncongruent triangles with five equal pairs of corresponding parts? yes

• Extension 5-2

Computers

The computer activity in the pupil's book can be completed using *GeoDraw*.

• **Computer Activities 5-2**
• **Computer Worksheet 5-2**

LESSON 5–3

Resources

Compass
Straightedge
  Teaching Aid 13, triangle
  methods
Visual Aid 13, triangle methods
Worksheet 5–3
Extension 5–3
Computer Worksheet 5–3

OBJECTIVES

Use the AAS Congruence Theorem to prove triangles congruent; use the AAS Theorem, the SAS Postulate and the ASA Postulate to prove right triangles congruent.

WORKSHEET

Name _____   Lesson **5-3**

Complete each proof below.

1. Given: $m\angle X \cong m\angle Y$; $m\angle 1 = m\angle 2$
Prove: $\triangle XWZ \cong \triangle YWZ$

Statements	Reasons
1. $m\angle X \cong m\angle Y$; $m\angle 1 = m\angle 2$	1. Given
2. $ZW = ZW$	2. Reflexive Prop.
3. $\triangle XWZ \cong \triangle YWZ$	3. AAS for ≅ △s [1, 2]

2. Given: D is the midpoint of $\overline{AB}$; $m\angle ADC = m\angle BDC$
Prove: $\triangle ADC \cong \triangle BDC$

Statements	Reasons
1. D is the midpoint of $\overline{AB}$.	1. Given
2. $m\angle ADC = m\angle BDC$	2. Given
3. $AD = DB$	3. Def. of midpoint [1]
4. $DC = DC$	4. Reflexive Prop.
5. $\triangle ADC \cong \triangle BDC$	5. SAS for ≅ △s [2, 3, 4]

3. Given: $\angle 1 \cong \angle 2$; $\angle 3$ and $\angle 4$ are right angles.
Prove: $\triangle ADC \cong \triangle BDC$

Statements	Reasons
1. $\angle 1 \cong \angle 2$	1. Given
2. $\angle 3$ and $\angle 4$ are rt. ∠s.	2. Given
3. $CD = CD$	3. Reflexive Prop.
4. $m\angle 3 = m\angle 4$	4. All rt. ∠s are =. [2]
5. $\triangle ADC \cong \triangle BDC$	5. ASA for ≅ △s [1, 3, 4]

32   For use with Lesson 5–3.   SCOTT, FORESMAN GEOMETRY © Scott, Foresman and Company

---

5-3 The AAS Congruence Theorem and Right Triangles

When cabinetmaker Mary Chin attached the braces on a dropfront desk, she knew that $\angle ABC$ and $\angle DEF$ were equal, as were AC and DF. She then needed only to sight along $\overleftrightarrow{AD}$ to see if $\angle BAC$ and $\angle EDF$ were equal. If they were, then the AAS Congruence Theorem below assured her that the triangles formed were congruent and that the braces were attached correctly.

Theorem 5-2   *AAS Congruence Theorem*

If two angles and the side opposite one of the angles in one triangle are equal to the corresponding parts of another triangle, then the triangles are congruent.

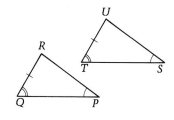

Given $m\angle P = m\angle S$; $m\angle Q = m\angle T$; $QR = TU$

Prove $\triangle PQR \cong \triangle STU$

Plan for Proof   Show $m\angle R = m\angle U$ by Theorem 4-15. Then use the ASA Postulate.

The proof of the AAS Congruence Theorem is left to Exercise 11.

The next three examples use the AAS Theorem, the SAS Postulate, and the ASA Postulate, respectively, to prove that two right triangles are congruent.

Example 1

Suppose the hypotenuse and an acute angle of one right triangle are equal to the corresponding parts of another right triangle. Prove that the triangles are congruent.

Solution

Given: $\angle N$ and $\angle S$ are right angles; $MP = RT$; $m\angle P = m\angle T$
Prove: $\triangle MNP \cong \triangle RST$

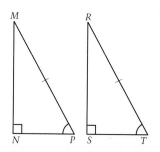

Statements	Reasons
1. $MP = RT$; $m\angle P = m\angle T$	1. Given
2. $\angle N$ and $\angle S$ are rt. ∠s.	2. Given
3. $m\angle N = m\angle S$	3. All rt. ∠s are =. [2]
4. $\triangle MNP \cong \triangle RST$	4. AAS Theorem [1, 3]

Example 2

The legs of one right triangle are equal to the corresponding legs of another right triangle. Prove that the triangles are congruent.

Solution

Given: $\angle B$ and $\angle E$ are right angles; $AB = DE$; $BC = EF$
Prove: $\triangle ABC \cong \triangle DEF$

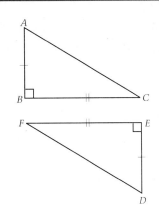

Statements	Reasons
1. $AB = DE$; $BC = EF$	1. Given
2. $\angle B$ and $\angle E$ are rt. $\angle$s.	2. Given
3. $m\angle B = m\angle E$	3. All rt. $\angle$s are =. [2]
4. $\triangle ABC \cong \triangle DEF$	4. SAS Postulate [1, 3]

Another special case for right triangles is the following: If a leg and an acute angle of one right triangle are equal to the corresponding parts of another right triangle, then the triangles are congruent.

The proofs of this statement differ depending upon whether or not the equal sides are included between the given acute angles and the right angles. The proof of the first case is in Example 3. The proof of the second case is left to Exercise 12.

Example 3

Given: $\angle N$ and $\angle S$ are right angles; $MN = RS$; $m\angle M = m\angle R$
Prove: $\triangle MNP \cong \triangle RST$

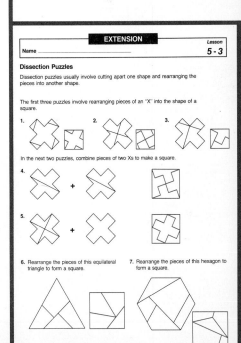

Solution

Statements	Reasons
1. $MN = RS$; $m\angle M = m\angle R$	1. Given
2. $\angle N$ and $\angle S$ are rt. $\angle$s.	2. Given
3. $m\angle N = m\angle S$	3. All rt. $\angle$s are =. [2]
4. $\triangle MNP \cong \triangle RST$	4. ASA Postulate [1, 3]

No

Do you think there is an SSA Congruence Theorem? The pencils at the right form two noncongruent triangles with side lengths 19 cm and 14 cm and a nonincluded angle of 40°. So SSA cannot be used to prove that triangles are congruent.

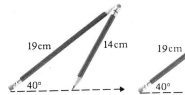

19cm   14cm   40°

19cm   14cm   40°

Assignment Guide

Basic: 1–11, 24–30
Average: 1–11 (odd), 12–21, 24–30
Extended: 2–14 (even), 16–30

Additional Examples

Example 1

Given: $\overline{CD} \perp \overline{CB}$; $\overline{CD} \perp \overline{ED}$;
$CB = ED$ Prove: $\triangle ACB \cong \triangle ADE$

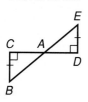

1. $\overline{CD} \perp \overline{CB}$; $\overline{CD} \perp \overline{ED}$ (Given); 2. $\angle C$ and $\angle D$ are rt. $\angle$s (Def. of $\perp$ [1]); 3. $\angle C = \angle D$ (All rt. $\angle$s are =.); 4. $\angle CAB = \angle EAD$ (Vert. $\angle$s are =.); 5. $CB = ED$ (Given); 6. $\triangle ACB \cong \triangle ADE$ (AAS [3, 4, 5])

Example 2

Given: $\overline{KT}$ and $\overline{GP}$ bisect each other. Prove: $\triangle KHG \cong \triangle THP$

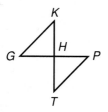

1. $\overline{KT}$ and $\overline{GP}$ bisect each other. (Given); 2. $KH = HT$ (Def. of bisector [1]); 3. $\angle KHG = \angle PHT$ (Vert. $\angle$s are =.); 4. $GH = HP$ (Def. of bisector [1]); 5. $\triangle KHG \cong \triangle THP$ (SAS [2, 3, 4])

Example 3

Given: $\overline{KG}$ bisects $\angle HKL$;
$\overline{HL} \perp \overline{KG}$
Prove: $\triangle KGH \cong \triangle KGL$

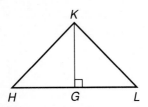

Checking for Understanding

1. What can you add to the inventory of geometric facts?   AAS Thm.

Which postulate or theorem justifies $\triangle MIN \cong \triangle SEC$?

2. Given: $SE = MI$; $m\angle M = m\angle S$; $m\angle I = m\angle E$ ASA Post.

3. Given: $NI = CE$; $m\angle M = m\angle S$; $m\angle I = m\angle E$ AAS Thm.

4. Given: Right $\angle$s at C and N; $MN = SC$; $m\angle M = m\angle S$ ASA Post.

5. Given: Right $\angle$s at C and N; $MN = SC$; $IN = EC$ SAS Post.

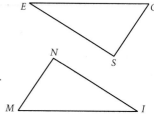

Written Exercises

Set A   The goal is to prove $\triangle TAN \cong \triangle RED$.

1. Given $TA = RE$ and $m\angle T = m\angle R$, to use the AAS Theorem, show $m\angle \underline{?N} = m\angle \underline{?}$. D

2. Given right $\angle$s at A and E, to use the SAS Postulate, show $TA = \underline{?}$ and $\underline{?} = \underline{?}$. RE; AN = ED

3. Given right $\angle$s at A and E and $m\angle T = m\angle R$, to use the AAS Theorem, show $\underline{?} = \underline{?}$. AN; ED or TN; RD

4. Given right $\angle$s at A and E and $m\angle N = m\angle D$, to use the AAS Theorem, show $\underline{?} = \underline{?}$; to use the ASA Postulate, show $\underline{?} = \underline{?}$. TN; RD or TA; RE   AN; ED

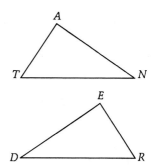

5. Given: $\overline{BC} \perp \overline{AD}$; $m\angle A = m\angle D$
   Prove: $\triangle ABC \cong \triangle DBC$

Statements	Reasons
1. $\underline{?}$ $\overline{BC} \perp \overline{AD}$	1. Given
2. $\angle ACB$ and $\angle DCB$ are rt. $\angle$s.	2. $\underline{?}$ 2 $\perp$ lines form 4 rt. $\angle$s [1]
3. $\underline{?}$ $m\angle ACB = m\angle DCB$	3. All rt. $\angle$s are =. [2]
4. $BC = BC$	4. $\underline{?}$ Reflexive Prop.
5. $m\angle A = m\angle D$	5. $\underline{?}$ Given
6. $\triangle ABC \cong \triangle DBC$	6. $\underline{?}$ AAS Thm.

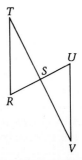

6. Write the steps of this proof in a correct order.
   Given: S is the midpoint of $\overline{RU}$ and $\overline{TV}$.   c, d, a, b
   Prove: $\triangle RST \cong \triangle USV$

Statements	Reasons
a. $m\angle RST = m\angle USV$	a. Vert. $\angle$s are =.
b. $\triangle RST \cong \triangle USV$	b. SAS Post. [2, 3]
c. S is midpt. of $\overline{RU}$ and $\overline{TV}$.	c. Given
d. $RS = SU$; $TS = SV$	d. Def. of midpt. [1]

Prove: △AOB ≅ △DOC

7. Given: m∠A = m∠D; AB = DC

8. Given: O is the midpoint of $\overline{AD}$; m∠B = m∠C

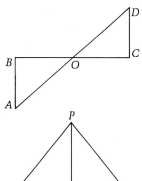

Prove: △TIP ≅ △TQP

9. Given: $\overrightarrow{PT}$ bisects ∠IPQ; m∠I = m∠Q

10. Given: $\overline{PT} \perp \overline{IQ}$; m∠I = m∠Q

11. Prove the AAS Congruence Theorem.

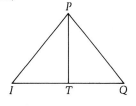

Set B **12.** Prove for the case in which the leg is not included between the acute angle and the right angle: If a leg and an acute angle of one right triangle are equal to the corresponding parts of another right triangle, then the triangles are congruent.

13. Given: $\overleftrightarrow{RT}$ bisects ∠SRW and ∠STW.
Prove: △RST ≅ △RWT

14. Given: $\overline{RS} \perp \overline{ST}$; $\overline{RW} \perp \overline{WT}$; $\overline{ST} \parallel \overline{RW}$
Prove: △RST ≅ △TWR

15. Given: $\overline{WT} \parallel \overline{RS}$; $\overline{RW} \parallel \overline{ST}$
Prove: △RSW ≅ △TWS

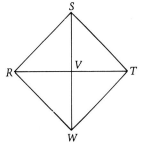

Given: P, Q, R, and S are noncoplanar; ∠RSP, ∠RSQ, and ∠QSP are right angles.

16. Given: PS = RS
Prove: △PSQ ≅ △RSQ

17. Given: m∠PQS = m∠PRS
Prove: △PQS ≅ △PRS

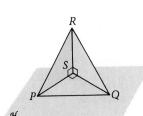

Cele wants to cut endpiece ABCDE of a magazine rack. B' is the midpoint of $\overline{RS}$.

18. Explain how Cele could use the SAS Congruence Postulate to cut the endpiece.

19. Explain how Cele could use the ASA Congruence Theorem to cut the endpiece for the other end.

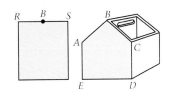

5-3 *The AAS Congruence Theorem and Right Triangles*

1. $\overline{KG}$ bisects ∠HKL (Given); 2. m∠HKL = m∠LKG (Def. of ∠ bisector [1]); 3. KG = KG (Reflexive Prop.); 4. $\overline{HL} \perp \overline{KG}$ (Given); 5. ∠HGK and ∠LGK are rt. ∠s. (Def. of ⊥ [4]); 6. m∠HGK = m∠LGK (All rt. ∠s are =.); 7. △KGH ≅ △KGL (ASA [2, 3, 6])

Error Analysis Students have difficulty with the fact that there is no SSA criterion for proving triangles congruent. Have students construct a triangle given an angle and two line segments. Point out that two triangles are possible although they are obviously not congruent to each other.

ANSWERS

Written Exercises

7. Proof: 1. m∠A = m∠D; AB = DC (Given) 2. m∠AOB = m∠DOC (Vert. ∠s are =.) 3. △AOB ≅ △DOC (AAS Thm. [1, 2])

8. Proof: 1. O is midpt. of $\overline{AD}$; m∠B = m∠C (Given) 2. AO = DO (Def. of midpt. [1]) 3. m∠AOB = m∠DOC (Vert. ∠s are =.) 4. △AOB ≅ △DOC (AAS Thm. [1, 2, 3])

9. Proof: 1. $\overrightarrow{PT}$ bisects ∠IPQ; m∠I = m∠Q (Given) 2. m∠IPT = m∠QPT (Def. of ∠ bisector [1]) 3. PT = PT (Reflexive Prop.) 4. △TIP ≅ △TQP (AAS Thm. [1, 2, 3])

10. Proof: 1. $\overline{PT} \perp \overline{IQ}$; m∠I = m∠Q (Given) 2. ∠ITP and ∠QTP are rt. ∠s. (2 ⊥ lines form 4 rt. ∠s. [1]) 3. m∠ITP = m∠QTP (All rt. ∠s are =. [2]) 4. PT = PT (Reflexive Prop.) 5. △TIP ≅ △TQP (AAS Thm. [1, 3, 4])

20. Proof: 1. $\overline{BD} \perp \overline{AB}$; $\overline{BD} \perp \overline{BC}$; $AB = BC$ (Given) 2. $\angle ABD$ and $\angle CBD$ are rt. $\angle$s. (2 $\perp$ lines form 4 rt. $\angle$s. [1]) 3. $m\angle ABD = m\angle CBD$ (All rt. $\angle$s are =. [2]) 4. $BD = BD$ (Reflexive Prop.) 5. $\triangle ABD \cong \triangle CBD$ (SAS Post. [1, 3, 4])

21. Proof: 1. $AB = CB = EC = EA$ (Given) 2. $BE = EB$ (Reflexive Prop.) 3. $\triangle ABE \cong \triangle CBE$ (SSS Post. [1, 2])

22. Proof: 1. $AC = EC$; $m\angle CAD = m\angle CEB$ (Given) 2. $m\angle C = m\angle C$ (Reflexive Prop.) 3. $\triangle CAD \cong \triangle CEB$ (ASA Post. [1, 2])

23. Proof: 1. $\overline{EB} \perp \overline{AC}$; $\overline{AD} \perp \overline{EC}$; $AC = EC$ (Given) 2. $\angle CBE$ and $\angle CDA$ are rt. $\angle$s. (2 $\perp$ lines form 4 rt. $\angle$s. [1]) 3. $m\angle CBE = m\angle CDA$ (All rt. $\angle$s are =. [2]) 4. $m\angle C = m\angle C$ (Reflexive Prop.) 5. $\triangle CAD \cong \triangle CEB$ (AAS Thm. [1, 3, 4])

20. Given: $\overline{BD} \perp \overline{AB}$; $\overline{BD} \perp \overline{BC}$; $AB = BC$
Prove: $\triangle ABD \cong \triangle CBD$

21. Given: $AB = CB = EC = EA$
Prove: $\triangle ABE \cong \triangle CEB$

Set C **22.** Given $\overline{EB} \perp \overline{AC}$, $\overline{AD} \perp \overline{EC}$, $AC = EC$, and $m\angle CAD = m\angle CEB$, prove $\triangle CAD \cong \triangle CEB$.

23. Repeat Exercise 22 without using the given information that $m\angle CAD = m\angle CEB$.

▲ Review **24.** Which postulate justifies the fact that $\triangle GEF \cong \triangle XYZ$?

25. In $\triangle ABC$ and $\triangle RTK$, $m\angle C = m\angle K$ and $BC = TK$. What other pair of parts must be equal in order to use the SAS Postulate to prove $\triangle ABC \cong \triangle RTK$?

26. If $\triangle DHM \cong \triangle QPS$, then $\triangle MDH \cong \underline{?}$. $\triangle SQP$

27. Draw an obtuse triangle.

28. The coordinates of A are $(-6, 3)$ and the coordinates of M are $(-7, 5)$. Find the coordinates of B so that M is the midpoint of $\overline{AB}$. $(-8, 7)$

Thinking Ahead **29.** Draw $\overline{AB}$ with length 2 in. and midpoint M. Draw line r, the perpendicular bisector of $\overline{AB}$. Mark any point P ($\neq M$) on r. Draw $\triangle AMP$ and $\triangle BMP$. How are $\triangle AMP$ and $\triangle BMP$ related? $\overline{AP}$ and $\overline{BP}$? $\cong$; =

30. Repeat the activity of Exercise 29 for another point, Q, on r. $\cong$; =

ASA Post.

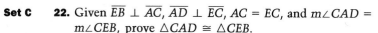

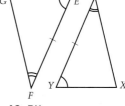

25. AC, RK

27. Sample:

29-30. (Not actual size)

Algebra Review: Solving Linear Inequalities

Examples

1. Solve $5x \geq 365$ for x.

2. Solve $32 - 4d < 4$ for d.

Solutions

1. $5x \geq 365$

$(\frac{1}{5})(5x) \geq (\frac{1}{5})(365)$

$x \geq 73$

2. $32 - 4d < 4$

$-32 + 32 - 4d < -32 + 4$

$-4d < -28$

$(-\frac{1}{4})(-4d) > (-\frac{1}{4})(-28)$

$d > 7$

Solve each inequality.

1. $x + 17 < 48$
$x < 31$

2. $y - 32 > -88$
$y > -56$

3. $\frac{2}{3}g \geq 66$ $g \geq 99$

4. $-12h < 30$
$h > -2.5$

5. $9 + \frac{7}{8}x \leq 30$
$x \leq 24$

6. $14 - \frac{5}{2}a < -21$
$a > 14$

7. $151 - 3m \geq 142$
$m \leq 3$

8. $12x - 7 < 4x + 73$
$x < 10$

Excursion: Congruent Triangles on a Sphere

If you have ever seen a map of the airline flight paths between cities that are a great distance apart, you were probably surprised to see that many of the paths do not appear to be straight lines. Since the earth is a *sphere*, the shortest distance or path between two cities, staying on or slightly above the earth's surface, follows a *great circle*—a circle whose center is the center of the earth and whose points lie on the surface of the earth.

Chicago

London

1. Describe the path of an airplane flying from New York City to London. **The smaller part of the great circle containing New York and London.**

A triangle on the surface of the earth consists of segments like *NR*, *NS*, and *RS*, which are shown at the right. In spherical geometry, "lines" are great circles. Therefore, "segments" are parts of great circles. In the diagram, the intersection of the great circles containing *NR* and *RS* form a right "angle." Since ∠*NRS* is a right angle, △*NRS* is a right "triangle."

2. Explain how a triangle on a sphere can have three right angles. Draw a diagram.

It can be proved using appropriate axioms that the SSS, SAS, ASA, and AAS congruence criteria are true for triangles on a sphere. But a major surprise is that there is an AAA criterion for congruent triangles.

If three angles of one triangle on the surface of a sphere are equal to three angles of another, then the triangles are congruent.

To see that this is true, try to draw two triangles on a sphere that have the same corresponding angle measures but different lengths for sides.

2 great circles intersect a 3rd great circle to form 2 rt. ∠s, and they intersect each other to form the 3rd rt. ∠.

3. In the diagram at the right, *ABC* is *not* a triangle. Why?
"Segment" *BC* does not lie on a great circle.

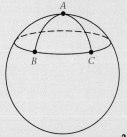

Warm-Up Review

1. How many pairs of corresponding parts are equal if two triangles are congruent? Six
2. Angle 3 and angle __?__ are corresponding angles. 7
3. Name two pairs of alternate interior angles. ∠3 and ∠5; ∠4 and ∠6
4. If $r \parallel s$, which angles are equal to ∠2? ∠4; ∠6; ∠8

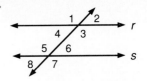

LESSON 5-4

Resources

Teaching Aid 13, triangle methods
Visual Aid 13, triangle methods
Worksheet 5-4
Extension 5-4
Quiz 5

OBJECTIVE

Use congruent triangles to prove segments or angles equal and to prove lines parallel or perpendicular.

5-4 Proving Corresponding Parts Equal

One way to prove that segments or angles are equal is to first show that they are corresponding parts of congruent triangles. The definition of congruent triangles then assures us that corresponding parts are equal.

Example 1

Show that if the legs of the chair are attached at their midpoints, then the edge of the seat is parallel to the floor.

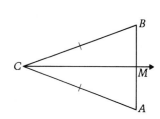

Solution

Draw $\overline{AC}$ and $\overline{BD}$ to represent the legs of the chair. The edge of the seat and the floor are then represented by $\overline{AB}$ and $\overline{DC}$, respectively.

Given: E is the midpoint of $\overline{AC}$ and $\overline{BD}$.
Prove: $\overline{AB} \parallel \overline{CD}$

Statements	Reasons
1. E is midpt. of $\overline{AC}$ and $\overline{BD}$.	1. Given
2. $AE = EC$; $DE = EB$	2. Def. of midpoint [1]
3. $m\angle AEB = m\angle CED$	3. __?__ Vert. ∠s are =.
4. $\triangle ABE \cong \triangle CDE$	4. SAS Post. [2, 3]
5. $m\angle ABE = m\angle CDE$	5. Corr. parts of $\cong \triangle$s are =. [4]
6. $\overline{AB} \parallel \overline{CD}$	6. Alt. int. ∠s = $\Rightarrow$ lines ∥. [5]

Example 2

Prove that the bisector of the vertex angle of an isosceles triangle is perpendicular to the base.

Solution

Given: $\overrightarrow{CM}$ bisects $\angle ACB$; $AC = BC$
Prove: $\overline{CM} \perp \overline{AB}$

Statements	Reasons
1. $\overrightarrow{CM}$ bisects $\overline{AB}$; $AC = BC$	1. Given
2. $m\angle ACM = m\angle BCM$	2. Def. of bisector [1]
3. $CM = CM$	3. Reflexive Prop.
4. $\triangle ACM \cong \triangle BCM$	4. __?__ [1, 2, 3] SAS Post.
5. $m\angle CMA = m\angle CMB$	5. Corr. parts of $\cong \triangle$s are =. [4]
6. $\overline{CM} \perp \overline{AB}$	6. __?__ [5] If the ∠s in a lin. pr. are =, then the lines containing their sides are ⊥

Summary Ways to Prove Triangles Congruent

Show that the triangles are congruent to the same triangle.

Show that the following parts are equal:

All six pairs of corresponding parts (Definition)

Three pairs of corresponding sides (SSS Congruence Postulate)

Two pairs of corresponding sides and their included angles
(SAS Congruence Postulate)

Two pairs of corresponding angles and their included sides
(ASA Congruence Postulate)

Two pairs of corresponding angles and a pair of corresponding,
nonincluded sides (AAS Congruence Theorem)

The diagram below shows how the proof of the AAS Congruence
Theorem is built upon various postulates and theorems.

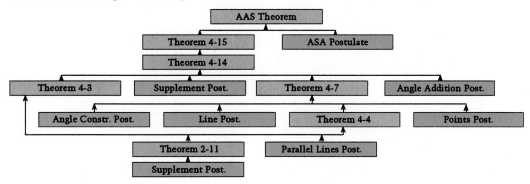

Checking for Understanding

Given $AD = CB$, $AB = CD$, the goal is to prove $\overline{AB} \parallel \overline{CD}$.

1. $\overleftrightarrow{AC}$ is a transversal cutting $\overleftrightarrow{AB}$ and $\overleftrightarrow{CD}$. Name a pair of
   alternate interior angles. ∠1, ∠2

2. It follows that $\overline{AB} \parallel \overline{CD}$, if you show that ∠1 and ∠2 are $\underline{\ ?\ }$. =

3. $m\angle 1 = m\angle 2$ if $\triangle ABC \cong \underline{\ ?\ }$. △CDA

4. The triangles are congruent by the $\underline{\ ?\ }$ Postulate. SSS

Which triangles might you prove congruent to justify each statement?

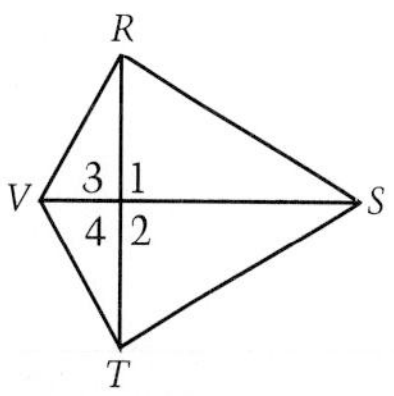

5. $RS = TS$

6. $RU = TU$

7. $m\angle 1 = m\angle 2$

8. $m\angle SVR = m\angle SVT$

9. $m\angle RSV = m\angle TSV$

10. $\overline{SV} \perp \overline{RT}$

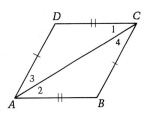

TEACHING NOTES

To begin this lesson, review the
definition of congruent triangles.
Because it is an "if and only if"
statement, it consists of two
conditionals:
1. If corresponding parts are
equal, then the triangles are
congruent; and
2. If two triangles are congruent,
then their corresponding parts are
equal.
The second conditional is introduced in this lesson.

Additional Examples

Example 1

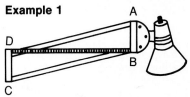

EXTENSION

Name _____   *Lesson* **5-4**

Quilt Designs

For hundreds of years people have used quilt designs that often start with a
square with a geometric design. The design is repeated many times to create a
complicated pattern. With the endless variations in colors, shadings, and
materials, there is no limit to the variety of possible quilt designs.

Today, many quilts are treasured, not only as family heirlooms, but as works of
art.

A few basic quilt designs are shown below. Common names are given, although
names vary from one region of the country to another.

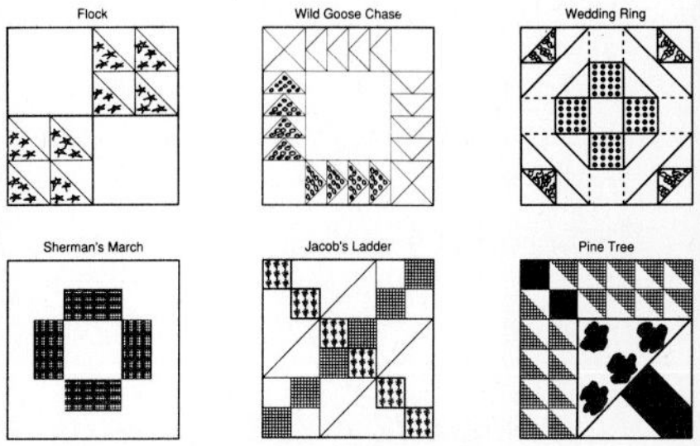

Flock   Wild Goose Chase   Wedding Ring

Sherman's March   Jacob's Ladder   Pine Tree

1. Pick a design above and copy it. Repeat the design to make a 4-by-4 array
   of squares. Use colored pencils to make an attractive design. **student art**

2. Create your own quilt pattern and name it. **student art**

Assignment Guide

Basic: 1–11, 18–23
Average: 2–10 (even, 12–15, 18–23
Extended: 2–10 (even), 12–23

Show that if the braces $\overline{DA}$ and $\overline{CB}$ of the wall lamp are the same length, and if bracket $\overline{AB}$ is the same length as $\overline{CD}$, then bracket $\overline{AB}$ will always be parallel to the wall. $DB = DB$ by Reflexive Prop.; use SSS to get $\triangle ABD \cong \triangle CDB$. By corresponding parts, $m\angle ABD = m\angle CDB$, and $\overline{AB} \parallel \overline{DC}$.

Example 2
Show that the median to the base of an isosceles triangle is perpendicular to the base. Use SSS to prove triangles equal.

Error Analysis   When using congruent triangles to prove parts equal, students must use only corresponding pairs of sides or angles. If they try to conclude that noncorresponding sides or angles are equal, have them write out the correspondences.

ANSWERS

Written Exercises

1. Proof: 1. $WZ = YZ$; $m\angle 1 = m\angle 2$ (Given) 2. $XZ = XZ$ (Reflexive Prop.) 3. $\triangle XWZ \cong \triangle XYZ$ (SAS Post. [1, 2]) 4. $m\angle 3 = m\angle 4$ (Corr. parts of $\cong \triangle$s are =. [3])
2. Proof: 1. $m\angle 1 = m\angle 2$; $m\angle 3 = m\angle 4$ (Given) 2. $XZ = XZ$ (Reflexive Prop.) 3. $\triangle XWZ \cong \triangle XYZ$ (ASA Post. [1, 2]) 4. $WZ = YZ$ (Corr. parts of $\cong \triangle$s are =. [3])
3. Proof: 1. $WX = YX$; $WZ = YZ$ (Given) 2. $XZ = XZ$ (Reflexive Prop.) 3. $\triangle XWZ \cong \triangle XYZ$ (SSS Post. [1, 2]) 4. $m\angle 1 = m\angle 2$ (Corr. parts of $\cong \triangle$s are =. [3])
4. Proof: 1. $m\angle W = m\angle Y$; $m\angle 1 = m\angle 2$ (Given) 2. $XZ = XZ$ (Reflexive

Written Exercises
Set A

1. Given: $WZ = YZ$; $m\angle 1 = m\angle 2$
Prove: $m\angle 3 = m\angle 4$

2. Given: $m\angle 1 = m\angle 2$; $m\angle 3 = m\angle 4$
Prove: $WZ = YZ$

3. Given: $WX = YX$; $WZ = YZ$
Prove: $m\angle 1 = m\angle 2$

4. Given: $m\angle W = m\angle Y$; $m\angle 1 = m\angle 2$
Prove: $WX = YX$

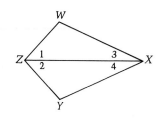

5. Given: $PK = NM$; $KL = ML$; right angles at K and M
Prove: $PL = NL$

6. Given: $m\angle P = m\angle N$; $m\angle 1 = m\angle 2$; $PK = NM$
Prove: $m\angle K = m\angle M$

7. Given: $PL = NL$; $PK = NM$; L is the midpoint of $\overline{KM}$.
Prove: $m\angle K = m\angle M$

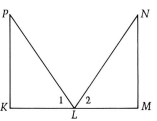

8. Given: $m\angle 2 = m\angle 3$; $m\angle B = m\angle D$
Prove: $AB = CD$

9. Given: $AB = CD$; $m\angle 2 = m\angle 3$
Prove: $\overline{AD} \parallel \overline{CB}$

10. Given: $\overline{AD} \perp \overline{CD}$; $\overline{AB} \perp \overline{BC}$; $m\angle 1 = m\angle 4$
Prove: $AB = CD$

11. Given: $\overline{AB} \perp \overline{BC}$; $AD = CB$; $m\angle 1 = m\angle 4$
Prove: $\overline{AD} \perp \overline{DC}$

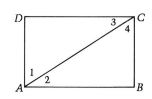

Set B

12. In order to draw the bisector of $\angle Y$, carpenter Jon James places his square in the interior of $\angle Y$ so that $XY = ZY$ and $XW = ZW$. Explain why $\overrightarrow{YW}$ bisects $\angle Y$.

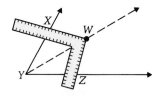

13. In the Blazing Star quilt design, $\triangle CED$ and $\triangle CAB$ are cut from the same pattern, so that $CE = CA$, $CD = CB$, and $m\angle DCE = m\angle BCA$. Explain why the other corresponding parts of the triangles will be equal; that is, $DE = BA$, $m\angle CED = m\angle CAB$, and $m\angle CDE = m\angle CBA$.

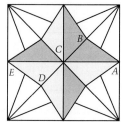

14. The sail of a hang glider is shown at right. $PQ =$ PS and $RQ = RS$. Are $\angle Q$ and $\angle S$ equal in measure? Explain.

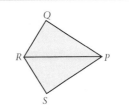

15. When a billiard ball bounces off a side of a billiard table, the angles at which the ball hits and rebounds are equal. Show that a ball shot from P to the midpoint B of the end of the table will rebound to a point P' such that $CP = AP'$.

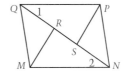

Set C **16.** Show that a ball shot from Q to B will rebound to a point Q' such that $DQ = EQ'$.

17. Given: $QR = NS$; $MR = PS$; $m\angle QRM = m\angle NSP$
Prove: $m\angle 1 = m\angle 2$

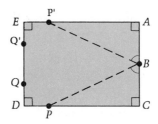

Review **18.** Given: $\angle B$ and $\angle D$ are right angles; C is the midpoint of $\overline{BD}$; $m\angle A = m\angle E$
Prove: $\triangle ABC \cong \triangle EDC$

19. Suppose the legs of one right triangle are equal to the corresponding parts of another right triangle. Are the triangles congruent? Explain. **Yes, by SAS Post.**

20. If $WX = YZ$ and $WZ = YX$, then the $\underline{\ ?\ }$ Postulate can be used to prove $\triangle WXY \cong \triangle YZW$. **SSS**

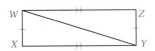

21. $\underline{\ ?\ }$ are always understood to be "if and only if" statements. **Definitions**

22. If $\overrightarrow{GJ}$ bisects $\angle HGK$, then $m\angle 1 = \underline{\ ?\ }$. **21**

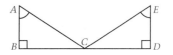

Thinking Ahead **23.** List all pairs of triangles in the figure at the right that appear to be congruent. $\triangle RWS$, $\triangle TWV$; $\triangle RWV$, $\triangle TWS$; $\triangle RST$, $\triangle TVR$; $\triangle RSV$, $\triangle TVS$

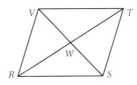

Prop.) 3. $\triangle XWZ \cong \triangle XYZ$ (AAS Thm. [1, 2]) 4. $WX = YX$ (Corr. parts of $\cong \triangle$s are =. [3])

5. Proof: 1. $PK = NM$; $KL = ML$; rt. $\angle$s at K and M (Given) 2. $m\angle K = m\angle M$ (All rt. $\angle$s are =. [1]) 3. $\triangle PKL \cong \triangle NML$ (SAS Post. [1, 2]) 4. $PL = NL$ (Corr. parts of $\cong \triangle$s are =. [3])

6. Proof: 1. $m\angle P = m\angle N$; $m\angle 1 = m\angle 2$; $PK = NM$ (Given) 2. $\triangle PKL \cong \triangle NML$ (AAS Thm. [1]) 3. $m\angle K = m\angle M$ (Corr. parts of $\cong \triangle$s are =. [2])

7. Proof: 1. $PL = NL$; $PK = NM$; L is midpt. of $\overline{KM}$. (Given) 2. $KL = ML$ (Def. of midpt. [1]) 3. $\triangle PKL \cong \triangle NML$ (SSS Post. [1, 2]) 4. $m\angle K = m\angle M$ (Corr. parts of $\cong \triangle$s are =. [3])

8. Proof: 1. $m\angle 2 = m\angle 3$; $m\angle B = m\angle D$ (Given) 2. $AC = CA$ (Reflexive Prop.) 3. $\triangle ABC \cong \triangle CDA$ (AAS Thm. [1, 2]) 4. $AB = CD$ (Corr. parts of $\cong \triangle$s are =. [3])

9. Proof: 1. $AB = CD$; $m\angle 2 = m\angle 3$ (Given) 2. $AC = CA$ (Reflexive Prop.) 3. $\triangle ABC \cong \triangle CDA$ (SAS Post. [1, 2])

10. Proof: 1. $\overline{AD} \perp \overline{CD}$; $\overline{AB} \perp \overline{BC}$; $m\angle 1 = m\angle 4$ (Given) 2. $\angle D$ and $\angle B$ are rt. $\angle$s. (2 $\perp$ lines form 4 rt. $\angle$s. [1]) 3. $m\angle D = m\angle B$ (All rt. $\angle$s are =. [2]) 4. $CA = AC$ (Reflexive Prop.) 5. $\triangle CDA \cong \triangle ABC$ (AAS Thm. [1, 3, 4]) 6. $AB = CD$ (Corr. parts of $\cong \triangle$s are =. [5])

FOLLOW-UP

More Practice

Have students bring in pictures from magazines that incorporate congruent triangles.
• Worksheet 5-4

Extension

• Extension 5-4

Warm-Up Review

1. If $\triangle YOE \cong \triangle MAN$, what side is equal to $\overline{YE}$? $\overline{MN}$
2. If $\triangle BAD \cong \triangle SAD$, what angle is equal to $\angle ADB$? $\angle ADS$
3. State four methods used to prove two triangles are congruent.   SSS; SAS; ASA; AAS
4. A polygon with all sides equal and all interior angles equal is ___?___.   Regular
5. What is a five-sided polygon called?   Pentagon

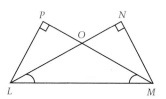

5-5 Overlapping Triangles

The five-pointed star, called a *pentagram*, is often found in nature. In the diagram at the right, a pentagram is drawn inside a regular pentagon. How many triangles are there in the figure? Be sure to count triangles that overlap one another.

The identification and use of overlapping triangles is important in the study of geometry.

Example 1

By SAS Post.

In regular pentagon $ABCDE$, $\triangle ABE \cong \triangle BAC$. Why? List the six pairs of corresponding parts.

Solution

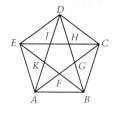

By drawing the triangles separately at the right, we can see their corresponding parts more clearly. In particular, we have $\overline{AB} \leftrightarrow \overline{BA}$, $\overline{AE} \leftrightarrow \overline{BC}$, $\overline{BE} \leftrightarrow \overline{AC}$, $\angle BAE \leftrightarrow \angle ABC$, $\angle ABE \leftrightarrow \angle BAC$, and $\angle BEA \leftrightarrow \angle ACB$.

Example 2

Given: $\overline{LN} \perp \overline{NM}$; $\overline{LP} \perp \overline{MP}$; $m\angle LMP = m\angle MLN$
Prove: $LP = MN$

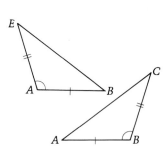

Solution

Statements	Reasons
1. $\overline{LN} \perp \overline{NM}$; $\overline{LP} \perp \overline{MP}$	1. Given
2. $\angle LNM$ and $\angle MPL$ are rt. $\angle$s.	2. __?__ 2 $\perp$ lines form 4 rt. $\angle$s. [1]
3. $m\angle LNM = m\angle MPL$	3. __?__ All rt. $\angle$s are = [2]
4. $m\angle LMP = m\angle MLN$	4. Given
5. $LM = ML$	5. __?__ Reflexive Prop.
6. $\triangle LMP \cong \triangle MLN$	6. AAS Theorem [3, 4, 5]
7. $LP = MN$	7. __?__ Corr. parts of $\cong \triangle$s are =. [6]

To show one pair of triangles congruent, it is sometimes necessary to first prove that another pair are congruent.

Example 3

Given: Regular pentagon $ABCDE$
Prove: $\triangle ACE \cong \triangle BEC$

Solution

Draw $\triangle ACE$ and $\triangle BEC$ separately. $AE = BC$ by the definition of a regular pentagon. By the Reflexive Property, $EC = CE$. We can use the SSS Postulate if we know $AC = BE$, so we should first try to prove $\triangle ABE \cong \triangle BAC$.

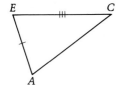 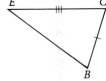

Statements	Reasons
1. $ABCDE$ is a regular pentagon.	1. Given
2. $AE = BC$; $m\angle EAB = m\angle CBA$	2. Def. of reg. polygon [1]
3. $AB = BA$	3. __?__ **Reflexive Prop.**
4. $\triangle ABE \cong \triangle BAC$	4. SAS Post. [2, 3]
5. $BE = AC$	5. Corr. parts of $\cong \triangle$s are =. [4]
6. $EC = CE$	6. Reflexive Prop.
7. $\triangle ACE \cong \triangle BEC$	7. SSS Post. [2, 5, 6]

Checking for Understanding

Given: $m\angle UXY = m\angle UZY$; $\overrightarrow{YU}$ bisects $\angle XYZ$. The goal is to prove $m\angle 1 = m\angle 2$.

1. To show $m\angle 1 = m\angle 2$, which pair of triangles should you prove congruent? **$\triangle XVY$, $\triangle ZVY$**

2. Which pairs of corresponding parts of the two triangles are equal? Are you given enough pairs of equal parts to prove the triangles congruent? Explain.

3. a. Which pair of equal corresponding parts are needed if you use the SAS Postulate? **$\overline{XY}$, $\overline{ZY}$**

   b. Which other triangles should you prove congruent in order to find these equal parts? **$\triangle UXY$, $\triangle UZY$**

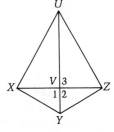

2. $VY = VY$ and $m\angle XYV = m\angle ZYV$;
no, need one more pair

---

activity, have students count the triangles and identify any pairs they think are congruent.

Example 3 uses parts from one pair of congruent triangles to prove another pair of triangles congruent.

Additional Examples

Example 1

In quadrilateral *MATH*, if $\triangle MTH \cong \triangle AHT$, name the six pairs of corresponding parts.

$\angle HMT \leftrightarrow \angle TAH$; $\angle MTH \leftrightarrow \angle AHT$;
$\angle THM \leftrightarrow \angle ATH$; $\overline{MT} \leftrightarrow \overline{AH}$; $\overline{TH} \leftrightarrow \overline{HT}$;
$\overline{HM} \leftrightarrow \overline{TA}$

EXTENSION		Lesson
Name _____		**5-5**

Counting Triangles

All the puzzles below involve counting triangles in a figure composed of overlapping triangles. You may find more triangles than you might suppose.

1. How many equilateral triangles does the figure contain?

2. How many triangles does the figure contain?

27 triangles   29 triangles

3. How many triangles can you form by joining the points on this circle?

4. How many triangles does the figure contain?

35 triangles   40 triangles

5. How many triangles congruent to each numbered triangle does the square contain? 1: 36; 2: 36; 3: 24; 4: 8

Assignment Guide

Basic: 1–11, 25–32
Average: 2–10 (even), 12–22, 25–32
Extended: 2–16 (even), 17–32

Example 2

Use the above diagram.
Given: $\overline{MH} \perp \overline{HT}$; $\overline{AT} \perp \overline{HT}$;
$m\angle HMT = m\angle TAH$
Prove: $MH = AT$
Use AAS to get $\triangle MTH \cong \triangle AHT$,
with $HT = HT$. Then use corresponding parts.

Example 3

Given: Regular octagon
Prove: $\triangle VSU \cong \triangle SVT$

Use SAS to get $\triangle TVU \cong \triangle UST$.
By corresponding parts, $TV = US$;
then use SSS.

Error Analysis Many students have trouble "seeing" overlapping triangles and their parts. Draw the overlapping triangles separately or trace over each of the overlapping triangles in a different color.

ANSWERS

Written Exercises

1. Proof: 1. $m\angle UXY = m\angle UZY$; $\overline{YU}$ bisects $\angle XYZ$. (Given) 2. $m\angle XYU = m\angle ZYU$ (Def. of $\angle$ bisector [1]) 3. $UY = UY$ (Reflexive Prop.) 4. $\triangle UXY \cong \triangle UZY$ (AAS Thm. [1, 2, 3]) 5. $XY = ZY$ (Corr. parts of $\cong$ $\triangle$s are =. [4]) 6. $VY = VY$ (Reflexive Prop.) 7. $\triangle XVY \cong \triangle ZVY$ (SAS Post. [2, 5, 6]) 8. $m\angle 1 = m\angle 2$ (Corr. parts of $\cong$ $\triangle$s are =. [7])
5. yes; SAS Post.
6. yes; AAS Thm.
7. yes; ASA Post.
8. no

Written Exercises

Set A

1. Use Exercises 1–3 in Checking for Understanding to write a two-column proof that $m\angle 1 = m\angle 2$.

Does this information show that $\triangle KGH \cong \triangle JHG$? If so, give a postulate or a theorem to support your answer. **Yes, ASA Post.**

2. $m\angle GHK = m\angle HGJ$; $m\angle KGH = m\angle JHG$

3. $KH = GJ$; $KG = HJ$ **Yes; SSS Post.**

4. $m\angle GKH = m\angle HJG$; $KG = HJ$ **No**

Does this information show that $\triangle XYV \cong \triangle ZYU$? If so, give a postulate or a theorem to support your answer.

5. $XY = ZY$; $YU = YV$ 6. $m\angle X = m\angle Z$; $XV = ZU$

7. $m\angle X = m\angle Z$; $XY = ZY$ 8. $XY = ZY$; $XV = ZU$

9. Write the steps of this proof in a correct order.

Given: $AD = BC$; $m\angle DAB = m\angle CBA$ **b, d, c, a**
Prove: $\triangle ADB \cong \triangle BCA$

Statements	Reasons
a. $\triangle ADB \cong \triangle BCA$	a. SAS Post. [1, 2, 3]
b. $AD = BC$	b. Given
c. $AB = BA$	c. Reflexive Prop.
d. $m\angle DAB = m\angle CBA$	d. Given

10. Supply the missing reasons.

Given: $m\angle TVR = m\angle TUS$; $RV = SU$
Prove: $\triangle RTV \cong \triangle STU$

Statements	Reasons
1. $m\angle TVR = m\angle TUS$	1. __?__ Given
2. $m\angle T = m\angle T$	2. __?__ Reflexive Prop.
3. $RV = SU$	3. __?__ Given
4. $\triangle RTV \cong \triangle STU$	4. __?__ AAS Thm. [1, 2, 3]

11. Given: $\overline{RT} \perp \overline{US}$; $\overline{TS} \perp \overline{RV}$; $m\angle URS = m\angle VSR$
Prove: $\triangle RUS \cong \triangle SVR$

Set B   Refer to Checking for Understanding Exercises 1–2.

12. **a.** Which pair of equal corresponding parts are needed if you use the AAS Theorem? $\angle VXY$, $\angle VZY$

b. Which other triangles should you prove congruent in order to help you find these equal parts?

13. Write a two-column proof.

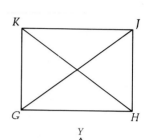

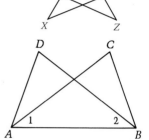

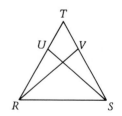

14. Given: $\overline{AB} \perp \overline{BE}$; $\overline{FE} \perp \overline{BE}$; $AB = EF$; $BC = DE$
  Prove: $\triangle ABD \cong \triangle FEC$

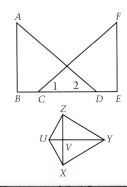

15. Given: V is the midpoint of $\overline{XZ}$; $\overline{UY} \perp \overline{XZ}$
  Prove: $m\angle UXY = m\angle UZY$

16. Given: $XU = ZU$; $XY = ZY$
  Prove: $\overline{UY} \perp \overline{XZ}$

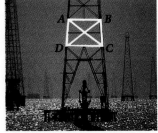

In the offshore oil rig at the right, piece $\overline{AC}$ must be replaced. $AD = BC$ and $m\angle ADC = m\angle BCD$.

17. Name the overlapping triangles that can be proved congruent using the given information. △ADC, △BCD

18. Prove that the triangles in Exercise 17 are congruent.

19. The replacement piece $\overline{AC}$ will be equal to which segment? Why? $\overline{BD}$; corr. parts of ≅ △s are =.

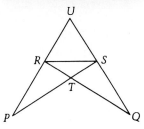

20. Name three pairs of triangles which appear to be congruent. △PSR, △QRS; △PRT, △QST; △PUS, △QUR

21. If $PR = QS$ and $PS = QR$, what postulate or theorem explains why $\triangle PRS \cong \triangle QSR$? **SSS Post.**

22. If $UP = UQ$ and $UR = US$, what postulate or theorem explains why $\triangle UPS \cong \triangle UQR$? **SAS Post.**

Set C   **23.** Given $PR = QS$ and $SU = RU$, prove $m\angle URS = m\angle USR$.

24. Given $PR = QS$ and $m\angle URS = m\angle USR$, prove $SU = RU$.

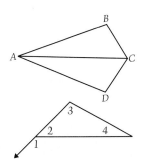

◆ **Review**   **25.** List six ways to prove that two triangles are congruent.

26. Given: $\overrightarrow{AC}$ bisects $\angle BAD$; $\overrightarrow{CA}$ bisects $\angle BCD$.
  Prove: $BC = DC$

27. Explain why there is no SSA Theorem for congruent triangles.

28. In the diagram at the right, $m\angle 1 = \underline{} + \underline{}$. $m\angle 3 \quad m\angle 4$

29. Predict the next number in this sequence:
4 5 7 11 19. What type of reasoning did you use?
35; inductive

11. Proof: 1. $\overline{RT} \perp \overline{US}$; $\overline{TS} \perp \overline{RV}$; $m\angle URS = m\angle VSR$ (Given) 2. $\angle RUS$ and $\angle SVR$ are rt. $\angle$s. (2 $\perp$ lines form 4 rt. $\angle$s. [1]) 3. $m\angle RUS = m\angle SVR$ (All rt. $\angle$s are =. [2]) 4. $RS = SR$ (Reflexive Prop.) 5. $\triangle RUS \cong \triangle SVR$ (AAS Thm. [1, 3, 4])

13. Proof: 1. $m\angle UXY = m\angle UZY$; $\overrightarrow{YU}$ bisects $\angle XYZ$. (Given) 2. $m\angle XYU = m\angle ZYU$ (Def. of $\angle$ bisector [1]) 3. $UY = UY$ (Reflexive Prop.) 4. $\triangle UXY \cong \triangle UZY$ (AAS Thm. [1, 2, 3]) 5. $m\angle VUX = m\angle VUZ$; $XU = ZU$ (Corr. parts of $\cong$ △s are =. [4]) 6. $UV = UV$ (Reflexive Prop.) 7. $\triangle UXV \cong \triangle UZV$ (SAS Post. [5, 6]) 8. $m\angle UXV = m\angle UZV$ (Corr. parts of $\cong$ △s are =. [7]) 9. $m\angle UXY = m\angle UXV + m\angle VXY$; $m\angle UZY = m\angle UZV + m\angle VZY$ ($\angle$ Add. Post.) 10. $m\angle UXV + m\angle VXY = m\angle UZV + m\angle VZY$ (Substitution Prop. [1, 9]) 11. $m\angle VXY = m\angle VZY$ (Subtraction Prop. [8, 10]) 12. $VY = VY$ (Reflexive Prop.) 13. $\triangle XVY \cong \triangle ZVY$ (AAS Thm. [2, 11, 12]) 14. $m\angle 1 = m\angle 2$ (Corr. parts of $\cong$ △s are =. [13])

14. Proof: $\overline{AB} \perp \overline{BE}$; $\overline{FE} \perp \overline{BE}$; $AB = EF$; $BC = DE$ (Given) 2. $\angle B$ and $\angle E$ are rt. $\angle$s. (2 $\perp$ lines form 4 rt. $\angle$s. [1]) 3. $m\angle B = m\angle E$ (All rt. $\angle$s are =. [2]) 4. $CD = CD$ (Reflexive Prop.) 5. $BC + CD = DE + CD$ (Add. Prop. [1, 4]) 6. $BC + CD = BD$; $DE + CD = EC$ (Seg. Add. Post.) 7. $BD = EC$ (Substitution Prop. [5, 6]) 8. $\triangle ABD \cong \triangle FEC$ (SAS Post. [1, 3, 7])

15. Proof: 1. V is midpt. of $\overline{XZ}$; $\overline{UY} \perp \overline{XZ}$ (Given) 2. $XV = ZV$ (Def. of midpt. [1]) 3. $\angle XVY$ and $\angle ZVY$ are rt. $\angle$s. (2 $\perp$ lines form 4 rt. $\angle$s. [1]) 4. $m\angle XVY = m\angle ZVY$ (All rt. $\angle$s are =. [3]) 5. $VY = VY$ (Reflexive Prop.) 6. $\triangle XVY \cong \triangle ZVY$ (SAS Post. [2, 4, 5]) 7. $XY = ZY$; $m\angle XYV = m\angle ZYV$ (Corr. parts of $\cong$ △s are =. [6]) 8. $UY = UY$ (Reflexive Prop.) 9. $\triangle UXY \cong \triangle UZY$ (SAS Post. [7, 8]) 10. $m\angle UXY = m\angle UZY$ (Corr. parts of $\cong$ △s are =. [9])

Thinking Ahead

30–31. By construction; the compass is held with a fixed radius.
32. $\triangle VPT \cong \triangle FGH$ by SSS $\cong$ Post. So, $m\angle VPT = m\angle AGB$ because corres. parts of $\cong$ $\triangle$s are =.

Draw a six-pointed star inside a hexagon. How many triangles are in the figure? 32 triangles

Draw an eight-pointed star inside an octagon. How many triangles are in the figure?
40 triangles

• **Worksheet 5–5**

Extension

• **Extension 5–5**

Progress Check

8. Proof: 1. $\overrightarrow{AC}$ bisects $\angle BAD$; $\overline{AB} \perp \overline{BC}$; $\overline{AD} \perp \overline{DC}$ (Given) 2. $m\angle BAC = m\angle DAC$ (Def. of $\angle$ bisector) 3. $\angle B$ and $\angle D$ are rt. $\angle$s. ($2 \perp$ lines form 4 rt. $\angle$s. [1]) 4. $m\angle B = m\angle D$ (All rt. $\angle$s are =. [3]) 5. $AC = AC$ (Reflexive Prop.) 6. $\triangle ABC \cong \triangle ADC$ (AAS Thm. [2, 4, 5])

Thinking Ahead Consider Construction 2 from page 31.
Construct an angle equal to a given angle.

Given $\angle AGB$

Construct $\angle VPT$ so that $m\angle VPT = m\angle AGB$

30. How do you know that $PT = GH$? that $PV = GF$?

31. How do you know that $TV = HF$?

32. Explain why $m\angle VPT = m\angle AGB$.

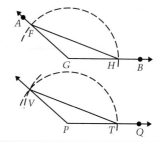

Progress Check

Lesson 5-1, page 191
Given $\triangle ABC \cong \triangle DEF$, list the pairs of

1. corresponding sides.
AB, DE; AC, DF; BC, EF

2. corresponding angles.
$\angle A, \angle D$; $\angle B, \angle E$; $\angle C, \angle F$

Lesson 5-2, page 195
Which postulate justifies that $\triangle XYZ \cong \triangle SRT$?

3. Given: $XY = RS$; $m\angle Y = m\angle R$; $YZ = RT$ **SAS Post.**

4. Given: $XY = RS$; $XZ = ST$; $YZ = RT$ **SSS Post.**

5. Given: $m\angle Z = m\angle T$; $m\angle X = m\angle S$; $XZ = ST$ **ASA Post.**

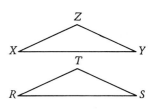

Lesson 5-3, page 200
Which theorem or postulate justifies that $\triangle MPR \cong \triangle NPR$?

6. Given: $\overline{RP} \perp \overline{MN}$; $m\angle M = m\angle N$ **AAS Thm.**

7. Given: $\overline{RP} \perp \overline{MN}$; $MP = PN$ **SAS Post.**

8. Given: $\overrightarrow{AC}$ bisects $\angle BAD$; $\overline{AB} \perp \overline{BC}$; $\overline{AD} \perp \overline{DC}$
Prove: $\triangle ABC \cong \triangle ADC$

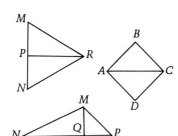

Lesson 5-4, page 206
Name triangles that you might show congruent to prove

9. $m\angle MNP = m\angle ONP$.

10. $\overrightarrow{NP}$ bisects $\overline{MO}$.

11. Given: $\overline{YZ} \parallel \overline{XW}$; $YZ = XW$
Prove: $XY = WZ$

9. $\triangle MNP$, $\triangle ONP$; or $\triangle MNQ$, $\triangle ONQ$
10. $\triangle MNQ$, $\triangle ONQ$; or $\triangle MPQ$, $\triangle OPQ$

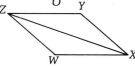

Lesson 5-5, page 210
13. $\triangle ABE$, $\triangle DCE$; $\triangle ADE$, $\triangle CBE$
Name a pair of congruent triangles.

12. Given: $AB = CD$; $m\angle ABC = m\angle BCD$ $\triangle ABC$, $\triangle DCB$

13. Given: $AB = CD$; E bisects $\overline{AC}$ and $\overline{BD}$.

14. Given: $m\angle ABD = m\angle DCA$; $m\angle CAD = m\angle ADB$
$\triangle ABD$, $\triangle DCA$

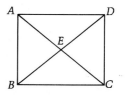

Using Logo: Designs with Congruent Triangles

The Logo primitives, POS and SETPOS, are useful in defining procedures that locate vertices and draw triangles.

POS—outputs the coordinates of the turtle's position
SETPOS—moves the turtle to a position specified by its coordinates

The procedure DRAWTRIANGLE can be used to draw a triangle for which the coordinates of its vertices (X, Y, and Z) are known.

```
TO DRAWTRIANGLE
SETPOS :Z
SETPOS :X
SETPOS :Y
SETPOS :Z
END
```

1. In the procedure TRIANGLE, the MAKE command assigns the coordinates of the vertices of the triangle to the variables :X, :Y, and :Z. The procedure then calls DRAWTRIANGLE to draw the triangle.

   Do TRIANGLE. Type RT 160 and then do TRIANGLE again. What postulate explains why the triangles are congruent? **SAS Post.**

```
TO TRIANGLE
MAKE "Z POS
FD 60
MAKE "X POS
SETPOS :Z
RT 35
FD 30
MAKE "Y POS
DRAWTRIANGLE
END
```

2. This procedure creates a pinwheel through repeated use of TRIANGLE. The variable :H determines the direction of the first side that is drawn in each triangle.

   Do PINWHEEL. Use the Logo editor to change the shape of the pinwheel by varying values in TRIANGLE and PINWHEEL. **Answers will vary.**

```
TO PINWHEEL
MAKE "H 0
REPEAT 8(RT :H TRIANGLE
  MAKE "H :H + 45)
END
```

3. Modify PINWHEEL and TRIANGLE to create the design below using congruent isosceles triangles.

4. Write procedures to create the "Blazing Star" pattern shown below using eight congruent scalene triangles.

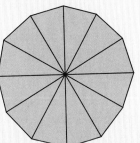

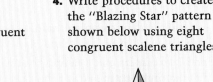

Using Logo

4. Sample:
```
TO TRIANGLE        TO TRIANGLE
  1                  2
MAKE "Z POS        MAKE "Z POS
FD 60              FD 60
MAKE "X POS        MAKE "X POS
SET POS :Z         SET POS :Z
RT 45              LT 45
FD 30              FD 30
MAKE "Y POS        MAKE "Y POS
DRAW               DRAW
  TRIANGLE           TRIANGLE
END                END


TO BSTAR
REPEAT 4 [TRIANGLE2
RT45 TRIANGLE1 RT 45]
END
```

3. Change 3rd line in PINWHEEL to: REPEAT 12 [RT: H TRIANGLE MAKE "H: H + 30]

Warm-Up Review

1. A(n) __?__ divides an angle into two equal angles.   Angle bisector
2. A(n) __?__ divides a line segment into two equal line segments.   Midpoint
3. __?__ lines intersect to form right angles.   Perpendicular
4. How many lines can be drawn through a point on a line, perpendicular to the given line?   One

LESSON 5-6

Resources

Compass
Straightedge
Worksheet 5-6
Extension 5-6

OBJECTIVE

Justify constructions using congruent triangles.

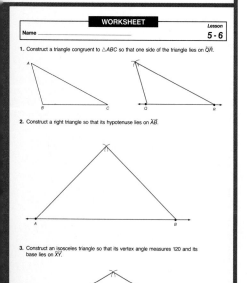

WORKSHEET   Lesson 5-6

Name _____

1. Construct a triangle congruent to △ABC so that one side of the triangle lies on $\overleftrightarrow{QR}$.

2. Construct a right triangle so that its hypotenuse lies on $\overline{AB}$.

3. Construct an isosceles triangle so that its vertex angle measures 120 and its base lies on $\overleftrightarrow{XY}$.

5-6 Using Congruence to Justify Constructions

Constructions are based on the fact that all radii of a circle are equal. Using the congruent-triangle postulates and theorems, you can now justify these constructions. Constructions 3 and 4 from pages 31 and 38 are justified below.

Construction 3

Construct the bisector of a given angle.

Given   ∠ABC

Construct $\overrightarrow{BD}$, the bisector of ∠ABC

Method   Step 1: With B as center, construct an arc that intersects $\overrightarrow{BA}$ and $\overrightarrow{BC}$ at X and Y, respectively.

Step 2: With X and Y as centers and a radius greater than $\frac{1}{2}XY$, construct two arcs intersecting in the interior of ∠ABC. Label the intersection D.

Step 3: Draw $\overrightarrow{BD}$. $\overrightarrow{BD}$ bisects ∠ABC.

Plan for Justifying   Draw $\overline{XD}$ and $\overline{YD}$; $BX = BY$ and $XD = YD$ by construction. Show $\triangle BXD \cong \triangle BYD$ by the SSS Postulate. Then $m\angle XBD = m\angle YBD$ by corresponding parts.

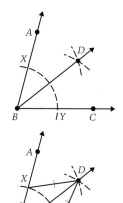

Construction 4

Through a point on a given line, construct a line perpendicular to the given line.

Given   Point P on line m

Construct $\overleftrightarrow{PQ} \perp m$

Method   Step 1: With P as center and a convenient radius, construct arcs intersecting m at points A and B.

Step 2: With A and B as centers and a radius greater than AP, construct two intersecting arcs. Label the point of intersection Q.

Step 3: Draw $\overleftrightarrow{PQ}$. $\overleftrightarrow{PQ} \perp m$ at P.

Plan for Justifying   Draw $\overline{AQ}$ and $\overline{BQ}$; $AQ = BQ$ and $AP = BP$ by construction. Show $\triangle AQP \cong \triangle BQP$. Then $m\angle APQ = m\angle BPQ$ by corresponding parts, and $\overleftrightarrow{PQ} \perp m$.

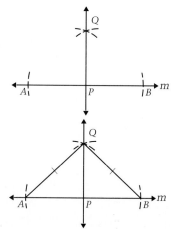

We define three special segments in a triangle. These can be constructed with compass and straightedge.

Definition *Angle Bisector, Median, Altitude of a Triangle*

An angle bisector is the segment from any vertex to the opposite side on the ray bisecting the angle; a median is the segment from any vertex to the midpoint of the opposite side; an altitude is the segment from any vertex perpendicular to the line containing the opposite side.

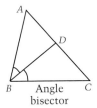

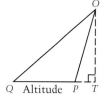

$\overline{BD}$ is an angle bisector. $\overline{BH}$ is a median. $\overline{BN}$ and $\overline{OT}$ are altitudes. Notice that in some cases an altitude may be *outside* the triangle. The construction of an altitude of a given triangle is considered next. You are expected to construct the other special segments in the exercises.

Construction 8

Construct the altitude from a given vertex of a triangle.

Given $\triangle ABC$

Construct $\overleftrightarrow{CG}$ with G on $\overleftrightarrow{AB}$ and $\overleftrightarrow{CG} \perp \overleftrightarrow{AB}$

Method   **Step 1:** With C as center, draw an arc that intersects $\overleftrightarrow{AB}$ at two points E and F; extend $\overleftrightarrow{AB}$ if necessary.

         Step 2: With E and F as centers and radius greater than $\frac{1}{2}EF$, construct a pair of arcs intersecting at D.

         Step 3: Draw $\overleftrightarrow{CD}$. Label the intersection of $\overleftrightarrow{CD}$ and $\overleftrightarrow{AB}$ as G. $\overline{CG}$ is the desired altitude.

Plan for   Draw $\overline{CE}$, $\overline{CF}$, $\overline{DE}$, and $\overline{DF}$. $CE = CF$ and $DE = DF$
Justifying   by construction. Show $\triangle CDE \cong \triangle CDF$ by the SSS Postulate. Show $m\angle GCE = m\angle GCF$ and $CG = CG$. Then $\triangle GCE \cong \triangle GCF$ by the SAS Postulate. $\angle EGC$ and $\angle FGC$ form a linear pair and are equal, so $\overline{CG} \perp \overline{AB}$. Why?   If the $\angle$s in a lin. pr. are =, then the lines containing their sides are $\perp$.

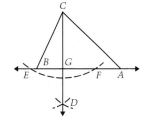
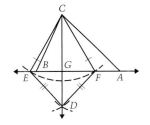

TEACHING NOTES

Review Construction 3. Ask students to explain why the steps yield two equal angles. This should lead into the development of the justification given.

Discuss the assumptions made in compass and straightedge constructions. For example, we assume that a line that has a point inside a circle intersects the circle in two points.

EXTENSION   *Lesson*
Name _____ **5-6**

Three Famous Problems

A great variety of constructions are possible by using only a compass and a straightedge. However, three constructions have perplexed mathematicians throughout the ages.

(1) Duplication of the cube
Construct the edge of a cube having twice the volume of a given cube.

(2) Trisection of an angle
Divide a given angle into three congruent parts.

(3) Quadrature of the circle
Construct a square having an area equal to that of a given circle.

Although the constructions were simple to state, no one could accomplish them. However, in the process a number of important mathematical discoveries were made.

In the nineteenth century it was proven that all of these are impossible to solve by using only a compass and straightedge.

1. According to mythology, King Minos was dissatisfied with the tomb erected for his son Glaucus. The king ordered the tomb doubled in size. One assistant doubled the dimensions of the tomb. If the tomb was a cube, what happened to the volume? **The volume would be 8 times as large.**

2. Nearly 4,000 years ago, the Egyptians "solved" the problem of constructing a square equal in area to a given circle by constructing a side of the square that is $\frac{8}{9}$ of the circle's diameter. Draw a large circle on grid paper, measure its radius, and compute its area. Then construct a square with a side that is $\frac{8}{9}$ of the circle's diameter. Compare the areas. **student construction**

Assignment Guide

Basic: 1–16, 26–32
Average: 2–16 (even), 17–24, 26–32
Extended: 2–16 (even), 17–32

EXERCISE NOTES

Exercises 1–6 involve a step-by-step justification of the equal angle construction.

Exercise 10 is completed correctly if the medians intersect at one point called the centroid of the triangle.

Exercise 11 is completed correctly if the altitudes intersect at one point called the orthocenter of the triangle.

Exercises 12–15 should lead students to conjecture in **Exercise 16** that in an isosceles triangle the bisector of the vertex angle, the median to the base and the altitude to the base coincide.

ANSWERS

Review

26. Proof: 1. $AB = AE$; $AC = AD$; $BC = ED$ (Given) 2. $CD = DC$ (Reflexive Prop.) 3. $BC + CD = ED + DC$ (Add. Prop. [1, 2]) 4. $BC + CD = BD$; $ED + DC = EC$ (Seg. Add. Post.) 5. $BD = EC$ (Substitution Prop. [3, 4]) 6. $\triangle ABD \cong \triangle AEC$ (SSS Post. [1, 5])

27. Proof: 1. $m\angle 1 = m\angle 2$; $m\angle 3 = m\angle 4$; $AC = AD$ (Given) 2. $m\angle CAD = m\angle DAC$ (Reflexive Prop.) 3. $m\angle 1 + m\angle CAD = m\angle 2 + m\angle DAC$ (Addition Prop. [1, 2]) 4. $m\angle 1 + m\angle CAD = m\angle BAD$; $m\angle 2 + m\angle DAC = m\angle EAC$ (∠ Add. Post.) 5. $m\angle BAD = m\angle EAC$ (Substitution Prop. [3, 4]) 6. $\triangle BAD \cong \triangle EAC$ (AAS Thm. [1, 5]) 7. $BD = EC$ (Corr. parts of $\cong \triangle$s are =. [6])

28. $\triangle WZU$; $\triangle YZU$ or $\triangle WZX$; $\triangle YZX$

29. $y = -2x - 4$

Checking for Understanding

1. In Construction 3, Step 2, why must the radius be greater than $\frac{1}{2}XY$? **So that the arcs intersect**

2. In Construction 3, why do we say $BX = BY$ and $XD = YD$ "by construction"?

3. In Construction 4, Step 2, why must the radius be greater than AP? **So that the arcs intersect**

4. In Construction 4, how do you know that $\triangle AQP = \triangle BQP$? that $PQ \perp m$?

5. F; a straightedge is unmarked.

Tell whether each statement is *true* or *false*. Explain.

5. A straightedge can be used to measure a segment.

6. If A is the center of an arc through B and C, then $AB = AC$.

7. If an arc is drawn with the compass radius used in Exercise 6 and with D as center, then $DE = AB$.
6–7. T; radii of a circle are =.

2. In the construction BX and BY are radii of a circle; XD and YD are radii of another circle.

4. By SSS Post.; if the ∠s in a lin. pr. are =, then the lines containing their sides are ⊥.

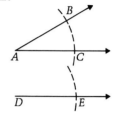

Written Exercises

Set A   Refer to this construction of an angle equal to a given angle. (Construction 2, page 31)   **1–3. Equal; radii of a circle are =.**

1. How are BD and BE related? Why?

2. How are QP and QR related? Why?

3. How are BE and QP related? Why?

4. P is the intersection of two arcs drawn so $QP = $ __?__ and $RP = $ __?__. Why are these pairs of segments equal? **BE; DE; radii of a circle are =.**

5. How are $\triangle BDE$ and $\triangle QRP$ related? Why? **≅; by SSS Post.**

6. Which definition, postulate, or theorem guarantees that $m\angle Q = m\angle B$? **Def. of ≅ △s (Corr. parts of ≅ △s are =.)**

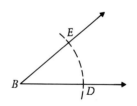

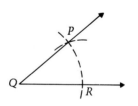

Trace $\triangle ABC$ and construct

7. the bisector of $\angle B$.   **8.** an angle equal to $\angle B$.

9. a segment twice as long as $\overline{AB}$.

10. the three medians of $\triangle ABC$.

11. the three altitudes of $\triangle ABC$.

Trace isosceles $\triangle DEF$ and construct

12. the bisector of $\angle D$.   **13.** the median from D.

14. the altitude from D.

15. the perpendicular bisector of $\overline{EF}$.

16. What do you observe in Exercises 12–15?

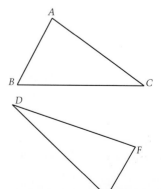

Set B Construct each of the following, and write a plan to justify your construction. Trace the figures as needed.

17. An angle equal to ∠R

18. A triangle congruent to △XYZ, using the SAS Postulate

19. A triangle congruent to △RST, using the ASA Postulate

20. A triangle congruent to △HJK, using the SSS Postulate

21. The perpendicular bisector of $\overline{XZ}$

22. A line perpendicular to $\overleftrightarrow{RS}$ through T

23. A 45° angle   **24.** A 60° angle

Set C **25.** Construct a triangle with angles of 120° and 15° and write a plan to justify your construction.

◆ Review **26.** Given: AB = AE; AC = AD; BC = ED
Prove: △ABD ≅ △AEC

27. Given: m∠1 = m∠2; m∠3 = m∠4; AC = AD
Prove: BD = EC

28. Which triangles might you prove congruent to justify that WZ = YZ?

29. Write the equation of a line through P(0, −4) perpendicular to the line with equation $y = \frac{1}{2}x + 5$.

30. Given the diagram in Exercise 28, list three things you *may* assume and three things you *may not* assume.

Thinking Ahead **31.** Construct an equilateral triangle. Measure the angles. How are the angles related? Is this true for any equilateral triangle? **Equal; yes**

32. Construct an equiangular triangle. Begin by constructing a 60° angle, ∠ABC. Then at A construct an angle equal to ∠ABC with side $\overrightarrow{AB}$ so that the other side intersects $\overrightarrow{BC}$. Draw $\overline{AC}$. Why is m∠BCA = 60? Measure the sides of the triangle. How are the sides related? Is this true for any equiangular triangle? **The sum of the meas. of ∠s of a △ = 180; sides =; yes.**

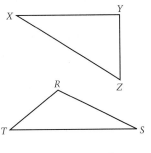
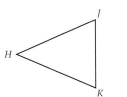
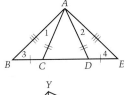
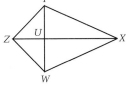
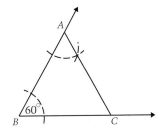

30. Sample answer: You *may* assume (1) U is between Y and W; (2) X, U and Z are collinear; (3) $\overline{YW}$ intersects $\overline{XZ}$ at U. You *may not* assume (1) $\overline{YW} \perp \overline{XZ}$; (2) U is midpt. of $\overline{YW}$; (3) $\overline{WZ} \parallel \overline{XY}$.

Thinking Ahead

31.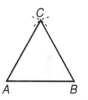
m∠A = m∠B = m∠C = 60
32.

FOLLOW-UP

More Practice
• Worksheet 5–6

Extension
Challenge students to divide an angle into more than two equal parts. The following should be noted.
1. Trisecting an angle with just compass and straightedge has been proven impossible.
2. Dividing an angle into four equal parts is easily done by bisecting the angle and then bisecting each of the halves.
3. The above can be extended to divide an angle into 2^n equal parts for any positive integer n.
• Extension 5–6

Warm-Up Review

1. A triangle with two equal sides is ___?___. **Isosceles**
2. A triangle with three equal sides is ___?___. **Equilateral**
3. A triangle with three equal angles is ___?___. **Equiangular**
4. If the three angles of a triangle are equal, what is the measure of one of them? **60**

LESSON 5-7

Resources

Compass
Straightedge
Worksheet 5-7
Extension 5-7
💻 Computer Activities 5-7

OBJECTIVES

Use the Isosceles Triangle Theorem and its converse; use the HL Theorem to prove right triangles congruent.

TEACHING NOTES

Use the following construction **activity** to introduce the HL Theorem.

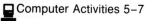

WORKSHEET

Name _____ Lesson **5-7**

State the postulate or theorem that supports the conclusion that △ABC ≅ △RST.

1. Given: $\overline{BC} \perp \overline{AC}$; $\overline{RT} \perp \overline{TS}$; $AB = RS$; $m\angle B = m\angle S$
Postulate or Theorem: **AAS**

2. Given: $BC = ST$; $AB = RS$; $\angle C$ and $\angle T$ are right ∠s.
Postulate or Theorem: **HL**

Complete each proof below.

3. Given: $\angle 1$ and $\angle 2$ are rt. ∠s; $RT = TS$
Prove: △RTQ ≅ △STQ

Statements	Reasons
1. $\angle 1$ and $\angle 2$ are right ∠s.	1. Given
2. $RT = TS$	2. Given
3. $m\angle 1 = m\angle 2$	3. All rt. ∠s are =. [1]
4. $TQ = TQ$	4. Reflexive Prop.
5. △RTQ ≅ △STQ	5. HL Theorem [2, 3, 4]

4. Given: △EHG is isosceles; $\overline{HF} \perp \overline{EG}$
Prove: $EF = FG$

Statements	Reasons
1. △EHG is isosceles.	1. Given
2. $m\angle E = m\angle G$ (or $HE = HG$)	2. Base ∠s of an isosc. △ are =. (or Def. of isosc. △) [1]
3. $\overline{HF} \perp \overline{EG}$	3. Given
4. $\angle HFE$ and $\angle HFG$ are rt. ∠s.	4. Def. of ⊥ [3]
5. $m\angle HFE = m\angle HFG$	5. All rt. ∠s are =. [4]
6. $HF = HF$	6. Reflexive Prop.
7. △HFE ≅ △HFG	7. AAS (or HL) [2, 5, 6]
8. $EF = FG$	8. Corr. pts. of ≅ △s are =. [7]

5-7 Isosceles Triangles and the HL Congruence Theorem

The rafters which support most roofs are the legs of isosceles triangles. In the diagram at the right, legs YX and YZ are equal. How do base angles ∠X and ∠Z appear to be related? Your answer suggests the Isosceles Triangle Theorem. **Equal**

Theorem 5-3   Isosceles Triangle Theorem

If two sides of a triangle are equal, then the angles opposite those sides are equal.

Given △ABC with $AC = BC$

Prove $m\angle A = m\angle B$

Plan for Proof Draw $\overline{CD}$ so that D is the midpoint of $\overline{AB}$. Show △ADC ≅ △BDC. Then use corresponding parts.

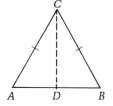

Proof

Statements	Reasons
1. $AC = BC$	1. Given
2. Let D be midpt. of $\overline{AB}$.	2. Midpoint Postulate
3. Draw $\overline{CD}$.	3. Line Postulate
4. $AD = DB$	4. Def. of midpoint [2]
5. $CD = CD$	5. Reflexive Prop.
6. △ADC ≅ △BDC	6. SSS Postulate [1, 4, 5]
7. $m\angle A = m\angle B$	7. Corr. parts of ≅ △s are =. [6]

Example 1

Given $AC = BC$, find $m\angle C$.

Solution

Since $m\angle A = m\angle B$ by the Isosceles △ Theorem, $2x = x + 20$, and $x = 20$. Therefore, $m\angle A = m\angle B = 40$. The sum of the measures of the angles of a triangle is 180, so $m\angle C = 180 - (40 + 40) = 100$.

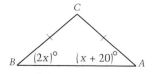

We can also prove the converse of the Isosceles Triangle Theorem. The proof is left to Exercise 14.

Theorem 5-4

If two angles of a triangle are equal, then the sides opposite those angles are equal.

Given $\triangle ABC$ with $m\angle A = m\angle B$

Prove $AC = BC$

Plan for Proof Draw $\overrightarrow{CE}$, the bisector of $\angle ACB$. Let D be the intersection of $\overleftrightarrow{AB}$ and $\overleftrightarrow{CE}$. Show $\triangle ACD \cong \triangle BCD$ by the AAS Theorem. Then $\overline{AC}$ and $\overline{BC}$ are corresponding parts.

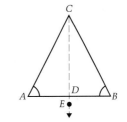

Example 2
Give a Plan for Proof: If $m\angle 1 = m\angle 3$, then $AB = BC$.

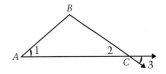

Solution
Show $m\angle 3 = m\angle 2$ by vertical angles. By transitivity, $m\angle 1 = m\angle 2$. Use the converse of the Isosceles $\triangle$ Theorem to show $AB = BC$.

Theorems 5-5 and 5-6 follow directly from Theorems 5-4 and 5-3, respectively. Their proofs are left to Exercises 15 and 16.

Theorem 5-5

An equiangular triangle is also equilateral.

Theorem 5-6

An equilateral triangle is also equiangular.

Example 3
Show that the measure of an exterior angle of an equilateral triangle is 120.

Solution
An equilateral triangle is also equiangular, so the measure of each angle is 60. An exterior angle is supplementary to one of these 60° angles, so its measure is 120.

The next theorem is useful in proving that two right triangles are congruent. Its proof is left to Exercise 25. An indirect proof is requested in Exercise 33.

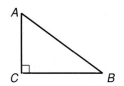

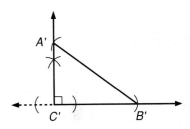

1. Given right $\triangle ABC$, draw $\overline{C'B'}$ having length equal to CB.
2. Construct $\overleftrightarrow{C'A} \perp \overleftrightarrow{C'B'}$.
3. Set compass to BA and place point at B'. There is only one possible location for A', and $\triangle A'B'C' \cong \triangle ABC$. Allow students to try this with various shapes and sizes of right triangles.

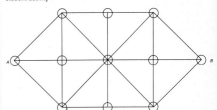

Assignment Guide

Basic: 1–20, 35–42
Average: 2–20 (even), 21–31, 35–42
Extended: 2–20 (even), 21–42

Additional Examples

Example 1
Given: $PR = QR$
Find $m\angle R$. 36

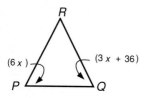

Example 2
Given: $m\angle 1 = m\angle 2$
Prove: $WY = XY$ Because supplements of equal angles are equal, $m\angle 3 = m\angle 4$; then use the converse of the Isosceles Triangle Theorem.

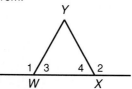

Example 3
If the vertex angle of an isosceles triangle measures 40, find the measure of an exterior angle at the base. 110

Error Analysis Students tend to want to use the HL Theorem when right triangles are not involved. Point out that the "H" in the HL Theorem stands for "hypotenuse" and stress that you only have a hypotenuse when you have a right triangle.

EXERCISE NOTES

Exercises 17–20 use the **proof subskills** of drawing a diagram and writing the "Given" and the "Prove" for a proof.

Theorem 5-7 *HL Congruence Theorem*

If the hypotenuse and a leg of one right triangle are equal to the corresponding parts of another right triangle, then the triangles are congruent.

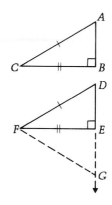

Given $\triangle ABC$ and $\triangle DEF$ with right angles at B and E;
$AC = DF$; $BC = EF$

Prove $\triangle ABC \cong \triangle DEF$

Plan for Draw $\overleftrightarrow{DE}$. Choose G on the ray opposite $\overrightarrow{ED}$ so $EG =$
Proof AB and draw $\overline{FG}$. Show $\triangle ABC \cong \triangle GEF$. Show $AC = GF$. Use $AC = DF$ to show $DF = GF$. Apply the Isosceles $\triangle$ Theorem. Show $\triangle GEF \cong \triangle DEF$. Use transitivity (Theorem 5-1) to show $\triangle ABC \cong \triangle DEF$.

Checking for Understanding

1. Combine Theorems 5-3 and 5-4 into one "if and only if" statement.

2. In the Plan for Proof of Theorem 5-7, how do you know that $\triangle ABC \cong \triangle GEF$? that $AC = GF$? that $\triangle GEF \cong \triangle DEF$?

Tell whether each statement is *always*, *sometimes*, or *never* true.

3. If $\triangle ABC$ is isosceles, then it is equiangular. Sometimes

4. An equiangular triangle is also isosceles. Always

5. If two angles of $\triangle DEF$ are equal, then $\triangle DEF$ is equilateral. Sometimes

6. A right triangle is not equilateral. Always

7. The measure of each angle of an equilateral triangle is 60. Always

(right column answers)
1. Two sides of a triangle are equal if and only if the angles opposite those sides are equal.
2. SAS Post.; corr. parts of $\cong$ $\triangle$s are =; SSS Post., SAS Post., ASA Post., or AAS Thm.

Written Exercises

Set A

1. A base angle of an isosceles triangle measures 50. Find the measures of the other two angles. 50; 80

Given: $AC = BC$; $m\angle 1 = 100$

2. $m\angle 2 = \underline{?}$ 80
3. $m\angle 4 + m\angle 5 = \underline{?}$ 100
4. $m\angle 4 = \underline{?}$ 50
5. $m\angle 3 = \underline{?}$ 130

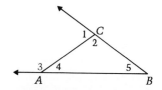

Given: $m\angle 4 = m\angle 5$

6. $AC = 12$ and $BC = 2x + 4$. Find x. 4

7. $AC = x - 3$ and $BC = 2x - 8$. Find AC. 2

8. Find the measure of $\angle P$ at the peak of the roof at the right and the length of $\overline{QR}$. 60; 5 m

9. Prove the conditional in Example 2.

10. Given: $AC = BC$; $\overline{CD}$
is an altitude of $\triangle ABC$.
Prove: $\triangle ACD \cong \triangle BCD$

11. Given: $m\angle A = m\angle B$; $\overline{CD}$
is a median of $\triangle ABC$.
Prove: $\triangle ACD \cong \triangle BCD$

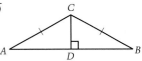

12. Given: $m\angle 2 = m\angle 4$
Prove: $\triangle MNP$ is isosceles.

13. Given: $MP = NP$
Prove: $m\angle 1 = m\angle 3$

Prove each theorem.

14. Theorem 5-4   **15.** Theorem 5-5

16. Theorem 5-6

Draw a figure and write a Given and Prove for
each statement.

17. If a triangle is isosceles, then the median from the
vertex angle bisects the vertex angle.

18. If an altitude of a triangle is also a median, then
the triangle is isosceles.

19. The median from the vertex angle of an isosceles
triangle is the perpendicular bisector of the base.

20. Use the Distance Formula to show that $\triangle AOB$
is isosceles. Why can you conclude that
$m\angle A = m\angle B$? $OA = OB = \sqrt{17}$; by the Isos. $\triangle$ Thm.

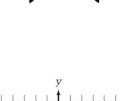

Set B Prove the statement in each exercise.

21. Exercise 17   **22.** Exercise 18   **23.** Exercise 19

24. Write the converse of the statement in Exercise 19.
Is the converse true?

25. Prove the HL Theorem (Theorem 5-7).

26. Prove: The medians to the equal sides of an
isosceles triangle are equal.

27. Use Exercise 26 to prove that the three medians of
an equiangular triangle are equal.

28. Given: $AC = BC$; $m\angle 1 = m\angle 2$
Prove: $m\angle CAD = m\angle CBD$

29. Given: $\overline{AB} \perp \overline{CD}$; $m\angle CAB = m\angle CBA$
Prove: $m\angle DAB = m\angle DBA$

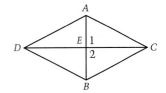

24. The $\perp$ bisector of the
base of an isos. $\triangle$ is the
median of the vertex $\angle$;
yes.

Written Exercises

9. Proof: 1. $m\angle 1 = m\angle 3$ (Given)
2. $m\angle 3 = m\angle 2$ (Vert. $\angle$s are =.)
3. $m\angle 1 = m\angle 2$ (Transitive Prop.
[1, 2]) 4. $AB = BC$ (If 2 $\angle$s of a $\triangle$
are =, then the sides opp. those
$\angle$s are =. [3])

10. Proof: 1. $AC = BC$; $\overline{CD}$ is an
altitude of $\triangle ABC$. (Given) 2. $\overline{CD} \perp$
$\overline{AB}$ (Def. of altitude of a $\triangle$ [1]) 3.
$\angle ADC$ and $\angle BDC$ are rt. $\angle$s. (2 $\perp$
lines form 4 rt. $\angle$s. [2]) 4. $\triangle ACD$
and $\triangle BCD$ are rt. $\triangle$s. (Def. of rt.
$\triangle$ [3]) 5. $CD = CD$ (Reflexive
Prop.) 6. $\triangle ACD \cong \triangle BCD$ (HL
Thm. [1, 4, 5])

11. Proof: 1. $m\angle A = m\angle B$; $\overline{CD}$ is
a median of $\triangle ABC$. (Given) 2. AC
$= BC$ (If 2 $\angle$s of a $\triangle$ are =, then
the sides opp. those $\angle$s are =.
[1]) 3. D is midpt. of $\overline{AB}$. (Def. of
median [2]) 4. $AD = BD$ (Def. of
midpt. [3]) 5. $\triangle ACD \cong \triangle BCD$
(SAS Post. [1, 2, 4])

12. Proof: 1. $m\angle 2 = m\angle 4$ (Given)
2. $m\angle 2 = m\angle PMN$; $m\angle 4 = m\angle$
PNM (Vert. $\angle$s are =.) 3. $m\angle PMN$
$= m\angle PNM$ (Substitution Prop. [1,
2]) 4. $PM = PN$ (If 2 $\angle$s of a $\triangle$ are
=, then the sides opp. those $\angle$s
are =. [3]) 5. $\triangle MNP$ is isosceles.
(Def. of isos. $\triangle$ [4])

More Practice

• **Worksheet 5–7**

Extension

Challenge students to draw a diagram that illustrates why the SSA
Theorem cannot be used to prove
two triangles congruent.
 Challenge students to draw a
diagram of a polygon that is equilateral but not equiangular.
• **Extension 5–7**

Computers

This computer activity can be completed using *The Geometric preSupposer: Points and Lines, The Geometric Supposer: Triangles* or *Circles,* or *GeoDraw.*

To introduce students to concepts of triangle inequalities, have students draw any isosceles triangle. Ask students what must be true about the base angles based on the Isosceles Triangle Theorem. **The base angles must be equal.** Measure the base angles in the drawing to see that this is true. Have students draw an extension of one of the legs of the isosceles triangle from the vertex. Label any point *D* on the extension (other than the vertex itself). Have students draw the new triangle formed by the base of the original isosceles triangle and point *D* on the extension △*ABD.* Where is side *BD* with respect to ∠*DAB*? **opposite the angle** Is *BD* longer or shorter than *BC*? **longer** Is ∠*DAB* greater or smaller than ∠ *CAB*? **greater** Have students label any point on the leg of the isosceles triangle opposite ∠*A* other than one of the endpoints of the leg, and repeat the process of measuring the new angle formed at *A* and the side opposite. Guide students to develop a conjecture as to the size of an angle of a triangle with respect to the length of the opposite side: As the size of the angle increases, the length of the opposite side __?__. **increases**

30. Two braces of equal length support a shelf. Explain why you would attach the braces to the wall the same distance below the shelf.

31. Ben needs to cut 10 right isosceles triangles with legs 12 in. long from a 12-in.-wide board. How long must the board be? **60 in.**

Set C **32.** Prove: Base angles of an isosceles triangle are acute.

33. Write an indirect proof of the HL Theorem.

34. Prove Theorem 5-3 without auxiliary lines. (See Exercises 14 and 16, page 193.)

Sometimes

▲ **Review** Is each statement *always, sometimes,* or *never* true?

35. A median of a triangle bisects one of the angles.

36. All three angle bisectors of a triangle are in the triangle's interior. **Always**

37. If one altitude of a triangle is in the triangle's exterior, then a second altitude is also in the triangle's exterior. **Always**

38. At the right, △*MNP* is a(n) __?__ triangle. Identify the legs, the base angles, and the vertex angle.

39. By Theorem 5-1, if △*NQU* ≅ △*BJK,* and △*BJK* ≅ △*YZX,* then △*NQU* ≅ __?__. △*YZX*

≡ **Thinking** **40.** Draw a right triangle. Which side is longest?
▼ **Ahead** Which angle has greatest measure?

41. Draw an obtuse triangle. Which angle has greatest measure? Which side is longest?

42. Try to draw triangles with sides of these lengths:

 a. 4 cm, 3 cm, 5 cm   **b.** 4 cm, 2 cm, 6 cm

Make a conjecture about the lengths of three segments that form a triangle.

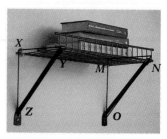

30. With the shelf level, $\overline{XY}$ ⊥ *XZ* and *MN* ⊥ *MQ.* Shelf width is constant, so *XY* = *MN.* △*XYZ* ≅ △*MNO* by the HL Thm; and *XZ* = *MO.*

38. Isosceles; legs: $\overline{MP}$, $\overline{MN}$; base angles: ∠*N*, ∠*P* vertex angle: ∠*M*

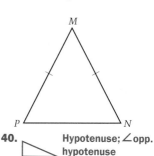

40. Hypotenuse; ∠opp. hypotenuse

41. Obtuse ∠; side opp. obtuse ∠

42. (Not actual size)
 a. **b.** Not possible

The sum of the lengths of any 2 sides is greater than the length of the third side.

Challenge

Point *E* is inside square *ABCD* with m∠*EAD* = m∠*EDA* = 15. Show that △*CBE* is equilateral. (HINT: Draw equilateral triangle *ADG,* and use a congruent-triangle proof.)

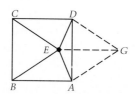

5-8 Angle and Side Inequalities in Triangles

Recall from algebra that $a > b$ means there is a positive real number c such that $a = b + c$. For real numbers, a, b, c, and d, we say that a and b are **unequal in the same order** as c and d if (1) $a > b$ and $c > d$, or (2) $a < b$ and $c < d$.

Theorem 5-8 is the counterpart of the Isosceles Triangle Theorem for triangles with unequal angles and unequal sides. Its proof is omitted.

Theorem 5-8

If the lengths of two sides of a triangle are unequal, then the measures of the angles opposite those sides are unequal in the same order.

Given $\triangle ABC$, $CB > CA$

Prove $m\angle CAB > m\angle B$

Plan for Proof   Choose D on $\overline{CB}$ so $CD = CA$; draw $\overline{AD}$. Show $m\angle 1 = m\angle 3$ by the Isosceles $\triangle$ Theorem. Show $m\angle 3 > m\angle B$ by Theorem 4-19. Substitute to show $m\angle 1 > m\angle B$. $m\angle CAB = m\angle 1 + m\angle 2$ by the Angle Addition Postulate. Finally, use definition of $>$ and transitivity.

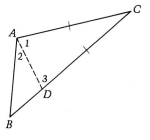

We can prove the converse of Theorem 5-8 indirectly.

Theorem 5-9

If the measures of two angles of a triangle are unequal, then the lengths of the sides opposite those angles are unequal in the same order.

Given $\triangle ABC$; $m\angle A > m\angle B$

Prove $CB > CA$

Proof   Either (1) $CB > CA$ or (2) $CB \not> CA$.

Suppose $CB \not> CA$.

Then either $CB = CA$ or $CB < CA$.

If $CB = CA$ then $m\angle A = m\angle B$ by the Isosceles $\triangle$ Theorem. But this contradicts the Given. Thus, $CB \neq CA$.

If $CB < CA$, then $m\angle A < m\angle B$ by Theorem 5-8. But this contradicts the Given. Thus, $CB \not< CA$.

Therefore, the assumption that $CB \not> CA$ is false. We conclude that $CB > CA$.

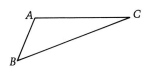

LESSON 5-8

Resources

Worksheet 5-8
Extension 5-8

OBJECTIVE

Recognize and apply inequalities in one triangle or a pair of triangles.

TEACHING NOTES

Introduce Theorem 5-8 by considering the inverse of Theorem 5-3. Its inverse is true, but this only tells us that the angles are not equal. Have students make conjectures about the order of the inequality. This should lead to Theorem 5-8.

Use pencils for an **activity** to motivate the Hinge Theorem.

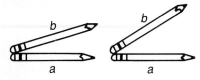

Ask students to compare the distances between the tips of the two pairs of pencils.

Additional Example

If the lengths of two sides of a triangle are 15 and 21, find the range of possible lengths for the third side. $6 < x < 36$

The following important inequality relates the lengths of the sides of a triangle. Its proof is left to Exercise 19.

Theorem 5-10   *Triangle Inequality Theorem*

The sum of the lengths of any two sides of a triangle is greater than the length of the third side.

Given $\triangle ABC$

Prove $AC + CB > AB$

Plan for Proof   Choose D on the ray opposite to $\overrightarrow{CB}$ so $DC = AC$. Draw $\overline{AD}$ and show $m\angle 1 = m\angle 2$. Show $m\angle BAD > m\angle 2$. Use Theorem 5-9 to show $DB > AB$. Show $DB = DC + CB$, and then substitute AC for DC.

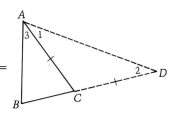

Example 1

The lengths of two sides of a triangle are 6 and 8. Find the range of possible lengths x for the third side.

Solution

By the Triangle Inequality Theorem, $6 + 8 > x$, $x + 6 > 8$, and $x + 8 > 6$. Solving each inequality for x, we have $x < 14$, $x > 2$, and $x > -2$. The numbers between 2 and 14 satisfy all three inequalities, so $2 < x < 14$.

Top views of a door are shown below. The door and the opening in the frame are each 70 cm wide. As the door is opened, what happens to $\angle PHQ$? How does PQ change? Your answer suggests Theorem 5-11, the Hinge Theorem. The proof is omitted. *$m\angle PHQ$ Increases; PQ Increases*

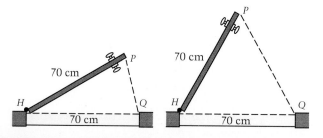

Theorem 5-11   *Hinge Theorem*

If two sides of one triangle are equal to two sides of another triangle and the included angles are unequal, then the lengths of the third sides are unequal in the same order.

Given $AC = DF$; $AB = DE$; $m\angle A > m\angle D$

Prove $BC > EF$

Plan for Proof   Draw $\overrightarrow{AG}$ so $m\angle BAG = m\angle EDF$. $\overrightarrow{AG}$ is in the interior of $\angle BAC$. Why? Choose H on $\overrightarrow{AG}$ so that $AH = DF$; draw $\overline{BH}$. Since $AB = DE$, $\triangle ABH \cong \triangle DEF$ by the SAS Postulate. Show $BH = EF$. *$m\angle A = m\angle D$; Angle Add.*

Case I H lies on $\overline{BC}$.
$BH + HC = BC$ by the Segment Addition Postulate. Show $BC > EF$. Substitute to show $BC > EF$.

Case II H does not lie on $\overline{BC}$.
Draw $\overrightarrow{AJ}$, the bisector of $\angle CAH$. Let K be the intersection of $\overrightarrow{AJ}$ and $\overline{CB}$. Draw $\overline{KH}$. Use transitivity to show $AC = AH$. Show $\triangle ACK \cong \triangle AHK$ by the SAS Postulate. Show $KC = KH$. Use the Triangle Inequality Theorem to show $BK + KH > BH$. Substitute to show $BK + KC > BH$. Use the Segment Addition Postulate and substitution to show $BC > EF$.

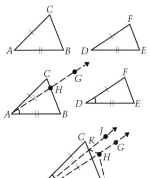

We can prove Theorem 5-12, the converse of the Hinge Theorem, indirectly.

Theorem 5-12

If two sides of one triangle are equal to two sides of another triangle and the lengths of the third sides are unequal, then the measures of the angles included between the equal sides are unequal in the same order.

Given $XY = RS$; $XZ = RT$; $ZY > TS$

Prove $m\angle X > m\angle R$

Proof   *Either $m\angle X > m\angle R$ or $m\angle X \ngtr m\angle R$.*

Suppose $m\angle X \ngtr m\angle R$.

Then either $m\angle X < m\angle R$ or $m\angle X = m\angle R$.

If $m\angle X < m\angle R$ then $ZY < TS$ by the Hinge Theorem. But this contradicts the Given. Thus, $m\angle X < m\angle R$ is false.

If $m\angle X = m\angle R$, then $\triangle XYZ \cong \triangle RST$ by the SAS Postulate and $ZY = TS$. But this contradicts the Given. Thus, $m\angle X = m\angle R$ is false.

Therefore, the assumption that $m\angle X \ngtr m\angle R$ is false.

We conclude that $m\angle X > m\angle R$.

Error Analysis   Because the statements for Theorems 5–8 and 5–12 are very similar, students may confuse them. Point out that one is used in a single triangle and the other in a pair of triangles. Make the same distinction between Theorems 5–9 and 5–11.

ANSWERS

Written Exercises

13. Since $AH = BH$, $m\angle A = m\angle B$. If $AB < 8$ cm, $m\angle H < m\angle A$. So $m\angle H$ can be 40 when $m\angle A = m\angle B = 70$. If $AB = 8$ cm, $m\angle H = 60$ because $\triangle ABH$ is equilateral. $m\angle H$ cannot be 70, because then $m\angle A = m\angle B = 55$, and then $AB > 8$ cm, which contradicts the given information.

14. Proof: Either (1) $\overline{AB} \not\parallel \overline{DE}$ or (2) $\overline{AB} \parallel \overline{DE}$. Suppose $\overline{AB} \parallel \overline{DE}$. Then $m\angle A = m\angle D$ and $m\angle B = m\angle E$ because lines $\parallel \Rightarrow$ alt. int. $\angle$s =. Since $AC > BC$, $m\angle B > m\angle A$. By substitution, $m\angle B > m\angle D$. Since $CE > CD$, $m\angle D > m\angle E$. By the Transitive Prop., $m\angle B > m\angle E$. But this contradicts $m\angle B = m\angle E$. Hence, it is false that $\overline{AB} \parallel \overline{DE}$. We conclude that $\overline{AB} \not\parallel \overline{DE}$.

15. Proof: 1. $ST > RS$ (Given) 2. $m\angle SRT > m\angle STR$ (If 2 sides of a $\triangle$ are $\neq$, the $\angle$s opp. them are $\neq$ in the same order. [1]) 3. $m\angle 1 = m\angle 2$; $m\angle 3 = m\angle 4$ (Given) 4. $m\angle STR = m\angle 1 + m\angle 2$; $m\angle SRT = m\angle 3 + m\angle 4$ ($\angle$ Add. Post.) 5. $m\angle STR = m\angle 2 + m\angle 2 = 2(m\angle 2)$; $m\angle SRT = m\angle 3 + m\angle 3 = 2(m\angle 3)$ (Substitution Prop. [3, 4]) 6. $2(m\angle 3) > 2(m\angle 2)$ (Substitution Prop. [2, 5]) 7. $m\angle 3 > m\angle 2$ (Mult. Prop. [6]) 8. $TU > UR$ (If 2 $\angle$s of a $\triangle$ are $\neq$, the sides opp. them are $\neq$ in the same order. [7])

16. Proof: 1. $LJ = MJ$; $m\angle LJK < m\angle MJK$ (Given) 2. $JK = JK$ (Reflexive Prop.) 3. $LK < MK$ (Hinge Thm. [1, 2])

17. Proof: 1. $m\angle MLJ = m\angle LMJ$; $MN < LN$ (Given) 2. $LJ = MJ$ (If 2 $\angle$s of a $\triangle$ are =, then the sides opp. those $\angle$s are =. [1]) 3. $NJ = NJ$ (Reflexive Prop.) 4. $m\angle MJN < m\angle LJN$ (If 2 sides of one $\triangle$ are =

Checking for Understanding

1. List four numbers a, b, c, and d such that a and b are unequal in the same order that c and d are.

Can a triangle have sides of the given lengths?

2. 11, 9, 16 **Yes**   **3.** 5, 7, 9 **Yes**   **4.** $2y$, $2y - 7$, $2y + 9$ **Yes, if $y > 8$**

Fill in each blank with > or <.

5.

$m\angle R \underline{\ ?\ } m\angle Q$
$<$

6.

$XY \underline{\ ?\ } RS$
$>$

7.

$MN \underline{\ ?\ } NP$
$<$

Written Exercises

Set A   The lengths of two sides of a triangle are given. Find the range of possible lengths x for the third side.

1. 5, 7   **2.** 3.6, 2.1   **3.** 2.5, 7.5
    $2 < x < 12$ $1.5 < x < 5.7$ $5 < x < 10$

4. Name the shortest and longest sides in $\triangle MNP$.
    MN; MP

5. Name the angles of least and greatest measure in $\triangle TUV$. **$\angle U$; $\angle V$**

Is each statement *always*, *sometimes*, or *never* true?

6. In $\triangle ABC$, if $AB > BC$ then $m\angle C > m\angle A$. **Always**

7. If $\angle A$ is acute, $\overline{BC}$ is the shortest side of $\triangle ABC$. **Sometimes**

8. A scalene triangle has no equal angles. **Always**

9. The sum of the measures of two angles of a **Sometimes** triangle is greater than the measure of the third angle.

10. The median to the hypotenuse of a right triangle is longer than either leg. **Never**

Fill in the blank with > or <.

11. If $m\angle R = m\angle V$, $RT = 13$, and $TV = 10$, then $m\angle RWT \underline{\ ?\ } m\angle VWT$. **>**

12. If $ST = TU$, $m\angle WTS = 92$, and $m\angle WTU = 88$, then $SW \underline{\ ?\ } UW$. **>**

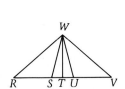

13. Spring $\overline{AB}$ will stretch to a maximum length of 8 cm. Can $m\angle AHB$ be 40? 60? 70? Explain.
Yes; yes; no

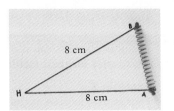
8 cm
8 cm
H

Set B **14.** Given: $AC > BC$; $CE > CD$
Prove: $AB \not\parallel DE$

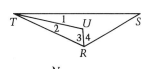

15. Given: $ST > RS$; $m\angle 1 = m\angle 2$; $m\angle 3 = m\angle 4$
Prove: $TU > UR$

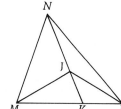

16. Given: $LJ = MJ$; $m\angle LJK < m\angle MJK$
Prove: $LK < MK$

Set C **17.** Given: $m\angle MLJ = m\angle LMJ$; $MN < LN$
Prove: $m\angle LJK < m\angle MJK$

18. Given: $LJ = MJ$; $LK < MK$
Prove: $m\angle MJN < m\angle LJN$

19. Prove the Triangle Inequality Theorem.

▲ Review **20.** The measure of the vertex angle of an isosceles triangle is 80. Find the measures of the base angles. 50, 50

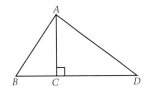

21. State the HL Theorem.

22. $\overline{AC}$ is a(n) __?__ of $\triangle ABD$. altitude

23. Tell which postulate or definition supports this statement: For two points G and H, $GH \neq -5$.
Ruler Post.

24. A polygon with 12 sides is a __?__.
dodecagon

≡ Thinking **25.** Draw a line r, and locate a point P not on r. Draw
▼ Ahead several segments from P to points on r and measure each segment. Make a conjecture about the shortest distance from P to r.

21. If the hypotenuse and a leg of one rt. $\triangle$ are = to the corr. parts of another rt. $\triangle$, then the $\triangle$s are $\cong$.

25.

The shortest distance is the length of the $\perp$ segment.

26. Points $A(1, 1)$, $B(3, 3)$, and $C(4, 4)$ lie on the line with equation $y = x$. Use the Distance Formula and find an equation relating AB, BC, and AC.
$AB + BC = AC$: $2\sqrt{2} + \sqrt{2} = 3\sqrt{2}$

to 2 sides of another $\triangle$ and the lengths of the third sides are $\neq$, then the measures of the $\angle$s included between the = sides are $\neq$ in the same order. [2, 3]) 5. $\angle MJN$ and $\angle MJK$ are supp. $\angle$s; $\angle LJN$ and $\angle LJK$ are supp. $\angle$s. (Supplement Post.) 6. $m\angle MJN + m\angle MJK = 180$; $m\angle LJN + m\angle LJK = 180$ (Def. of supp. $\angle$s [5]) 7. $m\angle MJN = 180 - m\angle MJK$; $m\angle LJN = 180 - m\angle LJK$ (Subtraction Prop.) 8. $180 - m\angle MJK < 180 - m\angle LJK$ (Substitution Prop. [4, 7]) 9. $m\angle LJK < m\angle MJK$ (Add. Prop. [8])

FOLLOW-UP

More Practice

• **Worksheet 5-8**

Extension

The following suggestions will be helpful in working with more capable students to develop a proof of the Hinge Theorem.
1. To show $\overrightarrow{AG}$ is in the interior of $\angle BAC$, use an indirect proof involving the Plane Separation Postulate and a contradiction of the Angle Addition Postulate.
2. To show that K lies on both $\overrightarrow{AJ}$ and $\overline{BC}$, use an indirect proof. If K is not a point of intersection, we can show that $m\angle C + m\angle JAC = 180$, and we have a triangle with an angle sum of more than 180. If $\overleftrightarrow{AK}$ intersects $\overleftrightarrow{BC}$ outside $\overline{BC}$, we can contradict the definition of angle bisector.
3. Case III: Depending on how the diagram is drawn, H may fall outside $\triangle ABC$. The proof is similar to Case II.
• **Extension 5-8**

LESSON 5-9

Resources

Worksheet 5–9
Extension 5–9
Algebra Review 5
Chapter 5 Test, Form I
Chapter 5 Test, Form II
Chapter 5 Test, Form III

OBJECTIVE

Apply the Triangle Inequality
Theorem.

TEACHING NOTES

Begin this lesson by having students solve the following application as a **group activity**.
   Two factories are at A and B on opposite sides of power line p.

5-9 Using the Triangle Inequality Theorem

Business planners can use the Triangle Inequality Theorem to locate sites for their facilities, as shown in Example 1.

Example 1

Four stores, located at the vertices of $ABCD$, are supplied from a warehouse at P, the intersection of the diagonals. Show that the sum of the distances from each store to P is less than the sum of the distances to any other point such as Q.

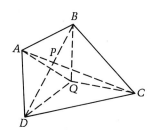

Solution

The sum of the distances from each point to P is $(AP + PC) + (BP + PD)$. $AP + PC = AC$, $BP + PD = BD$, and $(AP + PC) + (BP + PD) = AC + BD$. Why? By the Triangle Inequality Theorem, $AC < AQ + QC$ and $BD < BQ + QD$. Thus, $AC + BD < (AQ + QC) + (BQ + QD)$. The sum of the distances from each store to P is less than the sum of the distances to Q.

By Seg. Add. Post. and Substitution Prop.

Theorem 5-13 follows directly from the Triangle Inequality Theorem. Its indirect proof is requested in Exercise 17.

Theorem 5-13

If $AB + BC = AC$, then points A, B, and C are collinear and B is between A and C.

Theorems 5-14 and 5-15 restate the Triangle Inequality Theorem.

Theorem 5-14

The perpendicular segment from a point to a line is the shortest segment from the point to the line.

Given $\overleftrightarrow{XY}$; P not on $\overleftrightarrow{XY}$; $\overline{PQ} \perp \overleftrightarrow{XY}$; M on $\overleftrightarrow{XY}$; M is not Q.

Prove $PM > PQ$

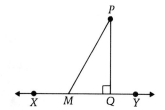

Proof

Statements	Reasons
1. $\overline{PQ} \perp \overleftrightarrow{XY}$; Q and M on $\overleftrightarrow{XY}$; M is not Q.	1. Given
2. ∠PQM and ∠PQY are rt. ∠s.	2. Two ⊥ lines form four rt. ∠s. [1]
3. $m\angle PQM = m\angle PQY$	3. All rt. ∠s are =. [2]
4. $m\angle PQY > m\angle PMQ$	4. The meas. of an ext. ∠ of a △ is greater than __?__.
5. $m\angle PQM > m\angle PMQ$	5. Substitution Prop. [3, 4]
6. $PM > PQ$	6. If the meas. of two ∠s of a △ are ≠, then __?__. [5]

the measure of either of its remote interior ∠s.

The lengths of the sides opp. those ∠s are ≠ in the same order.

Mathematicians often prove theorems in paragraph form. In a *paragraph proof*, statements and reasons are given in a less structured way than in a two-column proof. A paragraph proof for Theorem 5-14 follows.

Paragraph Proof In $\triangle PQM$, $\overline{PQ} \perp \overleftrightarrow{XY}$; so $\angle PQM$ and $\angle PQX$ are right angles because perpendicular lines form right angles. Since all right angles are equal, $m\angle PQM = m\angle PQY$. Because the measure of an exterior angle of a triangle is greater than the measure of either remote interior angle, $m\angle PQY$ is greater than $m\angle PMQ$. Substituting, we have $m\angle PQM > m\angle PMQ$. By Theorem 5-9, the sides opposite $\angle PQM$ and $\angle PMQ$ are unequal in the same order, so $PM > PQ$.

Theorem 5-15, the space counterpart of Theorem 5-14, is to be proved in Exercise 14.

Theorem 5-15

The perpendicular segment from a point to a plane is the shortest segment from the point to the plane.

"The shortest distance between two points is a straight line" is the concept formalized in Theorems 5-14 and 5-15. The distance from a point to a line or to a plane is also defined to be the length of the "shortest path."

Definition   *Distance from a Point to Line (or Plane)*

The distance from a point to a line (or plane) not containing the point is the length of the perpendicular segment from the point to the line (or plane).

Example 2
Find the distance from $(-5, -5)$ to the line with equation $y = 3$.

Solution
The distance is 8 units, as we see in the figure.

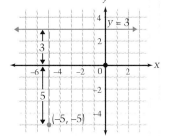

Checking for Understanding
1. Describe a possible location of R, S, and T if $RS + ST = RT$.

2. How is Theorem 5-13 different from the Seg. Add. Post.?

3. Find the distance from $(2, -4)$ to the line $y = 5$. 9
1. R, S, and T, are collinear, and S is between R and T.
2. Thm. 5-13 is the converse of the Seg. Add. Post.

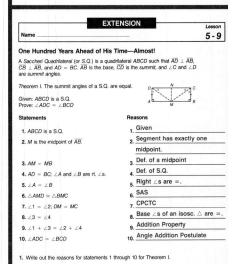

Where should a transformer *T* be located on *p* so that the transformer is as close as possible to both factories?

Have students write a previous two-column proof in paragraph form, such as the proof of Theorem 5–3.
Review the definition of a line perpendicular to a plane before studying Theorem 5–15.

EXERCISE NOTES

Exercises 3–4 may be done by sketching a graph and drawing the perpendicular from the point to the line.

EXTENSION		Lesson
Name		5-9

One Hundred Years Ahead of His Time—Almost!

A *Saccheri Quadrilateral* (or *S.Q.*) is a quadrilateral ABCD such that $\overline{AD} \perp \overline{AB}$, $\overline{CB} \perp \overline{AB}$, and AD = BC. $\overline{AB}$ is the base, $\overline{CD}$ is the *summit*, and $\angle C$ and $\angle D$ are *summit* angles.

Theorem I. The summit angles of a S.Q. are equal.

Given: ABCD is a S.Q.
Prove: $\angle ADC = \angle BCD$

Statements	Reasons
1. ABCD is a S.Q.	1. Given
2. M is the midpoint of $\overline{AB}$.	2. Segment has exactly one midpoint.
3. AM = MB	3. Def. of a midpoint
4. AD = BC; $\angle A$ and $\angle B$ are rt. $\angle$s.	4. Def. of S.Q.
5. $\angle A = \angle B$	5. Right $\angle$s are =.
6. $\triangle AMD = \triangle BMC$	6. SAS
7. $\angle 1 = \angle 2$; DM = MC	7. CPCTC
8. $\angle 3 = \angle 4$	8. Base $\angle$s of an isosc. $\triangle$ are =.
9. $\angle 1 + \angle 3 = \angle 2 + \angle 4$	9. Addition Property
10. $\angle ADC = \angle BCD$	10. Angle Addition Postulate

1. Write out the reasons for statements 1 through 10 for Theorem I.

Theorem II. The segment joining the midpoints of the base and summit of a S.Q. is perpendicular to each of them.

2. Write a proof of Theorem II.
   see Additional Answers, p. 124

Additional Examples

Example 1

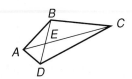

Alice, Billy, Claire, Danny and Elaine live on the corners of the streets indicated by *A*, *B*, *C*, *D* and *E*. Show that the sum of the distances from Elaine's house to each of the other houses is less than the sum of the distances from Alice's house to Billy's, Claire's and Danny's houses. $AE + BE + EC + ED = (AE + EC) + (BE + ED) = AC + BD$; by triangle inequality, $BD < AD + AB$, so $AC + BD < AC + AD + AB$

Example 2
Find the distance from $(4, -3)$ to the line whose equation is $x = -2$. 6

Error Analysis Students may use the length of any segment from a point to a line (or plane) as the distance from the point to the line (or plane). Drawings showing several different segments should clarify the fact that the perpendicular is the shortest segment.

ANSWERS

Written Exercises

9. $AP + PC = AC$ and $BP + PD = BD$ by the Seg. Add. Post. $AC < AR + RC$ and $BD < BR + RD$ by the △ Inequality Thm. So, $AC + BD < (AR + RC) + (BR + RD)$. By substitution, $(AP + PC) + (BP +$

Written Exercises

$\overline{BC}$; $\overline{AC}$

Set A **1.** Name the shortest and longest sides of △*ABC*.

2. If $PQ = 6$, $QR = 13$, and $PR = 7$, what theorem ensures that *P*, *Q*, and *R* are collinear? Which of the three points lies between the other two? Thm 5-13; *P*

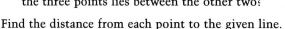

Find the distance from each point to the given line.

3. $(3, 2)$; line $x = -4$ 7   **4.** $(0, 4)$; line $y = -\frac{2}{3}$ $4\frac{2}{3}$

Use the Distance Formula and Theorem 5-13 to decide whether each triple of points are collinear.

5. $(0, 1)$, $(-1, 3)$, $(2, -3)$ Yes **6.** $(3, 2)$, $(-1, -2)$, $(1, 1)$ No

A is between *B* and *C*. In Exercises 7 and 8, *AB*, *AC*, and *BC*, respectively, are expressed in terms of x. Find *AB*, *AC*, and *BC*.

7. x; $2x$; $2x + 4$ **8.** $3x + 2$; $5x$; $x + 5$
   4; 8; 12 $3\frac{2}{7}$; $2\frac{1}{7}$; $5\frac{3}{7}$

Set B Refer to Example 1.

9. If *R* is in the exterior of quadrilateral *ABCD*, show that $(AP + PC) + (BP + PD) < (AR + RC) + (BR + RD)$.

10. If *S* is a point, different from *P*, on $\overline{AC}$, show that $(AP + PC) + (BP + PD) < (AS + SC) + (BS + SD)$.

Given △*XYZ*, find the distance from *Y* to $\overline{XZ}$.

11. $m\angle Z = 90$; $XY = 5$; $XZ = 3$; $YZ = 4$ 4

12. Altitude $\overline{YN}$; median $\overline{YM}$; $YN = 11$; $YM = 15$ 11

13. Prove in paragraph form that if $\overline{AM}$ is a median and $\overline{AD}$ is an altitude, with *M* not *D*, of △*ABC*, then $AD < AM$.

14. Write a paragraph proof of Theorem 5-15.

15. Two factories, *A* and *B*, are on opposite sides of power line *p*. Where should a transformer *T* be located on *p* so that the transformer is as close as possible to both factories; that is, $AT + BT$ is as small as possible? Explain.

16. Air distances from New York to Chicago, Montreal, and Washington, D.C., are 714 mi., 331 mi., and 205 mi., respectively. Use the Triangle Inequality Theorem to find maximum and minimum air distances between Chicago and Montreal, Montreal and Washington, and Chicago and Washington.

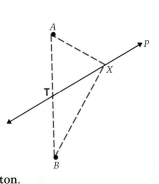

Set C

17. Write an indirect proof of Theorem 5-13.

18. Write a paragraph proof: The perimeter of a quadrilateral is greater than the sum of its diagonal lengths.

$4 < x < 22$

▲ **Review** **19.** The lengths of two sides of a triangle are 9 and 13. Find the range of possible lengths of the third side.

20. In $\triangle ABC$, $AB = 14$, $BC = 17$, and $AC = 21$. $\angle C$; $\angle B$ Which angle has the smallest measure? the largest?

21. The measure of a base angle of an isosceles **48; 84** triangle is 48. Find the measures of the other angles.

22. If $a \parallel b$, which other angles are equal to $\angle 1$?

23. Given $a \not\parallel b$ and $t \perp a$, prove indirectly that $t \not\perp b$.

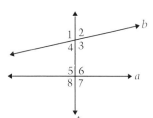

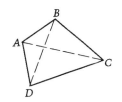

⚡ Progress Check

Lesson 5-6, page 216
1. Draw obtuse $\triangle BIG$. Construct the altitude from B to $\overline{IG}$. Write a plan to justify your construction.

Lesson 5-7, page 220
2. Given $YX = YZ$ and $m\angle Y = 50$, $m\angle YXZ = \underline{\ ?\ }$. **65**

3. Given: $\overline{YX} \perp \overline{ZT}$; $\overline{YZ} \perp \overline{XV}$;
$TW = VW$
Prove: $m\angle WXZ = m\angle WZX$

4. Given: $XY = ZY$;
$XW = ZW$
Prove: $\triangle XTW \cong \triangle ZVW$

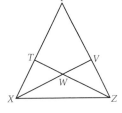

Lesson 5-8, page 225
5. Given $\triangle FDE$ with $m\angle F = 48$ and $m\angle D = 52$, which side is longest? shortest? $\overline{DF}$; $\overline{DE}$

6. Given: $MQ = NQ$; $PN = RM$;
$PQ > QR$
Prove: $LM > LN$

7. Given: $MQ = NQ$;
$PN = RM$; $LN < LM$
Prove: $QR < PQ$

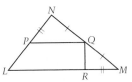

Lesson 5-9, page 230
Write a paragraph proof for each exercise.

8. Given: $VW = XY$; $WZ = XZ$;
$WY > VX$
Prove: $m\angle YXZ > m\angle VWZ$

9. Given: $VW = XY$;
$m\angle WXY > m\angle VWX$
Prove: $WY > VX$

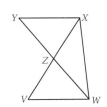

$PD) < (AR + RC) + (BR + RD)$.
10. $AP + PC = AC$ and $BP + PD = BD$ by the Seg. Add. Post. $AC < AS + SC$ and $BD < BS + SD$ by the $\triangle$ Inequality Thm. So, $AC + BD < (AS + SC) + (BS + SD)$. By substitution, $(AP + PC) + (BP + PD) < (AS + SC) + (BS + SD)$.
13. Given $\overline{AM}$ is a median of $\triangle ABC$; $\overline{AD}$ is an altitude; M is not D. Prove: $AD < AM$

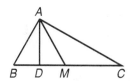

Proof: Since $\overline{AD}$ is an altitude, $\overline{AD} \perp \overline{BC}$ by the def. of altitude. Since M is not D, median $\overline{AM} \not\perp \overline{BC}$ because through a pt. not on a given line, there is exactly one line $\perp$ to the given line. So $AD < AM$ because the $\perp$ seg. from a pt. to a line is the shortest seg. from the pt. to the line.

FOLLOW-UP

More Practice
• **Worksheet 5–9**

Extension

Challenge your better students to solve the variation of the factory problem mentioned above, where A and B are on the same side of p.

The trick is to reflect B in line p to B'. Because $B'T = BT$, T will be the intersection of $\overline{AB'}$ with p.
• **Extension 5–9**

Chapter 5 Summary

Important Terms

AAS Congruence
  Theorem (200)
Altitude of a triangle (217)
Angle bisector of a
  triangle (217)
ASA Congruence
  Postulate (196)
Congruent triangles (191)

Corresponding parts (191)
Distance from a point to
  a line or a plane (231)
Hinge Theorem (226)
HL Congruence
  Theorem (222)
Included angle (192)
Included side (192)

Isosceles Triangle
  Theorem (220)
Median of a triangle (217)
SAS Congruence
  Postulate (196)
SSS Congruence
  Postulate (195)
Triangle Inequality
  Theorem (226)

Important Ideas

1. Corresponding parts of congruent triangles are equal. (192)

2. Two triangles are congruent if
   a. three sides of one are equal to the corresponding sides of the other
      (SSS Postulate). (195)
   b. two sides and the included angle of one are equal to the
      corresponding parts of the other (SAS Postulate). (196)
   c. two angles and the included side (ASA Postulate) or two angles and a
      nonincluded side (AAS Theorem) of one are equal to the
      corresponding parts of the other. (196, 200)

3. Two sides of a triangle are equal if and only if the angles opposite those
   sides are equal. (220, 221)

4. Two right triangles are congruent if the hypotenuse and a leg of one
   are equal to the corresponding parts of the other (HL Theorem). (222)

5. Two sides of a triangle are unequal in a given order if and only if the
   angles opposite those sides are unequal in the same order (225)

6. The sum of the lengths of any two sides of a triangle is greater than the
   length of the third side (Triangle Inequality Theorem). (226)

7. If two sides of one triangle are equal to two sides of another triangle
   and the measures of the included angles are unequal, then the lengths of
   the third sides are unequal in the same order (Hinge Theorem). (226)

8. If two sides of one triangle are equal to two sides of another triangle and
   the lengths of the third sides are unequal, then the measures of the angles
   included between the equal sides are unequal in the same order. (227)

9. The perpendicular segment from a point to a line (or plane) is the
   shortest segment from the point to the line (or plane). (231)

Chapter 5 Review

Lesson 5-1, Page 191

Given: $\triangle KLM \cong \triangle RST$

1. List the pairs of equal sides. **KL, RS; KM; RT; LM; ST**

2. List the pairs of equal angles. **∠K, ∠R; ∠L; ∠S; ∠M, ∠T**

3. Name the side included between $\angle RST$ and $\angle STR$. $\overline{ST}$

Lesson 5-2, Page 195

4. If $m\angle B = m\angle E$, then $\triangle ABC \cong \triangle DEF$ by the $\underline{\ ?\ }$ Postulate. **SAS**

5. If $AC = DF$, then $\triangle ABC \cong \triangle DEF$ by the $\underline{\ ?\ }$ Postulate. **SSS**

6. Given: $\triangle HJK$ and $\triangle MNO$; $JK = NO$; $m\angle HJK = m\angle MNO$; $m\angle JKH = m\angle NOM$. What conclusion can you draw and why? **$\triangle HJK \cong \triangle MNO$ by ASA Post.**

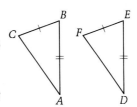

Lesson 5-3, Page 200

Which postulate or theorem justifies $\triangle RST \cong \triangle WXY$ given right angles at R and W? **AAS Thm.**   **SAS Post.**

7. $RT = WY$; $m\angle S = m\angle X$ **8.** $RS = WX$; $RT = WY$

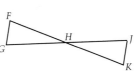

9. Given: C is the midpoint of $\overline{BD}$; $m\angle A = m\angle E$; $m\angle B = m\angle D$
Prove: $\triangle ABC \cong \triangle EDC$

10. Given: C is the midpoint of $\overline{BD}$; $\overline{AC} \parallel \overline{ED}$; $AC = DE$
Prove: $\triangle ABC \cong \triangle ECD$

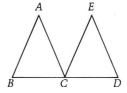

Lesson 5-4, Page 206

11. Given: $\overline{FG} \perp \overline{KF}$; $\overline{JK} \perp \overline{KF}$; $GH = JH$
Prove: $FH = KH$

12. Given: H is the midpoint of $\overline{KF}$ and $\overline{GJ}$.
Prove: $\overline{FG} \parallel \overline{JK}$

13. Newport (N) is due north of Tiffin (T). Fairfield (F) is 52 km due west of Tiffin, and Grove City (G) is 52 km due east of Tiffin. Show that $\triangle FTN \cong \triangle GTN$. Explain why Fairfield and Grove City are equal distances from Newport.

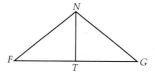

Lesson 5-5, Page 210

14. Given: $\overline{XY} \perp \overline{VZ}$; $\overline{VW} \perp \overline{XZ}$; $VW = XY$
Prove: $\triangle XYZ \cong \triangle VWZ$

15. Given: $YT = WT$; $VT = TX$
Prove: $YZ = ZW$

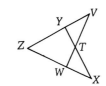

ANSWERS

Chapter Review

9. Proof: 1. C is midpt. of $\overline{BD}$; $m\angle A = m\angle E$; $m\angle B = m\angle D$ (Given) 2. $BC = DC$ (Def. of midpt. [1]) 3. $\triangle ABC \cong \triangle EDC$ (AAS Thm. [1, 2])

10. Proof: 1. C is midpt. of $\overline{BD}$; $\overline{AC} \parallel \overline{ED}$; $AC = DE$ (Given) 2. $BC = CD$ (Def. of midpt. [1]) 3. $m\angle ACB = m\angle EDC$ (Lines $\parallel \Rightarrow$ corr. $\angle$s =. [1]) 4. $\triangle ABC \cong \triangle ECD$ (SAS Post. [1, 2, 3])

11. Proof: 1. $\overline{FG} \perp \overline{KF}$; $\overline{JK} \perp \overline{KF}$; $GH = JH$ (Given) 2. $\angle F$ and $\angle K$ are rt. $\angle$s. (2 $\perp$ lines form 4 rt. $\angle$s. [1]) 3. $m\angle F = m\angle K$ (All rt. $\angle$s are =. [2]) 4. $m\angle FHG = m\angle KHJ$ (Vert. $\angle$s are =.) 5. $\triangle FGH \cong \triangle KJH$ (AAS Thm. [1, 3, 4]) 6. $FH = KH$ (Corr. parts of $\cong \triangle$s are =. [5])

12. Proof: 1. H is midpt. of $\overline{KF}$ and $\overline{GJ}$. (Given) 2. $FH = KH$; $GH = JH$ (Def. of midpt. [1]) 3. $m\angle FHG = m\angle KHJ$ (Vert. $\angle$s are =.) 4. $\triangle FGH \cong \triangle KJH$ (SAS Post. [2, 3]) 5. $m\angle F = m\angle K$ (Corr. parts of $\cong \triangle$s are =. [4]) 6. $\overline{FG} \parallel \overline{JK}$ (Alt. int. $\angle$s = $\Rightarrow$ lines $\parallel$. [5])

13. $FT = GT = 52$ km. $\angle FTN$ and $\angle GTN$ are rt. $\angle$s, so they are =. $NT = NT$. Hence, $\triangle FTN \cong \triangle GTN$ by SAS Post. Then $FT = GT$ by corr. parts, so Fairfield and Grove City are = distances from Tiffin.

14. Proof: 1. $\overline{XY} \perp \overline{VZ}$; $\overline{VW} \perp \overline{XZ}$; $VW = XY$ (Given) 2. $\angle XYZ$ and $\angle VWZ$ are rt. $\angle$s. (2 $\perp$ lines form 4 rt. $\angle$s. [1]) 3. $m\angle XYZ = m\angle VWZ$ (All rt. $\angle$s are =. [2]) 4. $m\angle Z = m\angle Z$ (Reflexive Prop.) 5. $\triangle XYZ \cong \triangle VWZ$ (AAS Thm. [1, 3, 4])

15. Proof: 1. $YT = WT$; $VT = TX$ (Given) 2. $m\angle YTV = m\angle WTX$ (Vert. $\angle$s are =.) 3. $\triangle YTV \cong \triangle WTX$ (SAS Post. [1, 2]) 4. $m\angle V$

= m∠X (Corr. parts of ≅ △s are =. [3]) 5. m∠Z = m∠Z (Reflexive Prop.) 6. YT + TX = WT + TV (Add. Prop. [1]) 7. YT + TX = YX; WT + VT = WV (Seg. Add. Post.) 8. YX = WV (Substitution Prop. [6, 7]) 9. △XYZ ≅ △VWZ (AAS Thm. [4, 5, 8]) 10. YZ = WZ (Corr. parts of ≅ △s are =. [9])

16.

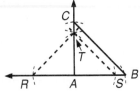

Plan for justifying: Draw $\overline{RT}$ and $\overline{ST}$. AR = AS and RT = ST by construction. Show △RAT ≅ △SAT by SSS Post. Use corr. parts to show m∠RAT = m∠SAT. Then $\overrightarrow{AT}$ ⊥ $\overleftrightarrow{AB}$ because if the ∠s in a lin. pr. are =, then the lines containing their sides are ⊥. So ∠SAT is a rt. ∠. AB = AC by construction, so △ABC is an isos. △ by def.

17.

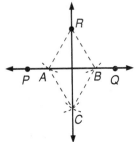

Plan for justifying: Draw $\overline{AR}$, $\overline{BR}$, $\overline{AC}$ and $\overline{BC}$. AR = BR and AC = BC by construction. Show △RAC ≅ △RBC by SSS Post. Then show m∠ARD = m∠BRD by corr. parts and show △ARD ≅ △BRD by SAS Post. Use corr. parts to show m∠ADR = m∠BDR. So $\overleftrightarrow{RD}$ ⊥ $\overleftrightarrow{PQ}$ because if the ∠s in a lin. pr. are =, then the lines containing their sides are ⊥.

24. Proof: 1. XZ = YZ (Given) 2. m∠ZXY = m∠ZYX (Isos. △ Thm. [1]) 3. ∠1 and ∠ZXY are supp. ∠s; ∠2 and ∠ZYX are supp. ∠s. (Supp. Post.) 4. m∠1 = m∠2 (Supp. of = ∠s are =. [2, 3])

Lesson 5-6, Page 216

♠ 16. Draw $\overline{AB}$. Construct an isosceles right triangle with $\overline{AB}$ as a leg. Write a plan to justify your construction.

♠ 17. Draw $\overleftrightarrow{PQ}$. Choose a point R not on $\overleftrightarrow{PQ}$. Construct a line through R perpendicular to $\overleftrightarrow{PQ}$. Write a plan to justify your construction.

Tell whether each statement is *always*, *sometimes*, or *never* true.

18. The median of △ABC through A is parallel to $\overleftrightarrow{BC}$. **Never**

19. The altitude of △ABC from A intersects $\overline{BC}$ at a right angle. **Sometimes**

20. A triangle has three angle bisectors. **Always**

Lesson 5-7, Page 220

21. m∠B = _?_ **60** **22.** AB = _?_ cm **10** **23.** BC = _?_ cm

24. Given: XZ = YZ
Prove: m∠1 = m∠2

25. Given: m∠1 = m∠2
Prove: XZ = YZ

26. Given: XZ = YZ; $\overline{ZW}$ ⊥ $\overline{XY}$
Prove: $\overline{ZW}$ bisects $\overline{XY}$.

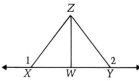

Lesson 5-8, Page 225

27. The smallest angle of △DEF is _?_. **∠D** Its largest angle is _?_. **∠E**

28. In △FED, $\overline{FG}$ is the median from F, $\overline{FH}$ is the altitude from F, and $\overline{FJ}$ is the angle bisector from F. Which of the three segments is shortest? **$\overline{FH}$**

29. The distance from F to $\overleftrightarrow{DE}$ is less than or equal to 5. Explain why. **The ⊥ seg. from a pt. to a line is the shortest seg. from the pt. to the line.**

30. Given: AD = BC; m∠CAD < m∠ACB
Prove: CD < AB

31. Given: AD = BC; AB > CD
Prove: m∠ACB > m∠CAD

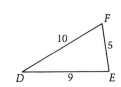

Lesson 5-9, Page 230

32. Find the possible values for x. **1 < x < 25**

33. If m∠J > m∠K, what are possible values for x? **13 < x < 25**

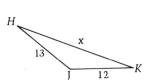

Chapter 5 Test

Tell whether each statement *always*, *sometimes*, or *never* true.

1. If $\triangle ABC \cong \triangle DEF$, then $BC = EF$. **Always**

2. If $\triangle ABC \cong \triangle DEF$, then $CB = ED$. **Sometimes**

3. The base angles of an isosceles right triangle are 30° angles. **Never**

4. The base of an isosceles triangle is longer than either of the other two sides. **Sometimes**

5. An altitude of a triangle joins a vertex to a point on the opposite side of the triangle. **Sometimes**

6. A median of a triangle bisects a side of the triangle. **Always**

7. The sum of the lengths of two sides of a triangle is greater than the length of the third side. **Always**

8. Solve for x in $\triangle KMN$. **20**

Which postulate or theorem justifies $\triangle ABC \cong \triangle DEF$?

9. $m\angle C = m\angle F$; $AC = DF$; $BC = EF$ **SAS Post.**

10. $m\angle C = m\angle F$; $m\angle D = m\angle A$; $AB = DE$ **AAS Thm.**

11. $\angle C$ and $\angle F$ are right $\angle$s; $AB = DE$; $BC = EF$ **HL Thm.**

12. To measure the height AC of a pole, a surveyor stood at B and measured $\angle ABC$. He then marked off $\overrightarrow{BE}$ so $m\angle ABE = m\angle ABC$. He next marked off $\overrightarrow{AF}$ so $m\angle BAF = 90$ with D the intersection of $\overrightarrow{AF}$ and $\overrightarrow{BE}$. Explain why $\triangle ABC \cong \triangle ABD$. What ground measurement could the surveyor make to find the height of the pole? **By ASA Post.; AD**

13. The coordinates of A, B, and C are (1, 1), (4, 3), and (3, 4), respectively. Use the Distance Formula to show that $\triangle ABC$ is isosceles. **AB = AC = $\sqrt{13}$**

14. Given: $PQ = QR$; $m\angle PQS < m\angle RQS$
Prove: $PS < RS$

15. Given: $AF = DE$; $m\angle A = m\angle D$; $m\angle F = m\angle E$
Prove: $AB = CD$

16. Given: $AF = BE$; $\overline{AF} \parallel \overline{BE}$; $AC = BD$
Prove: $\overline{FC} \parallel \overline{DE}$

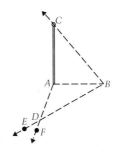

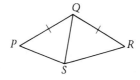

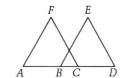

Chapter Test

14. Proof: 1. $PQ = QR$; $m\angle PQS < m\angle RQS$ (Given) 2. $QS = QS$ (Reflexive Prop.) 3. $PS < RS$ (Hinge Thm. [1, 2])

15. Proof: 1. $AF = DE$; $m\angle A = m\angle D$; $m\angle F = m\angle E$ (Given) 2. $\triangle AFC \cong \triangle DEB$ (ASA Post. [1]) 3. $AC = BD$ (Corr. parts of $\cong \triangle$s are =. [2]) 4. $AC = AB + BC$; $BD = BC + CD$ (Seg. Add. Post.) 5. $AB + BC = BC + CD$ (Substitution Prop. [3, 4]) 6. $BC = BC$ (Reflexive Prop.) 7. $AB = CD$ (Subtraction Prop. [5, 6])

16. Proof: 1. $AF = BE$; $\overline{AF} \parallel \overline{BE}$; $AC = BD$ (Given) 2. $m\angle A = m\angle EBD$ (2 lines $\parallel \Rightarrow$ corr. $\angle$s =. [1]) 3. $\triangle FAC \cong \triangle EBD$ (SAS Post. [1, 2]) 4. $m\angle FCA = m\angle D$ (Corr. parts of $\cong \triangle$s are =. [3]) 5. $\overline{FC} \parallel \overline{DE}$ (Corr. $\angle$s = $\Rightarrow$ lines $\parallel$. [4])

CHAPTER

6

Quadrilaterals

Chapter Overview

Students have been familiar with various types of quadrilaterals for years. In some cases, their recollections may contain erroneous notions. In this chapter, various types of quadrilaterals are defined and their properties are proved.

It will be helpful to refer students to the organizational structure of the set of quadrilaterals.

The study of quadrilaterals begins with a study of parallelograms, and the methods of proving that a quadrilateral is a parallelogram. Certain types of parallelograms (rectangles, rhombuses and squares) are similarly treated. Many of the proofs involve applications of congruent triangles.

The properties of parallelograms lead to some parallel line theorems. Trapezoids, especially isosceles trapezoids, are investigated.

In the last part of this chapter, the concept of locus in geometry is introduced. Some locus theorems are proved, and an intuitive approach is taken to locus problems. Students may use the **problem-solving strategy** of drawing a diagram often.

Perspectives

Lesson 6-1 begins the study of various quadrilaterals by defining the parallelogram. Students discover the basic properties of a parallelogram and prove them.

Lesson 6-2 shows methods of proving that a given quadrilateral is a parallelogram. Two of these methods are the converses of Theorems 6–1 and 6–3.

When coordinates of vertices are given, coordinate geometry can be used to show that a quadrilateral is a parallelogram.

Lesson 6-3 introduces rectangles, rhombuses and squares as subsets of the set of parallelograms. They are distinguished by their definitions and by the properties of their diagonals.

Lesson 6-4 introduces useful theorems involving parallel lines. The proofs of these theorems provide further applications of the properties of the parallelogram.

Lesson 6-5 completes the classification of quadrilaterals by introducing the subset of trapezoids. The relationship of the median of a trapezoid to its bases is studied, and the properties of the isosceles trapezoid are investigated and proved.

Lesson 6-6 introduces the concept of locus in an informal setting. Students are encouraged to approach locus problems by sketching the given information, locating a few points that satisfy the locus condition(s) and then sketching the full locus as an aid to describing it.

Lesson 6-7 formalizes the concept of locus using a series of theorems that may be applied in certain situations.

Pacing Chart for Chapter 6

Lesson	Objectives	Basic Course	Average Course	Extended Course
6–1	State and apply theorems concerning the properties of parallelograms.	1	1	1
6–2	State and apply theorems that prove a given quadrilateral is a parallelogram.	1	1	1
6–3	State and apply theorems concerning the properties of rectangles, rhombuses and squares.	1	1	1
6–4	Use the properties of parallelograms to establish geometric relationships for triangles and parallel lines.	1	1	1
6–5	State and apply theorems relating to the properties of trapezoids.	1	1	1
6–6	Sketch and describe solutions to locus problems.	$1\frac{1}{2}$	2	$1\frac{1}{2}$
6–7	State and apply theorems relating to locus.	$1\frac{1}{2}$	2	$1\frac{1}{2}$
Review		1	1	1
Test		1	1	1
Cumulative Test		2	2	2
Practice for Standardized Tests 2		1	1	1
Total		13 days	14 days	13 days

Quadrilaterals

Chapter 6

The designer and the builder of the deck shown have applied many of the properties of the quadrilaterals that will be presented in this chapter.

1. What two relationships seem to be true about the boards that form the top and bottom edges of the stair railings?

2. What seems to be true about the vertical supports at each end of the stair railings? the vertical slats, or *balusters*?

Warm-Up Review

Warm-Up Review

1. Name four methods used to prove triangles congruent. SSS; SAS; ASA; AAS
2. If two parallel lines are cut by a transversal, then interior angles on the same side are __?__. Supplementary
3. A(n) __?__ separates a segment or angle into two ≅ parts. Bisector
4. A four-sided polygon is a(n) __?__. Quadrilateral

6-1 Parallelograms and Their Properties

The stair railing of the deck on page 238 is shaped like quadrilateral *ABCD*. The answers to the questions on page 238 suggest that *ABCD* is a parallelogram.

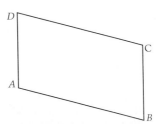

Definition *Parallelogram*

A parallelogram is a quadrilateral in which both pairs of opposite sides are parallel.

We write parallelogram *ABCD* as ▱*ABCD*.

Several properties of parallelograms are evident in the stair railing. For instance, the balusters are the same length. This property is stated in Theorem 6-1, for which a paragraph proof is shown.

Theorem 6-1

Both pairs of opposite sides of a parallelogram are equal.

Given ▱*ABCD*

Prove $AB = DC$ and $BC = AD$

Proof Draw $\overline{BD}$. By the Reflexive Property, $BD = DB$. Since $\overline{AB} \parallel \overline{DC}$ and $\overline{BC} \parallel \overline{AD}$, $m\angle 1 = m\angle 2$ and $m\angle 3 = m\angle 4$ because they are alternate interior angles. So, $\triangle ABD \cong \triangle CDB$ by the ASA Postulate. Therefore, $AB = DC$ and $BC = AD$, because corresponding parts of congruent triangles are equal.

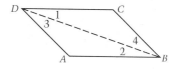

Example 1

Given ▱*PQRS*, if $PS = 6x + 5$, $PQ = 4x + 15$, and $QR = 5x + 7$, then $SR = \underline{?}$.

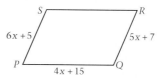

Solution

$$PS = QR \qquad \text{Theorem 6-1}$$
$$6x + 5 = 5x + 7$$
$$x = 2$$

Substitute 2 for x in $PQ = 4x + 15$.
$$PQ = 4(2) + 15 = 8 + 15 = 23$$
Since $PQ = SR$, $SR = 23$.

LESSON 6–1

Resources

Ruler
Teaching Aid 1, protractor
Visual Aid 1, protractor
Readiness Worksheet 3
Worksheet 6–1
Extension 6–1
Computer Activities 6–1

OBJECTIVE

State and apply theorems concerning the properties of parallelograms.

TEACHING NOTES

You may wish to introduce this lesson by using **concrete materials**. Have students measure the

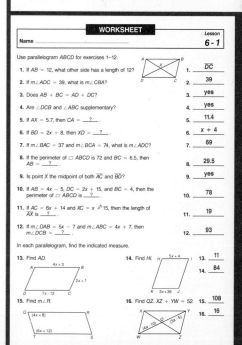

WORKSHEET

Name _____

Lesson 6-1

Use parallelogram *ABCD* for exercises 1–12.

1. If $AB = 12$, what other side has a length of 12? **1.** $\overline{DC}$
2. If $m\angle ADC = 39$, what is $m\angle CBA$? **2.** 39
3. Does $AB + BC = AD + DC$? **3.** yes
4. Are $\angle DCB$ and $\angle ABC$ supplementary? **4.** yes
5. If $AX = 5.7$, then $CA = \underline{?}$. **5.** 11.4
6. If $BD = 2x + 8$, then $XD = \underline{?}$. **6.** $x + 4$
7. If $m\angle BAC = 37$ and $m\angle BCA = 74$, what is $m\angle ADC$? **7.** 69
8. If the perimeter of ▱ *ABCD* is 72 and $BC = 6.5$, then $AB = \underline{?}$. **8.** 29.5
9. Is point *X* the midpoint of both $\overline{AC}$ and $\overline{BD}$? **9.** yes
10. If $AB = 4x - 5$, $DC = 2x + 15$, and $BC = 4$, then the perimeter of ▱ *ABCD* is $\underline{?}$. **10.** 78
11. If $AC = 6x + 14$ and $XC = x + 15$, then the length of $\overline{AX}$ is $\underline{?}$. **11.** 19
12. If $m\angle DAB = 5x - 7$ and $m\angle ABC = 4x + 7$, then $m\angle DCB = \underline{?}$. **12.** 93

In each parallelogram, find the indicated measure.

13. Find *AD*. **13.** 11
14. Find *HI*. **14.** 84
15. Find $m\angle R$. **15.** 108
16. Find *QZ*. $XZ + YW = 52$ **16.** 16

sides and angles of several different parallelograms with a ruler and protractor, and ask them for conclusions. Try having students fold, crease and tear parallelograms along a diagonal, and then compare the various parts of the two triangles. To determine how to prove the triangles congruent, have students move the triangles back and forth between their original and superimposed positions. Practicing the **proof subskill** of writing a plan for a proof could follow this **activity**.

Theorem 6–3 may also be introduced by having students either measure the two parts of each diagonal or fold the parallelogram and observe how one segment of a diagonal reflects exactly onto the other.

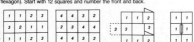
The opposite angles of each baluster are equal. This property is stated in Theorem 6-2, which is to be proved in Exercise 11.

Theorem 6-2

Both pairs of opposite angles of a parallelogram are equal.

Given $\square ABCD$

Prove $m\angle DAB = m\angle BCD$; $m\angle ABC = m\angle CDA$

Plan for Proof   Draw the diagonals. Show $\triangle ABD \cong \triangle CDB$ and $\triangle ADC \cong \triangle CBA$.

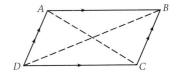

Another property of parallelograms is stated in Theorem 6-3. Its proof is left to Exercise 21.

Theorem 6-3

The diagonals of a parallelogram bisect each other.

Given $\square ABCD$ with diagonals $\overline{AC}$ and $\overline{BD}$ intersecting at Q

Prove $\overline{AC}$ and $\overline{BD}$ bisect each other.

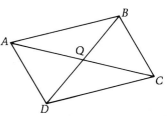

Example 2

Given $\square QRST$, if QS is 6 more than 2 times RT, and $RV = 9$, then $QV = \underline{\ ?\ }$.

Solution

By Theorem 6-3, $RT = 2RV$. Since $RV = 9$, $RT = 18$.

Substitute 18 for RT in $QS = 6 + 2RT$.
$QS = 6 + 2(9) = 6 + 18 = 24$

By Theorem 6-3, $QS = 2QV$. Substitute 24 for QS.
$24 = 2QV$ and $QV = 12$.

Summary Properties of Parallelograms

Opposite sides are parallel.	Opposite angles are equal.
Opposite sides are equal.	Diagonals bisect each other.

Assignment Guide

Basic: 1–15, 27–33
Average: 1–24, 27–33
Extended: 2–14 (even), 15–33

The distance between two parallel lines is the length of a segment drawn from any point on one line perpendicular to the other line. Thus, the distance between parallel lines m and n at the right is AB, CD, or EF. Theorem 6-4, to be proved in Exercise 22, establishes that these distances are equal.

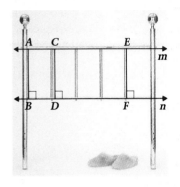

Theorem 6-4

The distance between two given parallel lines is constant.

Given $\ell \parallel k$; P and Q are any two points on ℓ; $\overline{PR} \perp k$; $\overline{QS} \perp k$

Prove $PR = QS$

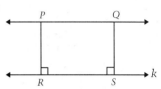

Checking for Understanding

1. Write Theorem 6-1 in "if . . . then" form.

2. In $\square ABCD$, if $AB = 12$ and $BC = 7$, then $CD = \underline{?}$. **12**

3. In $\square QRST$, if $m\angle Q = 130$, then $m\angle S = \underline{?}$ **130** and $m\angle T = \underline{?}$. **50**

4. Tell why $m\angle 1 = m\angle 2$ in the proof of Theorem 6-1.   **4. 2 lines $\parallel \Rightarrow$ alt. int. $\angle$s=.**

5. In $\square ABCD$, if $\overline{AC}$ intersects $\overline{BD}$ at Q, $AQ = 6$, and $DQ = 10$, then $DB = \underline{?}$. **20**

6. How do you know that $PRSQ$ in Theorem 6-4 is a parallelogram?

7. In $\square ABCD$, angles A and B are *consecutive angles* of the polygon. Explain why any two consecutive angles of a parallelogram are supplementary. **2 lines $\parallel \Rightarrow$ int. $\angle$s on same side of transversal supp.**

Written Exercises

Set A   Given $\square HIJK$

1. If $HI = 18$, find KJ. **18**   2. If $HO = 10$, find HJ. **20**

3. If $m\angle HIJ = 135$, find $m\angle HKJ$. **135**

4. If the distance from K to $\overleftrightarrow{HI}$ is 15, what is the distance from I to $\overleftrightarrow{KJ}$? **15**

In the road sign at the right, the black portion is formed by congruent parallelograms $ABCD$ and $CDEF$.

5. If $m\angle ADE = 117$, then $m\angle B = \underline{?}$. **$58\frac{1}{2}$**

6. AD is 5 more than AB and $EF = 5.75$. Find FC. **10.75**

Additional Examples

Example 1

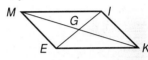

Given: $\square SUAN$;
$SU = 5x - 4$;
$UA = 2x + 5$;
$NA = 4x + 3$
Find SN. 19

Example 2

Given: $\square MIKE$, with diagonals intersecting at point G. If the length of MK is two less than four times the length of $\overline{IE}$, and $IG = 5$, then $MG = \underline{?}$. 19

Example 3
Given: $\square WXYZ$; $m\angle W = 6x + 10$;
$m\angle Y = 8x - 14$
Find $m\angle W$. 82

Error Analysis   In algebraic problems, remind students to reread the problem after solving the equation(s) and check what is asked for. Students have a tendency to stop when a value for the variable is obtained.

ANSWERS

Checking for Understanding

1. If a quadrilateral is a $\square$, then both pairs of opposite sides are =.
6. Since $\ell \parallel k$, $\overline{PQ} \parallel \overline{RS}$. $\overline{PR} \parallel \overline{QS}$ because both $\overline{PR}$ and $\overline{QS}$ are $\perp$ to the same line.

Written Exercises

16. Proof: 1. ▱CTGD (Given) 2. CD = GT (Opp. sides of a ▱ are =. [1]) 3. m∠D = m∠T (Opp. ∠s of a ▱ are =. [1]) 4. $\overleftrightarrow{CO}$ ⊥ $\overleftrightarrow{DG}$ and $\overleftrightarrow{AG}$ ⊥ $\overleftrightarrow{CT}$ (Given) 5. ∠COD and ∠GAT are rt. ∠s. (Def. of ⊥ lines [4]) 6. m∠COD = m∠GAT (All rt. ∠s are =. [5]) 7. △COD ≅ △GAT (AAS Thm. [2, 3, 6])

17. Proof: 1. ▱GRIN; ▱GLAD (Given) 2. m∠G = m∠I; m∠G = m∠A (Opp. ∠s of a ▱ are =. [1]) 3. m∠I = m∠A (Subs. Prop. [2])

21. Proof: 1. ▱ABCD (Given) 2. AB = CD (Opp. sides of a ▱ are =. [1]) 3. $\overline{AB}$ ∥ $\overline{CD}$ (Def. of ▱ [1]) 4. m∠ABD = m∠CDB; m∠BAC = m∠DCA (2 lines ∥ ⇒ alt. int. ∠s =. [3]) 5. △ABQ ≅ △CDQ (ASA ≅ Post. [2, 4]) 6. AQ = CQ; BQ = DQ (Corres. parts of ≅ △s are =. [5]) 7. Q is the midpt. of both $\overline{AC}$ and $\overline{BD}$. (Def. of midpt. [6]) 8. $\overline{AC}$ and $\overline{BD}$ bisect each other. (Def. of seg. bisector [7])

22. Proof: 1. ℓ ∥ k; P and Q are any two pts. on ℓ; $\overrightarrow{PR}$ ⊥ k; $\overrightarrow{QS}$ ⊥ k (Given) 2. $\overrightarrow{PR}$ ∥ $\overrightarrow{QS}$ (In a plane, 2 lines ⊥ to the same line ⇒ 2 lines ∥. [1]) 3. PQSR is a ▱. (Def. of ▱ [1, 2]) 4. PR = QS (Opp. sides of a ▱ are =. [3])

23. Proof: 1. ▱EFGH; EG = FH (Given) 2. $\overline{EF}$ ∥ $\overline{HG}$ (Def. of ▱ [1]) 3. ∠HEF and ∠EHG are supp. (2 lines ∥ ⇒ int. ∠s on same side supp. [2]) 4. m∠HEF + m∠EHG = 180 (Def. of supp. ∠s [3]) 5. EF = HG (Opp. sides of ▱ are =. [1]) 6. HE = EH (Reflexive Prop.) 7. △HEF ≅ △EHG (SSS ≅ Post. [1, 5, 6]) 8. m∠HEF = m∠EHG (Corres. parts of ≅ △s are =. [7]) 9. m∠HEF + m∠HEF = 180 or 2(m∠HEF) = 180. (Substitution Prop. [4, 8]) 10. m∠HEF = 90 (Mult. Prop. [9]) 11. ∠HEF is a rt. ∠. (Def. of rt. ∠ [10])

25. Proof: 1. △MNQ is equilateral; m∠1 = m∠2 = m∠N (Given) 2. △MNQ is equiangular. (Equilateral △ is equiangular. [1]) 3. m∠Q = m∠N (Def. of equiangular △ [2])

---

7. The DeCarlo family needs to replace several balusters in a railing. Which theorem guarantees that the balusters have the same length? **Thm. 6-4**

Given ▱ABCD

8. m∠A = 5x + 9 and m∠C = 2x + 24. Find x. **5**

9. AB = 3y + 5; AD = y + 2; DC = 2y + 10. Find BC. **7**

10. $\overline{AC}$ and $\overline{BD}$ intersect at Q. AQ = 7r − 12 and QC = 4r + 27. Find AC. **158**

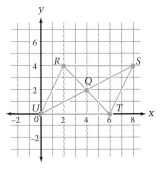

11. Complete this proof of Theorem 6-2.
Given: ▱ABCD
Prove: m∠DAB = m∠BCD; m∠ADC = m∠CBA

Statements	Reasons
1. ▱ABCD	1. Given
2. Draw $\overline{AC}$ and $\overline{BD}$.	2. $\underline{\ ?\ }$ Line Post.
3. AC = CA; BD = DB	3. $\underline{\ ?\ }$ Reflexive Post.
4. AB = CD; BC = DA	4. $\underline{\ ?\ }$ Opp. sides of a ▱ are =. [1]
5. $\underline{\ ?\ }$ △DAB ≅ △BCD	5. SSS Post. [3, 4]
6. m∠DAB = m∠BCD	6. $\underline{\ ?\ }$ Def. of ≅ △s [5]
7. $\underline{\ ?\ }$ △ADC ≅ △CBA	7. SSS Post. [3, 4]
8. m∠ADC = m∠ABC	8. $\underline{\ ?\ }$ Def. of ≅ △s [7]

Given ▱RSTU; $\overline{RT}$ and $\overline{SU}$ intersect at Q.

12. Find TS. **2√5** **13.** Find RT. **4√2** **14.** Find US. **4√5**

15. Find the coordinates for point Q. **(4, 2)**

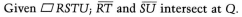

Set B

16. Given: ▱CTGD; $\overline{CO}$ ⊥ $\overline{DG}$ and $\overline{AG}$ ⊥ $\overline{CT}$
Prove: △COD ≅ △GAT

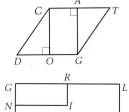

17. Given: ▱GRIN; ▱GLAD
Prove: m∠A = m∠I

Given: ▱TAXI

18. If TM = 3x and TX = 3x + 18, find TM. **18**

19. If MI = 6y − 5 and AI = 2y + 15, find AI. **20**

20. If m∠ATI = x + 20, m∠AXI = 2x + y, and m∠TIX = x − y, find m∠ATI. **80**

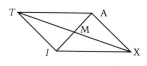

21. Prove Theorem 6-3. **22.** Prove Theorem 6-4.

23. Given: ▱ EFGH; EG = FH
Prove: ∠HEF is a right angle.

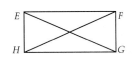

24. Given ▱ ABCD with diagonals intersecting at Q;
A(−3, 9), B(6, 9), and Q(3, 4). Find the coordinates
of C and D. **C(9, −1); D(0, −1)**

Set C **25.** Given: △MNQ is equilateral; m∠1 = m∠2 = m∠N
Prove: PQRS is a parallelogram.

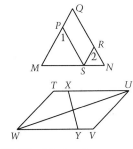

26. Given: ▱ TUVW; TX = VY
Prove: $\overline{XY}$ bisects $\overline{UW}$.

▲ Review **27.** If $\overleftrightarrow{PD} \perp \overleftrightarrow{CD}$, which of the following is true? Why?

$PD > PC \qquad PD < PC \qquad PD = PC$

27. PD<PC; the ⊥ segment
from a pt. to a line is the
shortest segment from the pt.
to the line.

28. Find the distance from A(6, 3) to line ℓ whose
equation is x = 1. **5**

29. In △QSV, m∠S = 44 and m∠V = 55. Which side
of △QSV is longest? **S̄V̄**

30. Planes G and H are both perpendicular to line m.
How are planes G and H related? **G ‖ H**

31. Write an "if . . . then" statement for the Venn
diagram at the right. **If a figure is a pentagon,
then it is a convex polygon.**

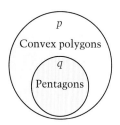

≡ Thinking Ahead **32.** Close to the left side of a lined paper, draw a
segment on a line. Several lines down and to the
right, draw another segment on a line equal in
length to the first. Connect the endpoints to form
a quadrilateral. Describe the quadrilateral. **It is a ▱**

33. Use two strips of paper of one length and two of
another length to form a quadrilateral. Place the
strips of equal length opposite each other. What
kind of quadrilateral is formed? **▱**

💻 Computer Activities: Drawing and Measuring

Draw two segments that bisect each other. Connect the four
endpoints of the segments to form a quadrilateral.

1. What kind of quadrilateral is formed? **▱**

2. Repeat the activity with three more pairs of segments. What conjecture can
you make regarding a quadrilateral whose diagonals bisect each other?
If the diagonals of a quad. bisect each other, then the quad is a ▱

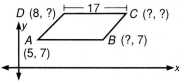

4. m∠Q = m∠2; m∠Q = m∠1
(Substitution Prop. [1, 3]) **5.** $\overline{PQ}$ ‖
$\overline{SR}$; $\overline{QR}$ ‖ $\overline{PS}$ (Corres. ∠s = ⇒
lines ‖. [4]) **6.** PQRS is a ▱. (Def.
of ▱ [5])
26. Proof: **1.** ▱ TUVW; TX = VY
(Given) **2.** TU = WV (Opp. sides of
▱ are =. [1]) **3.** TU = TX + XU;
WV = WY + YV (Seg. Add. Post.)
4. TX + XU = WY + YV (Substitution Prop. [2, 3]) **5.** XU = WY
(Subtraction Prop. [1, 4]) **6.** m∠
XZU = m∠YZW (Vert. ∠s are =.)
7. $\overline{TU}$ ‖ $\overline{WV}$ (Def. of ▱ [1]) **8.**
m∠XUZ = m∠YWZ (Lines ⇒ alt.
int. ∠s =. [7]) **9.** △XZU ≅ △YZW
(AAS ≅ Thm. [5, 6, 8]) **10.** WZ =
UZ (Corres. parts of ≅ △s are =.
[9]) **11.** Z is the midpt. of WU.
(Def. of midpt. [10]) **12.** $\overline{XY}$ bisects
$\overline{WU}$. (Def. of seg. bisector [11])

FOLLOW-UP

More Practice

• **Worksheet 6–1**

Extension

Solve the following problems.

1. Find the missing coordinates of
vertices B, C and D. (22, 7);
(25, 11); (8, 11)
2. Find the coordinates of the
point of intersection of diagonals
$\overline{AC}$ and $\overline{BD}$. (15, 9)
• **Extension 6–1**

Computers

The computer activity in the pu-
pil's book can be completed using
*The Geometric preSupposer:
Points and Lines* or *GeoDraw*.
• **Computer Activities 6–1**

LESSON 6–2

Resources

Compass
Construction paper
Straightedge
Straws
Teaching Aid 5, graphs
Visual Aid 5, graphs
Worksheet 6–2
Extension 6–2
Computer Activities 6–2

OBJECTIVE

State and apply theorems that prove a given quadrilateral is a parallelogram.

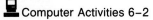

WORKSHEET

Name _____   Lesson **6-2**

Determine the value of x and y to change each quadrilateral to a parallelogram.

1. $x = \underline{3}$; $y = \underline{2}$
2. $x = \underline{2}$; $y = \underline{6}$
3. $x = \underline{4.5}$; $y = \underline{7.5}$
4. $x = \underline{8}$; $y = \underline{7}$
5. $x = \underline{-8}$; $y = \underline{0}$
6. $x = \underline{12}$; $y = \underline{8.5}$

6-2 Quadrilaterals That Are Parallelograms

To make a pattern for the roof in the schoolhouse quilt block, Ellen Huerta drew a segment 6 inches long on a line of ruled paper. Then she drew a 60° angle at one end of the segment. She drew another segment 6 inches long on another line and formed a quadrilateral as shown. Theorem 6-5 guarantees that the quadrilateral is a parallelogram.

Theorem 6-5

If two sides of a quadrilateral are parallel and equal, then the quadrilateral is a parallelogram.

Given Quadrilateral $ABCD$; $\overline{AB} \parallel \overline{DC}$; $AB = CD$

Prove $ABCD$ is a parallelogram.

Plan for Proof Draw $\overline{BD}$. Show $\triangle ABD \cong \triangle CDB$. Then show $\overline{AD} \parallel \overline{BC}$.

Proof

Statements	Reasons
1. Quadrilateral $ABCD$; $\overline{AB} \parallel \overline{DC}$; $AB = CD$	1. Given Line
2. Draw $\overline{BD}$.	2. _?_ Postulate
3. $BD = DB$	3. _?_ Reflexive Prop.
4. $m\angle 1 = m\angle 2$	4. 2 lines $\parallel \Rightarrow$ _?_. [1] alt. int. $\angle$s =
5. $\triangle ABD \cong \triangle CDB$	5. SAS Post. [1, 3, 4]
6. $m\angle 3 = m\angle 4$	6. _?_ [5]Corr. parts of $\cong \triangle$s are =.
7. $\overline{AD} \parallel \overline{BC}$	7. Alt. int. $\angle$s = $\Rightarrow$ _?_. [6]
8. $ABCD$ is a $\square$.	8. Def. of $\square$ [1, 7]2 lines $\parallel$

You found in Exercises 32 and 33 of Lesson 6-1 that a quadrilateral whose opposite sides have equal length is a parallelogram. This conclusion is supported by Theorem 6-6, which is to be proved in Exercise 15. What kind of figure is formed if pairs of equal sides are adjacent? A kite

Theorem 6-6

If both pairs of opposite sides of a quadrilateral are equal, then the quadrilateral is a parallelogram.

Given Quadrilateral $ABCD$; $AB = CD$; $BC = AD$

Prove $ABCD$ is a parallelogram.

Plan for Proof Draw $\overline{BD}$. Show $\triangle ABD \cong \triangle CDB$. Then show $m\angle 1 = m\angle 2$, so that $\overline{AB} \parallel \overline{CD}$. Then use Theorem 6-5.

Example 1

$QUAD$ is a quadrilateral with $Q(-3, -2)$, $U(2, -1)$, $A(4, 5)$, and $D(-1, 4)$. Show that $QUAD$ is a parallelogram.

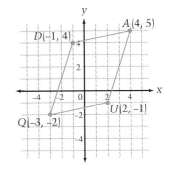

Solution

By Theorem 6-6, $QUAD$ is a parallelogram if *both* pairs of opposite sides are equal. Use the Distance Formula.

$UQ = \sqrt{(-3-2)^2 + (-2-(-1))^2} = \sqrt{25+1} = \sqrt{26}$

$DA = \sqrt{(4-(-1))^2 + (5-4)^2} = \sqrt{25+1} = \sqrt{26}$

$AU = \sqrt{(2-4)^2 + (-1-5)^2} = \sqrt{4+36} = \sqrt{40}$

$QD = \sqrt{(-1-(-3))^2 + (4-(-2))^2} = \sqrt{4+36} = \sqrt{40}$

$UQ = DA$ and $AU = QD$, so $QUAD$ is a parallelogram.

You could also use the definition of parallelogram.

The slope of $\overleftrightarrow{DQ}$ $\left(\frac{4-(-2)}{-1-(-3)}\right)$ and of $\overleftrightarrow{AU}$ $\left(\frac{5-(-1)}{4-2}\right)$ is $\frac{6}{2}$, so $\overline{DQ} \parallel \overline{AU}$.

The slope of $\overleftrightarrow{DA}$ $\left(\frac{5-4}{4-(-1)}\right)$ and of $\overleftrightarrow{QU}$ $\left(\frac{-1-(-2)}{2-(-3)}\right)$ is $\frac{1}{5}$, so $\overline{DA} \parallel \overline{QU}$.

The following theorem is the converse of Theorem 6-3.
The proof of Theorem 6-7 is left to Exercise 16.

Theorem 6-7

If the diagonals of a quadrilateral bisect each other, then the quadrilateral is a parallelogram.

Given $ABCD$; diagonals $\overline{AC}$ and $\overline{BD}$ bisect each other.

Prove $ABCD$ is a parallelogram.

Plan for Proof Show $\triangle AOB \cong \triangle COD$, so that $AB = CD$. Then show $\overline{AB} \parallel \overline{CD}$. Finally use Theorem 6-5.

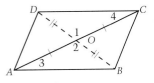

Example 2

How do you know that quadrilateral $GRAM$ is a parallelogram,

a. if $AM = GR$; $MG = AR$?   **b.** if $\overline{MG} \parallel \overline{AR}$; $\overline{MA} \parallel \overline{GR}$?

c. if $m\angle 3 = m\angle 4$; $MG = 10$; $AR = 10$?

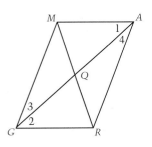

Solution

a. If both pairs of opposite sides of a quadrilateral are equal, then the quadrilateral is a parallelogram. (Theorem 6-6)

b. A parallelogram is a quadrilateral in which both pairs of opposite sides are parallel. (Definition)

c. If two sides of a quadrilateral are parallel and equal, then the quadrilateral is a parallelogram. (Theorem 6-5)

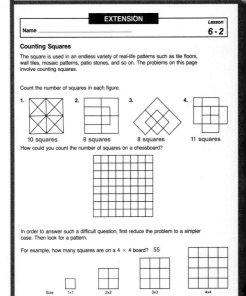

Additional Examples

Example 1

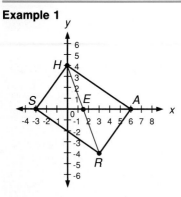

SHAR is a quadrilateral with vertices $S(-3, 0)$, $H(0, 4)$, $A(6, 0)$ and $R(3, -4)$. Show that *SHAR* is a parallelogram. $SH = RA = 5$; slope $SH =$ slope $RA = \frac{4}{3}$

Example 2

State the definition or theorem that shows that quadrilateral *SHAR* is a parallelogram.

(a) $SH = AR$; $\overline{SH} \parallel \overline{AR}$ If a pair of opposite sides is = and $\parallel$, the quadrilateral is a $\square$.

(b) $EH = \frac{1}{2}RH$; $EA = \frac{1}{2}SA$ Diagonals of a $\square$ bisect each other.

(c) $m\angle S = m\angle A$; $m\angle H = m\angle R$ Opposite $\angle$s of a $\square$ are =.

(d) $SH = RA$; $SR = HA$ Definition of a $\square$

Error Analysis It should be stressed that the application of Theorem 6–5 requires the use of the same pair of sides for both the parallel and equal parts of the example. It is not sufficient to show that one pair of opposite sides is parallel and the other pair equal (counterexample: isosceles trapezoid).

Summary Ways to Prove a Quadrilateral is a Parallelogram

Show that: both pairs of opposite sides are parallel.
one pair of opposite sides are parallel and equal.
both pairs of opposite sides are equal.
the diagonals bisect each other.

Checking for Understanding

1. Why are the triangles congruent in the proof for Theorem 6-6? SSS Post.

2. Why are the triangles congruent in the proof for Theorem 6-7? SAS Post.

Which definition or theorem justifies that *ABCD* is a parallelogram?

3. Given: $CD = AB$; $\overline{CD} \parallel \overline{AB}$ Thm. 6-5

4. Given: $m\angle 1 = m\angle 2$; $m\angle 3 = m\angle 4$ Thm. 4-4, def. of $\square$

5. Given: X is the midpoint of $\overline{BD}$ and $\overline{AC}$. Thm. 6-7

6. Quadrilateral *EFGH* has a pair of equal sides and a pair of parallel sides. Is it necessarily a parallelogram? Explain. No: the same two sides must be $\parallel$ and =.

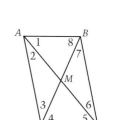

Written Exercises **3.** $x = 50$; Thm. 4-4, def of $\square$.

Set A Find x so that *ABCD* is a parallelogram. Tell which definition or theorem justifies your answer.

1. $MA = 10$; $MC = 10$; $MD = 9$; $MB = x$ $x = 9$; Thm. 6-7

2. $AD = 7$; $AB = 12$; $CD = 12$; $BC = x$ $x = 7$; Thm. 6-6

3. $m\angle 1 = x$; $m\angle 3 = 40$; $m\angle 5 = 50$; $m\angle 7 = 40$

4. $MD = 6$; $MB = 6$; $CA = 17$; $CM = x$ $x = 8.5$; Thm. 6-7

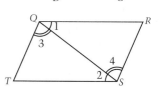

5. Given: $m\angle 1 = m\angle 2$; $m\angle 3 = m\angle 4$
Prove: *QRST* is a parallelogram.

Statements	Reasons
1. $m\angle 1 = m\angle 2$	1. _?_ Given
2. $\overline{QR} \parallel \overline{ST}$	2. _?_ Alt. int. $\angle$s = $\Rightarrow$ 2 lines $\parallel$. [1]
3. $m\angle 3 = m\angle 4$	3. _?_ Given
4. $\overline{QT} \parallel$ _?_	4. _?_ $\overline{RS}$; alt. int. $\angle$s = $\Rightarrow$ 2 lines $\parallel$. [3]
5. *QRST* is a $\square$.	5. _?_ Def. of $\square$. [2, 4]

Sketch a counterexample to show that each statement does *not* guarantee a quadrilateral is a parallelogram.

Samples:

6. The diagonals are perpendicular.

6.   **7.**

7. One diagonal is the perpendicular bisector of the other.

Prove that *JKLM* is a parallelogram.

8. Given: $\overline{JK} \parallel \overline{ML}$; $JX = LX$

9. Given: $m\angle 1 = m\angle 2$; $m\angle MJK = m\angle KLM$

10. Give two ways to show that *PARE* is a parallelogram given the quadrilateral with vertices $P(-2, 0)$, $A(4, 0)$, $R(6, 3)$, and $E(0, 3)$.

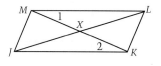

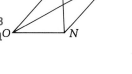

Set B Find x and y so that *KMNO* is a parallelogram. $x = 13$; $y = 6$

11. $KM = x + y$; $MN = 2y + 6$; $ON = 2x - 7$; $KO = 3y$

12. $KM = x + y$; $ON = 3x - 4y$; $m\angle MKN = x + 5$; $m\angle KNO = 2x - 10$ $x = 15$; $y = 6$

13. $m\angle KOM = 6y + 1$; $m\angle KMO = 3x + 2$; **13.** $x = 6$; $y = 3$ $m\angle MON = 2x + 8$; $m\angle OMN = 4y + 7$ **14.** $x = 5$; $y = 1$

14. $KP = 2x + 4$; $MP = 6 + 3y$; $NP = 15 - y$; $OP = x + 4$

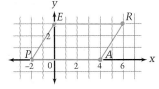

15. Prove Theorem 6-6. **16.** Prove Theorem 6-7.

17. Given: $\Box HIJK$; $m\angle 1 = m\angle 2$
Prove: *HXJY* is a parallelogram.

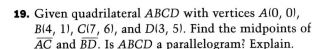

18. Given a quadrilateral *DEFG* with vertices $D(-3, 2)$, $E(2, -3)$, $F(6, 0)$, and $G(1, 5)$. Is *DEFG* a parallelogram? Support your answer in two ways.

19. Given quadrilateral *ABCD* with vertices $A(0, 0)$, $B(4, 1)$, $C(7, 6)$, and $D(3, 5)$. Find the midpoints of $\overline{AC}$ and $\overline{BD}$. Is *ABCD* a parallelogram? Explain.

20. Given: $AX = CX$; $CY = BY$; $XY = YZ$
Prove: *ABZX* is a parallelogram.

21. State and prove the converse of Theorem 6-2.

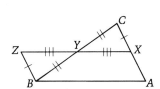

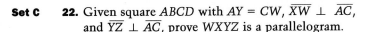

Set C **22.** Given square *ABCD* with $AY = CW$, $\overline{XW} \perp \overline{AC}$, and $\overline{YZ} \perp \overline{AC}$, prove *WXYZ* is a parallelogram.

23. Prove: If the sum of the lengths of every two consecutive sides of a quadrilateral is constant, then the quadrilateral is a parallelogram.

24. Given: *FINE*; $IF = FE = EN$; $m\angle E = m\angle I$
Prove: *FINE* is a parallelogram.

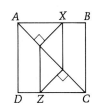

Written Exercises

10. Use = slopes to show opp. sides are ∥; use the Distance Formula to show opp. sides are =.

15. Proof: 1. Quadrilateral *ABCD*; $AB = CD$; $BC = AD$ (Given) 2. Draw $\overline{BD}$. (Line Post.) 3. $BD = BD$ (Reflexive Prop.) 4. $\triangle BCD \cong \triangle DAB$ (SSS ≅ Post. [1, 3]) 5. $m\angle 1 = m\angle 2$ (Corres. parts of ≅ △s are =. [4]) 6. $\overleftrightarrow{CD} \parallel \overleftrightarrow{AB}$ (Alt. int. ∠s = ⇒ lines ∥.) 7. *ABCD* is a ▱ (If 2 sides of a quad. are ∥ and =, then the quad. is a ▱. [1, 6])

16. Proof: 1. Quadrilateral *ABCD*; $\overline{AC}$ and $\overline{BD}$ bisect each other. (Given) 2. *O* is midpt. of $\overline{AC}$; *O* is midpt. of $\overline{BD}$. (Def. of seg. bisector [1]) 3. $AO = OC$; $DO = OB$ (Def. of midpt. [2]) 4. $m\angle 1 = m\angle 2$ (Vert. ∠s are =.) 5. $\triangle JOC \cong \triangle BOA$ (SAS ≅ Post. [3, 4]) 6. $DC = AB$ and $m\angle 3 = m\angle 4$ (Corres. parts of ≅ △s are =. [5]) 7. $\overrightarrow{DC} \parallel \overrightarrow{AB}$ (Alt. int. ∠s = ⇒ lines ∥. [6]) 8. *ABCD* is a ▱. (If 2 sides of a quad. are ∥ and =, then the quad. is a ▱. [6, 7])

17. Proof: 1. $\Box HIJK$; $m\angle 1 = m\angle 2$ (Given) 2. $HK = JI$ (Opp. sides of ▱ are =. [1]) 3. $m\angle K = m\angle I$ (Opp. ∠s of ▱ are =. [1]) 4. $\triangle KXH \cong \triangle IYJ$ (ASA ≅ Post. [1, 2, 3]) 5. $m\angle KXH = m\angle IYJ$ and $HX = JY$. (Corres. parts of ≅ △s are =. [4]) 6. $\overline{HI} \parallel \overline{KJ}$ (Def. of ▱ [1]) 7. $m\angle IYJ = m\angle KJY$ (Lines ∥ ⇒ alt. int. ∠s =. [6]) 8. $m\angle KXH = m\angle KJY$ (Transitive Prop. [5, 7]) 9. $\overline{HX} \parallel \overline{JY}$ (Corres. ∠s = ⇒ lines ∥. [8]) 10. *HXJY* is a ▱. (If 2 sides ∥ and =, then quad. is ▱. [5, 9])

18. Yes: 1) slope of $\overleftrightarrow{DE}$ = slope of $\overleftrightarrow{FG}$ = -1 ⇒ $\overleftrightarrow{DE} \parallel \overleftrightarrow{FG}$ and slope of $\overleftrightarrow{EF}$ = slope of $\overleftrightarrow{DG}$ = $\frac{3}{4}$ ⇒ $\overleftrightarrow{EF} \parallel \overleftrightarrow{DG}$; 2) midpt. of $\overline{DF}$ = midpt. of $\overline{EG}$ = $\left(\frac{3}{2}, 1\right)$ ⇒ $\overline{DG}$ and $\overline{EG}$ bisect each other.

19. Midpt. of $\overline{AC}$ = $\left(\frac{7}{2}, 3\right)$ = midpt. of $\overline{BD}$; this means *ABCD* is a ▱ because the diags. bisect each other.

Review

26. Opp. sides are ∥; opp. sides are =; opp. ∠s are =; diagonals bisect each other.

30. Proof: 1. *Z* is the midpt. of $\overline{XJ}$ and $\overline{KY}$. (Given) 2. *XZ* = *JZ* and *YZ* = *KZ* (Def. of midpt. [1]) 3. *m*∠*XZY* = *m*∠*KZJ* (Vert. ∠s are =.) 4. △*XYZ* ≅ △*JKZ* (SAS ≅ Post. [2, 4])

25. Do the lines $y = x - 4$, $2y = -5x + 62$, $y = x + 3$, and $2y = -5x + 34$ form a parallelogram? Support your answer in two ways.

Review **26.** Give four properties of parallelograms.

27. *ABCD* is a parallelogram. Find the lengths of the sides.

AB = *CD* = 7; *AD* = *BC* = 11

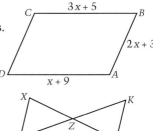

28. Are points *P*(−1, 0), *Q*(0, 1), and *R*(2, 4) collinear? No

29. Give the property of real numbers that justifies the following statement. If 12*x* = 84, then *x* = 7. Division Prop.

30. Given: *Z* is the midpoint of $\overline{YK}$ and $\overline{XJ}$.
Prove: △*XYZ* ≅ △*JKZ*

Thinking Ahead Graph each set of ordered pairs. Join the points in order. Give the most specific name for each figure.

31. *A*(4, 6); *B*(4, 10); *C*(9, 10); *D*(9, 6)

32. *Q*(−2, 5); *R*(1, 5); *S*(1, 8); *T*(−2, 8)

33. *X*(4, −4); *Y*(6, 0); *Z*(4, 4); *W*(2, 0)

34. Use the Distance Formula to find the lengths of the diagonals of *ABCD* and *QRST*. What is true in each case?

35. What appears to be true about the diagonals in *XYZW*?

34. Lengths of diagonals are =.
35. Diagonals are ⊥ bisectors of each other.

💻 Computer Activities: Drawing and Measuring

Draw any quadrilateral *ABCD* with all four sides equal and diagonals intersecting at *E*.

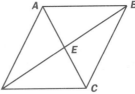

1. Measure the angles at *E*.

2. Measure the two angles at each vertex.

3. Repeat the activity above with five other quadrilaterals whose four sides are equal.

4. Complete this conjecture: If a quadrilateral has all four sides equal, then its diagonals are ⎯?⎯ and each diagonal ⎯?⎯ a pair of opposite angles. ⊥; bisects

Challenge

Find the total number of parallelograms in the drawing at the right. The ten vertical segments are parallel and equal.
9 + 8 + 7 + 6 + 5 + 4 + 3 + 2 + 1 = 45

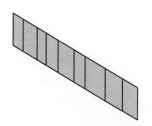

Warm-Up Review

1. If two lines intersect to form right angles, the lines are ___?___. Perpendicular
2. If $m\angle XYZ = 36$ and $\overrightarrow{YX}$ bisects $\angle WYZ$, find $m\angle WYZ$. 72
3. Are all quadrilaterals parallelograms? No
4. Are all parallelograms quadrilaterals? Yes
5. Name the diagonals of quadrilateral SOUP. $\overline{SU}$; $\overline{OP}$

6-3 Rectangles, Rhombuses, and Squares

This stained-glass panel contains three special parallelograms: a rectangle, a rhombus, and a square.

Definition *Rectangle, Rhombus, and Square*

A rectangle is a parallelogram with four right angles.
A rhombus is a parallelogram with four equal sides.
A square is a rectangle with four equal sides.

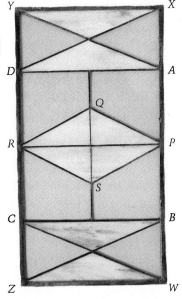

Example 1

In the panel, classify parallelograms *PQRS*, *WXYZ*, and *ABCD*.

Solution

$\square$ *PQRS* has four equal sides, so it is a rhombus.
$\square$ *WXYZ* has four right angles, so it is a rectangle.
$\square$ *ABCD* has four right angles *and* four equal sides, so it is a square.
$\square$ *XADY* also appears to be a rectangle.

Theorem 6-8 guarantees that if $XD = AY$, then $\square$ *XADY* is a rectangle. The proof is left to Exercises 21 and 22.

Theorem 6-8

A parallelogram is a rectangle if and only if its diagonals are equal.

Part I   If $AC = BD$, then $\square$ *ABCD* is a rectangle.

Given $\square$ *ABCD* with $AC = BD$

Prove   *ABCD* is a rectangle.

Plan for Proof   Show $\triangle ABD \cong \triangle BAC$ by SSS. $\angle DAB$ and $\angle CBA$ are equal and supplementary, so the angles are right angles. Similarly, $\angle ADC$ and $\angle BCD$ are right angles, and $\square$ *ABCD* is a rectangle.

Part II   If $\square$ *ABCD* is a rectangle, then $AC = BD$.

Given   *ABCD* is a rectangle.

Prove $AC = BD$

Plan for Proof   Show $\triangle ABD \cong \triangle BAC$ by SAS. Then $AC = BD$. $AD = BC$ and $m\angle DAB = m\angle CBA$.

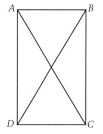

LESSON 6-3

Resources

Teaching Aid 14, quadrilaterals chart
Visual Aid 14, quadrilaterals chart
Worksheet 6–3
Extension 6–3
Computer Activities 6–3
Computer Worksheet 6–3

OBJECTIVE

State and apply theorems concerning the properties of rectangles, rhombuses and squares.

TEACHING NOTES

One way to introduce this lesson is to use **concrete materials** such

---

WORKSHEET   *Lesson* **6-3**

Name _____

Tell whether each statement is *always, sometimes,* or *never* true.

1. A square is a parallelogram.   1. **always**
2. The diagonals of a parallelogram bisect each other.   2. **always**
3. A rectangle is a square.   3. **sometimes**
4. A square is a rectangle.   4. **always**
5. The diagonals of a quadrilateral are perpendicular.   5. **sometimes**
6. A parallelogram is a rhombus.   6. **sometimes**
7. Each diagonal of a rectangle bisects the angles of the rectangle. 7. **sometimes**
8. A square is a rhombus.   8. **always**
9. A rhombus is a square.   9. **sometimes**
10. The diagonals of a rhombus are equal.   10. **sometimes**

Tell whether *ABCD* is a *parallelogram, rectangle, rhombus, square,* or *none of these.* Write the best answer.

11. Given: $AB = DC$ and $BC = AD$ 11. **parallelogram**
12. Given: $\overline{AC}$ and $\overline{BD}$ bisect each other and $\overline{AC} \perp \overline{BD}$ 12. **rhombus**
13. Given: $\overline{AC}$ and $\overline{BD}$ bisect each other and $AC = BD$ 13. **rectangle**
14. Given: $\overline{AC}$ and $\overline{BD}$ are perpendicular bisectors of each other and $AC = BD$ 14. **square**
15. Given: $AB = BC = DC$ 15. **none of these**
16. *QRST* is a rhombus with diagonals $\overline{QS}$ and $\overline{RT}$. If $m\angle SRT = 2(m\angle TQS)$ and the perimeter of the rhombus is 42, then $RT = $ ___?___.   16. **10.5**
17. *ABCD* is a rectangle. The diagonals $\overline{AC}$ and $\overline{BD}$ intersect at point Q. If $m\angle AQB = 4(m\angle BQC)$, find $m\angle QDC$.   17. **18**

as strips of paper to represent the diagonals of a quadrilateral.

1. Label the endpoints of two strips of equal length *A* and *B*, *P* and *Q*.

2. Locate the midpoint of each by folding and marking.

3. Place the midpoint of one directly over the midpoint of the other and draw quadrilateral *APBQ*.

Why must *APBQ* be a parallelogram? Diagonals bisect each other. What kind of quadrilateral does it appear to be? rectangle

Repeat the **activity** with the strips perpendicular. What does *APBQ* appear to be? square

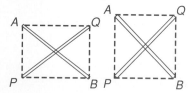

Use strips of unequal lengths to illustrate Theorem 6–9.

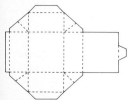
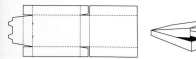

Example 2

Find the value of x so that $\square ABCD$ is a rectangle. $AC = 4x + 15$ and $BD = 2x + 27$.

Solution

By Theorem 6-8, $\square ABCD$ is a rectangle if $AC = BD$. Substitute $4x + 15$ for AC and $2x + 27$ for BD, and solve for x.

$4x + 15 = 2x + 27$, and $x = 6$.

How are $\overline{PR}$ and $\overline{QS}$, the diagonals of rhombus *PQRS* in the stained-glass panel, related? What seems to be true regarding the two angles at each vertex? $\overline{PR} \perp \overline{QS}$; they are =.

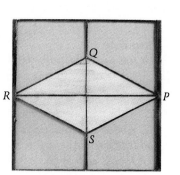

The answers to these questions suggest Theorems 6-9 and 6-10, which are to be proved in Exercises 23 and 24.

Theorem 6-9

A parallelogram is a rhombus if and only if its diagonals are perpendicular.

Theorem 6-10

A parallelogram is a rhombus if and only if each diagonal bisects a pair of opposite angles of the parallelogram.

Example 3

PQRS is a parallelogram with diagonals intersecting at *E* and $m\angle PEQ = 3x + 6$. Find x so that $\square PQRS$ is a rhombus.

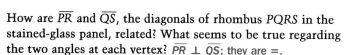

Solution

By Theorem 6-9, $\square PQRS$ is a rhombus if $\overline{PR} \perp \overline{QS}$, or $m\angle PEQ = 90$. Substitute $3x + 6$ for $m\angle PEQ$, and solve for x.

$3x + 6 = 90$, and $x = 28$.

Summary Properties of Quadrilaterals

Properties of Rectangles	Properties of Rhombuses	Properties of Squares
All properties of parallelograms	All properties of parallelograms	All properties of parallelograms
Four right angles	Four equal sides	All properties of rectangles
Equal diagonals	Diagonals that bisect the angles	All properties of rhombuses
	Perpendicular diagonals	

Assignment Guide

Basic: 1–16, 32–37
Average: 1–29, 32–37
Extended: 1–37

Checking for Understanding

1. What is a rhombus with four right angles? **A square**

2. Give the hypothesis and the conclusion for each part of Theorem 6-9.

3. In rectangle $ABCD$, if $AC = 12$, then $BD = \underline{?}$. **12**

4. Given rhombus $QRST$, if $\overline{QS}$ and $\overline{RT}$ intersect at point M, then $m\angle QMR = \underline{?}$. **90**

5. In what type of parallelogram are the diagonals both perpendicular and equal? **Square**

6. Give the hypothesis and the conclusion for each part of Theorem 6-10.

7. If the diagonals of a quadrilateral are perpendicular and bisect each other, is the quadrilateral a rhombus? Explain.

Written Exercises

Set A   The template shown is used to draw flow charts. List all the figures that appear to be

    1. quadrilaterals. **A, B, L, M, O**

    2. rectangles. **B, M**

    3. parallelograms. **A, B, M, O**

    4. rhombuses. **M, O**

    5. rectangles that are not rhombuses. **B**

    6. rhombuses that are not rectangles. **O**

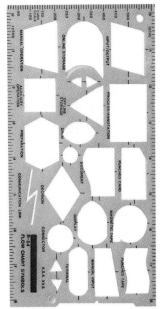

In rectangle $ABCD$, with $\overline{AC}$ and $\overline{BD}$ intersecting at X,

    7. if $AC = 15$ feet, then $BD = \underline{?}$. **15 ft.**

    8. if $BD = 7.5$ yards, then $XC = \underline{?}$. **3.75 yd.**

    9. if $AX = 4y + 12$ and $CX = 2y + 48$, find y and AC. **18; 168**

    10. if $AC = 9p - 35$ and $BD = 4p + 70$, then $p = \underline{?}$. **21**

    11. if $AC = 3x - 8.75$ and $BD = 2x - 4.75$, find x and BD. **4; 3.25**

    12. if $DX = 7s + 11$ and $CX = 3s + 83$, then $AC = \underline{?}$. **2.74**

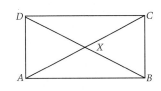

Additional Examples

Example 1

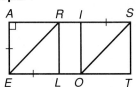

In this design, classify parallelograms $ASTE$ **rectangle**; $ARLE$ **square**; $RIOL$ **rectangle**; and $RSOE$ **rhombus** if $RS = SO$.

Example 2

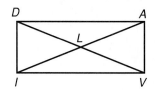

Given: $DV = 5y + 3$; $IA = 7y - 7$
Find DL if $\square DAVI$ is a rectangle. **5**

Example 3

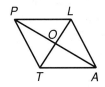

Given: Rhombus $PLAT$ with diagonals intersecting at 0; $m\angle TOP = 8x - 6$
Find x. **12**

Error Analysis   Students tend to think of the set of squares as disjoint from the sets of rectangles, rhombuses and parallelograms. Stress that a square is a rectangle, a rhombus is a parallelogram and so on.

ANSWERS

Written Exercises

13. Sometimes; = diags. proves only that it is a rect.
14. always (Thm. 6–8)
15. Sometimes; the diags. of a ▱ are ⊥ only if the ▱ is a rhombus or a square.
16. Sometimes; it is a rhombus only if the diags. also bisect each other. The diags. of a kite are ⊥.
21. Given: ▱*ABCD*; *AC* = *BD*
Prove: *ABCD* is a rect. Proof: By hypothesis, *ABCD* is a ▱ with *AC* = *BD*. Since *AD* = *BC* and *AB* = *AB*, △*ABD* ≅ △*BAC* by SSS ≅ Post. Then *m∠DAB* = *m∠CBA*. Since *AD* ∥ *BC*, ∠*DAB* and ∠*CBA* are supp. and *m∠DAB* + *m∠CBA* = 180. By the Substitution Prop. and Div. Prop., *m∠DAB* = *m∠CBA* = 90. Therefore, ∠*DAB* and ∠*CBA* are rt. ∠s. Since the opp. ∠s of a ▱ are = and all rt. ∠s are =, ∠*ADC* and ∠*BCD* are rt. ∠s. Then ▱*ABCD* has four rt. ∠s. Therefore, ▱*ABCD* is a rectangle.
22. Given: *ABCD* is a rect. Prove: *AC* = *BD* Proof: By hypothesis, *ABCD* is a rect.; then by the def. of a rect., ∠*DAB* and ∠*CBA* are rt. ∠s. Since all rt. ∠s are =, *m∠DAB* = *m∠CBA*. Since *ABCD* is also a ▱, and opp. sides of a ▱ are =, *AD* = *BC*. By the Reflexive Prop. *AB* = *AB*. So △*ABD* ≅ △*BAC* by SAS ≅ Post. and *AC* = *BD*.
23.

Part I: Given: ▱*ABCD*; *AC* ⊥ *BD*
Prove: *ABCD* is a rhombus. Proof: By hypothesis, *ABCD* is a ▱ with *AC* ⊥ *BD*. Since 2 ⊥ lines inter-

---

Tell whether each statement is *always*, *sometimes*, or *never* true. Explain each answer.

13. A parallelogram with equal diagonals is a square.

14. The diagonals of a rectangle are equal.

15. The diagonals of a parallelogram are perpendicular.

16. If the diagonals of a quadrilateral are perpendicular, then the quadrilateral is a rhombus.

Set B In rhombus *RHOM* with $\overline{HM}$ and $\overline{OR}$ intersecting at *X*,

17. if *m∠RHX* = 62, then *m∠HOX* = ? and *m∠MRX* = ? . **28; 28**

18. find the perimeter if *HO* = 7*p* − 15 and *MO* = 3*p* + 5. **80**

19. find *m∠RMO* and *m∠MOH* if *m∠RMX* = 6*x* + 5 and *m∠MOX* = 4*x* + 10. **100; 80**

20. Find the perimeter of square *JKLM* if *JK* = 4*y* + 12 and *ML* = 6*y* − 3. **168**

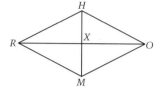

Write a paragraph proof for each of the following.

21. Part I of Theorem 6-8   **22.** Part II of Theorem 6-8

23. Theorem 6-9   **24.** Theorem 6-10

Classify each parallelogram. Support each answer with both a definition and a theorem.

25. ▱*ABCD* with vertices *A*(0, 0), *B*(5, 1), *C*(6, 6), and *D*(1, 5)

26. ▱*EFGH* with vertices *E*(6, 1), *F*(3, −2), *G*(6, −5), and *H*(9, −2)

27. In rhombus *QRST*, *m∠QRS* = 2(*m∠TQR*), and the sum of the lengths of two sides equals 21*n*. Find the length of the shorter diagonal in terms of *n*. *RT* = $\frac{21n}{2}$

28. Given: Rectangle *HELP*; $\overline{OA}$ ⊥ $\overline{PL}$
Prove: △*HAE* ≅ △*POL*

29. How can a contractor be sure that a concrete slab is rectangular without measuring its angles?

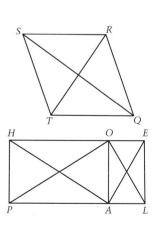

Set C 30. Write a paragraph proof.
Given: Rectangle *ABCD*; *BC* = *DX*
Prove: *m∠BXC* = 60

31. Prove: The length of the median to the hypotenuse of a right triangle is one half the length of the hypotenuse. (HINT: Use auxiliary lines to develop a rectangle with diagonals.)

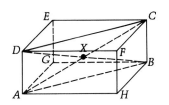

▲ **Review** 32. Complete the following statement in four ways. If __?__, then *PQRS* is a parallelogram.

33. *PQ* = 7x + y, *QR* = 4x + 1, and *PS* = 2x + 7. Find *RS* so that *PQRS* is a parallelogram. **21 + y**

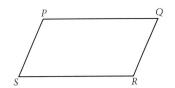

34. The trademark of AZ Lighting is based on a parallelogram. Why are the red bars equal?

35. The hypotenuse and an acute angle of a right triangle are equal to the corresponding parts of another right triangle. Are the triangles congruent? Explain. **Yes, by the AAS Thm.**

36. ∠*U* and ∠*V* are supplementary angles. *m∠U* is 5 more than 6 times *m∠V*. Find *m∠U* and *m∠V*.
155; 25

≋ **Thinking** 37. Draw a large triangle *QRS* on a sheet of paper.
▼ **Ahead** Fold the paper to locate the midpoints *A* and *B* of the two sides *RQ* and *RS*. Draw the line segment joining *A* and *B*. Place another sheet of paper over △*QRS* and copy *AB*. How many times will *AB* fit on *SQ*? **2**

🖳 Computer Activities: Drawing and Measuring

Draw four parallel lines the same distance apart. Then draw a transversal intersecting the four lines.

1. Measure the segments formed on the transversal. How are the lengths related? **They are =.**

2. Draw three different transversals to the original four parallel lines. What is true of the lengths of the segments on each transversal? **They are =.**

sect to form 4 rt. ∠s and all rt. ∠s are =, *m∠AEB* = *m∠CEB*. We know *AE* = *CE* because the diags. of a ▱ bisect each other. Then △*AEB* ≅ △*CEB* (SAS ≅ Post.). Therefore, *AB* = *BC*. Since *ABCD* is a ▱, *AB* = *DC* and *AD* = *BC*. Therefore, by the Substitution Prop., *AB* = *BC* = *CD* = *DA*. So ▱*ABCD* is a rhombus. *Part II*: Given: *ABCD* is a rhombus. Prove: *AC* ⊥ *BD* Proof: By hypothesis, *ABCD* is a rhombus and by the def. of a rhombus, *AB* = *BC*. Since a rhombus is also a ▱, and the diags. of a ▱ bisect each other, *AE* = *EC*. Since *BE* = *BE*, △*ABE* ≅ △*CBE* by SSS ≅ Post. Then *m∠AEB* = *m∠CEB*. Since ∠*AEB* and ∠*CEB* form a lin. pr., *AC* ⊥ *BD*. (If the ∠s of a lin. pr. are =, then the lines containing their sides are ⊥.)

FOLLOW-UP

More Practice

Use a Venn diagram to show the relationship between various classes of quadrilaterals. Sketch quadrilaterals on the chalkboard and ask students to place each in the correct region of the diagram.
• **Worksheet 6–3**

Extension
• **Extension 6–3**

Computers

The computer activity in the pupil's book can be completed using *The Geometric preSupposer: Points and Lines* or *GeoDraw*.
• **Computer Activities 6–3**
• **Computer Worksheet 6–3**

Using Logo

```
1.  TO PARALLELOGRAM
      CT CG
      REPEAT 2[FD 70 RT 55
      FD 40 RT 125]
    END
2.  TO PARALLELOGRAM
      :ANGLE :SIDE1
        :SIDE2
      CT CG
      REPEAT 2[FD :SIDE1
      RT :ANGLE FD :SIDE2
      RT 180- :ANGLE]
    END
3.  TO RHOMBUS :ANGLE
        :SIDE
      CT CG
      REPEAT 2[FD :SIDE RT
        :ANGLE FD :SIDE RT
        180- :ANGLE]
    END
5a. TO QUAD .PAR
      CT CG
      PU SETPOS [30 5] PD
      SETPOS [-25 30]
      SETPOS [-25 -20]
      SETPOS [30 -45]
      SETPOS [30 5]
    END
b.  TO QUAD .RHOM
      CT CG
      PU SETPOS [0 40] PD
      SETPOS [60 15]
      SETPOS [21 -37]
      SETPOS [-39 -12]
      SETPOS [0 40]
    END
c.  TO QUAD .RECT
      CT CG
      PU SETPOS [30 50] PD
      SETPOS [102 -46]
      SETPOS [62 -76]
      SETPOS [-10 20]
      SETPOS [30 50]
    END
```

Using Logo: Parallelograms

1. Define a procedure called PARALLELOGRAM to draw a parallelogram with an angle of 55 and sides of length 40 and 70. Use the figure as a guide.

2. Modify PARALLELOGRAM so that it can be used to draw any parallelogram with a variable :ANGLE for the measure of one angle and variables :SIDE1 and :SIDE2 for the lengths of adjacent sides.

3. Define a procedure called RHOMBUS to draw any rhombus using the variable :ANGLE for the measure of one angle and the variable :SIDE for the length of any side.

4. The procedure QUAD draws a quadrilateral by connecting four points in order, starting and finishing at the same point. Do QUAD. Use the Logo editor to change the coordinates of the vertices to (50, 20), (−20, 20), (−40, −40), and (30, −40). Do QUAD again. What kind of quadrilateral is drawn? □

```
TO QUAD
PU
SETPOS [-20 10]
PD
SETPOS [50 20]
SETPOS [30 -40]
SETPOS [-60 -25]
SETPOS [-20 10]
END
```

5. For each quadrilateral below, the coordinates of three vertices are given in order. Find coordinates for a fourth vertex and modify QUAD to draw the quadrilateral.

   a. Parallelogram: (30, 5), (−25, 30), (−25, −20) **(30, −45)**

   b. Rhombus: (0, 40), (60, 15), (21, −37) **(−39, −12)**

   c. Rectangle: (30, 50), (102, −46), (62, −76) **(−10, 20)**

6. Define a procedure to draw a rhombus with variables :DIAG1 and :DIAG2 for the lengths of its diagonals.

Warm-Up Review

1. If M is the midpoint of $\overline{QR}$ and $QR = 13.5$, then $MR = \underline{\ ?\ }$. 6.75
2. When are corresponding angles equal? When the lines are parallel
3. A $\underline{\ ?\ }$ is a line that intersects a set of lines. Transversal
4. If the diagonals of a parallelogram are equal, the parallelogram is a $\underline{\ ?\ }$. Rectangle

6-4 Parallelograms and Parallel Lines

The design specifications for the truss, or bridge support, have points P and F as the midpoints of $\overline{CH}$ and $\overline{AH}$, respectively. Segments FP and AC appear to be parallel. What appears to be true about the lengths of $\overline{FP}$ and $\overline{AC}$?
$$FP = \tfrac{1}{2}AC$$
Your observations should be consistent with Theorem 6-11. Its proof is left to Exercise 21.

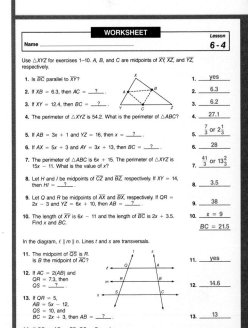

LESSON 6-4

Resources

Teaching Aid 14, quadrilaterals chart
Visual Aid 14, quadrilaterals chart
Teaching Aid 16, triangles
Visual Aid 16, triangles
Worksheet 6-4
Extension 6-4
Computer Activities 6-4
Quiz 6

OBJECTIVE

Use the properties of parallelograms to establish geometric relationships for triangles and parallel lines.

Theorem 6-11

If a segment joins the midpoints of two sides of a triangle, then it is parallel to the third side, and its length is one half the length of the third side.

Given $\triangle ABC$; X and Y are the midpoints of $\overline{AC}$ and $\overline{BC}$.

Prove $\overline{XY} \parallel \overline{AB}$ and $XY = \tfrac{1}{2}AB$

Plan for Proof Locate Z on $\overrightarrow{XY}$ so that $YZ = XY$. Show $\triangle BZY \cong \triangle CXY$. Show $\overline{AX} \parallel \overline{BZ}$ and $BZ = AX$ to show that $ABZX$ is a parallelogram.

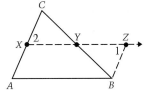

Example 1

In $\triangle ABC$, X and Y are midpoints of $\overline{AC}$ and $\overline{BC}$, respectively. If $AB = 9x - 1$ and $XY = 2x + 7$, then $AB = \underline{\ ?\ }$ and $XY = \underline{\ ?\ }$.

Solution

By Theorem 6-11, $XY = \tfrac{1}{2}AB$. Substitute $9x - 1$ for AB and $2x + 7$ for XY, and solve for x.

$$2x + 7 = \tfrac{1}{2}(9x - 1)$$
$$4x + 14 = 9x - 1, \text{ and } x = 3.$$

Then, $AB = 3(9) - 1 = 26$, and $XY = 2(3) + 7 = 13$.

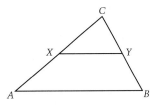

WORKSHEET		Lesson 6-4

Name _____

Use $\triangle XYZ$ for exercises 1–10. A, B, and C are midpoints of $\overline{XY}$, $\overline{XZ}$, and $\overline{YZ}$, respectively.

1. Is $\overline{BC}$ parallel to $\overline{XY}$? **1.** yes
2. If $XB = 6.3$, then $AC = \underline{\ ?\ }$. **2.** 6.3
3. If $XY = 12.4$, then $BC = \underline{\ ?\ }$. **3.** 6.2
4. The perimeter of $\triangle XYZ$ is 54.2. What is the perimeter of $\triangle ABC$? **4.** 27.1
5. If $AB = 3x + 1$ and $YZ = 16$, then $x = \underline{\ ?\ }$. **5.** $\frac{7}{3}$ or $2\frac{1}{3}$
6. If $AX = 5x + 3$ and $AY = 3x + 13$, then $BC = \underline{\ ?\ }$. **6.** 28
7. The perimeter of $\triangle ABC$ is $6x + 15$. The perimeter of $\triangle XYZ$ is $15x - 11$. What is the value of x? **7.** $\frac{41}{3}$ or $13\frac{2}{3}$
8. Let H and I be midpoints of $\overline{CZ}$ and $\overline{BZ}$, respectively. If $XY = 14$, then $HI = \underline{\ ?\ }$. **8.** 3.5
9. Let Q and R be midpoints of $\overline{AX}$ and $\overline{BX}$, respectively. If $QR = 2x - 3$ and $YZ = 6x + 10$, then $AB = \underline{\ ?\ }$. **9.** 38
10. The length of $\overline{XY}$ is $6x - 11$ and the length of $\overline{BC}$ is $2x + 3.5$. Find x and BC. **10.** $x = 9$, $BC = 21.5$

In the diagram, $\ell \parallel m \parallel n$. Lines t and s are transversals.

11. The midpoint of $\overline{QS}$ is R. Is B the midpoint of $\overline{AC}$? **11.** yes
12. If $AC = 2(AB)$ and $QR = 7.3$, then $QS = \underline{\ ?\ }$. **12.** 14.6
13. If $QR = 5$, $AB = 5x - 12$, $QS = 10$, and $BC = 2x + 3$, then $AB = \underline{\ ?\ }$. **13.** 13
14. If $QR = AB = RS$, $QS = 7x - 1$, and $BC = 2x + 10$, then $AC = \underline{\ ?\ }$. **14.** 48

TEACHING NOTES

The following **group activity** may be used to introduce this lesson.
1. Have each student draw a triangle and locate the midpoints *M* and *N* of any two sides.
2. Draw and measure $\overline{MN}$. Does $\overline{MN}$ appear to be parallel to the third side? yes
3. How does it compare to the length of the third side? one-half
Theorem 6–11 may be discussed and proved at this point.

Have students try dividing a line segment into four equal parts using the method described before Theorem 6–12.

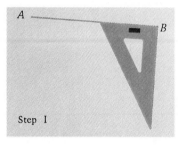

Step I

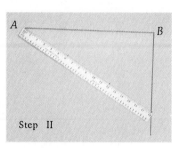

Step II

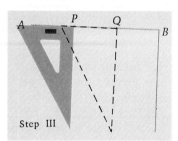

Step III

Cheryl Hollatz, a student in a mechanical drawing class, must divide a line segment into three equal parts. Her technique, using a triangle and a ruler, is shown above. Theorem 6-12 guarantees that $AP = PQ = QB$. Its proof is left to Exercise 22.

Theorem 6-12

If three or more parallel lines cut off equal segments on one transversal, then they cut off equal segments on every transversal.

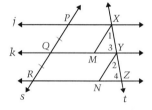

Given $j \parallel k \parallel \ell$; j, k, and ℓ are cut by transversals s and t; $PQ = QR$

Prove $XY = YZ$

Plan for Proof   Draw $\overline{XM} \parallel s$ and $\overline{YN} \parallel s$ to form $\square\,PQMX$ and $\square\,QRNY$. Show $\triangle XMY \cong \triangle YNZ$ so that $XY = YZ$.

Example 2

$j \parallel k \parallel \ell$; j, k, and ℓ are cut by transversals s and t; $PQ = QR = 12$. If $XY = 15$, then $XZ = \underline{\ ?\ }$.

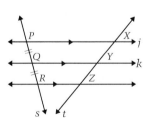

Solution

By Theorem 6-12, $XY = YZ$.
Since $XY = 15$, $YZ = 15$ and $XZ = 30$.

Checking for Understanding

Use the diagram for Theorem 6-11.

1. Explain why $\triangle XYC \cong \triangle ZYB$.   **2.** Explain why $XZ = AB$.

3. In the diagram, if $XY = 11$, then $AB = \underline{\ ?\ }$. 22

Use the diagram for Theorem 6-12. Both pairs of opposite sides
4. Explain why $PQMX$ and $QRNY$ are parallelograms.   are ∥.

5. Explain why $m\angle 1 = m\angle 2$. 2 lines ∥ ⇒ corr. ∠s =.

6. If $PQ = 6$, $XZ = 13$, and $QR = 6$, then $XY = \underline{\ ?\ }$. 6.5

7. Explain the mechanical drawing method used by Cheryl Hollatz to divide the segment into equal parts.

8. Cheryl drew a right angle at point B. Do you think the angle *must* be a right angle? Explain.

Written Exercises

Set A Given: $\triangle ABC$; X and Y are midpoints of $\overline{AB}$ and $\overline{BC}$.

1. If $AC = 13$, then $XY = \underline{\ ?\ }$. $6\frac{1}{2}$

2. If $XY = 3.3$, then $AC = \underline{\ ?\ }$. 6.6

3. If $XY = r$ and $AC = 3r - 30$, then $r = \underline{\ ?\ }$. 30

4. If $AC = 4t + 5$ and $XY = t + 40$, then $XY = \underline{\ ?\ }$. $77\frac{1}{2}$

5. Given $X(-5, 7)$ and $Y(7, 7)$, $AC = \underline{\ ?\ }$. 24

6. Given $A(-1, -1)$, $C(12, -1)$, and $X(2, 4)$, Y has coordinates $(\underline{\ ?\ }, \underline{\ ?\ })$. (15, 4)

7. Given $X(0, 0)$, $Y(8, 0)$, and $A(-6, -11)$, C has coordinates $(\underline{\ ?\ }, \underline{\ ?\ })$. (10, −11)

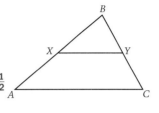

Show that $\overline{XY}$ is parallel to $\overline{AC}$

8. in Exercise 6. 9. in Exercise 7.

Given: $\overleftrightarrow{AX} \parallel \overleftrightarrow{BY} \parallel \overleftrightarrow{CZ} \parallel \overleftrightarrow{DW}$

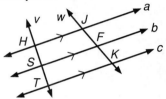

10. If $AB = BC = CD$ and $XY = 10$, then $ZW = \underline{\ ?\ }$. 10

11. If $AB = 17$ and $XY = YZ = ZW$, then $CD = \underline{\ ?\ }$. 17

12. If $BC = 9$ and $WZ = XY = ZW$, then $AB = CD = \underline{\ ?\ }$. 9

13. If $BC = CD$ and $WY = 21$, then $ZW = \underline{\ ?\ }$. 10.5

Mike is building a model plane. He needs to divide a strip of balsa wood into five congruent rectangles to glue onto the wing section.

14. Explain how Mike can use the ruled paper to mark the balsa wood.

15. Which theorem justifies your answer in Exercise 14? Thm. 6-12

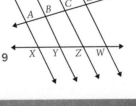

Set B In the diagram, X, Y, and Z are midpoints.

16. Prove: $XY + YZ + XZ = \frac{1}{2}(AB + AC + BC)$

17. If $XZ + XY = 30$, find $BC + AC$. 60

18. If $AB = 15$, $BC = 14$, and $AC = 21$, find $XY + YZ + XZ$. 25

19. If $XY = u$, $AZ = 4v + 6$, and $ZC = u + 4v$, find XY and AC. 6; 12

Additional Examples

Example 1

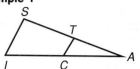

In $\triangle SAI$, T and C are midpoints of $\overline{SA}$ and $\overline{IA}$, respectively. If $SI = 7x - 10$ and $TC = 3x + 4$, then $SI = \underline{\ ?\ }$ and $TC = \underline{\ ?\ }$. 116; 58

Example 2

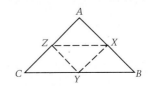

Given: $a \parallel b \parallel c$; transversals v and w; $JF = FK = 15$
If $HT = 40$, then $ST = \underline{\ ?\ }$. 20

ANSWERS

Written Exercises

8. Slope of $\overleftrightarrow{XY}$ = slope of $\overleftrightarrow{AC}$ = 0
9. Slope of $\overleftrightarrow{XY}$ = slope of $\overleftrightarrow{AC}$ = 0
14. Place pt. A on any line and pt. B on the line that is 5 lines below A. Mark the 4 pts. of intersection of $\overline{AB}$ with the lines of the paper. Repeat this process on the other edge of the balsa strip and cut along the $\parallel$ segs. that are determined.
16. Proof: 1. X, Y and Z are midpts. (Given) 2. $XY = (\frac{1}{2})AC$; $YZ = (\frac{1}{2})AB$; $XZ = (\frac{1}{2})BC$; (If a seg. joins the midpts. of 2 sides of a $\triangle$, then its length is $\frac{1}{2}$ the length of the 3rd side) 3. $XY + YZ + XZ = (\frac{1}{2})(AB + AC + BC)$ (Add. Prop. [2])

21. Proof: 1. In △ABC, X and Y are midpts. of $\overline{AC}$ and $\overline{BC}$, respectively. (Given) 2. CX = XA; CY = YB (Def. of midpt. [1]) 3. Locate Z on $\overrightarrow{XY}$ so that YZ = XY (Seg. Construction Post.) 4. m∠CYX = m∠ BYZ (Vert. ∠s are =.) 5. △CYX ≅ △BYZ (SAS ≅ Post. [2, 4]) 6. m∠1 = m∠2 (Corres. parts of ≅ △s are =. [5]) 7. $\overline{AX}$ ∥ $\overline{BZ}$ (Alt. int. ∠s = ⇒ 2 lines ∥. [6]) 8. CX = BZ (Corres. parts of ≅ △s are △. [5]) 9. AX = BZ (Substitution Prop. [2, 8]) 10. AXZB is a ▱. (If 2 sides of a quad. are ∥ and =, then the quad. is a ▱. [7, 9]) 11. $\overline{XY}$ ∥ $\overline{AB}$ (Def. of ▱ [10]) 12. XZ = AB (Both prs. of opp. sides of a ▱ are =. [10]) 13. XY + YZ = XZ (Seg. Add. Post.) 14. XY + XY = XZ, or 2(XY) = XZ (Substitution Prop. [3, 13]) 15. XY = $(\frac{1}{2})$XZ (Mult. Prop. [14]) 16. XY = $(\frac{1}{2})$AB (Substitution Prop. [12, 15])

22. Proof: 1. j ∥ k ∥ ℓ; j, k and ℓ are cut by transversals s and t. (Given) 2. Draw $\overline{XM}$ ∥ s and $\overline{YN}$ ∥ s. (Through a given pt. not on a given line there exists exactly 1 line ∥ to the given line.) 3. PXMQ and QRNY are ▱s. (Def. of ▱ [1, 2]) 4. PQ = XM; QR = YN (Opp. sides of a ▱ are =. [3]) 5. PQ = QR (Given) 6. XM = YN (Substitution Prop. [4, 5]) 7. $\overline{XM}$ ∥ $\overline{YN}$ (If 2 lines are ∥ to the same line, then they are ∥ to each other. [2]) 8. m∠1 = m∠2 (2 lines ∥ ⇒ corr. ∠s =. [7]) 9. m∠3 = m∠4 (2 lines ∥ ⇒ corr. ∠s =. [1]) 10. △XMY ≅ △YNZ (AAS Thm. [6, 8, 9]) 11. XY = YZ (Corres. parts of ≅ △s are =. [10])

More Practice

Introduce Theorem 6–11 by drawing the following diagram on the board.

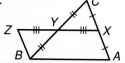

20. In the diagram of a truss for a house, Y, W, and D are the midpoints of $\overline{AD}$, $\overline{BD}$, and $\overline{AB}$, respectively. X and Z are the midpoints of $\overline{AC}$ and $\overline{BC}$. If XY = 3x − 5 and ZW = 5x − 11, then CD = _?_. **8**

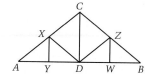

21. Prove Theorem 6-11.

22. Prove Theorem 6-12. Use three parallel lines.

Debbie needs to replace a panel on her garage door. On a new rectangular panel, she made a design by locating the midpoints of each side and connecting the points.

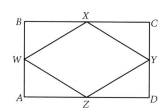

23. Use Theorem 6-11 to show that WXYZ is a parallelogram.

24. Explain why WXYZ is a rhombus.

In quadrilateral HIJK, X, Y, Z, and W are the midpoints of sides $\overline{HI}$, $\overline{IJ}$, $\overline{JK}$, and $\overline{KH}$.

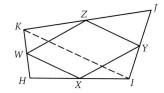

25. If KI = 12, then WX = _?_. **6**

26. If KI = 16, then YZ = _?_. **8**

27. Prove: WX ∥ ZY

28. Prove: If the midpoints of the sides of any quadrilateral are connected in order, the quadrilateral formed is a parallelogram.

Set C

29. Prove a second case of Theorem 6-12.
Given: j ∥ k ∥ ℓ; transversal s intersects transversal t at a point between lines j and k; PQ = QR
Prove: XY = YZ

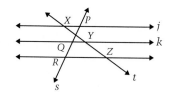

30. Prove: If a line contains the midpoint of one side of a triangle and is parallel to a second side, then it contains the midpoint of the third side.

31. Given △ABC with vertices A(x, y), B(x₁, y₁), and C(x₂, y₂); D is the midpoint of $\overline{AB}$; E is the midpoint of $\overline{CB}$. Show that DE = $\frac{1}{2}$AC.

◆ Review

32. State three facts about the diagonals of a rhombus.

33. Can a quadrilateral be both a rhombus and a rectangle? Explain. **Yes; it can be a square.**

34. Given: D is the midpoint of $\overline{MJ}$; $m\angle 1 = m\angle 2$
Prove: $HJKM$ is a parallelogram.

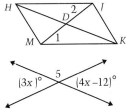

35. The measure of an exterior angle of a regular polygon is 18. How many sides does the polygon have? **20**

36. Find $m\angle 5$ at the right. **144**

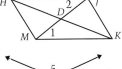

≡ Thinking Ahead Draw $ABCD$ with $A(2, 7)$, $B(16, 7)$, $C(12, 1)$, and $D(4, 1)$.

37. Explain why $ABCD$ is not a parallelogram.

38. What is the length of $\overline{AB}$? of $\overline{DC}$? **14; 8**

39. What is the length of the segment containing the midpoints of the nonparallel sides? **11**

Repeat with $P(-1, 2)$, $Q(5, 6)$, $R(5, -4)$, and $S(-1, -2)$.

40. How does the length of the segment that joins the midpoints of the nonparallel sides compare to the lengths of the parallel sides?

40. It is half the sum of the lengths of the ∥ sides.

⚗ Construction Exercises

Construction 9

Divide a segment into three equal segments.

Given $\overline{AB}$

Construct Points M and N such that $AM = MN = NB$

Method Step 1: Draw $\overrightarrow{AQ}$ not containing $\overline{AB}$.

Step 2: On $\overrightarrow{AQ}$ mark off $AX = XY = YZ$, using any convenient length for $\overline{AX}$.

Step 3: Draw $\overline{ZB}$. Through points X and Y construct lines parallel to $\overline{ZB}$ that intersect $\overline{AB}$. Label the points of intersection M and N, respectively. Then $AM = MN = NB$.

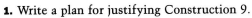

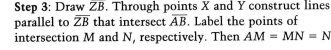

1. Write a plan for justifying Construction 9.

Divide a segment

2. of 7 cm into three equal segments.

3. of 4 inches into five equal segments.

4. of 7 cm into four equal segments.

5. Repeat Exercise 4 using a different method of construction.

Ask the following questions.
1. Name the midpoints of $\overline{AC}$ and $\overline{BC}$. **X; Y**
2. Name two pairs of parallel sides. $\overline{BZ}$ and $\overline{AX}$; $\overline{ZX}$ and $\overline{BA}$
3. How does XY compare to YZ? **equal** To ZX? **half** To BA? **half**
• **Worksheet 6–4**

Extension

• **Extension 6–4**

Computers

This computer activity can be completed using *The Geometric Supposer: Quadrilaterals* or *Circles* or *GeoDraw*.

To introduce students to properties of trapezoids, have students use the computer drawing tool to do the following.

Draw an isosceles trapezoid. Identify the two angles that form each pair of base angles. Measure the four angles of the trapezoid. What do you notice about the measures of the two angles in each pair of base angles? They are equal.

Now label the midpoint on each leg of the trapezoid. Draw the segment that connects the midpoints. Measure the two acute angles formed by this segment and the two legs. What is the relationship between these two acute angles and the two acute base angles of the trapezoid? They are equal. What does this tell you about the segment that connects the midpoints of the legs of the trapezoid? The segment lies on a line that is parallel to the bases.

Measure the length of the segment that connects the midpoints of the legs. Measure the lengths of the two bases of the trapezoid and find their sum. What is the relationship between the length of the segment that connects the midpoints of the legs to the sum of the lengths of the two bases? The length of the segment that connects the midpoints is half the sum of the lengths of the bases.

Repeat this activity for two or three more isosceles trapezoids.

• **Computer Activities 6–4**

Progress Check

Lesson 6-1, page 239

Is each statement *always, sometimes,* or *never* true?

1. The diagonals of a parallelogram are equal. Sometimes
2. The diagonals of a parallelogram bisect each other. Always

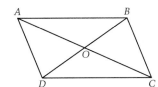

Given $\square ABCD$

3. If $m\angle DAB = 56$, find $m\angle DCB$. 56
4. If $DO = 4.5$, then $DB = \underline{?}$. 9
5. If $m\angle DCB = 47$, then $m\angle CDA = \underline{?}$. 133

Lesson 6-2, page 244

Tell how to justify that $QRST$ is a parallelogram.

6. Given: $QR = ST$; $m\angle 1 = m\angle 2$ Thm. 6-5
7. Given: $RM = \frac{1}{2}RT$; $QM = 4$; $QS = 8$ Thm. 6-7
8. Given: $QT = RS$; $QR = ST$ Thm. 6-6

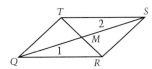

Lesson 6-3, page 249

9. In rhombus $ABCD$, with $A(4, 2)$ and $B(-5, 2)$, $BC = \underline{?}$. 9
10. In rectangle $QRST$, if $QS = 9$, then $RT = \underline{?}$. 9
11. In rectangle $TANG$, $TN = 4x - 11$ and $AG = 2x + 9$. Find x and TN. 10; 29

Lesson 6-4, page 255

Given $\triangle EFG$ with X, Y, and Z midpoints of $\overline{EG}$, $\overline{FG}$, and $\overline{EF}$, respectively.

12. If $EF = 21$, find XY. 10.5
13. If $XZ = 3x$ and $GF = x + 5$, then $XZ = \underline{?}$ and $GF = \underline{?}$. 3; 6
14. If $XY + YZ = 14.5$, find $EF + EG$. 29
15. Given $\ell \parallel m \parallel n$, $PQ = QR$, if $MN = 13$, then $MK = \underline{?}$. 26

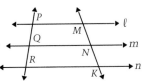

Algebra Review: Multiplying Monomials and Binomials

Examples

1. Multiply $4x$ and $(3x - 5)$.
2. Multiply $(2x + 4)$ and $(x - 7)$.

Solutions

1. $(4x)(3x - 5) = (4x)(3x) + (4x)(-5)$
   $= 12x^2 - 20x$

2. $(2x + 4)(x - 7) = 2x^2 - 14x + 4x - 28$
   $= 2x^2 - 10x - 28$

Multiply. 1. $-2x^2 - 18x$ 2. $2ab^2 + 10ab$ 3. $-12xy + 6y^2$ 4. $14x^2 + 7xy - 35x$

1. $(-2x)(x + 9)$ 2. $2ab(b + 5)$ 3. $(4x - 2y)(-3y)$ 4. $7x(2x + y - 5)$

5. $(x + 7)(x + 2)$ 6. $(3x - 8)(x - 1)$ 7. $(3x + 4y)(2x + 6y)$ 8. $(x - 6)^2$

5. $x^2 + 9x + 14$ 6. $3x^2 - 11x + 8$ 7. $6x^2 + 26xy + 24y^2$ 8. $x^2 - 12x + 36$

Warm-Up Review

1. The line segment formed by connecting a vertex of a triangle to the midpoint of the opposite side is a(n) __?__. Median
2. A(n) __?__ triangle has two congruent sides. Isosceles
3. In $\triangle ABC$, if X and Y are midpoints of $\overline{AB}$ and $\overline{AC}$, respectively, and $XY = 12.4$, then $BC = $ __?__. 24.8

6-5 Trapezoids

The buildings in the photo are the *Pyramids*, located in Indianapolis, Indiana. They have sides shaped like quadrilaterals in which exactly one pair of sides are parallel. These figures are called trapezoids.

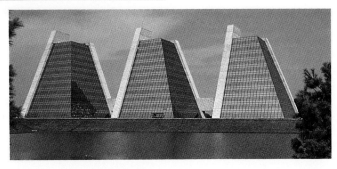

Definition *Trapezoid*

A trapezoid is a quadrilateral with exactly one pair of opposite sides parallel.

In a trapezoid, the parallel sides are called *bases*. The nonparallel sides are called *legs*.

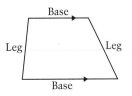

Definition *Median of a Trapezoid*

The median of a trapezoid is the segment joining the midpoints of the legs of the trapezoid.

$\overline{MN}$ is the median of trapezoid $TRAP$.

Theorem 6-13 expresses the relationship of the median of a trapezoid to the bases. Its proof is left to Exercise 29.

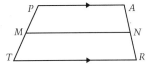

Theorem 6-13

The median of a trapezoid is parallel to the bases and its length is one half the sum of the lengths of the bases.

Given   Trapezoid $ABCD$; $\overline{AB} \parallel \overline{CD}$; median $\overline{XY}$

Prove $\overline{XY} \parallel \overline{AB}$; $\overline{XY} \parallel \overline{CD}$; $XY = \frac{1}{2}(AB + CD)$

Plan for Proof   Draw $\overline{BD}$ with midpoint M, $\overline{MX}$, and $\overline{MY}$. Use Theorem 6-11 to show $\overline{MX} \parallel \overline{AB}$; $\overline{MY} \parallel \overline{CD}$; $MX = \frac{1}{2}AB$ and $MY = \frac{1}{2}CD$. Show $\overline{MY} \parallel \overline{AB}$ and X, Y, and M are collinear. Then $\overline{XY} \parallel \overline{AB}$ and $\overline{XY} \parallel \overline{CD}$. Use the Seg. Add. Post. and the Addition Prop. to show $XY = XM + MY = \frac{1}{2}(AB + CD)$.

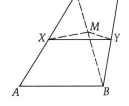

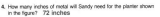

Example 1

ABCD is a trapezoid. $\overline{XY}$ is the median.

a. If *AB* = 15 and *DC* = 28, find *XY*.

b. If *XY* = 15 and *AB* = 7, find *DC*.

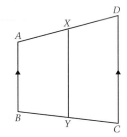

Solution

Use Theorem 6-13.

a. $XY = \frac{1}{2}(AB + DC)$

$XY = \frac{1}{2}(15 + 28)$

$XY = \frac{1}{2}(43)$

$XY = 21.5$

b. $XY = \frac{1}{2}(AB + DC)$

$15 = \frac{1}{2}(7 + DC)$

$30 = 7 + DC$

$23 = DC$

In the outdoor lamp, each glass panel is a trapezoid with nonparallel sides that are equal in length. This type of trapezoid is an isosceles trapezoid.

Definition *Isosceles Trapezoid*

An isosceles trapezoid is a trapezoid whose legs are equal.

In isosceles trapezoid *ABCD*, *AD* = *BC*. ∠*A* and ∠*B* are a pair of **base angles**. ∠*C* and ∠*D* are another pair of base angles. What appears to be true about a pair of base angles? Your answer suggests Theorem 6-14, the proof of which is left to Exercise 16. **They appear to be =.**

Theorem 6-14

Each pair of base angles of an isosceles trapezoid are equal.

Given Isosceles trapezoid *ABCD* with *AD* = *BC*

Prove $m\angle A = m\angle B;\ m\angle C = m\angle D$

Plan for Proof Draw $\overline{DX} \perp \overline{AB}$ and $\overline{CY} \perp \overline{AB}$. Prove that the triangles formed are congruent. Show that ∠*D* and ∠*C* are supplements of ∠*A* and ∠*B*.

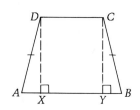

Example 2

ABCD is an isosceles trapezoid with $m\angle A = 6x + 10$ and $m\angle B = 4x + 50$. Find $m\angle A$.

Solution

By Theorem 6-14, $m\angle A = m\angle B$.

$6x + 10 = 4x + 50$

$2x = 40$

$x = 20$

$m\angle A = 6(20) + 10 = 130$

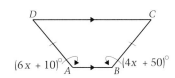

Example 3

Coordinates of the vertices of trapezoid $QRST$ are $Q(0, -2)$, $R(10, -2)$, $S(8, 3)$, and $T(2, 3)$. $\overline{TS}$ is parallel to $\overline{QR}$. Is $QRST$ an isosceles trapezoid?

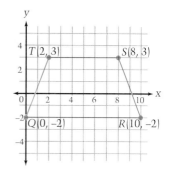

Solution

Determine the length of each leg.

$$QT = \sqrt{(2 - 0)^2 + (3 - (-2))^2} \qquad RS = \sqrt{(8 - 10)^2 + (3 - (-2))^2}$$
$$= \sqrt{4 + 25} \qquad\qquad\qquad = \sqrt{4 + 25}$$
$$= \sqrt{29} \qquad\qquad\qquad\qquad = \sqrt{29}$$

Since $QT = RS$, trapezoid $QRST$ is isosceles.

Sometimes lamps have decorative wire inserts in front of the glass panels. These wires represent the diagonals of an isosceles trapezoid. What appears to be true about $\overline{QS}$ and $\overline{TR}$? The answer to this question is verified by Theorem 6-15, which is to be proved in Exercise 17.

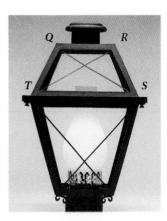

Theorem 6-15

The diagonals of an isosceles trapezoid are equal.

Given Isosceles trapezoid $QRST$; with $\overline{QR} \parallel \overline{TS}$ and $\overline{QT} = \overline{RS}$ diagonals $\overline{QS}$ and $\overline{TR}$

Prove $QS = TR$

Plan for Proof Use the definition of isosceles trapezoid and Theorem 6-14. Show $\triangle QTS \cong \triangle RST$, and thus $QS = RT$.

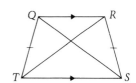

Checking for Understanding

Given trapezoid $ABCD$; $\overline{AB} \parallel \overline{DC}$; X and Y are midpoints of $\overline{AD}$ and $\overline{BC}$, respectively.

1. Name the bases of $ABCD$. $\overline{AB}, \overline{CD}$

2. What is the segment $\overline{XY}$ called? Median

3. Give an equation relating the lengths of AB, DC, and XY.

4. Find XY if $AB = 30$ and $DC = 18$. 24 $\quad XY = \frac{1}{2}(AB + DC)$

5. Find AB if $DC = 5$ and $XY = 8$. 11

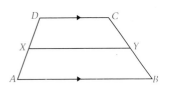

3. Draw $\overline{QR}$. What kind of quadrilateral is $QRCB$? isosceles trapezoid

4. How do angles C and B compare? equal

5. Draw $\overline{QC}$ and $\overline{RB}$. How do they compare? equal

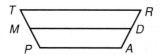

Additional Examples

Example 1

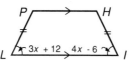

$TRAP$ is a trapezoid and MD is the median.

(a) If $TR = 23$ and $PA = 13$, find MD. 18

(b) If $MD = 21$ and $TR = 35$, find PA.

Example 2

$PHIL$ is an isosceles trapezoid. If $m\angle L = 3x + 12$ and $m\angle I = 4x - 6$, find $m\angle L$ and $m\angle P$. 66; 114

Example 3

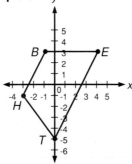

In quadrilateral *BETH*, the coordinates of the vertices are $B(-1, 3)$, $E(4, 3)$, $T(0, -5)$ and $H(-3, -1)$. Is *BETH* a trapezoid? yes; slope of BH = slope of ET = 2/1 If so, is it an isosceles trapezoid? yes; $BE = HT = 5$

Error Analysis Students often apply the properties of isosceles trapezoids to all trapezoids. Stress that a trapezoid is a quadrilateral with only one pair of parallel sides.

ANSWERS

Written Exercises

16. Proof: 1. *ABCD* is an isos. trap. with $AD = BC$. (Given) 2. $\overline{CD} \parallel \overline{AB}$ (Def. of isos. trap. [1]) 3. Draw $\overline{DX} \perp \overline{AB}$ and $\overline{CY} \perp \overline{AB}$. (Through a pt. not on a given line there exists exactly 1 line $\perp$ to the given line.) 4. $DX = CY$ (The distance between 2 given $\parallel$ lines is constant. [2, 3]) 5. $\angle DXA$ and $\angle CYB$ are rt. $\angle$s. (2 $\perp$ lines form 4 rt. $\angle$s. [3]) 6. $\triangle AXD$ and $\triangle BYC$ are rt. $\triangle$s. (Def. of rt. $\triangle$ [5]) 7. $\triangle AXD \cong \triangle BYC$ (HL Thm. [1, 4, 6]) 8. $m\angle A = m\angle B$ (Corres. parts of $\cong \triangle$s are =. [7]) 9. $\angle ADC$ and $\angle A$ are supp.; $\angle BCD$ and $\angle B$ are supp. (2 lines $\parallel \Rightarrow$ int. $\angle$s on same side of trans. supp. [2]) 10. $m\angle ADC = m\angle BCD$ (Supplements of $= \angle$s are =. [8, 9])

17. Proof: By hypothesis, *QRST* is an isos. trap. and by def. $QT = RS$. $m\angle QTS = m\angle RST$ because each pair of base $\angle$s of an isos. trap. are =. Since $ST = ST$, $\triangle QTS \cong \triangle RST$ by SAS $\cong$ Post. Thus, $QS = RT$ (Corres. parts of $\cong \triangle$s are =.).

Given trapezoid *WXYZ*; $\overline{WX} \parallel \overline{ZY}$; $ZW = YX$

6. Explain why $\angle Z$ is supplementary to $\angle W$.

7. If $ZX = 2x$ and $WY = x + 6$, find the length of $\overline{ZX}$. 12

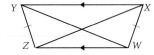

Written Exercises

Set A Tell whether each statement is *always*, *sometimes*, or *never* true.

1. The median of a trapezoid is equal in length to a base of the trapezoid. Never
   Sometimes
2. Lengths of the diagonals of a trapezoid are equal. Sometimes
3. A trapezoid has two right angles. Sometimes
4. A trapezoid has exactly one right angle. Never
5. Opposite angles of a trapezoid are supplementary. Sometimes

Given: $\overline{AB}$ is the median of trapezoid *QRST*.

6. If $QR = 6$ and $TS = 12$, then $AB = \underline{\ ?\ }$. 9
7. If $QR = 55$ and $TS = a$, find AB. $\frac{1}{2}(a + 55)$
8. If $m\angle T = 63$, find $m\angle Q$. 117
9. If $TA = \frac{1}{2}SR$ and $m\angle R = 130$, find $m\angle T$. 50
10. $AB = 21$ and $TS = 28$. Find QR. 14
11. If $ST = 2c$, $QR = 4c$, and $AB = 12$, find c. 4
12. If $ST = 2x + 3$, $QR = x + 4$, and $AB = 23$, find ST. 29
13. If $TQ = SR$, $m\angle T = 3y + 27$, and $m\angle S = 5y - 3$, find $m\angle T$. 72
14. If X is the midpoint of $\overline{TA}$, Y is the midpoint of $\overline{SB}$, $TS = 28$, and $QR = 12$, then $XY = \underline{\ ?\ }$. 24
15. Trapezoid *ABCD* has vertices at $A(-4, -1)$, $B(-1, 2)$, $C(5, 2)$, and $D(-4, -7)$ and $\overline{AB}$ parallel to $\overline{DC}$. Is *ABCD* isosceles? Explain. Yes; $AD = BC = 6$
16. Write a two-column proof of Theorem 6-14.
17. Write a paragraph proof of Theorem 6-15.
18. In the birdhouse shown at the right, find the length of $\overline{IR}$. $10\frac{1}{2}$ inches

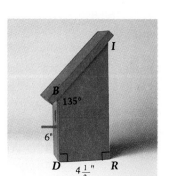

Set B A knife blade is shaped like an isosceles trapezoid. 58
19. If $m\angle K = 3x + 7$ and $m\angle N = 5x - 27$, find $m\angle K$.
20. If $m\angle E = 5x + 12$ and $m\angle N = 2x - 7$, find $m\angle F$. 137

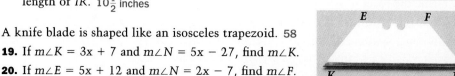

21. Given isosceles trapezoid *BROW* with $\overline{BR} \parallel \overline{OW}$, prove △*WON* is isosceles.

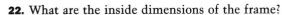

Krista makes picture frames with a line of trim joining the midpoints of $\overline{BX}$, $\overline{CY}$, $\overline{DZ}$, and $\overline{AW}$. The distance between the inner and outer rectangles is 3 inches. *DA* = 14 inches and *CD* = 16 inches. **8 in.; 10 in.**

22. What are the inside dimensions of the frame?

23. How much trim is needed for the frame? **48 in.**

24. Given isosceles trapezoid *SCEL*; median $\overline{XY}$; $m\angle E = 60$; *LE* = 6*a* − 13; and *LS* = *EC* = *SC* = 2*a* + 1. Find the length of the median. (HINT: Draw a line parallel to $\overline{LS}$ through *C*.) **24**

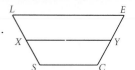

25. Given trapezoid *QRST*; median $\overline{XY}$; $\overline{QR} \perp \overline{QT}$; $\overline{ST} \perp \overline{QT}$; *QR* = 4*a* + 5; *QT* = 2*a* + 13; *TS* = 9*a* + 12; and $m\angle R = 135$. Find *XY*. (HINT: Draw a line perpendicular to $\overline{TS}$ through *R*.) **21.5**

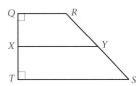

Quadrilateral *RSTV* has vertices *R*(−4, 2), *S*(1, 4), *T*(5, 0), and *V*(−5, −4). *M* is the midpoint of $\overline{RV}$ and *N* is the midpoint of $\overline{ST}$.

26. Is *RSTV* a trapezoid? If so, it is isosceles? **Yes; no**

27. Find the length of median $\overline{MN}$. $\frac{3\sqrt{29}}{2}$

28. Show that $\overline{MN}$ is parallel to $\overline{RS}$.

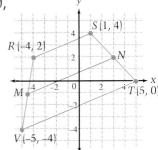

Set C

29. Prove Theorem 6-13.

30. Prove: If one pair of base angles of a trapezoid are equal, the trapezoid is isosceles.

21. Proof: 1. *BROW* is an isos. trap. with $\overline{BR} \parallel \overline{OW}$. (Given) 2. *BW* = *RO* (The legs of an isos. trap. are =. [1]) 3. $m\angle BWO = m\angle ROW$ (Each pair of base ∠s of an isos. trap. are =.) 4. *OW* = *OW* (Reflexive Prop.) 5. △*BWO* ≅ △*ROW* (SAS ≅ Post. [2, 3, 4]) 6. $m\angle NWO = m\angle NOW$ (Corres. parts of ≅ △s are =. [5]) 7. *NW* = *NO* (If 2 ∠s of a △ are =, then the sides opp. them are =. [6]) 8. △*WON* is isos. (Def. of isos. △ [7])

28. The coordinates of *M* and *N* are $(-4\frac{1}{2}, -1)$ and (3, 2). The slope of $\overline{MN}$ is $\frac{2}{5}$. Since the slope of $\overline{RS}$ is also $\frac{2}{5}$, $\overline{MN}$ is ∥ to $\overline{RS}$.

29. Proof: 1. Trap. *ABCD* has $\overline{AB} \parallel \overline{CD}$ and median $\overline{XY}$. (Given) 2. Draw $\overline{BD}$. (2 pts. determine a line.) 3. Let *M* be midpt. of $\overline{BD}$. (Seg. has exactly 1 midpt.) 4. Draw $\overline{MX}$ and $\overline{MY}$. (2 pts. determine a line.) 5. *X* is midpt. of $\overline{AD}$; *Y* is midpt. of $\overline{BC}$. (Def. of median of trap. [1]) 6. $\overline{MX} \parallel \overline{AB}$; $\overline{MY} \parallel \overline{DC}$; $MX = \frac{1}{2}(AB)$; $MY = \frac{1}{2}(DC)$ (Seg. joining midpts. of 2 sides of △ is ∥ to third side and half its length. [3, 5]) 7. $\overline{MY} \parallel \overline{AB}$ (2 lines ∥ to same line are ∥ to each other. [1, 6]) 8. $\overline{MY}$ and $\overline{XM}$ lie on same line: $\overleftrightarrow{XY}$. (Through a pt. not on a given line, there is exactly 1 line ∥ to the given line. [6, 7]) 9. $\overline{XY} \parallel \overline{AB}$ and $\overline{XY} \parallel \overline{CD}$ (Def. of ∥ segs. [6, 7, 8]) 10. *XY* = *MX* + *MY* (Seg. Add. Post.) 11. $XY = \frac{1}{2}(AB) + \frac{1}{2}(CD) = \frac{1}{2}(AB + CD)$ (Substitution Prop. [6, 10])

Review

36. SSS ≅ Post.; SAS ≅ Post.;
ASA ≅ Post.; AAS Thm.; HL Thm.

Thinking Ahead

38. The line drawn in Exercise 37
is the ⊥ bisector of $\overline{AB}$.

39.

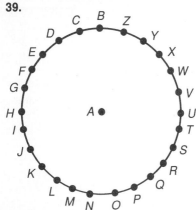

31. In isosceles trapezoid $ABCD$, $\overline{AB} \parallel \overline{CD}$, $\overline{XY} \parallel \overline{CD}$,
$AD = k$, $AB = s$, and $CD = t$. Find DX and CY
such that the perimeter of $ABYX$ equals the
perimeter of $XYCD$. DX = CY = $\frac{2k + s - t}{4}$

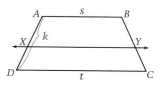

▲ Review In $\triangle ABC$, B is the midpoint of $\overline{AC}$, and E is the
midpoint of $\overline{AD}$.

32. $BE = $ __?__ 9   **33.** $m\angle C = $ __?__ 84

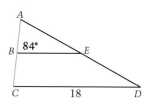

34. Complete the following statement with the names
of quadrilaterals. A square is also a __?__, a __?__,
and a __?__. □, rect., rhombus

35. Write an equation of a line through $P(-1, 4)$ and
parallel to the line whose equation is $2x - y = 1$.
Sample: y = 2x + 6

36. List as many ways as you can to prove two
triangles are congruent.

Thinking Ahead Draw segment AB on a sheet of paper. Carefully
locate point C such that $AC = BC$. Locate other points
$D, E, F, \ldots$, on either side of $\overline{AB}$ such that $AD = BD$,
$AE = BE$, $AF = BF, \ldots$

37. Connect points $C, D, E, F, \ldots$ Do the points
appear to be collinear? Yes

38. What seems to be the relationship between the
figure you drew in Exercise 37 and segment AB?

Mark point A and locate points $B, C, D, \ldots$,
X, Y, Z such that $AB = AC = AD = \ldots = AX =$
$AY = AZ = 2$ inches.

39. Connect $B, C, D, \ldots, X, Y, Z$ and B in order.
Describe the figure you drew. Polygon approaching a circle

40. Suppose you could locate at least 200 or more
points, each 2 inches from A. What kind of figure
would be formed by a smooth curve through the
points? Circle

41. What kind of figure would be formed in Exercise
2 if the points are not restricted to a plane? Sphere

Excursion: Nonperiodic Tessellations

The first two tessellations, or tilings, use the same isosceles triangle. The one on the right uses a combination of "kites" and "darts."

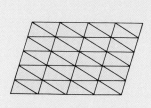 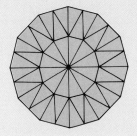 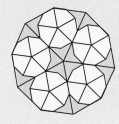 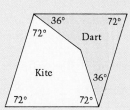

A tiling that fits on itself when slid is called *periodic*. One that cannot fit onto itself when slid is called *nonperiodic*. Which of the tessellations above are periodic? Which are nonperiodic?

Many polygonal shapes, such as the triangles above, will tile *both* periodically and nonperiodically. Many shapes, such as squares, will tile *only* periodically, but, a single shape that tiles *only* nonperiodically has not yet been found.

The kites and darts in the tessellations above were discovered in 1974 by Roger Penrose, a British mathematician at the Oxford University. The two shapes are obtained from a particular rhombus, shown at the right. If the kite and dart are combined to form the rhombus, the pieces can tessellate periodically. However, if the rhombus is not allowed, the kite and dart can tessellate only nonperiodically.

Make a set of darts and kites. To get elaborate patterns, you will need at least 100 kites and 60 darts. Then create two nonperiodic tessellations using the two figures. Remember, do *not* include any rhombuses.

Warm-Up Review

1. The set of points the same distance from a point is a(n) __?__. Circle
2. True or false: The perpendicular bisector of a line segment is at right angles to the segment. True
3. If $\overrightarrow{OC}$ bisects $\angle AOB$, $m\angle AOC = 3x + 5$ and $m\angle COB = 6x - 16$, find $m\angle AOB$. 52

6-6 Locus

An adventurer found fragments of an old treasure map. From the note at the bottom of the map, he assumed that the treasure was buried the same distance from the tall palm tree, the ceremonial pole, and the wrecked boat—all marked on the map. How did the adventurer and his crew decide where to begin their search for the treasure?

The cabin boy determined the set of points on the map that were the same distance, or *equidistant*, from the palm tree and the ceremonial pole. These points are marked on the map. They suggest a figure called a locus.

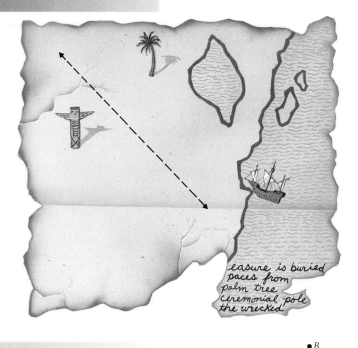

Definition *Locus*

A locus is the set of all points, and only those points, that satisfy a given condition.

Example 1 illustrates the steps used by the cabin boy.

Example 1

In a plane, what is the locus of points equidistant from two given points A and B?

Solution

Sketch the given information.
   Show two points and label them A and B.

Locate several points that satisfy the given condition(s).
   Sketch points that are equidistant from A and B until you begin to see a pattern.

Draw a line or a smooth curve through the points.

Describe the pattern of points as the required locus.
   In a plane, the locus of points equidistant from two given points A and B is the perpendicular bisector of $\overline{AB}$.

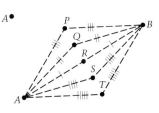

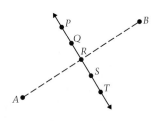

The cabin boy then located all the points on the map equidistant from the tree and the boat. After drawing the locus for these points, he said he could mark the spot where the treasure might be. The spot would be equidistant from the tree, the pole, and the boat. Where did he mark the spot? **At the pt. of the intersection of the 2 loc.**

The first mate thought the treasure might be buried 20 paces from both the palm tree and the ceremonial pole, which are 15 paces apart. He used the method described in Example 2 to determine the spot for the treasure.

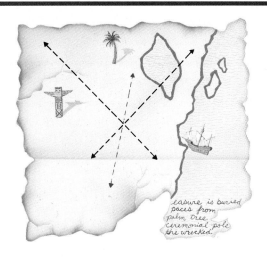

Treasure is buried paces from palm tree ceremonial pole the wrecked.

Example 2

In a plane, find the locus of points at a distance of 2 cm from point P and 3 cm from point Q. Points P and Q are 4 cm apart.

Solution

Sketch the given information.
   Show the two points P and Q.

Locate several points that satisfy the given conditions.
   Sketch points 2 cm from P and 3 cm from Q.

Draw a smooth curve through each set of points.

Describe the locus.
   In a plane, the locus of points 2 cm from P is a circle with center P and radius 2 cm. The locus of points 3 cm from Q is a circle with center Q and radius 3 cm. The locus consists of the two points at which the circles intersect.

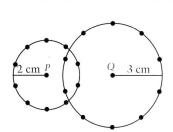

A description of a locus is correct if it describes *all points* that satisfy the conditions and *only those points*. If a locus is not restricted to a plane, think in terms of three dimensions.

Example 3

What would be the solution to Example 1 if the phrase *in a plane* were omitted?

Solution

The locus is a *plane* containing the midpoint of the segment joining the given points and which is perpendicular to this segment. The plane is perpendicular to and bisects the segment.

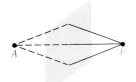

TEACHING NOTES

You may wish to introduce this lesson with a discussion of the term "equidistant." Locate two points, T and V. Ask students to locate a point equidistant from T and V. Most students will name the midpoint of $\overline{TV}$. Ask for another point. Have students first estimate a location and check the distances with a ruler. Then have them find the intersection of two arcs. Students should recall the perpendicular bisector construction and should discover the solution to **Example 1**. **Example 3** introduces the circle as the locus of points at a given distance (radius) from a given point (center).

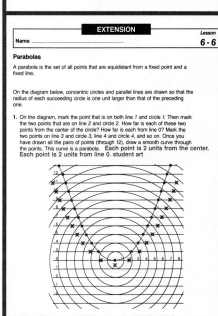

Example 1

In a plane, what is the locus of points equidistant from parallel lines k and ℓ? a line halfway between k and ℓ that is parallel to both

Example 2

In a plane, what is the locus of points equidistant from two intersecting lines k and ℓ? two lines through the point of intersection, bisecting the angles

Example 3

What would be the solution to **Example 2** if the phrase "in a plane" were omitted? a plane containing the point of intersection that bisects the angles

Error Analysis Students should be reminded that the phrase "equidistant from" must be followed by two geometric figures. Many will confuse it with "a given distance from."

ANSWERS

Checking for Understanding

2. The locus is a 3rd line ∥ to each of the 2 given lines and midway between them.

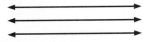

3. The locus is the lateral surface of a cylinder with radius 1 in.

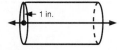

Checking for Understanding

1. Sketch the treasure map on page 269. Show how pairing the tree and the pole and then the pole and the boat will give the same solution as the cabin boy's.

For each exercise, draw a figure and describe the locus.

2. In a plane, all points equidistant from two parallel lines

3. All points at a distance of 1 inch from a given line

4. In a plane, all points equidistant from the sides of a given acute angle

5. In a plane, all points equidistant from A and B and 3 cm from point B, if $AB = 5$ cm

6. In space, all points 3 inches from point P.

Describe the locus for Example 2 if Q and P are
7. 5 cm apart. **8.** 8 cm apart.

Written Exercises

Set A For each exercise, draw a figure and describe the locus.

1. The points 10 cm from a given plane

2. In a half-plane, the points 1 inch from the edge of the half-plane

3. In a plane, the points equidistant from the four vertices of a square

4. In a plane, the midpoints of all segments joining point C to points of $\overline{AB}$, if C is not on $\overline{AB}$

5. In a triangle, the locus of points equidistant from the sides of the triangle

6. In a plane, all points 1 inch from line $\overleftrightarrow{AB}$ and 1 inch from point A

7. In a plane, all points 2 inches from line $\overleftrightarrow{AB}$ and 1 inch from point A

8. In a plane, all points equidistant from noncollinear points A, B, and C

9. The Park Commission wants to locate a fountain in a rectangular play lot equidistant from the corners of the lot. Where should the fountain be?

2. A 3rd line ∥ to each of the 2 given lines and midway between them

3. The lateral surface of a cylinder with radius 1 in.

4. The ray that bisects the ∠, excluding its endpoint

5. The 2 pts. at which ⊙B intersects the ⊥ bisector of AB

6. A sphere with radius 3 cm and center P

7. A single point on $\overline{PQ}$, where the circles touch

8. There is none.

Assignment Guide

Basic: 1–10, 28–35
Average: 1–25, 28–35
Extended: 1–35

1.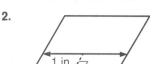

10. The broadcasting range of a television station is 50 miles. What is the locus of points that can receive a signal from the station?

2.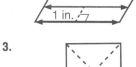

Set B Write a locus problem for which the figure in blue is the solution.

11. 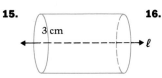 $\ell \parallel k$

12.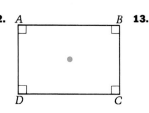

13.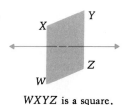

$WXYZ$ is a square.

3.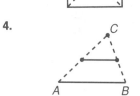

14.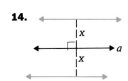

15. 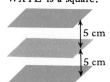 3 cm

16. 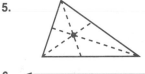 5 cm 5 cm

4.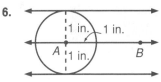

5.

Sketch each locus.

17. The points in a plane 3 cm from a given circle with a 5-cm radius

18. The points in the exterior of an angle that are 2 cm from the angle

19. The points equidistant from two parallel planes

6.

20. The points in a plane 1 inch from a given ray

21. The locus of points equidistant from collinear points A, B, and C

22. In a plane, all points 1 inch from a given line $\overleftrightarrow{RS}$ and 3 inches from point S

7.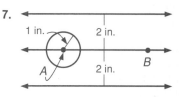

23. The points a dog can reach when it is tied 6 feet from the corner of a house with a 12-foot leash

24. The captain thought that the treasure was buried 20 paces from the ceremonial pole and equidistant from the pole and the palm tree. Where would the captain dig for the treasure?

8.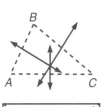

25. Given $\angle A$ and points B and C on one ray of the angle as shown, what is the locus of points in the plane of the angle equidistant from the sides of the angle and equidistant from B and C?

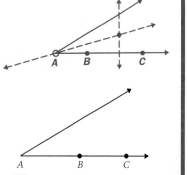

The intersection of the bisector of $\angle A$ and the $\perp$ bisector of $\overline{BC}$

9.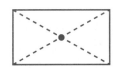

26. Depending on the placement of the 2 pts. in the int. of the ∠, the locus is (a) the pt. of intersection of the bisector of the ∠ and the ⊥ bisector of the seg. joining the 2 pts. in the int. of the ∠; if the line containing the seg. joining the 2 pts. is ⊥ to the ∠ bisector, then there is (b) no locus of points or (c) infinitely many pts. (the ∠ bisector, excluding its endpt.).

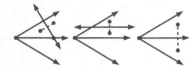

FOLLOW-UP

More Practice

• Worksheet 6–6

Extension

Have students locate the points $T(0, 0)$ and $P(10, 0)$ on graph paper. Ask them to locate and name coordinates of points that are equidistant from T and P. **(5, 0); (5, 1); (5, −1); etc.** What do these points have in common? **The x-coordinate is 5.** What is the equation of the locus of points equidistant from T and P? $x = 5$

The exercise may be repeated for $T(0, 0)$ and $Q(8, 0)$. $x = 4$ Ask students to determine a general equation for the locus of points equidistant from the origin and a point $(a, 0)$. $x = a/2$

• Extension 6–6

Computers

• Computer Worksheet 6–6

Set C   **26.** In a plane, what is the locus of points equidistant from the sides of an angle and equidistant from two points that lie in the interior of the angle?

27. In a plane, what is the locus of points 6 cm from a given line and equidistant from two points which lie in opposite half-planes formed by the given line?

▲ **Review**   **28.** What is the median of a trapezoid?

29. Describe two properties of isosceles trapezoids that are also properties of isosceles triangles.

30. If $\overleftrightarrow{AE} \parallel \overleftrightarrow{BF} \parallel \overleftrightarrow{CG} \parallel \overleftrightarrow{DH}$, then $EH = \underline{\ ?\ }$. **12**

31. Draw a large triangle XYZ. Then draw $\overline{XU}$, the altitude from X, $\overline{YV}$, the median from Y, and $\overline{ZW}$, the angle bisector of $\angle Z$.

32. In $\triangle JKM$ and $\triangle PQR$, $JK = PQ$, $KM = QR$, $m\angle K = 85$, and $m\angle Q = 60$. Which segment is longer, $\overline{JM}$ or $\overline{PR}$? $\overline{JM}$

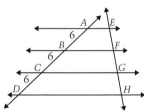

≡ **Thinking Ahead**   Draw a pair of lines ℓ and m intersecting at point P.

33. Position a pencil at P so that it is perpendicular to line ℓ but *not* perpendicular to m. Is the pencil perpendicular to the paper? **No**

34. Next position the pencil so that it is perpendicular to both lines ℓ and m at P. Is the pencil perpendicular to the paper? **Yes**

35. Now position the pencil perpendicular to the **Yes** paper at P. Is the pencil perpendicular to ℓ? to m? **Yes**

Algebra Review: Factoring Algebraic Expressions

Examples

1. Factor $45x^2y - 30x$.   **2.** Factor $25x^2 - 4y^2$.   **3.** Factor $3x^2 - 2x - 8$.

Solutions

1. $45x^2y - 30x$
$15x(3xy) - 15x(2)$
$15x(3xy - 2)$

2. $25x^2 - 4y^2$
$(5x)^2 - (2y)^2$
$(5x + 2y)(5x - 2y)$

3. Factors of $3x^2$: x, 3x
Factors of -8: 1, −8; −1, 8
2, −4; −2, 4
$(x - 2)(3x + 4)$

Factor each expression.   **1.** $4b(3a + b)$ **2.** $7x^2y^2 (1 - y)$ **3.** $(x - 7)(x + 7)$ **4.** $(x - 6)^2$

1. $12ab + 4b^2$ **2.** $7x^2y^2 - 21x^2y^3$ **3.** $x^2 - 49$ **4.** $x^2 - 12x + 36$

5. $6x^2 - 5x - 4$ **6.** $3a^3b^3 - a^2b^2 + 9ab$ **7.** $16a^2 - 9y^2$ **8.** $2x^2 + 16x + 30$

5. $(3x - 4)(2x + 1)$ **6.** $ab (3a^2b^2 - ab + 9)$ **7.** $(4a - 3y)(4a + 3y)$ **8.** $2(x + 3)(x + 5)$

Warm-Up Review

1. The set of all points that satisfy a given condition is a __?__. Locus
2. If point P is on line ℓ, how many lines can be drawn through P, perpendicular to ℓ? One
3. If P is not on ℓ, how many perpendicular lines can be drawn? One

6-7 Locus Theorems

A bus company wants to build a garage equidistant from the two schools on the map. From Lesson 6-6, you know that the garage should be built on the perpendicular bisector of the segment joining the two schools.

A locus statement is a powerful, yet concise, statement. To prove a locus theorem, you must show that: (1) if a point is on the locus, then it must satisfy the given condition(s), and (2) if a point satisfies the given condition(s), then it is on the locus.

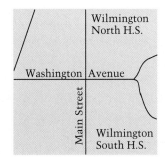

The locus described in the garage situation is expressed as: The locus of points in a plane equidistant from two given points is the perpendicular bisector of the segment joining the points.

To prove the two parts of this statement, you can rewrite the statement in "if and only if" form: In a plane, a point is equidistant from two given points if and only if the point lies on the perpendicular bisector of the segment joining the points.

This locus statement is Theorem 6-16, the proof of which is left to Exercise 2.

Theorem 6-16

In a plane, the locus of points equidistant from two given points is the perpendicular bisector of the segment joining the two points.

Part I In a plane, if a point is on the perpendicular bisector of a segment (the locus), then it is equidistant from the endpoints of the segment (given condition).

Given ℓ is the perpendicular bisector of $\overline{AB}$; P is on ℓ.

Prove $PA = PB$

Plan for Proof Draw $\overline{AP}$ and $\overline{BP}$; prove $\triangle AMP \cong \triangle BMP$. Then $PA = PB$.

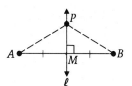

Part II In a plane, if a point is equidistant from the endpoints of a segment (given condition), then it is on the perpendicular bisector of the segment (the locus).

Given $QA = QB$; ℓ is the perpendicular bisector of $\overline{AB}$.

Prove Q is on ℓ.

Plan for Proof Draw $\overline{QA}$, $\overline{QB}$, and $\overline{QM}$. Prove $\triangle QAM \cong \triangle QBM$. Show $\overline{QM} \perp \overline{AB}$ at M. Then $\overleftrightarrow{QM}$ must be ℓ.

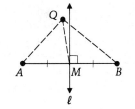

LESSON 6-7

Resources

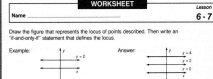

Teaching Aid 3, grid paper
Visual Aid 3, grid paper
Teaching Aid 5, four-quadrant grids
Visual Aid 5, four-quadrant grids
Worksheet 6-7
Extension 6-7
Algebra Review 6
Chapter 6 Test, Form I
Chapter 6 Test, Form II
Chapter 6 Test, Form III
Cumulative Test Chapters 1-6, Form I
Cumulative Test Chapters 1-6, Form II
Practice for Standardized Tests

OBJECTIVE

State and apply theorems relating to locus.

WORKSHEET   *Lesson* **6-7**

Name _____

Draw the figure that represents the locus of points described. Then write an "if-and-only-if" statement that defines the locus.

Example:

Locus of points 2 units away from the line $y = 2$

Answer:

Statement: A point is 2 units away from the line $y = 2$ if and only if it lies on the line $y = 4$ or on the line $y = 0$.

1. Locus of points equidistant from point $P(0, 0)$ and $Q(4, 0)$
Statement: A point is equidistant from P and Q if and only if it lies on the line $x = 2$.

2. Locus of points equidistant from points $L(0, 3)$ and $M(3, 0)$
Statement: A point is equidistant from L and M if and only if it lies on the line $x = y$.

3. Locus of points equidistant from $\overline{AB}$ and $\overline{AC}$
Statement: A point is equidistant from $\overline{AB}$ and $\overline{AC}$ if and only if it lies on the line $y = 0$ (x-axis).

4. Locus of points equidistant from $\overline{SR}$ and $\overline{ST}$
Statement: A point is equidistant from $\overline{SR}$ and $\overline{ST}$ if and only if it lies on the line $x - y = 0$.

5. Locus of points 2 units away from point $P(0, 0)$
Statement: A point is 2 units away from (0, 0) if and only if it lies on the circle $x^2 + y^2 = 4$.

6. Locus of points 1 unit away from point $B(4, 1)$
Statement: A point is 1 unit away from (4, 1) if and only if it lies on the circle $(x - 4)^2 + (y - 1)^2 = 1$.

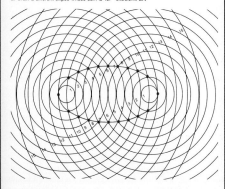
Theorem 6-16 describes a locus of points in a plane. Theorem
6-17 describes a locus with similar conditions; but since the
words *in a plane* are absent, the locus is a set of points
in space.

Theorem 6-17

The locus of points equidistant from two given points is the plane
perpendicular to and bisecting the segment joining the given points.

Example 1

Write the two parts to be proved for Theorem 6-17.

Solution

In the theorem, the locus is the plane perpendicular to and
bisecting the segment. The given condition is that the points in
space must be equidistant from two given points.

Part I   If a point is on the plane perpendicular to and
           bisecting a given segment, then it is equidistant from
           the endpoints of the segment.

Part II If a point is equidistant from the endpoints of a
           segment, then it lies on the plane perpendicular to and
           bisecting the segment.

Example 2

In the coordinate plane, what is the locus of points equidistant
from the points $R(3, 2)$ and $S(7, 2)$?

Solution

Use Theorem 6-16. The locus of points equidistant from R and
S is the perpendicular bisector of segment $\overline{RS}$. The midpoint of
$\overline{RS}$ is point $M(5, 2)$. The equation of the line passing through M
and perpendicular to $\overline{RS}$ is $x = 5$.

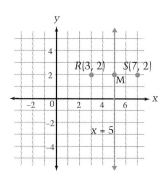

Theorem 6-18

In a plane, the locus of points equidistant from the sides of an
angle is the bisecting ray of the angle, excluding its endpoint.

Theorems 6-17 and 6-18 are to be proved in Exercises 16, 17,
and 22. Theorem 6-19 shows how a locus theorem is used in a
proof. You are asked to prove it in Exercise 20.

Theorem 6-19

If a line is perpendicular to each of two intersecting lines at their point of intersection, then it is perpendicular to the plane containing the two lines.

Given ℓ is perpendicular to m and n; m and n lie in $\mathcal{E}$.

Prove ℓ is perpendicular to $\mathcal{E}$.

Plan for Proof To satisfy the definition of a line perpendicular to a plane, prove ℓ is perpendicular to *any* line in $\mathcal{E}$ passing through X, the point of intersection of m and n. Draw any line k in $\mathcal{E}$ through X. Choose A and B on ℓ so that $AX = BX$. Then m and n are perpendicular bisectors of $\overline{AB}$. Choose C on m, and D on n, and let $\overline{CD}$ intersect k at Y. Show $AC = BC$ and $AD = BD$. Show $\triangle ACD \cong \triangle BCD$; then $\triangle ACY \cong \triangle BCY$. If $AY = BY$, then k is the $\perp$ bisector of $\overline{AB}$, and $\ell \perp k$. So $\ell \perp \mathcal{E}$ by definition of a line perpendicular to a plane.

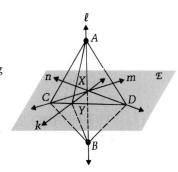

Checking for Understanding

1. On which street should the bus garage be built? Why?

2. In Theorem 6-16, Part I, why are the triangles congruent? SAS Post.

3. In Theorem 6-16, Part II, why are the triangles congruent? SSS Post.

4. Draw a diagram, and state the Given and the Prove for Theorem 6-17, Parts I and II.

5. In Theorem 6-18, why must the endpoint of the bisecting ray be excluded? Because it is on the sides of the ∠.

Written Exercises

Set A

1. If X and Y are each equidistant from A and B, explain why $\overleftrightarrow{XY}$ is the perpendicular bisector of $\overline{AB}$.

2. Prove Theorem 6-16.

Use this statement: In a plane, the locus of points equidistant from two parallel lines is a line parallel to the given lines and midway between them.

3. Write the two parts of this statement to be proved.

4. Draw a diagram and write the Given and the Prove for each part.

Additional Example

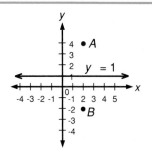

In the coordinate plane, what is the locus of points equidistant from points $A(2, 4)$ and $B(2, -2)$? $y = 1$

ANSWERS

Checking for Understanding

1. on Washington Ave., because it lies on the $\perp$ bisector of the seg. joining the 2 schools

4. *Part I:* Given: $\mathcal{E}$ is the $\perp$ bisecting plane of $\overline{AB}$; P lies in $\mathcal{E}$. Prove: $PA = PB$

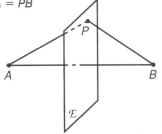

Part II: Given: $\mathcal{E}$ is the $\perp$ bisecting plane of $\overline{AB}$; $PA = PB$ Prove: P lies in $\mathcal{E}$.

Written Exercises

1. In a plane, the locus of pts. equidistant from 2 given pts. is the $\perp$ bisector of the seg. joining the 2 pts.

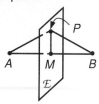

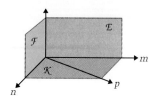

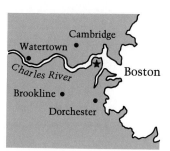

9. A point is *d* cm from a given point if and only if it lies on the circle with radius *d* and center at the given point.

16.

Given: Plane ε is $\perp \overleftrightarrow{AB}$ and bisects $\overline{AB}$; ε intersects $\overline{AB}$ at *M*; *P* lies in ε. Prove: *PA* = *PB* Proof: 1. Plane ε is $\perp$ to $\overleftrightarrow{AB}$ and bisects $\overline{AB}$; ε intersects $\overline{AB}$ at *M*; *P* lies in ε. (Given) 2. *M* is the midpt. of $\overline{AB}$. (Def. of seg. bisector [1]) 3. *MA* = *MB* (Def. of midpt. [2]) 4. Draw $\overline{PM}$. (2 pts. determine a line.) 5. $\overline{PM}$ lies in ε. (Flat Plane Post. [1, 4]) 6. $\overline{PM} \perp \overleftrightarrow{AB}$ (Def. of line $\perp$ to plane [1]) 7. $\angle PMB$ and $\angle PMA$ are rt. $\angle$s. (2 $\perp$ lines form 4 rt. $\angle$s. [6]) 8. $m\angle PMA = m\angle PMB$ (All rt. $\angle$s are =. [7]) 9. *PM* = *PM* (Reflexive Prop.) 10. $\triangle PMA \cong \triangle PMB$ (SAS $\cong$ Post. [3, 8, 9]) 11. *PA* = *PB* (Corres. parts of $\cong \triangle$s are =. [10])

17.

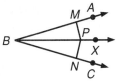

Part I: Given: *P* is on $\overrightarrow{BX}$; $\overrightarrow{BX}$ bisects $\angle ABC$; $\overline{PM} \perp \overline{BA}$; $\overline{PN} \perp \overline{BC}$; *P* ≠ *B* Prove: *PM* = *PN* Proof: 1. *P* is on $\overrightarrow{BX}$; $\overrightarrow{BX}$ bisects $\angle ABC$; $\overline{PM} \perp \overline{BA}$; $\overline{PN} \perp \overline{BC}$; *P* ≠ *B* (Given) 2. $m\angle MBP = m\angle NBP$ (Def. of $\angle$ bisector [1]) 3. $\angle PMB$ and $\angle PNB$ are rt. $\angle$s. (2 $\perp$ lines intersect to form 4 rt. $\angle$s. [1]) 4. $m\angle PMB = m\angle PNB$ (All rt. $\angle$s are =. [3]) 5. *BP* = *BP* (Reflexive Prop.) 6. $\triangle PMB \cong \triangle PNB$ (AAS Thm. [2, 4, 5]) 7. *PM* = *PN* (Corres. parts of $\cong \triangle$s are =. [6]) *Part II:* Given: $\overrightarrow{BX}$ bisects $\angle ABC$; *MP* = *NP*; $\overline{PM} \perp \overline{BM}$; $\overline{PN} \perp \overline{BN}$ Prove: *P* is on $\overrightarrow{BX}$. Proof: Either *P* is on $\overrightarrow{BX}$ or *P* is not on $\overrightarrow{BX}$. Suppose *P* is not on

Tell which line and plane are perpendicular.

5. Given: ℓ is perpendicular to *m* and *p*. $\ell \perp \mathcal{K}$

6. Given: *m* is perpendicular to ℓ and *n*. $m \perp \varepsilon$

7. Given: *m* and ℓ are perpendicular to *n*. $n \perp \varepsilon$

8. Given: ℓ is perpendicular to *m* and *n*. $\ell \perp \mathcal{K}$

9. Write an "if and only if" statement for this locus: In a plane, the points *d* cm from a given point.

In the coordinate plane, find the locus of points

10. 5 units from the line *y* = 3. Lines *y* = 8 and *y* = −2

11. equidistant from the lines *x* = −2 and *x* = 5. Line $x = \frac{3}{2}$

Set B **12..** The Franklins are moving to the Boston area. Ben will work in Brookline, and Kay will work in Cambridge. If they both want to travel the same distance to work and live on the Charles River, where should they look for a home? **Watertown**

In the coordinate plane, find the locus of points

13. in the first quadrant that are equidistant from the x-axis and y-axis. Lines *y* = *x*, *x* and *y* both > 0

14. equidistant from the lines *y* = *x* + 4 and *y* = *x* − 4. Line *y* = *x*

15. 5 units from *x* = 1 and equidistant from *y* = 2 and *y* = −4. Pts. (6, −1) and (−4, −1)

16. Prove Theorem 6-17, Part I.

17. Prove Theorem 6-18. (HINT: From a point in the bisecting ray, draw a perpendicular to each side of the angle.)

18. Prove: If the bisectors of two angles of a triangle intersect at a point *P*, then *P* is equidistant from the sides of the third angle.

19. Prove: If the perpendicular bisectors of two sides of a triangle intersect at a point *Q*, then *Q* is equidistant from the endpoints of the third side.

BX. Then $\overrightarrow{BP}$ does not bisect ∠
ABC. (An angle has exactly 1 bi-
sector.) However, by the HL Thm.,
△BPM ≅ △BPN. Thus, m∠PBM =
m∠PBN. And since m∠PBM = m∠
PBN, $\overrightarrow{BP}$ bisects ∠ABC. This contradicts the fact that $\overrightarrow{BP}$ does not
bisect ∠ABC. Therefore, the as-
sumption that P is not on $\overrightarrow{BX}$ is
false. We conclude that P is on
$\overrightarrow{BX}$.

Set C **20.** Write a paragraph proof for Theorem 6-19.

21. Use an indirect proof to prove this statement: If a plane is perpendicular to a line at a point P, then the plane contains all the lines perpendicular to the given line at P.

22. Prove Theorem 6-17, Part II. Use the statement in Exercise 21 as one of the reasons.

▲**Review** Draw a figure and describe the locus.

23. In a plane, all points 5 cm from a given line

24. In space, all points 5 cm from a given line

25. Given trapezoid $TRAP$ with $T(1, 1)$, $R(3, 1)$, $A(5, 5)$, and $P(2, 3)$, find the length of the median. $\frac{3\sqrt{5}}{2}$

26. At the right, $m\angle Y = \underline{\ ?\ }$. 29

27. Give several examples of surfaces in your classroom that suggest parallel planes.

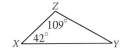

27. Samples: Ceiling and floor; opposite walls

Progress Check

Lesson 6-5, page 261 Bases: $\overline{AB}$ and $\overline{CD}$; legs: $\overline{BC}$ and $\overline{AD}$

1. In trapezoid $ABCD$ with $\overline{AB} \parallel \overline{CD}$, name the bases and the legs.

2. In isosceles trapezoid $QRST$ with $\overline{QR} \parallel \overline{ST}$, if $QS = 6x + 5$ and $RT = 4x + 17$, then $x = \underline{\ ?\ }$. 6

3. Given isosceles trapezoid $HJKL$ with $\overline{HJ} \parallel \overline{LK}$ and median $\overline{PQ}$, if $HJ = 42$ and $PQ = 27$, find LK. 12

Lesson 6-6, page 268

4. Draw a figure and describe the locus of points in a plane 3 in. from a given line.

Describe the locus of points

5. equidistant from two given parallel lines.

6. equidistant from the three sides of a triangle.

Lesson 6-7, page 273

7. In the coordinate plane, what is the locus of points equidistant from $y = -1$ and $y = 7$?

8. What two things must be proved when proving a locus theorem?

18.

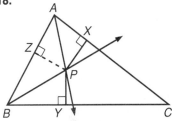

Given: $\overrightarrow{AP}$ bisects $\angle BAC$; $\overrightarrow{BP}$ bisects $\angle ABC$; $\overline{PX} \perp \overline{AC}$; $\overline{PY} \perp \overline{BC}$

Prove: $PX = PY$ Proof: 1. $\overrightarrow{AP}$ bisects $\angle BAC$; $\overrightarrow{BP}$ bisects $\angle ABC$; $\overline{PX} \perp \overline{AC}$; $\overline{PY} \perp \overline{BC}$ (Given) 2. Draw $\overline{PZ} \perp \overline{AB}$. (Through a given pt. not on a given line, there exists exactly one line ∥ to the given line.) 3. $PZ = PX$ and $PZ = PY$ (If a pt. is on the bisector of an ∠, then it is equidistant from the sides of the ∠.) 4. $PX = PY$ (Substitution Prop. [3])

FOLLOW-UP

More Practice

• **Worksheet 6–7**

Extension

Find the locus of points equidistant from the lines whose equations are (1) $y = 2x + 5$ and $y = 2x + 1$, (2) $y = x - 3$ and $y = x + 2$ and (3) $y = 3x - 4$ and $y = 3x$. $y = 2x + 3$; $y = x - \frac{1}{2}$; $y = 3x - 2$ Ask students to generalize and find the locus of points equidistant from $y = mx + b$ and $y = mx + c$. $y = mx + \frac{(b + c)}{2}$

• **Extension 6–7**

Chapter 6 Summary

Important Terms

Equidistant (268)

Bases of a trapezoid (261)

Isosceles trapezoid (262)

Legs of a trapezoid (261)

Locus (268)

Median of a trapezoid (239)

Parallelogram (239)

Rectangle (249)

Rhombus (249)

Square (249)

Trapezoid (261)

Important Ideas

1. A quadrilateral is a parallelogram if and only if
   a. both pairs of opposite sides are parallel. (239)
   b. both pairs of opposite sides are equal. (239, 244)
   c. the diagonals bisect each other. (240, 245)

2. Both pairs of opposite angles of a parallelogram are equal. (240)

3. The distance between two parallel lines is constant. (241)

4. If two sides of a quadrilateral are parallel and equal, then the quadrilateral is a parallelogram. (244)

5. A parallelogram is a rectangle if and only if its diagonals are equal. (249)

6. A parallelogram is a rhombus if and only if the diagonals are perpendicular and each diagonal bisects a pair of opposite angles. (250)

7. In a triangle, if a segment joins the midpoints of two sides, then it is parallel to the third side and its length is one half the length of the third side. (255)

8. If three or more parallel lines cut off equal segments on one transversal, then they cut off equal segments on every transversal. (256)

9. The median of a trapezoid is parallel to the bases and its length is one-half the sum of the lengths of the bases. (261)

10. In an isosceles trapezoid, the base angles are equal and the diagonals are equal. (262, 263)

11. A locus is the set of all points, and only those points, that satisfy a given condition. (268)

12. To prove a locus theorem, it must be shown that
    a. if point is on the locus, then it must satisfy the given condition(s);
    b. if a point satisfies the given condition(s), then it is on the locus. (273)

Chapter 6 Review

Lesson 6-1, page 239

Given: $\square ABCD$

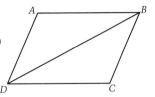

1. Name a pair of equal segments. **Sample: $\overline{AB}$ and $\overline{CD}$**
2. Name two pairs of equal angles. **Sample: $m\angle A$ and $m\angle C$; $m\angle ABD$ and $m\angle BDC$**
3. Name a pair of supplementary angles. **Sample: $\angle A$ and $\angle ADC$**
4. Given $A(-2, 1)$, $B(0, 5)$, and $C(6, 5)$, the coordinates of D are ___?___. **(4, 1)**

Lesson 6-2, page 244

Tell which definition or theorem is needed to prove that quadrilateral $EFGH$ is a parallelogram.

5. Given: $EF = GH$; $EH = FG$ **Thm. 6-6**
6. Given: $EF = GH$; $\overline{EF} \parallel \overline{GH}$ **Thm. 6-5**
7. Given: $\overline{FH}$ and $\overline{EG}$ bisect each other. **Thm. 6-7**
8. Given: $\overline{EF} \parallel \overline{GH}$; $\overline{EH} \parallel \overline{FG}$ **Def. of $\square$**

Lesson 6-3, page 249

Tell whether $\square ABCD$ is a rectangle, a rhombus, or a square.

9. Given: $AC = 13$; $DB = 13$ **Rect.**
10. Given: $AD = DC$ **Rhombus**
11. Given: $m\angle A = 90$; $AB = BC$ **Square**
12. Given: $\overline{AC} \perp \overline{BD}$ **Rhombus**
13. Given: $A(1, 4)$, $B(6, 1)$, $C(3, -4)$, $D(-2, -1)$ **Square**

If the statement is always true, write *true*. If it is not always true, write *false*.

14. A parallelogram is a square. **False**
15. A square is a rhombus. **True**
16. A square is a rectangle. **True**
17. A rhombus is a rectangle. **False**
18. A rhombus is a parallelogram. **True**

ANSWERS

Chapter Review

27.

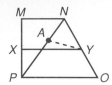

Given: Trapezoid MNOP with median $\overline{XY}$ and diagonal $\overline{PN}$ Prove: $\overline{XY}$ bisects $\overline{PN}$. Proof: 1. Trap. MNOP with median $\overline{XY}$ and diag. $\overline{PN}$ (Given) 2. X and Y are midpts. of $\overline{MP}$ and $\overline{NO}$, respectively. (Def. of median of a trap. [1]) 3. Locate A, the midpt. of $\overline{PN}$. (A seg. has exactly 1 midpt.) 4. Draw $\overline{AY}$. (2 pts. determine a line.) 5. $\overline{AY} \parallel \overline{PO}$ (Seg. joining midpts. of 2 sides of $\triangle$ is $\parallel$ to the third side. [2, 3]) 6. $\overline{XY} \parallel \overline{PO}$ (Median of trap. is $\parallel$ to bases. [1]) 7. A lies on $\overline{XY}$. (Through a pt. not on a line, there is exactly 1 line $\parallel$ to the given line. [5, 6]) 8. $\overline{XY}$ bisects $\overline{PN}$. (Def. of seg. bisector [3, 7])

28. Proof: 1. $\overline{XY}$ is the median of isosceles trap. MNOP. (Given) 2. $\overline{XY} \parallel \overline{PO}$ (The median of a trap. is $\parallel$ to the bases.) 3. XYOP is a trap. (Def. of trap. [2]) 4. MP = NO (Def. of isos. trap. [1]) 5. X and Y are midpts. of $\overline{MP}$ and $\overline{NO}$, resp. (Def. of median of trap. [1]) 6. MX = PX; NY = OY (Def. of midpt. [5]) 7. MX + XP = MP; NY + YO = NO (Seg. Add. Post.) 8. XP + XP = MP, or 2(XP) = MP; YO + YO = NO, or 2(YO) = NO (Substitution Prop. [6, 7]) 9. 2(XP) = 2(YO) (Substitution Prop. [4, 8]) 10. XP = YO (Div. Prop. [9]) 11. XYOP is isos. trap. (Def. of isos. trap. [3, 10])

29. The locus of pts. is a circle with a radius of r cm and center at the given pt.

30. The locus of pts. is a cylindrical surface determined by all circles with centers on the given line and with radius k inches, and the plane of each circle is $\perp$ to the given line.

Lesson 6-4, page 255

M and N are midpoints of $\overline{OJ}$ and $\overline{OK}$, respectively.

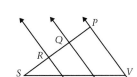

19. If MN = 8, find JK. **16**

20. If JK = 11, find MN. **5.5**

21. Given J(2, 2), K(13, 2), and M(5, 7), the coordinates of N are __?__. **(10.5, 7)**

22. If MN = x + 5 and JK = 4x − 15, find x, MN, and JK. **12.5; 17.5; 35**

Given: PQ = QR = RS; $\overleftrightarrow{RT} \parallel \overleftrightarrow{QU} \parallel \overleftrightarrow{PV}$

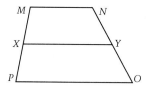

23. If ST = 6, find TU and UV. **6; 6**

24. If SV = 7.5, find ST. **2.5**

25. If ST = 4a − 9 and UV = 2a + 10, find TU. **29**

Lesson 6-5, page 261

Given: $\overline{XY}$ is the median of trapezoid MNOP.

26. If XY = 5k − 7, MN = k + 7, and PO = 3k + 3, find XY. **13**

27. Prove: $\overline{XY}$ bisects diagonal $\overline{PN}$.

28. Prove: If MNOP is isosceles, then XYOP is an isosceles trapezoid.

Lesson 6-6, page 268

Describe each locus.

29. In a plane, the points r cm from a given point

30. The points k inches from a given line

31. In a plane, the points equidistant from a pair of opposite sides of a rectangle

Lesson 6-7, page 273

Use this statement: The locus of points at a given distance from a given point is a sphere with the given point as the center and the given distance as the radius.

32. Write the two parts that must be proved in order to prove the locus statement.

33. Draw a diagram and write the Given and the Prove for each part.

Chapter 6 Test

Is the statement *always true*, *sometimes true*, or *never true*?

1. A rectangle is a parallelogram with four right angles. **Always**

2. If the diagonals of a quadrilateral are equal, then it is a rectangle. **Sometimes**

3. The diagonals of a rhombus bisect each other. **Always**

4. In $\triangle ABC$, if X and Y are the midpoints of $\overline{AC}$ and $\overline{BC}$, respectively, then $XY = AB$. **Never**

5. If the diagonals of $\square DEFG$ are perpendicular, then $DEFG$ is a square. **Sometimes**

Draw a figure and describe the locus.

6. In a plane, all points 6 cm from a given line

7. In a plane, all points equidistant from two parallel lines

8. List three properties of a parallelogram.

9. What two parts are to be proved for this locus theorem? In a plane, the locus of points equidistant from the two sides of an angle is the bisecting ray of the angle, excluding its endpoint.

Does the given information guarantee that $PQRS$ is a parallelogram?

10. $PQ = RS$; $QR = PS$ **Yes**   11. $m\angle 1 = m\angle 2$; $PQ = RS$ **No**

12. $P(-1, -3)$; $Q(4, 4)$; $R(11, 4)$; $S(5, -3)$ **No**

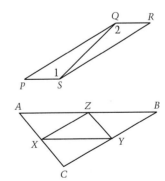

Given: X, Y, and Z are midpoints of $\overline{AC}$, $\overline{BC}$, and $\overline{AB}$, respectively.

13. If $XY = 12$, find AB. **24**

14. If $AC = 17$, find YZ. **8.5**

15. If $AB = 14$, find the length of the median of trapezoid $ABYX$. **10.5**

16. Given: Quadrilateral $ABCD$; $\overline{AC} \perp \overline{BD}$; $\overline{AC}$ and $\overline{BD}$ bisect each other.
    Prove: $ABCD$ is a rhombus.

---

6. The locus is 2 lines ∥ to the given line and 6 cm on either side of the given line.

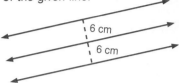

7. The locus is a line ∥ to each of the 2 given lines and lying midway between the 2 given lines.

8. Opp. sides are =; opp. ∠s are =; diags. bisect each other.

9. *Part I:* In a plane, if a pt. is on the bisecting ray of an ∠, excluding its endpt., then it is equidistant from the 2 sides of the ∠. *Part II:* In a plane, if a pt. is equidistant from the sides of an ∠, then it lies on the bisecting ray of the ∠, excluding its endpt.

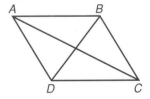

16. Proof: 1. Quad. $ABCD$; $\overline{AC}$ and $\overline{BD}$ bisect each other. (Given) 2. $ABCD$ is a $\square$. (If the diags. of a quad. bisect each other, then the quad. is a $\square$. [1]) 3. $\overline{AC} \perp \overline{BD}$ (Given) 4. $ABCD$ is a rhombus. (If the diags. of a $\square$ are $\perp$, then the $\square$ is a rhombus. [3])

Cumulative Review   Chapters 1–6

Select the best answer for each item.

1. Points _?_ are coplanar.
  A. A, B, F, and H
  B. E, A, C, and D
  C. B, F, D, and H
  D. E, F, D, and H

2. B is between A and C. $AB = 5$; $BC = 10$.
  Find AC.
  A. 15   **B.** 10   **C.** 5   **D.** 20

3. D lies in the exterior of $\angle ABC$;
  $m\angle ABC = 30$; $m\angle CBD = 10$. Find
  $m\angle ABD$.
  A. 20   **B.** 40   **C.** 90   **D.** 180

4. Use inductive reasoning to predict the
  next number in this sequence: 52, 53,
  56, 61.
  A. 62   **B.** 64   **C.** 66   **D.** 68

5. Angles 1 and 2 form a linear pair. Which
  statement is not necessarily true?
  A. The sum of the measures of $\angle 1$ and
    $\angle 2$ is 180.
  B. $\angle 1$ and $\angle 2$ form perpendicular lines.
  C. $\angle 1$ and $\angle 2$ are supplementary.
  D. Two rays from $\angle 1$ and $\angle 2$ are
    opposite rays.

6. If $m\angle 1 = m\angle 2$,
  then _?_.
  A. $\ell_1 \parallel \ell_2$
  B. ℓ_1 and ℓ_2 are skew
  C. $m\angle 2 + m\angle 3 = 180$
  D. $m\angle 4 = m\angle 2$

7. The hypothesis of the statement "All
  ravens are black" is "_?_."
  A. If a creature is a raven, then it is
    black.
  B. A creature is a raven.
  C. All ravens are not black.
  D. The creature is black.

8. Given $\overleftrightarrow{EA} \parallel \overleftrightarrow{DB}$, it
  is correct to
  conclude that _?_.
  A. $m\angle ACB = m\angle ABC$
  B. $m\angle FAB = m\angle EAC$
  C. $m\angle FAE = m\angle ACB$
  D. $m\angle GAF = m\angle EAB$

9. Given: $m\angle A = m\angle B$; $m\angle B = m\angle C$
  Prove: $m\angle A = m\angle C$
  Which reason justifies the Prove?
  A. Transitive Property
  B. Definition of equal angles
  C. Reflexive Property
  D. Symmetric Property

10. In a proof using
  this diagram,
  you may assume
  that _?_.
  A. $\overleftrightarrow{AB} \parallel \overleftrightarrow{ED}$
  B. E, D, and C are collinear
  C. C is the midpoint of $\overline{ED}$
  D. $m\angle ACB = 90$

11. If in a plane, $\ell_1 \perp \ell_2$ and $\ell_2 \perp \ell_3$,
  then _?_.
  A. $\ell_3 \parallel \ell_1$ **B.** $\ell_3 \perp \ell_1$
  C. $\ell_1 \parallel \ell_2$ **D.** ℓ_1 and ℓ_3 are
                                        skew

12. Given $\ell_1 \parallel \ell_2$, find $m\angle 3$.

A. 19

B. 13

C. 84

D. 60

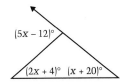

13. The perimeter of a regular octagon is 72. The length of a side is __?__.

A. 8   **B.** 9   C. 12   D. 6

14. A triangle with three 60° angles is __?__.

A. Acute, equilateral, and right

B. Regular, obtuse, and scalene

C. Scalene, isosceles, and equilateral

D. Equiangular, acute, and regular

15. You wish to prove this statement indirectly: Complementary angles are acute. What do you assume at the start?

A. Complementary angles are right.

B. Complementary angles are not acute.

C. Complementary angles have measures less than 90.

D. Complementary angles are not supplementary.

16. If $m\angle ABC = m\angle DBA$, then $\overleftrightarrow{AB}$ and $\overleftrightarrow{DC}$ are __?__.

A. Parallel

B. Perpendicular

C. Skew

D. Parallel or skew

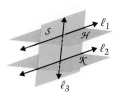

17. How many lines perpendicular to $\overleftrightarrow{AB}$ contain B?

A. One   B. Zero

C. Two   **D.** An infinite number

18. $m\angle 1 = 30$, and $\angle 1$ is an obtuse angle. This statement contradicts the __?__.

A. Definition of degree measure

B. Definition of obtuse angle

C. Protractor Postulate

D. Definition of angle measure

19. In the triangle below, x = __?__.

$(5x - 12)°$

$(2x + 4)°$ $(x + 20)°$

A. 21   **B.** 18   C. 78   D. 93

20. If planes $\mathcal{H}$ and $\mathcal{K}$ are parallel, which statement is true?

ℓ_1

S $\mathcal{H}$

ℓ_2

$\mathcal{K}$

ℓ_3

A. $\ell_1 \perp \ell_2$ B. Plane $\mathcal{H} \perp$ plane S

C. $\ell_1 \parallel \ell_2$ D. ℓ_1 and ℓ_2 are skew.

21. A six-sided polygon is a(n) __?__.

A. Pentagon   B. Heptagon

C. Octagon   **D.** Hexagon

22. A regular heptagon has sides of length 10. Its perimeter is __?__.

A. 90   B. 9   C. 7   **D.** 70

23. The sum of the measures of the interior angles of a polygon is 720. The polygon has __?__ sides.

A. 4   **B.** 6   **C.** 7   **D.** 12

24. Given $\triangle ABC \cong \triangle BDE$. Name the angle corresponding to $\angle BCA$.

A. $\angle DBE$

B. $\angle DEB$

C. $\angle EDB$

D. $\angle EBD$

25. If A is the midpoint of $\overline{BC}$ and $\overleftrightarrow{EB} \parallel \overleftrightarrow{CD}$, then $\triangle BAE \cong \triangle CAD$ by the __?__ Theorem (Postulate).

A. SSS

B. HL

C. SAS

D. AAS

26. The lengths of two sides of a triangle are 9 and 11. The length of the third side is between __?__.

A. 9 and 11   **B.** 9 and 20

C. 2 and 20   **D.** 2 and 11

27. If $\triangle ABC \cong \triangle DBC$, which statement is not necessarily true?

A. $m\angle DBC = m\angle CBA$

B. $AB = CD$

C. $m\angle D = m\angle A$

D. $AC = DC$

28. Triangle ABC is isosceles. Find $m\angle B$.

A. 10

B. 13

C. 62

D. 74

29. According to the Hinge Theorem, if __?__, then $m\angle A > m\angle D$.

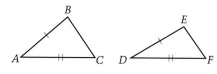

A. $AB > BC$ **B.** $DE > EF$

C. $BC > EF$ **D.** $AC > DE$

30. Which statement is not true?

A. A parallellogram is a rhombus.

B. A square is a rectangle.

C. A rectangle is a parallelogram.

D. A parallelogram is a quadrilateral.

31. Given $\square LMON$, find $m\angle O$.

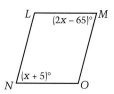

A. 105   **B.** 75   **C.** 70   **D.** 80

32. If $\overline{AB}$ is the median of trapezoid *LMNO*, which of the following statements is not necessarily true?

A. $MB = BN$

B. $\overleftrightarrow{AB} \parallel \overleftrightarrow{ON}$

C. $OL = NM$

D. $AB = \frac{1}{2}(ON + LM)$

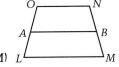

33. The locus of points equidistant from *A* and *B* is __?__ .

A. A line perpendicular to $\overline{AB}$ through the midpoint of $\overline{AB}$

B. A plane perpendicular to $\overline{AB}$ through the midpoint of $\overline{AB}$

C. A pair of circles centered at *A* and *B*

D. The midpoint of $\overline{AB}$

34. If __?__ , then *ABCD* is a parallelogram.

A. $m\angle 1 = m\angle 2$; $m\angle 3 = m\angle 4$

B. $\angle 1$ and $\angle 2$ are supplementary; $m\angle 4 = m\angle 5$

C. $m\angle 1 = m\angle 2 = m\angle 5$

D. $AD = BC$

35. Given: *ABCD* is a rhombus. To prove *ABCD* is a square, show that:

A. $DC = BC$

B. $\overline{BD}$ bisects $\overline{AC}$; $\overline{AC}$ bisects $\overline{BD}$.

C. $DB = AC$

D. $\overline{DB} \perp \overline{AC}$

36. If $\overrightarrow{BC}$ bisects $\angle ABD$, which of the following is true?

A. $BC = AB = AD$

B. A point on $\overrightarrow{BC}$ is equidistant from $\overrightarrow{AB}$ and $\overrightarrow{BD}$.

C. A plane containing $\overrightarrow{BC}$ is perpendicular to the plane containing *A*, *B*, and *D*.

D. *C* is equidistant from *A* and *D*.

37. The diagonals of quadrilateral *RSTU* bisect each other. *RSTU* is a(n) __?__ .

A. Parallelogram   **B.** Rhombus

C. Trapezoid   **D.** Rectangle

38. *A*, *B*, and *C* are midpoints. Which of the following statements is not necessarily true?

A. $2AB = EF$

B. $BF = CF$

C. $BC = \frac{1}{2}DE$

D. $\overline{AB} \parallel \overline{EF}$

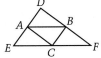

39. In $\triangle LMN$, *S* and *T* are midpoints of $\overline{LN}$ and $\overline{MN}$, respectively. If $LM = 6y + 6$ and $ST = 5y - 3$, then $ST = $ __?__ .

A. 3

B. 9

C. 12

D. 24

40. A(n) __?__ of a triangle is a segment from any vertex perpendicular to the line containing the opposite side.

A. Altitude   **B.** Angle bisector

C. Hypotenuse   **D.** Median

CHAPTER 7

Similarity

Chapter Overview

In this chapter ratio and proportion are reviewed, properties of a proportion are proved, and numerical and algebraic applications are shown.

Similarity is defined for all convex polygons, and similar triangles are introduced using the AA Similarity Postulate. Similarity of triangles is expanded with the SAS and SSS similarity theorems. Other segments in a triangle proportional to corresponding sides (i.e., altitudes, medians and angle bisectors) are also studied. Indirect measurement is shown as a major application of similarity.

Other applications related to ratio and proportion are presented, including segments divided by parallel lines and lines parallel to one side of a triangle.

The **problem-solving skill** of drawing a diagram is invaluable for most problems in this chapter. Some problems may offer an opportunity for students to use a **calculator**.

Perspectives

Lesson 7-1 reviews the concepts of ratio and proportion and includes application problems.

Lesson 7-2 introduces similar polygons and shows some applications of the proportionality of corresponding sides. Theorem 7-1 establishes that perimeters of similar polygons are proportional to the lengths of their corresponding sides.

Lesson 7-3 concentrates on the AA Similarity Postulate. It is postulated so that we can move quickly into writing proofs that triangles are similar. Students are asked to use given information to determine whether two triangles are similar and to solve for unknowns when they are.

Lesson 7-4 uses the AA Similarity Postulate to show that parallel lines cut off proportional line segments on two or more transversals drawn through them. Theorem 7-3 applies this to a line parallel to one side of a triangle.

Lesson 7-5 gives students two more methods for proving that triangles are similar. The SAS and SSS similarity theorems can be useful in numerical applications to verify that triangles are similar.

The proofs of these two theorems make extensive use of the AA Similarity Postulate and properties of similarity.

Pacing Chart for Chapter 7

Lesson	Objectives	Basic Course	Average Course	Extended Course
7–1	Use ratios and proportions to solve problems; use properties of equality to change the form of a proportion.	$1\frac{1}{2}$	1	1
7–2	Recognize and apply the properties of similar polygons, using ratios and proportions.	$1\frac{1}{2}$	1	1
7–3	Apply the AA Similarity Postulate to prove that triangles are similar.	2	2	$1\frac{1}{2}$
7–4	Use similar triangles to prove that parallel lines divide certain segments proportionally; apply this property to find unknown lengths.	2	2	$1\frac{1}{2}$
7–5	Apply the SAS and SSS similarity theorems to prove that triangles are similar.	$1\frac{1}{2}$	1	1
7–6	Apply ratios to the lengths of altitudes, angle bisectors and medians in similar triangles.	2	2	2
7–7	Solve real-world problems using similar figures.	2	2	2
Review		$1\frac{1}{2}$	1	1
Test		1	1	1
Total		15 days	13 days	12 days

Lesson 7–6 shows altitudes, medians and angle bisectors of similar triangles to be in the same ratio as the corresponding sides.

Theorem 7–10 proves that an angle bisector of a triangle divides the opposite side into segments proportional to the adjacent sides.

Lesson 7–7 uses similar triangles in various applications, most involving indirect measurement. This is one of the best examples of the usefulness of geometry.

The emphasis in this lesson is on proportions involving corresponding sides only.

Similarity

Chapter 7

CANADA

Montana
North Dakota
Minnesota
Lake Superior
Billings
Bismark
Duluth
South Dakota
Pierre
St. Paul
Wisconsin
Minneapolis
Michigan
Wyoming
Madison
Milwaukee
Lake Michigan
Cheyenne
Nebraska
Iowa
Des Moines
Chicago
Denver
Lincoln
Illinois
Indian
Colorado
Topeka
Kansas City
Springfield
Indianapolis
Kansas
Kansas City
St. Louis
Santa Fe
Jefferson City
Missouri
Kentucky
Louisv
New Mexico
Amarillo
Oklahoma City
Tulsa
Nashville
Tennessee
Lubbock
Oklahoma
Arkansas
Memphis
Little Rock
Mississippi
Alabama
Fort Worth
Birmingh
Texas
Dallas
Jackson
Montgomery
Louisiana
Baton Rouge
Austin
Houston
New Orleans
San Antonio
MEXICO
Laredo

Missouri River
Missouri
Arkansas River
Red River
Brazos
Rio Grande
River
Ohio River
Mississippi River

Legend:
- – – – International boundaries
- —— State boundaries
- ▬▬ Major highways
- ★ State capital
- ● Other cities or towns

```
0    100   200   300   Miles
0  100  200  300  400  Kilometers
```

1 inch → 300 miles
1cm → 190 kilometers

1. On this map of part of the United States, how many miles are represented by one inch? How many kilometers are represented by one centimeter?

2. Estimate the distance from Chicago, Illinois, to Minneapolis, Minnesota.

Warm-Up Review

1. If $x = 5$, then $6x = 30$ by applying the ___?___ Property for real numbers.   Multiplication
2. Find $\frac{5}{8}$ of 400.   250
3. Simplify: $3(7x - 2)$. $21x - 6$
4. Solve for x: $4x + 4x + x = 180$. $x = 20$
5. Solve for x: $4x + 12 = 7x - 6$. $x = 6$

7-1 Ratio and Proportion

The Josephs planned a driving vacation from Chicago, Illinois, to Houston, Texas. They wanted to cover between 350 and 450 miles each day. Mrs. Joseph used the scale on the map on page 286 to help her schedule the trip. The scale, 1 inch → 300 miles, is a ratio.

A *ratio* represents the comparison or relationship of two quantities. Ratios can be expressed in several ways:

6 to 10   6:10 $\frac{6}{10}$, or $\frac{3}{5}$ 0.6   60%

Example 1
The Josephs want to stay with friends in St. Louis the first night. Using the scale on the map, figure out in what town the Josephs might stop the second night of their trip to Houston. On what day after they leave Chicago will they arrive in Houston?

Solution
On the map, Little Rock, Arkansas, is approximately $1\frac{1}{4}$ inches from St. Louis, so it is approximately 375 miles away. The Josephs might stay in Little Rock the second night. Since Houston is about $1\frac{1}{2}$ inches from Little Rock, it is about 450 miles away. The Josephs will arrive there at the end of one more day of driving, the third day of their trip.

A *proportion* is an equation which states that two ratios are equal. $\frac{5}{6} = \frac{15}{18}$ and $\frac{4}{1} = \frac{2}{0.5}$ are proportions.
The numbers 5 and 6 are *proportional to* the numbers 15 and 18. The properties of equality can be used to change the way a proportion is written.

Example 2
Show that if $\frac{a}{b} = \frac{c}{d}$ for positive numbers a, b, c, and d, then $ad = bc$.

Solution
If $\frac{a}{b} = \frac{c}{d}$, then by the Multiplication Property, $\frac{a}{b}(bd) = \frac{c}{d}(bd)$.
Simplifying, we have $ad = bc$.

The summary on page 288 lists ways the properties of equality can be used to change the form of a proportion.

LESSON 7–1

Resources

Worksheet 7–1
Extension 7–1
Computer Activities 7–1
Computer Worksheet 7–1

OBJECTIVES

Use ratios and proportions to solve problems; use properties of equality to change the form of a proportion.

TEACHING NOTES

Begin this lesson by using examples as the material is introduced. Review ratios using **Example 1**. When the concept of proportion and its properties is introduced, use **Example 2** to justify the fact

WORKSHEET   Lesson 7-1

Name _____

1. Underline the proportions which are equivalent to $\frac{3}{x} = \frac{4}{5}$.
   $4x = 15$ $\frac{3}{4} = \frac{5}{x}$ $\frac{7}{3} = \frac{x+5}{4}$ $\frac{3+x}{4} = \frac{9}{5}$

2. Underline the proportions which are true if $2x = 15$.
   $\frac{2}{x} = \frac{5}{3}$ $\frac{3}{x} = \frac{5}{2}$ $\frac{x+3}{3} = \frac{7}{2}$ $\frac{x-3}{2} = \frac{3}{1}$

Solve for x.

3. $\frac{x}{2} = \frac{6}{3}$ $x = 4$
4. $\frac{3x}{6} = \frac{10}{2}$ $x = 10$
5. $\frac{x+3}{6} = \frac{7}{2}$ $x = 18$
6. $\frac{2x+1}{5} = \frac{4}{3}$ $x = 2\frac{5}{6}$
7. $\frac{4x-3}{9} = \frac{8}{-3}$ $x = -5\frac{1}{4}$
8. $\frac{1+x}{x-1} = \frac{x}{x+2}$ $x = -\frac{1}{2}$

9. Two complementary angles are in the ratio 2:3. What is the measure of each angle?   36; 54

10. Two consecutive angles of a parallelogram are in the ratio 7:8. What is the measure of each angle?   84; 96

11. The angles of a triangle are in the ratio 3:4:5. What is the measure of each angle?   45; 60; 75

The scale on a certain map is one inch equals 10 miles. Find the following.

12. How many miles does $2\frac{1}{2}$ inches represent?   25 miles

13. 175 miles is represented by how many inches on the paper? $17\frac{1}{2}$ inches

14. John averages two hits for every five times he is at bat. How many hits would he probably have if he batted 130 times?   52 hits

15. If $\frac{AB}{EB} = \frac{AD}{EF}$, $AB = 6$, $AD = 10$, and $AE = 4$, then $EF = $ ___$3\frac{3}{3}$___.

that cross-products are equal. **Examples 3** and **4** provide algebraic practice with this method. Discuss why 4x and 5x are used for angle measures in **Example 4**.

Additional Examples

Example 1
On a map, one centimeter represents 350 km. If Yellowstone National Park is approximately 1.2 cm from Missoula on the map, how many kilometers are between the locations? 420 km

Example 2
Show that if $\frac{(a + b)}{b} = \frac{(c + d)}{d}$ for positive numbers a, b, c and d, then $\frac{a}{b} = \frac{c}{d}$. Subtract 1, $\frac{b}{b}$, from the left side and $\frac{d}{d}$ from the right side.

Example 3
Solve this proportion for x:
$\frac{3x - 2}{5} = \frac{4x - 1}{7}$ x = 9

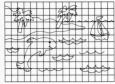
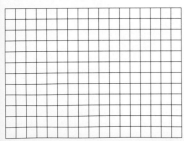

Assume $\frac{a}{b} = \frac{c}{d}$ for positive numbers a, b, c, and d.

Summary Proportions

If you do this to both sides of the proportion:	You will have:	By this property of equality:
1. Multiply by bd.	$ad = bc$	Multiplication Property
2. Multiply by $\frac{b}{c}$.	$\frac{a}{c} = \frac{b}{d}$	Multiplication Property
3. Multiply by $\frac{bd}{ac}$.	$\frac{d}{c} = \frac{b}{a}$	Multiplication Property
4. Add 1, $\frac{b}{b}$ on the left side and $\frac{d}{d}$ on the right.	$\frac{a + b}{b} = \frac{c + d}{d}$	Addition Property
5. Subtract 1, $\frac{b}{b}$ on the left side and $\frac{d}{d}$ on the right.	$\frac{a - b}{b} = \frac{b + d}{d}$	Subtraction Property

A proportion can be changed in yet another way using the **Summation Property of Proportions**: If $\frac{a}{b} = \frac{c}{d}$, then $\frac{a + c}{b + d} = \frac{a}{b}$. You are asked to derive this property in Exercise 34.

If you change the form of a proportion in a proof or an exercise in one of these six ways, use the corresponding property as the reason.

Example 3
Solve the proportion $\frac{2x - 1}{3} = \frac{3x + 1}{5}$ for x.

Solution
By the first entry in the summary, $(2x - 1)5 = 3(3x + 1)$. These products are called **cross-products**. Then $10x - 5 = 9x + 3$, and $x = 8$.

Example 4
Find the measures of the angles of a parallelogram in which a pair of consecutive angles have measures in the ratio 4 to 5.

Solution
$m\angle A$ and $m\angle B$ are in the ratio of 4 to 5, represent their measures as 4x and 5x. Then, $4x + 5x = 180$. Why? So $9x = 180$, and $x = 20$.

$m\angle A = m\angle C = 4x = 4(20) = 80$

2 lines ∥ ⇒ int. ∠s on the same side supp.

$m\angle B = m\angle D = 5x = 5(20) = 100$

Assignment Guide

Basic: 1–24, 35–42
Average: 1–13, 14–24 (even), 25–33, 35–42
Extended: 1–13, 14–24 (even), 25–42

Checking for Understanding

Given $\frac{a}{b} = \frac{c}{d}$, let $a = 18$, $b = 12$, $c = 3$, and $d = 2$ to verify that

1. $ad = bc$. **2.** $\frac{a}{c} = \frac{b}{d}$. **3.** $\frac{d}{c} = \frac{b}{a}$.

4. $\frac{a + b}{b} = \frac{c + d}{d}$. **5.** $\frac{a - b}{b} = \frac{c - d}{d}$. **6.** $\frac{a + c}{b + d} = \frac{a}{b}$.

1. $18(2) \stackrel{?}{=} 12(3), 36 = 36$
2. $\frac{18}{3} \stackrel{?}{=} \frac{12}{2}, 6 = 6$
3. $\frac{2}{3} \stackrel{?}{=} \frac{12}{18}, \frac{2}{3} = \frac{2}{3}$
4. $\frac{18 + 12}{12} \stackrel{?}{=} \frac{3 + 2}{2}, \frac{5}{2} = \frac{5}{2}$
5. $\frac{18 - 12}{12} \stackrel{?}{=} \frac{3 - 2}{2}, \frac{1}{2} = \frac{1}{2}$
6. $\frac{18 + 3}{12 + 2} \stackrel{?}{=} \frac{18}{12}, \frac{3}{2} = \frac{3}{2}$

Given $\frac{x}{y} = \frac{12}{21}$. If $x = 4$ and $y = 7$, which of the following are true? State the property which justifies each true statement.

7. $\frac{x}{12} = \frac{y}{21}$ **8.** $\frac{x + y}{x} = \frac{12 + 21}{21}$ **9.** $\frac{x - y}{y} = \frac{12 - 21}{21}$

10. If $\frac{4}{5} = \frac{8}{10} = \frac{12}{15}$, does $\frac{4 + 8 + 12}{5 + 10 + 15} = \frac{4}{5}$? Will the corresponding proportion be true if you include 2 more equal ratios? 5 more? n more? What property is illustrated?

10. Yes, yes; yes; Summation Prop. of Prop.

11. Mary's graduation photos came in two sizes, 5 in. by 7 in. and 8 in. by 10 in. Are these dimensions proportional?

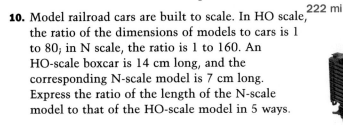

11. No; $5(10) = 50$ and $7(8) = 56$

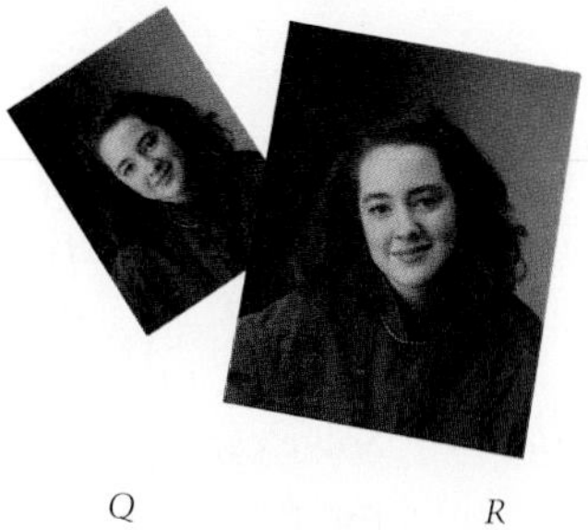

Written Exercises

Set A For each ratio, name three equal ratios.

1. $\frac{4}{7}$ **2.** $\frac{12}{20}$ **3.** $\frac{30}{6}$ **4.** $\frac{0.2}{5}$

5. In figure $QRST$, $\frac{QR}{AB} = \frac{RS}{BC}$. Find BC.

3

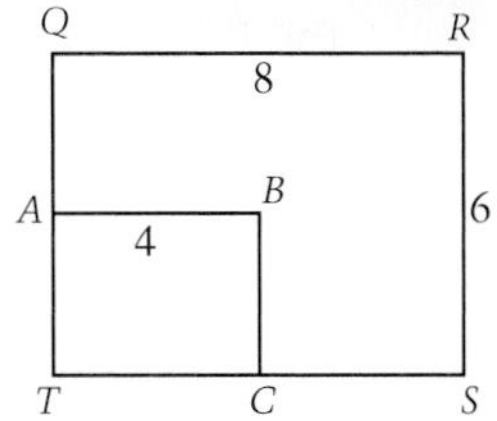

For each equation, write three equivalent proportions.

6. $\frac{3}{4} = \frac{6}{8}$ **7.** $\frac{3}{9} = \frac{5}{15}$ **8.** $\frac{a}{c} = \frac{x}{z}$

9. Houston and Dallas are $9\frac{1}{4}$ in. apart on a map with scale 1 in. → 24 mi. How far apart are the cities?

222 mi

10. Model railroad cars are built to scale. In HO scale, the ratio of the dimensions of models to cars is 1 to 80; in N scale, the ratio is 1 to 160. An HO-scale boxcar is 14 cm long, and the corresponding N-scale model is 7 cm long. Express the ratio of the length of the N-scale model to that of the HO-scale model in 5 ways.

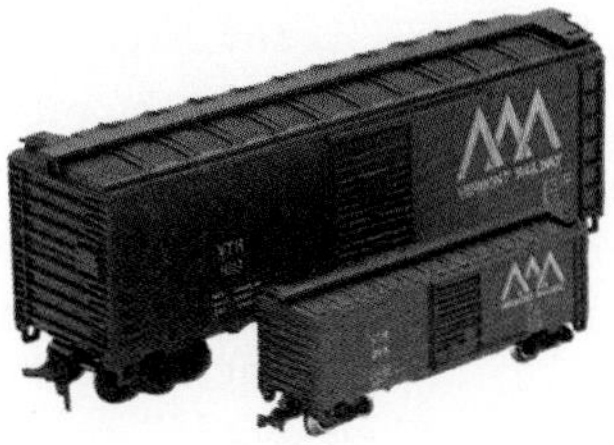

Example 4
Find the measures of the angles of a triangle if the angles are in the ratio 3 to 4 to 8. 36; 48; 96

Error Analysis Given $\frac{a}{b} = \frac{c}{d}$, students often come up with the following variations:

$\frac{a}{d} = \frac{b}{c}$ $\frac{a + x}{b} = \frac{c + x}{d}$

Be sure to show why these are incorrect.

EXERCISE NOTES

Exercises 26 and **29** illustrate a ratio expressed as one number:

$0.25 = 0.25 : 1$
$= 25 : 100$
$= 1 : 4$

Exercises 32–33 involve coordinate application of ratios involving line segments joining midpoints of the sides of a triangle.

ANSWERS

Checking for Understanding

7. true; Multiplication Prop.
8. false
9. true; Subtraction Prop.

Written Exercises

Samples:
1. $\frac{8}{14}, \frac{12}{21}, \frac{28}{49}$
2. $\frac{24}{40}, \frac{36}{60}, \frac{3}{5}$
3. $\frac{5}{1}, \frac{10}{2}, \frac{60}{12}$
4. $\frac{0.4}{10}, \frac{1}{25}, \frac{2}{50}$
6. $\frac{3}{6} = \frac{4}{8}; \frac{3 + 6}{4 + 8} = \frac{3}{4}; \frac{3 + 4}{4} = \frac{6 + 8}{8}$
7. $\frac{15}{5} = \frac{9}{3}; \frac{3 + 9}{9} = \frac{5 + 15}{15}; \frac{3 - 9}{9} = \frac{5 - 15}{15}$
8. $\frac{a}{x} = \frac{c}{z}; \frac{a + x}{c + z} = \frac{a}{c}; \frac{z}{x} = \frac{c}{a}$
10. 7 to 14; 7: 14; $\frac{7}{14}$, or $\frac{1}{2}$; 0.5; 50%

14. $\frac{3}{9} \stackrel{?}{=} \frac{5}{15}, \frac{1}{3} = \frac{1}{3}$

15. $3(15) \stackrel{?}{=} 5(9)$, $45 = 45$

16. $\frac{3+5}{5} \stackrel{?}{=} \frac{9+15}{15}, \frac{8}{5} = \frac{8}{5}$

17. $\frac{5}{3} \stackrel{?}{=} \frac{15}{9}, \frac{5}{3} = \frac{5}{3}$

18. $\frac{3+9+6+12}{5+15+10+20} \stackrel{?}{=} \frac{30}{50} \stackrel{?}{=} \frac{3}{5}, \frac{3}{5} = \frac{3}{5}$

19. $\frac{9-15}{15} \stackrel{?}{=} \frac{3-5}{5}, \frac{-6}{15} \stackrel{?}{=} \frac{-2}{5}, \frac{-2}{5} = \frac{-2}{5}$

30. 6 m; 3.6 m

31. 6 cm; 5 cm

34. Let $\frac{a}{b} = \frac{c}{d} = k$. Then $a = bk$ and $c = dk$ (Multiplication Prop.), and $a + c = bk + dk = (b + d)k$ (Addition Prop.). $\frac{a+c}{b+d} = R$ (Multiplication Prop.), and $\frac{a+c}{b+d} = \frac{c}{d}$ (Substitution Prop.).

Review

35–36.

$D = (-1, 3)$

$E = (1, 0)$

$F = (1, 3)$

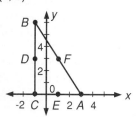

37.

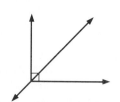

a line which bisects the right angle

The Josephs will return to Chicago from Houston by way of Denver, Colorado, traveling about 400 mi. a day.

11. On what day of the return trip will they reach Denver? **The third day**

12. How many days will the trip from Denver to Chicago take? **About $2\frac{1}{2}$ days**

13. Yuko is building a model of a log cabin to the scale of 3 in. to 2 ft. The cabin measures 18 ft. by 12 ft. by 8 ft. What dimensions will the model have? **27 in.; 18 in.; 12 in.**

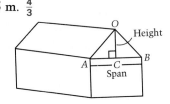

Given $\frac{p}{q} = \frac{r}{s} = \frac{t}{u} = \frac{v}{w}$, use $p = 3$, $q = 5$, $r = 9$, $s = 15$, $t = 6$, $u = 10$, $v = 12$, and $w = 20$ to verify each equation.

14. $\frac{p}{r} = \frac{q}{s}$ **15.** $ps = qr$ **16.** $\frac{p+q}{q} = \frac{r+s}{s}$

17. $\frac{q}{p} = \frac{s}{r}$ **18.** $\frac{p+r+t+v}{q+s+u+w} = \frac{p}{q}$ **19.** $\frac{r-s}{s} = \frac{p-q}{q}$

Complete each statement. Tell what was done to the original proportion.

20. If $\frac{m}{4} = \frac{n}{12}$, $\frac{m}{n} = \frac{?}{?}$.   **21.** If $\frac{r}{4} = \frac{5}{s}$, $\frac{r+4}{4} = \frac{?}{?}$.

20. $\frac{4}{12}$; each side was multiplied by $\frac{4}{n}$.

21. $\frac{5+s}{s}$; $\frac{4}{4}(1)$ was added to $\frac{r}{4}$ and $\frac{s}{s}(1)$ was added to $\frac{5}{s}$.

Solve each proportion for x.

22. $\frac{x+2}{x+5} = \frac{4}{7}$ **23.** $\frac{4x+5}{6} = \frac{2x+5}{4}$ **24.** $\frac{2x-1}{x+7} = \frac{3}{4}$

     $x = 2$ $x = 2.5$ $x = 5$

Set B   The pitch of a roof is the ratio: height:0.5 (span).

25. Find the pitch of a roof with height 4 m and span 6 m. $\frac{4}{3}$

26. The pitch of a roof is 0.25 and its span is 8 m. What is its height? **1 m**

27. Find two complementary angles with measures in the ratio 4 to 5. **40°; 50°**

28. Find the measures of angles in a triangle if their measures are in the ratio 2 to 3 to 5. **36; 54; 90**

29. Find the measures of the angles in an isosceles triangle if the ratio between the base and vertex angle measures is 2 to 1. **72; 72; 36**

30. What are the dimensions of the living room?

31. If the dimensions of the kitchen are 3.75 m by 4.5 m, what are the dimensions in the drawing?

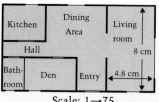

Scale: 1→75

Graph $\triangle ABC$ with $A(3, 0)$, $B(-1, 6)$, $C(-1, 0)$.
Find the midpoints D, E, and F of $\overline{BC}$, $\overline{AC}$, and
$\overline{AB}$, respectively.

32. How are AB and DE related? BC and FE? AC and FD?

$AB = 2DE$; $BC = 2FE$; $AC = 2FD$

33. What is the value of $\frac{DE}{AB}$? of $\frac{FE}{BC}$? of $\frac{FD}{AC}$? $\frac{1}{2}$; $\frac{1}{2}$; $\frac{1}{2}$

Set C   **34.** Show how $\frac{a+c}{b+d} = \frac{a}{b}$ can be derived from $\frac{a}{b} = \frac{c}{d}$.

 Review

35. In the proof of a locus theorem, what parts are proved?

35. If a point is on the locus, it satisfies the given conditions and vice versa.

36. In the coordinate plane, what is the locus of points equidistant from the lines $y = -4$ and $y = 5$?

36. A line with equation $y = \frac{1}{2}$

37. Draw a figure and describe the locus of points in a plane equidistant from the sides of a right angle.

38. The last step of a two-column proof is *always*, *sometimes*, or *never* the given. **Never**

39. Are $\angle EFG$ and $\angle HFG$ adjacent angles? Explain.
No; a side of $\angle HFG$ is in the interior of $\angle EFG$.

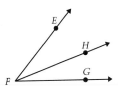

Thinking Ahead **40.** Tape a cartoon figure to a grid. Draw the lines of the grid across the figure. Find the dimensions of the rectangle that just encloses the figure.

41. Cut another rectangle whose dimensions are twice those of the rectangle in Exercise 40. Reproduce the original figure using a 2-by-2 square on the reproduction to represent a 1-by-1 square on the original. How are the figures related?

42. Repeat Exercise 41, using a 1-by-2 rectangle. What change does that make? What would happen if you used a 2-by-1 rectangle?

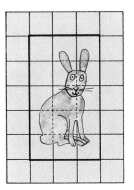

💻 Computer Activities: Drawing and Measuring

1. Draw two triangles with each side of the second triangle twice as long as the corresponding side of the first. What appears to be true for the two triangles? They have the same shape.

2. Measure the angles in the two triangles. How do the angles in the first triangle compare with the angles in the second? They are equal   **3.** They have the same shape.

3. Draw two different-sized triangles with the measures of two angles in one equal to the measures of two angles in the second. What appears to be true?

4. What is true of the ratios of the lengths of corresponding sides in the two triangles? They are equal

---

Thinking Ahead

40. Answers will vary.
41. The figures are the same shape, but the second has twice the dimensions of the first.
42. The second figure has the same width but is twice as tall; the second figure has the same height but is twice as wide.

FOLLOW-UP

More Practice

• Worksheet 7–1

Extension

Ask students to solve the following proportion:
$$\frac{2x + 8}{8} = \frac{7}{4} \quad x = 3$$
How could you simplify the problem? Subtracting $\frac{8}{8}$ on the left side and $\frac{4}{4}$ on the right side simplifies the problem to $\frac{2x}{8} =$, $\frac{3}{4}$, or $\frac{x}{4} = \frac{3}{4}$.

Ask students to come up with other proportions whose solutions are simplified by using a property of equality.

• Extension 7–1

Computers

The computer activity in the pupil's book can be completed using *The Geometric Supposer: Triangles*.

• Computer Activities 7–1
• Computer Worksheet 7–1

Warm-Up Review

1. If $\triangle ABC \cong \triangle PQR$, name the side that corresponds to $\overline{AC}$. $\overline{PR}$
2. If $\triangle XYZ \cong \triangle WBZ$, name the angle that corresponds to $\angle YZX$. $\angle BZW$
3. Define convex polygon. A polygon with sides made up of lines that contain no points in the interior of the polygon

LESSON 7–2

Resources

Colored transparency sheets or
  construction paper
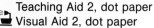 Teaching Aid 2, dot paper
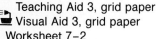 Visual Aid 2, dot paper
Teaching Aid 3, grid paper
Visual Aid 3, grid paper
Worksheet 7–2
Extension 7–2
Computer Activities 7–2

OBJECTIVE

Recognize and apply the properties of similar polygons, using ratios and proportions.

TEACHING NOTES

Begin this lesson by using **concrete materials** such as congru-

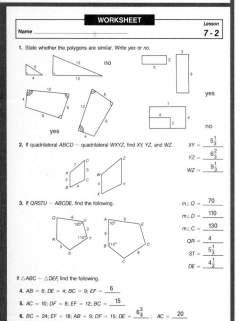

7-2 Similar Polygons

In Chapters 5 and 6 you studied congruent polygons, that is, polygons with the same size and shape. In this chapter you will study polygons that are the same shape but not necessarily the same size. Such figures are called similar.

The three balalaikas (Russian stringed instruments) in this picture are similar. Why? They have the same shape.

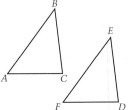

Definition *Similar Polygons*

Two convex polygons are similar if and only if there is a correspondence between their vertices such that corresponding angles are equal and the lengths of corresponding sides are proportional.

Quadrilaterals $ABCD$ and $EFGH$ are similar because their corresponding angles are equal and the lengths of the corresponding sides are proportional, as expressed below.

$$\frac{AB}{EF} = \frac{BC}{FG} = \frac{CD}{GH} = \frac{DA}{HE} = \frac{3}{2}$$

Thus, $ABCD \sim EFGH$. The symbol $\sim$ means "is similar to." Notice that with similar polygons, as with congruent polygons, the corresponding vertices are named in order.

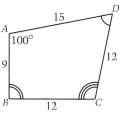

Example 1

Given: $\triangle ABC \cong \triangle DEF$
Prove: $\triangle ABC \sim \triangle DEF$

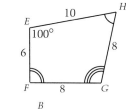

Solution

Statements	Reasons
1. $\triangle ABC \cong \triangle DEF$	1. Given
2. $AB = DE$; $AC = DF$; $BC = EF$; $m\angle A = m\angle D$; $m\angle B = m\angle E$; $m\angle C = m\angle F$	2. Corr. parts of $\cong$ $\triangle$s are $=$. [1]
3. $\frac{AB}{DE} = \frac{AB}{AB} = 1$; $\frac{AC}{DF} = \frac{AC}{AC} = 1$; $\frac{BC}{EF} = \frac{BC}{BC} = 1$	3. Substitution Prop. [2]
4. $\frac{AB}{DE} = \frac{AC}{DF} = \frac{BC}{DE}$	4. Substitution Prop. [3]
5. $\triangle ABC \sim \triangle DEF$	5. Definition $\sim$ polygons [2, 4]

Example 2

ABCD is similar to *EFGH*. Find *EF*, *FG*, and *GH*.

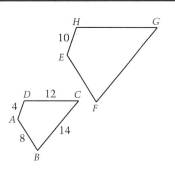

Solution

$$\frac{DA}{HE} = \frac{4}{10} = \frac{2}{5}$$

$\frac{AB}{EF} = \frac{DA}{HE}$	$\frac{BC}{FG} = \frac{DA}{HE}$	$\frac{CD}{GH} = \frac{DA}{HE}$
$\frac{AB}{EF} = \frac{2}{5}$	$\frac{BC}{FG} = \frac{2}{5}$	$\frac{CD}{GH} = \frac{2}{5}$
$\frac{8}{EF} = \frac{2}{5}$	$\frac{14}{FG} = \frac{2}{5}$	$\frac{12}{GH} = \frac{2}{5}$
$8(5) = EF(2)$	$14(5) = FG(2)$	$12(5) = GH(2)$
$EF = 20$	$FG = 35$	$GH = 30$

Example 3

Find the ratio of the perimeters of *ABCD* and *EFGH*.

Solution

$AB + BC + CD + DA = 8 + 14 + 12 + 4 = 38$

$EF + FG + GH + HE = 20 + 35 + 30 + 10 = 95$

$$\frac{\text{Perimeter } ABCD}{\text{Perimeter } EFGH} = \frac{38}{95} = \frac{2}{5}$$

Notice that this ratio is the same as the ratio of the lengths of corresponding sides of the quadrilaterals. This example suggests Theorem 7-1; you are asked to prove this theorem for two pentagons in Exercise 26.

Theorem 7-1

The perimeters of two similar polygons are proportional to the lengths of any pair of corresponding sides.

Checking for Understanding

Given Pentagon *ABCDE* ~ pentagon *FGHJK*

1. Name all pairs of corresponding vertices.

$A \leftrightarrow F, B \leftrightarrow G, C \leftrightarrow H, D \leftrightarrow J, K \leftrightarrow E$

2. Write all ratios of lengths of corresponding sides.

$\frac{AB}{FG}, \frac{BC}{GH}, \frac{CD}{GH}, \frac{DE}{JK}, \frac{EA}{KF}$

3. In Example 2, $\frac{AB}{EF} = \frac{BC}{FG} = \frac{CD}{GH} = \frac{DA}{HE} = \frac{2}{5}$.

In Example 3, $\frac{AB + BC + CD + DA}{EF + FG + GH + HE} = \frac{2}{5}$.

What property in Lesson 7-1 is illustrated?
Summation Prop. of Prop.

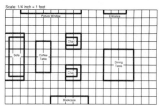

Assignment Guide

Basic: 1–15, 27–34
Average: 2–6 (even), 7–20, 24, 27–34
Extended: 2–14 (even), 15–34

Follow the pattern of proof for **Example 1** in the pupil's book, showing that corresponding angles are equal and the ratios of the lengths of corresponding sides are equal.

Example 2

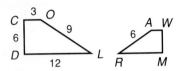

If quadrilateral *COLD* ~ quadrilateral *WARM*, find $\overline{AW}$, $\overline{WM}$ and $\overline{MR}$.   2; 4; 8

Example 3
Find the ratio of the perimeters of the quadrilaterals in **Example 2** above. $\frac{3}{2}$, the same as the ratio of the corresponding sides

Error Analysis As with congruent polygons, students may not always write the similar polygons with vertices in corresponding order. Be sure to stress that the similarity statement is used to determine which parts correspond (e.g., if $\triangle TAP \sim \triangle BIN$, the first two letters of each triangle should indicate a pair of corresponding sides; therefore, $\overline{TA}$ should correspond to $\overline{BI}$).

ANSWERS

Checking for Understanding

4. Since all angles and all sides of a regular polygon are equal, corresponding angles of one are equal to the corresponding angles of the other and corresponding sides of one are proportional to corresponding sides of the other.

4. Explain why two regular polygons having the same number of sides are similar.

5. State Theorem 7-1 in "if . . . then" form.

6. Why are a parallelogram and a trapezoid never similar?

Decide whether the polygons in each pair are similar. Answer *yes*, *no*, or *not enough information*.

7.

Yes

8.

Not enough information

9.

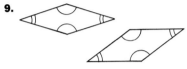

Not enough information

Written Exercises

Set A   Given: $\triangle ABC \sim \triangle ADE$

1. $AD = 8$; $AE = 6$; $AC = 15$; $AB = \underline{\ ?\ }$ 20
2. $AE = 6$; $AD = 9$; $AB = 15$; $AC = \underline{\ ?\ }$ 10
3. $AE = 6$; $EC = 4$; $AD = 8$; $DB = \underline{\ ?\ }$ $5\frac{1}{3}$
4. $AD = 6$; $DB = 9$; $AE = 5$; $EC = \underline{\ ?\ }$ $7\frac{1}{2}$
5. $AE = 3x$; $AC = 5x$; $AB = 10$; $AD = \underline{\ ?\ }$ 6
6. $AD = x + 3$; $AB = x + 8$; $AE = 12$; $AC = 16$; $AB = \underline{\ ?\ }$ 20

Tell whether the polygons in each pair are *always*, *sometimes*, or *never* similar. Explain. **7.** Sometimes

7. Two rectangles   **8.** Two squares Always

9. A regular hexagon and a regular octagon Never

10. Two parallelograms with 60° angles Sometimes

11. Two isosceles triangles with a 45° angle Sometimes

Given: Hexagon *ABCDEF* ~ hexagon *STWXYZ*

12. Find the lengths of the sides of hexagon *STWXYZ*.

13. Give the ratio of the perimeters of the hexagons. 4:3

14. Prove that if two quadrilaterals are congruent, then they are similar.

15. Give a Plan for Proof for Theorem 7-1 for two triangles.

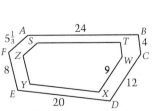

12. $ST = 18$; $TW = 3$; $WX = 9$
$XY = 15$; $YZ = 6$; $ZS = 4$

Set B   Given: $\square FADE \sim \square GLOW$

16. $\dfrac{FE}{GW} = \dfrac{ED}{\underline{}}$ WO

17. If $m\angle E = 60$, name two 60° angles in $\square GLOW$. $\angle W; \angle L$

18. If $ED = 9$ and $\dfrac{FA}{GL} = \dfrac{1}{3}$, find WO and GL.   27

19. If $m\angle D = 110$, then $m\angle W = \underline{}$.   70

20. Two similar polygons have perimeters of 164 and 205. The length of one side in the larger polygon is 3 more than the length of the corresponding side in the smaller polygon. Find the length of that side in the smaller polygon.   12

21. Is the statement in Exercise 14 true for any two congruent polygons? Explain.

22. Recall that Theorem 6-11 states: If a segment joins the midpoints of two sides of a triangle, then it is parallel to the third side, and its length is one half the length of the third side. What is the ratio of the lengths of the sides of $\triangle ABC$ and $\triangle XYC$? Why are the triangles similar?

23. Find the coordinates of points K, L, M, N, and P such that pentagons $ABCDE$ and $KLMNP$ are similar but not congruent and none of the corresponding sides of the two pentagons are parallel.

24. A yearbook company can reduce photos to fit a page, but the photo must first be cropped in proportion to the reduced size. If an original football candid measures 8 in. by 10 in., give three sets of possible cropped dimensions that can be reduced to fit in a 2-in.-by-3-in. space.

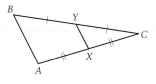

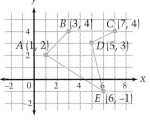

5. If two polygons are similar, then their perimeters are proportional to the lengths of any pair of corresponding sides.

6. Both pairs of opposite sides of a parallelogram are parallel, while only one pair of sides in a trapezoid are parallel.

Written Exercises

14. Given: $ABCD \cong EFGH$ Prove: $ABCD \sim EFGH$ Proof: 1. $ABCD \cong EFGH$ (Given) 2. $AB = EF$; $BC = FG$; $CD = GH$; $DA = HE$; $m\angle A = m\angle E$; $m\angle B = m\angle F$; $m\angle C = m\angle G$; $m\angle D = m\angle H$ (Def. of $\cong$ polygons [1]) 3. $\dfrac{AB}{EF} = \dfrac{AB}{AB} = 1$; $\dfrac{BC}{FG} = \dfrac{BC}{BC} = 1$; $\dfrac{CD}{GH} = \dfrac{CD}{CD} = 1$; $\dfrac{DA}{HE} = \dfrac{DA}{DA} = 1$ (Substitution Prop. [2]) 4. $\dfrac{AB}{EF} = \dfrac{BC}{FG} = \dfrac{CD}{GH} = \dfrac{DA}{HE}$ (Substitution Prop. [3]) 5. $ABCD \sim EFGH$ (Def. of similar polygons [2, 4])

15. Given: $\triangle ABC \sim \triangle DEF$ Prove: $\dfrac{\text{Perimeter } \triangle ABC}{\text{Perimeter } \triangle DEF} = \dfrac{AB}{DE}$ Plan for Proof: By definition of similar polygons, $\dfrac{AB}{DE} = \dfrac{BC}{EF} = \dfrac{CA}{FD}$. Use the Summation Prop. of Prop. to show that $\dfrac{AB + BC + CA}{DE + EF + FD} = \dfrac{AB}{DE}$.

21. Yes; corresponding angles are equal and the ratio of lengths of corresponding sides is 1 : 1.

22. 2 : 1; the triangles are similar because lengths of corresponding sides are proportional and corresponding angles are equal. (2 lines $\parallel \Rightarrow$ corr. $\angle$s =.)

23. Sample: $K(0, -1)$; $L(-4, 3)$; $M(-4, 11)$; $N(-2, 7)$; $P(6, 9)$

24. Samples: 2 in. by 3 in.; 4 in. by 6 in.; 6 in. by 9 in.

25. No; corresponding angles are equal, but lengths of corresponding sides (KF and EL, and HG and CM) are not proportional.

25. If $\overline{LM}$ is drawn parallel to $\overline{AB}$ such that $\overline{EA}$ and $\overline{CB}$ can be extended to form $\overline{EL}$ and $\overline{CM}$, respectively, is pentagon $LMCDE \sim$ pentagon $ABCDE$? Explain.

26. Prove Theorem 7-1 for two pentagons.

▲ **Review** **27.** Solve the proportion $\frac{x+6}{4x+7} = \frac{1}{3}$ for x. x = 11

28. Find the angle measures in a triangle if they are in the ratio 1 to 2 to 6. 20; 40; 120

29. In the coordinate plane, what is the locus of points 8 units from the line with equation y = x + 5?

30. Name as many properties of a rhombus as you can.

31. If pentagon $ABCDE$ is regular, then $m\angle B = \underline{\ ?\ }$. 108

Thinking Ahead **32.** Draw $\triangle ABC$ with $m\angle A = 65$, $m\angle B = 35$ and $\triangle DEF$ with $m\angle D = m\angle A$, $m\angle E = m\angle B$, and $DE \neq AB$. Measure the sides and compare $\frac{AB}{DE}$, $\frac{AC}{DF}$, and $\frac{BC}{EF}$.

33. Repeat Exercise 32 with different-sized angles. Compare your results with those of other students. What do you notice?

34. Based on these results, what general statement can you make about similarity of triangles?

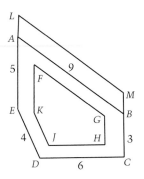

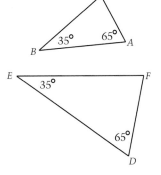

Algebra Review: Simplifying Radicals

Examples

1. Simplify $\sqrt{98}$.

2. Simplify $(5\sqrt{3})^2$.

3. Simplify $\sqrt{\frac{2}{7}}$.

Solutions

1. $\sqrt{98} = \sqrt{49}(\sqrt{2})$
$= 7\sqrt{2}$

2. $(5\sqrt{3})^2 = 5\sqrt{3}(5\sqrt{3})$
$= 5(5)(\sqrt{3})(\sqrt{3})$
$= 25(3)$
$= 75$

3. $\sqrt{\frac{2}{7}} = \frac{\sqrt{2}}{\sqrt{7}}$
$= \frac{\sqrt{2}(\sqrt{7})}{\sqrt{7}(\sqrt{7})}$
$= \frac{\sqrt{14}}{7}$

Simplify.

1. $\sqrt{81}$ 9

2. $\sqrt{72}$ $6\sqrt{2}$

3. $(2\sqrt{3})(\sqrt{3})$ 6

4. $\sqrt{3}(\sqrt{7})$ $\sqrt{21}$

5. $5\sqrt{288}$ $60\sqrt{2}$

6. $\sqrt{\frac{1}{4}}$ $\frac{1}{2}$

7. $\sqrt{\frac{3}{10}}$ $\frac{\sqrt{30}}{10}$

8. $\sqrt{\frac{1}{14}}$ $\frac{\sqrt{14}}{14}$

9. $(\sqrt{5})^2$ 5

10. $(4\sqrt{2})(\sqrt{6})$ $8\sqrt{3}$

11. $(8\sqrt{5})^2$ 320

12. $3\sqrt{\frac{7}{8}}$ $\frac{3\sqrt{14}}{4}$

13. $\frac{5}{\sqrt{15}}$ $\frac{\sqrt{15}}{3}$

14. $\frac{3\sqrt{2}}{2\sqrt{6}}$ $\frac{\sqrt{3}}{2}$

15. $\frac{(-\sqrt{3})^2}{\sqrt{5}}$ $\frac{3\sqrt{5}}{5}$

Warm-Up Review

1. The sum of the measures of the angles in a triangle is ___?___. 180
2. If lines are parallel and intersected by a transversal, ___?___ angles on the same side are supplementary. Interior
3. In △QED, name the angle included between sides $\overline{ED}$ and $\overline{DQ}$. ∠D
4. Polygons having the same shape are ___?___. Similar

7-3 Similar Triangles

Similar triangles are often used to find unknown distances. The surveyor shown is using similar triangles to plan measurements he must make in order to find the distance across the lake. By the definition of similar polygons, △ABC ~ △DEF shown below the photo if and only if

$$\frac{AB}{DE} = \frac{BC}{EF} = \frac{CA}{FD},$$

and $m\angle A = m\angle D$, $m\angle B = m\angle E$, and $m\angle C = m\angle F$.

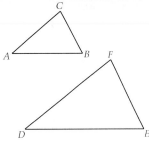

With this definition, the surveyor would have to know *all* angle measures and *all* distances, including a distance he is unable to measure.

Just as there are shorter ways than the definition to prove triangles congruent, there are ways to prove triangles similar without knowing the measures of all the sides and angles. Postulate 19 provides the first of several more efficient ways to prove that two triangles are similar.

Postulate 19 *AA Similarity Postulate*

If two angles of one triangle are equal to two angles of another triangle, the triangles are similar.

Example 1
Given △ABC and △DEF, find x.

Solution
Since the triangles are isosceles with one pair of base angles equal, the other pair of base angles are also equal. So △ABC ~ △EDF by Postulate 19.

$$\frac{AB}{ED} = \frac{BC}{DF}$$
$$\frac{x}{27} = \frac{16}{24}$$
$$x(24) = 27(16)$$
$$x = 18$$

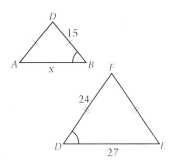

LESSON 7-3

Resources

Ruler
Teaching Aid 1, protractor
Visual Aid 1, protractor
Worksheet 7-3
Extension 7-3
Computer Activities 7-3
Computer Worksheet 7-3

OBJECTIVE

Apply the AA Similarity Postulate to prove that triangles are similar.

TEACHING NOTES

Introduce the AA Similarity Postulate with the following **group activity**.

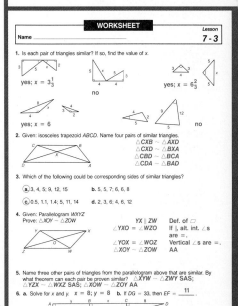

1. Have each student draw △*ABC* with m∠*A* = 30 and m∠*B* = 70.
2. Discuss why it was not necessary to measure ∠*C*.
3. Working in pairs, have students measure each side and compute the ratios of corresponding sides.

Discuss various situations in which pairs of angles can be proven congruent. Elicit responses such as vertical angles, alternate interior or corresponding angles when lines are parallel, base angles of an isosceles triangle and opposite angles of a parallelogram.

Additional Examples

Example 1

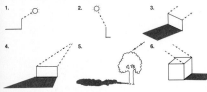
Example 2
The surveyor's sketch is shown. Given $\overleftrightarrow{WV} \parallel \overleftrightarrow{XY}$, identify the similar triangles. Which measures must you know to find *WV*?

Solution
∠*X* and ∠*V* and ∠*Y* and ∠*W* are alternate interior angles, so m∠*X* = m∠*V* and m∠*Y* = m∠*W*. Thus, △*XYZ* ~ △*VWZ* by Postulate 19. You must know the measures of $\overline{XY}$ and either $\overline{XZ}$ and $\overline{VZ}$ or $\overline{YZ}$ and $\overline{WZ}$.

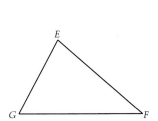

Theorem 5-1 states that congruence of triangles is reflexive, symmetric, and transitive. Theorem 7-2 is the corresponding similarity theorem.

Theorem 7-2

Similarity of triangles is reflexive, symmetric, and transitive.

Example 3
Prove that similarity of triangles is reflexive. (Theorem 7-2)

Solution
Given: △*EFG*
Prove: △*EFG* ~ △*EFG*

Statements	Reasons
1. △*EFG*	1. Given
2. m∠*E* = m∠*E*; m∠*F* = m∠*F*	2. Reflexive Prop.
3. △*EFG* ~ △*EFG*	3. AA Similarity Post. [2]

The remainder of the proof is requested in Exercises 15 and 16.

Checking for Understanding
Are the triangles in each exercise similar? Answer *yes*, *no*, or *not enough information*. Explain each answer.

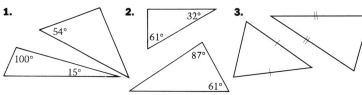

Given m∠*X* = m∠*H* and m∠*Z* = m∠*L*, complete each proportion.

5. $\dfrac{XY}{HK} = \dfrac{YZ}{?}$ *KL*   **6.** $\dfrac{XZ}{HL} = \dfrac{?}{LK}$ *ZY*   **7.** $\dfrac{KL}{YZ} = \dfrac{HL}{?}$ *XZ*

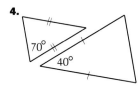

8. △*ABC* ~ △*GFC* and △*GFC* ~ △*EDC*. Explain why △*ABC* ~ △*EDC*.
Similarity of triangles is transitive.

Assignment Guide

Basic: 1–7, 18–25
Average: 1–16, 18–25
Extended: 1–25

Written Exercises

Set A   If the triangles in each exercise are similar, find x.

1.
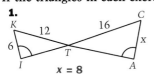
x = 8

2.
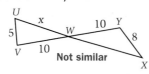
Not similar

3.
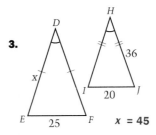
x = 45

Which could be corresponding sides of similar triangles?

4. 3, 5, 7 and 6, 10, 14 **Yes**   **5.** 1.5, 2.5, 3.5 and 6, 10, 12 **No**

6. Given: △ABC with AC = BC; $\overline{DE} \perp \overline{AB}$; $\overline{FG} \perp \overline{AB}$

Prove: △ADE ∼ △BFG

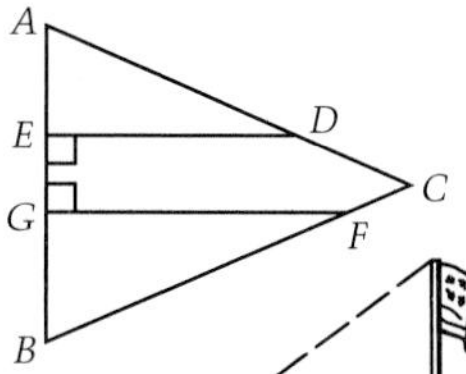

7. Allen's shadow and that of the flagpole are in line and have the same tip. Allen's height is 178 cm. His shadow measures 267 cm when the pole's shadow measures 921 cm. How tall is the pole?
614 cm

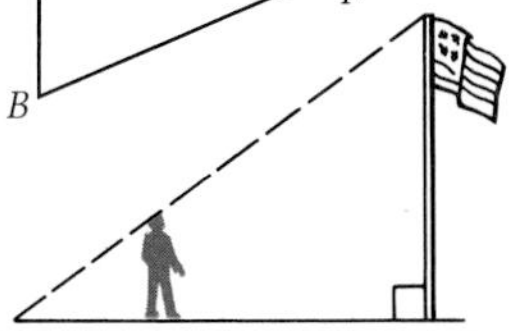

Set B   Find x in each exercise.

8.
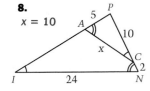
x = 10

9.
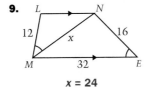
x = 24

10.
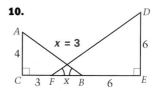
x = 3

11. Find the width of the Brasos River. **17 m**

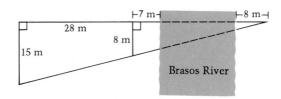

Brasos River

12. Given: Trapezoid HJKL; $\overline{HJ} \parallel \overline{LK}$
Prove: △HOJ ∼ △KOL

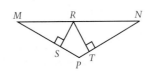

13. Given: △MNP; MP = NP; $\overline{RT} \perp \overline{PN}$; $\overline{RS} \perp \overline{PM}$
Prove: (RM)(RT) = (RS)(NR)

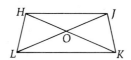

Given: △TRI with $\overline{AB} \parallel \overline{RI}$
Find TR. **15**

Example 2

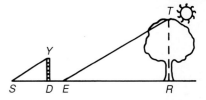

Explain how measuring the shadow $\overline{DS}$ cast by yardstick $\overline{YD}$ and measuring the shadow $\overline{RE}$ cast by tree $\overline{TR}$ will allow us to find the height of the tree indirectly. Assume that sun rays are parallel. △YDS ∼ △TRE

Error Analysis   Students may have difficulty writing proportions in the correct order if they do not take care in naming corresponding sides. Stress the order of the vertices in the similarity statement.

ANSWERS

Written Exercises

6. Proof: 1. △ABC with AC = BC; $\overline{DE} \perp \overline{AB}$; $\overline{FG} \perp \overline{AB}$ (Given) 2. m∠A = m∠B (Isos. △ Thm. [1]) 3. ∠AED and ∠FGB are rt. ∠s. (2 ⊥ lines form 4 rt. ∠s. [1])
4. △ADE ∼ △BFG (AA ∼ Post. [2, 3])
12. Proof: 1. Trapezoid HJKL; $\overline{HJ} \parallel \overline{LK}$ (Given) 2. m∠OJH = m∠OLK; m∠OHJ = m∠OKL (2 lines ∥ ⇒ alt. int. ∠s =. [1]) 3. △HOJ ∼ △KOL (AA ∼ Post. [2])

15. Given: $\triangle ABC \sim \triangle DEF$ Prove: $\triangle DEF \sim \triangle ABC$ Proof: 1. $\triangle ABC \sim \triangle DGF$ (Given) 2. $m\angle A = m\angle D$; $m\angle B = m\angle E$ (Def. of $\sim$ polygons [1]) 3. $m\angle D = m\angle A$; $m\angle G = m\angle B$ (Symmetric Prop. [2]) 4. $\triangle DEF \cong \triangle ABC$ (AA $\sim$ Post. [3])

16. Given: $\triangle ABC \sim \triangle DEF$; $\triangle DEF \sim \triangle GHI$ Prove: $\triangle ABC \sim \triangle GHI$ Proof: 1. $\triangle ABC \sim \triangle DEF$; $\triangle DEF \sim \triangle GHI$ (Given) 2. $m\angle A = m\angle D$; $m\angle B = m\angle E$; $m\angle D = m\angle G$; $m\angle E = m\angle H$ (Def. of $\sim$ polygons [1]) 3. $m\angle A = m\angle G$; $m\angle B = m\angle H$ (Transitive Prop. [2]) 4. $\triangle ABC \sim \triangle GHI$ (AA $\sim$ Post. [3])

17. Proof: 1. $\triangle HJK$; $\angle J$ is a rt. $\angle$; $\overline{JL} \perp \overline{HK}$ (Given) 2. $\angle JLK$ is a rt. $\angle$. (Two $\perp$ lines form 4 rt. $\angle$s. [1]) 3. $m\angle HJK = m\angle JLK$ (All rt. $\angle$s are =. [1, 2]) 4. $m\angle K = m\angle K$ (Reflexive Prop.) 5. $\triangle HJK \sim \triangle JLK$ (AA $\sim$ Post. [3, 4])

FOLLOW-UP

More Practice

• Worksheet 7-3

Extension

Challenge your students to do the following proof review to some properties of a parallelogram.

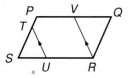

Given: $\square PQRS$; $\overline{TU} \parallel \overline{VR}$
Prove: $\triangle SUT \sim \triangle QVR$

• Extension 7-3

Computers

The computer activity in the pupil's book can be completed using *The Geometric Supposer: Triangles, The Geometric preSupposer: Points and Lines* or GeoDraw.

• Computer Activities 7-3
• Computer Worksheet 7-3

---

14. Given: $\triangle XYZ$; $m\angle Z = m\angle WXY$
Prove: $(YW)(YZ) = (YX)(YX)$

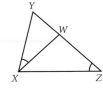

15. Prove that similarity of triangles is symmetric.

16. Prove that similarity of triangles is transitive.

Set C **17.** Given: $\triangle HJK$ with right angle at J; $\overline{JL} \perp \overline{HK}$
Prove: $\triangle HJK \sim \triangle JLK$

◆ Review Given: Hexagon $CDEFGH \sim$ hexagon $PQRSTU$

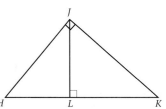

18. $m\angle S = \underline{\ ?\ }$ $m\angle F$

19. If $DE = 5$, $TU = 15$, and $GH = 8$, then $QR = \underline{\ ?\ }$.   9.375

20. Write three proportions equivalent to $\dfrac{d}{e} = \dfrac{s}{t}$.

Samples: $\dfrac{d}{s} = \dfrac{e}{t}$; $\dfrac{e}{d} = \dfrac{t}{s}$; $\dfrac{d+s}{e+t} = \dfrac{d}{e}$; $\dfrac{d-e}{e} = \dfrac{s-t}{t}$

21. For $\square VWXY$, write as many statements as you can about the angle measures.

22. Write this statement and its converse in "if . . . then" form: Two isosceles triangles with equal vertex angles are similar. Is the statement true? Is the converse true?

Thinking Ahead On lined paper, draw lines ℓ, m, and n on the 1st, 4th, and 9th lines as shown. Draw a segment from A perpendicular to n, intersecting n at B and m at X. Choose C on ℓ and draw $\overline{CB}$ and $\overline{CD}$ as shown, intersecting m at Z and Y. All are $\dfrac{3}{5}$.

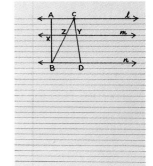

23. Measure $\overline{CZ}$, $\overline{ZB}$, $\overline{CY}$, and $\overline{YD}$. Compare the ratios $CZ:ZB$ and $CY:YD$ to the ratio $AX:XB$.

24. Repeat Exercise 23 using the 1st, 5th, and 6th lines. All ratios are $\dfrac{5}{1}$.

25. What relationships for parallel lines cut by transversals do your ratios suggest?

💻 Computer Activities: Drawing and Measuring

1. Draw any $\triangle ABC$. Draw a segment parallel to $\overline{AC}$ intersecting $\overline{AB}$ at D and $\overline{CB}$ at E. Measure $\overline{AD}$, $\overline{DB}$, $\overline{CE}$, and $\overline{EB}$. Compare the ratios $AD:DB$ and $CE:EB$. What do you notice?   1. The ratios are equal.

2. Repeat the activity in Exercise 1 with five other triangles.   2. The ratios are equal.

3. What conjecture can you make regarding a triangle and a line parallel to one side?

Using Logo: Similar Polygons

The POLYGON procedure below requires four inputs: the
number of sides in the polygon, the side lengths in order, the
angle measures in order, and the starting position. When
executed, POLYGON calls procedures SIDE and ANGLE to
produce the corresponding parts of the polygon.

```
TO POLYGON :N :SIDES :ANGLES :START      TO SIDE
PU                                        MAKE."SIDE ITEM :NO :SIDES
SETPOS :START                             FD :SIDE
PD                                        END
MAKE "NO 1
REPEAT :N (SIDE ANGLE MAKE "NO "NO + 1)   TO ANGLE
END                                       MAKE "ANGLE ITEM :NO :ANGLES
                                          LT 180 - :ANGLE
                                          END
```

1. Use POLYGON 5 [50 50 50 50 50] [108 108 108 108 108] [40 0] to draw
   a regular pentagon starting at (40, 0). On the same screen, draw
   POLYGON 5 [38 38 38 38 38] [108 108 108 108 108] [−60 0]. Why are
   the two pentagons similar?

2. Use POLYGON to draw each of the following pairs at different locations
   on the same screen:
   a. One parallelogram having an angle that measures 100 and side
      lengths of 36 and 48; a second having one angle that measures 80 and
      side lengths of 30 and 40. Are the parallelograms similar? Explain.
   b. Two parallelograms that are not similar, but in which the measures of
      the pairs of corresponding angles are equal.
   c. Two parallelograms that are not similar, but in which the ratios of the
      lengths of the pairs of corresponding sides are equal.

3. Use POLYGON to draw a triangle with side lengths 72, 81, and 63 and
   angle measures 48, 58, and 74. At a different position on the same
   screen, draw a second triangle similar to the first one with side lengths
   in the ratio of 4:3 with the corresponding sides of the first.

4. Compare these inputs for the sides, lengths, and angle measures of two
   triangles to be drawn using POLYGON: [72 81 63][48 58 74] and
   [54 54 54] [48 58 99].
   a. Use POLYGON to draw each figure on the same screen. Are the
      results what you expected?
   b. Are the triangles similar? Explain.
   c. What is the ratio of the lengths of each pair of corresponding sides?
   d. What are the actual lengths of the sides of the second triangle?

ANSWERS

Using Logo

1. Pairs of corresponding angles
have equal measures. Ratios of
lengths of pair of corres. sides
$= \frac{19}{25}$.

2a. Use POLYGON 4 [36 48 36
48] [100 80 100 80] [400] and
POLYGON 4 [30 40 30 40] [80 100
80 100] [−600]. The polygons are
similar. Corres. ∠ measures are
=. Ratios of corres. side lengths
are $\frac{5}{6}$.

b. Many answers. A sample is giv-
en: POLYGON 4 [30 35 30 35]
[130 50 130 50] [400] POLYGON 4
[30 50 30 50] [130 50 130 50]
[−600]

c. Many answers. A sample is giv-
en: POLYGON 4 [20 30 20 30]
[120 60 120 60] [400] POLYGON 4
[30 45 30 45] [105 75 105 75]
[−600]

3. For second △ use POLYGON 3
[96 108 84] [48 58 74] [−600]

4b. Yes; two pairs of corres. ∠s
have = measures.

c. 3 to 2

d. 48; 54; 42

LESSON 7–4

Resources

Compass
Ruler
Worksheet 7–4
Extension 7–4
🖥 Computer Worksheet 7–4
Quiz 7

OBJECTIVES

Use similar triangles to prove that parallel lines divide certain segments proportionally; apply this property to find unknown lengths.

TEACHING NOTES

Use the following **activity** to introduce Theorem 7–4.
1. Draw △XYZ.

7-4 Segments Divided Proportionally

The map at the right shows a section of some Chicago suburbs. If the east-west streets are parallel, then Theorems 7-3 and 7-4 guarantee that the north-south streets and Rand Road are *divided proportionally* by the east-west streets.

In symbols, $\dfrac{AB}{BC} = \dfrac{AE}{EF}$ and $\dfrac{BC}{CD} = \dfrac{EF}{FG}$.

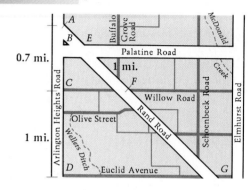

Theorem 7-3

If a line parallel to one side of a triangle intersects the other two sides, then it divides them proportionally.

Given △ABC; D on $\overline{AB}$; E on $\overline{AC}$; $\overline{DE} \parallel \overline{BC}$

Prove $\dfrac{AB}{BC} = \dfrac{AE}{EF}$

Proof We are given △ABC, with D on $\overline{AB}$, E on $\overline{AC}$, and $\overline{DE} \parallel \overline{BC}$. By the Reflexive Property, $m\angle A = m\angle A$. Because $\angle ADE$ and $\angle ABC$ are corresponding angles, $m\angle ADG = m\angle ABC$. Then △ADG ~ △ABC by AA similarity.

By definition, $\dfrac{AB}{AD} = \dfrac{AC}{AE}$. Seg. Add. Post.
But $AB = AD + DB$ and $AC = AE + EC$. Why?

Substituting, we have $\dfrac{AB}{AD} = \dfrac{AD + DB}{AD}$ and $\dfrac{AC}{AE} = \dfrac{AE + EC}{AE}$.
By addition and multiplication, $\dfrac{DB}{AD} = \dfrac{EC}{AE}$ and $\dfrac{AD}{DB} = \dfrac{AE}{EC}$.

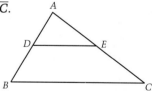

Example 1

On the map above, find the distance from Willow Road to Euclid Avenue along Rand Road.

Solution

Write a proportion. Then substitute known values and solve for FG.

$\dfrac{AC}{CD} = \dfrac{AF}{FG}$

$\dfrac{0.7}{1} = \dfrac{1}{FG}$

$0.7FG = 1$

$FG \approx 1.4$

The distance is about 1.4 miles.

Theorem 7-4

If three parallel lines intersect two transversals, then the parallel lines divide the transversals proportionally.

Given $\overleftrightarrow{BE} \parallel \overleftrightarrow{CF} \parallel \overleftrightarrow{DG}$

Prove $\dfrac{BC}{CD} = \dfrac{EF}{FG}$

Proof It is given that $\overleftrightarrow{BE}$, $\overleftrightarrow{CF}$, and $\overleftrightarrow{DG}$ are parallel lines. By the Line Postulate, we can draw $\overleftrightarrow{BG}$. $\overleftrightarrow{BG}$ cuts $\overleftrightarrow{CF}$ at H. Because $\overleftrightarrow{CF}$ is parallel to $\overline{DG}$ in $\triangle DBG$ and to $\overline{BE}$ in $\triangle EGB$, $\dfrac{BC}{CD} = \dfrac{BH}{HG}$ and $\dfrac{EF}{FG} = \dfrac{BH}{HG}$. Then, by substitution, $\dfrac{BC}{CD} = \dfrac{EF}{FG}$.

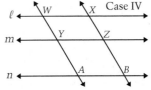

Case 1

The diagram above shows Case I in which the transversals intersect beyond the given parallels. Cases II–IV below show other possibilities. The transversals could intersect on or between the parallels, or they could themselves be parallel.

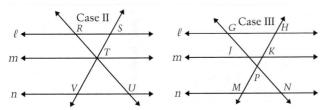

Case II

Case III

Case IV

In general, on any two transversals, parallel lines cut off segments whose lengths are proportional.

Example 2

Given $\overleftrightarrow{MP} \parallel \overleftrightarrow{NQ} \parallel \overleftrightarrow{OR}$; $MN = x + 4$, $MO = 3x + 4$, $PQ = x + 1$, and $PR = 3x - 1$. Find x.

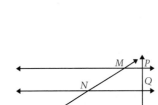

Solution

$$\frac{MN}{NO} = \frac{PQ}{QR}$$

$$\frac{MN}{MO - MN} = \frac{PQ}{PR - PQ}$$

$$\frac{x + 4}{(3x + 4) - (x + 4)} = \frac{x + 1}{(3x - 1) - (x + 1)}$$

$$\frac{x + 4}{2x} = \frac{x + 1}{2x - 2}$$

$$(x + 4)(2x + 2) = 2x(x + 1)$$

$$2x^2 + 6x - 8 = 2x^2 + 2x$$

$$4x = 8$$

$$x = 2$$

Theorem 7-4

$NO = MO - MN$;
$QR = PR - PQ$

7-4 *Segments Divided Proportionally*

---

2. Choose a point V on $\overline{XZ}$ and construct a line through V parallel to $\overline{XY}$. Label W the point of intersection of this line with $\overline{ZY}$.

3. Find XV, VZ, YW and WZ.

4. Compare the ratios $XV : VZ$ and $YW : WZ$. They are the same. Have students make a conjecture. Using the activity diagram, sketch a line through Z parallel to $\overline{VW}$ and $\overline{XY}$. This should motivate the statement and proof of Theorem 7–4.

Additional Examples

Example 1

Refer to the map used for **Example 1** in the text. If the distance from A to B is 0.2 miles, then find the distance from A to E. Using the proportion $\dfrac{.2}{.5} = \dfrac{x}{(1 - x)}$, $x \approx .28$ miles.

EXTENSION

Lesson
7-4

Name _____

Two Gems Help Locate the Prize

Certain theorems are gems because these theorems are either beautiful in their own right, their conclusions are astonishing, they are useful in a practical sense or in developing proofs of other theorems, they are used to prove their own converse, or for any combination of these reasons. Two such theorems are Ceva's Theorem (1678), and Menelaus's Theorem (c. 100 B.C.).

Ceva's Theorem If three lines $\overline{AO}$, $\overline{BO}$, and $\overline{CO}$, drawn through the vertices of $\triangle ABC$ and any point O of its plane, meet the lines containing the opposite sides of $\triangle ABC$ in L, M, and N respectively, then $\frac{AN}{NB} \cdot \frac{BL}{LC} \cdot \frac{CM}{MA} = 1$.

1. Use a straightedge to draw $\triangle ABC$. Choose any point O in the interior of $\triangle ABC$. Measure $\overline{AN}$, $\overline{BN}$, $\overline{BL}$, $\overline{LC}$, $\overline{CM}$, and $\overline{MA}$ very carefully. Use a calculator to find $\frac{AN}{NB} \cdot \frac{BL}{LC} \cdot \frac{CM}{MA}$. What integer value does this product approach? **1**

Menelaus's Theorem If a straight line intersects the lines containing the sides $\overline{BC}$, $\overline{CA}$, and $\overline{AB}$ of $\triangle ABC$ in the points L, M, and N respectively, then $\frac{AN}{NB} \cdot \frac{BL}{LC} \cdot \frac{CM}{MA} = -1$. (Note: The direction of LC is negative.)

2. Use a straightedge to draw any $\triangle ABC$. Let any line $\overline{NL}$ intersect the sides of the triangle as shown. Measure $\overline{AN}$, $\overline{NB}$, $\overline{BL}$, $\overline{LC}$, $\overline{CM}$, and $\overline{MA}$ very carefully. Find the product $\frac{AN}{NB} \cdot \frac{BL}{LC} \cdot \frac{CM}{MA}$. What integer value does this product approach? **−1**

3. Use Ceva's Theorem and Menelaus's Theorem along with your algebraic skills to locate the prize in the following problem. Drawing a diagram may help you. **see Additional Answers, p. 125**

The following directions were given at a party Matt attended. "Start at the intersection of First Street and Wilson Avenue. Proceeding north on First Street, find first a pine tree, then a maple. Return to the intersection. West on Wilson Avenue there is an elm and east on Wilson Avenue there is a spruce. One important point is the intersection of the spruce-pine line and the elm-maple line. The other important point is the intersection of the elm-pine line and the maple-spruce line. The line joining the two important points meets Wilson Avenue where the prize is located."

Matt's group found the elm four blocks from the intersection, and the spruce two blocks from the intersection. But, there was no trace of the maple or the pine. Nevertheless Matt's group found the prize. Where was the prize?

Assignment Guide

Basic: 1–19, 40–49
Average: 2–18 (even), 20–32, 40–49
Extended: 2–24 (even), 25–49

Example 2

In the figure for Case II of Theorem 7–4, we are given $RT = x - 2$, $ST = x + 1$, $TU = 2x - 2$ and $TV = 2x + 7$. Find x. Using $\frac{(x-2)}{(x+1)} \sim \frac{(2x-2)}{(2x+7)}$, $x = 4$.

Error Analysis   In problems with a segment parallel to one side of a triangle, students tend to confuse segments cut off with corresponding sides. For example, in the diagram shown they may conclude that $\frac{AB}{BC} = \frac{BE}{CF}$.

Be sure students are aware that they are working with either corresponding sides of similar triangles ($\overline{AB}$ and $\overline{AC}$, $\overline{BE}$ and $\overline{CF}$) or segments cut off ($\overline{AB}$ and $\overline{BC}$, $\overline{AE}$ and $\overline{EF}$).

EXERCISE NOTES

Exercises 10–15   should clarify the point made in the Error Analysis.

Exercises 27–28   could be solved with a **calculator**.

Exercise 34   extends Theorem 7–4 to include parallel planes.

ANSWERS

Checking for Understanding

5. Case II: $\overrightarrow{RV}$ or $\overrightarrow{SU}$; $\frac{RT}{TU} = \frac{ST}{TV}$
Case III: $\overrightarrow{GM}$ or $\overrightarrow{HN}$; $\frac{GJ}{JN} = \frac{HK}{KM}$ Case
IV: $\overrightarrow{WB}$ or $\overrightarrow{XA}$; $\frac{WY}{YA} = \frac{XZ}{ZB}$

Checking for Understanding

1. On the map of the Chicago suburbs, if $AB = 1$, $BC = 3$, $CD = 6$, and $AG = 20$, find AE, EF, and FG. 2; 6; 12

Given $\triangle ABC$ and $\overline{DE} \parallel \overline{BC}$, complete each proportion.

2. $\frac{AE}{EC} = \frac{AD}{\underline{?}}$ DB

3. $\frac{AD}{AB} = \frac{?}{AC}$ AE

4. $\frac{DE}{\underline{?}} = \frac{BC}{BA}$ DA

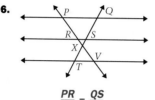

5. For Cases II-IV of Theorem 7-4, name an auxiliary line you can draw. State the proportions in the triangles formed.

Given $j \parallel k \parallel \ell$, state a proportion based on Theorem 7-4.

6.

$\frac{PR}{RV} = \frac{QS}{ST}$

7.

$\frac{HK}{KN} = \frac{JK}{KM}$

Given $\overleftrightarrow{MJ} \parallel \overleftrightarrow{NK} \parallel \overleftrightarrow{OL}$, complete each proportion.

8. $\frac{MN}{NO} = \frac{?}{KL}$ JK

9. $\frac{JK}{MN} = \frac{KL}{\underline{?}}$ NO

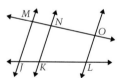

Written Exercises

Set A   Avenues A, B, C, and K are parallel.

1. How far is it from Avenue A to Avenue B along D Street? 1.2

2. How far is it from Avenue C to Avenue K along E Street? 5

Given: $\triangle XYZ$; $\overline{RS} \parallel \overline{YZ}$

3. $XR = 8$; $XS = 6$; $XZ = 15$; $XY = \underline{?}$ 20

4. $XS = 6$; $XR = 9$; $XY = 15$; $XZ = \underline{?}$ 10

5. $XS = 6$; $SZ = 4$; $XR = 8$; $RY = \underline{?}$ $5\frac{1}{3}$

6. $XR = 6n$; $RY = 2n$; $XS = 9$; $SZ = \underline{?}$ 3

Given $j \parallel k \parallel \ell$, find each missing length.

7. $AC = 9$; $BC = 6$; $DF = 15$; $EF = \underline{?}$ 10

8. $AB = 4$; $BC = 13$; $EF = 39$; $DE = \underline{?}$ 12

9. $AB = 5y$; $DE = 2y$; $EF = 12$; $BC = \underline{?}$ 30

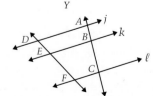

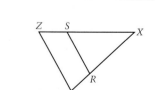

Given $\overline{OP} \parallel \overline{AD}$, tell whether each proportion is correct.

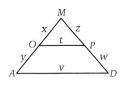

10. $\dfrac{x}{y} = \dfrac{z}{w}$ Yes **11.** $\dfrac{x+y}{y} = \dfrac{z+w}{z}$ No **12.** $\dfrac{z}{z+w} = \dfrac{t}{v}$ Yes

13. $\dfrac{w}{z} = \dfrac{t}{v}$ No **14.** $\dfrac{x+y}{z} = \dfrac{y}{t}$ No **15.** $\dfrac{z+w}{w} = \dfrac{t}{v}$ No

Photographers use the *diagonal test* for similarity of two rectangles: Place one rectangle on top of the other so that two right angles coincide and the longer side of one lies on the longer side of the other. Use the edge of a piece of paper and the diagonal test to tell if the rectangles in each exercise are similar.

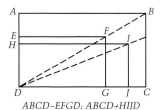

ABCD~EFGD; ABCD≁HIJD

16.

Similar

17.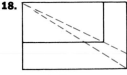

Not similar

18.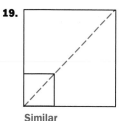

Not similar

19.

Similar

Set B

20. Using the diagonal test for similarity and the diagram above, explain why *ABCD* and *EFGD* are similar but *ABCD* and *HIJD* are not.

Given: $\triangle ABC$; $\overline{DE} \parallel \overline{BC}$

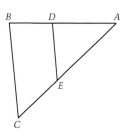

21. $AD = 2x + 3$; $DB = 10$; $AE = 2x$; $EC = 8$.
Find AD and AE. AD = 15; AE = 12

22. $AE = 2x + 2$; $AC = 3x$; $AB = 30$; $AD = 24$.
Find AE and AC. AE = 12; AC = 15

Given: $j \parallel k \parallel \ell$

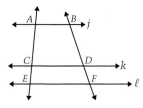

23. $AC = x + 2$; $CE = 9$; $BD = x + 3$; $DF = 12$.
Find AC and BD. AC = 3; BD = 4

24. $AE = 3x$; $AC = 16$; $BD = 20$; $BF = 4x - 1$.
Find AE and BF. AG = 12; BF = 15

25. The three segments below are divided proportionally. Find x, y, and z. x = 12; y = 30; z = 18

| 20 | 15 | y | | 16 | x | 24 | | 8 | ←z→ |

Written Exercises

20. Because $m\angle BDC = m\angle EDG$ and $m\angle C = m\angle G$, $\triangle BDC \sim \triangle EDG$ and $ABCD \sim EFGH$. Because $m\angle BDC \neq m\angle IDJ$, $\triangle BDC \not\sim \triangle IDJ$ and $ABCD \not\sim HIJD$.

26.

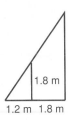

1.8 m

1.2 m 1.8 m

28. Gupta: $\frac{2}{5}$; Cox: $\frac{1}{5}$; West: $\frac{3}{10}$; Wu: $\frac{1}{10}$

29. Proof: 1. $\square ABCD$; $\overline{EF} \parallel \overline{DC}$; $\overline{GH} \parallel \overline{BC}$ (Given) 2. $\frac{AG}{GB} = \frac{AK}{KC}$; $\frac{AE}{ED} = \frac{AK}{KC}$ (If a line $\parallel$ to one side of a $\triangle$ intersects the other 2 sides, then it divides them proportionally. [1]) 3. $\frac{AG}{GB} = \frac{AE}{ED}$ (Substitution Prop. [2])

30. Proof: 1. Equilateral $\triangle ABC$; D on $\overline{BC}$; E on $\overline{AC}$; F on AB; $\overline{DE} \parallel \overline{BA}$; $\overline{EF} \parallel \overline{CB}$; $\overline{FD} \parallel \overline{AC}$ (Given) 2. $\frac{AF}{FB} = \frac{CD}{DB}$; $\frac{CD}{DB} = \frac{CE}{EA}$; $\frac{AF}{FB} = \frac{EA}{CE}$ (If a line $\parallel$ to one side of a $\triangle$ intersects the other 2 sides, then it divides them proportionally.) 3. $\frac{AF}{FB} = \frac{CE}{EA}$ (Transitive Prop. [2]) 4. $\frac{CE}{EA} = \frac{EA}{CE}$ (Substitution Prop. [2, 3]) 5. $(CE)^2 = (EA)^2$ and $CE = EA$ (Multiplication Prop. [4]) 6. $\frac{AF}{FB} = \frac{CE}{CE} = t$; $\frac{CD}{DB} = \frac{CE}{CE} = t$ (Substitution Prop. [2, 5]) 7. $AF = FB$; $CD = DB$ (Multiplication Prop. [6]) 8. D, E and F are midpts. of $\overline{BC}$, $\overline{CA}$ and $\overline{AB}$, respectively. (Def. of midpt. [5, 7])

32. If a line divides two sides of a triangle proportionally, then it is parallel to the third side; yes

33. Proof: 1. $\triangle ABC$; medians $\overline{AD}$ and $\overline{BE}$ (Given) 2. Draw $\overline{DE}$ (2 pts. determine a line.) 3. E is midpt. of $\overline{AC}$; D is midpt. of $\overline{BC}$. (Def. of median [1]) 4. $DE = \frac{1}{2}AB$; $\overline{DE} \parallel \overline{AB}$ (Seg. joining midpts. of 2 sides of a $\triangle$ is $\parallel$ to third side and its length is $\frac{1}{2}$ length of third side.) 5. $\frac{AB}{DE} = \frac{2}{1}$ (Multiplication Prop. [4]) 6. $m\angle EXA = m\angle DXB$ (Vertical $\angle$s are =.) 7. $m\angle XAB = m\angle XDE$ (2 lines $\parallel$ $\Rightarrow$ alt. int. $\angle$s are =. [4]) 8. $\triangle XAB \sim \triangle XDE$ (AA Post. [6, 7]) 9. $\frac{AX}{BX} = \frac{BX}{EX} = \frac{AE}{DE}$ (Def. of $\sim$ polygons [8]) 10. $\frac{AX}{DX} = \frac{BX}{EX} = \frac{2}{1}$ (Substitution Prop. [5, 9])

26. The foot of a ladder is 1.2 m from a fence that is 1.8 m high. The ladder touches the fence and rests against a building that is 1.8 m behind the fence. Draw a diagram, and determine the height on the building reached by the top of the ladder. **4.5 m**

27. A half-mile ramp begins 2,596 ft. west of a bridge. There is a pillar under the toll plaza which is located 1,500 ft. up the ramp. How far is the base of the pillar from the west end of the ramp? **1,475 ft.**

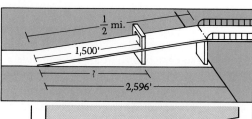

28. Residents are to pay for new curbs in proportion to the footage their lots have on Monroe Street. What part of the total cost must be paid by each resident?

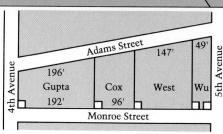

29. Given: $\square ABCD$; $\overline{EF} \parallel \overline{DC}$; $\overline{GH} \parallel \overline{BC}$
Prove: $\frac{AG}{GB} = \frac{AE}{ED}$

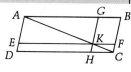

30. Given: Equilateral $\triangle ABC$; with D on $\overline{BC}$, E on $\overline{AC}$, and F on $\overline{AB}$ such that $\overline{DE} \parallel \overline{BA}$, $\overline{EF} \parallel \overline{CB}$, and $\overline{FD} \parallel \overline{AC}$
Prove: D, E, and F are midpoints of $\overline{BC}$, $\overline{AC}$, and $\overline{AB}$.

31. $\triangle TRC \sim \triangle TQS$ and $TR = CS$. Find TR. **$2\sqrt{2}$**

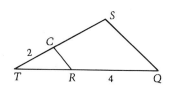

32. State the converse of Theorem 7-3. Is it true?

Set C

33. Given: $\triangle ABC$; medians $\overline{AD}$ and $\overline{BE}$
Prove: $\frac{AX}{DX} = \frac{BX}{EX} = \frac{2}{1}$

34. Given planes $\mathcal{R}$, $\mathcal{H}$, and $\mathcal{S}$; $\mathcal{R} \parallel \mathcal{H} \parallel \mathcal{S}$ and transversals ℓ and m, prove $\frac{AB}{BC} = \frac{DN}{NF}$.
(HINT: Draw $\overline{AF}$ intersecting plane $\mathcal{H}$ at G. Then draw $\overline{AD}$, $\overline{BG}$, $\overline{GN}$, $\overline{CF}$.)

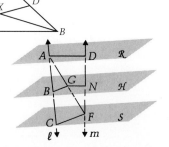

35. Given: $\square ABCD$; $\overline{TV}$, $\overline{PR}$, $\overline{AC}$ pass through O; $\overline{TP} \perp \overline{AC}$
Prove: $\overline{RV} \perp \overline{AC}$

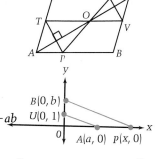

36. What are the coordinates of P if $\overline{AU} \parallel \overline{PB}$? **(ab, 0)**

Use figures in the other three quadrants to illustrate each statement.

37. $a(-b) = -ab$ **38.** $(-a)(-b) = ab$ **39.** $(-a)b = -ab$

Review   **40.** Given: Rectangle $ABCD$; $m\angle ABF = m\angle CBE$
Prove: $\triangle ABF \sim \triangle CBE$

41. In $\triangle XYZ$, $m\angle X = 31$ and $m\angle Z = 80$. In $\triangle PQR$, $m\angle Q = 69$ and $m\angle R = 80$. Are the triangles similar? Explain.

42. Are all equilateral hexagons similar? Explain.

43. The shortest segment from a point to a line is __?__.

44. In isosceles trapezoid $STUV$, $\overline{ST} \parallel \overline{VU}$. Which angles are equal? **∠S and ∠T; ∠V and ∠U**

Thinking Ahead Draw $\triangle ABC$ with coordinates $A(1, 2)$, $B(4, 3)$, and $C(2, 6)$. On the same grid, draw $\triangle A'B'C'$ with vertices whose coordinates are three times those of A, B, and C.

45. How are the two triangles related?

46. How do you think the side lengths of $\triangle A'B'C'$ compare to the side lengths of $\triangle ABC$?

47. Check your conjecture in Exercise 46 by computing the side lengths of $\triangle ABC$ and $\triangle A'B'C'$.

48. Now find $\dfrac{A'B'}{AB}$; $\dfrac{B'C'}{BC}$; and $\dfrac{A'C'}{AC}$.

49. What do you think would happen if you drew another triangle with vertices whose coordinates were five times the coordinates of A, B, and C?

Challenge

Trace the diagram at the right and continue to draw segments parallel to the sides of the triangle. Explain why you can draw no more than six distinct parallel segments. Is there a case for which there will be fewer than six segments? If so, how many will there be?

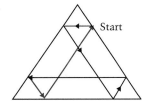

34. Proof: 1. Planes $\mathcal{R}$, $\mathcal{H}$, and $\mathcal{S}$; $\mathcal{R} \parallel \mathcal{H} \parallel \mathcal{S}$; transversals ℓ and m (Given) 2. Draw $\overline{AF}$ intersecting $\mathcal{H}$ at G and $\overline{AD}$, $\overline{BG}$, $\overline{GN}$ and $\overline{CF}$ (Line Post.) 3. $\overleftrightarrow{BG}$ and $\overleftrightarrow{CF}$ do not intersect; $\overleftrightarrow{GN}$ and $\overleftrightarrow{AO}$ do not intersect. (Def. of $\parallel$ planes [1]) 4. A, C and F determine a plane. (Plane Post.) 5. B, G and $\overline{BG}$ lie in plane ACF; G, N and $\overline{GN}$ lie in plane FAD. (Flat Plane Post.) 6. $\overline{BG} \parallel \overline{CF}$; $\overline{GN} \parallel \overline{AD}$ (Def. of $\parallel$ lines in a plane [3, 5]) 7. $\dfrac{AB}{BC} = \dfrac{AG}{GF}$; $\dfrac{AG}{GF} = \dfrac{DN}{NF}$ (If a line parallel to one side of a $\triangle$ intersects the other 2 sides, then it divides them proportionally. [6]) 8. $\dfrac{AB}{BC} = \dfrac{DN}{NF}$ (Transitive Prop. [7])

FOLLOW-UP

More Practice

- **Worksheet 7–4**

Extension

Assign **Exercise 29** and use the following questions to guide class discussion.
1. Is $AE : AD = AG : AB$? yes; by Addition Property
2. What does this suggest about $\square AGKE$ and $\square ABCD$? They are similar.
3. Compare your results with the diagonal test for similarity in **Exercises 16–19**. What does this suggest? an analogous test for similarity of parallelograms

- **Extension 7–4**

Computers

- **Computer Worksheet 7–4**

⚐ Construction Exercises

Construction 10

Separate a given segment into segments whose lengths are proportional to those of three other given segments.

Given $\overline{AB}$; segments with lengths x, y, and z

Construct Points C and D on $\overline{AB}$ such that $\dfrac{AC}{x} = \dfrac{CD}{y} = \dfrac{DB}{z}$

Method **Step 1:** Choose P not on $\overline{AB}$. Draw $\overrightarrow{AP}$.
Step 2: On $\overrightarrow{AP}$, mark off successive lengths $AT = x$, $TQ = y$, and $QR = z$. Draw $\overline{RB}$.
Step 3: Through T and Q, construct lines parallel to $\overline{RB}$ cutting $\overline{AB}$ at C and D, respectively.
Then, $\dfrac{AC}{x} = \dfrac{CD}{y} = \dfrac{DB}{z}$.

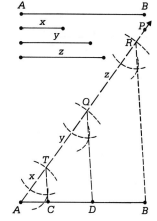

1. Tell which theorem justifies Construction 10.

2. Draw a segment. Separate it into 3 segments of equal length.

3. Draw a segment. Separate it into segments whose lengths are in the ratio 1 to 2 to 3.

4. How should the construction be modified to separate $\overline{AB}$ into segments with lengths proportional to x and y? to x, y, z, and w?

5. Draw a segment. Separate it into segments whose lengths are in the ratio 1 to 2 to 4 to 5.

6. Separate the hypotenuse $\overline{AB}$ of right $\triangle ABC$ into segments $\overline{AD}$ and $\overline{DB}$ such that $\dfrac{AC}{AD} = \dfrac{CB}{DB}$.

Construction 11

Given segments of lengths a, b, and c, construct a segment of length t such that $\dfrac{a}{b} = \dfrac{c}{t}$. The number t is called the fourth proportional of a, b, and c.

Given Segments of lengths a, b, and c

Construct A segment of length t, such that $\dfrac{a}{b} = \dfrac{c}{t}$

Method **Step 1:** Draw $\angle DEF$. On $\overrightarrow{ED}$, mark off successive lengths $EG = a$ and $GH = b$.
Step 2: On $\overrightarrow{EF}$, mark $EK = c$. Draw $\overline{KG}$.
Step 3: Through H, construct a line parallel to $\overline{KG}$ cutting $\overrightarrow{EF}$ at J. Let $KJ = t$. Then, $\dfrac{a}{b} = \dfrac{c}{t}$.

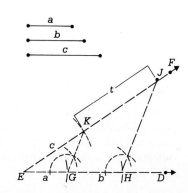

7. Tell which postulate or theorem justifies Construction 11.

8. Construct a segment of length t such that $\frac{2}{5} = \frac{1}{t}$.

9. Construct a segment of length r such that $\frac{1}{2} = \frac{r}{3}$.

Progress Check

Lesson 7-1, page 287

Solve each proportion for x.

1. $\frac{x + 3}{x + 6} = \frac{5}{8}$ $x = 2$ 2. $\frac{2x + 1}{3} = \frac{4x + 5}{7}$ $x = 4$ 3. $\frac{9}{x + 5} = \frac{4}{x + 2}$ $x = 0.4$

4. If $\frac{m}{n} = \frac{p}{q}$, then $mq = \underline{?}$ np and $\frac{m + n}{m} = \frac{p + q}{\underline{?}}$. q

Lesson 7-2, page 292

5. Are quadrilaterals $ABCD$ and $EFGH$ similar? Why or why not?

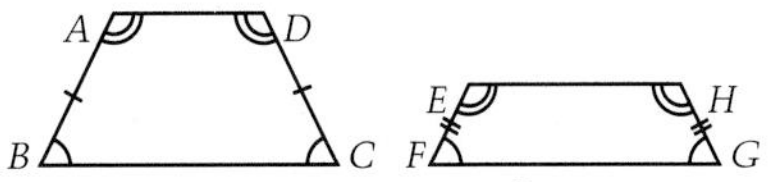

6. Given $\triangle MNO \sim \triangle PQR$, find RQ. 16

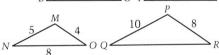

7. Given pentagon $STUVW \sim$ pentagon $HIJKL$, find IJ. 1.8

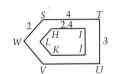

Lesson 7-3, page 297

In each exercise, name the similar triangles, and explain why they are similar. Then find the value of x.

8.

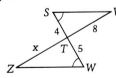

9.

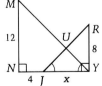

10.

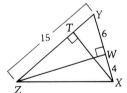

Lesson 7-4, page 302

Given $\overline{DE} \parallel \overline{AB}$, is each statement *true* or *false*? If false, explain why.

11. $\frac{CD}{CE} = \frac{DA}{BE}$ True

12. $\frac{CD}{DA} = \frac{DE}{EB}$ False; DE is not part of the intersected side of $\triangle ABC$.

13. $CD = 20$; $AD = 12$; $CB = 24$; $CE = \underline{?}$ 15; $EB = \underline{?}$ 9

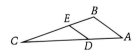

14. In trapezoid $SRTV$, $\overline{SR} \parallel \overline{VT} \parallel \overline{ZY}$. If $RT = 10$, $SV = 15$, and $\frac{RP}{PV} = \frac{2}{3}$, find RY, YT, SZ, and ZV. 4; 6; 6; 9

ANSWERS

Progress Check

5. Not necessarily; lengths of corresponding sides are not proportional.

8. $\triangle STV \sim \triangle WTZ$; AA $\sim$ Post.; $x = 10$

9. $\triangle MNY \sim \triangle RYJ$; AA $\sim$ Post.; $x = 8$

10. $\triangle ZYW \sim \triangle XYT$; AA $\sim$ Post.; $x = 4$

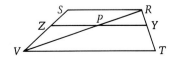

LESSON 7–5

Resources

Worksheet 7–5
Extension 7–5
Computer Activities 7–5

OBJECTIVE

Apply the SAS and SSS similarity theorems to prove that triangles are similar.

TEACHING NOTES

Discuss the following questions and elicit counterexamples for those that are false.
1. If two pairs of corresponding sides of two triangles are equal, must the triangles be congruent?
no

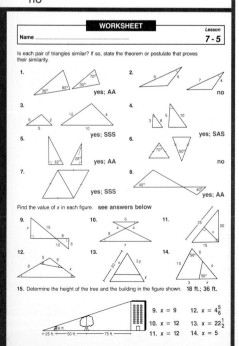

WORKSHEET   *Lesson* 7-5

Name _____

Is each pair of triangles similar? If so, state the theorem or postulate that proves their similarity.

1. 70° 30° 80° 30°   yes; AA
2. 9 6 7 4   no
3. 6 2 12 5 10 4   yes; SSS
4. 3 6 5 10   yes; SAS
5. 62° 28°   yes; AA
6. 70° 50°   no
7. yes; SSS
8. 40° 40°   yes; AA

Find the value of x in each figure. see answers below

9. x 15 8 10 6
10. 6 4 4 8 x
11. 25 20 x 15
12. 5 6 8 x
13. 3y x y
14. 50° 6 10 4 50° 3 x

15. Determine the height of the tree and the building in the figure shown. 18 ft.; 36 ft.

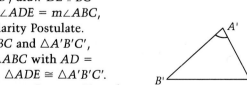
6 ft. 25 ft. 50 ft. 75 ft.

9. x = 9
10. x = 12
11. x = 12
12. x = 4⅚
13. x = 22½
14. x = 5

7-5 The SAS and SSS Similarity Theorems

A *pantograph* is an instrument that enlarges or reduces plane figures. The rods are hinged so that *ABCD* is always a parallelogram with *P*, *C*, and *C'* collinear. The instrument lies flat, fastened with a pivot at *P*. As a pointer at *C* traces from *R* to *S* along $\overline{RS}$, a pen at *C'* will draw from *R'* to a point collinear with *P* and *S*, say *S'*. As the pointer traces from *S* to *T*, the pen will draw from *S'* to a point collinear with *P* and *T*, say *T'*.

This arrangement of pointer and pen enlarges the figure. For a reduction, the pen and the pointer are interchanged.

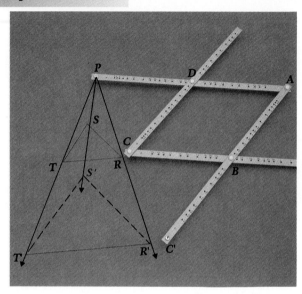

The proof that $\triangle R'S'T' \sim \triangle RST$ uses Theorems 7-5 and 7-6.

Theorem 7-5 *SAS Similarity Theorem*

If an angle of one triangle is equal to an angle of a second triangle, and if the lengths of the sides including these angles are proportional, then the triangles are similar.

Given $\triangle ABC$ and $\triangle A'B'C'$; $m\angle A = m\angle A'$; $\frac{AB}{A'B'} = \frac{AC}{A'C'}$

Prove $\triangle ABC \sim \triangle A'B'C'$

Plan for **Case I** $AB = A'B'$
Proof Show that the $\triangle$s are congruent and therefore similar.

Case II $AB \neq A'B'$
Locate *D* on $\overrightarrow{AB}$ such that $AD = A'B'$; draw $\overline{DE} \parallel \overline{BC}$ with *E* on $\overrightarrow{AC}$. $m\angle A = m\angle A$ and $m\angle ADE = m\angle ABC$, so $\triangle ADE \sim \triangle ABC$ by the AA Similarity Postulate. Use proportionality of sides of $\triangle ABC$ and $\triangle A'B'C'$, which is given, and of $\triangle ADE$ and $\triangle ABC$ with $AD = A'B'$ to show $AE = A'C'$. Therefore, $\triangle ADE \cong \triangle A'B'C'$. $m\angle D = m\angle B$ and $m\angle D = m\angle B'$, so $m\angle B = m\angle B'$, and $\triangle ABC \sim \triangle A'B'C'$.

Theorem 7-5, whose proof is left to Exercises 16 and 17, is analogous to the SAS Congruence Postulate.

Theorem 7-6 is analogous to the SSS Congruence Postulate. Its proof is requested in Exercise 18.

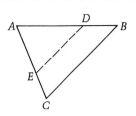

Theorem 7-6 *SSS Similarity Theorem*

If the lengths of the sides of one triangle are proportional to the lengths of the sides of a second triangle, then the triangles are similar.

Given $\triangle ABC$ and $\triangle A'B'C'$; $\dfrac{AB}{A'B'} = \dfrac{BC}{B'C'} = \dfrac{CA}{C'A'}$

Prove $\triangle ABC \sim \triangle A'B'C'$

Summary Ways to Prove Triangles Similar

Two triangles are similar if:

- all pairs of corresponding angles are equal, and lengths of all pairs of corresponding sides are proportional (Definition);
- two pairs of corresponding angles are equal (AA);
- they are congruent to each other;
- they are similar to the same triangle;
- lengths of two pairs of corresponding sides are proportional, and the included angles are equal (SAS Similarity);
- lengths of all pairs of corresponding sides are proportional (SSS Similarity).

Example

Given trapezoid $ABCD$ with $\overline{AD} \parallel \overline{BC}$, find x.

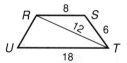

Solution

$m\angle CAD = 180 - (m\angle ACD + m\angle CDA) = 180 - (90 + 60) = 30$

Since $\overline{AD} \parallel \overline{BC}$, $m\angle BCA = m\angle CAD = 30$.

$\dfrac{BC}{CA} = \dfrac{CA}{AD} = \dfrac{5}{6}$. Thus, $\triangle ABC \sim \triangle DCA$. $\dfrac{AB}{DC} = \dfrac{BC}{CA}$, or $\dfrac{x}{18} = \dfrac{25}{30}$.

Therefore, x = 15.

Checking for Understanding 1. 2 lines $\parallel \Rightarrow$ corr. $\angle$s =.

In the Plan for Proof of Case II of Theorem 7-5, how do you know

1. $m\angle ADE = m\angle ABC$?   **2.** $\triangle ADE \cong \triangle A'B'C'$? SAS $\cong$ Post.

3. In the Example, how do you know $\triangle ABC \sim \triangle DCA$?

SAS $\sim$ Thm.

Refer to the pantograph on page 310.

4. If D is the midpoint of $\overline{PA}$, how are the side lengths of $\triangle RST$ and $\triangle R'S'T'$ related?

4. Side lengths of $\triangle RST = \frac{1}{2}$ side lengths of $\triangle R'S'T'$

5. To draw a figure whose dimensions are three times those of the figure being traced, where should D be?

PD should be $\frac{1}{3}PA$.

---

2. If two pairs of corresponding sides of two triangles are in proportion, must the triangles be similar? no

3. If three pairs of corresponding sides of two triangles are equal, must the triangles be congruent? yes

4. If three pairs of corresponding sides of two triangles are in proportion, must the triangles be similar? yes

Ask students to make conjectures and elicit the SAS and SSS similarity statements.

Additional Example

Given trapezoid $RSTU$ with $\overline{RS} \parallel \overline{TU}$, find **x**. x = 9

YELLOW···

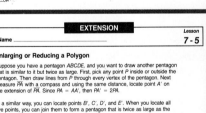
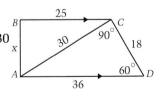

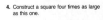

312

Assignment Guide

Basic: 1–5, 20–28
Average: 1–16, 20–28
Extended: 1–28

Error Analysis Students often forget that sides of similar triangles need only be proportional—not equal. Stress that to prove any triangles similar you either prove (1) pairs of angles are congruent (SAS or AA) or (2) pairs of sides are proportional (SAS or SSS).

ANSWERS

Written Exercises

4. $AX = BX = \frac{1}{2}CX$

10. Proof: 1. $\frac{CE}{AE} = \frac{3}{2}$, $\frac{BD}{AD} = \frac{1}{2}$; $\overline{DE} \parallel \overline{BF}$ (Given) 2. $\frac{FE}{AE} = \frac{BD}{AD}$ (If a line $\parallel$ to one side of a $\triangle$ intersects the other 2 sides, then it divides them proportionally. [1]) 3. $\frac{FE}{AE} = \frac{1}{2}$ (Substitution Prop. [1, 2]) 4. $AE = 2FE$; $2CE = 3AE$ (Multiplication Prop. [1, 3]) 5. $2CE = 6FE$ (Substitution Prop. [4]) 6. $\frac{CE}{FE} = \frac{3}{1}$ (Multiplication Prop. [5]) 7. $CE = CF + FE$ (Seg. Add. Post.) 8. $\frac{CF + FE}{FG} = \frac{3}{1}$ (Substitution Prop. [6]) 9. $\frac{CF}{FE} = \frac{2}{1}$ (Subtraction Prop. [8]) 10. $\frac{CM}{DM} = \frac{CF}{FE}$ (If a line $\parallel$ to one side of a $\triangle$ intersects the other 2 sides, then it divides them proportionally. [1]) 11. $\frac{CM}{DM} = \frac{2}{1}$ (Substitution Prop. [9, 10]) 12. $DM = \frac{CM}{2}$ (Multiplication Prop. [10])

16. Given: $\triangle ABC$ and $\triangle A'B'C'$; $m\angle A = m\angle A'$; $\frac{AB}{A'B'} = \frac{AC}{A'C'}$; $AB = A'B'$ Prove: $\triangle ABC \sim \triangle A'B'C'$ Proof: 1. $\triangle ABC$ and $\triangle A'B'C'$; $m\angle A = m\angle A'$; $\frac{AB}{A'B'} = \frac{AC}{A'C'}$; $AB = A'B'$ (Given) 2. $\frac{AB}{A'B'} = \frac{AC}{A'C'}$ (Substitution Prop. [1]) 3. $1 = \frac{AC}{A'C'}$ (Substitution Prop. [2]) 4. $A'C' = AC$ (Multiplication Prop. [3]) 5. $\triangle ABC \cong \triangle A'B'C'$ (SAS $\cong$ Post. [1, 4]) 6. $m\angle B = m\angle B'$ (Def. of $\sim$ polygons [5]) 7. $\triangle ABC \sim \triangle A'B'C'$ (AA $\sim$ Post. [1, 6])

Are the triangles in each exercise similar? If *so*, state the theorem or postulate that applies. If *not*, explain why not.

6. 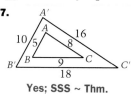 Yes; AA $\sim$ Post.

7. 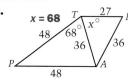 Yes; SSS $\sim$ Thm.

8. 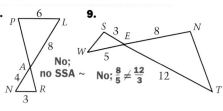 No; no SSA $\sim$

9. No; $\frac{8}{5} \ne \frac{12}{3}$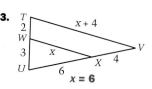

Written Exercises

Set A Find the value of x in each exercise.

1. $x = 6.5$

2. $x = 68$

3. 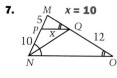 $x = 6$

4. Proportional dividers are used by cartographers to construct segments with proportional lengths. The legs $\overline{AC}$ and $\overline{BD}$ are of equal length, joined by a thumbscrew at X. The screw slides along the legs so that AX and BX remain equal. Describe where the screw should be located so that $CD = 2AB$.

5. A flashlight beam is directed horizontally at a flat vertical screen. A cardboard triangle with side lengths 4, 5, and 6 is positioned between the light and the screen, parallel to the screen. List several sets of possible dimensions for the shadow. Which theorem justifies your answers?
Samples: 8, 10, 12; 12, 15, 18; SSS $\sim$ Thm.

Set B Find the value of x in Exercises 6–9.

6. $x = 82$

7. $x = 10$

8. $x = 46$

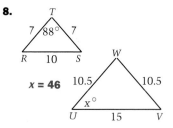

9.

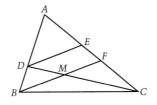

$$x = 12$$

10. Given: $\dfrac{CE}{AE} = \dfrac{3}{2}$; $\dfrac{BD}{AD} = \dfrac{1}{2}$; $\overline{DE} \parallel \overline{BF}$

Prove: $DM = \dfrac{CM}{2}$

The coordinates of A, B, and C are $A(0, 0)$, $B(2, 6)$, and $C(8, -2)$. Are the following triangles similar to $\triangle ABC$? If *so*, state the theorem or postulate which justifies similarity. If *not*, explain why not.

11. $\triangle DEF$ with $D(-2, 12)$, $E(-6, -4)$, and $F(-18, 0)$ Yes; SSS ~ Thm.

12. $\triangle XYZ$ with X, Y, and Z are the points where the lines with equations $y = 3x$, $-4y = x$, and $3y + 4x = 13$ Yes; SSS ~ Thm.

13. $\triangle AB'C'$ where the coordinates of B' and C' are double the coordinates of B and C Yes; SAS or SSS ~ Thm.

14. $\triangle GHK$ where the x-coordinates of G, H, and K are 2 less than the coordinates of A, B, and C Yes; SSS ~ Thm.

15. Find the height of the tree. 41.5 ft.

16. Prove Theorem 7-5, Case I.

Set C **17.** Prove Theorem 7-5, Case II.

18. Prove Theorem 7-6.

19. Given a quadrilateral and its diagonals, prove that the ratio of the segments on one diagonal is equal to the ratio of the segments on the other diagonal if and only if the quadrilateral is a parallelogram or a trapezoid.

▲ Review Given: $j \parallel k \parallel \ell$

20. Name a pair of similar triangles. $\triangle ABE$, $\triangle ACF$, $\triangle ADG$

21. If $AC = 6$, $FG = 10$, and $AF = 8$, then $CD = \underline{\ ?\ }$. 7.5

22. State the AA Similarity Postulate.

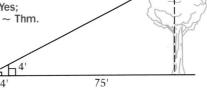

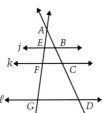

17. Given: $\triangle ABC$ and $\triangle A'B'C'$; $m\angle A = m\angle A'$; $\dfrac{AB}{A'B'} = \dfrac{AC}{A'C'}$ Prove: $\triangle ABC \sim \triangle A'B'C'$ Proof: 1. $\triangle ABC$ and $\triangle A'B'C'$; $m\angle A = m\angle A'$; $\dfrac{AB}{A'B'} = \dfrac{AC}{A'C'}$ (Given) 2. Locate D on $\overline{AB}$ such that $AD = A'B'$. (Seg. Const. Post.) 3. Draw $\overline{DE} \parallel \overline{BC}$ with E on $\overrightarrow{AC}$. (Through a point not on a given line, there is exactly one line $\parallel$ to the given line. [2]) 4. $m\angle A = m\angle A$ (Reflexive Prop.) 5. $m\angle B = m\angle ADE$ (2 lines $\parallel \Rightarrow$ corr. $\angle$s =. [3]) 6. $\triangle ABC \sim \triangle ADE$ (AA ~ Post. [4, 5]) 7. $\dfrac{AB}{AD} = \dfrac{AC}{AE}$ (Def. of ~ polygons [6]) 8. $\dfrac{AB}{A'B'} = \dfrac{AC}{AE}$ (Substitution Prop. [2, 7]) 9. $\dfrac{AC}{AE} = \dfrac{AC}{A'C'}$ (Substitution Prop. [1, 8]) 10. $(AC)(A'C') = (AE)(AC)$ (Multiplication Prop. [9]) 11. $A'C' = AE$ (Multiplication Prop. [10]) 12. $\triangle A'B'C' \cong \triangle ADE$ (SAS ~ Post. [1, 2, 11]) 13. $m\angle B' = m\angle ADE$ (Corr. parts of $\cong$ $\triangle$s are =. [12]) 14. $m\angle B = m\angle B'$ (Substitution Prop. [5, 13]) 15. $\triangle ABC \sim \triangle A'B'C'$ (AA ~ Post. [1, 14])

18. Given: $\triangle ABC$ and $\triangle A'B'C'$; $\dfrac{AB}{A'B'} = \dfrac{BC}{B'C'} = \dfrac{CA}{C'A'}$ Prove: $\triangle ABC = \triangle A'B'C'$ Proof: 1. $\triangle ABC$ and $\triangle A'B'C'$; $\dfrac{AB}{A'B'} = \dfrac{BC}{B'C'} = \dfrac{CA}{C'A'}$ (Given) 2. Locate D on $\overrightarrow{AB}$ and E on $\overrightarrow{AC}$ such that $AD = A'B'$ and $AE = C'A'$ (Seg. Constr. Post.) 3. $\dfrac{AB}{AD} = \dfrac{CA}{AE}$ (Substitution Prop. [1, 2]) 4. $m\angle A = m\angle A$ (Reflexive Prop.) 5. $\triangle ABC \sim \triangle ADE$ (SAS ~ Thm. [3, 4]) 6. $\dfrac{AB}{AD} = \dfrac{BC}{DE}$ (Def. of ~ polygons [5]) 7. $\dfrac{AB}{A'B'} = \dfrac{BC}{B'C'} = \dfrac{BC}{DE}$ (Substitution Prop. [1, 2, 6]) 8. $(BC)(B'C') = (DE)(BC)$ (Multiplication Prop. [7]) 9. $B'C' = DE$ (Division Prop. [8]) 10. $\triangle ADE \cong \triangle A'B'C'$ (SSS $\cong$ Post. [2, 9]) 11. $m\angle A = m\angle A'$ (Corr. parts of $\cong$ $\triangle$s are =. [10]) 12. $\triangle ABC \sim \triangle A'B'C'$ (SAS ~ Thm. [1, 11])

Thinking Ahead

25. $\triangle ABC \sim \triangle A'B'C'$; SSS ~
Thm.

26. $\frac{BH}{B'H'} = \frac{AC}{A'C'}$ $\left(\frac{4}{8} = \frac{6}{12} = \frac{1}{2}\right)$

27. $\frac{AM}{A'M'} = \frac{AC}{A'C'}$ $\left(\frac{\sqrt{13}}{2\sqrt{13}} = \frac{6}{12} = \frac{1}{2}\right)$

FOLLOW-UP

More Practice

• **Worksheet 7–5**

Extension

Challenge your better students to
do the following proof.
Given: $\square ABCD$
Prove: $\overline{TP} \parallel \overline{RV}$

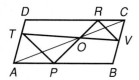

Use AA to prove $\triangle TOA \sim \triangle VOC$
and $\triangle AOP \sim \triangle COR$. Then use
the Transitive Property and the
SAS Similarity Theorem to get
$\triangle TOP \sim \triangle VOR$. Because alternate interior angles are equal, the
lines are parallel.

• **Extension 7–5**

Computers

The computer activity in the pupil's book can be completed using
The Geometric Supposer: Triangles
or *The Geometric preSupposer:
Points and Lines.*

Note: *GeoDraw* does not directly
offer the option to bisect an angle.
Because angle measures and
lengths in *GeoDraw* are displayed
to the nearest whole number, if
the activity is completed using
GeoDraw the effect may be ratios
that are approximately—but not
exactly—equal in terms of values
displayed in the program.

• **Computer Activities 7–5**

---

23. Can the complements of two supplementary
angles be equal? Can the supplements of two
complementary angles be equal? Explain.

24. List as many ways as you can to prove that a
quadrilateral is a parallelogram.

Thinking Ahead On a coordinate system, draw $\triangle ABC$ with $A(1, 0)$,
$B(3, 4)$, and $C(7, 0)$. Draw altitude $\overline{BH}$ and median $\overline{AM}$.
On the same grid, draw $\triangle A'B'C'$ with $A'(2, 0)$,
$B'(6, 8)$, and $C'(14, 0)$. Draw altitude $\overline{BH'}$ and
median $\overline{A'M'}$.

25. What is true about $\triangle ABC$ and $\triangle A'B'C'$? Why?

26. How does $\frac{BH}{B'H'}$ compare with $\frac{AC}{A'C'}$?

27. Find AM and $A'M'$. How does $\frac{AM}{A'M'}$ compare with $\frac{AC}{A'C'}$?

28. What conjectures can you make?

Computer Activities: Drawing and Measuring

1. Draw any triangle ABC. Draw the bisector of $\angle B$, intersecting
$\overline{AC}$ at D. Find the ratios $AD{:}CD$ and $AB{:}CB$. What is true?
The ratios are equal

2. Repeat the activity in Exercise 1 with five different triangles.
What is true of the two ratios for each triangle? They are equal

3. What generalization can you make regarding an angle
bisector of a triangle?

Algebra Review: Solving Quadratic Equations

Examples

1. Solve $x^2 + 4x - 12 = 0$
by factoring.

2. Solve $x^2 + 9x - 2 = 0$ by using
the quadratic formula at the right.

$$x = \frac{-b \pm \sqrt{b^2 - 4ac}}{2a}$$

Solutions

1. $x^2 + 4x - 12 = 0$
$(x + 6)(x - 2) = 0$
$x + 6 = 0$ or $(x - 2) = 0$
$x = -6$ or $x = 2$

2. $x = \frac{-9 \pm \sqrt{9^2 - (4)(1)(-2)}}{(2)(1)}$ *Here*, $a = 1, b = 9$,
and $c = -2$.

$= \frac{-9 \pm \sqrt{89}}{2}$

$x = \frac{-9 + \sqrt{89}}{2}$ or $\frac{-9 - \sqrt{89}}{2}$

Solve by the method of your choice.

1. $x^2 + 4x - 21 = 0$ **2.** $x^2 - 10x - 39 = 0$ $x = 13$ or -3 **3.** $x^2 - 3x = 3$ $x = \frac{3 \pm \sqrt{21}}{2}$

4. $x^2 - 16 = 0$ $x = \pm 4$ **5.** $x^2 + 4x - 2 = 0$ **6.** $x^2 + 5x = 0$ $x = 0$ or -5

7. $9x^2 + 12x = -4$ $x = -\frac{2}{3}$ **8.** $2x^2 - 3x - 20 = 0$ **9.** $x^2 = 81$ $x = \pm 9$
     1. $x = 3$ or -7 $x = 4$ or $-\frac{5}{2}$
                             5. $x = 2 \pm \sqrt{16}$

Excursion: The Golden Ratio

For centuries, people have been fascinated by the golden ratio. If a point P divides a segment $\overline{AB}$ into segments $\overline{AP}$ and $\overline{PB}$ such that $\frac{AB}{AP} = \frac{AP}{PB}$, then the ratio $\frac{AB}{AP}$ is called the *golden ratio*.

Sometimes referred to as the "divine proportion," the golden ratio appears frequently in nature and in art. To find its value, let $AB = 1$ and $AP = x$. Since $PB = 1 - x$, we have $\frac{1}{x} = \frac{x}{1 - x}$. Then $x^2 = 1 - x$ and $x^2 + x - 1 = 0$. By the quadratic formula, $x = \frac{1}{2}(-1 \pm \sqrt{5})$. $\frac{AB}{AP} = \frac{1}{x} = \frac{1}{\frac{1}{2}(-1 + \sqrt{5})} = \frac{1}{2}(1 + \sqrt{5}) \approx 1.618$. Why do we discard the value $x = \frac{1}{2}(-1 - \sqrt{5})$? **Lengths cannot be negative.**

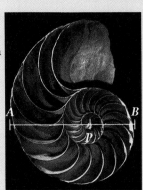
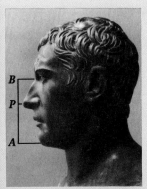

1. If P divides $\overline{AB}$ into the golden ratio, and $AB = 8$ cm, find AP.
About 4.944 cm

In a *golden rectangle*, the ratio of the length of the longer side to that of the shorter one is the golden ratio. The Greeks realized the pleasing proportions of this figure and used it in much of their architecture. Some properties of golden rectangles are suggested in these exercises.

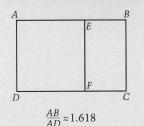

$$\frac{AB}{AD} \approx 1.618$$

Given: $ABCD$ is a golden rectangle; $AF = AD$; $EF \perp AB$

2. Show that $ABCD$ and $BCEF$ are similar rectangles.

3. Is $BCEF$ a golden rectangle? Why?

An isosceles triangle is a *golden triangle* if the ratio of the length of one leg to that of the base is the golden ratio.

Given: $\triangle ABC$ is a golden triangle; $AB = AC$; $BD = BC$

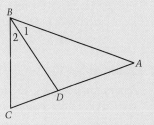

4. Prove: $\triangle ABC \sim \triangle BDC$ **5.** Prove: $\triangle ABD$ is isosceles.

6. Prove: $m\angle 1 = m\angle 2$ **7.** Prove: $m\angle A = 36$

8. Copy the golden rectangle in Exercises 2 and 3. Draw $\overline{AC}$ and $\overline{EB}$. Then prove that $\overline{AC}$ is perpendicular to $\overline{EB}$.

ANSWERS

Excursion

2. Because $AF = AD$, $ADEF$ is a square. Thus, $BCEF$ is a rectangle. Since $ABCD$ is a golden rectangle, $\frac{AB}{AD} = \frac{1}{2}(1 + \sqrt{5})$. Let $AD = 1$. Then $AB = \frac{1}{2}(1 + \sqrt{5})$. $BF = AB - AF = \frac{1}{2}(1 + \sqrt{5}) = 1$ and $\frac{EF}{BF} = \frac{1}{\frac{1}{2}(1 + \sqrt{5}) - 1} = \frac{1}{2}(1 + \sqrt{5})$. Thus, $ABCD \sim BCEF$.

3. $BCEF$ is a golden rectangle because $\frac{EF}{BF} = \frac{1}{2}(1 + \sqrt{5})$.

4. Proof: 1. $\triangle ABC$ is a golden $\triangle$; $AB = AC$; $BD = BC$ (Given) 2. $m\angle ABC = m\angle C$; $m\angle C = m\angle BDC$ (Isos. $\triangle$ Thm. [1]) 3. $m\angle ABC = m\angle BDC$ (Transitive Prop. [2]) 4. $m\angle C = m\angle C$ (Reflexive Prop.) 5. $\triangle ABC \sim \triangle BDC$ (AA $\sim$ Post. [3, 4])

5. Proof: 1. $\triangle ABC$ is a golden $\triangle$; $AB = AC$; $BD = BC$ (Given) 2. $\triangle ABC \sim \triangle BDC$ (Exercise 4) 3. $\frac{AC}{BC} = \frac{BC}{CD}$ (Corres. sides of $\sim \triangle$s are prop. [2]) 4. $\frac{AC}{BC} = \frac{BC}{CD} = \frac{1}{2}(1 + \sqrt{5})$ (Def. of golden $\triangle$ [1, 2]) 5. Let $BC = 1$. (A seg. has a unique length.) 6. $BD = 1$ (Substitution Prop. [1, 5]) 7. $\frac{AC}{1} = \frac{1}{CD} = \frac{1}{2}(1 + \sqrt{5})$ (Substitution Prop. [4, 5]) 8. $CD = \frac{2}{1 + \sqrt{5}}$ (Multiplication Prop. [7]) 9. $AC = AD + CD$ (Seg. Add. Post.) 10. $AD = AC - CD$ (Subtraction Prop. [9]) 11. $AD = \frac{1}{2}(1 + \sqrt{5}) - \frac{2}{1 + \sqrt{5}} = 1$ (Substitution Prop. [7, 8]) 12. $AD = BD$ (Substitution [6, 11]) 13. $\triangle ABD$ is isosceles. (Def. of isosceles $\triangle$ [12]) **6.** Proof: 1. $\triangle ABC$ is a golden $\triangle$; $AB = AC$; $BD = BC$ (Given) 2. $AD = BD$ (Exercise 5) 3. $m\angle A = m\angle 1$ (Isos. $\triangle$ Thm. [2]) 4. $\triangle ABC \sim \triangle BDC$ (Exercise 4) 5. $m\angle A = m\angle 2$ (Def. of $\sim$ polygons [4]) 6. $m\angle 1 = m\angle 2$ (Substitution Prop. [3, 5])

LESSON 7–6

Resources

Compass
Straightedge
Worksheet 7–6
Extension 7–6

OBJECTIVE

Apply ratios to the lengths of altitudes, angle bisectors and medians in similar triangles.

TEACHING NOTES

Have students construct a pair of similar triangles using the AA method. Then have them construct the corresponding altitudes. Compare the ratio of the altitude

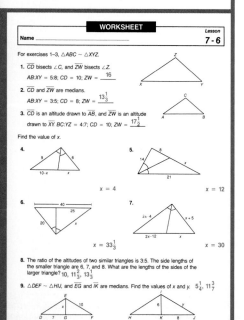

7-6 More Ratios in Similar Triangles

Engineer Calvin Browne, working with blueprints of the new college library, uses the fact that if two figures are similar, then the lengths of any two pairs of corresponding segments are proportional. Theorems 7-7, 7-8, and 7-9 express this relationship for angle bisectors, altitudes, and medians of similar triangles, respectively. The proofs of Theorems 7-7 and 7-9 are requested in Exercises 34 and 35.

Theorem 7-7

In similar triangles, the lengths of bisectors of corresponding angles are proportional to the lengths of corresponding sides.

Given $\triangle ABC \sim \triangle A'B'C'$; $\overrightarrow{CD}$ bisects $\angle ACB$; $\overrightarrow{C'D'}$ bisects $\angle A'C'B'$.

Prove $\dfrac{CD}{C'D'} = \dfrac{AC}{A'C'}$

Plan for Show $\triangle ACD \sim \triangle A'C'D'$ by AA similarity.

Proof By corresponding sides of similar triangles, $\dfrac{CD}{C'D'} = \dfrac{AC}{A'C'}$.

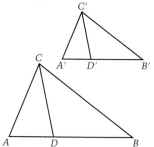

Theorem 7-8

In similar triangles, the lengths of altitudes from corresponding vertices are proportional to the lengths of corresponding sides.

Given $\triangle DEF \sim \triangle D'E'F'$; $\overline{FG} \perp \overline{DE}$; $\overline{F'G'} \perp \overline{D'E'}$

Prove $\dfrac{FG}{F'G'} = \dfrac{DF}{D'F'}$

Proof It is given that $\triangle DEF$ is similar to $\triangle D'E'F'$ and that $\overline{FG}$ and $\overline{F'G'}$ are perpendicular to $\overline{DE}$ and $\overline{D'E'}$. Because perpendicular lines form right angles, $\angle FGD$ and $\angle F'G'D'$ are right angles; and $m\angle FGD = m\angle F'G'D'$ because all right angles are equal. Thus $\triangle DFG$ is similar to $\triangle D'F'G'$ by AA similarity. Finally, $\dfrac{FG}{F'G'} = \dfrac{DF}{D'F'}$ by definition of similar polygons.

Theorem 7-9

In similar triangles, the lengths of medians from corresponding vertices are proportional to the lengths of corresponding sides.

Given $\triangle RST \sim \triangle R'S'T'$; $\overline{TM}$ is the median from $\angle T$; $T'M'$ is the median from $\angle T'$.

Prove $\dfrac{TM}{T'M'} = \dfrac{RT}{R'T'}$

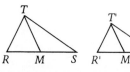

Example 1

The library window will be cut by support beam $\overline{DK}$ perpendicular to the base $\overline{EF}$, by beam $\overline{LF}$ bisecting $\angle DFE$, and by beam $\overline{NE}$ bisecting side $\overline{DF}$. How long will the beams need to be? In the blueprint, $JC = 13.5$ in., $AH = 9$ in., and $MB = 10.5$ in.

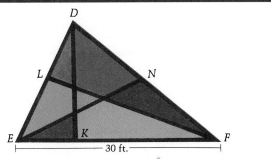

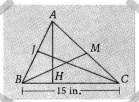

Solution

To find DK, use Theorem 7-8.	To find LF, use Theorem 7-7.	To find NE, use Theorem 7-9.
$\dfrac{DK}{AH} = \dfrac{EF}{BC}$	$\dfrac{LF}{JC} = \dfrac{EF}{BC}$	$\dfrac{NE}{MB} = \dfrac{EF}{BC}$
$\dfrac{DK}{9} = \dfrac{30}{15} = \dfrac{2}{1}$	$\dfrac{LF}{13.5} = \dfrac{30}{15} = \dfrac{2}{1}$	$\dfrac{NE}{10.5} = \dfrac{30}{15} = \dfrac{2}{1}$
$DK = 9(2) = 18$ ft.	$LF = 13.5(2) = 27$ ft.	$NE = 10.5(2) = 21$ ft.

One of the most surprising properties of triangles, stated in Theorem 7-10, is the proportionality of the segments created by the intersection of an angle bisector with the opposite side. The proof of this theorem is left to Exercise 36.

Theorem 7-10

The bisector of an angle of a triangle divides the opposite side into two segments whose lengths are proportional to the lengths of the two sides adjacent to the segments.

Given $\triangle ABC$; bisector of $\angle ABC$ intersects $\overline{AC}$ at D.

Prove $\dfrac{AD}{CD} = \dfrac{BA}{BC}$

Plan for Proof   Draw $\overleftrightarrow{EC} \parallel \overrightarrow{BD}$ with E on $\overrightarrow{AB}$. Use AA similarity to show $\triangle ADB \sim \triangle ACE$. Use the properties of angle bisector, alternate interior angles, and corresponding angles to show $\triangle BEC$ is isosceles with $BE = BC$. Then use Theorem 7-3 and substitution to show $\dfrac{AD}{CD} = \dfrac{BA}{BC}$.

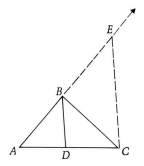

measures with that of a pair of corresponding sides. the same Repeat the activity with a pair of corresponding sides. the same Repeat the activity with a pair of corresponding medians and corresponding angle bisectors.

The proof of Theorem 7–10 uses the previous theorem concerning a line parallel to one side of a triangle.

Additional Examples

Example 1

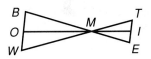

Given: $BW \parallel TE$

(a) $\overline{MO}$ bisects $\angle BMW$, $\overline{MI}$ bisects $\angle EMT$, $BM = 8$, $EM = 6$ and $MI = 5$. Find MO. $6\frac{2}{3}$

(b) $\overline{MO} \perp \overline{BW}$, $\overline{MI} \perp \overline{ET}$, $WM = 10$, $MO = 8$ and $MI = 3$. Find MT.   3.75

Example 2

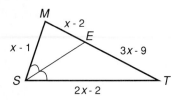

Given: $\triangle MST$; $\overline{SE}$ bisects $\angle MST$. Find MT. $MT = 9$

Error Analysis   Students may try to use any two altitudes (medians, angle bisectors) in the application of these theorems, rather than corresponding ones. Continue to stress the importance of establishing corresponding vertices.

EXERCISE NOTES

Exercise 37   may require a plan for a proof.

ANSWERS

Checking for Understanding

7. Given: $\triangle RST \sim \triangle R'S'T'$; $RM = MS$; $R'S' = M'S'$ Prove: $\frac{TM}{T'M'} = \frac{RT}{R'T'}$ Plan for Proof: Show $\triangle TRM \sim \triangle T'R'M'$ by AA $\sim$ Post. Then, using corr. sides of $\sim \triangle s \frac{TM}{T'M'} = \frac{RT}{R'T'}$.

Example 2
Given $\triangle DEF$ with $\overrightarrow{EB}$ bisecting $\angle DEF$, find DF.

Solution

$$\frac{DB}{FB} = \frac{ED}{EF} \qquad \textit{Theorem 7-10}$$
$$\frac{x+4}{x-2} = \frac{2x}{x}$$
$$x^2 + 4x = 2x^2 - 4x$$
$$x^2 - 8x = 0$$
$$x(x - 8) = 0, \text{ and } x = 0 \text{ or } x = 8$$

$DF = DB + BF = (x + 4) + (x - 2) = (8 + 4) + (8 - 2) = 18$
Why do we discard $x = 0$? **BF** would have a negative value.

Checking for Understanding
Given: $\triangle RST \sim \triangle XYZ$; altitudes $\overline{SU}$ and $\overline{YP}$; medians $\overline{RW}$ and $\overline{XV}$

1. $\frac{XZ}{RT} = \frac{?}{SU}$ YP   **2.** $\frac{RS}{XY} = \frac{RW}{?}$ XV   **3.** $\frac{XV}{YP} = \frac{?}{SU}$

4. $\frac{RS}{XY} = \frac{?}{YP}$ SU   **5.** $\frac{YZ}{ST} = \frac{XV}{?}$ RW   **6.** $\frac{SU}{YP} = \frac{RW}{?}$ XV

7. Give a Plan for Proof for Theorem 7-9.

Given $\triangle ABC \sim \triangle DEF$; $\overrightarrow{BG}$ bisects $\angle ABC$; $\overrightarrow{EH}$ bisects $\angle DEF$.

8. $\frac{AG}{CG} = \frac{?}{BC}$ BA   **9.** $\frac{DH}{?} = \frac{ED}{EF}$ FH

Written Exercises
Set A   Find x.

1. 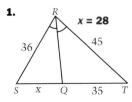 $x = 28$

2. 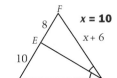 $x = 10$

3. 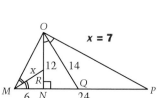 $x = 7$

Given: $\triangle HJK$; $\overrightarrow{JL}$ bisects $\angle J$.

4. $HJ = 9$; $HL = 6$; $JK = 10$; $LK = \underline{?}$ $6\frac{2}{3}$

5. $HJ = 20$; $JK = 8$; $LK = 6$; $HK = \underline{?}$ 15

6. $HJ = 8$; $JK = 10$; $HK = 9$; $HL = \underline{?}$ 4

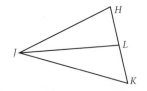

Given: $\triangle GHK \sim \triangle LMN$; $\overrightarrow{HX}$ bisects $\angle GHK$; $\overrightarrow{MY}$ bisects $\angle LMN$.

7. $GH = 15$; $HX = 10$; $LM = 24$; $MY = \underline{?}$ **16**

8. $YN = 12$; $XK = 8$; $HK = 10$; $MN = \underline{?}$ **15**

9. $GX = 18$; $MY = 14$; $LY = 21$; $HX = \underline{?}$ **12**

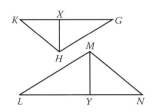

Given: $\triangle PQR \sim \triangle STU$; $\overline{VP} \perp \overline{QR}$; $\overline{WS} \perp \overline{TU}$

10. $TS = 8$; $WS = 6$; $QP = 32$; $VP = \underline{?}$ **24**

11. $PR = 16$; $SU = 12$; $WU = 18$; $VR = \underline{?}$ **24**

12. $QV = 9$; $SW = 8$; $TW = 6$; $PV = \underline{?}$ **12**

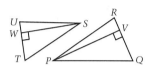

Given: $\triangle ABC \sim \triangle XYZ$; $\overline{AD} = \overline{DB}$; $\overline{XW} = \overline{WY}$

13. $XZ = 6$; $ZW = 15$; $AC = 4$; $CD = \underline{?}$ **10**

14. $BC = 20$; $YZ = 30$; $YW = 12$; $BD = \underline{?}$ **8**

15. $DA = 20$; $ZW = 18$; $WX = 30$; $CD = \underline{?}$ **12**

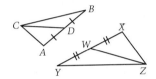

Given: $\triangle MNP \sim \triangle RST$; $\overrightarrow{NO}$ bisects $\angle MNP$; $\overrightarrow{SU}$ bisects $\angle RST$. Find x

16. $MN = 20$; $NP = 24$; $RS = 35$; $ST = x$ **x = 42**

17. $RU = 8$; $UT = 24$; $RS = 12$; $ST = x$ **x = 36**

18. $MP = 12$; $RT = 16$; $MN = x$; $RS = x + 6$ **x = 18**

19. $NP = 20$; $OP = 12$; $NM = x$; $OM = x - 8$ **x = 20**

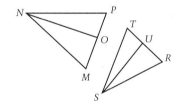

Refer to Example 1. State the postulate or theorem which justifies each pair of similar triangles.

20. $\triangle ACH \sim \triangle DFK$

21. $\triangle FEL \sim \triangle CBJ$

22. $\triangle AMB \sim \triangle DNE$

23. $\triangle FLD \sim \triangle CJA$

24. $\triangle KED \sim \triangle HBA$

25. $\triangle NEF \sim \triangle MBC$

Set B   Given: $\triangle ABC \sim \triangle DEF$

26. $DF = 10$; $AC = 4$; $EK = 6$; $BH = \underline{?}$ **2.4**

27. $AB = 9$; $DE = 12$; $NE = 15$; $MB = \underline{?}$ **11.25**

28. $AH = 9$; $DF = 12$; $DK = 18$; $AC = \underline{?}$ **6**

29. $AJ = 6$; $BJ = 8$; $BC = 20$; $AC = \underline{?}$ **15**

30. $MB = 12$; $NE = 8$; $AJ = 4x + 1$; $DL = 3x - 1$; $x = \underline{?}$ **5**

31. $AH = x$; $NF = x$; $MC = x - 2$; $DK = x + 3$; $x = \underline{?}$ **6**

32. $CJ = x - 2$; $EK = 2x - 1$; $BH = x + 2$; $FL = x + 1$; $x = \underline{?}$ **8**

33. $BC = 2x$; $AC = 4x$; $BJ = x + 2$; $AJ = 3x$; $x = \underline{?}$ **4**

Written Exercises

20. AA ~ Post.
21. AA ~ Post.
22. SAS ~ Thm.
23. AA ~ Post.
24. AA ~ Post.
25. SAS ~ Thm.

34. Given: $\triangle ABC \sim \triangle A'B'C'$; $\overline{CD}$ bisects $\angle ACB$; $\overline{C'D'}$ bisects $\angle A'C'B'$. Prove: $\frac{CD}{C'D'} = \frac{AC}{A'C'}$ Proof: 1. $\triangle ABC \sim \triangle A'B'C'$; $\overline{CD}$ bisects $\angle ACB$; $\overline{C'D'}$ bisects $\angle A'C'B'$. (Given) 2. $m\angle ACB = m\angle A'C'B'$; $m\angle A = m\angle A'$ (Def. of $\sim$ polygons [1]) 3. $m\angle ACD = m\angle DCB$; $m\angle A'C'D' = m\angle D'C'B'$ (Def. of $\angle$ bisector [1]) 4. $m\angle ACB = m\angle ACD + m\angle DCB$; $m\angle A'C'B' = m\angle A'C'D' + m\angle D'C'B'$ (Angle Add. Post.) 5. $m\angle ACB = 2(m\angle ACD)$; $m\angle A'C'B' = 2(m\angle A'C'D')$ (Substitution Prop. [3, 4]) 6. $2(m\angle ACD) = 2(m\angle A'C'D')$ (Substitution Prop. [2, 5]) 7. $m\angle ACD = m\angle A'C'D'$ (Division Prop. [6]) 8. $\triangle ACD \sim \triangle A'C'D'$ (AA $\sim$ Post. [2, 7]) 9. $\frac{CD}{C'D'} = \frac{AC}{A'C'}$ (Def. of $\sim$ polygons [8])

FOLLOW-UP

More Practice

- **Worksheet 7–6**

Extension

Theorem 7–10 may be applied as a construction—to divide a line segment in a given ratio. For example, divide $\overline{AB}$ in the ratio $5:3$.

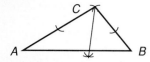

Describe an arc about A of radius 5 of any convenient unit, and about B with radius 3 units. Call the intersection of these arcs C and draw $\overline{AC}$ and $\overline{BC}$. Bisect $\angle ACB$. The bisector divides $\overline{AB}$ in the given ratio.

- **Extension 7–6**

---

34. Prove Theorem 7-7.   **35.** Prove Theorem 7-9.

36. Prove Theorem 7-10.

37. Given: $\triangle EFG$; $\overline{HJ} \parallel \overline{FG}$; $\overrightarrow{EK}$ bisects $\angle GEF$.
Prove: $\frac{JL}{HL} = \frac{GK}{FK}$

38. Given: $\triangle ABC \sim \triangle DEF$; $AJ = JB$; $DK = KE$; $\overline{CG} \perp \overline{AB}$; $\overline{FH} \perp \overline{DE}$
Prove: $\triangle CGJ \sim \triangle FHK$

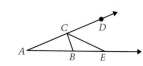

Set C **39.** Given: $\triangle ABC$; $AC \neq BC$; $\overrightarrow{CE}$ bisects $\angle BCD$.
Prove: $\frac{AE}{EB} = \frac{AC}{BC}$
(HINT: Draw a parallel to $\overline{CD}$ through B.)

◆ **Review** **40.** List all the ways you have learned for proving that two triangles are similar.

41. Given $\triangle ABC$ and $\triangle DEF$, find x. **x = 85**

42. If three parallel lines intersect two transversals, then ___?___ .

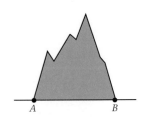

43. In isosceles triangle FGH, $FH = GH$, $m\angle H = x - 17$, and $m\angle F = 22$. Find $m\angle G$.
22

44. Explain how to use a sheet of ruled paper to mark six equal segments along the edge of an index card.

Thinking **45.** How could you use similarity to determine the
Ahead distance between two points A and B on opposite sides of the base of a mountain?

Challenge

Given rectangle $ABCD$ with $A(0, 0)$, $B(6, 0)$, $C(6, 4)$, and $D(0, 4)$, if the length and the width are both *increased* by 2, is the resulting figure similar to $ABCD$? If the length and the width are both multiplied by 2, is this resulting figure similar to $ABCD$? Check your answers by drawing the figures on a grid and applying the diagonal test described on page 305.

Yes; Yes

1. State three ways to prove that two triangles are similar. AA; SAS; SSS
2. Name three other segments in similar triangles that are in the same ratio as the corresponding sides. Altitudes; angle bisectors; medians
3. If $\triangle ABC \sim \triangle DEC$, give three ratios that are equal. $\frac{AB}{DE} = \frac{BC}{EC} = \frac{AC}{DC}$
4. In the diagram, if $PQ \parallel RS$, state which two triangles are similar. $\triangle TQP \sim \triangle TSR$

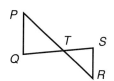

7-7 Additional Applications of Similarity

In Lesson 5-2, congruent triangles were used to find measures indirectly. In Lesson 7-3, indirect measures were found using similar triangles. In this lesson, we will explore additional methods of using similar figures to find measures indirectly.

Example 1 presents three different ways to find the height of Chicago's *Bat Column*, a sculpture by Claes Oldenburg. Other methods of indirect measurement will be studied in Chapter 8.

Example 1
Estimate the height of the *Bat Column*.

Solution
Method I: A regulation baseball bat with length 42 in. is held parallel to the sculpture, with the shadows of both bats in a line. The length of the shadows cast by the bat and the sculpture are found to be 21 in. and 49 ft., respectively. The sun's rays may be represented by parallel lines. Then $\triangle DEF \sim \triangle ABC$.

$$\frac{CB}{FE} = \frac{AB}{DE}$$
$$\frac{49}{21} = \frac{AB}{42}$$
$$49(42) = 21AB$$
$$AB = 98 \text{ ft.}$$

Method II: A mirror is placed on the ground as shown so that the viewer sees the top of the sculpture reflected in it. By direct measurement, $OE = 18$ in., $OB = 24.5$ ft., and $DE = 72$ in. A law of physics tells us that $m\angle DOE = m\angle AOB$. Thus, $\triangle DOE \sim \triangle AOB$.

$$\frac{AB}{DE} = \frac{OB}{OE}$$
$$\frac{AB}{72} = \frac{294}{18} \qquad 24.5 \text{ ft.} = 294 \text{ in.}$$
$$AB(18) = 72(294)$$
$$AB = 1{,}176 \text{ in., or } 98 \text{ ft.}$$

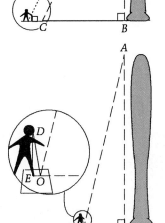

LESSON 7-7

Resources

Strips of wood
Tape measure
Teaching Aid 1, protractor
Visual Aid 1, protractor
Worksheet 7–7
Extension 7–7
Algebra Review 7
Chapter 7 Test, Form I
Chapter 7 Test, Form II
Chapter 7 Test, Form III

OBJECTIVE

Solve real-world problems using similar figures.

322

TEACHING NOTES

The use of similar triangles in indirect measurement can help determine inaccessible heights and distances. Have students construct a makeshift transit using **concrete materials** such as strips of wood fastened as shown.

Use the left angle as a line of sight while holding the other two strips horizontal and vertical. Then measure the angle.

To determine the height of a flagpole or any other inaccessible object, ask students to make necessary measurements using this device and a tape measure. Dis-

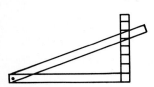

Method III: A 12-inch ruler is held vertically with the lower end at eye level. The viewer sights the top of the sculpture in line with the other end of the ruler. By direct measurement, EF = 8 in., CF = 62 ft., and FG = 5 ft. $\triangle DFE$ and $\triangle AFC$ are similar.

$$\frac{CF}{EF} = \frac{AC}{DE}$$
$$\frac{744}{8} = \frac{AC}{12} \qquad \textit{62 ft. = 744 in.}$$
$$744(12) = 8AC$$
$$AC = 1{,}116 \text{ in., or 93 ft.}$$
$$AB = AC + BC = 93 + 5 = 98 \text{ ft.}$$

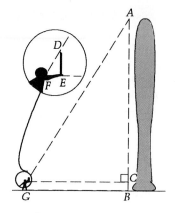

Example 2
Find the distance from one side of a river to a rock on the opposite side.

Solution
Method I: B and C are located across the river from the rock at A, so that $\overline{AB} \perp \overline{BC}$ and BC = 100 m. A transit shows $m\angle ACB$ to be 31. A second triangle, $\triangle A'B'C'$, is drawn with $m\angle B'$ = 90, $B'C'$ = 20 cm, and $m\angle C' = m\angle C$. $A'B'$ is found to be 12 cm. By the AA Similarity Postulate, $\triangle A'B'C' \sim \triangle ABC$.

$$\frac{AB}{A'B'} = \frac{BC}{B'C'}$$
$$\frac{AB}{12} = \frac{10{,}000}{20} \qquad \textit{100 m = 10,000 cm}$$
$$AB(20) = 12(10{,}000)$$
$$AB = 6{,}000 \text{ cm, or 60 m}$$

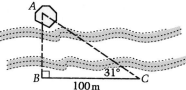

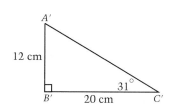

Method II: Similar triangles are arranged as shown at the right, with right angles at B and D. By sighting from C to A, the viewer locates O as the intersection of $\overline{BD}$ and $\overline{AC}$. By direct measurement, OB = 80 m, CD = 6 m, and OD = 8 m. By the AA Similarity Postulate, $\triangle BOA \sim \triangle DOC$.

$$\frac{AB}{CD} = \frac{OB}{OD}$$
$$\frac{AB}{6} = \frac{80}{8}$$
$$AB(8) = 6(80)$$
$$AB = 60 \text{ m}$$

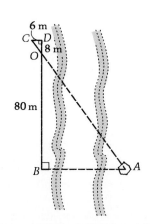

These problems and their solutions illustrate how similar triangles can be used to determine unknown distances indirectly. They also show that whatever the method, the results are the same. Of course, indirect measurements, like all others, are only approximations.

322 Chapter 7 *Similarity*

Checking for Understanding

The diagram at the right shows yet another solution to the problem in Example 2. B, C, D, and E are located across the river from A, with $\overline{BC} \perp \overline{AD}$ and $\overline{DE} \perp \overline{AD}$, as shown. By direct measurement, $BC = 40$ m, $DE = 60$ m, and $BD = 30$ m.

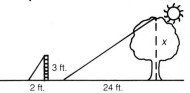

1. Name two similar triangles. Why are they similar?

2. Write a proportion to find AB. $AB = \underline{\ ?\ }$ $\dfrac{AB}{AB + 30} = \dfrac{40}{60}$; 60 m

Name the postulate or theorem which guarantees similarity for each method in Example 1. **3–5. AA ~ Post.**

3. Method I   **4.** Method II   **5.** Method III

6. What measurements are needed to find XY if there is a rock between X and Y? **ZB, ZY, ZA, ZX and BA**

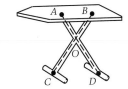

7. In the diagram of the ironing board, $OA = OB$ and $OC = OD$. Explain why the board is parallel to the floor.

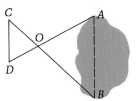

8. What measures are needed to find the distance from A to B across the lake? **CD, CO, BO, DO, and AO**

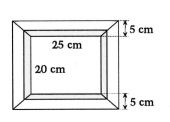

Written Exercises

Set A   **1.** A picture measures 20 cm by 25 cm. The width of the matting and frame at top and bottom is 5 cm. How wide should the matting and frame be at the sides so that the framed picture is similar to the picture alone? **6.25 cm**

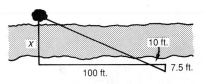

2. A 12-centimeter rod is held between a flashlight and a wall as shown at right. Find the length of the shadow if the rod is 45 cm from the wall and 15 cm from the light. **48 cm**

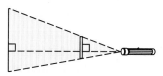

3. Find the length of the shadow of the rod in Exercise 2 if the rod is 30 cm from the wall and the flashlight is 75 cm from the wall. **20 cm**

cuss other possible methods of obtaining the same result.

Additional Examples

Example 1

If a tree casts a 24-foot shadow at the same time that a yardstick casts a 2-foot shadow, find the height of the tree.   36 ft.

Example 2

A bush is sighted on the other side of a canyon. Find the width of the canyon.   75 ft.

Error Analysis   In writing proportions from similar triangles, students sometimes write one ratio from one triangle and the second ratio from the other. This increases the chance that the proportion will be written in the wrong order. Encourage students to choose the first member of a ratio from one triangle and the second member from the other. Equivalent ratios may then be written using the properties of Lesson 7–1.

FOLLOW-UP

More Practice

• Worksheet 7–7

Extension

A more sophisticated device students could make for indirect measurement is a hypsometer, shown in the drawing.

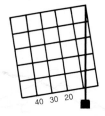

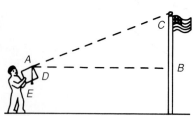

It is made from graph paper mounted on stiff cardboard and has a scale marked on one side. A string is attached to one corner, and a weight keeps it vertical.

If the student sights along *AC* to the top of the pole, △*ADE* will be similar to △*ABC*. *AD* is known, *DE* may be read from the scale and

---

4. An antique box camera, 4 in. deep, is held so that the image is parallel to the subject, who is 6 ft. tall and 10 ft. from the camera. Find the height of the image. **2.4 in.**

5. Find the distance between the subject and the camera in Exercise 4 so that the image will just fit on 2.5-in. film. **9.6 ft.**

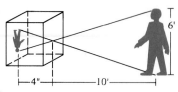

6. Luisa began walking up a hill at a spot where the elevation is 0.9 km. After she walked 3 km, she saw a sign giving the elevation as 0.95 km. How far will she have walked when she reaches an elevation of 1.1 km? Draw a diagram. **12 km**

7. The cheerleaders at City High make their own megaphones by cutting off the small end of a cone made from heavy paper. If the small end of the megaphone is to have radius of 2.5 cm, what should be the height of the cone that is cut off? **5.4 cm**

8. Using similar triangles, an archaeologist can determine the original height of a pyramid, though its top has worn away. Find the original height. **61 m**

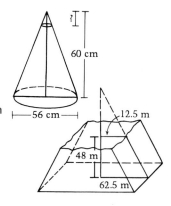

Set B **9.** A tourist on the observation deck of a 800-foot building looks toward a 600-foot building which is one block from the first. Her car is parked two blocks beyond the second building. If no other building intervenes, can she see her car?

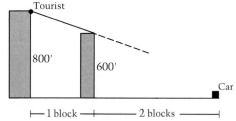

The Smiths, the Ortegas, and the Community Park all have lake frontage.

10. How many meters of lake frontage are on the Smiths' lot? **22.5 m**

11. How many are on the Community Park lot? **42.5 m**

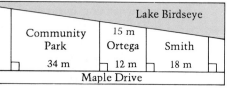

12. Find the mirror of minimum length that will permit Paco, who is 5 feet 8 inches tall, to see a full view of himself. The image is as far "behind" the mirror as Paco is in front of it, so $AD = DB$. $\overline{DE} \perp \overline{AB}$ and $\overline{BC} \perp \overline{AB}$. **2 ft. 10 in.**

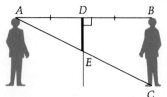

Set C Two poles are braced as shown. How high above the ground do the braces cross if the poles are

13. 24 m apart? **3 m**   **14.** 36 m apart? **3 m**

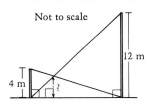

Not to scale

12 m

4 m

15. What can you conclude about the distance between the poles and the height at which the braces cross?

♦ **Review** **16.** If two triangles are similar, give three pairs of segments whose lengths are proportional to the lengths of corresponding sides of the triangles.

17. Give a proportion that is true for △KGD.

18. In △PQR and △ATU, m∠R = m∠U. What proportion would have to be true to prove that △PQR ~ △ATU by the SAS Similarity Theorem? **17.** $\frac{GE}{DE} = \frac{KG}{KD}$ **18.** $\frac{QR}{TU} = \frac{RP}{UA}$

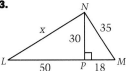

19. In your classroom, find an illustration of skew lines.

20. Draw a convex octagon and a nonconvex octagon. **19.** Answers will vary.

Progress Check

Lesson 7-5, page 310
In each exercise, can the triangles be proved similar? If so, find x.

1.
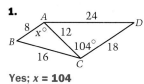
Yes; x = 104

2.
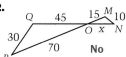
No

3.
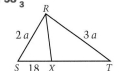
Yes; x = 58⅓

Lesson 7-6, page 316
4. $\overrightarrow{RX}$ bisects ∠SRT. ST = __?__ **45**

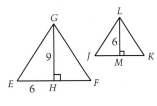

5. Given △EFG ~ △JKL, $\overline{GH} \perp \overline{EF}$, and $\overline{LM} \perp \overline{JK}$, find JM. **4**

6. Given: △ABC ~ △DEF, $\overrightarrow{CG}$ bisects ∠C; $\overrightarrow{FH}$ bisects ∠F.
Prove: $\frac{AG}{DH} = \frac{BC}{EF}$

Lesson 7-7, page 321
7. A 6-foot man casts a 5-foot shadow at the same time a tree casts a 30-foot shadow. What is the height of the tree? **36 ft.**

8. Draw diagrams showing two ways to find the width AB of the river. Write the proportions you would solve for AB.

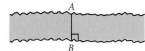

AB can be measured. When BC is calculated, the height of the pole can be determined.
• **Extension 7–7**

ANSWERS

Progress Check

2. Triangles cannot be proved similar because lines are not necessarily parallel.
6. Proof: 1. △ABC ~ △DEF; $\overrightarrow{CG}$ bisects ∠C; $\overrightarrow{FH}$ bisects ∠F. (Given) 2. m∠C = m∠F; m∠A = m∠D; $\frac{AC}{DF} = \frac{BC}{EF}$ (Def. of ~ polygons [1]) 3. m∠ACG = ½(m∠C); m∠DFH = ½(m∠F) (Def. of ∠ bis. [1]) 4. m∠C = 2(m∠ACG); m∠F = 2(m∠DFH) (Multiplication Prop. [3]) 5. 2(m∠ACG) = 2(m∠DFH) (Substitution Prop. [2, 4]) 6. m∠ACG = m∠DFH (Division Prop. [5]) 7. △ACG ~ △DFH (AA ~ Post. [2, 6]) 8. $\frac{AG}{DH} = \frac{AC}{DF}$ (Def. of ~ polygons [7]) 9. $\frac{AG}{DH} = \frac{BC}{EF}$ (Substitution Prop. [2, 8])
8. Samples:

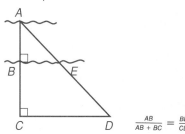

$\frac{AB}{AB + BC} = \frac{BE}{CD}$

$\frac{AB}{ED} = \frac{BC}{DC}$

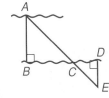

Chapter 7 Summary

Important Terms

AA Similarity Postulate (297)
Cross-product (288)
Proportion (287)
Proportional to (287)
Ratio (287)

SAS Similarity Theorem (310)
SSS Similarity Theorem (311)
Segments divided
   proportionally (302)
Similar polygons (292)

Similar triangles (297)
Summation Property of
   Proportions (288)

Important Ideas

1. The proportion $\frac{a}{b} = \frac{c}{d}$, with a, b, c, and d all positive numbers, can be changed to these equivalent forms using properties of equality. (288)

   a. $ad = bc$ **b.** $\frac{a}{c} = \frac{b}{d}$ **c.** $\frac{d}{c} = \frac{b}{a}$

   d. $\frac{a + b}{b} = \frac{c + d}{d}$ **e.** $\frac{a - b}{b} = \frac{c - d}{d}$ **f.** $\frac{a + c}{b + d} = \frac{a}{b}$

2. In similar polygons,
   a. corresponding angles are equal and the lengths of corresponding sides are proportional. (292)
   b. the perimeters are proportional to the lengths of corresponding sides. (293)

3. Two triangles can be shown to be similar by using the AA Similarity Postulate, the SAS Similarity Theorem, or the SSS Similarity Theorem. (297, 310–311)

4. Similarity of triangles is reflexive, symmetric, and transitive. (298)

5. If a line parallel to one side of a triangle intersects the other two sides, then it divides them proportionally. (302)

6. If three parallel lines intersect two transversals, then the parallel lines divide the transversals proportionally. (303)

7. In similar triangles, the lengths of corresponding sides are proportional to the lengths of angle bisectors, the altitudes, and the medians. (316)

8. The bisector of an angle in a triangle divides the opposite side into two segments whose lengths are proportional to the lengths of the other two sides. (317)

Chapter 7 Review

Lesson 7-1, Page 287

1. Write three proportions equivalent to the equation $ef = gh$.

2. Los Angeles and New York City are 8 inches apart on a map. If the scale of the map is 1 inch → 350 miles, about how far apart are the two cities? **2,800 mi**

Solve each proportion for x.

3. $\dfrac{5x - 2}{2} = \dfrac{3x + 10}{4}$ **x = 2**   **4.** $\dfrac{x}{x + 7} = \dfrac{5}{12}$ **x = 5**   **5.** $\dfrac{x - 2}{3x - 1} = \dfrac{1}{4}$
x = 7

Lesson 7-2, Page 292

Given: $\square STUV \sim \square ABCD$

6. Name all pairs of equal angles.

7. Write all ratios of the lengths of corresponding sides.

Given: $\triangle ABD \sim \triangle KED$

8. If $AK = 3$, $KD = 6$, and the perimeter of $\triangle ABD$ is 24, find the perimeter of $\triangle KED$. **16**

9. If $AK = 5$ and $KD = 10$, prove $BD = 3BE$.

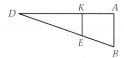

Lesson 7-3, Page 297

Can these lengths be the sides of similar triangles?

10. 12, 28, 32 and 30, 20, 50 **No**

11. 23, 28, 32 and 35, 15, 45 **No**

Find the value of x in each exercise.

12.

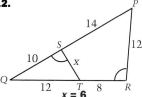

x = 6

13.
x = 6

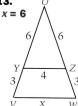

14. **x = 12.5**

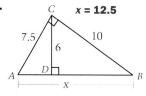

15. Given: $\square ABCD$
Prove: $\triangle BOE \sim \triangle DOC$

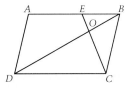

---

23. Proof: 1. $\frac{AE}{AC} = \frac{AD}{DB}$ (Given) 2. $m\angle A = m\angle A$ (Reflexive Prop.) 3. $\triangle AED \sim \triangle ACB$ (SAS $\sim$ Thm. [1, 2]) 4. $m\angle AED = m\angle ACB$ (Def. of $\sim$ polygons [3])

25. Proof: 1. $\triangle CNB \sim \triangle EMA$; $\overrightarrow{NO}$ bisects $\angle CNB$; $\overrightarrow{MD}$ bisects $\angle EMA$. (Given) 2. $m\angle C = m\angle E$; $m\angle CNB = m\angle EMA$ (Def. of $\sim$ polygons [1]) 3. $m\angle CNO = m\angle BNO$; $m\angle EMD = m\angle AMD$ (Def. of $\angle$ bis. [1]) 4. $m\angle CNB = m\angle CNO + m\angle BNO$; $m\angle EMA = m\angle EMD + m\angle AMD$ (Angle Add. Post.) 5. $m\angle CNB = 2(m\angle CNO)$; $m\angle EMA = 2(m\angle EMD)$ (Substitution Prop. [3, 4]) 6. $2(m\angle CNO) = 2(m\angle EMD)$ (Substitution Prop. [3, 5]) 7. $m\angle CNO = m\angle EMD$ (Division Prop. [6]) 8. $\triangle CNO \sim \triangle EMD$ (AA $\sim$ Post. [2, 7]) 9. $\frac{NO}{MD} = \frac{CO}{ED}$ (Def. of $\sim$ polygons [8]) 10. $\frac{NO}{CO} = \frac{MD}{ED}$ (Multiplication Prop. [9])

26. Proof: 1. $\triangle PTR \sim \triangle XYZ$; $\overline{TQ} \perp \overline{PR}$; $\overline{YU} \perp \overline{XZ}$; $TS = SR$; $YW = WZ$ (Given) 2. $\overline{TQ}$ is altitude of $\triangle PTR$; $\overline{YU}$ is altitude of $\triangle XYZ$. (Def. of altitude of $\triangle$ [1]) 3. $\overline{PS}$ is median of $\triangle PTR$; $\overline{XW}$ is median of $\triangle XYZ$. (Def. of median of $\triangle$ [1]) 4. $\frac{TQ}{YU} = \frac{TP}{YX}$ (In $\sim$ $\triangle$s, the lengths of medians from corr. vertices are proportional to lengths of corr. sides. [2]) 5. $\frac{PS}{XW} = \frac{TP}{YX}$ (In $\sim$ $\triangle$s, the lengths of altitudes from corr. vertices are proportional to lengths of corr. sides. [3]) 6. $\frac{TQ}{YU} = \frac{PS}{XW}$ (Substitution Prop. [4, 5])

Lesson 7-4, Page 302

Given: $\overline{DE} \parallel \overline{BC}$

16. $AD = 20$; $AB = 24$; $AE = 15$; $AC = \underline{\ ?\ }$ 18

17. $AD = 12$; $DB = 8$; $AE = 18$; $EC = \underline{\ ?\ }$ 12

18. $AB = 24$; $DB = 4$; $AC = 20$; $AE = \underline{\ ?\ }$ $16\frac{2}{3}$

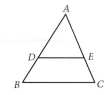

19. In $\square ABCD$, $BD = 16$, $AE = 2$, $EG = 4$, $CK = 2$, and $\overline{AD} \parallel EJ \parallel \overline{GK}$. Find DF, FH, and HB. 4; 8; 4

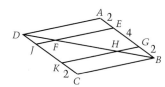

Lesson 7-5, Page 310

Find the value of x in each exercise.

20. $x = 14$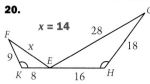

21. $x = 53$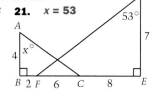

22. $x = 2$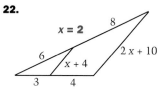

23. Given: $\frac{AE}{AC} = \frac{AD}{AB}$

Prove: $m\angle AED = m\angle ACB$

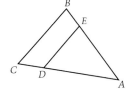

Lesson 7-6, Page 316

24. In $\triangle ABC$, $\overrightarrow{AX}$ bisects $\angle BAC$. If $AB = 18$, $AC = 10$, and $CX = 5$, find BX. 9

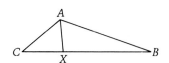

25. Given: $\triangle CNB \sim \triangle EMA$; $\overrightarrow{NO}$ bisects $\angle CNB$; $\overrightarrow{MD}$ bisects $\angle EMA$.

Prove: $\frac{NO}{CO} = \frac{MD}{ED}$

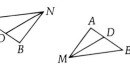

26. Given: $\triangle PTR \sim \triangle XYZ$; $\overline{TQ} \perp \overline{PR}$; $\overline{YV} \perp \overline{XZ}$; $TS = SR$; $YW = WZ$

Prove: $\frac{TQ}{YV} = \frac{PS}{XW}$

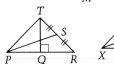

Lesson 7-7, Page 321

27. At a ground distance of 1.5 miles from takeoff, a plane's altitude is 1,000 yards. Assuming a constant angle of ascent, find its altitude 5 miles from takeoff. $3,333\frac{1}{3}$ yd.

28. Use the information in the diagram to find the width of the river. 20 m

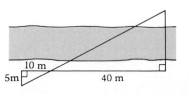

Chapter 7 Test

1. Solve this proportion for x: $\dfrac{3x-2}{4} = \dfrac{5x+1}{7}$ x = 18

2. If $\dfrac{x}{y} = \dfrac{r}{s}$, then $\dfrac{x+r}{y+s} = \dfrac{r}{\underline{?}}$ s

Name the postulate or theorem that guarantees the specified triangles are similar.

3.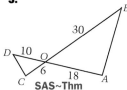

SAS~Thm

4.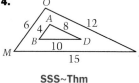

SSS~Thm

5.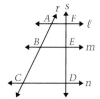

AA~Post

Given: Polygon $SRVT \sim$ polygon $KPQJ$

6. Find KJ, JQ, and QP in terms of a. 2a; a; $\dfrac{3a}{2}$

7. Find the ratio of the perimeters. 2:1 $(SRVT:KPQJ)$

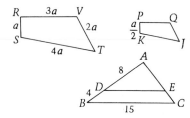

Given: $\overline{BC} \parallel \overline{DE}$; $AC = 10$

8. Find AE. $6\dfrac{2}{3}$ **9.** Find DE. 10

10. Given: $\ell \parallel m \parallel n$; $AB = x - 2$, $BC = x + 2$, $FE = 2x$, and $ED = 3x$. Find x. x = 10

11. In the diagram at the right, $ST = 24$ and $\overrightarrow{RU}$ bisects $\angle R$. Find RS. 18

12. Given: $GF = 3KF$; $HF = 3LF$
Prove: $GH = 3KL$

13. A man standing 16 ft. from an 18-ft. pole casts an 8-ft. shadow, the tip of which aligns with the tip of the pole's shadow. How tall is the man? 6 ft.

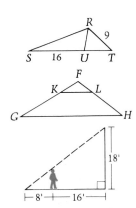

12. Proof: 1. $GF = 3KF$; $HF = 3LF$ (Given) 2. $m\angle F = m\angle F$ (Reflexive Prop.) 3. $\dfrac{GF}{KF} = 3$; $\dfrac{HF}{LF} = 3$ (Multiplication Prop. [1]) 4. $\triangle GFH \sim \triangle KFL$ (SAS $\sim$ Thm. [2, 3]) 5. $\dfrac{GH}{KL} = \dfrac{GF}{KF}$ (Def. of $\sim$ polygons [4]) 6. $\dfrac{GH}{KL} = 3$ (Transitive Prop. [3, 5]) 7. $GH = 3KL$ (Multiplication Prop. [6])

CHAPTER 8

Right Triangles

Chapter Overview

The concepts of similar triangles flow logically into the similarity relationships when an altitude is drawn to the hypotenuse of a right triangle. This in turn leads to the Pythagorean Theorem and its applications, including the 30-60-90 and 45-45-90 triangles.

Trigonometric ratios are defined, and their use in indirect measurement is studied. Allow students to use **calculators** so that they can concentrate on the process of setting up the problem.

Perspectives

Lesson 8–1 applies the concepts of similarity to the triangles formed when the altitude to the hypotenuse of a right triangle is drawn.

Applications that develop from the triangle similarity and the resulting geometric mean relationships are studied.

Lesson 8–2 introduces the Pythagorean Theorem, one of the most widely applicable results in geometry. This lesson presents a simple algebraic proof of this formula.

Lesson 8–3 concentrates on the 30-60-90 and the 45-45-90 triangles. The ratios of lengths of sides in these triangles are derived from the Pythagorean Theorem.

Lesson 8–4 applies the Pythagorean Theorem and the special cases of 30-60-90 and 45-45-90 triangles to practical problems.

Because approximations of irrational answers are preferable to radical form when dealing with real-world applications, **calculators** may be used.

Lesson 8–5 introduces the concept of trigonometric ratios using similar and right triangles. The sine, cosine and tangent ratios are defined and applied.

Using these ratios and the Pythagorean Theorem, some of the fundamental identities are also introduced.

Pacing Chart for Chapter 8

Lesson	Objectives	Basic Course	Average Course	Extended Course
8–1	Apply the ideas of similarity and geometric mean to right triangles.	2	$1\frac{1}{2}$	$1\frac{1}{2}$
8–2	State and apply the Pythagorean Theorem and its converse.	2	$1\frac{1}{2}$	$1\frac{1}{2}$
8–3	Determine and apply the properties of a 30-60-90 triangle and a 45-45-90 triangle.	2	2	$1\frac{1}{2}$
8–4	Use the Pythagorean Theorem to solve problems.	2	$1\frac{1}{2}$	1
8–5	Identify and evaluate the tangent, sine and cosine ratios for an acute angle of a right triangle.	2	$1\frac{1}{2}$	$1\frac{1}{2}$
8–6	Use a table of trigonometric ratios to find the measure of an angle or a ratio for a given angle.	2	2	$1\frac{1}{2}$
8–7	Use the trigonometric ratios to solve indirect measurement problems.	2	2	$1\frac{1}{2}$
Review		2	1	1
Test		1	1	1
Total		17 days	14 days	12 days

Lesson 8–6 presents the table of trigonometric ratios. The table is used in two ways: (1) given an angle, find the sine, cosine or tangent; and (2) given the value of the sine, cosine or tangent, find the measure of the angle.

Using **calculators** will allow students to concentrate on the process.

Lesson 8–7 uses the skills developed in the last few lessons to solve problems involving trigonometric ratios. Many problems are solved using indirect measurement. This lesson emphasizes the usefulness of geometry in real-world problem solving.

Right Triangles

The Pine River Park Board wants to put a bicycle path from the corner of Elm and Oak Streets to the river. Where is the shortest path? What information might help the board to compute the length of the path without actually measuring?

8-1 Similarity in Right Triangles

The Pine River Park Board members drew the diagram at the right. $\angle BCA$ represents the corner of Elm and Oak Streets, and $\overline{AB}$ represents the portion of the river bank between Elm and Oak. They drew a perpendicular from C to $\overline{AB}$ intersecting $\overline{AB}$ at D. $\overline{CD}$ represents the shortest path from the corner to the river. Why? The shortest distance from a pt. to a line is the ⊥ distance.

Theorem 8-1 shows a way to find the length of $\overline{CD}$. The proof is left to Exercise 10.

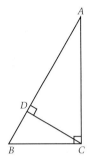

Theorem 8-1

If an altitude is drawn to the hypotenuse of a right triangle, then the new triangles formed are similar to the given triangle and to each other.

Given $\triangle ABC$ with right $\angle BCA$; $\overline{CD}$ is perpendicular to $\overline{AB}$.

Prove   *Part I* $\triangle ACD \sim \triangle ABC$

         Part II $\triangle CBD \sim \triangle ABC$

         Part III $\triangle ACD \sim \triangle CBD$

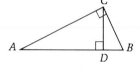

Plan for Proof   *Part I* Use the AA Similarity Postulate with the right angles and $\angle A$.

         Part II Use the AA Similarity Postulate with the right angles and $\angle B$.

         Part III Use symmetry and transitivity with Parts I and II.

Example 1

If BD is 18 meters and AD is 32 meters, how long is the path from the corner to the river?

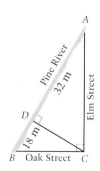

Solution

Since $\triangle ACD \sim \triangle CBD$, then $\frac{AD}{CD} = \frac{CD}{BD}$, or $\frac{32}{CD} = \frac{CD}{18}$.

Thus, $(CD)^2 = (32)(18) = 576$, and $CD = \pm 24$. Because distance is positive, we do not use -24. The path is 24 m long.

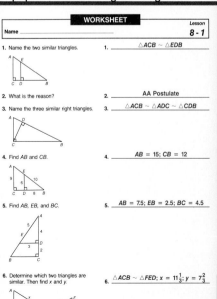

Cut one of the triangles along the altitude to the hypotenuse and re-align the triangles created so that corresponding sides are parallel. Point out that all three triangles are similar. The proof of Theorem 8–1 can be simplified by changing the alignment back and forth and noting equal angles.

Example 1 introduces the concept of geometric mean. Theorem 8–2 is a generalization of this example.

Additional Examples

Example 1

In right $\triangle PQR$, $\overline{RS} \perp \overline{QP}$, $QS = 8$ and $SP = 18$. Find RS. 12

Notice that CD appears twice in the proportion, $\frac{AD}{CD} = \frac{CD}{BD}$. CD is called the geometric mean of AD and BD.

Definition   *Geometric Mean*

The geometric mean of two positive numbers a and b is the positive number x such that $\frac{a}{x} = \frac{x}{b}$.

If $\frac{a}{x} = \frac{x}{b}$, then $x^2 = ab$, or $x = \sqrt{ab}$.

Thus, the geometric mean of two positive real numbers is the square root of their product. For example, the geometric mean of 9 and 4 is $\sqrt{36}$, or 6, and the geometric mean of 5 and 7 is $\sqrt{35}$. The next two theorems involve geometric means. Their proofs are left to Exercises 11 and 20.

Theorem 8-2

The length of the altitude to the hypotenuse of a right triangle is the geometric mean of the lengths of the segments into which the altitude separates the hypotenuse.

Given $\triangle ABC$ with right $\angle C$; $\overline{CD}$ is perpendicular to $\overline{AB}$.

Prove $\frac{AD}{CD} = \frac{CD}{BD}$

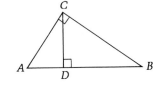

Theorem 8-3

If the altitude to the hypotenuse is drawn in a right triangle, then the length of either leg is the geometric mean of the lengths of the hypotenuse and the segment on the hypotenuse which is adjacent to that leg.

Given $\triangle ABC$ with right $\angle C$; $\overline{CD}$ is perpendicular to $\overline{AB}$.

Prove $\frac{AB}{AC} = \frac{AC}{AD}$ and $\frac{BA}{BC} = \frac{BC}{BD}$.

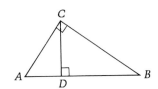

Summary Right Triangles and Altitudes

If $\triangle ABC$ is a right triangle and $\overline{CD}$ is the altitude to the hypotenuse $\overline{AB}$, then:

$\triangle ACD \sim \triangle CBD$, so $\frac{n}{h} = \frac{h}{m}$ and $h^2 = nm$;

$\triangle ACD \sim \triangle ABC$, so $\frac{c}{b} = \frac{b}{n}$ and $b^2 = cn$;

$\triangle CBD \sim \triangle ABC$, so $\frac{c}{a} = \frac{a}{m}$ and $a^2 = cm$.

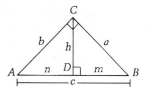

Example 2

a. Find h.   **b.** Find n. 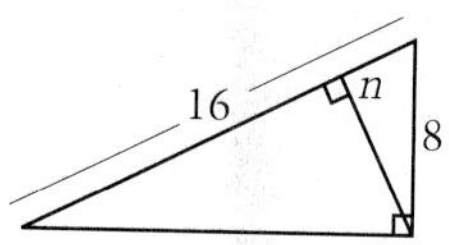   **c.** Find b. 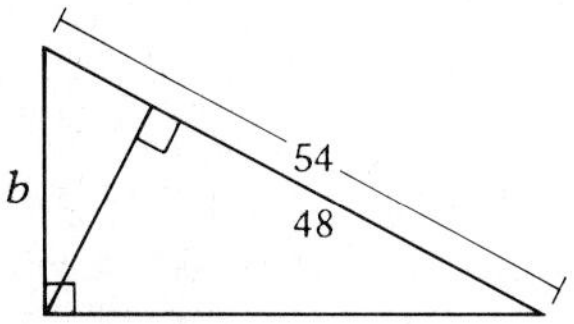   **d.** Find c.

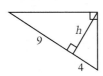   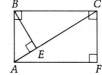 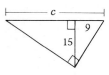

Solution

a. $h^2 = 9(4)$
$h^2 = 36$
$h = 6$

b. $8^2 = 16n$
$64^2 = 16n$
$4 = n$

c. $b^2 = 54(54 - 48)$
$b^2 = 324$
$b = 18$

d. $15^2 = 9(c - 9)$
$225^2 = 9c - 81$
$306 = 9c$
$34 = c$

Checking for Understanding

In each exercise, name all triangles that are similar to $\triangle ABC$.

1.
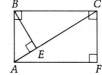
$\triangle AEB$
$\triangle BEC$
$\triangle CFA$

2. 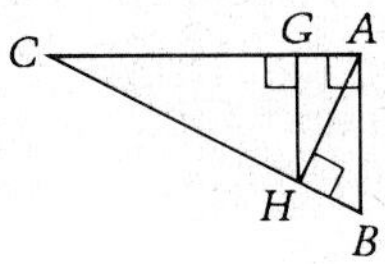
$\triangle GHC$
$\triangle GAH$
$\triangle HBA$
$\triangle HAC$

Use the diagram at the right to complete the exercises.

3. $\frac{?}{PO} = \frac{PO}{?}$ MP; PN   **4.** $\frac{?}{MO} = \frac{MO}{?}$ MN; MP   **5.** $\frac{?}{NO} = \frac{NO}{?}$ MN; PN

6. $MP = 3$; $MN = 12$; $MO = \underline{?}$ 6

7. $PN = 4$; $MN = 9$; $ON = \underline{?}$ 6

8. $PN = 28$; $PM = 7$; $OP = \underline{?}$ 14

9. $OP = 8$; $MP = NP$; $MN = \underline{?}$ 8

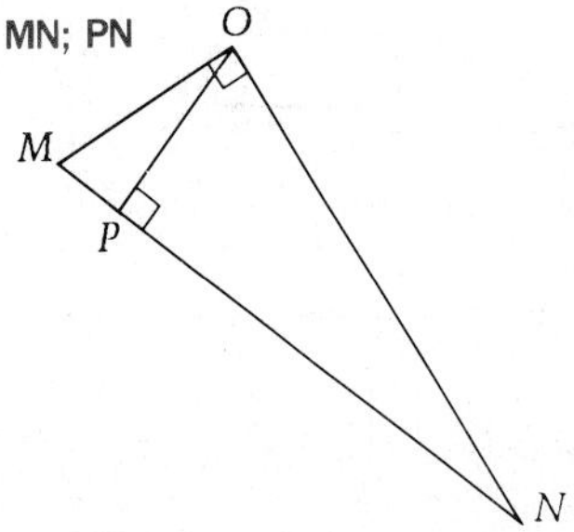

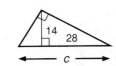

Example 2

(a)

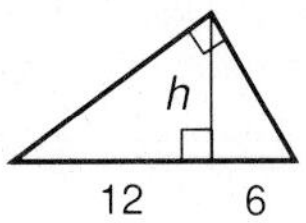

Find the length of h. $6\sqrt{2}$

(b)

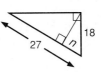

Find n. 12

(c)

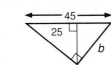

Find b. 30

(d)

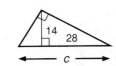

Find c. 35

Error Analysis Students will find the theorems on geometric means difficult to remember and apply. Have students think of the first ratio as comparing two parts out of "shorter" leg, "longer" leg and hypotenuse. The second ratio must compare the same two parts for a different triangle.

EXERCISE NOTES

Exercises 1–7 could be easier to solve if three separate triangles are drawn.

Exercises 12–17 are algebraic applications of the theorems.

ANSWERS

Written Exercises

8. Proof: 1. *ABCD* is a rectangle; $\overline{BE} \perp \overline{AC}$ (Given) 2. ∠*B* is a rt. ∠. (Def. of rect. [1]) 3. △*ABC* is a rt. △. (Def. of rt. △ [2]) 4. $\frac{AC}{AB} = \frac{AB}{AE}$ (If altitude is drawn to hypotenuse of a rt. △, length of either leg is geometric mean of lengths of hypotenuse and seg. on hypotenuse adj. to that leg. [1, 3]) 5. $(AB)^2 = (AC)(AE)$ (Mult. Prop. [4]) 6. *ABCD* is a ▱. (Def. of rect. [1]) 7. *AB* = *CD* (Opp. sides of ▱ are =. [6]) 8. $(CD)^2 = (AC)(AE)$ (Substitution Prop. [5, 7])

9. Proof: 1. △*FGH*; $\overline{FG} \perp \overline{GH}$; $\overline{GI} \perp \overline{FH}$; $\overline{FG} \parallel \overline{IJ}$ (Given) 2. *m*∠*JIC* = *m*∠*GFH* (2 lines ∥ ⇒ corres. ∠s =. [1]) 3. *m*∠*H* = *m*∠*H* (Reflexive Prop.) 4. △*IHJ* ~ △*FHG* (AA ~ Post. [2, 3]) 5. ∠*FGH* is a rt. ∠. (2 ⊥ lines form 4 rt. ∠s. [1]) 6. △*FGH* is a rt. △. (Def. of rt. △ [5]) 7. △*FHG* ~ △*FGI* (If altitude to hypotenuse is drawn in a rt. △, the new △s formed are ~ to each other and to the given △. [1, 6]) 8. △*IHJ* ~ △*FGI* (~ of △s is transitive. [4, 7])

10.

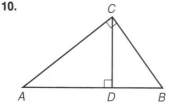

Given: △*ABC* with rt. ∠*BCA*; $\overline{CD}$ ⊥ $\overline{AB}$ Prove: Part I: △*ACD* ~ △*ABC* Part II: △*CBD* ~ △*ABC* Part III: △*ACD* ~ △*CBD* Proof: *Part I* 1. △*ABC* with rt. ∠ *BCA*; $\overline{CD}$ ⊥ $\overline{AB}$ (Given) 2. *m*∠*A* = *m*∠*A* (Reflexive Prop.) 3. ∠*CDA* is a rt. ∠. (2 ⊥ lines form 4 rt. ∠s. [1]) 4. *m*∠*CDA* = *m*∠*ACB* (All rt. ∠s are =. [1, 3]) 5. △*ACD* ~ △*ABC* (AA ~ Post. [2, 4]) *Part II* 1. △*ABC* with rt. ∠*BCA*; $\overline{CD}$ ⊥ $\overline{AB}$ (Given) 2. *m*∠*B* = *m*∠*B* (Reflexive Prop.) 3. ∠*CDB* is a rt. ∠. (2 ⊥ lines

Assignment Guide

Basic: 1–8, 12–17, 36–42
Average: 2–6 (even), 9–11, 12–16 (even), 18–29, 36–42
Extended: 2–28 (even), 30–42

Written Exercises

Set A

1. $c = 12$; $m = 6$; $a = \underline{?}$ $6\sqrt{2} \approx 8.48$

2. $m = 4$; $h = 25$; $n = \underline{?}$ 156.25

3. $n = 4$; $h = 64$; $m = \underline{?}$ 1024

4. $c = 18$; $n = 10$; $a = \underline{?}$ 12

5. $n = 4$; $m = 25$; $h = \underline{?}$ 10

6. $m = 15$; $n = 3$; $b = \underline{?}$ $3\sqrt{6} \approx 7.35$

7. $c = 12$; $m = 4$; $h = \underline{?}$ $4\sqrt{2} \approx 5.66$

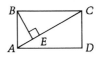
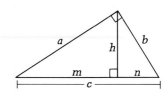

8. Given: Rectangle *ABCD*; $\overline{BE} \perp \overline{AC}$
Prove: $(CD)^2 = (AE)(AC)$

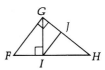

9. Given: △*FGH*; $\overline{FG} \perp \overline{GH}$; $\overline{GI} \perp \overline{FH}$; $\overline{FG} \parallel \overline{IJ}$
Prove: △*IHJ* ~ △*FGI*

10. Prove Theorem 8-1. **11.** Prove Theorem 8-2.

Write your answers in terms of x (x > 0).

12. $CD = x$; $BD = 4x$; $AD = \underline{?}$ 2x

13. $BC = x^2 + 9$; $BD = 9$; $AD = \underline{?}$ 3x

14. $CD = 2x$; $BD = 6x$; $AC = \underline{?}$ 4x

15. $BC = x^2 + 2x + 10$; $CD = 9$; $AD = \underline{?}$ 3x + 3

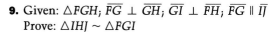

16. $AC = 8x$; $CD = 4x$; $BD = \underline{?}$ (HINT: Find *BC* first.) 12x

17. $BA = 12x$; $CB = 16x$; $CD = \underline{?}$ (HINT: Find *BD* first.) 7x

Set B

18. Is △*ABC* with vertices *A*(0, 0), *B*(4, 3), and *C*(4, 0) similar to △*ACD* if *D* has coordinates $\left(\frac{64}{25}, \frac{48}{25}\right)$? Explain your answer.

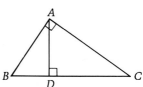

19. Given: ∠*ACB* is a right angle; *WXYZ* is a square.
Prove: $(WX)^2 = (AW)(XB)$

20. Prove Theorem 8-3.

21. $a = 30$; $c = 50$; $h = \underline{?}$ 24

22. $h = 12$; $m = 9$; $b = \underline{?}$ 20

23. $a = 24$; $m = 4$; $b = \underline{?}$ $24\sqrt{35} \approx 141.99$

24. $b = 45$; $n = 5$; $a = \underline{?}$ $180\sqrt{5} \approx 402.49$

25. $b = 8$; $m = 12$; $c = \underline{?}$ 16

26. $h = 14$; $c = 35$; $n = \underline{?}$ 7 or 28

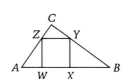

27. Find d. $6\frac{2}{3}$

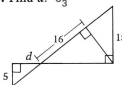

28. Find e. $6\frac{3}{4}$

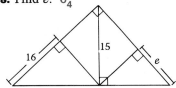

29. A carpenter's square is laid on the ground to find the length of a lake. Find AP if BA is 201 m and QA is 34 m. **178.5 m**

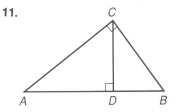

Set C

30. $a = 7\sqrt{5}$; $h = 14$; $c = $ __?__ ; $n = $ __?__ **35; 28**

31. $a = 6\sqrt{5}$; $b = 3\sqrt{5}$; $m = $ __?__ ; $h = $ __?__ **12; 6**

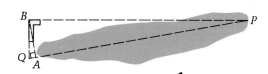

A right triangle has legs of lengths a and b. The altitude to the hypotenuse has length h; it divides the hypotenuse into segments of lengths m and n.

32. Prove: $h(m + n) = ab$

33. Prove: $a^2 + b^2 = (m + n)^2$

34. Given: $\triangle XYZ$; $m\angle YXZ = 2m\angle Z$; $\overline{XF}$ bisects $\angle YXZ$
Prove: XY is the geometric mean of ZY and FY.

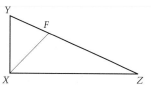

35. Given: $\triangle ABC$ with altitudes $\overline{AY}$, $\overline{BZ}$, and $\overline{CX}$ intersecting at P
Prove: $\left(\dfrac{AX}{XB}\right)\left(\dfrac{BY}{YC}\right)\left(\dfrac{CZ}{ZA}\right) = 1$

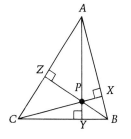

▲ Review

36. Tonya's cabin is at the edge of a river directly across from a tree on the other side. Without crossing the river, how can Tonya measure the distance from her cabin to the tree? Draw a diagram and describe your method.

37. Repeat Exercise 36 using a different method.

38. $\overline{WY}$ bisects $\angle XYZ$. Find XZ. **24**

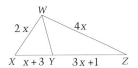

39. What is a locus?

40. List the steps in an indirect proof.

39. A locus is the set of all points and only those points, that satisfy a given condition.

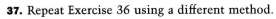

form 4 rt. $\angle$s. [1]) 4. $m\angle CDB = m\angle ACB$ (All rt. $\angle$s are =. [1, 3]) 5. $\triangle CBD \sim \triangle ABC$ (AA $\sim$ Post. [2, 4]) *Part III* 1. $\triangle ABC$ with rt. $\angle BCA$; $\overline{CD} \perp \overline{AB}$ (Given) 2. $\triangle ACD \sim \triangle ABC$ (Part I above) 3. $\triangle CBD \sim \triangle ABC$ (Part II above) 4. $\triangle ABC \sim \triangle CBD$ (Symmetric Prop. [3]) 5. $\triangle ACD \sim \triangle CBD$ (Transitive Prop. [2, 4])

11.

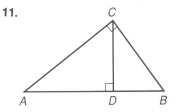

Given: $\triangle ABC$ with rt. $\angle BCA$; $\overline{CD} \perp \overline{AB}$ Prove: $\dfrac{AD}{CD} = \dfrac{CD}{BD}$ Proof: 1. $\triangle ABC$ with rt. $\angle BCA$; $\overline{CD} \perp \overline{AB}$ (Given) 2. $\triangle ACD \sim \triangle CBD$ (If altitude is drawn to hypotenuse of a rt. $\triangle$, the new $\triangle$s formed are $\sim$ to each other and to the given $\triangle$. [1]) 3. $\dfrac{AD}{CD} = \dfrac{CD}{BD}$ (Corres. sides of $\sim$ $\triangle$s are prop. [2])

18. Yes; since the slope of $\overline{AB}$ is $\frac{3}{4}$ and the slope of $\overline{CD}$ is $-\frac{4}{3}$, $\overline{CD} \perp \overline{AB}$ and $\overline{CD}$ is the altitude to the hypotenuse of $\triangle ABC$. The triangles are $\sim$ by Thm. 8–1.

19. Proof: 1. $\angle ACB$ is a rt. $\angle$; $WXYZ$ is a square. (Given) 2. $\angle ZWX$ and $\angle YXW$ are rt. $\angle$s. (Def. of square [1]) 3. $\overline{ZW} \perp \overline{AB}$; $\overline{YX} \perp \overline{AB}$ (Def. of $\perp$ [2]) 4. $\angle ZWA$ and $\angle YXB$ are rt. $\angle$s. (Def. of $\perp$ [3]) 5. $\triangle ACB$, $\triangle AWZ$ and $\triangle YXB$ are rt. $\triangle$s. (Def. of rt. $\triangle$ [1, 4]) 6. $\angle XYB$ and $\angle B$ are complementary; $\angle A$ and $\angle B$ are complementary. (2 acute $\angle$s of a rt. $\triangle$ are complementary. [5]) 7. $m\angle XYB = m\angle A$ (Complements of same $\angle$ are =. [6]) 8. $m\angle ZWA = m\angle YXB$ (All rt. $\angle$s are =. [4]) 9. $\triangle AWZ \sim \triangle YXB$ (AA $\sim$ Post. [7, 8]) 10. $\dfrac{AW}{YX} = \dfrac{WZ}{XB}$ (Corres. sides of $\sim$ $\triangle$s are prop. [9]) 11. $YX = WX$; $WZ = WX$ (Def. of square [1]) 12. $\dfrac{AW}{WX} = \dfrac{WX}{XB}$ (Substitution Prop. [10, 11]) 13. $(AW)(XB) = (WX)^2$ (Mult. Prop. [12])

FOLLOW-UP

More Practice

• Worksheet 8–1

Extension

Modify **Exercise 19** so that *WXYZ* is known only to be a rectangle. Through an intuitive limiting process, the exercise can be used as an alternate approach to Theorem 8–2.

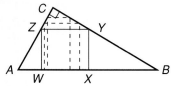

1. Which length is the geometric mean of *AW* and *XB*? *WZ* or *XY*
2. As *Z* and *Y* become closer to *C*, what length do *WZ* and *XY* approach? the altitude from *C*
3. What does *WX* approach? zero
4. What do *AW* and *XB* approach? the lengths cut off on the hypotenuse by the altitude

• Extension 8–1

Computers

The computer activity in theh pupil's book can be completed using *The Geometric Supposer: Triangles.*
Note: The activity can also be completed using *GeoDraw*, but because the program measures lengths to the nearest whole number, the measures given for the hypotenuse will be approximations.

• Computer Activities 8–1

Thinking Ahead **41.** Draw right $\triangle ABC$ in the middle of a sheet of grid paper. Let $m\angle C = 90$; $BC = 9$; and $AC = 12$. Draw square *BCPQ* using $\overline{BC}$ as one side. *P* and *Q* should not be on the *A* side of $\overleftrightarrow{BC}$. Similarly, draw squares *ACJK* and *ABGH* using $\overline{AC}$ and $\overline{AB}$, respectively, as sides.

a. What is *AB*? 15
b. What are the areas of the squares?
c. Write an equation that shows how the areas are related to one another. $BC^2 + AC^2 = AB^2$

42. Repeat the activity above with $BC = 12$ and $AC = 5$.
42. $AB = 13$; $5^2 + 12^2 = 13^2$

Sample:

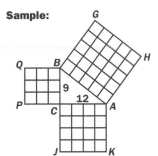

b. Area of *ABGH* = 225
Area of *BCPQ* = 81
Area of *ACJK* = 144

⌨ Computer Activities: Drawing and Measuring

1. Draw any right triangle. Measure the three sides and square the lengths. How are the squares related?

2. Repeat the activity with five different right triangles. Does the same relationship exist? Yes

3. Compare your results with those of your classmates, and then write a conjecture involving the hypotenuse and the legs of a right triangle.

1. The sum of the squares of lengths of the legs equals the square of the length of the hypotenuse

3. In a rt. △, the square of the length of the hypotenuse is equal to the sum of the squares of the lengths of the legs.

Algebra Review: Solving Equations with Perfect Squares

If $x^2 = a^2$, then $x^2 - a^2 = 0$ or $(x + a)(x - a) = 0$. So either $x + a = 0$ and $x = -a$, or $x - a = 0$ and $x = a$. Thus if $x^2 = a^2$ then $x = \pm a$.

Examples

1. Solve: $x^2 = 9a^2$

2. Solve: $x^2 = c^2 + 6c + 9$

Solutions

1. $x^2 = 9a^2$
$x^2 = (3a)^2$
$x = \pm 3a$

2. $x^2 = c^2 + 6c + 9$
$x^2 = (c + 3)^2$
$x = \pm(c + 3)$

Solve each equation for x.

1. $x^2 = 49$
2. $x^2 = (c - 7)^2$
3. $x^2 = a^2 + 10a + 25$
4. $x^2 = 441$
5. $x^2 = 169a^4b^2c^8$
6. $x^2 = 9b^2 + 24bd + 16d^2$
7. $x^2 = 64b^2$
8. $x^2 = 100d^4$
9. $x^2 = (a^2 + b^2)^2 - (2ab)^2$
10. $x^2 = 196e^{20}$
11. $x^2 - c^2 + c = 4 - 3c$
12. $x^2 - 3e - 1 = e^2 - 5e$

1. $x = \pm 7$
2. $x = \pm(c - 7)$
3. $x = \pm(a + 5)$
4. $x = \pm 21$
5. $x = \pm 13a^2bc^4$
6. $x = \pm(3b + 4d)$
7. $x = \pm 8b$
8. $x = \pm 10d^2$
9. $x = \pm(a^2 - b^2)$
10. $x = \pm 14e^{10}$
11. $x = \pm(c - 2)$
12. $x = \pm(e - 1)$

8-2 The Pythagorean Theorem

One of the most important relationships in all of geometry is stated in the Pythagorean Theorem. The ancient Egyptians used the relationship as early as 2000 B.C. It was also known to the Babylonians. The block print shown at the right is evidence that Chinese mathematicians knew the theorem as well. However, there is no record that any of these groups proved it. The theorem bears the name of the Greek mathematician Pythagoras, who lived about 500 B.C. and is credited with the first proof.

Proofs of this theorem for three special cases are shown below. In each case, the area of a square on the hypotenuse c or on one of the legs a or b represents the square of the length of that side.

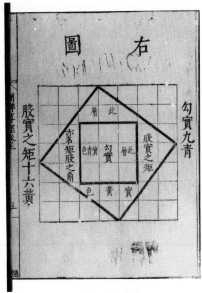

In the first case, each square is divided into triangular tiles. The four tiles which show a^2 and the four tiles which show b^2 can be rearranged to cover the eight tiles which show c^2. Thus if $a^2 = 4$, $b^2 = 4$, $c^2 = 8$, and $4 + 4 = 8$, then $a^2 + b^2 = c^2$ by the Substitution Property.

In the second case, each square is divided into square tiles. The nine tiles on a^2 and the sixteen tiles on b^2 can be arranged to cover 25 tiles on c^2. Thus, if $a^2 = 9$, $b^2 = 16$, $c^2 = 25$, and $9 + 16 = 25$, then $a^2 + b^2 = c^2$ by the Substitution Property.

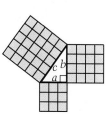

In the third case, congruent quadrilaterals 2, 3, 4, and 5 form the square whose area is a^2 can be combined with square 1 whose area is b^2 to cover the square whose area is c^2. Therefore, $a^2 + b^2 = c^2$.

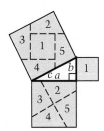

These are specific examples of the Pythagorean Theorem, Theorem 8-4. A paragraph proof for this theorem is given.

TEACHING NOTES

Use one or more of the geometric proofs to motivate the statement of the Pythagorean Theorem. Have students cut the two smaller squares of the Pythagorean Theorem model in numerous ways and place the parts on the third square. Discuss the equation that is represented. Point out that the four triangles formed by dotted lines in Square I (after the proof of Theorem 8–4) correspond to the four triangles in Square II. This shows $a^2 + b^2 = c^2$ visually.

Additional Examples

Example 1
In $\triangle PQR$, $\angle R$ is a right angle, $PR = 3$ and $QR = 9$. Find PQ. $3\sqrt{10}$

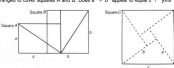

Theorem 8-4 *Pythagorean Theorem*

In a right triangle, the square of the length of the hypotenuse is equal to the sum of the squares of the lengths of the legs.

Given   Right $\triangle ABC$ with right $\angle C$; legs of lengths a and b, and hypotenuse of length c

Prove $a^2 + b^2 = c^2$

Proof   Because there is one line perpendicular to a given line through a point not on the line, the altitude from C can be drawn to $\overline{AB}$. Label the segment on $\overline{AB}$ so that $BD = x$ and $DA = y$. By the Segment Addition Postulate, $BD + DA = BA$; and by the Substitution Property, $x + y = c$. Then, by Theorem 8-3 and the definition of geometric mean, $a^2 = xc$ and $b^2 = yc$. By the Addition Property, $a^2 + b^2 = xc + yc = (x + y)c$. Finally, $a^2 + b^2 = c^2$ by the Substitution Property.

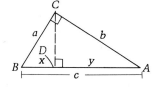

The Pythagorean Theorem has more different proofs than any other theorem in geometry. People with diverse backgrounds, such as Leonardo da Vinci and U.S. President James A. Garfield, have developed original proofs. The proof generally believed to be the one developed by Pythagoras and his followers is based on the areas of squares, rectangles, and triangles. The area of Square I at the right is the sum of the areas of two squares and two rectangles, or $a^2 + b^2 + 2ab$. The area of Square II is the sum of the area of a square and the areas of four triangles, or $c^2 + 4(\frac{1}{2}ab)$. Squares I and II have sides of length $a + b$ and consequently have equal areas. Therefore, $a^2 + b^2 + 2ab = c^2 + 4(\frac{1}{2}ab)$ which simplifies to $a^2 + b^2 = c^2$.

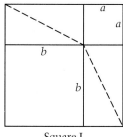

Square I

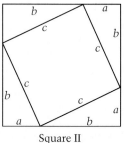

Square II

Example 1

Given $\triangle ABC$ with right $\angle C$, $BC = 8$, and $AC = 4$, find AB.

Solution

Since $\triangle ABC$ is a right triangle, use the Pythagorean Theorem.

$$AB^2 = BC^2 + AC^2$$
$$AB^2 = 8^2 + 4^2$$
$$AB^2 = 64 + 16$$
$$AB^2 = 80$$
$$AB = \sqrt{80} = \sqrt{16(5)} = 4\sqrt{5}$$

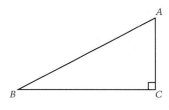

Example 2

Find an altitude of an equilateral triangle with side length 12.

Solution

In equilateral $\triangle ABC$, let $\overline{BD}$ be the altitude to $\overline{AC}$ which forms right $\triangle ABD$ with right $\angle ADB$. $\overline{BD}$ bisects $\overline{AC}$. Thus, $AD = \frac{1}{2}AC = 6$.

By the Pythagorean Theorem:

$$AD^2 + BD^2 = AB^2$$
$$6^2 + BD^2 = 12^2$$
$$36 + BD^2 = 144$$
$$BD^2 = 108$$
$$BD = \sqrt{108} = \sqrt{36(3)} = 6\sqrt{3}$$

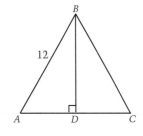

The Egyptian "rope stretchers" used the Pythagorean relation to survey land. To form a right angle, they divided a rope into twelve equal parts with eleven knots. Then they formed a triangle with sides of lengths 3, 4, and 5. The converse of the Pythagorean Theorem guarantees that the angle opposite the side of length 5 is a right angle. Its proof is requested in Exercise 33.

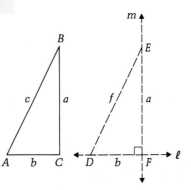

Theorem 8-5

If the sum of the squares of the lengths of two sides of a triangle is equal to the square of the length of the third side, then the triangle is a right triangle.

Given $\triangle ABC$ with side lengths of a, b, and c; $a^2 + b^2 = c^2$

Prove $\triangle ABC$ is a right triangle.

Plan for Proof   Draw $\ell \perp m$ at point F. Locate D on ℓ and E on m so that $DF = b$ and $EF = a$. Use the Pythagorean Theorem to show $f = c$. Show $\triangle ABC \cong \triangle DEF$ by SSS, and $\angle C$ is a right angle.

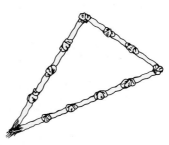

Example 2

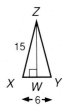

In isosceles $\triangle XYZ$, $XZ = YZ = 15$ and $XY = 6$. Find the length of $\overline{ZW}$. $6\sqrt{6}$

Example 3

Use the Pythagorean Theorem to show that $\triangle ABC$ with vertices A $(-10, 8)$, $B(-2, 2)$ and $C(-2, 8)$ is a right triangle. $AC = 8$, $CB = 6$ and $AB = 10$, so $8^2 + 6^2 = 10^2$

Error Analysis   In applications where the diagram is fairly involved, students may confuse legs with the hypotenuse. Have them first identify the hypotenuse by finding the side opposite the right angle. Stress that the hypotenuse is the longest line segment that forms the triangle.

Once students become comfortable with using the Pythagorean Theorem they will want to use it for any triangle. Stress that a triangle must be right to find an unknown measure.

Students will also give c^2 as the length of the hypotenuse. They often forget to find the square root.

Assignment Guide

Basic: 1–13, 39–50
Average: 2–12 (even), 14–35, 39–50
Extended: 2–32 (even), 33–50

EXERCISE NOTES

Exercise 28 develops the Distance Formula for the coordinate model.
Exercise 31 involves the **proof subskill** of writing plans for a proof.
Exercise 34 applies the Pythagorean Theorem to △*CDB* and △*CDA*.
Exercise 35 applies the Pythagorean Theorem to △*MAL* and △*MAN*.
Exercise 36 involves a three-dimensional application.

ANSWERS

Checking for Understanding

9. By the HL ≅ Thm., △*ABD* ≅ △*CBD*. Then *AD* = *CD* and *D* is the midpt. of $\overline{AC}$. By def. of midpt., $\overline{BD}$ bisects $\overline{AC}$.

Checking for Understanding

Use the Pythagorean Theorem to find x.

1. 13

2. 24

3. 8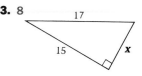

Which of the following number triples can be lengths of sides of a right triangle?

4. 4, 5, 7 No   **5.** 9, 40, 41 Yes   **6.** 20, 21, 29 Yes   **7.** 9, 12, 16 No

8. Show why a triangle with lengths of sides 3, 4, and 5, is a right triangle. $3^2 + 4^2 = 5^2$

9. In Example 2, explain why $\overline{BD}$ bisects $\overline{AC}$.
An altitude of an equilateral △ is also a median.

Written Exercises

Set A   Given: △*ABC* with right ∠*C*

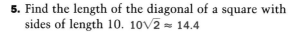

1. *BC* = 14; *AC* = 48; *AB* = ___?___ 50

2. *AC* = 1; *BC* = 3; *AB* = ___?___ $\sqrt{10} \approx 3.16$

3. *AC* = 2; *AB* = 4; *BC* = ___?___ $2\sqrt{3} \approx 3.46$

4. *AB* = $8\sqrt{3}$; *BC* = $4\sqrt{3}$; *AC* = ___?___ 12

5. Find the length of the diagonal of a square with sides of length 10. $10\sqrt{2} \approx 14.4$

6. Find the length of a diagonal of a rectangle with dimensions 8 inches by 20 inches. $4\sqrt{29} \approx 21.54$ in.

7. Find the length of the hypotenuse of an isosceles right triangle with legs of length 18. $18\sqrt{2} \approx 25.46$

8. Give at least three other rope lengths and arrangements of knots that the Egyptian rope stretchers might have used to get a right angle.
8, 15, 17; 5, 12, 13; 9,40, 41
Give the lengths of the segments pictured on the geoboard. $\sqrt{10}$

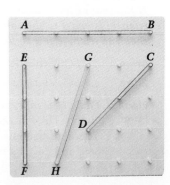

9. *AB* 4   **10.** *CD* $2\sqrt{2}$ **11.** *EF* 3   **12.** *GH*

13. What two labeled points could you connect on the geoboard to get a segment whose length is $\sqrt{5}$?
A and *G* or *G* and *B*

Set B   Given: Equilateral $\triangle ABC$ with altitude $\overline{AD}$

14. If $BC = 18$, find AD. $9\sqrt{3}$

15. If $AD = 4\sqrt{3}$, find AC. 8

16. If $AD = 7$, find AB. $\dfrac{14\sqrt{3}}{3}$

On grid paper, draw a segment with each length. Let the length of a side of a square equal 1 unit.

17. $\sqrt{2}$ **18.** $\sqrt{5}$ **19.** $\sqrt{3}$

Use Theorem 8-5 and the Distance Formula, if necessary, to show that

20. quadrilateral $ABCD$ with these coordinates is a rectangle: $A(0, 3)$, $B(2, 0)$, $C(8, 4)$, $D(6, 7)$.

21. quadrilateral $EFGH$ with these coordinates is a square: $E(1, 0)$, $F(0, 3)$, $G(-3, 2)$, $H(-2, -1)$.

Two cars are at point C when a tornado is sighted at T. The tornado is 1.6 km away and moving toward them. Car D drives along $\overrightarrow{CD}_1$ at a right angle to the path of the tornado. Car E drives along $\overrightarrow{CE}_1$ directly away from the tornado at the same speed as Car D. The tornado is moving along $\overrightarrow{TC}$ at twice the speed of the cars. Complete the table.

	Position			Distance from tornado	
	Tornado	Car D	Car E	Car D	Car E
	T	C	C	1.6	1.6
22.	T_1	D_1	E_1	? 0.9	1.2
23.	C	D_2	E_2	? 0.8	? 0.8
24.	? E_2	D_3	E_3	? 1.4	? 0.4
25.	? E_4	D_4	E_4	? 2.3	? 0

26. Which path is the safer course? The path taken by car D.

27. The minute hand of Big Ben is 14 feet long and the hour hand is 9 feet long. What is the distance between the tips of the hands when it is 3:00 P.M.? $\sqrt{277}$ ft.

17.

18.

19.
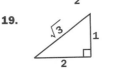

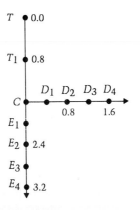

20. $\overline{AD} \parallel \overline{BC}$ because they have the same slope, $\frac{2}{3}$. $\overline{AB} \parallel \overline{CD}$ because they have the same slope, $\frac{-3}{2}$. Using the Distance Formula gives $AD = BC = \sqrt{52}$, $AB = CD = \sqrt{13}$ and $BD = AC = \sqrt{65}$. Since $AB^2 + AD^2 = BD^2$, $BC^2 + CD^2 = BD^2$, $AD^2 + DC^2 = AC^2$ and $AB^2 + BC^2 = AC^2$, by Thm. 8-5 $\triangle$s ADC, DCB, CBA and BAD are rt. $\triangle$s. Therefore, $\angle A$, $\angle B$, $\angle C$ and $\angle D$ are rt. $\angle$s. $ABCD$ is a parallelogram with 4 rt. $\angle$s. Thus, $ABCD$ is a rect.

21. $\overline{EF} \parallel \overline{GH}$ because they have the same slope, -3. $\overline{FG} \parallel \overline{HE}$ because they have the same slope, $\frac{1}{3}$. $EF = FG = GH = HE = \sqrt{10}$ and $EG = HF = 2\sqrt{5}$. Since $EF^2 + FG^2 = EG^2$, $FG^2 + GH^2 = FH^2$, $GH^2 + HE^2 = GE^2$ and $HE^2 + EF^2 = HF^2$, by Theorem 8-5, $\triangle EFG$, $\triangle FGH$, $\triangle GHE$ and $\triangle HEF$ are rt. $\triangle$s. Therefore, $\angle E$, $\angle F$, $\angle G$ and $\angle H$ are rt. $\angle$s. $EFGH$ is a rectangle with equal sides. Thus, $EFGH$ is a square.

28.

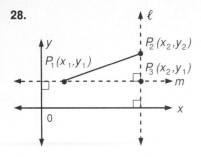

In the coordinate plane draw line ℓ through P_2 so that ℓ is $\perp$ to the x-axis. Draw line m through P so that m is $\perp$ to the y-axis. Then ℓ $\perp m$ and the intersection of ℓ and m is a point, say P_3, with coordinates (x_2, y_1). Then $P_1P_3 = |x_2 - x_1|$ and $P_2P_3 = |y_2 - y_1|$. Using right $\triangle P_1P_2P_3$ and substituting in the Pythagorean Theorem gives:
$(P_1P_2)^2 = (P_1P_3)^2 + (P_2P_3)^2$
$(P_1P_2)^2 = (|x_2 - x_1|)^2 + (|y_2 - y_1|)^2$
$(P_1P_2)^2 = (x_2 - x_1)^2 + (y_2 - y_1)^2$
$P_1P_2 = \sqrt{(x_2 - x_1)^2 + (y_2 - y_1)^2}.$

FOLLOW-UP

More Practice

• **Worksheet 8–2**

Extension

The Pythagorean Theorem is actually a special case of the Law of Cosines. Have students do the following proof.
Given: $\triangle ABC$ with altitude AD
Prove: $c^2 = a^2 + b^2 - 2ax$

Plan for proof: Express AD^2 using the Pythagorean Theorem for $\triangle ABD$ and $\triangle ACD$. Substitute and simplify.
• **Extension 8–2**

28. In Chapter 1, you found the distance d between two points $P_1(x_1, y_1)$ and $P_2(x_2, y_2)$ by using the formula $d = \sqrt{(x_2 - x_1)^2 + (x_2 - y_1)^2}$. Explain how the Pythagorean Theorem can be used to justify this formula.

29. Find AB, given $A(-1, 5)$ and $B(5, -1)$. $6\sqrt{2} \approx 8.49$

30. Is $\triangle DEF$ with $D(-2, -3)$, $E(-1, 4)$, and $F(5, -2)$ a right triangle? Explain.

31. What are two ways to show that a triangle in the coordinate plane is a right triangle?

32. If $XY = WY$ and $XZ = YZ = 4$, find XW.
$4\sqrt{4 + 2\sqrt{2}} \approx 10.45$

33. Prove Theorem 8-5.

34. Given: $\triangle ABC$ with altitude $\overline{CD}$
Prove: $a^2 - y^2 = b^2 - x^2$

35. Given: $\angle MAN$ is a right angle.
Prove: $NA^2 + ML^2 = MN^2 + AL^2$

Set C **36.** If $\triangle ABC$ is equilateral, $AB = 24$, $\overline{XA}$ is perpendicular to the plane of $\triangle ABC$, $XC = 2XA$, and M is the midpoint of $\overline{BC}$, find XM.
$4\sqrt{39} \approx 24.98$

37. Given: $\triangle ABC$; $m\angle C = 90$; $\overline{DC} \perp \overline{AB}$
Prove: $\dfrac{1}{a^2} + \dfrac{1}{b^2} = \dfrac{1}{h^2}$

38. Given: P is in the interior of rectangle $QRST$.
Prove: $x^2 + z^2 = w^2 + y^2$
(HINT: Use Exercise 34.)

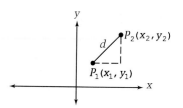
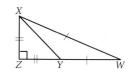
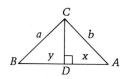
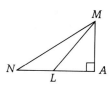
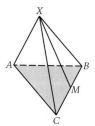
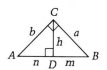
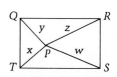

Computers

This computer activity can be completed using *The Geometric Supposer: Triangles* or *GeoDraw*.

Note: If you are using *GeoDraw*, the length of each side measured will be given to the nearest whole number and the ratios obtained may not be precisely those expected.

To alert students to the special relationships between the legs and hypotenuse of 30-60-90 and 45-45-90 triangles, have students do the following.

Draw a 30-60-90 triangle. Measure the hypotenuse and divide its length by the length of the shorter leg. Draw several similar, noncongruent (30-60-90) triangles and for each, repeat the measuring process. What generalization appears to be true about the relationship between the length of the hypotenuse of a 30-60-90 triangle and the length of its shorter leg? Hypotenuse ÷ 2 = length of shorter leg ÷ 2

Draw a 45-45-90 triangle. Measure the hypotenuse and divide its length by the length of either of the legs. Draw several similar, noncongruent (45-45-90) triangles and repeat the measuring process. What does the value of the ratio of the length of the hypotenuse of a 45-45-90 triangle to either of the triangle's legs always seem to approximate? √2, or 1.41

 Review In $\triangle RST$, $\angle S$ is a right angle, and $\overline{SU}$ is an altitude.

39. $\triangle RST \sim \underline{\ ?\ }$ and $\triangle RST \underline{\ ?\ }$. $\triangle RUS$; $\triangle SUT$

40. If $RU = 12$ and $UT = 3$, then $SU = \underline{\ ?\ }$. **6**

41. A 6-foot fence post casts a 2-foot shadow on level ground at the same time that a tower casts an 8-foot shadow on level ground. How tall is the tower? **24 ft.**

42. In $\triangle XYZ$, if the measure of an exterior angle at Y is 106, then $m\angle X + m\angle Z = \underline{\ ?\ }$. **106**

43. If $EF = GH$ and $\overline{EF} \parallel \overline{GH}$, then $EFGH$ is a $\underline{\ ?\ }$. **parallelogram**

Thinking Ahead Given: Equilateral $\triangle ABC$ with altitude $\overline{BD}$

44. What is the relationship between AD and AB? $AD = \frac{1}{2} AB$

45. What is $m\angle A$? $m\angle ABD$? **60; 30**

46. Complete the table.

AB	12	32	?	?	?	?
AD	?	?	9	8	?	?
BD	?	?	?	?	24	6

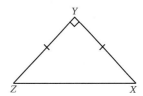

47. What patterns do you see in the table?

Given: $\triangle XYZ$; $XY = ZY$; $m\angle Y = 90$

48. What is $m\angle X$? $m\angle Z$? **45; 45**

49. Complete the table.

XY	10	12	?	?
XZ	?	?	16	6

50. What patterns do you see in the table?

Challenge

Trace this figure of nested squares without lifting your pencil or retracing any segment. What is the length of the path you traced? A side of the largest square measures 1 unit. **6 + 3√2 ≈ 10.2 units**

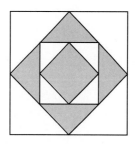

Construction Exercises

Construction 12

Construct a segment of length $\sqrt{5}$ times a given length.

Given A segment of length a

Construct $\overline{AC}$ of length $a\sqrt{5}$

Method Step 1: Draw $\overrightarrow{BZ}$. Construct $\overrightarrow{BW} \perp \overrightarrow{BZ}$.

Step 2: On $\overrightarrow{BZ}$, construct $\overline{AB}$ of length $2a$. On $\overrightarrow{BW}$, construct $\overline{BC}$ of length a.

Step 3: Draw $\overline{AC}$. Then $AC = a\sqrt{5}$.

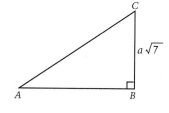

1. Write a plan for justifying Construction 12. Since $\overline{BW} \perp \overline{BZ}$, $\triangle ABC$ is a rt. $\triangle$. By Pythagorean Thm. $a^2 + (2a)^2 = (AC)^2$. Solving, $AC = a\sqrt{5}$

Construct segments of the given lengths. A segment of length a is given.

2. $a\sqrt{10}$ **3.** $a\sqrt{17}$ **4.** $a\sqrt{8}$

For Exercises 2–4, you constructed the required segment by thinking of the segment as the *hypotenuse* of a right triangle. To construct a segment of length $a\sqrt{7}$, think of the segment as a *leg* of a right triangle, say $\overline{BC}$. You want to find the lengths of $\overline{AB}$ and $\overline{AC}$ in terms of whole numbers and a. Since $AB^2 + BC^2 = AC^2$, substituting gives $AB^2 + 7a^2 = AC^2$. What perfect square can we choose for AB^2 so that $AB^2 + 7a^2$ is also a perfect square? When AB^2 is $9a^2$, AC^2 is $16a^2$ which is a perfect square. Therefore, construct $AB = 3a$ and $AC = 4a$. The Pythagorean Theorem guarantees that $BC = a\sqrt{7}$.

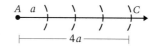

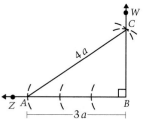

5. Justify the construction of the segment with length $a\sqrt{7}$.

Construct segments of the given lengths. A segment of length a is given.

6. $a\sqrt{15}$ **7.** $a\sqrt{12}$ **8.** $a\sqrt{6}$

5. Since $AB^2 + BC^2 = AC^2$, $(3a)^2 + (BC)^2 = (4a)^2$ Solving for BC yields $BC = a\sqrt{7}$

Excursion: Snowflake Curves

The sequence of figures on the right shows the evolution of an interesting curve called the *snowflake curve*. A procedure for drawing this curve a type of *fractal*, is described below.

1. Begin with an equilateral triangle with side length 1. The triangle is the curve labeled S_1.

2. Trisect each side of the triangle and in each center section construct an equilateral triangle outward. Erase the segments common to each new triangle and the previous triangle. This curve is S_2.

3. Trisect each side of S_2 and again construct an equilateral triangle outward on each center section. Erase the segments common to the new figure and S_2. This curve is S_3.

Repeat this process indefinitely. Stages S_4 and S_5 are shown.

Analyze the curves and complete this table.

	Curve	Number of sides	Perimeter	
1.	S_1	?	?	3; 3
2.	S_2	?	?	12; 4
3.	S_3	?	?	48; $5\frac{1}{3}$
4.	S_4	?	?	192; $7\frac{1}{9}$
5.	S_5	?	?	768; $9\frac{13}{27}$
6.	S_6	?	?	3,072; $12\frac{52}{81}$

7. At the seventh stage, snowflake curve S_7 will have
   a. __?__ sides. 12,288   b. a perimeter of __?__. $16\frac{208}{243}$

8. $3 + 1 + \frac{4}{3} + (\frac{4}{3})^2 + (\frac{4}{3})^4 + (\frac{4}{3})^5$ is the perimeter for which snowflake curve? S_7

9. Generalize your answers for snowflakes S_1 through S_7 to the case for S_n; that is, how many sides does a snowflake at the nth stage have, and what is its perimeter?

10. As the snowflake continues to evolve, what appears to be true for its perimeter?   The perimeter appears to be infinite
    9. $3(4)^{n-1}$; $3(\frac{4}{3})^{n-1}$

Ask students to find the length of an altitude for each new equilateral triangle. Then ask: As the snowflake continues to evolve, what appears to be true about its area? The area approaches a limit. It can be shown that the area has limit $\frac{23}{5}$.

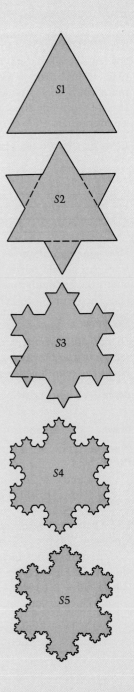

S1

S2

S3

S4

S5

Warm-Up Review

1. The sum of the measures of the angles of a triangle is ___?___. 180
2. A triangle with two congruent sides is ___?___. Isosceles
3. State the equation for the Pythagorean Theorem. $a^2 + b^2 = c^2$
4. True or false: The diagonals of a square are congruent and bisect each other. True

---

LESSON 8–3

Resources

Teaching Aid 18, square root table
Visual Aid 18, square root table
Worksheet 8–3
Extension 8–3

OBJECTIVE

Determine and apply the properties of a 30-60-90 triangle and a 45-45-90 triangle.

TEACHING NOTES

Introduce the 30-60-90 triangle by drawing an altitude of an equilateral triangle and asking the following questions.

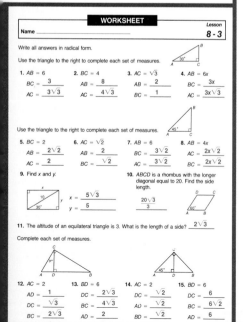

8-3 Special Right Triangles

An architect is going to use glass panels, many of which are shaped like equilateral triangles, to build a geodesic dome. She plans to first make a model of the dome using Plexiglas. How many equilateral triangles with sides of length 2.4 inches can she cut from one sheet of Plexiglas, 24 inches by 36 inches, if she minimizes the waste?

Rows of triangles can be arranged on the Plexiglas in two ways.

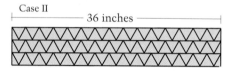 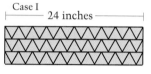

How many equilateral triangles are in each row? How many rows can be laid out in each case? What do you need to know about the triangular pieces in order to find the number of rows? Use Theorem 8-6 to help you. The proof is left to Exercise 29.

Case I has 19 △s across; Case II has 29 △s across; The number of rows in each case is determined by the altitude of the triangular piece.

Theorem 8-6

In a 30-60-90 triangle, the length of the hypotenuse is twice the length of the shorter leg, and the length of the longer leg is $\sqrt{3}$ times the length of the shorter leg.

Given Right $\triangle ABC$ with $m\angle A = 60$, $m\angle ABC = 30$, $AC = b$, $AB = c$, and $BC = a$

Prove $c = 2b$ and $a = b\sqrt{3}$

Plan for Proof Draw $\overrightarrow{AC}$. Label D on $\overrightarrow{AC}$ so that $CA = CD$. Draw $\overline{BD}$. Show $\triangle ABC \cong \triangle DBC$. Then $\triangle ABD$ is equilateral and $c = 2b$. Apply the Pythagorean Theorem, using $2b$ for c, to show $a = b\sqrt{3}$.

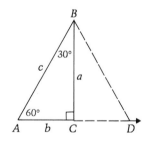

Use Theorem 8-6 to find the height of the triangular pieces. Since $c = 2.4$, $b = 1.2$ and $a = 1.2\sqrt{3}$. Therefore, the height is $1.2\sqrt{3}$ or about 2.1 inches. Divide the length of the remaining side of the Plexiglas by 2.1 to find the number of rows. For Case I, $36 \div 2.1$ gives 17 rows. For Case II, $24 \div 2.1$ gives 11 rows. Which arrangement should the architect use to get the most triangles and therefore minimize the waste? Case I
Case I has 17 × 19 or 323 triangles.
Case II gives 11 × 29 or 319 triangles.

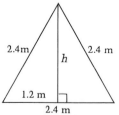

Theorem 8-7, which follows directly from Theorem 8-6, relates the altitude to the length of the side in an equilateral triangle. Its proof is left to Exercise 26.

Theorem 8-7

The length of an altitude of an equilateral triangle with sides of length s is $\frac{1}{2}s\sqrt{3}$.

Example 1
In the 30-60-90 triangle at the right, if $AC = 9$, find BC.

Solution
By Theorem 8-6, $AC = BC\sqrt{3}$. Therefore, $9 = BC\sqrt{3}$. Solving, $BC = \frac{9}{\sqrt{3}}$. Rationalizing the denominator, $BC = 3\sqrt{3}$.

Example 2
In the 30-60-90 triangle at the right, if $AC = 5\sqrt{21}$, find BC.

Solution
By Theorem 8-6, $BC = AC\sqrt{3}$. Therefore, $BC = (5\sqrt{21})\sqrt{3}$ $= 15\sqrt{7}$.

A baseball diamond is a square with sides that are 90 feet long. The distance d from home plate to second base is the length of a diagonal of the square. Since the diagonal divides the square into two 45-45-90 triangles, d is also the hypotenuse of the triangles. Theorem 8-8 shows a way to find d. Its proof is left to Exercise 27.

Theorem 8-8

In a 45-45-90 triangle, the length of the hypotenuse is $\sqrt{2}$ times the length of a leg.

Given Right $\triangle ABC$ with $m\angle A = m\angle B = 45$, $AB = c$, and $AC = a$

Prove $c = a\sqrt{2}$

Plan for Proof Show that $BC = a$. Use the Pythagorean Theorem to show $c = a\sqrt{2}$.

1. How does the altitude affect the base? It bisects the base.
2. How can we find the length of the altitude? Pythagorean Theorem The $1 : \sqrt{3} : 2$ ratio follows easily.

For the 45-45-90 triangle, draw a square and a diagonal and ask questions similar to those for the 30-60-90 triangle.

Reinforce the concept with several application problems. Given the length of one side, students should then be able to find the lengths of the sides of the triangle.

Additional Examples

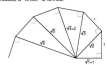

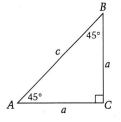

Example 1
In $\triangle PQR$, if $PR = 15$, find QR. $5\sqrt{3}$

Example 2
In $\triangle PQR$, if $QR = 2\sqrt{3}$, find PR. 6

Example 3
Find the length of the diagonal of a square 18 inches on each side. $18\sqrt{2}$

Example 4

In $\triangle XYZ$, if $XY = 14$, find XZ. $7\sqrt{2}$

Error Analysis Two common errors are associated with this topic:
1. Confusion of the $\sqrt{3}$ in the 30-60-90 triangle with the $\sqrt{2}$ in the 45-45-90 triangle.
2. Difficulty in dealing with irrational denominators if given a rational value for the side opposite the 60-degree angle or for the hypotenuse of the 45-45-90 triangle. Both problems will decrease with practice.

EXERCISE NOTES

   Exercise 14 involves the **proof subskill** of drawing a diagram.
   Exercises 16 and **19** require students to draw auxiliary lines.
   Exercise 24 foreshadows a theorem in Chapter 11.
   Exercise 32 could be solved by finding the measure of the altitude of the equilateral triangle formed by connecting the centers of the circles.

Example 3
Approximately how far does the ball travel when the catcher throws from home plate to second base? (See page 347.)

Solution
To find the distance from home plate to second base, use one of the 45-45-90 triangles formed by the diagonal of the square. Applying Theorem 8-8, $d = 90\sqrt{2} \approx 127$ feet.

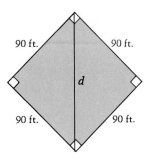

Example 4
In the 45-45-90 triangle at the right, if $DE = 8$, find EF.

Solution
By Theorem 8-8, $DE = EF\sqrt{2}$. Therefore, $8 = EF\sqrt{2}$.
Solving, $EF = \dfrac{8}{\sqrt{2}}$ which is not in simplest radical form.
Rationalizing the denominator, $EF = 4\sqrt{2}$.

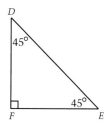

Checking for Understanding

1. In the Plan for Proof of Theorem 8-6, how would you show that $\triangle ABD$ is equilateral?

2. In Example 1, what is AB? $6\sqrt{3}$

3. In Example 2, what is AB? Use the Pythagorean Theorem to verify your answer.

4. In the solution to Example 3, show why $(5\sqrt{21})\sqrt{3} = 15\sqrt{7}$.
$(5\sqrt{21})(\sqrt{3}) = (5\sqrt{7}\,\sqrt{3})(\sqrt{3}) = (5\sqrt{7})(\sqrt{3})(\sqrt{3}) = (5\sqrt{7})(3) = 15\sqrt{7}$

Find x, y, or both x and y.

1. Since $\triangle ABC \cong \triangle DBC$, $m\angle D = m\angle A = 60$ and $m\angle DBC = m\angle ABC = 30$. Then, $m\angle ABC + m\angle DBC = m\angle ABD$ or $60 = m\angle ABD$. If $3\angle$s of a $\triangle$ are = then the $\triangle$ is equilateral.

5.
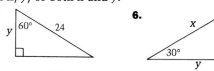
$x = 12$

6.
$x = 16$
$y = 8\sqrt{3}$

7.

$x = y = 8$

8.
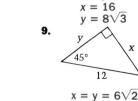
$x = 3\sqrt{3}$
$y = 6$

9.
$x = y = 6\sqrt{2}$

10.

$x = 8\sqrt{2}$

11. What is the relationship between the longer leg and the hypotenuse in a 30-60-90 triangle? The longer leg is $\dfrac{\sqrt{3}}{2}$ times the hypotenuse.

3. $10\sqrt{21}$; $(10\sqrt{21})^2 = (5\sqrt{21})^2 + (15\sqrt{7})^2$ or $2{,}100 = 525 + 1{,}575$

Written Exercises

Set A

1. $AC = 6$; $AB = \underline{?}$ 12
2. $AB = 8\sqrt{15}$; $AC = \underline{?}$ $4\sqrt{15}$
3. $AB = 4\sqrt{3}$; $BC = \underline{?}$ 6
4. $BC = 12$; $AB = \underline{?}$ $8\sqrt{3}$
5. $AC = 6\sqrt{6}$; $BC = \underline{?}$ $18\sqrt{2}$
6. $BC = 6\sqrt{3}$; $AC = \underline{?}$ 6

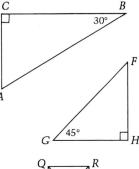

7. $FH = 6$; $FG = \underline{?}$ $6\sqrt{2}$
8. $FG = 12$; $FH = \underline{?}$ $6\sqrt{2}$
9. $GH = 9\sqrt{2}$; $FG = \underline{?}$ 18
10. $FG = 15\sqrt{2}$; $GH = \underline{?}$ 15
11. $FH = 14$; $FG = \underline{?}$ $14\sqrt{2}$
12. $FH = 5\sqrt{2}$; $FG = \underline{?}$ 10

13. Find ST, RT, and QS in the square at the right.
   15; $15\sqrt{2}$; $15\sqrt{2}$

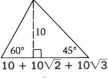

14. How many 30-60-90 triangles can be cut from a square piece of glass that measures 6 inches on a side, if the hypotenuse of the triangle is 6 inches? 4 Draw a diagram to show how you would arrange the triangles. Label the measures of all the segments and angles.

Set B Find the perimeter of each polygon.

15.
   20

16.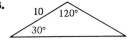
   $20 + 10\sqrt{3}$

17.
   $10 + 10\sqrt{2} + 10\sqrt{3}$

18.
   18

19.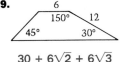
   $30 + 6\sqrt{2} + 6\sqrt{3}$

20.
   $12 + 4\sqrt{3}$

Find the lengths of the other two sides of each triangle in terms of x.

21.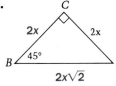

22.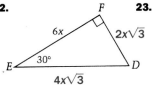

23.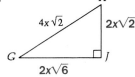

24. Find the length of a diagonal of a cube with side of length 12. $12\sqrt{3}$

25. In $\triangle PQR$, find QR. Is $\angle PQR$ a right angle? Explain.
   $3\sqrt{21}$; No; $PQ^2 + QR^2 \neq PR^2$

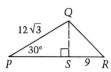

ANSWERS

Written Exercises

14. Samples:

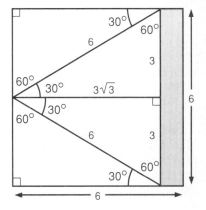

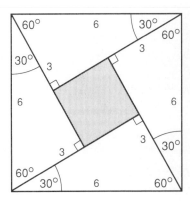

26. Theorem 8–7: The length of an altitude of an equilateral triangle with sides of length s is $\frac{1}{2}s\sqrt{3}$.

Given: Equilateral $\triangle ABC$; $AB = BC = AC = s$; $\overline{CD}$ is an altitude. Prove: $CD = \frac{1}{2}s\sqrt{3}$ Proof: 1. $\triangle ABC$ is equilateral; $AB = BC = AC = s$; $\overline{CD}$ is an altitude. (Given) 2. $\triangle ABC$ is equiangular. (Equilateral $\triangle$ is also equiangular. [1]) 3. $m\angle A = 60$ (Each $\angle$ of equiangular $\triangle$ has measure 60. [2]) 4. $\overline{CD} \perp \overline{AB}$ (Def. of altitude [1]) 5. $\angle CDA$ is a rt. $\angle$. (2 $\perp$ lines form 4 rt. $\angle$s. [4]) 6. $\triangle CDA$ is a rt. $\triangle$. (Def. of rt. $\triangle$ [5]) 7. $m\angle CDA = 90$ (Def. of rt. $\angle$ [5]) 8. $m\angle CDA + m\angle A + m\angle ACD = 180$ (Sum of measures of $\angle$s of $\triangle$ is 180.) 9. $90 + 60 + m\angle ACD = 180$ (Substitution [3, 7, 8]) 10. $m\angle ACD = 30$ (Add. Prop. [9]) 11. $CD = \frac{1}{2}s\sqrt{3}$ (In a 30–60–90 $\triangle$, length of leg opp. 30°$\angle$ is half length of hypotenuse; length of leg opp. 60°$\angle$ is $\sqrt{3}$ times length of other leg. [3, 7, 10])

FOLLOW-UP

More Practice

• Worksheet 8–3

Extension

Have students draw $\triangle ABC$ with vertices $A(0, 0)$, $B(6, 2\sqrt{3})$ and $C(3, 3\sqrt{3})$ and ask the following questions.
1. What kind of triangle is $\triangle ABC$? right triangle
2. What are the lengths of the sides? $AB = 4\sqrt{3}$; $BC = 2\sqrt{3}$; $AC = 6$
3. What are the measures of the angles? $m\angle A = 30$; $m\angle B = 60$; $m\angle C = 90$

• Extension 8–3

26. Prove Theorem 8-7.   **27.** Prove Theorem 8-8.

Set C **28.** The figure at the right is formed of four $4\sqrt{6}$ equilateral triangles with side length 12. Find AB.

29. Prove Theorem 8-6.

30. Find the dimensions of the square sheet of metal from which the stop sign was cut.
Since each side is $30 + 30\sqrt{2}$ cm the dimensions are about 72.43 cm by 72.43 cm.

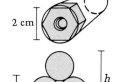

31. Find the diameter of the smallest iron rod from which the regular hexagonal nut at the right can be cut. $\frac{4}{3}\sqrt{3} \approx 2.31$ cm

32. Three pipes are stacked as shown. Find the height h of the stack if the diameter of each pipe is 8 inches. $8 + 4\sqrt{3} \approx 14.93$ in.

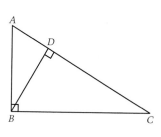

▲ Review **33.** $AB = 8$; $BC = 12$; $AC = \underline{?}$ $4\sqrt{13}$
34. $BC = 7$; $AC = 11$; $AB = \underline{?}$ $6\sqrt{2}$
35. $AC = 10$; $AD = 2$; $BC = \underline{?}$ $4\sqrt{5}$

36. Figures that are identical in size and shape are $\underline{?}$. congruent

37. If two angles are adjacent and complementary, then their noncommon sides are $\underline{?}$. perpendicular

Thinking Ahead **38.** What information would you need if you want to use the Pythagorean Theorem to solve a problem? A rt. $\triangle$ and the lengths of 2 of its sides

39. How would you use the Pythagorean Theorem to find the distance d across a lake? Draw a diagram to show what you would measure and how you would calculate the distance. Answers will vary.

40. Give a practical problem in which the Pythagorean Theorem would be useful in determining a distance or height that cannot be measured directly. Answers will vary.

39. Sample:

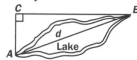

Measure $\overline{AC}$ and $\overline{CB}$ when $m\angle C = 90$ and use the Pythagorean Thm. to find d.

40. Sample:

How far up the building will a 12-foot ladder reach if the foot of the ladder is placed 3-feet from the building?

8-4 Applications of the Pythagorean Theorem

To apply the Pythagorean Theorem, you need to establish a right triangle. Then you must be able to measure two of the sides directly. When these conditions are met, you can use the Pythagorean Theorem to find numerical solutions to practical problems.

Three practical applications of the Pythagorean Theorem are worked in detail in this lesson.

Example 1

The Quans bought a 6-foot-square sheet of plywood to use as a base for a model railroad. Will the plywood fit into the back of their van if the opening is 44 inches high and 60 inches wide?

Solution

Use the Pythagorean Theorem to find the length of the diagonal of the van opening.

$d^2 = 44^2 + 60^2$
$d^2 = 1,936 + 3,600$
$d^2 = 5,536$
$d = \sqrt{5,536}$
$d \approx 74.4$

Since 74.4 inches is greater than 6 feet, the plywood will fit.

Example 2

The Draegers plan to purchase a television set with a 20-inch-diagonal screen to place in a wall unit. The width of the screen is about 15 inches. What is the minimum distance that must be allowed between two shelves of the wall unit to accommodate the set?

Solution

Use the Pythagorean Theorem to find the height of the screen.

$20^2 = 15^2 + h^2$
$400 = 225 + h^2$
$175 = h^2$
$h \approx 13.23$

The shelves must be at least $13\frac{1}{4}$ inches apart.

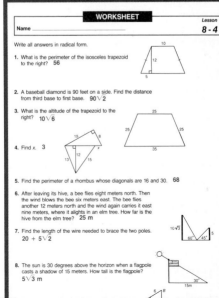

Assignment Guide

Basic: 1–9, 18–25
Average: 1–13, 18–25
Extended: 1–25

everyday situation. Discuss accuracy and rounding.

Example 3 offers an opportunity to discuss the change in length of wire as the position of *D* is changed.

Additional Examples

Example 1

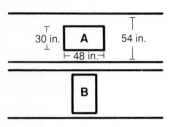

A desk in a hallway is to be turned around from position *A* to *B*. The desk is 48 in. by 30 in., and the hallway is 54 in. wide. Is there enough room to turn the desk without tilting it? No; diagonal of desk is 56.6 in.

Example 3

The frame for a trellis is made with two pieces of wood each 1.5 m long. *D* is the midpoint of $\overline{AB}$. Wire is to be strung from *A* to *C* to *B*. How much wire is needed?

Solution

$\triangle ADC \cong \triangle BDC$ by SAS and $AC = BC$. Since $AB = 1.5$, $AD = 0.75$.

$AC^2 = AD^2 + DC^2$
$AC^2 = (0.75)^2 + (1.5)^2$
$AC^2 = 0.5625 + 2.25$
$AC^2 = 2.8125$
$AC \approx 1.7$

$AC + BC \approx 3.4$, so about 3.4 m of wire is needed.

Checking for Understanding

Explain how the Pythagorean Theorem can be used to find x in each of the following diagrams. Tell what measurements are needed.

1. Width of lake

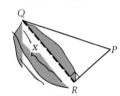

2. Amount of fencing

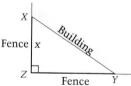

3. Length of brace

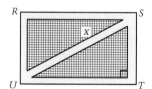

4. Distance between ships

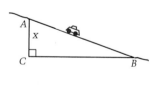

5. Height of ramp

6. Amount of wire

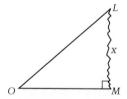

Written Exercises

Set A   The ladder is 15 feet long. **1.** $7.5\sqrt{3} \approx 12.99$ ft.

1. How high will the ladder reach if $m\angle A = 60$?

2. How high will the ladder reach if $m\angle A = 45$?

3. If the top of the ladder reaches a window sill 12 feet above the ground, how far from the house is the foot of the ladder? 9 ft.

2. $7.5\sqrt{2} \approx 10.61$ ft.

Two poles are arranged as shown in the diagram.

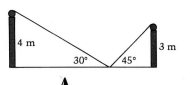

4. Find the total length of wire needed to brace the two poles. $8 + 3\sqrt{2} \approx 12.24$ m

5. Find the ground distance between the two poles. $3 + 4\sqrt{3} \approx 9.43$ m

6. The tower is 10.5 m high, and each wire brace is attached 4.5 m from the center of the tower's base. Find the total length of the three braces. About 34.26 m

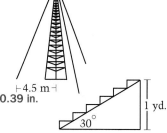

7. A carpenter built the stairs at the right. How high and how deep is each step? Height = 6 in.; depth ≈ 10.39 in.

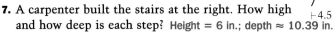

8. Explain how a carpenter might use a yardstick to determine if two boards are perpendicular.

Set B **9.** The glass for a picture window is 7.5 feet wide. About how high must a doorway be in order for a contractor to get the glass through the door? The doorway is 3 feet wide. $\sqrt{47.25} \approx 6.9$ ft.

10. The frame for a kite is made from two strips of wood, one 27 inches long and one 18 inches long. In the diagram, $AD = BD = CD$. What is the perimeter of the kite? Would the perimeter change if the vertical and horizontal strips were attached at some point other than D? $18\sqrt{2} + 18\sqrt{5} \approx 65.7$ in.; yes

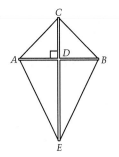

11. Find the dimensions not given in the drawing of the two lots at the right.
Lot A: 96 ft. and 238 ft.
Lot B: 144 ft. and 280 ft.

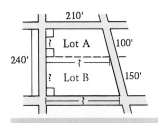

12. How much ribbon is needed for the package with a square base 1 foot on a side and 9 inches high if each diagonal piece of ribbon passes through the midpoint of an edge? $36 + (24\sqrt{2}) \approx 70$ in.

13. A tree originally 36 feet high was broken by a storm so that its top just touched the ground 12 feet from the base of the tree. How much of the tree is left standing? 16 ft.

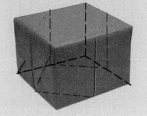

Example 2

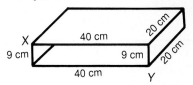

Steven has a cardboard box with two open ends and the dimensions shown. If points X and Y are 41 cm apart, will the faces of the box be perpendicular? yes; $9^2 + 40^2 = 41^2$

Example 3

A utility pole 9 m high is supported by two guy wires, each anchored to a point 3 m from the base of the pole. How many meters of wire are needed? about 19 m

Error Analysis If a **calculator** is used, students tend to trust every digit displayed, with no thought to errors inherent in given information. Emphasize that no result can be obtained that is more accurate than the given information and insist that every approximate answer be rounded off appropriately.

FOLLOW-UP

More Practice

• Worksheet 8–4

Extension

The following problem involves a challenging algebraic application of the Pythagorean Theorem. In right $\triangle ABC$, D is a point on $\overline{BC}$ such that $AC + CD = AB + BD$. If $AC = 6$ and $CD = 1$, find BD. $\frac{3}{4}$

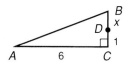

• Extension 8–4

Computers

The computer activity in the pupil's book can be completed using *The Geometric Supposer: Triangles.*

• Computer Activities 8–4
• Computer Worksheet 8–4

Set C Exercises 14 and 15 show how to find the width of a river by measuring angles A and B and finding the distance between points A and B. Find each width.

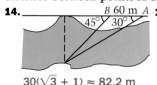 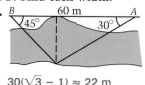

14.   **15.**

$30(\sqrt{3} + 1) \approx 82.2$ m $30(\sqrt{3} - 1) \approx 22$ m

16. Find the length of wire needed to brace the two poles shown if the angles made by the wire with the ground are equal. $5\sqrt{41} \approx 32$ m

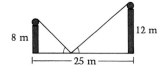

17. $\triangle ABC$ is equilateral; $AB = 24$; $\overline{XA}$ is perpendicular to the plane of $\triangle ABC$; $m\angle XBA = 30$; $MB = MC$. Find XM. $4\sqrt{39} \approx 24.98$

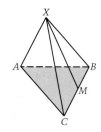

◆ **Review**   **18.** Find the length of an altitude in an equilateral triangle with 8-inch sides. $4\sqrt{3}$

19. In a 45-45-90 triangle, if the length of the hypotenuse is 18, how long are the legs? $9\sqrt{2}$

20. Can a right triangle have sides with lengths 9, 13, and 18? No

21. Write two conditionals for the following statement: I receive a trophy if and only if I am the winner.

21. If I am the winner, then I receive a trophy. If I received a trophy, then I am the winner.

22. Define *rectangle*. A rectangle is a parallelogram with 4 rt. ∠s.

⬇ **Thinking Ahead**   Draw the line whose equation is $y = 2x$ on a set of axes. Locate any 3 points, A, B, and C, on the line. Draw perpendicular lines from each point to the x-axis, intersecting the x-axis at point A', B', and C'.

23. Evaluate $\frac{AA'}{OA'}$; $\frac{BB'}{OB'}$; and $\frac{CC'}{OC'}$. All ratios = 2.

24. If you locate another point D on the line, what do you think the value of $\frac{DD'}{OD'}$ will be? 2

25. Check your conjecture by actually choosing a point D and evaluating $\frac{DD'}{OD'}$.

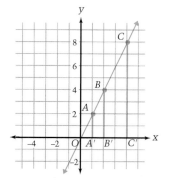

💻 Computer Activities: Drawing and Measuring

Draw three similar noncongruent triangles, $A_1B_1C_1$, $A_2B_2C_2$, and $A_3B_3C_3$, with right angles C_1, C_2, and C_3. Measure each hypotenuse and the sides opposite angles A_1, A_2, and A_3.

Sample:

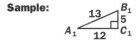

1. $\dfrac{B_1C_1}{B_1A_1} = \underline{\ ?\ }$; $\dfrac{B_2C_2}{B_2A_2} = \underline{\ ?\ }$; $\dfrac{B_3C_3}{B_3A_3} = \underline{\ ?\ }$ All three ratios are =.

Measure the sides adjacent to angles A_1, A_2, and A_3.

2. $\dfrac{A_1C_1}{A_1B_1} = \underline{\ ?\ }$; $\dfrac{A_2C_2}{A_2B_2} = \underline{\ ?\ }$; $\dfrac{A_3C_3}{A_3B_3} = \underline{\ ?\ }$ All three ratios are =.

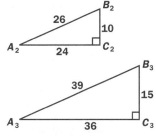

3. Given similar right triangles, what two ratios remain constant for every triangle with respect to one of the corresponding acute angles?

3. The ratio of the lengths of the side opposite and the hypotenuse, and the ratio of the lengths of the side adjacent and the hypotenuse.

Progress Check

Lesson 8-1, page 331

1. $a = 12$; $m = 8$; $c = \underline{\ ?\ }$ 18

$6\sqrt{2} \approx 8.49$

2. $c = 17$; $n = 8$; $h = \underline{\ ?\ }$

3. $c = 10$; $n = 8$; $b = \underline{\ ?\ }$
$\sqrt{5} \approx 2.24$

4. $b = 15$; $c = 50$; $m = \underline{\ ?\ }$
45.5

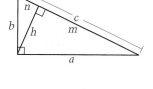

Lesson 8-2, page 337

Which of the following number triples can be the lengths of sides of a right triangle?

5. $5, 7, 10$ No   6. $11, 60, 61$ Yes   7. $7, 24, 25$ Yes

Given: Right $\triangle ABC$ with hypotenuse c and legs a and b

8. $b = 2$; $a = 4$; $c = \underline{\ ?\ }$
$2\sqrt{5} \approx 4.47$

12

9. $c = 37$; $a = 35$; $b = \underline{\ ?\ }$

Lesson 8-3, page 346

$25\sqrt{2}$

10. $AT = 10$; $RA = \underline{\ ?\ }$ $5\sqrt{2}$ 11. $AR = 25$; $AT = \underline{\ ?\ }$

12. $CA = 10\sqrt{3}$; $AR = \underline{\ ?\ }$ $5\sqrt{3}$ 13. $CR = 8\sqrt{3}$; $CA = \underline{\ ?\ }$
16

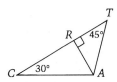

Lesson 8-4, page 351

14. How far from the base of a building must a 12-foot ladder be placed to make an angle of 60° with the ground? 6 ft.

15. If a car is driven 12 km due north and 10 km due east, to the nearest kilometer, how far is the car from its starting point? 16 km

16. Use the diagram at the right. What is the height of the roof?
$8\sqrt{2} \approx 11.31$ m

💻 Using BASIC: Academic Placement Testing

A school offers a special reading and writing course for new students. Section A places more emphasis on reading skills, whereas Section B concentrates more on writing skills. For Section A, the average reading and writing scores on a placement test are 64.2 and 73.8, respectively. For Section B the average reading and writing scores are 74.4 and 57.6, respectively. In which section should each of the four new students, whose scores are given at the right, be placed?

	Reading Score	Writing Score
Emily	68	64
Jim	67	67
Anne	70	62
Jennifer	66	69

Each student's pair of scores can be represented by a point in the coordinate plane. The distance formula, which is a direct application of the Pythagorean Theorem, can be used to assess the "proximity" of a student's scores to the average scores in each of the sections. Assume that the scales on both tests are the same.

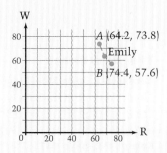

The program below applies the distance formula to decide student placement.

```
100  REM PLACEMENT IN READING AND WRITING SECTIONS
110  INPUT "STUDENT'S READING SCORE:" ;R
120  INPUT "STUDENT'S WRITING SCORE:" ;W
130  LET DR = SQR((64.2  R)^2 ÷ (73.8  W)^2)
140  LET DW = SQR((74.4  R)^2 ÷ (57.6  W)^2)
150  IF DR < DW THEN 180
160  PRINT "PLACE STUDENT IN SECTION B."
170  GOTO 200
180  PRINT "PLACE STUDENT IN SECTION A."
200  END
```

1. Use the program to determine the proper placement of the four students. Emily and Anne in B; Jim and Jennifer in A.

2. Modify the program so that the user can input the number of students to be placed and so that placements can be done during a single run.

Insert these lines: 105 Input 'NUMBER OF STUDENTS'; N
107 FOR I = 1 TO N
Then change line 200 and add line 210:
200 NEXT I
210 END

8-5 Right-Triangle Trigonometry

You can use similar triangles and the Pythagorean Theorem to write several useful relations. The study of these relations is called *trigonometry*.

Trigonometry is an example of a branch of mathematics that developed because of its practical applications.

In the diagram, $\overrightarrow{AB}$ (the flight path of the airplane) and $\overrightarrow{AC}$ (along the ground) contain two sides of right triangles whenever perpendicular lines are drawn to the ground from points on the plane's path. By the AA Similarity Postulate, $\triangle AJK \sim \triangle AFG \sim \triangle ADE \sim \triangle ABC$. This means that the corresponding sides are proportional and there are three special ratios which can be used to solve problems involving right triangles:

$\dfrac{BC}{AC} = \dfrac{DE}{AE} = \dfrac{FG}{AG} = \dfrac{JK}{AK}$ Each ratio is the *tangent ratio* for $\angle A$ (tan A).

$\dfrac{BC}{AB} = \dfrac{DE}{AD} = \dfrac{FG}{AF} = \dfrac{JK}{AJ}$ Each ratio is the *sine ratio* for $\angle A$ (sin A).

$\dfrac{AC}{AB} = \dfrac{AE}{AD} = \dfrac{AG}{AF} = \dfrac{AK}{AJ}$ Each ratio is the *cosine ratio* for $\angle A$ (cos A).

Definition *Trigonometric Ratios*

In a right $\triangle ABC$ with acute $\angle A$:

$\tan A = \dfrac{\text{length of side opposite } \angle A}{\text{length of side adjacent to } \angle A} = \dfrac{a}{b}$

$\sin A = \dfrac{\text{length of side opposite } \angle A}{\text{length of hypotenuse}} = \dfrac{a}{c}$

$\cos A = \dfrac{\text{length of side adjacent to } \angle A}{\text{length of hypotenuse}} = \dfrac{b}{c}$

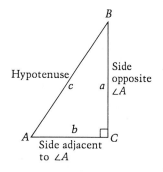

If an acute angle of one right triangle is equal to the corresponding angle of another right triangle, then the triangles are similar. So, for a given acute angle, each of the three trigonometric ratios is constant. This means that the value of the ratio depends only upon the size of the angle, as shown.

LESSON 8-5

Resources

Teaching Aid 1, protractor
Visual Aid 1, protractor
Teaching Aid 16, right triangles
Visual Aid 16, right triangles
Worksheet 8–5
Extension 8–5
Computer Activities 8–5

OBJECTIVE

Identify and evaluate the tangent, sine and cosine ratios for an acute angle of a right triangle.

TEACHING NOTES

Review the terms "opposite" and "adjacent." Have students do the following group activity.

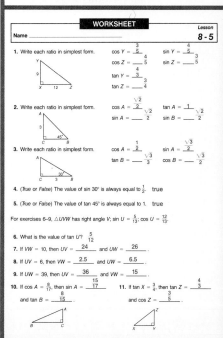

1. Draw a 40-degree angle using a protractor.

2. Draw several line segments perpendicular to one of the rays. Several right triangles are formed.

3. Measure the sides and angles. Complete a table like this:

	Length Opp. $\angle A$	Length Adj. $\angle A$	Hyp. Hyp.
1st $\triangle$			
2nd $\triangle$			
3rd $\triangle$			

	Opp. Hyp.	Adj. Hyp.	Opp. Adj.
1st $\triangle$			
2nd $\triangle$			
3rd $\triangle$			

Repeat using a different angle measure. What conclusion can you draw? Show that in each triangle the three trigonometric ratios of a given angle have constant value, which emphasizes that they are dependent only on the angle.

Example 1

Give the tangent, the sine, and the cosine for

a. $\angle P$.

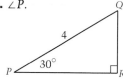

b. $\angle B$.

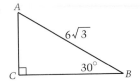

Solution

a. Since $\triangle PQR$ is a 30-60-90 triangle, $QR = 2$ and $PR = 2\sqrt{3}$.

$$\tan P = \frac{2}{2\sqrt{3}} = \frac{1}{\sqrt{3}} = \frac{\sqrt{3}}{3}$$

$$\sin P = \frac{2}{4} = \frac{1}{2}$$

$$\cos P = \frac{2\sqrt{3}}{4} = \frac{\sqrt{3}}{2}$$

b. Since $\triangle ABC$ is a 30-60-90 triangle, $AC = 3\sqrt{3}$ and $BC = 9$.

$$\tan B = \frac{3\sqrt{3}}{9} = \frac{\sqrt{3}}{3}$$

$$\sin B = \frac{3\sqrt{3}}{6\sqrt{3}} = \frac{1}{2}$$

$$\cos B = \frac{9}{6\sqrt{3}} = \frac{3}{2\sqrt{3}} = \frac{\sqrt{3}}{2}$$

Example 2

Compare the sines and the cosines of the acute angles in a right triangle. Then, give a generalization.

Solution

In $\triangle DEF$ with right $\angle F$, hypotenuse f, and legs d and e, $\sin D = \frac{d}{f}$, $\cos D = \frac{e}{f}$, $\sin E = \frac{e}{f}$, and $\cos E = \frac{d}{f}$. So $\sin D = \cos E$ and $\cos D = \sin E$. Since the acute angles in a right triangle are complementary, you can write this generalization: The sine of an acute angle equals the cosine of its complement.

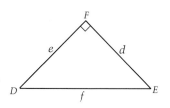

Example 3

a. Evaluate $(\sin X)^2 + (\cos X)^2$ in $\triangle XYZ$.

b. Evaluate $(\sin L)^2 + (\cos L)^2$ in $\triangle LMN$.

Solution

a. $\sin X = \frac{3}{5}$ and $\cos X = \frac{4}{5}$. Therefore, $(\sin X)^2 + (\cos X)^2 = \left(\frac{3}{5}\right)^2 + \left(\frac{4}{5}\right)^2 = \frac{9}{25} + \frac{16}{25} = 1$.

b. $\sin L = \frac{5}{13}$ and $\cos L = \frac{12}{13}$. Therefore, $\left(\sin L\right)^2 + (\cos L)^2 = \left(\frac{5}{13}\right)^2 + \left(\frac{12}{13}\right)^2 = \frac{25}{169} + \frac{144}{169} = 1$.

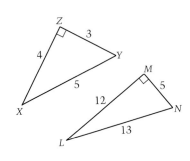

Example 3 gives two specific cases of Theorem 8-8, which states this relationship for all right triangles. Its proof is left to Exercise 24.

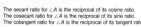

Theorem 8-9

In right △ABC with right ∠C, (sin A)² + (cos A)² = 1

Given Right $\triangle ABC$ with right $\angle C$

Prove $(\sin A)^2 + (\cos A)^2 = 1$

Plan for Proof Use the Pythagorean Theorem to show $a^2 + b^2 = c^2$. Divide both sides of the equation by c^2. Then use the definition of sine and cosine.

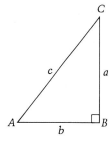

Checking for Understanding

Name each of the following parts of right $\triangle QRP$.

1. Side opposite $\angle P$ $\overline{QR}$
2. Side opposite $\angle Q$ $\overline{PR}$
3. Side adjacent to $\angle P$ $\overline{PR}$
4. Side adjacent to $\angle Q$ $\overline{QR}$

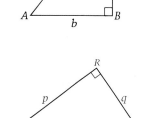

Name each trigonometric ratio for $\angle P$.

5. $\dfrac{p}{r}$ sine
6. $\dfrac{q}{r}$ cosine
7. $\dfrac{p}{q}$ tangent

8. What are the tangent, sine, and cosine for $\angle Q$? $\dfrac{q}{p}, \dfrac{q}{r}, \dfrac{p}{r}$

If $p = 24$ and $q = 7$, find

9. $\cos Q$. $\dfrac{24}{25}$
10. $\sin P$. $\dfrac{24}{25}$
11. $\tan Q$. $\dfrac{7}{24}$

12. Write two statements that Theorem 8-8 implies about $\triangle QRP$.
$(\sin Q)^2 + (\cos Q)^2 = 1$ and $(\sin P)^2 + (\cos P)^2 = 1$

Written Exercises

Set A Write each ratio in simplest form.

1. $\tan X$ $\dfrac{3}{4}$
2. $\sin X$ $\dfrac{3}{5}$
3. $\cos X$ $\dfrac{4}{5}$
4. $\tan Y$ $\dfrac{4}{3}$
5. $\sin Y$ $\dfrac{4}{5}$
6. $\cos Y$ $\dfrac{3}{5}$

In right $\triangle ABC$, name the trigonometric ratio represented for the given angle.

7. $\dfrac{15}{8}$; $\angle A$ $\tan A$
8. $\dfrac{15}{17}$; $\angle A$ $\sin A$
9. $\dfrac{8}{17}$; $\angle A$ $\cos A$
10. $\dfrac{8}{15}$; $\angle B$ $\tan B$
11. $\dfrac{8}{17}$; $\angle B$ $\sin B$
12. $\dfrac{15}{17}$; $\angle B$ $\cos B$

13. Use the dimensions of triangles XYZ and ABC in Exercises 1–12 to verify Theorem 8-8.

Draw square $PQRS$ with diagonal $\overline{PR}$ and $PQ = 4$ cm.

14. Find the length of $\overline{PR}$. $4\sqrt{2}$

15. Find sin 45°, cos 45°, and tan 45°. $\dfrac{\sqrt{2}}{2}; \dfrac{\sqrt{2}}{2}$; and 1

Additional Examples

Example 1

Give the tangent, sine and cosine for $\angle X$ and $\angle G$. For both, tan = $\dfrac{\sqrt{3}}{1}$, sin = $\dfrac{\sqrt{3}}{2}$ and cos = $\dfrac{1}{2}$.

Example 2

(a) In $\triangle CAW$, find the values of sin C, cos C, sin A and cos A. $\dfrac{5}{13}, \dfrac{12}{13}, \dfrac{12}{13}, \dfrac{5}{13}$

(b) Make a conjecture. sin of an $\angle$ = cos of its complement

Example 3
In $\triangle CAW$, find the value of (sin C)² + (cos C)². 1

Error Analysis Students often confuse the equations for the sine, cosine and tangent ratios. Have them use a memory trick like "soh, cah, toa" or have them make up a sentence or phrases to help them remember the correct ratios.

ANSWERS

Written Exercises

13. For $\triangle XYZ$, $(\sin X)^2 + (\cos X)^2 = \left(\frac{15}{25}\right)^2 + \left(\frac{20}{25}\right)^2 = \left(\frac{3}{5}\right)^2 + \left(\frac{4}{5}\right)^2 = \frac{9}{25} + \frac{16}{25} = 1$ and $(\sin Y)^2 + (\cos Y)^2 = \left(\frac{20}{25}\right)^2 + \left(\frac{15}{25}\right)^2 = 1$. For $\triangle ABC$, $(\sin A)^2 + (\cos A)^2 = \left(\frac{15}{17}\right)^2 + \left(\frac{8}{17}\right)^2 = \frac{225}{289} + \frac{64}{289} = \frac{289}{289} = 1$ and $(\sin B)^2 + (\cos B)^2 = \left(\frac{8}{17}\right)^2 + \left(\frac{15}{17}\right)^2 = 1$.

22 c. For $\triangle XYZ$, $(\tan X)(\tan Y) =$ $\left(\frac{15}{20}\right)\left(\frac{20}{15}\right) = \frac{300}{300} = 1$. For $\triangle ABC$, $(\tan A)(\tan B) = \left(\frac{15}{8}\right)\left(\frac{8}{15}\right) = \frac{120}{120} = 1$.

23 c. For $\triangle XYZ$, $\frac{\sin X}{\cos X} = \frac{\left(\frac{15}{25}\right)}{\left(\frac{20}{25}\right)} = \frac{15}{20} =$

$\tan X$ and $\frac{\sin Y}{\cos Y} = \frac{\left(\frac{20}{25}\right)}{\left(\frac{15}{25}\right)} = \frac{20}{15} = \tan Y$.

For $\triangle ABC$, $\frac{\sin A}{\cos A} = \frac{\left(\frac{15}{17}\right)}{\left(\frac{8}{17}\right)} = \frac{15}{8} = \tan A$

and $\frac{\sin B}{\cos B} = \frac{\left(\frac{8}{17}\right)}{\left(\frac{15}{17}\right)} = \frac{8}{15} = \tan B$.

24. Proof: 1. Rt. $\triangle ABC$ has rt. $\angle C$. (Given) 2. $a^2 + b^2 = c^2$ (Pythagorean Thm. [1]) 3. $\frac{a^2}{c^2} + \frac{b^2}{c^2} = \frac{c^2}{c^2}$ (Mult. Prop. [2]) 4. $\left(\frac{a}{c}\right)^2 + \left(\frac{b}{c}\right)^2 = 1$ (Algebra [3]) 5. $\sin A = \frac{a}{c}$ (Def. of sine [1]) 6. $\cos A = \frac{b}{c}$ (Def. of cosine [1]) 7. $(\sin A)^2 + (\cos A)^2 = 1$ (Substitution Prop. [4, 5, 6])

25.

In a right $\triangle ABC$ with right $\angle C$, $(\tan A)(\tan B) = 1$. Given: Rt. $\triangle ABC$ with right $\angle C$ Prove: $(\tan A)(\tan B) = 1$ Proof: 1. Rt. $\triangle ABC$ with rt. $\angle C$ (Given) 2. $\tan A = \frac{a}{b}$ and $\tan B = \frac{b}{a}$ (Def. of tangent [1]) 3. $(\tan A)(\tan B) = \left(\frac{a}{b}\right)\left(\frac{b}{a}\right) = 1$ (Mult. Prop. [2])

26.

In right $\triangle ABC$ with right $\angle C$, $\frac{\sin A}{\cos A} = \tan A$. Given: Rt. $\triangle ABC$ with right $\angle C$ Prove: $\frac{\sin A}{\cos A} = \tan A$ 1. Rt. $\triangle ABC$ with rt. $\angle C$ (Given) 2. $\sin A = \frac{a}{c}$ (Def. of sine [1]) 3. $\cos A = \frac{b}{c}$ (Def. of cosine [1]) 4. $\frac{\sin A}{\cos A} =$ $\frac{\left(\frac{a}{c}\right)}{\left(\frac{b}{c}\right)} = \frac{a}{b}$ (Mult. Prop. [2, 3]) 5. $\tan A = \frac{a}{b}$ (Def. of tangent [1]) 6. $\frac{\sin A}{\cos A} = \tan A$ (Substitution Prop. [4, 5])

Set B   Given: $\triangle UVW$ with right $\angle W$; $\sin U = \frac{3}{5}$; $\cos U = \frac{4}{5}$

16. What is the value of $\tan U$? $\frac{3}{4}$

17. If $VW = 9$, then $UW =$ _?_ and $UV =$ _?_. 12; 15

18. If $UW = 6$, then $VW =$ _?_ and $UV =$ _?_. 4.5; 7.5

Given: Right $\triangle ABC$ with vertices $A(1, 2)$, $B(5, 6)$, and $C(5, 2)$ $AC = 4$; $BC = 4$; $AB = 4\sqrt{2}$

19. Find $\sin A$. $\frac{\sqrt{2}}{2}$ **20.** Find $\tan B$. 1   **19-20.**

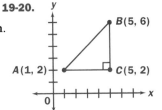

Draw $\triangle ABC$ with right $\angle C$, $AC = 7$ cm, and $BC = 24$ cm.

21. How long is the hypotenuse? 25 cm

22. a. Evaluate $\tan A$ and $\tan B$. $\tan A = \frac{24}{7}$; $\tan B = \frac{7}{24}$

21.

   b. Write an equation to show a relationship between $\tan A$ and $\tan B$. $(\tan A)(\tan B) = 1$

   c. Show that the equation in b is also true for $\tan X$ and $\tan Y$ in Exercises 1 and 4.

23. a. Evaluate $\frac{\sin A}{\cos A}$ and $\frac{\sin B}{\cos B}$. $\frac{24}{7}$, $\frac{7}{24}$

   b. What general statement can you make about $\frac{\sin A}{\cos A}$ and $\frac{\sin B}{\cos B}$? $\frac{\sin A}{\cos A} = \tan A$; $\frac{\sin B}{\cos B} = \tan B$

   c. Check your statement for the triangles in Exercises 1–6.

Set C   **24.** Prove Theorem 8-9.

25. State and prove a theorem based on your conjecture in Exercise 22b.

26. State and prove a theorem based on your conjecture in Exercise 23b.

▲ Review   **27.** The foot of a 20-foot ladder is 8 feet from a house. The top of the ladder just reaches the gutters. How high off the ground are the gutters? $4\sqrt{21} \approx 18.33$ ft.

28. How high will a 22-foot ladder reach if the ladder and the level ground meet to form a 60° angle? 19 ft.

29. Find the perimeter of a square with 16-in. diagonal. $32\sqrt{2}$

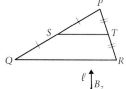

30. In $\square ABCD$, $\overline{AC}$ and $\overline{BD}$ intersect at W, $AW = 4x + 3$, and $AC = 9x - 3$. Find AC. 78

31. In $\triangle PQR$, $m\angle PST = \underline{\ ?\ }$ and $ST = \underline{\ ?\ }$.
$$\frac{}{m\angle PQR} \qquad \frac{1}{2}QR$$

Thinking Ahead At the bottom of a sheet of paper, draw $AC = 10$ cm and ℓ perpendicular to $\overline{AC}$ at C. Locate $B_1, B_2, \ldots, B_7$, so that $m\angle CAB_1 = 10$, $m\angle CAB_2 = 20$, $\ldots$, $m\angle CAB_7 = 70$.

32. Measure $\overline{CB}_1, \overline{CB}_2, \ldots, \overline{CB}_7$.

33. Find $\tan \angle CAB_1$, $\tan \angle CAB_2$, $\ldots$, $\tan \angle CAB_7$.

34. How does increasing the measure of the angle at A affect the tangent ratio? The tangent ratio increases.

35. If $AC = 20$ cm, how would the tangent ratios be affected? The tangent values for angles with measures of 10, 20, ... 70 would remain the same.

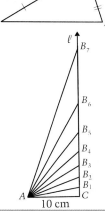

Computer Activities: Drawing and Measuring

Draw $\overline{AB}$ with length equal to some whole number. Draw a line perpendicular to $\overline{AB}$ at B. Locate seven points on the perpendicular so that angles are formed with measures of $10, 20, \ldots, 70$. Measure the distance from each point on the perpendicular to B.

1. Find the sine of each angle formed with vertex A.

2. How does increasing the measure of the angle at A affect the sine ratio?

3. Find the cosine of each angle formed with vertex A.

4. How does increasing the measure on the angle at A affect the cosine ratio?

1. 0.17; 0.34; 0.50; 0.64; 0.77; 0.87; 0.94
2. Increase the sine ratio
3. 0.98; 0.94; 0.87; 0.77; 0.64; 0.50; 0.34
4. Decreases the cosine ratio.

Challenge

A butterfly and a caterpillar are in a cage as shown. If the butterfly were to fly in a direct path to escape through the opening, what is the shortest path? How long is it? What is the shortest path the caterpillar could take to escape from the cage?

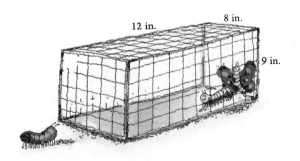

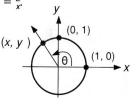

FOLLOW-UP

More Practice
• Worksheet 8–5

Extension

Challenge better students to investigate the sine, cosine and tangent of angles greater than 90. Introduce the following coordinate definitions: $\sin \theta = y$, $\cos \theta = x$, $\tan \theta = \frac{y}{x}$.

Show that these definitions are equivalent to the right triangle definitions for acute angles. Students can then define the sine, cosine or tangent of virtually any angle.
• **Extension 8–5**

Computers

The computer activity in the pupil's book can be completed using *GeoDraw*.

Note: The activity can be completed using *The Geometric Supposer: Triangles* if the activity is modified so that students draw a series of seven triangles using the "your own" and "angle/side/angle" options for each triangle, and by measuring and finding the sine and cosine before drawing a new triangle. In *GeoDraw*, the seven segments to be measured can be closely approximated, but the student may not be able to place the points along the perpendicular at the precise intersection of the angle leg and the perpendicular.
• **Computer Activities 8–5**

Warm-Up Review

1. Define sine ratio. Opp./Hyp.
2. Define cosine ratio. Adj./Hyp.
3. Define tangent ratio. Opp./Adj.
4. Express the sine of the smallest angle in a 3-4-5 right triangle as a decimal. .6
5. Express the cosine of 60 degrees as a decimal. .5

Warm-Up Review

1. Define sine ratio. Opp./Hyp.
2. Define cosine ratio. Adj./Hyp.
3. Define tangent ratio. Opp./Adj.
4. Express the sine of the smallest angle in a 3-4-5 right triangle as a decimal. .6
5. Express the cosine of 60 degrees as a decimal. .5

LESSON 8–6

Resources

Teaching Aid 19, trigonometric
    ratios table
Visual Aid 19, trigonometric
    ratios table
Worksheet 8–6
Extension 8–6
Computer Worksheet 8–6

OBJECTIVE

Use a table of trigonometric ratios
to find the measure of an angle or
a ratio for a given angle.

TEACHING NOTES

Have students draw a right triangle with an angle of 25 degrees
and measure the lengths of the

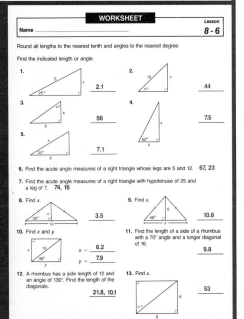

8-6 Trigonometric Ratios

Joan Mesa is an engineer with the state highway department.
She uses trigonometric ratios to determine the measures of
angles and distances. The values of these trigonometric ratios
can be found by using a calculator or tables like the one on
page 617. Each ratio is expressed as a decimal. Since many of
these ratios involve irrational numbers, most of the decimals
are approximations. Portions of the table are shown at the right
of Examples 1 and 2.

Example 1
Find tan 23°.

Solution
On most calculators, this key sequence gives tan 23°: 23 [TAN]
The display, 0.4244748, can be rounded to 0.4245.

To use a table, find the angle measure in the first column. In
the same row and in the second column is an approximate
value of tan 23°. Thus, tan 23° ≈ 0.4245.

From this portion of the table, you can see that sin 20° ≈
0.3420 and cos 25° ≈ 0.9063.

The table can also be used to find the measure of an angle to
the nearest degree, given one of its trigonometric ratios.

Example 2
If sin A ≈ 0.8746, find $m\angle A$.

Solution
First find 0.8746 in the "sin A" column. Then in the same
row, read the entry in the first column which shows $m\angle A$ ≈ 61.

Example 3
Find the measure of the angle formed by the sun's rays with
the ground when a 4-meter pole casts a 3-meter shadow.

Solution
Draw a diagram; label the angle $\angle A$. Then tan $A = \frac{4}{3}$ ≈ 1.3333.

This value is not in the table, but it lies between 1.3270 and
1.3764, which correspond to tan 53° and tan 54°, respectively.
Since 1.3333 is closer to 1.3270, the measure of the angle
formed by the sun's rays and the ground is about 53°.

$m\angle A$ in degrees	tan A	sin A	cos A
20	.3640	.3420	.9397
21	.3839	.3584	.9336
22	.4040	.3746	.9272
23	.4245	.3907	.9205
24	.4452	.4067	.9135
25	.4663	.4226	.9063
26	.4877	.4384	.8988
⋮	⋮	⋮	⋮
60	1.7321	.8660	.5000
61	1.8040	.8746	.4848
62	1.8807	.8829	.4695
63	1.9626	.8910	.4540
64	2.0503	.8988	.4384
65	2.1445	.9063	.4226
66	2.2460	.9135	.4067

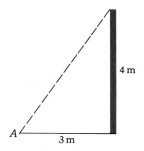

Assignment Guide

Basic: 1–15, 23–29
Average: 1–19, 23–29
Extended: 1–29

Checking for Understanding

Use the table on page 617.

1. As you read down the column entitled $m\angle A$, do the values increase or decrease? Increase

2. As $m\angle A$ increases, does sin A increase or decrease? Increase

3. As $m\angle A$ increases, does tan A increase or decrease? Increase

4. As $m\angle A$ increases, does cos A increase or decrease? Decrease

5. For what values of $\angle A$ does sin A = cos A? 45

6. For what values of $\angle A$ is sin A > cos A? sin A < cos A?

7. For what values of $\angle A$ is tan A = 1? tan A > 1? tan A < 1?

8. For what values of $\angle A$ is sin A > 1? cos A > 1?

9. For what values of $\angle A$ and $\angle B$ does sin A = cos B? How are these angles related?

6. $m\angle A>45$; $m\angle A<45$
7. 45; $m\angle A>45$; $m\angle A<45$
8. None; None
9. All values of A and B where A and B are complementary $\angle$s.

Written Exercises

For exercises in this lesson, use a calculator or the table on page 617 as needed.

Set A Give a decimal value for each ratio.

1. sin 29° 0.4848   **2.** tan 35° 0.7002   **3.** cos 81° 0.1564

4. sin 73° 0.9563   **5.** cos 42° 0.7431   **6.** tan 54° 1.3764

Find $m\angle A$ to the nearest degree.

7. sin A ≈ 0.1564 9   **8.** cos A ≈ 0.6157 52

9. tan A ≈ 2.9042 71   **10.** sin A ≈ 0.8988 64

11. cos A ≈ 0.8910 27   **12.** tan A ≈ 0.8098 39

Determine, to the nearest degree, the measures of the acute angles of a right triangle with legs of length

13. 7 and 24.   **14.** 8 and 15.   **15.** 9 and 40.
    16° and 74°   28° and 62°   13° and 77°

Set B **16.** If the base of an isosceles triangle has length 16 and the measure of the vertex angle is 72, what is the length of each leg? 13.6

17. If the length of each leg of an isosceles triangle is 24 and a base angle has measure 55, how long is the base? 27.6

legs. Find tan 25 by dividing. Point out that this process is tedious and not accurate enough at times. Then introduce the trigonometric table and have students practice using it.

If students have scientific **calculators**, explain when to use the inverse key.

Because we are primarily concerned with the concept at this point, have students find angles to the nearest degree.

Have students practice interpolation as shown in **Example 3**.

Additional Examples

Example 1
Use the trigonometric table to find sin 62°. 0.8829

Example 2
If cos X = .9135, find $m\angle X$. 24

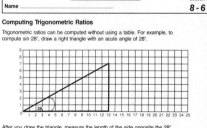

Example 3

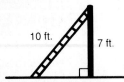

10 ft.   7 ft.

If a 10-foot ladder leans against the top of a 7-foot wall, find the angle the ladder makes with the ground. 44

Error Analysis The most common error at this level is using the wrong column (e.g., tan instead of sin). Encourage students to consult the column heading every time the table is used.

FOLLOW-UP

More Practice

• Worksheet 8-6

Extension

Have students study the sine and cosine columns of the trigonometric table. Look at the sine of 1, 2, 3 and so on and compare with the cosine of 89, 88, 87 and so on. What do you notice? They are the same.

• Extension 8-6

Computers

• Computer Worksheet 8-6

---

18. How tall is the tree? 20.1 m **19.** How wide is the lake? 23.8 m

76°

5 m

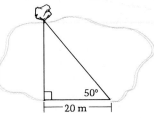

50°

20 m

Set C **20.** Find the measures of the angles of $\triangle PQR$ to the nearest degree if its vertices are $P(1, 9)$, $Q(6, 1)$, and $R(1, 1)$. $m\angle R = 90$; $m\angle P \approx 32$; $m\angle Q \approx 58$

21. Prove that $\tan A > \sin A$ for every $\angle A$. Why does the table show some values for which $\tan A = \sin A$?

22. Prove that $\sin A > \cos A$ for $m\angle A > 45$ and that $\sin A < \cos A$ for $m\angle A < 45$.

▲ **Review** **23.** Give the ratio for $\tan A$. $\frac{a}{b}$

24. Give the ratio for $\sin A$. $\frac{a}{c}$

25. Is a 10-foot board long enough to make two diagonal braces for the back of a shelving unit that is 2 feet wide and 4 feet tall? Yes

26. Give a geometric description of the number-line graph of $x \leq -2$ or $x \geq 7$.

27. Explain the similarities and differences between the SAS Congruence Postulate and the SAS Similarity Theorem.

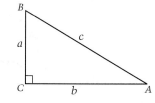

B
a
c
C b A

≡ **Thinking Ahead** Rose O'Sharon, a landscape architect, is planning several gardens for a shopping mall. One flower bed has the shape of a regular polygon with 18 sides. To position the stakes at the vertices of the polygon, Rose first places a stake at point C, the center of the polygon. Then she uses a rope 2.5 m long to measure the distance from C to each vertex.

28. How can Rose find the measures of the angles of each triangle formed?

29. Explain how Rose can use trigonometry to determine the distance between the stakes for the vertices of the polygon. Use the diagram and equations $\sin 10° = \frac{AD}{2.5}$ and $2AD = AD$; Thus, $AB = 0.868$ m

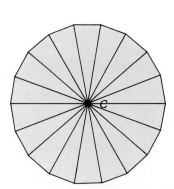

Assignment Guide

Basic: 1–15, 23–29
Average: 1–19, 23–29
Extended: 1–29

Checking for Understanding
Use the table on page 617.

1. As you read down the column entitled $m\angle A$, do the values increase or decrease? **Increase**

2. As $m\angle A$ increases, does sin A increase or decrease? **Increase**

3. As $m\angle A$ increases, does tan A increase or decrease? **Increase**

4. As $m\angle A$ increases, does cos A increase or decrease? **Decrease**

5. For what values of $\angle A$ does sin A = cos A? **45**

6. For what values of $\angle A$ is sin A > cos A? sin A < cos A?

7. For what values of $\angle A$ is tan A = 1? tan A > 1? tan A < 1?

8. For what values of $\angle A$ is sin A > 1? cos A > 1?

9. For what values of $\angle A$ and $\angle B$ does sin A = cos B? How are these angles related?

6. $m\angle A{>}45;\ m\angle A{<}45$
7. 45; $m\angle A{>}45;\ m\angle A{<}45$
8. None; None
9. All values of A and B where A and B are complementary $\angle$s.

Written Exercises
For exercises in this lesson, use a calculator or the table on page 617 as needed.

Set A Give a decimal value for each ratio.

1. sin 29° **0.4848**   **2.** tan 35° **0.7002**   **3.** cos 81° **0.1564**

4. sin 73° **0.9563**   **5.** cos 42° **0.7431**   **6.** tan 54° **1.3764**

Find $m\angle A$ to the nearest degree.

7. sin A ≈ 0.1564 **9**   **8.** cos A ≈ 0.6157 **52**

9. tan A ≈ 2.9042 **71**   **10.** sin A ≈ 0.8988 **64**

11. cos A ≈ 0.8910 **27**   **12.** tan A ≈ 0.8098 **39**

Determine, to the nearest degree, the measures of the acute angles of a right triangle with legs of length

13. 7 and 24.   **14.** 8 and 15.   **15.** 9 and 40.
   16° and 74°   28° and 62°   13° and 77°

Set B **16.** If the base of an isosceles triangle has length 16 and the measure of the vertex angle is 72, what is the length of each leg? **13.6**

17. If the length of each leg of an isosceles triangle is 24 and a base angle has measure 55, how long is the base? **27.6**

legs. Find tan 25 by dividing. Point out that this process is tedious and not accurate enough at times. Then introduce the trigonometric table and have students practice using it.

If students have scientific **calculators**, explain when to use the inverse key.

Because we are primarily concerned with the concept at this point, have students find angles to the nearest degree.

Have students practice interpolation as shown in **Example 3**.

Additional Examples

Example 1
Use the trigonometric table to find sin 62°. **0.8829**

Example 2
If cos X = .9135, find $m\angle X$. **24**

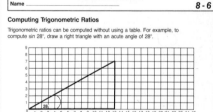

Example 3

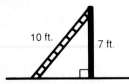

10 ft. 7 ft.

If a 10-foot ladder leans against the top of a 7-foot wall, find the angle the ladder makes with the ground. 44

Error Analysis The most common error at this level is using the wrong column (e.g., tan instead of sin). Encourage students to consult the column heading every time the table is used.

18. How tall is the tree? **19.** How wide is the lake? 23.8 m

20.1 m

76°

5 m

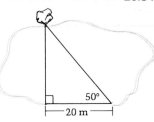

50°

20 m

Set C **20.** Find the measures of the angles of $\triangle PQR$ to the nearest degree if its vertices are $P(1, 9)$, $Q(6, 1)$, and $R(1, 1)$. $m\angle R = 90$; $m\angle P \approx 32$; $m\angle Q \approx 58$

21. Prove that $\tan A > \sin A$ for every $\angle A$. Why does the table show some values for which $\tan A = \sin A$?

22. Prove that $\sin A > \cos A$ for $m\angle A > 45$ and that $\sin A < \cos A$ for $m\angle A < 45$.

▲ Review **23.** Give the ratio for $\tan A$. $\frac{a}{b}$

24. Give the ratio for $\sin A$. $\frac{a}{c}$

25. Is a 10-foot board long enough to make two diagonal braces for the back of a shelving unit that is 2 feet wide and 4 feet tall? Yes

26. Give a geometric description of the number-line graph of $x \le -2$ or $x \ge 7$.

27. Explain the similarities and differences between the SAS Congruence Postulate and the SAS Similarity Theorem.

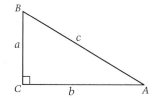

B

a   c

C   b   A

Thinking Ahead Rose O'Sharon, a landscape architect, is planning several gardens for a shopping mall. One flower bed has the shape of a regular polygon with 18 sides. To position the stakes at the vertices of the polygon, Rose first places a stake at point C, the center of the polygon. Then she uses a rope 2.5 m long to measure the distance from C to each vertex.

28. How can Rose find the measures of the angles of each triangle formed?

29. Explain how Rose can use trigonometry to determine the distance between the stakes for the vertices of the polygon. Use the diagram and equations $\sin 10° = \frac{AD}{2.5}$ and $2AD = AD$; Thus, $AB = 0.868$ m

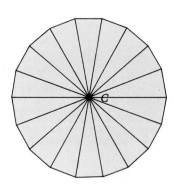

Warm-Up Review

1. Use the trigonometric table to find tan 27°. .5095
2. If cos A = .6018, find m∠A. 53
3. Which trigonometric ratio involves only the legs of a right triangle? Tangent
4. What is the ratio of the opposite leg to the hypotenuse? Sine
5. What is the ratio of the adjacent leg to the hypotenuse? Cosine

8-7 Applications of Trigonometric Ratios

In this chapter you have learned how to solve some practical problems by using the Pythagorean Theorem. Trigonometric ratios provide another way to solve practical problems involving indirect measurement and the angles defined here.

The angle between a horizontal line and the line of sight to a point above the observer is the *angle of elevation*.
The angle between a horizontal line and the line of sight to a point below the observer is the *angle of depression*.

In the diagram at the right, ∠BAC is an angle of depression and ∠ACD is an angle of elevation. Since the horizontal lines are parallel lines cut by a transversal, ∠BAC and ∠ACD are alternate interior angles. Therefore, the angle of depression and the angle of elevation have equal measures.

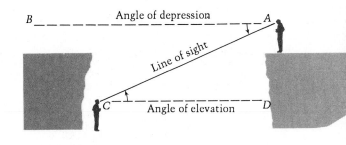

Example 1
An observer stands atop a building 25 m above the ground and the angle of depression to a car on the ground has measure of 27. About how far is the car from the building?

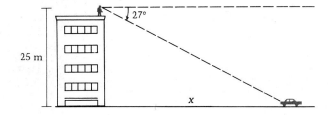

Solution
Since the angles of depression and elevation have equal measure, m∠A = 27. Since you want to find the length of the side adjacent to ∠A and you know the length of the side opposite ∠A and m∠A, use the tangent ratio.

$$\tan 27° = \frac{25}{x}$$
$$0.5095 \approx \frac{25}{x}$$
$$x \approx \frac{25}{0.5095} \approx 49 \text{ m}$$

LESSON 8-7

Resources

Teaching Aid 19, trigonometric ratios table
Visual Aid 19, trigonometric ratios table
Worksheet 8-7
Extension 8-7
Algebra Review 8
Chapter 8 Test, Form I
Chapter 8 Test, Form II
Chapter 8 Test, Form III

OBJECTIVE

Use the trigonometric ratios to solve indirect measurement problems.

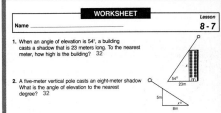

WORKSHEET

Name _____ Lesson 8-7

1. When an angle of elevation is 54°, a building casts a shadow that is 23 meters long. To the nearest meter, how high is the building? 32

2. A five-meter vertical pole casts an eight-meter shadow. What is the angle of elevation to the nearest degree? 32

3. A kite is flying at an angle of 42° with the ground. All 70 meters of string have been let out. Ignoring the sag in the string, find the height of the kite to the nearest 10 meters. 50 m

4. Martha is 66 inches tall and her daughter Heidi is 33 inches tall. Who casts the longer shadow, Martha when the sun is 80° above the horizon, or Heidi when the sun is 40° above the horizon? By how much? Heidi; 27.7 in.

5. A truck drives up a 30-meter incline. The angle that the truck drives up is 23°. To the nearest meter, how high (vertically) did the truck rise? 12 m

6. The steepness of a hill is sometimes measured by the grade. A grade of 1: 5 means the hill rises one unit for every 5 horizontal units.

   a. For a grade of 1: 5, what is the measure of angle A, the angle the hill makes with the horizontal? 11

   b. The force of gravity pulling an object down the hill is its weight multiplied by the sine of ∠A. On a 1: 5 grade, what is the force on a 3000-pound car? 572 lb.

7. To find the distance from point A on the shore of a lake to point B on an island in the lake, surveyors locate point P with m∠PAB = 62 and m∠APB = 28. If PA = 350 m, find AB. 164 m

8. Find the length of the shortest diagonal of a regular hexagon with side 10. 10√3 or 17.3

TEACHING NOTES

Introduce the terms "angle of depression" and "angle of elevation." Then have students solve a problem as a **group activity**. Choose an inaccessible object such as a tall flagpole.
1. Measure a given distance from the base.
2. Use a large protractor to measure the angle between the line of sight to the top and the horizontal line.
3. Use the tangent ratio to find the height.
   Examples 1 and **2** can then be used to illustrate other situations.

ANSWERS

Checking for Understanding

1. angle of elevation; opp. side and adj. side; $\tan 50° = \frac{x}{7}$; $x \approx 8.3$

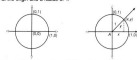
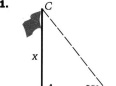

Example 2

A ladder mounted on a fire truck is 6 feet above the ground. If the maximum length of the ladder is 120 feet and the measure of the largest angle that the ladder can safely make with the truck is 75, about how high will it reach?

120 ft.

x

75°

6 ft.

Solution

Since you want to find the length of the side opposite the given angle and you know the hypotenuse and the measure of the angle, use the sine ratio.

$$\sin 75° = \frac{x}{120}$$
$$0.9659 \approx \frac{x}{120}$$
$$x \approx (0.9659)(120) \approx 115.9$$

Therefore, $h \approx 115.9 + 6 \approx 121.9$. The ladder can reach a point about 122 feet above the ground.

Checking for Understanding

First identify the given angle as either an angle of depression or an angle of elevation. Then identify the unknown distance and the given distance with respect to a known angle. Finally, use a trigonometric ratio to find *x*.

1.   2.   3.

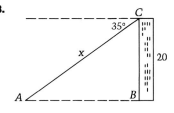

Written Exercises

Give the lengths to the nearest tenth of a unit and the angle measures to the nearest degree.

57.4 ft.   28.6 m

Set A   **1.** How high is the kite?   **2.** How wide is the river?

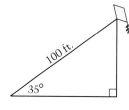

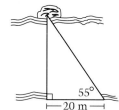

3. How tall is the building? **364 m**

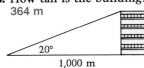

20°

1,000 m

4. How high is the hill? **321.4 ft.**

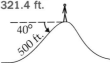

40°

500 ft.

5. How far up will the ladder reach? **11.3 m**

12 m

70°

6. What is the depth of the submarine? **206.0 m**

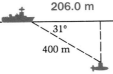

31°

400 m

7. How tall is the San Jacinto Monument? **571.5 ft.**

8. A rock dropped 182 feet from the top of the Leaning Tower of Pisa falls to a point 14 feet from its base. What angle does the tower make with the ground? **86°**

85°

182 ft.

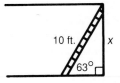

14 ft.

Set B

9. A mine shaft is 300 meters deep and makes an angle of 65° with the ground. How long is the shaft? **331 m**

65°

300 m

10. A 90-foot escalator rises 28 feet vertically. Find the angle that the escalator makes with the lower level. **18°**

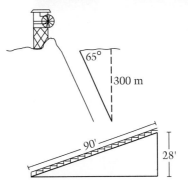

90'

28'

11. The angles of depression to the near and far banks of a river measure 49 and 11, respectively. If the observer is 6 feet tall, how wide is the river? **25.7 ft.**

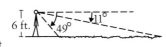

6 ft.

49°

11°

Additional Examples

Example 1

From the top of a 100-foot cliff at the shore, the angle of depression to a ship on the water is 32 degrees. About how far is the ship from shore? **160 ft.**

32°

100 ft.

x

Example 2

When a 10-foot ladder is pushed so that its top is in the corner between a wall and the ceiling, it makes an angle of 63 degrees with the floor. How tall is the wall? **8.9 ft.**

10 ft.

x

63°

Error Analysis Students often use the given angle measure to solve a problem when they should use the complement of the given angle. Stress the definitions of angle of depression and angle of elevation and point out that the angle adjacent to the angle of depression or elevation is its complement. Diagrams also help clarify the angle measure needed.

ANSWERS

Written Exercises

14.

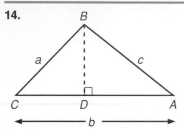

Proof: 1. Acute △ABC with sides of lengths a, b and c (Given) 2. Draw $\overline{BD} \perp \overline{AC}$ (Through a pt. not on a given line, there is exactly 1 line ⊥ to the given line.) 3. ∠BDA and ∠BDC are rt. ∠s. (2 ⊥ lines form 4 rt. ∠s [2]) 4. △s BDA and BDC are rt. △s (Def. of rt. △ [3]) 5. b = AD + DC (Def. of between) 6. AD = b − CD (Add. Prop. [5]) 7. $c^2 = BD^2 + AD^2$ and $a^2 = BD^2 + CD^2$ (Pythagorean Thm. [3, 4]) 8. $c^2 = BD^2 + (b − CD)^2 = BD^2 + b^2 − 2b(CD) + CD^2$ (Substitution Prop. [6, 7]) 9. $BD^2 = a^2 − CD^2$ (Add. Prop. [7]) 10. $c^2 = a^2 − CD^2 + b^2 − 2b(CD) + CD^2$ (Substitution Prop. [8, 9]) 11. cos $C = \frac{CD}{a}$ (Def. of cosine [1, 4]) 12. a (cos C) = CD (Mult. Prop. [11]) 13. $c^2 = a^2 + b^2 − 2ab$ (cos C) (Substitution Prop. [10, 12])

FOLLOW-UP

More Practice

• Worksheet 8–7

Extension

Have students draw △ABC so that m∠C = 90 and ask the following questions.
1. What is the relationship between a, b and c? $a^2 + b^2 = c^2$
2. If $c^2 = a^2 + b^2 − 2ab$(cos C), what must 2ab(cos C) equal? zero
3. What is the value of cos 90? zero
• Extension 8–7

---

12. Because of the pitch of the roof, a chest that is 5 ft. high must be placed as shown. What is the measure of the angle formed by the roof and the floor? **68°**

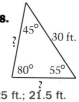

13. A car is driven up a slope of 6° for 150 meters and it is driven another 100 meters at a slope of 9°. How far has the car climbed vertically? **31.32 m**

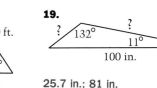

Set C Given: △ABC is an acute triangle with sides of length a, b, and c.

14. Prove: $c^2 = a^2 + b^2 − 2ab(\cos C)$

15. Prove: $\frac{a}{c} = \frac{\sin A}{\sin C}$

Given: △ABC with obtuse ∠C and sides with lengths of a, b, and c

16. Prove: $c^2 = a^2 + b^2 + 2ab((\cos (180 − C))$, where C represents m∠C

17. Prove: $\frac{a}{c} = \frac{\sin A}{\sin (180 − C)}$, where C represents m∠C

Use the formulas in Exercises 15 and 17 to find the missing length in each triangle. Then use the formulas in Exercises 14 and 16 to check your answers.

18.
25 ft.; 21.5 ft.

19.
25.7 in.; 81 in.

▲ **Review** Use a calculator or the table on page 617 as needed.

20. sin 66° ≈ _?_ 0.9135

21. If tan A = 3.4874, then m∠A ≈ _?_. 74

22. cos P = _?_ $\frac{3}{5}$

23. Find the distance between E(4, −3) and H(−1, 7). $5\sqrt{5} ≈ 11.18$

24. On a map of Wyoming, a distance of 2 cm represents 15 miles. How many miles are represented by a distance of 7 cm? **52.5 miles**

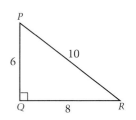

Progress Check

Lesson 8-5, page 357
Write each ratio in simplest form.

1. sin A $\frac{8}{17}$

2. cos A $\frac{15}{17}$

3. tan B $\frac{15}{18}$

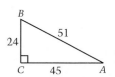

Name the trigonometric ratio represented for the given angle.

4. $\dfrac{m}{m+2}$; $\angle Q$ **tangent**

5. $\dfrac{m+2}{3m}$; $\angle P$ sine

6. $\dfrac{1}{3}$; $\angle Q$ sine

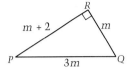

Lesson 8-6, page 362

Use a calculator or the table on page 617. Give the decimal value for each trigonometric ratio.

7. sin 30° **0.5000**   **8.** cos 45° **0.7071**   **9.** tan 50° **1.1918**

Find $m\angle A$ to the nearest degree.

10. sin $A \approx 0.5868$ **36°**   **11.** cos $A \approx 0.5868$ **54°**

12. tan $A \approx 0.5868$ **30°**   **13.** tan $A \approx 55.7$ **89°**

14. The vertex angle of an isosceles triangle is an 80° angle, and each leg measures 10 inches. How long is the base?

12.9 or 13 inches

Lesson 8-7, page 365

Use a calculator or the table on page 617.

15. How wide is the river? **112 ft.**   **16.** How wide is the flag? **6 ft.**

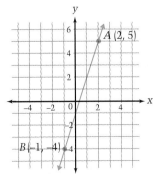

17. The angle of elevation from an observer on the roof of Building A to the roof of Building B is a 10° angle. The buildings are 1,500 feet apart. How much taller is B than A? **264 ft.**

Algebra Review: Writing Equations of Lines Given Two Points

Example

Write an equation of the line that contains $A(2, 5)$ and $B(-1, -4)$ in the form $y = mx + b$.

Solution

Find m, the slope of $\overleftrightarrow{AB}$. Then solve for b.

$$m = \frac{y_2 - y_1}{x_2 - x_1} = \frac{-4 - 5}{-1 - 2} = \frac{-9}{-3} = 3$$

$y = mx + b$

$5 = 3(2) + b$ *Substitute 3 for m and the coordinates of*

$b = -1$ *A (or B) for x and y. Use 3 for m and −1 for b.*

The equation of the line is $y = 3x - 1$.

Write an equation of the line that contains the given points.

1. $C(2, 3)$; $D(4, 7)$
  $y = 2x - 1$

2. $E(1, 1)$; $F(3, -1)$
  $y = -x + 2$

3. $D(-2, -3)$; $Q(5, 2)$
  $y = \dfrac{5}{7}x - \dfrac{11}{7}$

Chapter 8 Summary

Important Terms

30-60-90 triangle (346)

45-45-90 triangle (347)

Cosine ratio (cos) (357)

Geometric mean (332)

Pythagorean Theorem (338)

Sine ratio (sin) (357)

Tangent ratio (tan) (357)

Trigonometric ratios (357)

Important Ideas

1. The geometric mean of two positive real numbers a and b is equal to $\sqrt{ab}$. (332)

2. In a right triangle, the altitude to the hypotenuse
   a. divides the triangle into two triangles that are similar to each other and to the original triangle. (331)
   b. is the geometric mean of the lengths of the segments into which it separates the hypotenuse. (332)
   c. separates the hypotenuse into two segments such that each leg is the geometric mean of the lengths of the hypotenuse and the segment on the hypotenuse adjacent to that leg. (332)

3. A triangle is a right triangle if and only if the square of the length of the hypotenuse is equal to the sum of the squares of the lengths of the legs. (338, 339)

4. In a 30-60-90 triangle with a shorter leg of length b,
   a. the length of the hypotenuse is $2b$, and
   b. the length of the longer leg is $b\sqrt{3}$. (346)

5. In a 45-45-90 triangle with legs of length a, the length of the hypotenuse is $a\sqrt{2}$. (347)

6. The trigonometric ratios in right $\triangle ABC$ with acute $\angle A$ are
   a. $\tan A = \dfrac{\text{length of side opposite } \angle A}{\text{length of side adjacent to } \angle A} = \dfrac{a}{b}$;
   b. $\sin A = \dfrac{\text{length of side opposite } \angle A}{\text{length of hypotenuse}} = \dfrac{a}{c}$;
   c. $\cos A = \dfrac{\text{length of side adjacent to } \angle A}{\text{length of hypotenuse}} = \dfrac{b}{c}$. (353)

7. For any acute $\angle A$, $(\sin A)^2 + (\cos A)^2 = 1$. (359)

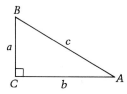

Chapter 8 Review

Lesson 8-1, Page 331

1. $m = 9; c = 25; a = \underline{\ ?\ }$ 15

2. $m = 16; c = 20; h = \underline{\ ?\ }$ 8

3. $a = 6; c = 9; n = \underline{\ ?\ }$ 5

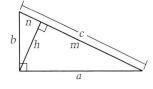

4. Given: $\overline{CD} \perp \overline{AB}; \overline{CD} \parallel \overline{EF}; m\angle ACB = 90$
Prove: $\triangle ACD \sim \triangle EBF$

Lesson 8-2, Page 337

In $\triangle ABC$, $\angle C$ is a right angle.

5. $AC = 15; BC = 20; AB = \underline{\ ?\ }$ 25

6. $AB = 36; AC = 4; BC = \underline{\ ?\ }$ $16\sqrt{5} \approx 35.78$

7. Find the length of the diagonal of a rectangle that is 9 cm by 18 cm. $9\sqrt{5} \approx 20.12$ cm

Lesson 8-3, Page 346

8. $AB = 8\sqrt{2}; AC = \underline{\ ?\ }$ 8

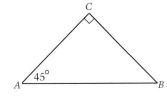

9. YZ = 36; XZ = $\underline{\ ?\ }$ $12\sqrt{3}$

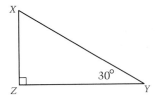

10. Find the length of a diagonal of a square with sides of length 64 cm. $64\sqrt{2}$ cm $\approx$

11. Find the length of an altitude of an equilateral triangle with sides of length 20 cm. $10\sqrt{3}$ cm $\approx$

ANSWERS

Chapter Review

4. Proof: 1. $\overline{CD} \perp \overline{AB}; \overline{CD} \parallel \overline{EF};$ $m\angle ACB = 90$ (Given) 2. $m\angle CDB = m\angle EFB$ (2 lines $\parallel \Rightarrow$ corres. $\angle$s =. [1]) 3. $m\angle B = m\angle B$ (Reflexive Prop.) 4. $\triangle CDB \sim \triangle EFB$ (AA Post. [2, 3]) 5. $\angle ACB$ is a rt. $\angle$. (Def. of rt. $\angle$ [1]) 6. $\triangle ACB$ is a rt. $\triangle$. (Def. of rt. $\triangle$ [5]) 7. $\triangle ADC \sim \triangle CDB$ (If alt. is drawn to hypotenuse of rt. $\triangle$, the new $\triangle$s formed are $\sim$ to each other and to the given $\triangle$ [1, 6]) 8. $\triangle ADC \sim \triangle EFB$ ($\sim$ of $\triangle$s is transitive. [4, 7])

Lesson 8-4, Page 351

Give answers to the nearest unit.

12. The dimensions of a football field are 160 ft. by 300 ft.
What is the distance between opposite corners of the field?
340 ft.

13. If the sun's rays make an angle
of 60° with the ground, how
long is the shadow of a person
who is 180 cm tall? **104 cm.**

14. How much more wire is needed
to brace the sapling than
the aerial pictured at the right? **2 ft.**

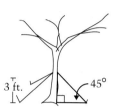

Lesson 8-5, Page 357

Write each ratio.

15. tan A $\frac{a}{b}$ **16.** tan B $\frac{b}{a}$ **17.** sin B $\frac{b}{c}$ **18.** cos B $\frac{a}{c}$

In △XYZ, identify the trigonometric ratio for the given angle.

19. $\frac{24}{25}$; ∠X cos x   **20.** $\frac{24}{7}$; ∠Y tan y   **21.** $\frac{7}{24}$; ∠X tan x

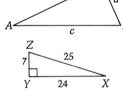

Lesson 8-6, Page 362

Use a calculator or the table on page 617. Give the decimal
value for each trigonometric ratio.

22. sin 39° **0.6293**   **23.** cos 85° **0.0872**   **24.** tan 52° **1.2799**
25. cos 1° **0.9998**   **26.** sin 89° **0.9998**   **27.** tan 89° **57.2900**

Find m∠A to the nearest degree.

28. cos A ≈ 0.3746   **29.** tan A ≈ 0.5310
    m∠A = 68   m∠A = 28

Lesson 8-7, Page 365

Use a calculator or the table on page 617. Give each answer to
the nearest degree or unit.

30. How long is the
wire brace? **98 m**

31. How far is the boat from the
base of the cliff? **1099 m**

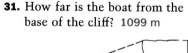

32. A treasure chest is buried 150 ft. under a building. If the
entrance to a tunnel leading to the treasure is 850 ft. from
the building, what angle must the tunnel form with the
surface in order to reach the treasure? **10°**

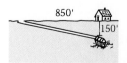

Chapter 8 Test

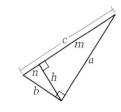

1. $a = 12$; $m = 6$; $c = $ ___?___ **24**

2. $m = 4$; $h = 10$; $c = $ ___?___ **29**

3. $c = 26$; $n = 8$; $h = $ ___?___ **12**

Given: $\triangle ABC$ with right $\angle C$

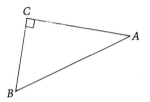

4. $AC = 14$; $BC = 48$; $AB = $ ___?___ **50**

5. $AB = 9$; $AC = 7$; $BC = $ ___?___ **$4\sqrt{2} \approx 5.66$**

6. $AB = 18$; $m\angle A = 45$; $AC = $ ___?___ **$9\sqrt{2}$**

7. $BC = 24$; $m\angle A = 30$; $AC = $ ___?___ **$24\sqrt{3}$**

8. $BC = 20\sqrt{3}$; $m\angle A = 60$; $AB = $ ___?___ **40**

9. Write a ratio that represents $\tan P$. $\frac{20}{21}$

10. What trigonometric ratio does $\frac{20}{29}$ represent with respect to $\angle Q$? **Cos Q**

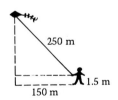

Use a calculator or the table on page 617.

11. Give a decimal approximation for $\sin 48°$. **0.7431**

12. If $\tan A \approx 4.0108$, find $m\angle A$. **76**

Use a calculator or the table on page 617 as needed. Give each answer to the nearest degree or unit.

13. A rectangular enclosure is 75 m by 100 m. How much fencing is needed to divide the enclosure diagonally? **125 m**

14. If 250 m of string have been let out as the kite passes over a point 150 m away, how high is the kite? **202 m**

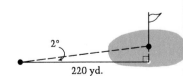

15. An observer stood atop a building 80 feet high. Since there were trees and shrubs blocking the base of a 10-foot statue, the observer measured the angle of depression to the top of the statue and found the measure to be 32. How far was the statue from the building? **112 ft.**

16. The golf ball was driven 220 yd. How long must the putt be to reach the hole? **7.7 yd**

CHAPTER 9

Circles

Chapter Overview

This chapter presents the terms associated with circles, including the equation of a circle. Tangents and chords are studied from a quantitative point of view, and the Pythagorean Theorem is applied.

Circumscribed and inscribed circles provide a vehicle for studying points of concurrency of altitudes, perpendicular bisectors, angle bisectors and medians in a triangle.

All cases of angle-arc relationships are proved and applied. Also proved are theorems about segments formed by intersecting chords, tangent segments and secant segments.

The proofs in this chapter provide an opportunity to apply similar and congruent triangle methods.

Perspectives

Lesson 9–1 lays the groundwork for studying circles and spheres. The terms "radius" and "diameter" refer to both the segment and its length.

The terms and concepts associated with spheres offer an opportunity for students to develop an increased awareness of spatial relationships.

Lesson 9–2 presents two important theorems about tangents and the definitions related to common tangents and tangent circles.

Theorem 9–2 is stated in "if and only if" form. Students should realize that either conditional may be used as a reason in subsequent proofs.

Lesson 9–3 introduces two theorems about chords. Congruent circles are also defined.

Emphasis in this lesson is again placed on applications, many using the Pythagorean Theorem.

Lesson 9–4 studies circumscribed and inscribed circles, because all three vertices of any triangle can be positioned on a circle.

The centroid, orthocenter and circumcenter of any triangle are collinear.

Lesson 9–5 defines the degree measure of an arc in terms of its central angle. The Arc Addition Postulate and a theorem relating arcs to their corresponding chords are introduced.

Pacing Chart for Chapter 9

Lesson	Objectives	Basic Course	Average Course	Extended Course
9–1	Recognize circles and spheres and lines, segments and planes related to them.	1	1	1
9–2	Use theorems about tangents to circles.	1	1	1
9–3	Use theorems involving chords of circles.	1	1	1
9–4	Recognize circles and polygons that are inscribed or circumscribed; recognize points of concurrency.	1	1	1
9–5	Recognize central angles, arcs and congruent arcs in circles; use postulates and theorems involving arcs of circles.	1	1	1
9–6	Recognize inscribed angles and other angles with vertices on circles; use theorems involving such angles.	1	1	$1\frac{1}{2}$
9–7	Use theorems involving angles with vertices not on circles and segments formed by chords, secants and tangents.	1	1	$1\frac{1}{2}$
Review		1	1	1
Test		1	1	1
Cumulative Test		1	1	1
Practice for Standardized Tests 3		1	1	1
Total		11 days	11 days	12 days

Lesson 9–6 continues the study of angle-arc relationships, inscribed angles and tangent-chord angles. The measure of either type of angle is one-half the measure of the intercepted arc, and each vertex is on the circle.

Lesson 9–7 concludes the theorems dealing with the measures of angles as they compare with the measures of intercepted arcs. It also studies relationships among segments on chords intersecting in a circle and among tangent and secant segments.

Circles

Chapter 9

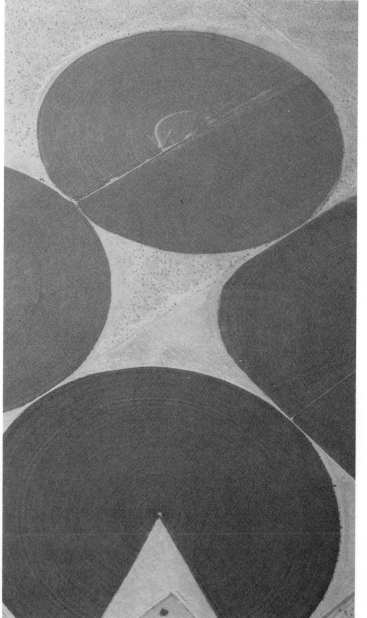

In center-point irrigation, fields are watered by dozens of sprinkler outlets positioned on a pipe that runs from the center of the field to its outer edge. The pipe is mounted on wheels and is driven by electrical power. It sweeps around the entire field.

As the pipe sweeps, what is the locus of all points determined by a sprinkler outlet 20 feet from the center point? Does the locus of points described contain the center point? Explain.

Warm-Up Review

1. On a plane, what is the locus of points a given distance from a point? Circle
2. Name the equation of a line through $P(3, -2)$ with a slope of 1. $y = x + (-5)$
3. If $5 - x = 5 + 6$, find the value of x. -6
4. Find the distance between $(-3, 5)$ and $(3, 13)$. 10

9-1 Circles and Spheres

A sprinkler outlet is positioned on an irrigation pipe 20 feet from the center point. As the pipe sweeps around the irrigation field, the sprinkler outlet travels the path of a circle.

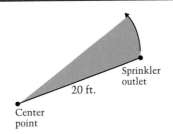

Definition *Circle*

A circle is the set of coplanar points at a given distance from a given point in the plane. The given point is called the center.

The segment determined by the sprinkler outlet and the center point represents a radius of the circle.

Definition *Radius of a Circle*

A radius of a circle is a segment determined by the center and a point on the circle.

Radius is also used to mean the *length* of this segment.

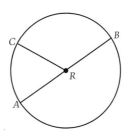

The diagram shows a circle with center R (denoted $\odot R$). $\overline{RA}$, $\overline{RB}$, and $\overline{RC}$ are radii.

Example 1
Find the radius of $\odot P$ whose center is $P(0, 0)$.

Solution
Since A, B, C, and D are on $\odot P$, $\overline{PA}$, $\overline{PB}$, $\overline{PC}$, and $\overline{PD}$ are all radii. Each segment is 3 units long, so the radius of $\odot P$ is 3 units.

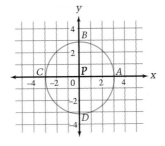

Using the definition of a circle and the distance formula, an equation of a circle with radius r and center $A(h, k)$ can be derived. Let $P(x, y)$ be any point on the circle. The radius r, the distance from A to P, is given by this following equation:
$r = AP = \sqrt{(x - h)^2 + (y - k)^2}$. Thus, $r^2 = (x - h)^2 + (y - k)^2$ or $(x - h)^2 + (y - k)^2 = r^2$.

Example 2
Find an equation for $\odot Q$ with a radius 6 and center $Q(3, 4)$.

Solution
Substitute 6 for r, 3 for h, and 4 for k in the equation of a circle.
$(x - h)^2 + (y - k)^2 = r^2$
$(x - 3)^2 + (y - 4)^2 = 6^2$
So an equation of $\odot Q$ is $(x - 3)^2 + (y - 4)^2 = 36$.

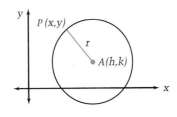

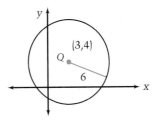

LESSON 9-1

Resources

String
  Teaching Aid 20, circular geoboard
  Visual Aid 20, circular geoboard
  Teaching Aid 21, circles
  Visual Aid 21, circles
  Worksheet 9-1
  Extension 9-1
  Computer Activities 9-1

OBJECTIVE

Recognize circles and spheres and lines, segments and planes related to them.

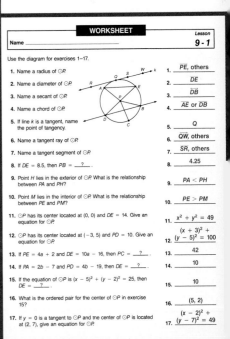

WORKSHEET
Lesson **9-1**

Name _____

Use the diagram for exercises 1–17.

1. Name a radius of $\odot P$.
2. Name a diameter of $\odot P$.
3. Name a secant of $\odot P$.
4. Name a chord of $\odot P$.
5. If line k is a tangent, name the point of tangency.
6. Name a tangent ray of $\odot P$.
7. Name a tangent segment of $\odot P$.
8. If $DE = 8.5$, then $PB = $ __?__ .
9. Point H lies in the exterior of $\odot P$. What is the relationship between PA and PH?
10. Point M lies in the interior of $\odot P$. What is the relationship between PE and PM?
11. $\odot P$ has its center located at $(0, 0)$ and $DE = 14$. Give an equation for $\odot P$.
12. $\odot P$ has its center located at $(-3, 5)$ and $PD = 10$. Give an equation for $\odot P$.
13. If $PE = 4a + 2$ and $DE = 10a - 16$, then $PC = $ __?__ .
14. If $PA = 2b - 7$ and $PD = 4b - 19$, then $DE = $ __?__ .
15. If the equation of $\odot P$ is $(x - 5)^2 + (y - 2)^2 = 25$, then $DE = $ __?__ .
16. What is the ordered pair for the center of $\odot P$ in exercise 15?
17. If $y = 0$ is a tangent to $\odot P$ and the center of $\odot P$ is located at $(2, 7)$, give an equation for $\odot P$.

1. $\overline{PE}$, others
2. DE
3. $\overline{DB}$
4. $\overline{AE}$ or $\overline{DB}$
5. Q
6. $\overrightarrow{QW}$, others
7. $\overline{SR}$, others
8. 4.25
9. $PA < PH$
10. $PE > PM$
11. $x^2 + y^2 = 49$
12. $(x + 3)^2 + (y - 5)^2 = 100$
13. 42
14. 10
15. 10
16. (5, 2)
17. $(x - 2)^2 + (y - 7)^2 = 49$

In the diagram of $\odot W$, $\overline{AB}$ and $\overline{CD}$ are not radii. Why? Both segments are chords. $\overline{AB}$ is also a diameter.

Definition   *Chord of a Circle*

A chord of a circle is a segment whose endpoints lie on the circle.

Definition   *Diameter of a Circle*

A diameter of a circle is a chord that contains the center of the circle.

Diameter is also used to mean the *length* of the segment.

How does AB compare to WB? Why?
$AB = 2WB$; diameter is 2 radii.

Example 3

Find the diameter and the center of a circle whose equation is $x^2 + (y + 3)^2 = 25$.

Solution

$x^2 + (y + 3)^2 = 25$
$(x - 0)^2 + (y - (-3))^2 = 5^2$
Since $r = 5$, the diameter is 10. The center is at $(0, -3)$.

A study of the circular region suggested by the photograph indicates that a circle separates a plane into three distinct sets of points. They are the circle and its interior and exterior.

Definition   *Interior and Exterior of a Circle*

The interior of a circle is the set of points in a plane whose distance from the center is less than the radius. The exterior of a circle is the set of points in the plane whose distance from the center is greater than the radius.

Suppose $ST = 4$, $SE < 4$, and $SD > 4$. By definition, E is in the interior and D is in the exterior of $\odot S$.

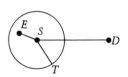

Example 4

The equation of $\odot Q$ is $(x + 1)^2 + (y - 2)^2 = 49$. Is $R(5, -1)$ on $\odot Q$ or in its interior or its exterior?

Solution

The coordinates of Q are $(-1, 2)$. Use the Distance Formula to find QR: $QR = \sqrt{(5 - (-1))^2 + (-1 - 2)^2} = \sqrt{36 + 9} = \sqrt{45}$
Since $r^2 = 49$, $r = 7$. $\sqrt{45} < 7$, so $QR < r$. Hence R is in the interior of $\odot Q$.

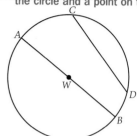

Now consider the relationships between lines and circles.

Definition *Secant of a Circle*

A secant is a line that intersects a circle in two points.

In the diagram shown at the right, $\overleftrightarrow{VW}$ is a secant. Is $\overleftrightarrow{OC}$ a secant? Suppose a line in the plane of $\odot O$ is drawn so it **Yes** contains interior point A, would that line be a secant? Your **Yes** answer should suggest Theorem 9-1, which is to be proved in Exercise 37.

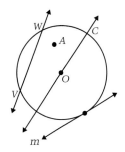

Theorem 9-1

A line that lies in the plane of a circle and contains an interior point of the circle is a secant.

Line m intersects $\odot O$ in exactly one point. How is line m different from a secant? Such a line is called a tangent.
A secant intersects a circle in 2 pts.

Definition *Tangent to a Circle*

A tangent to a circle is a line in the plane of the circle that intersects the circle in exactly one point. The point of intersection is called the point of tangency.

$\overleftrightarrow{ST}$ is a tangent to $\odot D$, and point S is the point of tangency.

A ray or segment is tangent to a circle if and only if it is a subset of a tangent line and contains the point of tangency. In $\odot D$, $\overrightarrow{ST}$ and $\overrightarrow{TR}$ are tangent rays, and $\overline{TR}$, $\overline{ST}$, and $\overline{SR}$ are tangent segments. $\overrightarrow{QU}$ is *not* a tangent ray. Why?
$\overrightarrow{QU}$ would intersect $\odot D$ in 2 pts.

In space, the counterpart of a circle is a sphere. These bubbles suggest spheres.

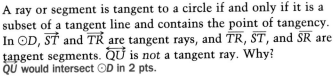

Definition *Sphere*

A sphere is the set of all points in space that are a given distance from a given point. The given point is called the center of the sphere.

A *radius of a sphere* is a segment determined by the center and a point on the sphere. $\overline{OA}$ is a radius of sphere O. Name two **$\overline{OB}$, $\overline{OC}$** other radii. A *diameter of a sphere* is a segment that contains the center and has its endpoints on the sphere. $\overline{AB}$ is a diameter of sphere O. *Radius* and *diameter* also mean the *lengths* of these segments.

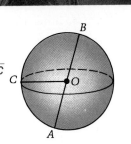

Additional Examples

Example 1

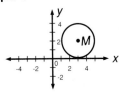

Find the radius of $\odot M$, whose center is at $M(3, 2)$. 2

Example 2

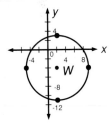

Find an equation for $\odot W$ with radius 7 and center $W(2, -4)$. $49 = (x - 2)^2 + (y + 4)^2$

Example 3
Find the diameter and center of a circle whose equation is $(x - 5)^2 + y^2 = 16$. diameter $= 8$; center at $(5, 0)$

Example 4
Is $P(-2, 5)$ in the interior, the exterior or on $\odot S$, whose equation is $64 = (x - 4)^2 + (y + 1)^2$? The radius of $\odot S = 8$; $PS = 6\sqrt{2}$, which is greater than the radius of $\odot S$; P is exterior to $\odot S$.

Assignment Guide

Basic: 1–14, 15–25 (odd), 32, 40–46
Average: 2–14 (even), 17, 18, 21–25, 28, 29, 32–35, 40–46
Extended: 2–14 (even), 18, 22–24, 28, 31–35, 37–46

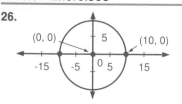
The intersection of a sphere and a plane containing the center of the sphere is a **great circle** of the sphere. At the right, ⊙P is a great circle of sphere P.

The intersection of a sphere and a plane containing an interior point of the sphere, but not containing the center, is a **small circle** of the sphere. ⊙D is a small circle of sphere P.

A line or a plane containing exactly one point of a sphere is tangent to the sphere. At the right, line ℓ is tangent to sphere T at point M. Also, plane 𝓔 is tangent to sphere T at M.

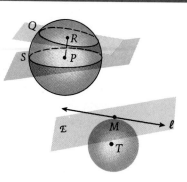

Checking for Understanding

1. How can a circle be drawn using chalk and a piece of string? Why does this work?

2. Explain why a compass works for drawing circles.

3. In ⊙P, is P part of the circle? Explain.

4. If the radius of ⊙S is 7.5 units, then the diameter is ___.    15 units

5. Write an equation of ⊙G with G(0, 0) and radius 10.   **5.** $x^2 + y^2 = 10^2 = 100$

6. Given ⊙M with equation $x^2 + (y + 4)^2 = 36$, find the radius and give the coordinates of M. $r = 6; M = (0, -4)$

7. How are chords and secants of a circle related?   **7.** Both intersect the circle in 2 pts.

8. What is the difference between a great circle and a small circle of sphere S?   **8.** The plane of the great circle contains the center of the circle; a great circle is larger.

9. Define *chord of a sphere*.   **10.** Define *secant of a sphere*.

Written Exercises

Set A   Name each item in circle O.   **1.** $\overline{OA}, \overline{OB}, \overline{OC}$

1. Three radii   **2.** A secant Line ℓ $\overleftrightarrow{BD}$ **3.** A diameter

4. A chord $\overline{BD}, \overline{BC}$ **5.** A tangent ray $\overrightarrow{BX}$ $\overline{BC}$

6. If OA = 12, then BC = ___.   24   OW<OA

7. How are OW and OA related? OX and OA?   OX>OA

8. If line t is a tangent, name the point of tangency.   B

9. Is $\overleftrightarrow{CW}$ a secant? Why?   Yes, W is in interior of ⊙O.

Name each item in sphere S.   **10.** $\overline{SO}, \overline{ST}, \overline{SR}, \overline{SQ}$

10. Three radii   **11.** A diameter $\overline{OT}$

12. A small circle ⊙P   **13.** A great circle ⊙S

14. Which line appears to be tangent to sphere S?
Line *m*

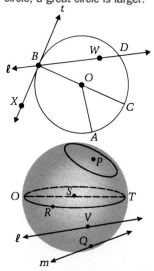

Find the radius of a circle with the given diameter.

15. 10 5 **16.** 9.4 4.7 **17.** $6\frac{1}{4}$ $3\frac{1}{8}$ **18.** $k + 1$ $\frac{k+1}{2}$

Find the diameter of a sphere with the given radius.

19. 6 12 **20.** 8.6 17.2 **21.** $\frac{2}{5}$ $\frac{4}{5}$ **22.** $k - 5$ $2(k - 5)$

23. The endpoints of the diameter of $\odot P$ are (5, 9) and (−3, −1). Find the coordinates of P. (1, 4)

24. If the radius of $\odot O$ is 5 and its center is $O(2, 3)$, give an equation for $\odot O$. $(x - 2)^2 + (y - 3)^2 = 25$

25. The tool at the right cuts holes in drywall. Point A is the pivot point and point C is the tip of the cutter. What length should $\overline{AC}$ be if the hole to be cut has a diameter of $11\frac{7}{8}$ in.? $5\frac{15}{16}$ in.

Set B Find the center and radius for each circle. Sketch graphs for Exercises 26 and 27.

(2, 6); 4

26. $x^2 + y^2 = 100$ **27.** $(x - 2)^2 + (y - 6)^2 = 16$

(0, 0); 10

28. $81 = (x + 1)^2 + y^2$ **29.** $x^2 + (y - 4)^2 = 1$ (0, 4);1

(−1, 0); 9

Given a circle with equation $(x + 3)^2 + (y - 1)^2 = 4$, is each point on the circle or in its interior or exterior?

30. $P(-1, 1)$ On **31.** $Q(-5, 0)$ **32.** $R(-2, 2)$

Exterior Interior

33. The window shown is a half circle. The diameter, including the wood trim, is 100 in. If the wood trim is 8 in. wide, how long is each "spoke" that radiates from the "hub"? The hub's diameter is 10 in. 38 in.

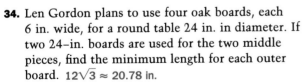

34. Len Gordon plans to use four oak boards, each 6 in. wide, for a round table 24 in. in diameter. If two 24–in. boards are used for the two middle pieces, find the minimum length for each outer board. $12\sqrt{3} \approx 20.78$ in.

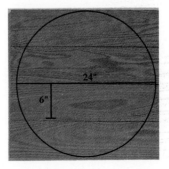

35. $\odot A$ has the equation $x^2 + y^2 = 36$. If line ℓ contains $P(1, 1)$, in how many points does ℓ intersect $\odot A$? Explain your answer. 2 pts; Thm. 9–1

27.

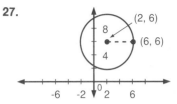

37.

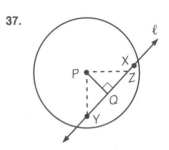

Given: Line ℓ and $\odot P$ are coplanar; X lies on ℓ; X is an interior pt.
Prove: Line ℓ is a secant of $\odot P$.
Proof: 1. Line ℓ and $\odot P$ are coplanar; X lies on ℓ; X is an interior pt. of $\odot P$. (Given) 2. Let r be the radius of $\odot P$. (Def. of $\odot$)
3. Draw $\overline{PQ} \perp \ell$ at Q. (In a plane, through a pt. not on a given line, there is exactly 1 line $\perp$ to the given line.) 4. On ℓ and on opp. sides of Q, mark pts. Y and Z so that $YQ = QZ = \sqrt{r^2 - (PQ)^2}$. (On a ray, there is exactly 1 pt. a given distance from the endpt. of the ray.) 5. Draw $\overline{PY}$ and $\overline{PZ}$. (2 pts. determine a line.) 6. $\angle PQY$ and $\angle PQZ$ are rt. $\angle$s. (2 $\perp$ lines form 4 rt. $\angle$s. [3]) 7. $\triangle PQY$ and $\triangle PQZ$ are rt. $\triangle$s. (Def. of rt. $\triangle$)
8. $(PY)^2 = (YQ)^2 + (PQ)^2$; $(PZ)^2 = (QZ)^2 + (PQ)^2$ (Pythagorean Thm. [6, 7]) 9. $(PY)^2 = (\sqrt{r^2 - (PQ)^2})^2 + (PQ)^2$; $(PZ)^2 = (\sqrt{r^2 - (PQ)^2})^2 + (PQ)^2$ (Substitution Prop. [4, 8])
10. $(PY)^2 = r^2 - (PQ)^2 + (PQ)^2 = r^2$; $(PZ)^2 = r^2 - (PQ)^2 + (PQ)^2 = r^2$ (Algebra [9]) 11. $(PY)^2 = (PZ)^2 = r^2$ (Substitution Prop. [10]) 12. $PY = PZ = r$ (Algebra [11]) 13. Y and Z are on $\odot P$. (Def. of $\odot$ [12]) 14. Line ℓ intersects $\odot P$ in 2 pts.: Y and Z. (Steps 4 and 13) 15. Line ℓ is a secant of $\odot P$. (Def. of secant)

38. interior of circle with center (1, −2) and radius 7

FOLLOW-UP

More Practice

• Worksheet 9–1

Extension

Challenge your better students to discuss methods for proving that a tangent does not contain any interior points of the circle.
• Extension 9–1

Computers

This computer activity can be completed using *The Geometric Supposer: Circles* or *GeoDraw*.

To give students the opportunity to explore tangents to a circle, have students do the following.

Draw any circle and label a point on the circle. Draw a radius to the point and a line perpendicular to the radius at the point on the circle. What appears to be true of that line? It is a tangent. Repeat this activity several times. Does it appear to be possible to draw a line through a point on the circle and perpendicular to the radius that also passes through the interior of the circle? no Draw any circle and label a point outside the circle. Draw two different tangents to the circle through that point. Measure the segments formed by the exterior point and the points of intersection with the circle. What is true about the lengths of the two segments? Their lengths are equal. Repeat the activity several times for circles of different sizes and different locations of the exterior point. What generalization can you make? Tangent segments drawn to a circle from an exterior point are equal.
• Computer Activities 9–1

36. Sphere O has small circle $\odot R$ and great circle $\odot O$. $\overline{OR} \perp \overline{RQ}$, $OS = 2$, and $RQ = 1$. $OR = \underline{\ ?\ }$. $\sqrt{3} \approx 1.73$

Set C **37.** Prove Theorem 9-1.

38. What set of points is determined by the inequality $(x - 1)^2 + (y + 2)^2 < 49$?

39. The equation of line m is $y = x + 10$, and the equation of $\odot T$ is $x^2 + y^2 = 50$. Is line m a tangent, a secant, or neither? Tangent at (−5, 5)

▲ **Review** Use a calculator or the table on page 617.

40. Find the distance across the river. 42 ft.

41. Find the distance between the trees. 65 ft.

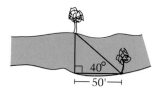

42. Give the decimal value for tan 20°. 0.3640

43. $\triangle DEF$ is a 30-60-90 triangle. $\angle E$ is the right angle and $DF = 12$. Find DE and EF. 6; 6√3 ≈ 10.39

44. $\angle A$ and $\angle B$ are supplementary. $m\angle A = 2x + 7$ and $m\angle B = 3x + 8$. Find x. 33

Thinking Ahead **45.** Draw $\odot O$ and label a point G on the circle. Draw $\overleftrightarrow{FG}$ tangent to $\odot O$ at G. What appears to be true about $\angle OGF$? Label another point K on the circle. Now draw $\overleftrightarrow{JK}$ tangent to $\odot O$ at K. What appears to be true about $\angle OKJ$?

46. $\overline{PA}$ and $\overline{PB}$ are segments tangent to $\odot Q$ from point P in the exterior of $\odot Q$. $\overleftrightarrow{PQ}$ intersects $\odot Q$ at R. If $PQ = 14$ and $m\angle APB = 60$, then $PR = \underline{\ ?\ }$. 7

Algebra Review: Writing an Equation for a Line

Example

Write an equation for the line perpendicular to the line $y = 5x - 8$ through the point $P(3, 7)$.

Solution

The equation of a line perpendicular to $y = 5x - 8$ has slope $-\frac{1}{5}$.

$y = mx + b$

$7 = -\frac{1}{5}(3) + b$ *Substitute 7 for y, $-\frac{1}{5}$ for m, and*

$7\frac{3}{5} = b$ *3 for x. Then solve for b.*

$y = -\frac{1}{5}x + 7\frac{3}{5}$ *Rewrite the equation.*

For each exercise, write an equation for the line perpendicular to the given line and through the given point.

1. $y = 2x + 3$; (0, 0)
$y = -\frac{1}{2}x$

2. $y = x - 3$; (2, 1)
$y = -x + 3$

3. $y = 3x - 4$; (5, 2)
$y = -\frac{1}{3}x + \frac{11}{3}$

Warm-Up Review

1. What is the point called where a tangent intersects a circle? Point of tangency
2. In $\triangle ABC$ and $\triangle XYZ$, $\angle C$ and $\angle Z$ are right angles, $AB = XY$ and $AC = XZ$.
   By what reason are the triangles congruent? HL, or hypotenuse-leg
3. In $\triangle FED$, if $m\angle D = 70$ and $m\angle F = 65$, then what is the relationship
   between DE and EF? $EF > DE$

9-2 Tangents to a Circle

The Kitchen Place is a company that remodels kitchens. Many of their countertop designs have rounded corners. To round the corners of a countertop, the cabinetmakers use the ideas in Theorems 9-2 and 9-3, which deal with tangents to circles.

Theorem 9-2

In a plane, a line is tangent to a circle if and only if it is perpendicular to a radius drawn to the point of tangency.

Part I   If a line is tangent to a circle, then it is perpendicular to a radius at its endpoint on the circle.

Given   Line m is tangent to $\odot P$ at Q.

Prove $m \perp PQ$

Plan for Proof   Use indirect proof. Suppose $\overline{PQ} \not\perp m$. Draw $\overline{PR} \perp m$. By Theorem 5-14, $PQ > PR$ and R is in the interior of $\odot P$. So m is a secant. This contradicts the Given.

Part II   In a plane, if a line is perpendicular to a radius at its endpoint on the circle, then the line is tangent to the circle.

Given   Line m and $\odot P$ are coplanar; $m \perp \overline{PQ}$ at Q on $\odot P$.

Prove m is tangent to $\odot P$.

Plan for Proof   Let R be any other point on m. Use Theorem 5-14 to show $PR > PQ$.

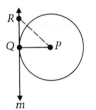

Theorem 9-3

Segments drawn tangent to a circle from an exterior point are equal.

Given $\overline{QA}$ and $\overline{QB}$ tangent to $\odot O$ at A and B, respectively.

Prove $QA = QB$

Plan for Proof   Draw $\overline{QO}$, $\overline{OA}$, and $\overline{OB}$. Show $\triangle QOA \cong \triangle QOB$. Use corresponding parts.

The proofs of Theorems 9-2 and 9-3 are requested in Exercises 18, 19, and 20.

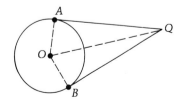

LESSON 9-2

Resources

Compass
Straightedge
   Teaching Aid 20, circular
   geoboard
Visual Aid 20, circular geoboard
Teaching Aid 21, circles
Visual Aid 21, circles
Worksheet 9-2
Extension 9-2

OBJECTIVE

Use theorems about tangents to circles.

TEACHING NOTES

Begin this lesson with the following construction **activity**.

WORKSHEET   Lesson **9-2**

Name _____

Determine the number of common tangents for each pair of circles.

1. $(x - 5)^2 + (y - 3)^2 = 25$; $(x + 4)^2 + (y - 3)^2 = 16$ 1. __3__
2. $(x + 2)^2 + (y + 2)^2 = 49$; $(x - 6)^2 + (y + 3)^2 = 9$ 2. __2__
3. $(x + 3)^2 + (y - 4)^2 = 36$; $(x - 3)^2 + (y - 10)^2 = 4$ 3. __4__
4. $(x - 10)^2 + (y - 8)^2 = 100$; $(x - 9)^2 + (y - 6)^2 = 16$ 4. __0__
5. $(x - 6)^2 + (y - 6)^2 = 36$; $(x - 2)^2 + (y - 6)^2 = 4$ 5. __1__

In the diagram, $\overline{AB}$ and $\overline{BC}$ are tangent segments.

6. What is the relationship between AB and BC?   6. $AB = BC$
7. What is the relationship between $m\angle ABO$ and $m\angle ABC$?   7. $m\angle ABO = \frac{1}{2}m\angle ABC$
8. If $\overline{OA}$ is drawn, then $m\angle OAB = $ _?_.   8. __90__
9. If $m\angle ABC = 60$ and $OE = 7$, then $OB = $ _?_.   9. __14__
10. If $m\angle ABD = 45$ and $AB = 5$, then $OB = $ _?_.   10. $5\sqrt{2}$
11. If $OB = 13$ and $OE = 5$, then $BC = $ _?_.   11. __12__
12. If $AB = 7$ and $OB = 13$, what is the diameter of $\odot O$?   12. $4\sqrt{30}$
13. If $OE = 4$ and $BD = 8$, then $AB = $ _?_.   13. $8\sqrt{2}$
14. If $BC = OE$, then $m\angle ABC = $ _?_.   14. __90__
15. If $BC = 16$ and $OE = 12$, then $BD = $ _?_.   15. __8__
16. If $BD = 4$ and $AB = 9$, then $OE = $ _?_.   16. $\frac{65}{8}$ or $8\frac{1}{8}$
17. If $OB = 4x + 2$, $m\angle ABD = 30$, and $AB = 12\sqrt{3}$, then $x = $ _?_.   17. $5\frac{1}{2}$ or $\frac{11}{2}$

---

1. Have students draw ⊙O with point A on the circle.
2. Draw $\overrightarrow{OA}$.
3. Construct a line perpendicular to $\overrightarrow{OA}$ at A.
4. What do you notice about this line? **tangent to ⊙O**
Discuss Theorem 9–2.
  Example 1 may be used as a **group activity**.

Additional Example

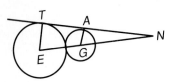

If $\overline{NT}$ is tangent to both ⊙G and ⊙E, how would you prove that △NAG ~ △NTE? **AA, using the common ∠N and right ∠ETN = right ∠GAN**

 EXTENSION

Name _____ Lesson **9-2**

Tree Planting Schemes

Horticulturists and landscape architects often use geometric principles in their work. The challenge in planting a small orchard, for example, is to find the most economical use of the space available. The maximum number of trees is limited by the fact that each tree must be planted a certain distance from each of its neighbors.

1. The diagrams represent two planting schemes. Which arrangement of trees is most economical? **2nd one**

2. Make a sketch showing a circular planting scheme. Is this arrangement better than either of those in exercise 1? **Answers will vary. An example is shown.**

Example

Show how to use Theorems 9-2 and 9-3 to round a square corner. A circle of radius $1\frac{1}{2}$ inches is to be used.

Solution

The goal is to find the center of a circle with radius $1\frac{1}{2}$ in. such that the sides of the corner are tangent to the circle. Let right ∠RQT be the square corner, as in the first diagram at the right. On $\overrightarrow{QR}$ and $\overrightarrow{QT}$, locate points A and B so QA = QB = $1\frac{1}{2}$ in. Points A and B are to be the points of tangency.

At A and B, draw rays perpendicular to $\overline{QA}$ and $\overline{QB}$ and intersecting at point O, as shown in the second diagram. Point O is the center of the desired circle. Using $\overline{OA}$ (or $\overline{OB}$) as a radius, draw part of ⊙O *from A to B.*

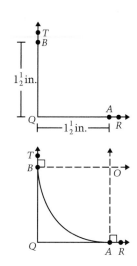

Now consider lines that are tangent to more than one circle. The artist's sketch below shows the path of the moon during a lunar eclipse. The moon appears the darkest when it is in the earth's umbra. The umbra and penumbra, regions in the earth's shadow, are bounded by lines tangent to both the sun and the earth.

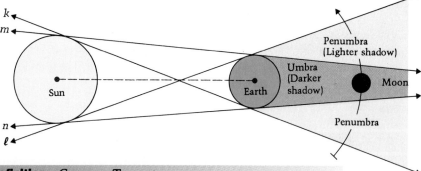

Definition *Common Tangent*

A common tangent is a line that is tangent to each of two coplanar circles.

At the right, line s is a common tangent to ⊙P and ⊙X. Line t is also a common tangent.

Common external tangents do not intersect the segment joining the centers of the circles. Line s is a common external tangent. *Common internal tangents* intersect the segment joining the centers of the circles. Line t is a common internal tangent. Which lines in the artist's sketch are common external tangents? common internal tangents? **Lines *m* and *n*; lines *k* and *ℓ***

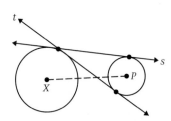

Assignment Guide

Basic: 1–6, 7, 10, 12, 13, 15, 22, 31–41
Average: 2–18 (even), 20, 21, 23, 24, 26–28, 31–41
Extended: 2–18 (even), 20, 21–27 (odd), 28–41

The pennies shown at the right suggest tangent circles.

Definition   *Tangent Circles*

Tangent circles are two coplanar circles that are tangent to the same line at the same point.

In the diagram at the right, ⊙P and ⊙Q are **externally tangent circles**. ⊙S and ⊙Q are **internally tangent circles**.

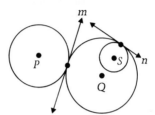

Checking for Understanding

1. The measure of the angle formed by a tangent ray and a radius drawn to the point of tangency is __?__. 90

2. $\overline{PA}$ and $\overline{PB}$ are tangent to ⊙O. P is in the exterior of ⊙O. If $PA = 3x + 1$ and $PB = 4x - 5$, then $x =$ __?__. 6

Draw two circles that have

3. one common external tangent.   **4.** no common tangents.

5. two common external tangents and one common internal tangent.

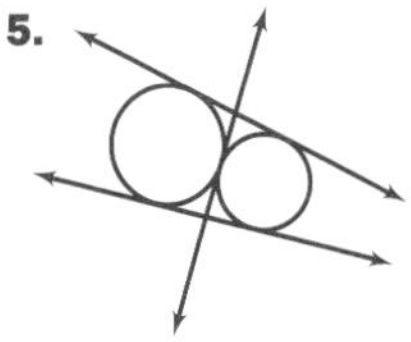

6. What is the greatest number of nonoverlapping circles that can be drawn externally tangent to a given circle? All circles are of the same size. 6

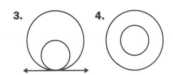

Written Exercises

Set A   How many common tangents could be drawn to each pair of circles?

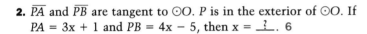

1.

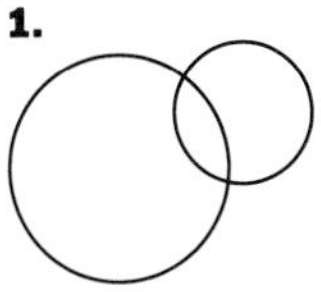

2 external

2.

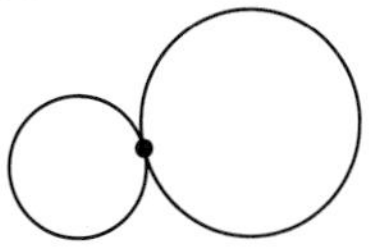

2 external
1 internal

3.

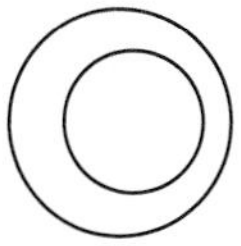

4.

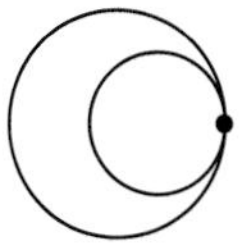

1 external

Error Analysis   Errors of omission are likely to be made in application problems. Students often forget to try drawing auxiliary lines to form rectangles, 30-60-90 triangles and so on, which usually leads to easy solutions.

EXERCISE NOTES

Exercises 11, 12 and **22–23** are applications of the Pythagorean Theorem.
Exercises 21–23 and **30**   are solved by drawing auxiliary lines.
Exercises 25 and **26**   are applications of the equation of a circle.

ANSWERS

Checking for Understanding

5.

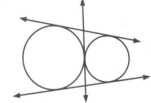

Written Exercises

5. Proof: 1. $\overline{AB}$ is diameter of $\odot O$; lines ℓ and k are tangent to $\odot O$ at A and B, resp. (Given) 2. $k \perp \overline{OB}$; $\ell \perp \overline{OA}$ (A line tangent to a $\odot$ is $\perp$ to a radius drawn to the pt. of tangency. [1]) 3. $k \perp \overleftrightarrow{AB}$; $\ell \perp \overleftrightarrow{AB}$ (Def. of a line $\perp$ to a segment [2]) 4. $k \parallel \ell$ (In a plane, 2 lines $\perp$ to the same line are $\parallel$. [3])

10. As the radius increases, the corner becomes more rounded and farther from the vertex of the rt. $\angle$.

13. Proof: 1. $\overline{QA}$ and $\overline{QB}$ are tangent to $\odot O$ at A and B, respectively. (Given) 2. $QA = OB$ (Segments drawn tangent to a circle from an exterior pt. are =. [1]) 3. $OA = OB$ (Def. of $\odot$ [1]) 4. $QO = QO$ (Reflexive Prop.) 5. $\triangle OAQ \cong \triangle OBQ$ (SSS $\cong$ Post. [2, 3, 4]) 6. $m\angle AQO = m\angle BQO$ (Corres. parts of $\cong \triangle$s are =. [5]) 7. $\overrightarrow{QO}$ bisects $\angle AQB$ (Def. of $\angle$ bis. [6])

18. Proof: Alternatives: *Either $\overleftrightarrow{PQ} \perp m$ or $\overleftrightarrow{PQ} \not\perp m$* Assumption: *Suppose $\overleftrightarrow{PQ} \not\perp m$*; Argument: *Then*, since through a given pt. not on a given line there exists exactly 1 line $\perp$ to the given line, draw $\overleftrightarrow{PR} \perp m$ at R; since the $\perp$ seg. from a pt. to a line is the shortest seg. from the pt. to the line, $PR < PQ$ and R is in the interior of $\odot P$. If a line contains a pt. in the interior of a $\odot$, then it is a secant. Therefore, m is a secant. Contradiction: *But this contradicts the given information that m is a tangent to $\odot P$. False assumption: Therefore the assumption that $\overleftrightarrow{PQ} \not\perp m$ is false.* Conclusion: *We conclude that $\overleftrightarrow{PQ} \perp m$.*

19. Proof: 1. Line m and $\odot P$ are coplanar; $m \perp \overline{PQ}$ at Q (Given) 2. Let R be any other pt. on m. (A line contains at least 2 pts.) 3. Draw $\overline{PR}$. (2 pts. determine a line.) 4. $PR > PQ$ (The $\perp$ seg. from a pt. to a line is the shortest seg. from the pt. to the line. [1, 3])

---

5. Given: $\odot O$; diameter $\overline{AB}$; ℓ and k tangent to $\odot O$ at A and B, respectively
Prove: $\ell \parallel k$

6. $\overline{GE}$ and $\overline{GF}$ are tangent to $\odot X$. If $m\angle EGX = 30$ and $GX = 12$, then $XE = \underline{\,?\,}$. **6**

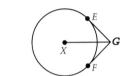

For each exercise, draw a right angle. Then round the corner using a circle with the given radius.

7. 1 in.   **8.** 2 in.   **9.** 3 in.

10. Study your work in Exercises 7–9. Describe how the radius of the circle affects the appearance of the rounded corner.

$\overleftrightarrow{AC}$ is tangent to $\odot P$.

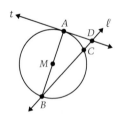

11. $BC = 13$; $AC = 5$; $AB = \underline{\,?\,}$ **12**

12. $BC = 12$; $AC = 6$; $PB = \underline{\,?\,}$ **$3\sqrt{3} \approx 5.20$**

13. Refer to the diagram and the Given in Theorem 9-3. Prove that $\overrightarrow{QO}$ bisects $\angle AQB$.

Use the converse of the Pythagorean Theorem to find the indicated lengths so that line t is a tangent to $\odot M$. Lines ℓ and t are in the plane of $\odot M$.

14. $MB = 4$; $AD = 6$; $BD = \underline{\,?\,}$ **10**

15. $BD = 13$; $AD = 5$; $AM = \underline{\,?\,}$ **6**

16. $CD = BC$; $BM = 4$; $AD = 8$; $CD = \underline{\,?\,}$ **$4\sqrt{2} \approx 5.66$**

17. $CD = BC + 2$; $AM = 2\sqrt{7}$; $AD = 12$; $CD = \underline{\,?\,}$ **9**

Set B   **18.** Prove Theorem 9-2, Part I.

19. Prove Theorem 9-2, Part II.

20. Prove Theorem 9-3.

21. To manufacture the triangular rack for pool balls, the corners of an equilateral triangle are rounded. If each pool ball has a diameter of $2\frac{1}{4}$ in., how far is the point of tangency, P, from A, the vertex of the equilateral triangle? **$\frac{9\sqrt{3}}{8} \approx 1.95$ in.**

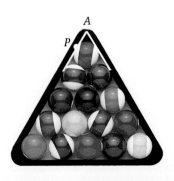

$\overleftrightarrow{AB}$ is a common external tangent.

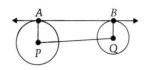

22. $AP = 24$; $BQ = 14$; $PQ = 46$; $AB = \underline{\ ?\ }$ **24**

23. $AB = 16$; $PQ = 20$; $AP = 18$; $BQ = \underline{\ ?\ }$ **6**

24. How many tangent lines can be drawn to a sphere at a given point on the sphere? **Infinitely many**

Sketch the graphs of each pair of circles on the same grid. Then tell how many common tangents could be drawn to each pair of circles.

25. $(x - 3)^2 + (y - 5)^2 = 9$ and $(x - 9)^2 + (y - 1)^2 = 4$ **4**

26. $x^2 + (y - 3)^2 = 9$ and $x^2 + (y + 4)^2 = 16$ **3**

27. In this pulley system, the distance between the centers of the wheels is 25 in. The length of the belt between the two wheels is 24 in. Find the diameter of each wheel if the diameter of the larger wheel is twice the diameter of the smaller wheel. **14; 28**

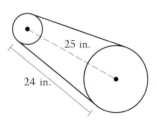

28. Given $\odot P$ with $P(0, 0)$, write the equation of a line tangent to $\odot P$ at $N(4, 5)$. $y = -\frac{4}{5}x + \frac{41}{5}$

29. Given $\odot Q$ with $Q(3, 2)$, write the equation of a line tangent to $\odot Q$ at $M(5, 7)$. $y = -\frac{2}{5}x + 9$

30. $\overline{AB}$, $\overline{BC}$, and $\overline{AC}$ are segments tangent to $\odot K$; $\overline{AC} \perp \overline{BC}$; $AC = 6$; $AB = 10$. Find the length of a radius of $\odot K$. **2**

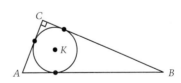

Set C $\overleftrightarrow{UR}$ and $\overleftrightarrow{ST}$ are common internal tangents of $\odot P$ and $\odot Q$.

31. Prove $UR = ST$.

32. $PU = 6$; $QS = 5$; $m\angle 1 = 60$; $PQ = \underline{\ ?\ }$. **22**

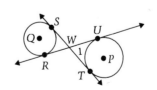

▲ Review **33.** What is the longest chord of a circle? **Diameter**

34. Define *sphere*. **The set of all points which are a given distance from a given pt.**

---

5. *R* lies in the exterior of $\odot P$. (Def. of exterior of a $\odot$ [2, 4]) 6. *m* is tangent to $\odot P$. (Def. of tangent [1, 2, 5])

20. Proof: 1. $\overline{QA}$ and $\overline{QB}$ are tangent to $\odot O$ at A and B, respectively. (Given) 2. Draw $\overline{OA}$, $\overline{QO}$ and $\overline{OB}$. (2 pts. determine a line.) 3. $OA = OB$ (Def. of $\odot$ [1]) 4. $QO = QO$ (Reflexive Prop.) 5. $\overline{OA} \perp \overleftrightarrow{AQ}$ and $\overline{OB} \perp \overleftrightarrow{BQ}$ (A tangent is $\perp$ to the radius drawn to the pt. of tangency.) 6. $\angle QAO$ and $\angle QBO$ are rt. $\angle$s. (Def. of $\perp$ lines [5]) 7. $\triangle QAO$ and $\triangle QBO$ are rt. $\triangle$s. (Def. of rt. $\triangle$ [6]) 8. $\triangle QAO \cong \triangle QBO$ (HL Thm. [3, 4]) 9. $QA = QB$ (Corres. parts of $\cong \triangle$s are =. [8])

25.

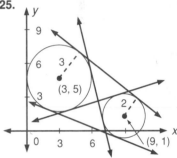

4 common tangents

26.

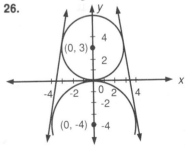

3 common tangents

31. Proof: 1. $\overleftrightarrow{UR}$ and $\overleftrightarrow{ST}$ are common internal tangents of $\odot P$ and $\odot Q$. (Given) 2. $WU = WT$; $WR = WS$ (Tangent segs. drawn from an ext. pt. to pts. on the $\odot$ are =. [1]) 3. $WU + WR = WT + WS$ (Add. Prop. [2]) 4. $WU + WR = UR$ and $WT + WS = ST$ (Seg. Add. Post.) 5. $UR = ST$ (Substitution Prop. [3, 4])

Thinking Ahead

38–39.

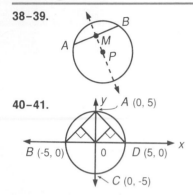

40–41.

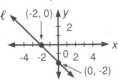

ANSWERS

Challenge

3. *T* has coordinates (x, y). Then if the taxi-cab distance from $T(x, y)$ to $P(-3, 5)$ is 4, $4 = (-3 - x) + (5 - y)$. When $x = 0$, $y = -2$, and when $x = -2$, $y = 0$.

ℓ is the set of all points T such that the taxi-cab distance from T to $P(-3, 5)$ is 4.

---

35. Use a calculator or the table on page 617 to find the height of the tower. **373.21 ft.**

36. $\triangle ABC \sim \triangle QRS$, $AB = 5$, $QR = 8$, and $AC = 12$. Find QS. $19\frac{1}{5}$

37. How many congruent triangles are formed by joining the midpoints of the sides of a triangle? **4**

Thinking Ahead Draw $\odot P$. Draw chord $\overline{AB}$ so that it is not a diameter. By folding, locate the midpoint of $\overline{AB}$.

38. Why is the line along the crease a secant of $\odot P$?

39. Describe two relationships that appear true for $\overline{AB}$ and the secant suggested by the crease.

Graph $x^2 + y^2 = 25$. Draw the chord with endpoints $A (0, 5)$ and $B(-5, 0)$, and another chord with endpoints $A(0, 5)$ and $D(5, 0)$.

40. What appears to be true about $\overline{AB}$ and $\overline{AD}$?

41. Find the distance from the center to each chord.

38. It intersects $\odot P$ in 2 pts.
39. The secant is the $\perp$ bisector of $\overline{AB}$.
40. $AB \perp AD$; $AB = AD$
41. $5\sqrt{2} \approx 3.54$

Challenge

In *taxi-cab geometry*, the distance from point R to point S is given by the formula $D = x_2 - x_1 + y_2 - y_1$.

Find the taxi-cab distance between the points in each pair.

1. $P(4, 5)$; $Q(2, 1)$ -6 **2.** $A(-5, 7)$; $B(4, -3)$ -1

3. Graph the set of all points T such that the taxi-cab distance from T to $P(-3, 5)$ is 4.

4. What name would be given to the figure in Exercise 3 in plane geometry?
Line with equation $y = -x - 2$

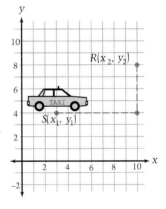

Algebra Review: Solving Systems of Linear Equations

Solve each system of linear equations. You might want to refer to the Algebra Review on page 113.

1. $y = -x + 7$
$y = 2x + 1$

2. $c = h + 5$
$c = 0.5h + 7$

3. $2x + y = -5$
$x + 3y = 10$

4. $x - 2y = 5$
$3x - 6y = 12$

5. $b = 3a + 4$
$2a = b - 3$
$a = -1, b = 1$

6. $2u - v = 7$
$u - 4 = 0$
$u = 4, a = 1$

7. $x + 2y = 7$
$4y + 2x = -5$
No solution

8. $5x - 32 = y$
$x - 19 = 2y$
$x = 5, y = -7$

1. $x = 2, y = 5$
2. $c = 9, h = 4$
3. $y = -5, y = 5$ 4. No solution

9-3 Chords of a Circle

Sally Jepson designs barbecue grills. She wants to modify the circular grill shown by inserting support wires $\overline{AD}$ and $\overline{BC}$ of the same length as shown.

To determine the length and position of the support wires, Sally can use the ideas in Theorems 9-4 and 9-5 dealing with chords of a circle.

Theorem 9-4

If a line through the center of a circle is perpendicular to a chord, then it bisects the chord.

Given $\odot P$; line ℓ contains P; chord $\overline{AB}$; $\overleftrightarrow{PC} \perp \overline{AB}$

Prove ℓ bisects $\overline{AB}$.

Plan for Proof   Draw $\overline{PA}$ and $\overline{PB}$. Show $\triangle PAC \cong \triangle PBC$. Thus $AC = CB$.

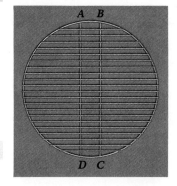

Theorem 9-4 is to be proved in Exercise 15.

Example 1

Suppose the radius of the grill above is 10 in. and the distance from the center to support wire $\overline{AD}$ is 5 in. How can Sally use Theorem 9-4 to find AD?

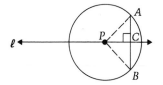

Solution
Draw $\overline{OA}$. Draw $\overleftrightarrow{OT} \perp AD$. By the Pythagorean Theorem, $(OT)^2 + (AT)^2 = (AO)^2$. By substitution, $5^2 + (AT)^2 = 10^2$, so $AT = \sqrt{75} \approx 8.7$ in. By Theorem 9-4, $\overleftrightarrow{OT}$ bisects $\overline{AD}$. Thus, $AD = 2(AT) \approx 2(8.7) \approx 17.4$ in.

Many of the circular grills being manufactured have the same radius, so they are congruent.

Definition   Congruent Circles

Congruent circles are circles with equal radii.

If $GX = HY$, then $\odot G \cong \odot H$. Conversely, if $\odot G \cong \odot H$, then $GX = HY$.

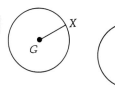

LESSON 9-3

Resources

Compass
Transparencies
   Teaching Aid 20, circular
      geoboard
Visual Aid 20, circular geoboard
Worksheet 9-3
Extension 9-3
Computer Activities 9-3

OBJECTIVE

Use theorems involving chords of circles.

TEACHING NOTES

Theorem 9–4 can be visualized by drawing a chord of a circle on a transparency and a radius on an

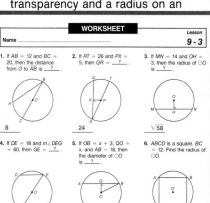

overlay. Using a compass point to hold the center fixed, rotate the radius until it is perpendicular to the chord. What do you think is also true? **It bisects the chord.**
   Repeat this exercise with a different chord if necessary. Also show the radii at the endpoints of the chord. **Example 1** practices applying the results.

Additional Examples

Example 1

In a circle with radius 10, how far from the center is a chord whose length is 16? **6**

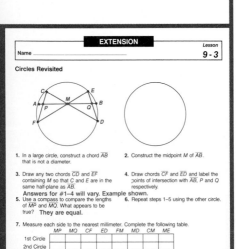

Theorem 9-5

In the same circle or in congruent circles, two chords have the same length if and only if they are the same distance from the center(s) of the circle(s).

Part I In the same circle or in congruent circles, if two chords are the same distance from the center(s), then the chords have the same length.

Given $\odot P \cong \odot Q$; chords $\overline{AB}$ and $\overline{CD}$; $\overline{PX} \perp \overline{AB}$; $\overline{QY} \perp \overline{CD}$; $PX = QY$

Prove $AB = CD$

Plan for Proof Draw $\overline{PB}$ and $\overline{QD}$. Show $\triangle QDY \cong \triangle PBX$ and $XB = YD$. Use Theorem 9-4 to show $AB = 2XB$ and $CD = 2YD$. Thus, $AB = CD$.

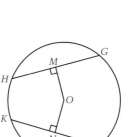

Part II In the same circle or in congruent circles, if two chords have the same length, then they are the same distance from the center(s).

The proof of Theorem 9-5 is requested in Exercises 23 and 24.

Example 2
In $\odot O$, if $GH = JK$, which other segments are equal?

Solution
By Theorem 9-4, $\overleftrightarrow{OM}$ and $\overleftrightarrow{ON}$ bisect $\overline{GH}$ and $\overline{JK}$, respectively. So $HM = MG = KN = NJ$. Also, by Theorem 9-5, $OM = ON$.

Checking for Understanding
1. Refer to the Plan for Proof for Theorem 9-4. What theorem or postulate can be used to show $\triangle PAC \cong \triangle PBC$? **HL Thm.**

2. Under what conditions are two circles congruent? **=radii**

In $\odot P$, $\overline{PX} \perp \overline{AB}$ and $\overline{PY} \perp \overline{CD}$.

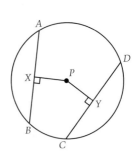

3. $CY = \underline{\ ?\ }$ **YD**   4. If $PY = PX$, then $AB = \underline{\ ?\ }$. **CD**

5. If $CD = BA$, then $PX = \underline{\ ?\ }$. **PY**

6. If $PX = PY$, does $BX = YD$? Why?

7. If $PX = PY$ and $YD = 7$, then $AB = \underline{\ ?\ }$. **14**

Refer to the diagram in Example 1.

8. If $AO = 25$ and $OT = 7$, then $AD = \underline{\ ?\ }$. **48**

9. If $AD = 24$ and $OT = 5$, then $AO = \underline{\ ?\ }$. **13**

Assignment Guide

Basic: 1–19, 37–43
Average: 1–10, 14–22 (even), 25–31, 37–43
Extended: 1–19 (odd), 20–43

Written Exercises

Set A $\overline{AC}$ is a diameter of $\odot P$, $\overline{AB}$ is a chord, and $\overline{PD} \perp \overline{AB}$.

1. $AP = 10$; $PD = 6$; $AB = \underline{\ ?\ }$. **16**

2. $AB = 24$; $PD = 6$; $AP = \underline{\ ?\ }$. **$6\sqrt{5} \approx 13.42$**

3. $AC = 30$; $AB = 24$; $PD = \underline{\ ?\ }$. **9**

Is each statement *always*, *sometimes*, or *never* true? Explain.

4. Two circles with equal diameters are congruent. **Always**

5. A circle is congruent to itself. **Always**

6. Two circles with equal chords are congruent. **Sometimes**

7. A line perpendicular to a chord bisects the chord. **Sometimes**

8. A line through the center of a circle bisects a radius. **Never**

9. A diameter perpendicular to a chord bisects the chord. **Always**

10. Two chords the same distance from the centers of two circles are the same length. **Sometimes**

In $\odot Q$, $\overline{QX} \perp \overline{YZ}$.

11. $YZ = 56$; $QY = 35$; $QX = \underline{\ ?\ }$. **21**

12. $QX = 10$; $YZ = 48$; $QY = \underline{\ ?\ }$. **26**

13. $QY = 2QX$; $YZ = 16\sqrt{3}$; $QY = \underline{\ ?\ }$. **16**

14. $QX = QW$; $YZ = 2QX$; $QY = 14\sqrt{2}$; $YW = \underline{\ ?\ }$. **$14\sqrt{2} - 14 \approx 5.80$**

15. Prove Theorem 9-4.

16. Prove: If a line through the center of a circle bisects a chord that is not a diameter, it is perpendicular to the chord.

17. Is the statement in Exercise 16 true for a chord that *is* a diameter? Explain.

Some square tables in restaurants have four curved drop leaves. When the leaves are raised, the tabletop is circular. Suppose the length of $\overline{AB}$ is 3 feet.

18. Find the radius of the circular tabletop. **$\frac{3\sqrt{2}}{2} \approx 2.12$ ft.**

19. Find the distance from the center of the circular tabletop to $\overline{AB}$. **1.5 ft.**

Example 2

Given: $\odot O$, $OA = OB$, $\overline{OA} \perp \overline{RS}$ and $\overline{OB} \perp \overline{RT}$. $\triangle SRT$ must be what kind of triangle? isosceles, with $RS = RT$

ANSWERS

Checking for Understanding

6. Yes; since $PX = PY$, $AB = DC$ by Thm. 9–5. By Thm. 9–4, the chords are bisected; so $AX = BX = \frac{1}{2}AB$ and $CY = DY = \frac{1}{2}CD$. By the Div. Prop. and substitution, $BX = YD$.

Written Exercises

6. if chords are same distance from centers of $\odot$s

7. if line passes through center of $\odot$

10. if $\odot$s are $\cong$

15. Proof: 1. $\odot P$; line ℓ contains pt. P; chord $\overline{AB}$; $\overrightarrow{PC} \perp \overline{AB}$ (Given) 2. Draw $\overline{PA}$ and $\overline{PB}$. (2 pts. determine a line.) 3. $PA = PB$ (Def. of $\odot$ [1]) 4. $PC = PC$ (Reflexive Prop.) 5. $\angle PCA$ and $\angle PCB$ are rt. $\angle$s. (2 $\perp$ lines form 4 rt. $\angle$s. [1]) 6. $\triangle PCA$ and $\triangle PCB$ are rt. $\triangle$s. (Def. of rt. $\triangle$ [5]) 7. $\triangle PCA \cong \triangle PCB$ (HL Thm. [3, 4, 6]) 8. $AC = CB$ (Def. of $\cong \triangle$s [7]) 9. C is the midpt. of $\overline{AB}$. (Def. of midpt. [8]) 10. ℓ bisects $\overline{AB}$. (Def. of seg. bisector [9])

22. Using the method from Exercise 21, find the length of each horizontal wire in half the grill. Then multiply by 2 and add the amount needed for the two support wires.

23. Proof: 1. ⊙P ≅ ⊙Q; $\overline{AB}$ and $\overline{CD}$ are chords; $\overline{PX} \perp \overline{AB}$; $\overline{QY} \perp \overline{CD}$; PX = QY (Given) 2. Draw $\overline{PB}$ and $\overline{QD}$. (2 pts. determine a line.) 3. ∠PXB and ∠QYD are rt. ∠s. (2 ⊥ lines form 4 rt. ∠s. [1]) 4. △PXB and △QYD are rt. △s. (Def. of rt. △ [3]) 5. PB = QD (Def. of ≅ ⊙s [1]) 6. △PXB ≅ △QYD (HL Thm. [1, 4, 5]) 7. XB = YD (Corres. parts of ≅ △s are =. [6]) 8. $\overline{PX}$ bisects $\overline{AB}$; $\overline{QY}$ bisects $\overline{CD}$. (If line through center of ⊙ is ⊥ to a chord, it bisects the chord. [1]) 9. X is the midpt. of $\overline{AB}$; Y is midpt. of $\overline{CD}$. (Def. of bisects [8]) 10. AX = XB; CY = YD (Def. of midpt. [9]) 11. AB = AX + XB; CD = CY + YD (Seg. Add. Post.) 12. AB = XB + XB = 2(XB); CD = YD + YD = 2(YD) (Substitution Prop. [10, 11]) 13. $\frac{1}{2}$(AB) = XB; $\frac{1}{2}$(CD) = YD (Mult. Prop. [12]) 14. $\frac{1}{2}$(AB) = $\frac{1}{2}$(CD) (Substitution Prop. [7, 13]) 15. AB = CD (Mult. Prop. [14])

24. Given: ⊙P ≅ ⊙Q; $\overline{AB}$ and $\overline{CD}$ are chords; AB = CD; $\overline{PX} \perp \overline{AB}$; $\overline{QY} \perp \overline{CD}$ Prove: PX = QY Proof: 1. ⊙P ≅ ⊙Q; $\overline{AB}$ and $\overline{CD}$ are chords; AB = CD; $\overline{PX} \perp \overline{AB}$; $\overline{QY} \perp \overline{CD}$ (Given) 2. Draw $\overline{PA}$, $\overline{PB}$, $\overline{QC}$ and $\overline{QD}$. (2 pts. determine a line.) 3. PA = QC; PB = QD (Def. of ≅ ⊙s) 4. △PAB ≅ △QCD (SSS ≅ Post. [1, 3]) 5. m∠PBX = m∠QDY (Corres. parts of ≅ △s are =. [4]) 6. ∠PXB and ∠QYD are rt. ∠s. (2 ⊥ lines form 4 rt. ∠s. [1]) 7. △PXB and △QYD are rt. △s. (Def. of rt. △ [6]) 8. △PXB ≅ △QYD (HA Thm. [3, 5, 7]) 9. PX = QY (Corres. parts of ≅ △s are =. [8])

25. Given: ⊙P with chord $\overline{AB}$; ℓ is ⊥ bisector of $\overline{AB}$. Prove: ℓ contains P.

Set B A circular grill 22 inches in diameter has 28 horizontal wires. The distance from the center to the first wire is $\frac{1}{4}$ inch. Thereafter, the distance between any two consecutive horizontal wires is $\frac{3}{4}$ inch. The distance between the two support wires is 6 inches.

20. Find the length of a support wire. $8\sqrt{7} \approx 21.17$ in.

21. Find the length of the shortest horizontal wire.

22. How could the total amount of wire for all 30 wires be found? **21.** $2\sqrt{21} \approx 9.17$ in

23. Prove Theorem 9-5, Part I.

24. Prove Theorem 9-5, Part II.

25. Prove: In a plane, the perpendicular bisector of a chord of a circle passes through the center of the circle.

26. Pictured at the right is a portion of a plate. Use Exercise 25 to describe a method for finding the diameter of the plate.

27. In a circle, what is the locus of midpoints of all chords equal to a given chord? Explain.

⊙P is a great circle and ⊙Q is a small circle of sphere P. Point X and ⊙Q are coplanar. $\overline{AB}$ is a chord of both circles. $\overline{PQ} \perp \overline{AB}$; $\overline{QX} \perp \overline{AB}$; $\overline{PQ} \perp \overline{QX}$

28. AB = 24; PA = 20; XA = 13; PX = $\underline{?}$. $\sqrt{281} \approx 16.76$

29. XA = 10; PX = 12; PQ = $6\sqrt{3}$; PA = $\underline{?}$. $2\sqrt{43} \approx 13.11$

30. Write a definition for *congruent spheres*.

31. What diameter rod must be used to make the machine part pictured at the right? **1 cm**

Set C $\overline{AB}$ is a chord of coplanar circles P and Q; $\overleftrightarrow{QP} \perp \overline{AB}$

32. Prove: If QX = PX, then QA = PA.

33. Prove: If QX > PX, then QA > PA.

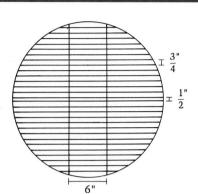

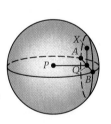

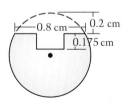

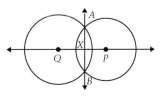

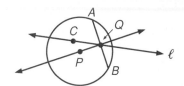

34. The sunburst pattern above the door is part of a circular region bounded by a chord and part of a circle. The pattern's width is 200 in. and the height is 50 in. Find the radius of the full circular region. **125 in.**

35. Find the center and the radius of a circle that contains points $A(-3, -1)$, $B(2, 4)$, and $C(5, 3)$. (HINT: Use Exercise 25.) **$(2, -1)$; 5**

36. Prove: If two chords of a circle have unequal lengths, then the shorter chord is a greater distance from the center of the circle.

 Review
37. Draw 2 circles with 2 common internal tangents.

38. $\overline{AB}$ and $\overline{AC}$ are tangent segments. Prove $m\angle 1 = m\angle 2$.

39. The radius of $\odot X$ is 7. If $XM = 9$, locate M.

40. Name two equilateral parallelograms.

41. $\overline{PQ}$ and $\overline{RS}$ are the bases of trapezoid $PQRS$. $PQ = 10$ and $RS = 13$. Find the length of the median. $11\frac{1}{2}$

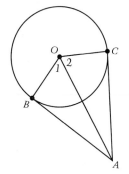

 Thinking Ahead
Draw $\odot P$, $\odot Q$, and $\odot R$. Draw acute $\triangle ABC$ so that A, B, and C are on $\odot P$. Draw obtuse $\triangle XYZ$ so that X, Y, and Z are on $\odot Q$. Draw right $\triangle DEF$ with $\angle E$ the right angle and so that D, E, and F are on $\odot R$.

42. Is the center of each circle in the triangle's interior or exterior, or on a side of the triangle?

43. Given $\triangle LMN$ with $m\angle N = 90$, how could you draw $\odot O$ so that L, M, and N are all on $\odot O$?

💻 Computer Activities: Drawing and Measuring

1. Draw $\triangle ABC$. Then draw the perpendicular bisector of each side. Do the perpendicular bisectors intersect? **Yes**

2. If the bisectors intersect, label the intersection and find the distance from the point of intersection to point A. Draw a circle with the point of intersection as the center and radius equal to this distance. How are the circle and $\triangle ABC$ related?

3. Draw $\triangle ABC$. Then draw the angle bisector of each angle. Do the angle bisectors intersect? **Yes**

4. If the angle bisectors intersect, find the distance from the point of intersection to $\overline{AB}$. Draw a circle with the point of intersection as the center and radius equal to this distance. How are the circle and $\triangle ABC$ related?

2. The vertices of $\triangle ABC$ lie on the circle.
4. AB, BC and AC are tangent to the circle.

1.

3.
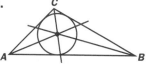

Proof: *Either* ℓ contains P or ℓ does not contain P. *Suppose* ℓ does not contain P. Draw $\overleftrightarrow{PQ} \perp \overline{AB}$. (Through a pt. not on a line, there is exactly 1 line $\perp$ to the given line.) Then $\overleftrightarrow{PQ}$ is the $\perp$ bisector of $\overline{AB}$. (If a line through the center of a $\odot$ is $\perp$ to a chord, it bisects the chord.) *But this contradicts* the given information that ℓ is $\perp$ bisector of $\overline{AB}$ and Thm. 4–10. (In a plane a segment has exactly one $\perp$ bisector.) *Therefore the assumption* that ℓ does not contain P is false. *We conclude that* ℓ contains P.

Warm-Up Review

1. If the vertices of a triangle lie on a circle, then each side of the triangle is a(n) __?__ of the circle. Chord
2. If each side of a triangle intersects a circle in exactly one point, then each side of the triangle is a(n) __?__ segment of a circle. Tangent
3. What is the locus of points equidistant from the sides of an angle? Line that bisects the angle

LESSON 9–4

Resources

Compass
Straightedge
  Teaching Aid 20, circular
    geoboard
Visual Aid 20, circular geoboard
  Teaching Aid 21, circles
Visual Aid 21, circles
Worksheet 9–4
Extension 9–4
Computer Worksheet 9–4
Quiz 9

OBJECTIVES

Recognize circles and polygons that are inscribed or circumscribed; recognize points of concurrency.

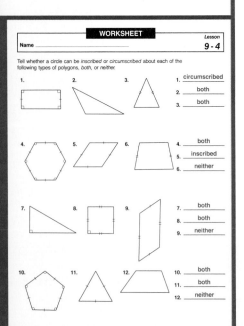

9-4 Circumscribed and Inscribed Circles

Stained-glass art often combines circles and polygons. In the panel shown, each side of the smaller square is a chord of the smaller circle. The smaller circle is said to be circumscribed about the smaller square.

How is each side of the larger square related to the larger circle? This circle is said to be inscribed in the larger square.
Each side is tangent to the circle

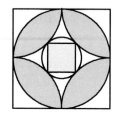

Definition *Circumscribed Circle*

A circle is circumscribed about a polygon when the vertices of the polygon lie on the circle. The polygon is inscribed in the circle.

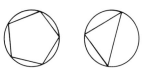

Definition *Inscribed Circle*

A circle is inscribed in a polygon when the sides of the polygon are tangent to the circle. The polygon is circumscribed about the circle.

The designer of the stained-glass panel at the right had to separate an equilateral triangle into three congruent triangles. He used the following definition and Theorem 9-6.

Definition *Concurrent Lines*

Concurrent lines are two or more lines that intersect in a single point. The point is called the point of concurrency.

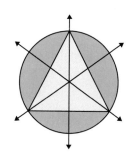

Theorem 9-6

The perpendicular bisectors of the sides of a triangle are concurrent in a point equidistant from the vertices of the triangle.

Given $\triangle ABC$ with ℓ_1, ℓ_2 and ℓ_3, the perpendicular bisectors of $\overline{AB}$, $\overline{AC}$, and $\overline{BC}$, respectively

Prove ℓ_1, ℓ_2 and ℓ_3 are concurrent, and the point of concurrency is equidistant from A, B, and C.

Plan for Proof Use indirect proof to show that ℓ_1 and ℓ_2 intersect. Suppose $\ell_1 \parallel \ell_2$. Since $\ell_1 \perp \overline{AB}$, $\ell_2 \perp \overline{AB}$. But $\ell_2 \perp \overline{AC}$. So $\overline{AB} \parallel \overline{AC}$. This contradicts that A is on $\overline{AB}$ and $\overline{AC}$. So ℓ_1 intersects ℓ_2 at some point P. Use Theorem 6-16 to show $PB = PA = PC$. Thus, P is on ℓ_3.

The proof of Theorem 9-6 is left to Exercise 42.

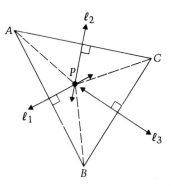

Theorem 9-6 establishes that points A, B, and C are equidistant from P. Thus, A, B, and C all lie on the circle with center P. This suggests the following theorem and definition.

Theorem 9-7

A circle can be circumscribed about any triangle.

The proof of Theorem 9-7 is left to Exercise 43.

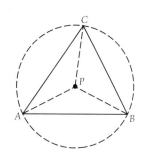

Definition   *Circumcenter and Circumcircle of a Triangle*

The circumcenter of a triangle is the point of concurrency of the perpendicular bisectors of the sides of the triangle. The circumcircle is the circumscribed circle.

Example 1

$\triangle ABC$ has vertices $A(0, 0)$, $B(6, 0)$, and $C(0, 8)$. Find the coordinates of the circumcenter of $\triangle ABC$.

Solution

The perpendicular bisectors of the sides of $\triangle ABC$ intersect at the circumcenter. The perpendicular bisector of $\overline{AB}$ is a vertical line through $(3, 0)$, with equation $x = 3$. The perpendicular bisector of $\overline{CA}$ is a horizontal line through $(0, 4)$, with equation $y = 4$. The lines intersect at $(3, 4)$, the circumcenter of $\triangle ABC$.

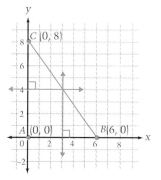

The beginning of a design is shown at the right. Two of the three angle bisectors of $\triangle DEF$ have been constructed. Will the third angle bisector contain point Q? Your answer should agree with Theorem 9-8. It is to be proved in Exercise 44. **Yes**

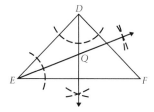

Theorem 9-8

The angle bisectors of a triangle are concurrent in a point equidistant from the sides of the triangle.

Given $\triangle ABC$; $\overline{AX}$, $\overline{BY}$, and $\overline{CZ}$ bisect $\angle A$, $\angle B$, and $\angle C$.

Prove $\overline{AX}$, $\overline{BY}$, and $\overline{CZ}$ are concurrent, and the point of concurrency is equidistant from $\overline{AB}$, $\overline{BC}$, and $\overline{AC}$.

Plan for   Use indirect proof to show $\overline{AX}$ and $\overline{BY}$ intersect.
Proof   Suppose $\overline{AX} \parallel \overline{BY}$. Then $m\angle ABY + m\angle BAX = 180$. So $m\angle ABC + m\angle BAC = 360$. But this contradicts Theorem 4-14. So $\overline{AX}$ intersects $\overline{BY}$ in a point P. Use Theorem 6-18 to show $PR = PS = PT$. Thus, P is on $\overline{CZ}$.

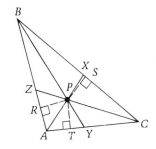

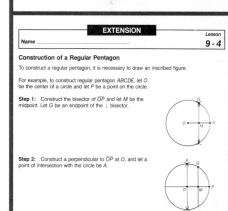

Additional Examples

Example 1

△RST has vertices R(−2, 2), S(4, 2) and T(−2, −6). Find the coordinates of the circumcenter of △RST. The ⊥ bisector of $\overline{RS}$ is a vertical line through (1, 2), with equation x = 3. The ⊥ bisector of $\overline{RT}$ is a horizontal line through (−2, −2), with equation y = −2. The lines intersect at (1, −2), the circumcenter of △RST.

Example 2

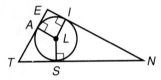

If L is the incenter of △ENT, $\overline{TE}$ ⊥ $\overline{EN}$, LS = 3 and TA = 5, find EN. x = 12; EN = 15

Error Analysis

Error Analysis Students are likely to get confused over the various points of concurrency. Point out that (1) angle bisectors are equidistant from sides and therefore intersect at the center of the inscribed circle, and (2) perpendicular bisectors are equidistant from vertices and therefore intersect at the center of the circumscribed circle.

ANSWERS

Checking for Understanding

5.

Since PR = PS = PT, points R, S, and T all lie on the same circle with center P. This suggests the following theorem and definition. Theorem 9-9 is to be proved in Exercise 45.

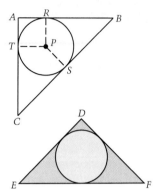

Theorem 9-9

A circle can be inscribed in any triangle.

Definition *Incenter and Incircle of a Triangle*

The incenter of a triangle is the point of concurrency of the angle bisectors of the triangle. The inscribed circle is called the incircle.

The finished stained-glass panel shows the incircle of △DEF.

Example 2

O is the incenter of △UVB; $\overline{UV}$ ⊥ $\overline{VB}$; AB = 4; OC = 2. Find UV.

Solution

Since the sides of △UVB are tangent to ⊙O, BA = BC, UA = UD, and VC = VD by Theorem 9-3. ODVC is a square. Why? So OC = VC = VD = 2. Let UD = x. Then UV = x + 2 and UB = x + 4. Since △UVB is a right triangle, the Pythagorean Theorem can be used.

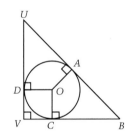

$$(UV)^2 + (VB)^2 = (UB)^2$$
$$(x + 2)^2 + (2 + 4)^2 = (x + 4)^2$$
$$x^2 + 4x + 4 + 36 = x^2 + 8x + 16$$
$$24 = 4x$$
$$6 = x$$

Since UV = x + 2, UV = 8.

Other sets of concurrent lines determine the orthocenter and centroid of a triangle. The *orthocenter* of a triangle, point S at the right, is the point of concurrency of the lines containing the altitudes of the triangle. The *centroid* of a triangle, point T at the right, is the point of concurrency of the medians of the triangle.

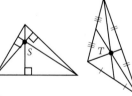

Checking for Understanding

1. If a circle is circumscribed about a pentagon, how many points of the pentagon lie on the circle? Describe them.

2. If a circle is inscribed in a pentagon, how many points of the pentagon lie on the circle? Describe them.

1. 5; vertices of the pentagon
2. 5; pts. at which sides of the pentagon are tangent to circle

Assignment Guide

Basic: 1–11 (odd), 12–25, 47–55
Average: 2–24 (even), 26–41, 47–55
Extended: 2–24 (even), 26–55

3. How many triangles can be inscribed in a given circle? circumscribed about it? **Infinitely many; infinitely many**

4. How many circles can be inscribed in a given triangle? circumscribed about it? **1; 1**

5. Draw an isosceles triangle. Locate its incenter.

6. Draw an obtuse triangle. Locate its circumcenter.

7. In Example 1, verify that the perpendicular bisector of $\overline{BC}$ passes through the circumcenter.

8. Draw an obtuse triangle. Verify with a carefully drawn sketch that the lines containing its altitudes are concurrent.

9. Draw a right triangle. Verify with a carefully drawn sketch that the medians are concurrent.

Written Exercises

Set A   Tell whether each polygon appears to be *inscribed* in the circle, *circumscribed* about the circle, or *neither*.

1. Inscribed   **2. Neither**   **3. Circumscribed**   **4. Neither**

Refer to the second stained-glass panel on page 392.

5. Describe a possible method used by the designer to create the panel.

6. Given that the designer located the circumcenter of the equilateral triangle, prove that the three obtuse triangles are congruent.

Tell whether each statement is *always*, *sometimes*, or *never* true.

7. A circle can be circumscribed about an obtuse triangle. **Always**

8. A circle can be circumscribed about a rectangle. **Always**

9. The orthocenter of a triangle lies in its interior.

10. The incenter of a triangle lies in its exterior.

11. A circle can be inscribed in a rhombus.

9. Sometimes
10. Never
11. Always

9-4 *Circumscribed and Inscribed Circles*

6.

7. Using the Midpoint Formula, the midpoint of $\overline{BC}$ is (3, 4). The circumcenter is the midpt. of $\overline{BC}$ and the ⊥ bisector of a seg. passes through the midpt. of the seg.

8.

9.

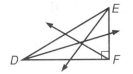

Written Exercises

5. She located the circumcenter of the equilateral triangle by constructing the ⊥ bisectors of the sides. This enabled her to construct the circumcircle. Drawing the segments from the circumcenter to each vertex gave her the smaller ≅ △s.

6.

Given: G is the circumcenter of equilateral △ABC. Prove: △AGB ≅ △BGC ≅ △CGA Proof: 1. G is the circumcenter of equilateral △ABC. (Given) 2. AB = BC = CA (Def. of equilateral △ [1]) 3. G is on the ⊥ bisector of $\overline{AB}$, $\overline{BC}$ and $\overline{CA}$. (Def. of circumcenter [1]) 4. GA = GC = GB (The locus of pts. equidistant from the endpts. of a seg. is the ⊥ bisector of the seg. [3]) 5. △AGB ≅ △BGC ≅ △CGA (SSS ≅ Post. [2, 4])

13.

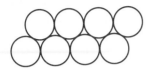

Yes; the above arrangement uses the area more efficiently, allowing another row of circles to be drawn.

14. orthocenter
15. incenter
16. centroid
17. circumcenter
20. 10√2 in. by 10√2 in. by 12 ft.
21. Proof: 1. △ABC is inscribed in ⊙P; $\overline{PY} \perp \overline{AC}$; $\overline{PX} \perp \overline{AB}$; XD = EY (Given) 2. PX = PY (Def. of a ⊙ [1]) 3. PX = PD + DX; PY = PE + EY (Seg. Add. Post.) 4. PD + DX = PE + EY (Substitution Prop. [2, 3]) 5. PD = PE (Subtraction Prop. [1, 4]) 6. AB = AC (If 2 chords are the same distance from the center of ⊙, they are =. [5]) 7. △ABC is isosceles. (Def. of isos. △ [6])

Amy is making a geometric mobile. She plans to draw nonoverlapping circles with radius 2 cm on a sheet of paper 38 cm by 48 cm.

12. If Amy draws the circles in a rectangular array as shown, how many can she draw on the paper? **108**

13. Is there a different way Amy can arrange the circles so that she can draw more of them on the same sheet of paper? Explain.

Give a name for the point of concurrency in each triangle.

14.   **15.** 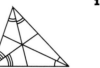   **16.**   **17.**

A portion of a stained-glass window is shown for each exercise below.

18. The square has side length 16. What is the radius of the inscribed circle? **8**

19. The rectangle inscribed in the circle has sides of lengths 12 and 5. What is the radius of the circle? **6.5**

20. A twelve-foot circular log has a 10-inch radius. Find the dimensions of the largest beam with a square cross section that can be cut from the log.

21. Given: △ABC inscribed in ⊙P; $\overline{PY} \perp \overline{AC}$; $\overline{PX} \perp \overline{AB}$; XD = EY Prove: △ABC is isosceles.

△ABC is circumscribed about ⊙P. X, Y, and Z are the points of tangency.

22. XC = 12; BC = 21; BY = _?_ **9**
23. AX = 8; AB = 24; BZ = _?_ **16**
24. BZ = 2m; CY = 3m + 5; BC = 35; m = _?_ **6**
25. CY = n + 3; AX = 2n − 1; AC = 23; n = _?_ **7**

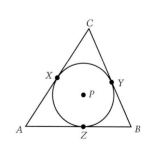

Set B Equilateral triangle *ABC* is inscribed in ⊙*P*.

26. If *AB* = 12, then *PA* = __?__. **4√3 ≈ 6.93**

27. If *PB* = 10, then *BC* = __?__. **10√3 ≈ 17.32**

28. Find *m∠APB*. **120**

29. If *PC* = x, find the radius of the incircle of △*ABC*. **$\frac{x}{2}$**

30. What is the relationship between the circumcenter, the incenter, the orthocenter, and the centroid of △*ABC*? Explain.

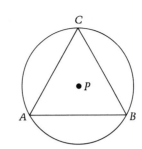

Q is the incenter of △*DEF* at the right and *m∠E* = 90.

31. *DF* = 13; *EF* = 12; *DJ* = 3. Find *QH*. **2**

32. *QK* = 5; *FH* = 12. Find *DH*. **$12\frac{1}{7}$**

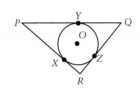

33. *BLUE* is a rhombus. *m∠BLU* = 60; *UE* = 8. Find the radius of the inscribed circle. **2√3 ≈ 3.46**

34. △*PQR* is a right triangle; ∠*R* is the right angle. *X*, *Y*, and *Z* are the points of tangency on incircle *O* as shown at the right. *PY* = 5; *QZ* = 4. Find the radius of ⊙*O*. **$\frac{-9 + \sqrt{161}}{2}$ ≈ 1.84**

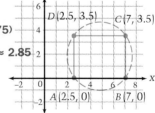

Rectangle *ABCD* is shown on a coordinate grid.

35. Find the center of the circumscribed circle. **(4.75, 1.75)**

36. Find the radius of the circumscribed circle. **√8.125 ≈ 2.85**

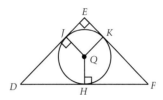

△*AOB* is has vertices *A*(5, 5), *B* (5, 0), and *C* (0, 0).

37. Find the coordinates of the circumcenter of △*AOB*.

38. Find the radius of the circumcircle.

39. Write the equation of the circumcircle.

40. △*ABC* has vertices *A*(−2, 0), *B*(3, 0), and *C*(1, 4). Find the coordinates of its centroid. **$\left(\frac{2}{3}, \frac{4}{3}\right)$**

37. **$\left(\frac{5}{2}, \frac{5}{2}\right)$**

38. **$\frac{5\sqrt{2}}{2}$ ≈ 3.54**

39. **$\left(x - \frac{5}{2}\right)^2 + \left(y - \frac{5}{2}\right)^2 = \frac{25}{2} = 12.5$**

41. The Pyle Corporation wants to build a new lodge the same distance from the hiking trail, Lake Road, and Golfcourse Lane. Trace the map shown at the right. Then determine the correct location for the lodge.

30. They are the same pt. because the lines containing the bisectors of the ∠s, the ⊥ bisectors of the sides, the medians and the altitudes of an equilateral △ all are coincident.

41. Bisect the ∠s formed by the intersection of the roads. The lodge should be built at the intersection of the ⊥ bisectors.

42. Proof: *Either* ℓ_1 *and* ℓ_2 *intersect or* $\ell_1 \parallel \ell_2$. *Suppose* $\ell_1 \parallel \ell_2$. $\ell_1 \perp \overline{AB}$ (Given), so $\ell_2 \perp \overline{AB}$. (In a plane, if a transversal is $\perp$ to one of 2 $\parallel$ lines, it is $\perp$ to the other.) Since $\ell_2 \perp \overline{AC}$, it follows that $\overline{AC} \parallel \overline{AB}$. (In a plane, 2 lines $\perp$ to the same line are $\parallel$.) *This contradicts* the fact that $\overline{AC}$ and $\overline{AB}$ intersect at A. Thus, *the assumption that* $\ell_1 \parallel \ell_2$ *is false. We conclude that* ℓ_1 and ℓ_2 intersect at a point P. Furthermore, since ℓ_1 and ℓ_2 are the $\perp$ bisectors of $\overline{AB}$ and $\overline{AC}$ respectively, $PA = PB$ and $PA = PC$. (The $\perp$ bisector of a segment is the locus of pts. equidistant from the endpts. of the segment.) Thus, $PB = PC$, and by the same locus theorem, P is on ℓ_3. Hence, ℓ_1, ℓ_2 and ℓ_3 are concurrent at P, and $PA = PB = PC$.

43. Given: Any triangle ABC
Prove: A circle can be circumscribed about $\triangle ABC$. Proof:
1. $\triangle ABC$ is any $\triangle$. (Given) 2. Let P be the pt. of concurrency of the $\perp$ bisectors of the sides so that $PA = PC = PB = r$. (The $\perp$ bisectors of the sides of a $\triangle$ are concurrent in a pt. equidistant from the vertices of the $\triangle$.) 3. The circle with center P and radius r contains pts. A, B and C. (Def. of a circle [2]) 4. $\odot P$ circumscribes $\triangle ABC$. (Def. of circumscribe [3])
44. Proof: *Either* $\overleftrightarrow{AX}$ *intersects* $\overleftrightarrow{BY}$ *at a pt. P or* $\overleftrightarrow{AX} \parallel \overleftrightarrow{BY}$. *Suppose* $\overleftrightarrow{AX} \parallel \overleftrightarrow{BY}$. Then $\angle ABY$ and $\angle BAX$ are supp. $\angle$s ($\parallel$ lines $\Rightarrow$ int. $\angle$s on same side of trans. supp.) and $m\angle ABY + m\angle BAX = 180$. (Def. of supp. $\angle$s) Since $\overrightarrow{BY}$ bisects $\angle ABC$ and $\overrightarrow{AX}$ bisects $\angle BAC$, $m\angle ABC = 2(m\angle ABY)$ and $m\angle BAC = 2(m\angle BAX)$. By the Add. Prop. and Substitution Prop., $m\angle ABC + m\angle BAC = 360$. Then $m\angle ABC + m\angle BAC + m\angle BCA > 360$. *But this contradicts* the fact that the sum of the measures of the $\angle$s of a $\triangle = 180$. *Therefore the assumption that* $\overleftrightarrow{AX} \parallel \overleftrightarrow{BY}$ *is false. We conclude that* $\overleftrightarrow{AX}$ *intersects* $\overleftrightarrow{BY}$ *at a pt. P.*

Set C   **42.** Prove Theorem 9-6.   **43.** Prove Theorem 9-7.

44. Prove Theorem 9-8.   **45.** Prove Theorem 9-9.

46. Show that the ratio of the radius of the inscribed circle to the radius of the circle circumscribed about a square is $\sqrt{2}$ to 2.

Congruent $\odot$s are
$\odot$s with = radii

▲ **Review**   **47.** Define *congruent circles*.

48. Given $OD = OF$ and $GD = 4$, find EF.   **4**

49. Draw a pair of externally tangent circles. $\sqrt{58} \approx 7.62$

50. $ABCD$ is a rectangle. $AB = 3$; $BC = 7$; $AC = \underline{}$

51. What is a regular polygon?

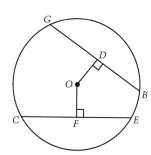

≡ **Thinking Ahead**   Many familiar objects and designs suggest circles. The circular region can be separated into congruent parts by drawing rays whose endpoints are the center of the circle. For each figure below, determine the measure of the indicated angle.

52. 60   **53.** 30   **54.** 45   **55.** 72

⚔ **Construction Exercises**

Construction 13

Construct a line tangent to a circle at a given point on the circle.

Given   Point Q on $\odot P$.

Construct   A tangent to $\odot P$ at point Q

Method   **Step 1:** Draw $\overleftrightarrow{PQ}$.
         Step 2: Construct $\ell \perp \overleftrightarrow{PQ}$ at Q. Then ℓ is tangent to $\odot P$ at point Q.

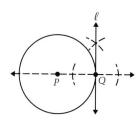

Draw $\overleftrightarrow{PR} \perp \overline{AB}$, $\overleftrightarrow{PS} \perp \overline{BC}$ and $\overleftrightarrow{PT}$ $\perp \overline{AC}$. (Through a given pt. not on a given line, there exists exactly 1 line $\perp$ to the given line.) Then $PR = PS$ and $PR = PT$. (The locus of pts. equidistant from the sides of an $\angle$ is the bisector of the $\angle$.) Thus $PS = PT$ (Substitution Prop.) and P lies on $\overleftrightarrow{CZ}$ by the same locus theorem.

1. Draw a large circle and mark a point on the circle. Construct a tangent at the given point.

2. Write a plan for justification of your construction in Exercise 1. (HINT: Use Theorem 9-2.)

3. Draw $\odot X$. Construct $\triangle ABC$ circumscribing $\odot X$. (HINT: Use Construction 13.)

4. Draw a large acute triangle. Construct the circumcircle. (HINT: Use Theorem 9-6.)

5. Draw a large acute triangle. Construct the incircle. (HINT: Use Theorem 9-8.)

6. Draw a large right triangle. Construct $\odot C$, the circumcircle. The hypotenuse is a __?__ of $\odot C$.

7. Draw a large scalene triangle. By methods of construction, locate the circumcenter, the centroid, and the orthocenter. These three points should be collinear. They lie on a line called the *Euler Line*.

Progress Check

Lesson 9-1, page 375
For $\odot A$, identify each of the following.

1. A radius $\overline{AB}$, $\overline{AC}$ 2. A diameter $\overline{BC}$

3. A secant $\overleftrightarrow{BD}$ 4. A chord $\overline{BC}$, $\overline{BD}$

5. Write the equation of $\odot A$. $(x - 3)^2 + (y + 1)^2 = 4$

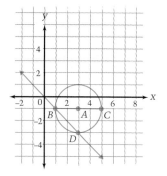

Lesson 9-2, page 381
$\overleftrightarrow{PS}$ and $\overleftrightarrow{PT}$ are tangent to $\odot W$ at S and T.

6. $PS = $ __?__ PT 7. $m\angle PSW = $ __?__ $90 = m\angle PTW$

8. Draw two internally tangent circles.

Lesson 9-3, page 387
In $\odot Q$, $AB = 24$, $QA = 13$, and $QX = QY$.

9. $XB = $ __?__ 12   10. $QX = $ __?__ 5   11. $CD = $ __?__ 24

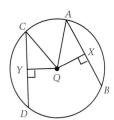

Lesson 9-4, page 392 12. An incircle is a $\odot$ inscribed in a $\triangle$.

12. Define *incircle*.   13. Define *circumcenter*.

14. The __?__ of $\triangle FGH$ is equidistant from F, G, and H. circumcenter

15. The __?__ of $\triangle FGH$ is equidistant from $\overline{FG}$, $\overline{GH}$, and $\overline{HF}$. incenter

FOLLOW-UP

More Practice

• **Worksheet 9–4**

Extension

Have students locate the circumcenter, centroid and orthocenter on various types of triangles. Observe what happens when the triangle is
1. acute. All three are inside the $\triangle$.
2. obtuse. Two are outside the $\triangle$.
3. right. Two are on the $\triangle$.
4. equilateral. They coincide.
• **Extension 9–4**

Computers

• **Computer Worksheet 9–4**

ANSWERS

8.

13. A circumcenter is the pt. of concurrency of $\perp$ bisectors of sides of a $\triangle$.

LESSON 9–5

Resources

Compass
Spinner
    Teaching Aid 20, circular
        geoboard
    Visual Aid 20, circular geoboard
Worksheet 9–5
Extension 9–5

OBJECTIVES

Recognize central angles, arcs and congruent arcs in circles; use postulates and theorems involving arcs of circles.

9-5 Arcs of a Circle

Spinner A   Spinner B   Spinner C   Spinner D

Many game spinners show a circle with angles whose vertices are at the center of the circle. These angles are called central angles.

Definition   *Central Angles*

A central angle of a circle is an angle that lies in the plane of the circle and whose vertex is the center of the circle.

$\angle 1$ is a central angle of $\odot O$.

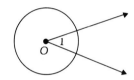

Definition   *Minor Arc*

A minor arc of a circle is the set of points on the circle that lie on or in the interior of a central angle.

In $\odot P$, arc AB (written $\overarc{AB}$ or $\overarc{BA}$) is a minor arc. Notice that $\angle APB$ "cuts off" $\overarc{AB}$. We say that $\overarc{AB}$ is *intercepted* by $\angle APB$. The arc formed by A and B and the points of the circle in the exterior of $\angle APB$ is called a *major arc*.

$\overarc{AQB}$ (or $\overarc{BQA}$) is a major arc. To avoid confusion, we will always use three letters to name a major arc. A minor arc may be named with either two or three letters.

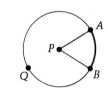

In Spinner C above, a diameter separates the circle into two arcs. These arcs are neither minor or major arcs. They are semicircles.

Definition   *Semicircle*

A semicircle is the set of points which includes the endpoints of a diameter and the points of the circle in a given half-plane formed by the line containing the diameter.

Three letters are used to name a semicircle. $\overarc{XYZ}$ and $\overarc{ZWX}$ are semicircles of $\odot P$.

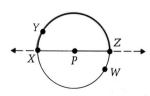

Just as we can give the degree measure of an angle, we can also give the degree measure of an arc.

Definition   *Degree Measure of a Minor Arc*

The degree measure of a minor arc is the measure of its central angle.

Definition   *Degree Measure of a Major Arc*

The degree measure of a major arc, $\overparen{ACB}$, is 360 minus the measure of the corresponding minor arc.

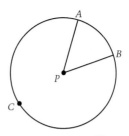

$m\,\overparen{AB} = m\angle ABP$

$m\,\overparen{ACB} = 360 - m\,\overparen{AB}$

Example 1
In $\odot P$, if $m\angle APB = 50$, find $m\overparen{ACB}$.

Solution
Since $m\angle APB = 50$, $m\overparen{AB} = 50$. Why? $m\overparen{ACB} = 360 - m\overparen{AB}$, so $m\overparen{ACB} = 360 - 50 = 310$. The degree of measure of a minor arc is the measure of its central $\angle$.

Definition   *Degree Measure of a Semicircle*

The degree measure of a semicircle is 180.

The next postulate is similar to the Angle Addition Postulate.

Postulate 20   *Arc Addition Postulate*

If P is on $\overparen{AB}$, then $m\overparen{AP} + m\overparen{PB} = m\overparen{APB}$.

If $m\overparen{AP} = 70$ and $m\overparen{PB} = 30$, then $m\overparen{APB} = 100$.

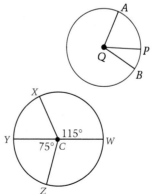

Example 2
$\overline{WY}$ is a diameter of $\odot C$. Find $m\overparen{XY}$ and $m\overparen{WYZ}$.

Solution
Since $m\overparen{WX} + m\overparen{XY} = m\overparen{WXY}$, $m\overparen{XY} = m\overparen{WXY} - m\overparen{WX}$. By substitution, $m\overparen{XY} = 180 - 115 = 65$. By arc addition, $m\overparen{WYZ} = m\overparen{WXY} + m\overparen{YZ} = 180 + 75 = 255$.

A useful relationship between measures of arcs and corresponding chords is given in Theorem 9-10. The proof of this theorem is left to Exercises 21 and 22.

Theorem 9-10

In the same circle or in congruent circles, two minor arcs have equal measures if and only if their chords have the same length.

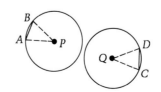

Part I   If $\odot X \cong \odot Y$ and $m\overparen{AB} = m\overparen{CD}$, then $AB = CD$.

Part II   If $\odot X \cong \odot Y$ and $AB = CD$, then $m\overparen{AB} = m\overparen{CD}$.

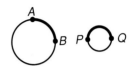

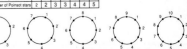

Additional Examples

Example 1

In ⊙S, if *mGLD* = 200, find
m∠GSD. **80**

Example 2

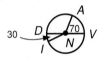

DV is the diameter of ⊙N. Find
mAD and *m AVI*. *mAD* = 110;
m AVI = 250

Error Analysis Students may
confuse degree measure with arc
length when it is studied in Chapter 10. Stress the definition of degree measure of an arc.

In Theorem 9-10, the arcs and chords are in the same or in
congruent circles. Suppose the circles are *not* congruent.
Consider the concentric circles at the right. ***Concentric circles***
are coplanar circles with the same center.

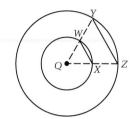

∠Q intercepts both *WX* and *YZ*, so *WX* and *YZ* have equal
measure. Why? Now examine the corresponding chords, *WX*,
and *YZ*. Do they appear to be equal? **Both arcs have
measure = m∠Q; no**
This should help you to understand that Theorem 9-10 is true
only for the same or for congruent circles.

Checking for Understanding

In ⊙Q at the right, *FG* is a diameter. Name each item.

1. A minor arc *FJ*; *JG*   2. A major arc *FGJ*; *JFG*
3. The arc intercepted by ∠1 *JG*
4. A central angle *∠FQJ*; ∠JQG   5. A semicircle *FJG*
6. The measure of a minor arc is _?_ than 180, and the
   measure of a major arc is _?_ than 180.
7. What is the measure of a minor arc that is intercepted by a
   central angle whose measure is 52? **52**
8. The measure of a minor arc is 107. What is the measure of
   the corresponding major arc? **253**

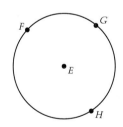

9. *AB* is a chord of ⊙P, and *CD* is a chord of ⊙O. ⊙P ≅ ⊙Q.
   If *AB* = *CD* and *mAB* = 73, then *mCD* = _?_. **73**
10. In ⊙E at the right, *mFG* + *mGH* + *mHF* = _?_. **360**
11. In Spinner B on page 400, if the HR region makes up 15%
    of the circular region, what is the measure of the central
    angle? **54**
12. In Spinner C, what are the chances that the pointer will
    land on red when it is spun? $\frac{1}{2}$
13. Explain why the circles in the computer graphic at the right
    are concentric circles. **They are coplanar and they
    have the same center.**

Assignment Guide

Basic: 2–22 (even), 41–53
Average: 1–16, 17–39 (odd), 41–53
Extended: 2–32 (even), 34–53

Written Exercises

Set A   Spinner A is used when playing a game. The measure of each acute central angle is 60.

1. What are the chances that the pointer will land on 1 when it is spun? $\frac{1}{6}$

2. What are the chances that the pointer will land on an even number when it is spun? $\frac{1}{2}$

Spinner A

$\overline{AB}$ is a diameter of $\odot P$.

3. Name a pair of arcs that have equal measure. **Sample:** $\widehat{BG}, \widehat{BC}$

4. Name a pair of equal chords. **Sample:** $\overline{BG}, \overline{BC}$

5. $m\widehat{BC} = \underline{\ ?\ }$ 60   6. $m\widehat{BD} = \underline{\ ?\ }$ 80

7. $m\widehat{FA} + \underline{\ ?\ } = m\widehat{FE} \quad \widehat{AE}$ 8. $m\widehat{BFD} = \underline{\ ?\ }$ 280

9. $m\widehat{AD} + m\widehat{DG} = \underline{\ ?\ }$ 240   10. $m\widehat{CEA} = \underline{\ ?\ }$ 120 360

11. $m\widehat{BD} + m\widehat{BFD} = \underline{\ ?\ }$ 360   12. $m\widehat{AE} + m\widehat{ECA} = \underline{\ ?\ }$

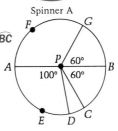

Mary and Dan are making a quilt. The instructions show a quarter of the design for the center of the quilt. The letters indicate the colors of the fabrics to be used. The red and blue triangles are all cut from the same pattern.

13. What is the measure of each central angle? Explain. **15; 90 ÷ 6 = 15**

14. Find the diameter of the circle circumscribed about the finished design in the center of the quilt. **17 in.**

15. How do you know that all the green triangles are congruent?

16. Mary wants to change the design by making the red and blue triangles isosceles. She will not change the size of the central angle. What effect will the changes have on the green triangles? Draw a diagram to illustrate your answer.

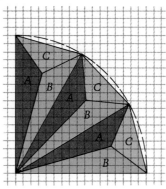

Scale: 1 square = $\frac{1}{2}$"

Points A, B, C, and D are on $\odot P$ as shown.

17. If $m\widehat{AC} = m\widehat{BD}$, prove $m\widehat{AB} = m\widehat{CD}$.

18. If $m\widehat{AB} = m\widehat{CD}$, prove $m\widehat{AC} = m\widehat{BD}$.

ANSWERS

Written Exercises

15. Since the blue and red △s are all ≅, the green triangles can be proved ≅ by SSS ≅ Post. Two sets of corres. sides of the green △s are = because they are corresponding sides of triangles A and B; Thm. 9–10 shows that the third sides of green △s are =. (They are chords with equal arcs that are measured by = central angles.)

16. Assuming that the base of each isos. △ is to be a radius of the ⊙, the green △ will be equilateral (see figure below).

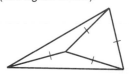

17. Proof: 1. $m\widehat{AC} = m\widehat{BD}$ (Given) 2. $m\widehat{AB} + m\widehat{BC} = m\widehat{AC}$ and $m\widehat{BC} + m\widehat{CD} = m\widehat{BD}$ (Arc Add. Post.) 3. $m\widehat{AB} + m\widehat{BC} = m\widehat{BC} + m\widehat{CD}$ (Substitution Prop. [1, 2]) 4. $m\widehat{BC} = m\widehat{BC}$ (Reflexive Prop.) 5. $m\widehat{AB} = m\widehat{CD}$ (Subtraction Prop. [3, 4])

18. Proof: 1. $m\widehat{AB} = m\widehat{CD}$ (Given) 2. $m\widehat{BC} = m\widehat{BC}$ (Reflexive Prop.) 3. $m\widehat{AB} + m\widehat{BC} = m\widehat{BC} + m\widehat{CD}$ (Add. Prop. [1, 2]) 4. $m\widehat{AB} + m\widehat{BC} = m\widehat{AC}$ and $m\widehat{BC} + m\widehat{CD} = m\widehat{BD}$ (Arc Add. Post.) 5. $m\widehat{AC} = m\widehat{BD}$ (Substitution Prop. [3, 4])

19.

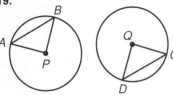

Given: $\odot P \cong \odot Q$; $m\widehat{AB} = m\widehat{CD}$
Prove: $m\angle APB = m\angle CQD$ Proof:
1. $\odot P \cong \odot Q$; $m\widehat{AB} = m\widehat{CD}$ (Given)
2. $m\widehat{AB} = m\angle APB$; $m\widehat{CD} = m\angle CQD$ (Def. of arc measure) 3. $m\angle APB = m\angle CQD$ (Substitution Prop. [1, 2])

20.

Given: $\odot P \cong \odot Q$; $m\angle APB = m\angle CQD$ Prove: $m\widehat{AB} = m\widehat{CD}$
Proof:
1. $\odot P \cong \odot Q$; $m\angle APB = m\angle CQD$ (Given) 2. $m\widehat{AB} = m\angle APB$; $m\widehat{CD} = m\angle CQD$ (Def. of arc measure)
3. $m\widehat{AB} = m\widehat{CD}$ (Substitution Prop. [1, 2])
21. Proof: 1. $\odot P \cong \odot Q$ (Given)
2. $PB = QD$; $PA = QC$ (Def. of $\cong$ $\odot$s [1]) 3. $m\widehat{AB} = m\widehat{CD}$ (Given) 4. $m\widehat{AB} = m\angle APB$; $m\widehat{CD} = m\angle CQD$ (Def. of arc measure) 5. $m\angle APB = m\angle CQD$ (Substitution Prop. [3, 4]) 6. $\triangle APB \cong \triangle CQD$ (SAS $\cong$ Post. [2, 5]) 7. $AB = CD$ (Corres. parts of $\cong \triangle$s are =. [6])
22. Proof: 1. $\odot P \cong \odot Q$ (Given)
2. $PB = QD$; $PA = QC$ (Def. of $\cong$ $\odot$s [1]) 3. $AB = CD$ (Given) 4. $\triangle APB \cong \triangle CQD$ (SSS $\cong$ Post. [2, 3]) 5. $m\angle APB = m\angle CQD$ (Corres. parts of $\cong \triangle$s are =. [4]) 6. $m\widehat{AB} = m\angle APB$; $m\widehat{CD} = m\angle CQD$ (Def. of arc measure) 7. $m\widehat{AB} = m\widehat{CD}$ (Substitution Prop. [5, 6])
28. Freshmen: 54; Sophomores: 72; Juniors: 99; Seniors: 135
30. Given: $\overline{AB}$ is a diameter of $\odot P$; $XZ = YW$ Prove: $m\widehat{XY} = m\widehat{ZW}$
Proof: 1. In $\odot P$, $XZ = YW$ (Given)

19. Prove: In the same or in congruent circles, if two minor arcs have the same measure, then their central angles are equal.

20. Prove: In the same or in congruent circles, if two central angles are equal, then their minor arcs have the same measure.

21. Prove Theorem 9-10, Part I.

22. Prove Theorem 9-10, Part II.

Set B Refer to the diagram at the right. Find the measure of each arc.

23. $\widehat{DE}$ 95   **24.** $\widehat{DEF}$ 175   **25.** $\widehat{EF}$ 80   **26.** $\widehat{GDE}$ 215

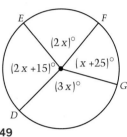

27. Write an equation of a circle that is concentric with the circle whose equation is $(x + 3)^2 + (y - 7)^2 = 64$. **Sample:** $(x + 3)^2 + (y - 7)^2 = 49$

Refer to the circle graph at the right.

28. Use the percents shown to calculate the measure of the central angle in each region.

29. Suppose there are 120 band members. How many of the members are freshmen? sophomores? juniors? seniors? **18; 24; 33; 45**

$\overline{AB}$ is a diameter of $\odot P$.

30. If $XZ = YW$, prove $m\widehat{XY} = m\widehat{ZW}$.

31. If $m\widehat{XY} = m\widehat{ZW}$, prove $XZ = YW$.

32. If $m\widehat{BC} = 2(m\widehat{AC})$, prove $\angle A$ and $\angle B$ are complementary.

Set C **33.** In $\odot P$, if $m\widehat{BC} = 2x$ prove that $\angle BCA$ is a right angle.

34. In $\odot P$, if $m\widehat{XY} = m\widehat{WZ}$, prove $m\angle XYV = m\angle WZV$.

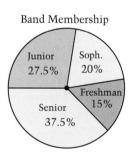

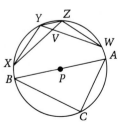

In the circle at the right, $m\widehat{AD} = 3(m\widehat{AB})$, $m\widehat{AC} = 90$, $m\widehat{DC} = 3(m\widehat{BC})$, and $m\widehat{BCD} = 5(m\widehat{AB})$. Find each measure.

35. $m\widehat{AB}$ 40   **36.** $m\widehat{BC}$ 50   **37.** $m\widehat{CD}$ 50

38. $m\widehat{AD}$ 120   **39.** $m\angle DAC$ 75   **40.** $m\angle ACD$ 60

Band Membership

▲ Review Define each of the following.
  41. Polygon inscribed in a circle
  42. Polygon circumscribed about a circle
  43. If $m\widehat{DE} = m\widehat{XY}$, does $DE = XY$? Explain.
  44. $\overline{YW}$ is the altitude drawn to the hypotenuse of right triangle XYZ. Name three similar triangles.
  45. Give the converse of this statement and tell if it is *true* or *false*: If x = 19, then x < 25.
  If x < 25, then x = 19; false

Thinking Ahead Eighteen equally spaced pins form the "circle" on the geoboard.
  $\overline{AB}$ is a diameter of $\odot O$. Do the following exercises without measuring.
  46. Find $m\angle AOC$. 40   **47.** Find $m\widehat{AC}$. 40
  48. What type of triangle is $\triangle COB$? Obtuse and isos.
  49. Find $m\angle CBA$. 20   **50.** $m\widehat{AC} = \underline{\ ?\ } (m\angle CBA)$ 2
  Use Exercises 46–50 to help you with Exercises 51–53.
  51. Find $m\angle ABQ$. 60   **52.** Find $m\widehat{AQ}$. 120
  53. $m\angle ABQ = \underline{\ ?\ } (m\widehat{AQ})$ $\frac{1}{2}$

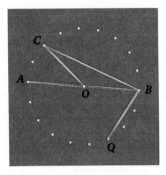

41. A polygon whose vertices lie on the $\odot$.
42. A polygon whose sides are tangent to the $\odot$.
43. Yes, if $\widehat{DE}$ and $\widehat{XY}$ are minor arcs of the same $\odot$ or $\cong \odot$s
44. $\triangle XYZ$, $\triangle XWY$, $\triangle YWZ$

2. $m\widehat{XZ} = m\widehat{YW}$ (In same or $\cong \odot$s, = chords $\Rightarrow$ = corres. minor arcs. [1]) **3.** $m\widehat{XZ} = m\widehat{XY} + m\widehat{YZ}$; $m\widehat{YW} = m\widehat{YZ} + m\widehat{ZW}$ (Arc Add. Post.) **4.** $m\widehat{XY} + m\widehat{YZ} = m\widehat{YZ} + m\widehat{ZW}$ (Substitution Prop. [2, 3]) **5.** $m\widehat{XY} = m\widehat{ZW}$ (Subtraction Prop. [4])
31. Given: $\overline{AB}$ is a diameter of $\odot P$; $m\widehat{XY} = m\widehat{ZW}$ Prove: $XZ = YW$ Proof: **1.** In $\odot P$, $m\widehat{XY} = m\widehat{ZW}$ (Given) **2.** $m\widehat{XY} + m\widehat{YZ} = m\widehat{YZ} + m\widehat{ZW}$ (Add. Prop. [1]) **3.** $m\widehat{XZ} = m\widehat{XY} + m\widehat{YZ}$; $m\widehat{YW} = m\widehat{YZ} + m\widehat{ZW}$ (Arc Add. Post.) **4.** $m\widehat{XZ} = m\widehat{ZW}$ (Substitution Prop. [2, 3]) **5.** $XZ = YW$ (In same or $\cong \odot$s, = minor arcs $\Rightarrow$ = corres. chords. [4])

FOLLOW-UP

More Practice

Consider one of the following **activities** to introduce the lesson.
1. Make a transparency of the diagram in **Exercise 28**. Discuss the mathematics needed to construct such a graph.
2. Make a spinner either for the chalkboard or for the overhead projector. Discuss the related circle concepts.
• **Worksheet 9-5**

Extension

• **Extension 9-5**

Challenge

1. What is the length of each side of square $PQRO$ if $OE = 1$? 2? 3? r? $\frac{\sqrt{2}}{2}$; $\sqrt{2}$; $\frac{3\sqrt{2}}{2}$; $\frac{r\sqrt{2}}{2}$

2. What is the length of each side of square $ABCD$ if $NM = 1$? 2? 3? r? $\frac{\sqrt{10}}{5}$, $\frac{2\sqrt{10}}{5}$, $\frac{3\sqrt{10}}{5}$, $\frac{r\sqrt{10}}{5}$

3. If $\odot O \cong \odot N$, what is the ratio of the length of each side of square $PQRO$ to the length of each side of square $ABCD$? $\frac{\sqrt{5}}{2}$

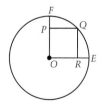

LESSON 9-6

Resources

Teaching Aid 20, circular geoboard
Visual Aid 20, circular geoboard
Teaching Aid 21, circles
Visual Aid 21, circles
Worksheet 9-6
Extension 9-6
Computer Activities 9-6
Computer Worksheet 9-6

OBJECTIVES

Recognize inscribed angles and other angles with vertices on circles; use theorems involving such angles.

WORKSHEET

Name _____ Lesson 9-6

Supply the missing reasons.

1. Given: Equilateral △ABC inscribed in ⊙P
   Prove: m⌢AC = 120

Statements	Reasons
1. Equilateral △ABC inscribed in ⊙P	1. Given
2. △ABC is equiangular.	2. An equilateral △ is also equiangular. [1]
3. m∠B = 60	3. Each ∠ of an equiangular △ has measure 60. [2]
4. m∠B = ½m⌢AC	4. m(inscr. ∠) = ½ m(intercepted arc)
5. 60 = ½m⌢AC	5. Substitution [3, 4]
6. 120 = m⌢AC	6. Multiplication [5]

In ⊙O, UR is a diameter. m⌢UQ = 125; m⌢QS = 95; m∠UOT = 35

2. Name an inscribed angle. 2. ∠QUR, others
3. What is the intercepted arc of angle TSQ? 3. TQ
4. Name a pair of equal angles. 4. ∠QUR, ∠QSR
5. m∠UQR = __?__. 5. 90
6. m∠UQS + m∠UTS = __?__. 6. 180
7. m∠URQ = __?__. 7. 62.5
8. m∠UQS = __?__. 8. 70
9. If TO intersects ⊙O at point A, then m⌢AS = __?__. 9. 75
10. m∠QRS = __?__. 10. 132.5

9-6 Inscribed and Related Angles of a Circle

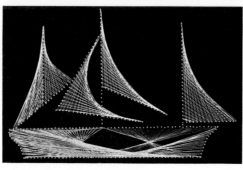
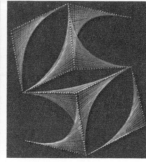
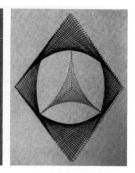

Juliana is making string designs for Artfest. The beginning of one of her designs is shown at the right. The angle formed by the strings is not a central angle. Why? In geometry, such an angle is called an inscribed angle. *Vertex of ∠ is not at center of ⊙.*

Definition *Inscribed Angle*

An angle inscribed in a circle is an angle whose vertex is on the circle and whose sides contain chords of the circle.

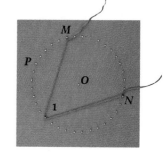

∠1 is inscribed in ⊙O. It also is said that ∠1 is inscribed in ⌢MPN. ⌢MN is intercepted by ∠1.

The geoboards below show three different cases in which ⌢GE is intercepted both by inscribed angle GFE and by central angle GOE.

Case I	Case II	Case III

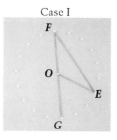
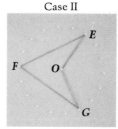
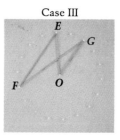

How do you think m∠GFE compares with m∠GOE? with m⌢GE?

The relationship between these measures is stated in Theorem 9-11, which is to be proved in Exercises 30–32.

$$m\angle GFE = \tfrac{1}{2}m\angle GDE$$
$$m\angle GFE = \tfrac{1}{2}\,m\,\widehat{GE}$$

Theorem 9-11

The measure of an inscribed angle is one half the measure of its intercepted arc.

Given $\odot P$; $\angle ACB$ is an inscribed angle.

Prove $m\angle ACB = \frac{1}{2}(m\widehat{AB})$

Plan for Proof

Case I P lies on $\angle ACB$. Draw $\overline{AP}$ and show $m\angle ACB = m\angle 1$. Show $m\angle ACB + m\angle 1 = m\angle 2$. Since $m\angle 2 = m\widehat{AB}$, $2(m\angle ACB) = m\widehat{AB}$.

Case II P is in the interior of $\angle ACB$. Draw $\overrightarrow{CP}$ and use Case I to show $m\angle 1 = \frac{1}{2}(m\widehat{AD})$ and $m\angle 2 = \frac{1}{2}(m\widehat{BD})$. Use Angle and Arc Addition Postulates.

Case III P is in the exterior of $\angle ACB$. Draw $\overrightarrow{CP}$ and show $m\angle ACB = m\angle DCB - m\angle 1$. Use Case I and Angle and Arc Addition Postulates.

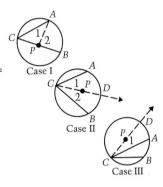

Case I

Case II

Case III

Example 1

Find the measure of $\angle H$.

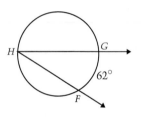

Solution

By Theorem 9-11, $m\angle H = \frac{1}{2}(m\widehat{GF})$. Since $m\widehat{GF} = 62$, $m\angle H = \frac{1}{2}(62) = 31$.

Example 2

In $\odot O$, find the measure of $\widehat{SQ}$.

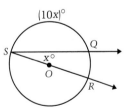

Solution

By Theorem 9-11, $m\angle QSR = \frac{1}{2}(m\widehat{QR})$. Since $m\angle QSR = x$, $m\widehat{QR} = 2x$. $\widehat{SQR}$ is a semicircle, so $m\widehat{SQ} + m\widehat{QR} = 180$.

$$m\widehat{SQ} + m\widehat{QR} = 180$$
$$10x + 2x = 180$$
$$12x = 180$$
$$x = 15$$

Since $m\widehat{SQ} = 10x$, $m\widehat{SQ} = 10(15) = 150$.

The photos on page 408 suggest three theorems which follow directly from Theorem 9-11. Proofs are left to Exercises 16, 17, and 33.

TEACHING NOTES

Use a transparency of a circular geoboard to begin this lesson.

Theorem 9–15 follows almost intuitively from Theorem 9–11. Starting with an inscribed angle, ask students to imagine moving the vertex until one type of angle changes into the other. Show students that both have the same relationship to the intercepted arc.

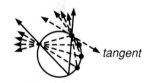

tangent

Examples 1 and **2** provide practice with inscribed angles. Theorem 9–15 is applied in **Example 3**.

EXTENSION   *Lesson* **9-6**

Name _____

Residue Designs

In modular arithmetic, all numbers that have the same remainder when divided by a given number (called the *modulus* or *mod*) are said to be congruent. For example, 7, 16, and 22 are congruent in *mod 3* arithmetic because when each number is divided by 3, the remainder is 1.

To denote this, you can use the symbol ≡ which means "is congruent to."

$7 \equiv 1$ *(mod 3)* $16 \equiv 1$ *(mod 3)* $22 \equiv 1$ *(mod 3)*

When numbers are multiplied in modular arithmetic, the result equals the remainder obtained when the product is divided by the modulus. For example, in *mod 7*,
$3 \times 5 = 15$
$15 \div 7 = 2$ R1
$15 \equiv 1$ *(mod 7)*

The complete multiplication for *mod 7* is shown in the table.

To create *mod 7* art, connect points on a circle according to the table, as shown. If you shade alternate regions, you obtain an interesting design called a *residue design*.

Draw residue designs for each table.

1.   2.   3.

Additional Examples

Example 1

Find the measure of $\widehat{SM}$. 70

Example 2

In $\odot A$, find the measure of $\widehat{CE}$.
$x = 12$; $m\widehat{CE} = 156$

Example 3

$\overline{RI}$ is tangent to $\odot S$ at A. Find $m\angle$ HAI. 105

Error Analysis   Students often mistake the type of angle pictured here for one formed by a tangent and a secant. Extend both sides so they can see that both sides are secants and that there is no definite relationship between the angle and the arc.

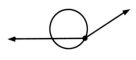

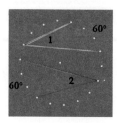

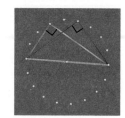

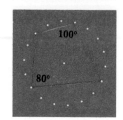

Theorem 9-12

If two inscribed angles intercept the same arc or arcs of equal measure, then the angles are equal.

Theorem 9-13

If an angle is inscribed in a semicircle, then it is a right angle.

Theorem 9-14

If a quadrilateral is inscribed in a circle, then the opposite angles are supplementary.

In $\odot P$ at the right, how is $\angle ACB$ formed? The relationship between the measure of $\angle ACB$ and the measure of its intercepted arc $\widehat{AXC}$ is the same as it is for inscribed angles. This relationship is stated in Theorem 9-15, which is to be proved in Exercises 34–36.

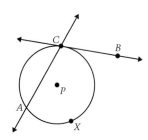

Theorem 9-15

The measure of an angle formed by a tangent and a secant that intersect at the point of tangency is one half the measure of the intercepted arc.

Given $\odot P$ tangent $\overleftrightarrow{BC}$ and secant $\overleftrightarrow{AC}$; C is the point of tangency.

Prove $m\angle ACB = \frac{1}{2}(m\widehat{AXC})$

Plan for   **Case I** P lies on $\angle ACB$.
Proof   Show $\angle ACB$ is a right angle. Since $\widehat{AXC}$ is a semicircle, $m\widehat{AXC} = 180$. Thus, $m\angle ACB = \frac{1}{2}(m\widehat{AXC})$.

Case II P lies in the interior of $\angle ACB$.
Use a method similar to the plan for proof of Theorem 9-11, Case II.

Case III P lies in the exterior of $\angle ACB$.
Use a method similar to the plan for proof of Theorem 9-11, Case III.

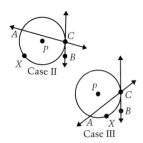

Example 3

$\overrightarrow{TU}$ is tangent to $\odot Q$ at T. Find $m\angle 1$.

Solution

Since $m\angle Q = 120$, $m\widehat{ST} = 120$. Why? By Theorem 9-15,
$m\angle 1 = \frac{1}{2}(m\widehat{ST}) = \frac{1}{2}(120) = 60$.   The degree measure of a minor arc is the measure of its central $\angle$.

Checking for Understanding 1. $\angle YZW$; $\angle YVW$; $\angle YWX$

W is a point of tangency on the circle at the right.

1. Name every angle whose measure is equal to $\frac{1}{2}(m\widehat{WY})$.

2. Name a pair of supplementary inscribed angles. $\angle ZVW$
$\angle ZYW$

3. Look at the beginning of Juliana's string design. What is the measure of the angle formed by the strings? **60**

4. Refer to the circular geoboards on page 406. Find $m\angle EFG$ in each of the three cases. **30; 60; 20**

5. In Example 1, $\angle H$ is inscribed in arc ___?___. **GHF**

6. Name the intercepted arc in Example 2. $\widehat{QR}$

7. In Example 2, if T is a point on $\widehat{QSR}$, then $m\angle QTR = $ ___?___. **15**

8. If point A is on $\odot O$ and $\overrightarrow{AB}$ and $\overrightarrow{AC}$ contain the endpoints of a diameter, then $m\angle BAC = $ ___?___. **90**

9. Draw a quadrilateral that cannot be inscribed in a circle.

10. Refer to Example 3. How can you find $m\angle 1$ without using Theorem 9-15?

Written Exercises

Set A $\overline{HF}$ is a diameter of $\odot O$ and $\overleftrightarrow{DF}$ is tangent to $\odot O$ at F.

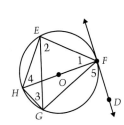

1. If $m\widehat{EH} = 65$, then $m\angle 1 = $ ___?___. **32.5**

2. If $m\angle 4 = 45$, then $m\widehat{EF} = $ ___?___. **90**

3. If $m\widehat{HG} = 44$, then $m\angle 2 = $ ___?___. **68**

4. If $m\widehat{EF} = 124$, then $m\angle 3 = $ ___?___. **28**

5. If $m\widehat{FG} = 140$, then $m\angle 5 = $ ___?___. **70**

6. $m\angle HEF = $ ___?___ **90**

7. $m\angle EFG + m\angle GHE = $ ___?___ **180**

EXERCISE NOTES

Exercises 18 and **19**   involve applications of angles inscribed in a semicircle.
Exercise 27   involves coordinate geometry.
Exercises 28 and **29**   are locus problems.

ANSWERS

Checking for Understanding

9.

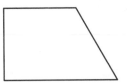

10. $m\angle QST = m\angle QTS = \frac{1}{2}(180 - 120) = 30$. Since $\angle QTS$ and $\angle 1$ are comp., $m\angle 1 = 60$.

Written Exercises

15. Proof: 1. *ABCD* is inscribed in ⊙*P*. (Given) 2. *m*∠1 = *m*∠4; *m*∠2 = *m*∠3 (If 2 inscribed ∠s intercept the same arc on a ⊙, then they are =.) 3. *m*∠1 + *m*∠2 = *m*∠3 + *m*∠4 (Add. Prop. [2])

16.

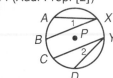

Given: ⊙*P*; ∠1 and ∠2 are inscribed ∠s; *m*$\widehat{AB}$ = *m*$\widehat{CD}$ Prove: *m*∠1 = *m*∠2 Proof: 1. *m*$\widehat{AB}$ = *m*$\widehat{CD}$ (Given) 2. *m*∠1 = $\frac{1}{2}$(*m*$\widehat{AB}$) and *m*∠2 = $\frac{1}{2}$(*m*$\widehat{CD}$) (The measure of an inscribed ∠ is $\frac{1}{2}$ the measure of its intercepted arc.) 3. $\frac{1}{2}$(*m*$\widehat{AB}$) = $\frac{1}{2}$(*m*$\widehat{CD}$) (Mult. Prop. [1]) 4. *m*∠1 = *m*∠2 (Substitution Prop. [2, 3])

17.

Given: ∠1 is inscribed in semicircle $\widehat{BCA}$ of ⊙*P*. Prove: ∠1 is a rt. ∠. Proof: 1. $\widehat{BCA}$ is a semicircle of ⊙*P*. (Given) 2. $\overline{AB}$ is a diameter of ⊙*P*. (Def. of semicircle [1]) 3. $\widehat{BDA}$ is a semicircle. (Def. of semicircle [2]) 4. *m*$\widehat{BDA}$ = 180 (Def. of measure of semicircle) 5. *m*∠1 = 90 (Measure of an inscribed ∠ is $\frac{1}{2}$ the measure of its intercepted arc.) 6. ∠1 is a rt. ∠. (Def. of rt. ∠ [5])
18. Place the corner of the card on the circle and mark the points on the circle where the edges of the card intersect the circle. These two points are the endpoints of a diameter.
19. Use the procedure from #18 above to locate a second diameter. The pt. of intersection of 2 diameters of a ⊙ is the center of the ⊙.

$\overleftrightarrow{RS}$ is tangent to ⊙*Q* at *R*, *m*$\widehat{OP}$ = 70, *m*$\widehat{MN}$ = 20, and *m*$\widehat{MR}$ = 100.

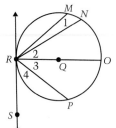

8. *m*∠1 = ___ 10   **9.** *m*∠2 = ___ 30

10. *m*∠3 = ___ 35   **11.** *m*∠4 = ___ 55

ABCD is inscribed in ⊙*P*.

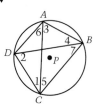

12. If *m*∠*DAB* = 95, then *m*∠*DCB* = ___. 85

13. If *m*∠*ADC* = 70 and *m*∠7 = 75, then *m*∠4 = ___. 35

14. If *m*∠*DAB* = 110 and *m*∠2 = 35, then *m*∠6 = ___. 75

15. Prove: *m*∠1 + *m*∠2 = *m*∠3 + *m*∠4.

16. Prove Theorem 9-12.

17. Prove Theorem 9-13.

Set B Judy has a drawing of a circle whose center is not marked.

18. How can she draw a diameter of this circle using only the corner of a 3-by-5 index card?

19. How can she find the center of the circle?

The Wankel engine is designed around a curve called a *Reuleaux triangle*. The curve is formed by drawing $\widehat{AB}$, $\widehat{BC}$, and $\widehat{AC}$ which are arcs of circles whose centers are *C*, *A*, and *B*, respectively. △*ABC* is an equilateral triangle.

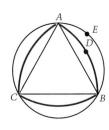

20. Find *m*$\widehat{ADB}$ of the Reuleaux triangle. 60

21. Find *m*$\widehat{AEB}$ of the circle that circumscribes △*ABC*. 120

QRST is inscribed in a circle.

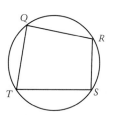

22. *m*∠*Q* = 2*x* + 12 and *m*∠*S* = 3*x* + 18. Find *m*∠*Q*. 72

23. *m*∠*R* = 2*x* + 15 and *m*∠*T* = 8*x* − 5. Find *m*∠*T*. 131

24. *m*∠*Q* = 4*x* + 5, *m*∠*R* = 7*x* + 2, and *m*∠*T* = 5*x* − 2. Find *m*∠*S*. 115

25. *m*∠*Q* = 6*x* − 5, *m*∠*R* = 2*x* + 30, and *m*∠*S* = 9*x* − 10. Find *m*∠*T*. 124

On a grid, graph the circle whose equation is $x^2 + y^2 = 25$. Label points $A(-5, 0)$, $B(5, 0)$, and $C(3, 4)$.

26. Use algebra to show that A, B, and C are on the circle.

27. Without using Theorem 9-13, show that $\triangle ABC$ is a right triangle.

26. A: $(-5)^2 + 0^2 = 25$
B: $5^2 + 0^2 = 25$
C: $3^2 + 4^2 = 25$

27. $AB = 10$;
$BC = \sqrt{2^2 + (-4)^2} = \sqrt{20}$;
$AC = \sqrt{8^2 + 4^2} = \sqrt{80}$; $AB^2 = 100$
and $BC^2 + AC^2 = 20 + 80 = 100$

Draw a figure for each exercise.

28. In $\odot O$, what is the locus of vertices of inscribed angles that intercept $\overset{\frown}{KM}$?

29. In a plane, what is the locus of vertices of right triangles with hypotenuse $\overline{VP}$?

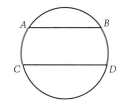

Prove each case of Theorem 9-11.

30. Case I   **31.** Case II   **32.** Case III

33. Prove Theorem 9-14.

Prove each case of Theorem 9-15.

34. Case I   **35.** Case II   **36.** Case III

37. Prove: If two chords in a circle are parallel, then the arcs they cut off between them are of equal measure. (HINT: Draw $\overline{BC}$ and use Theorem 9-11.)

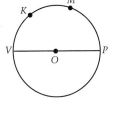

Set C   Quadrilateral $QRST$ is inscribed in $\odot P$.

38. $m\angle QTS = x^2 + 2x + 115$ and $m\angle QRS = 3x + 71$. Find $m\angle QTS$. **115 or 118**

39. If $m\angle QRS = m\angle TSR - k$, prove that $m\angle TQR = m\angle QTS - k$.

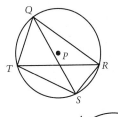

▲ Review   Refer to $\odot O$ at the right.

40. Name a minor arc.   **40.** $\overset{\frown}{AB}$; $\overset{\frown}{BC}$; $\overset{\frown}{CA}$

41. Name a major arc.   **41.** $\overset{\frown}{ABC}$; $\overset{\frown}{ACB}$; $\overset{\frown}{BAC}$

42. Is $\triangle ABC$ inscribed in $\odot O$ or circumscribed about $\odot O$? **Inscribed in**

43. $\triangle RST \sim \triangle MNP$, $RT = x + 1$, and $PM = 3x - 2$. Find x. **4**

44. Suppose lines j and k do not intersect. Is j parallel to k? Explain. **Not necessarily; if j and k are coplanar, they are parallel; if j and k are not coplanar, they are skew.**

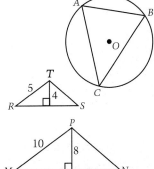

29. a circle with center at midpt. M of $\overline{VP}$, excluding points V and P

30. Proof: 1. $\odot P$ with inscribed $\angle ACP$; P lies on $\angle ACB$. (Given) 2. Draw $\overline{AP}$. (2 pts. determine a line.) 3. $CP = AP$ (Def. of $\odot$ [1]) 4. $m\angle 1 = m\angle ACB$ (In a $\triangle$, 2 sides $=$ $\Rightarrow$ angles opp. them are $=$. [3]) 5. $m\angle 2 = m\angle 1 + m\angle ACB$ (Meas. of an ext. $\angle$ $=$ sum of measures of its 2 remote int. $\angle$s.) 6. $m\angle 2 = m\angle ACB + m\angle ACB = 2(m\angle ACB)$ (Substitution Prop. [4, 5]) 7. $m\angle 2 = m\overset{\frown}{AB}$ (Def. of arc meas.) 8. $2(m\angle ACB) = m\overset{\frown}{AB}$ (Substitution Prop. [6, 7]) 9. $m\angle ACB = \frac{1}{2}(m\overset{\frown}{AB})$ (Mult. Prop. [8])

31. Proof: 1. $\odot P$ with inscribed $\angle ACB$; P is in the interior of $\angle ACB$. (Given) 2. Draw $\overleftrightarrow{CP}$. (2 pts. determine a line.) 3. $m\angle 1 = \frac{1}{2}(m\overset{\frown}{AD})$; $m\angle 2 = \frac{1}{2}(m\overset{\frown}{DB})$ (Case I, Exercise 30) 4. $m\angle 1 + m\angle 2 = \frac{1}{2}(m\overset{\frown}{AD}) + \frac{1}{2}(m\overset{\frown}{DB}) = \frac{1}{2}(m\overset{\frown}{AD} + m\overset{\frown}{DB})$ (Add. Prop. [3]) 5. $m\angle ACB = m\angle 1 + m\angle 2$ (Angle Add. Post.) 6. $m\overset{\frown}{AB} = m\overset{\frown}{AD} + m\overset{\frown}{DB}$ (Arc Add. Post.) 7. $m\angle ACB = \frac{1}{2}(m\overset{\frown}{AB})$ (Substitution Prop. [4, 5, 6])

32. Proof: 1. $\odot P$ with inscribed $\angle ACB$; P is in the exterior of $\angle ACB$. (Given) 2. Draw $\overleftrightarrow{CP}$. (2 pts. determine a line.) 3. $m\angle 1 = \frac{1}{2}(m\overset{\frown}{DA})$; $m\angle DCB = \frac{1}{2}(m\overset{\frown}{DB})$ (Case I, Exercise 30) 4. $m\angle 1 + m\angle ACB = m\angle DCB$ (Angle Add. Post.) 5. $m\angle ACB = m\angle DCB - m\angle 1$ (Subtraction Prop. [4]) 6. $m\angle ACB = \frac{1}{2}(m\overset{\frown}{DB}) - \frac{1}{2}(m\overset{\frown}{DA}) = \frac{1}{2}(m\overset{\frown}{DB} - m\overset{\frown}{DA})$ (Substitution Prop. [3, 5]) 7. $m\overset{\frown}{DB} = m\overset{\frown}{DA} + m\overset{\frown}{AB}$ (Arc Add. Post.) 8. $m\overset{\frown}{AB} = m\overset{\frown}{DB} - m\overset{\frown}{DA}$ (Subtraction Prop. [7]) 9. $m\angle ACB = \frac{1}{2}(m\overset{\frown}{AB})$ (Substitution Prop. [6, 8])

Thinking Ahead Draw a large circle. Then draw two secants $\overleftrightarrow{AC}$ and $\overleftrightarrow{BD}$ that intersect in the interior of the circle. Draw $\overline{BC}$. Label your figure as shown at the right. **Samples are** Find the following measures in your figure. **given**

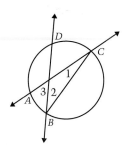

45. $m\angle 1$ 25   **46.** $m\widehat{AB}$ 50   **47.** $m\angle 2$ 20
48. $m\widehat{CD}$ 40   **49.** $m\angle 3$ 45

50. Compare $m\angle 3$ to $m\widehat{AB} + m\widehat{DC}$. What relationship exists? $m\angle 3 = \frac{1}{2}(m\,\widehat{AB} + m\,\widehat{DC})$

51. Repeat Exercises 45–50 with a new drawing. Does the relationship still hold? **Yes**

Now try a similar activity with two secants that intersect in an exterior point of the circle. Draw and label a diagram like the one at the right. Find the following measures. **Samples are given.**

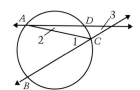

52. $m\angle 1$ 29   **53.** $m\widehat{AB}$ 58   **54.** $m\angle 2$ 5
55. $m\widehat{CD}$ 10   **56.** $m\angle 3$ 24

57. Compare $m\angle 3$ to $m\widehat{AB} - m\widehat{CD}$. What relationship exists? $m\angle 3 = \frac{1}{2}(m\widehat{AB} - m\widehat{CD})$

58. Repeat Exercises 52–57 with a new drawing. Does the relationship still hold? **Yes**

💻 Computer Activities: Drawing and Measuring

1. Draw a circle with two intersecting chords. For each chord, find the lengths of the two segments formed. Then find the product for each pair of lengths. What is true of the two products? **They are =.**

2. Repeat the activity five more times. Are your results the same? **Yes**

3. Based on your results, what conjecture can you make?

Challenge

CATH is a square; $CA = 20$; $\overline{CA}$ and $\overline{CH}$ are tangent to $\odot Y$; $\overline{TA}$ and $\overline{TH}$ are tangent to $\odot Q$; $\odot Q$ contains the center of $\odot Y$; the diameter of $\odot Y$ is 12.

Find the diameter of $\odot Q$. $56 - 28\sqrt{2} \approx 16.40$

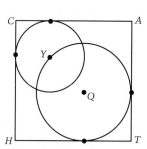

Construction Exercises

Construction 14

Construct the tangents to a circle from a given exterior point.

Given   ⊙P and point R in the exterior of ⊙P

Construct Tangents to ⊙P from R

Method   **Step 1:** Draw $\overline{PR}$. Construct ℓ, the perpendicular bisector of $\overline{PR}$. Let O be the point of intersection of ℓ and $\overline{PR}$.

Step 2: Using $\overline{OP}$ as the radius, draw ⊙O. Let A and B be the points of intersection of ⊙O and ⊙P.

Step 3: Draw $\overleftrightarrow{RA}$ and $\overleftrightarrow{RB}$. Then $\overleftrightarrow{RA}$ and $\overleftrightarrow{RB}$ are tangents to ⊙P from point R.

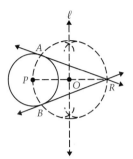

1. Draw a circle and mark a point in its exterior. Construct tangents to the circle from the exterior point.

2. Write a plan for justification of your construction in Exercise 1. (HINT: In the given circle, draw a radius to a point of tangency. Then use Theorem 9-13.)

3. Draw ⊙T with diameter $\overline{AB}$. Construct a 30-60-90 triangle whose hypotenuse is $\overline{AB}$. (HINT: Use Theorem 8-6.)

4. Write a plan for justification of your construction in Exercise 3.

5. Draw two segments, $\overline{AB}$ and $\overline{CD}$. Construct a segment whose length is the geometric mean of AB and CD. (HINT: Construct a circle with diameter equal to AB + CD and use Theorem 8-2.)

6. Draw two segments, $\overline{PQ}$ and $\overline{RS}$. Construct a segment of length $\sqrt{3(PQ)(RS)}$. (HINT: Use a method similar to the one in Exercise 5.)

7. Draw a segment $\overline{VW}$. Assume VW = 1. Construct a segment of length $\sqrt{7}$.

8. Draw a segment, $\overline{XY}$. Assume XY = 1. Construct a right triangle such that the hypotenuse has length 5 and the altitude to the hypotenuse has length $\sqrt{3}$.

Computer Activities

1. Sample:

3. If 2 chords intersect in a ⊙, then the product of the lengths of the segs. on 1 chord is = to the product of the lengths of the segs. on the other chord.

Warm-Up Review

1. State three ways to prove that two triangles are similar. AA; SAS; SSS
2. Find the measure of a central angle whose intercepted arc measures 82. 82
3. Find the measure of an inscribed angle whose intercepted arc measures 82. 41
4. If $\triangle AOD \sim \triangle COB$, state three ratios that are equal. $\frac{AO}{CO} = \frac{OD}{OB} = \frac{AD}{CB}$
5. In $\triangle ABC$, $m\angle C = 72$ and the measure of an exterior angle at A is 135. Find $m\angle B$. 63

9-7 Other Angles and Chords of a Circle

In the previous lesson, you studied the relationships between the measures of arcs and angles whose vertices are on a circle. This lesson deals with the measures of angles whose vertices are *not* on a circle.

In the diagram, $\angle 1$ is formed by two secants that intersect in the interior of a circle. $\angle 1$ and its vertical angle intercept arcs $\overset{\frown}{QT}$ and $\overset{\frown}{RS}$. The measure of $\angle 1$ is related to the measures of these two arcs. This relationship is stated in Theorem 9-16. Its proof is left to Exercise 24.

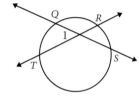

Theorem 9-16

The measure of an angle formed by two secants that intersect in the interior of a circle is one half the sum of the measures of the arcs intercepted by the angle and its vertical angle.

Given $\overleftrightarrow{QS}$ and $\overleftrightarrow{RT}$ intersect in the interior of the circle.

Prove $m\angle 1 = \frac{1}{2}(m\overset{\frown}{QT} + m\overset{\frown}{RS})$

Plan for Proof   Draw $\overline{TS}$. Show $m\angle 1 = m\angle 2 + m\angle 3$. Use Theorem 9-11 to show $m\angle 2 = \frac{1}{2}(m\overset{\frown}{RS})$ and $m\angle 3 = \frac{1}{2}(m\overset{\frown}{QT})$.

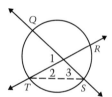

Example 1

Find $m\angle 1$ at the right.

Solution

By Theorem 9-16, $m\angle 1 = \frac{1}{2}(m\overset{\frown}{AB} + m\overset{\frown}{CD})$.
So $m\angle 1 = \frac{1}{2}(30 + 50) = 40$.

Angles that intercept arcs of a circle and whose vertices are in the exterior of the circle can be formed as follows.

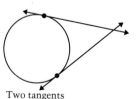

Two secants

A secant and a tangent

Two tangents

Theorem 9-17 states the relationship between the measures of these angles and the intercepted arcs. Its proof is requested in Exercises 25-27.

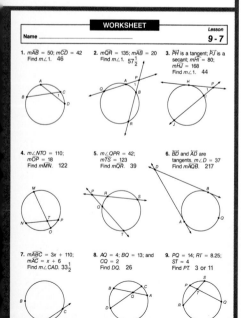

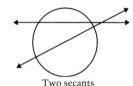

Theorem 9-17

The measure of an angle formed by two secants, a secant and a tangent, or two tangents that intersect in the exterior of a circle is one half the difference of the measures of the intercepted arcs.

Given **Case I** $\overleftrightarrow{BC}$ and $\overleftrightarrow{ED}$ intersect in the exterior of a circle.

Prove $m\angle 1 = \frac{1}{2}(m\overparen{CE} - m\overparen{BD})$

Plan for Proof Draw $\overline{BE}$. Show $m\angle 1 = m\angle 2 - m\angle 3$.
Show $m\angle 2 = \frac{1}{2}(m\overparen{CE})$ and $m\angle 3 = \frac{1}{2}(m\overparen{BD})$.

Case I

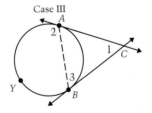

Given **Case II** $\overleftrightarrow{CQ}$ is tangent to the circle at Q; $\overleftrightarrow{BC}$ is a secant.

Prove $m\angle 1 = \frac{1}{2}(m\overparen{BQ} - m\overparen{AQ})$

Plan for Proof Draw $\overline{BQ}$. Show $m\angle 1 = m\angle 2 - m\angle 3$.
Show $m\angle 2 = \frac{1}{2}(m\overparen{BQ})$ and $m\angle 3 = \frac{1}{2}(m\overparen{AQ})$.

Case II

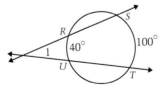

Given **Case III** $\overleftrightarrow{BC}$ and $\overleftrightarrow{AC}$ are tangent to the circle at B and A, respectively.

Prove $m\angle 1 = \frac{1}{2}(m\overparen{BYA} - m\overparen{BA})$

Plan for Proof Draw $\overline{AB}$. Show $m\angle 1 = m\angle 2 - m\angle 3$.
Show $m\angle 2 = \frac{1}{2}(m\overparen{BYA})$ and $m\angle 3 = \frac{1}{2}(m\overparen{BA})$.

Case III

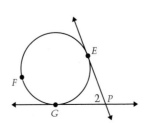

Example 2

Find $m\angle 1$ at the right.

Solution

By Case I of Theorem 9-17, $m\angle 1 = \frac{1}{2}(m\overparen{ST} - m\overparen{RU})$.
So $m\angle 1 = \frac{1}{2}(100 - 40) = 30$.

Example 3

$\overleftrightarrow{EP}$ and $\overleftrightarrow{GP}$ are tangents. Find $m\angle 2$ if $m\overparen{EFG} = 250$.

Solution

If $m\overparen{EFG} = 250$, then $m\overparen{EG} = 360 - 250 = 110$. By Case III of Theorem 9-17, $m\angle 2 = \frac{1}{2}(m\overparen{EFG} - m\overparen{EG}) = \frac{1}{2}(250 - 110) = 70$.

OBJECTIVE

Use theorems involving angles with vertices not on circles and segments formed by chords, secants and tangents.

TEACHING NOTES

Sketch a circle with an inscribed angle on an overlay. Move the vertex of the angle outside the circle and have students make observations about the intercepted arcs. Lead into the specifics of Theorem 9–17.

Theorem 9–18 is easily developed using similar triangles. Do not neglect relationships

EXTENSION Lesson 9-7

Name _____

Polar Coordinates

In the coordinate plane, you can locate any point P by an ordered pair (x, y), where x shows the distance of P from the y-axis and y shows the distance of P from the x-axis. Such coordinates are called *rectangular* coordinates.

Another coordinate system is the *polar coordinate system*. In this system, any point in a plane can be located by an ordered pair of the form (r, θ). In this case, r represents the distance of P from the origin and θ represents an angle measure. In the figure shown, one ray of the angle being measured is the positive side of the x-axis, and the other ray extends from the origin through point P.

All angles are measured counterclockwise from the positive side of the x-axis.

Give polar coordinates for each point.

1. A (4, 30°) 2. B (3, 75°) 3. C (3, 165°)
4. D (2, 225°) 5. E (4, 270°) 6. F (2, 330°)
7. G (4, 120°) 8. H (4, 195°) 9. I (5, 315°)

You can convert from polar coordinates to rectangular coordinates by using the following formulas:

$$x = r\cos\theta \qquad y = r\sin\theta$$

Find the rectangular coordinates for each point. Give answers in simplest radical form.

10. (4, 60°) $(2, 2\sqrt{3})$ 11. (3, 45°) $\left(\frac{3}{2}\sqrt{2}, \frac{3}{2}\sqrt{2}\right)$ 12. (10, 30°) $(5\sqrt{3}, 5)$

among tangent and secant segments.

Additional Examples

Example 1

Find $m\widehat{RS}$. 40

Example 2

If $m\angle AED = 20$ and $m\widehat{BC} = 80$, find $m\widehat{AD}$. 40

Example 3

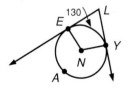

$\overleftrightarrow{EL}$ and $\overleftrightarrow{YL}$ are tangents to circle N. Find $m\angle L$ if $m\widehat{EY} = 130$. 50

Example 4

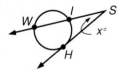

$\overleftrightarrow{SH}$ is a tangent. If $m\widehat{WH} = 136$ and $m\widehat{IH} = 6x$, find $m\widehat{IH}$. 102

Example 4

$\overleftrightarrow{ST}$ is a tangent. If $m\widehat{SU} = 4x$ and $m\widehat{SV} = 60$, find $m\widehat{SU}$.

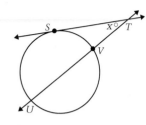

Solution

By Case II of Theorem 9-17, $m\angle STV = \frac{1}{2}(m\widehat{SU} - m\widehat{SV})$. Use substitution and solve the equation.

$$m\angle STV = \frac{1}{2}(m\widehat{SU} - m\widehat{SV})$$
$$x = \frac{1}{2}(4x - 60)$$
$$x = 2x - 30$$
$$x = 30$$

Since $m\widehat{SU} = 4x$, $m\widehat{SU} = 4(30) = 120$.

Just as there are relationships between the measures of certain angles and the measures of the arcs they intercept, there are relationships for the lengths of certain segments that intersect a circle.

Theorem 9-18 expresses the relationship for the lengths of the segments formed by two chords intersecting in a circle. Its proof is left to Exercise 28. Other segment relationships are to be proved in Exercises 29–30.

Theorem 9-18

If two chords intersect in a circle, then the product of the lengths of the segments on one chord is equal to the product of the lengths of the segments on the other.

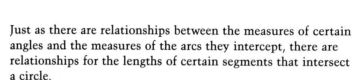

Given In $\odot P$, chords $\overline{AB}$ and $\overline{CD}$ intersect at O.

Prove $(AO)(OB) = (DO)(OC)$

Plan for Proof Draw $\overline{AD}$ and $\overline{BC}$. Use AA Similarity Post. to show $\triangle AOD \sim \triangle COB$. Thus, $\frac{AO}{OC} = \frac{DO}{OB}$.

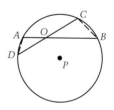

Example 5

In the circle at the right, $VX = 8$, $WV = 6$, and $VY = 4$. Find ZV.

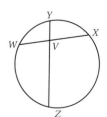

Solution

By Theorem 9-18, $(WV)(VX) = (ZV)(VY)$. So $6(8) = (ZV)(4)$. Thus, $ZV = 12$.

Assignment Guide

Basic: 1–15, 37–41
Average: 2–34 (even), 37–41
Extended: 1–35 (odd), 36–41

Checking for Understanding

In each exercise, find x.

1. 62.5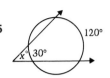

2. 45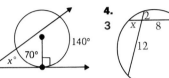

3. 35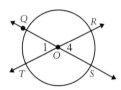

4. 3

5. Suppose $\overleftrightarrow{QS}$ and $\overleftrightarrow{RT}$ intersect at the center of the circle as shown at the right. Use the definition of degree measure of a minor arc, but *not* Theorem 9-16 to give a Plan for Proof that $m\angle 1 = \frac{1}{2}(m\widehat{QT} + m\widehat{RS})$.

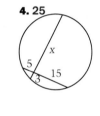

Written Exercises

Set A In each exercise, find x

1. 60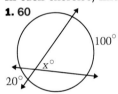

2. 50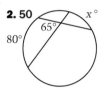

3. 110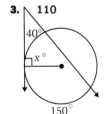

4. 25

5. 230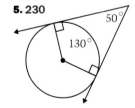

6. 130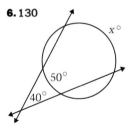

7. 100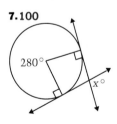

8. 10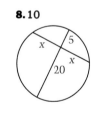

$\overleftrightarrow{AD}$ and $\overleftrightarrow{AE}$ are tangents, $\overleftrightarrow{AC}$ is a secant, and $\overline{GD}$ and $\overline{FE}$ are chords.

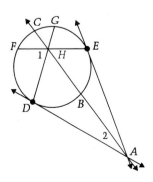

9. $m\widehat{DC} = 110$; $m\widehat{DB} = 43$; $m\angle 2 = \underline{\ ?\ }$ 33.5

10. $m\widehat{FD} = 70$; $m\widehat{GE} = 50$; $m\angle 1 = \underline{\ ?\ }$ 60

11. $m\widehat{DCE} = 300$; $m\angle DAE = \underline{\ ?\ }$ 120

12. $m\angle DAE = 60$; $m\widehat{DE} = \underline{\ ?\ }$ 120

13. $m\widehat{FD} = 65$; $m\angle 1 = 60$; $m\widehat{GE} = \underline{\ ?\ }$ 55

14. $m\widehat{BD} = 50$; $m\angle 2 = 20$; $m\widehat{CD} = \underline{\ ?\ }$ 90

15. $FH = 5$; $HG = 4$; $DH = 10$; $HE = \underline{\ ?\ }$ 8

Example 5

If $LN = 4$, $LG = 3$ and $LB = 9$, find LS. 12

Error Analysis Students sometimes confuse an angle formed by two secants intersecting inside a circle with a central angle. The difference can be emphasized by placing a dot at the center of the circle.

EXERCISE NOTES

Exercises 29–34 involve relationships between tangent and secant segments.

ANSWERS

Checking for Understanding

5. Since $\angle 1$ and $\angle 4$ are vert. $\angle$s, $m\angle 1 = m\angle 4$; then, since the measure of a minor arc is = to the measure of its central $\angle$, $m\widehat{QT} = m\widehat{RS}$; then $m\angle 1 + m\angle 4 = m\widehat{QT} + m\widehat{RS}$, $2m\angle 1 = m\widehat{QT} + m\widehat{RS}$, and $m\angle 1 = \frac{1}{2}(m\widehat{QT} + m\widehat{RS})$.

Written Exercises

22. Proof: 1. $\overleftrightarrow{RQ}$ and $\overleftrightarrow{RS}$ are tangent to $\odot U$. (Given) 2. $m\angle R = \frac{1}{2}(m\widehat{QTS} - m\widehat{QS})$ (The measure of an $\angle$ formed by tangents to a $\odot$ is = to $\frac{1}{2}$ the difference between the measures of the intercepted arcs.) 3. $m\widehat{QTS} = 360 - m\widehat{QS}$ (Def. of measure of major arc) 4. $m\angle R = \frac{1}{2}(360 - m\widehat{QS} - m\widehat{QS}) = 180 - m\widehat{QS}$ (Substitution Prop. [2, 3]) 5. $m\widehat{QS} + m\angle R = 180$ (Add. Prop. [4])

23. Proof: 1. $\overleftrightarrow{RQ}$ and $\overleftrightarrow{RS}$ are tangent to $\odot U$. (Given) 2. $m\angle R = \frac{1}{2}(m\widehat{STQ} - m\widehat{QS})$ (The measure of an $\angle$ formed by tangents to a $\odot$ is = to $\frac{1}{2}$ the difference between the measures of the intercepted arcs.) 3. $m\widehat{STQ} = 360 - m\widehat{QS}$ (Def. of measure of major arc) 4. $m\widehat{QS} = 360 - m\widehat{STQ}$ (Subtraction Prop. [3]) 5. $m\angle R = \frac{1}{2}(m\widehat{STQ} - (360 - m\widehat{STQ})) = m\widehat{STQ} - 180$ (Substitution Prop. [2, 3]) 6. $m\widehat{STQ} = 180 + m\angle R$ (Add. Prop. [5])

24. Proof: 1. Secants $\overleftrightarrow{QS}$ and $\overleftrightarrow{RT}$ intersect in the interior of the $\odot$. (Given) 2. Draw $\overline{TS}$. (2 pts. determine a line.) 3. $m\angle 1 = m\angle 3 + m\angle 2$ (Measure of exterior $\angle$ of a $\triangle$ = sum of measures of the 2 remote int. $\angle$s.) 4. $m\angle 2 = \frac{1}{2}(m\widehat{RS})$; $m\angle 3 = \frac{1}{2}(m\widehat{QT})$ (Measure of inscribed $\angle = \frac{1}{2}$ measure of intercepted arc.) 5. $m\angle 1 = \frac{1}{2}(m\widehat{QT}) + \frac{1}{2}(m\widehat{RS}) = \frac{1}{2}(m\widehat{QT} + m\widehat{RS})$ (Substitution Prop. [3, 4])

25. Proof: 1. Secants $\overleftrightarrow{BC}$ and $\overleftrightarrow{DE}$ intersect in the exterior of a $\odot$. (Given) 2. Draw $\overline{BE}$. (2 pts. determine a line.) 3. $m\angle 2 = m\angle 1 + m\angle 3$ (Measure of an exterior $\angle$ of a $\triangle$ = sum of two remote interior $\angle$s.) 4. $m\angle 1 = m\angle 2 - m\angle 3$ (Subtraction Prop. [3]) 5. $m\angle 2 = \frac{1}{2}(m\widehat{CE})$; $m\angle 3 = \frac{1}{2}(\widehat{BD})$ (Measure of inscribed $\angle = \frac{1}{2}$ measure of intercepted arc.) 6. $m\angle 1 = \frac{1}{2}(m\widehat{CE}) - \frac{1}{2}(m\widehat{BD}) = \frac{1}{2}(m\widehat{CE} - m\widehat{BD})$ (Substitution Prop. [4, 5])

Set B   Refer to $\odot O$ at the right.

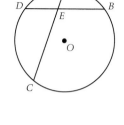

16. $m\widehat{AD} = 3x$; $m\widehat{BC} = 2x + 5$; $m\angle AED = 2x + 11$; $m\angle AED = \underline{\ \ ?\ \ }$ 45

17. $m\widehat{AB} = 2x$; $m\widehat{DC} = x + 55$; $m\angle DEC = x + 33$; $m\angle DEC = \underline{\ \ ?\ \ }$ 44

18. $m\widehat{DC} = 7x + 4$; $m\widehat{AB} = x^2$; $m\angle DEC = 3x + 5$; $m\angle DEC = \underline{\ \ ?\ \ }$ 11

19. $m\widehat{AD} = x^2 + 4$; $m\widehat{BC} = x^2 - 2x$; $m\angle AED = \frac{1}{2}x + 12$; $m\angle AED = \underline{\ \ ?\ \ }$ 10.75 or 14

20. $CE = 9$; $AE = 4$; $DB = 12$; $EB = \underline{\ \ ?\ \ }$ 6

21. $AE = 3$; $EC = 16$; $DB = 14$; $BE = \underline{\ \ ?\ \ }$ 6 or 8

$\overleftrightarrow{RQ}$ and $\overleftrightarrow{RS}$ are tangent to $\odot U$.

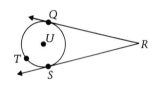

22. Prove that $m\widehat{QS} + m\angle R = 180$.

23. Prove that $m\widehat{STQ} = 180 + m\angle R$.

24. Prove Theorem 9-16.

25. Prove Theorem 9-17, Case I.

26. Prove Theorem 9-17, Case II.

Prove Theorem 9-17, Case III.

ء. Prove Theorem 9-18.

Each statement below gives a relationship for the lengths of segments contained in secants and tangents. Use similar triangles to prove each statement.

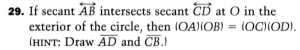

29. If secant $\overleftrightarrow{AB}$ intersects secant $\overleftrightarrow{CD}$ at O in the exterior of the circle, then $(OA)(OB) = (OC)(OD)$. (HINT: Draw $\overline{AD}$ and $\overline{CB}$.)

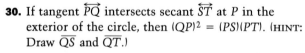

30. If tangent $\overleftrightarrow{PQ}$ intersects secant $\overleftrightarrow{ST}$ at P in the exterior of the circle, then $(QP)^2 = (PS)(PT)$. (HINT: Draw $\overline{QS}$ and $\overline{QT}$.)

Use the statements in Exercises 29 and 30 to find x.

31. 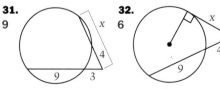 9

32. 6

33. 18

34. 7

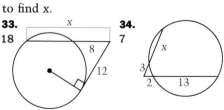
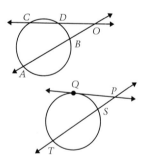

Set C **35.** $\overleftrightarrow{FG}$ is tangent to $\odot P$. $\overline{JH}$ is a diameter. If $FG = 12$ and $GH = 8$, then $m\widehat{FH} = \underline{\ ?\ }$. **67.4**

36. $\overrightarrow{RQ}$ and $\overrightarrow{RS}$ are tangent to $\odot T$ at Q and S, respectively. $m\angle R = 120$ and $TQ = x$. Show that the radius of the circle circumscribed about $\triangle TQR$ is $\frac{1}{3}(x\sqrt{3})$.

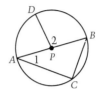

▲ **Review** $\overline{AB}$ is a diameter of $\odot P$.

37. If $m\widehat{BC} = 68$, $m\angle 1 = \underline{\ ?\ }$. **34** **38.** $m\angle ACB = \underline{\ ?\ }$ **90**

39. If $m\widehat{AD} = 80$, $m\angle 2 = \underline{\ ?\ }$. **100**

40. Describe how to construct a 45° angle.

41. Draw an obtuse scalene triangle.

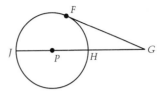

Progress Check

Lesson 9-5, page 400

$\overline{FG}$ is a diameter of $\odot M$. Find the measure of each arc.

1. $\widehat{FJ}$ 35 **2.** $\widehat{KG}$ 652 **3.** $\widehat{FHJ}$ 325 **4.** $\widehat{KGJ}$ 210

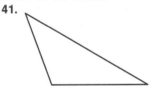

Lesson 9-6, page 406

$\overline{DB}$ is a diameter of $\odot P$ and $\overleftrightarrow{CO}$ is tangent at C.

5. If $m\widehat{AB} = 60$, then $m\angle ADB = \underline{\ ?\ }$. **30**

6. If $m\angle DAE = 75$, then $m\widehat{DC} = \underline{\ ?\ }$. **150**

7. If $m\widehat{DC} = 140$, then $m\angle DCO = \underline{\ ?\ }$. **70**

8. Name a right angle. ∠*BAD* or ∠*BCD*

9. Name a pair of equal inscribed angles. ∠*ABD* and ∠*ACD*

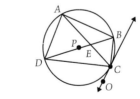

Lesson 9-7, page 414

$\overleftrightarrow{UV}$ and $\overleftrightarrow{UY}$ are tangent to the circle at V and Y, respectively.

10. $m\widehat{ST} = 30$; $m\widehat{WZ} = 60$; $m\angle 3 = \underline{\ ?\ }$ **15**

11. $m\widehat{VW} = 80$; $m\widehat{TV} = 35$; $m\angle 2 = \underline{\ ?\ }$ **22.5**

12. $m\angle 1 = 45$; $m\widehat{WZ} = 50$; $m\widehat{SY} = \underline{\ ?\ }$ **40**

13. $m\widehat{VZY} = 260$; $m\angle VUY = \underline{\ ?\ }$ **80**

14. $SX = 10$; $XW = 12$; $XY = 8$; $XZ = \underline{\ ?\ }$ **9.6**

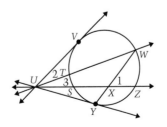

36.

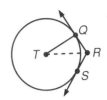

Draw $\overline{RT}$, which bisects $\angle R$; $m\angle QRT = 60$. Since $\overrightarrow{RQ}$ is tangent to $\odot T$ at Q, $m\angle TQR = 90$. Therefore, $\triangle TQR$ is a 30–60–90 $\triangle$. Since $TQ = x$, then $RQ = \frac{x\sqrt{3}}{3}$ and $RT = \frac{2x\sqrt{3}}{3}$.

Since $\triangle TQR$ is a rt. $\triangle$, its hypotenuse (RT) is a diameter of the circumcircle; therefore, the radius of the circumcircle $= \frac{1}{2}RT = x\frac{\sqrt{3}}{3}$.

40. Construct 2 ⊥ lines, and bisect 1 of the rt. ∠s.

41.

FOLLOW-UP

More Practice

• Worksheet 9–7

Extension

After assigning **Exercise 29**, ask students to redraw the diagram with the secants intersecting in the interior of the circle. Is it still true? yes; Theorem 9–18 Discuss the case of the secants intersecting on the circle. D, O and B coincide; $OB = 0$ and $OD = 0$, and it is trivially true.

• Extension 9–7

Computers

• Computer Worksheet 9–7

Excursion: Circling the Seas

As a ship nears the coastline, it must avoid dangerous rocks and shoals. Based on sailors' observations, the hazardous waters are charted. Then the region is represented by a circle, as shown below. The circle passes through lighthouses *A* and *B*. Point *C* is any other point on the part of the circle passing through the water.

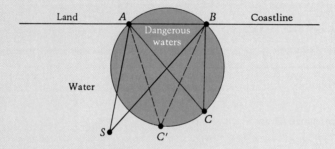

1. ∠*C* is called the *horizontal danger angle.* In geometry, we say that ∠*C* is a(n) __?__ angle. **inscribed**

2. Use your protractor to find the measure of ∠*C*. **43**

3. Why is the measure of ∠*C* the same for all locations of *C*? For example, why does $m\angle C' = m\angle C$? **The sides of the angles intercept the same arc.**

4. Let *S* be the location of the ship. Instruments mounted on the ship can determine the measure of ∠*ASB*. Measure ∠*ASB*. How does its measure compare with the measure of ∠*C*? $m\angle ASB < m\angle C$

5. Trace the diagram above. Choose another point *S'* outside the circle. Measure ∠*AS'B*. How does its measure compare with the measure of ∠*C*? $m\angle AS'B < m\angle C$

6. Now choose two points S_1 and S_2 *inside* the circle to represent the ship sailing in dangerous waters. Measure $\angle AS_1B$ and $\angle AS_2B$. How do these measures compare with the measure of ∠*C*? $m\angle AS_1B > m\angle C$; $m\angle AS_2B > m\angle C$

7. Explain how sailors use the horizontal danger angle to keep out of dangerous waters. (HINT: Consider your answers to Exercises 4, 5, and 6.) **They keep the ship positioned so that $m\angle ASB < m\angle ACB$.**

⌨ Using BASIC: Perimeters of Regular Polygons

Given the length of a side of a regular polygon of n sides, it is possible to find the length of a side of a polygon of the same radius with $2n$ sides. The radius of a regular polygon is the radius of the circle circumscribed about the polygon.

$\overline{AB}$ is a side of length s of a regular n-gon inscribed in a circle of radius r, and $\overline{AC}$ is a side of a regular $2n$-gon inscribed in the same circle.

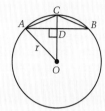

$$(DO)^2 + (AD)^2 = (OA)^2$$
$$(DO)^2 + (\tfrac{1}{2}s)^2 = r^2$$
$$DO = \sqrt{r^2 - (\tfrac{1}{2}s)^2}$$
$$(AD)^2 + (CD)^2 = (AC)^2$$
$$(\tfrac{1}{2}s)^2 + (r - \sqrt{r^2 - (\tfrac{1}{2}s)^2})^2 = (AC)^2$$
$$2r^2 - r\sqrt{4r^2 - s^2} = (AC)^2$$

The program below uses the final equation to compute perimeters of regular polygons, given an initial regular polygon with N sides, radius R, and sides of length S.

```
100 REM COMPUTING PERIMETER OF REGULAR POLYGONS
110 PRINT "WHAT ARE N,R, AND S (SEPARATED BY COMMAS)";
120 INPUT N,R,S
130 PRINT "R = ";R
140 PRINT "N","PERIMETER"
150 PRINT N,N*S
160 LET S = SQR(2*R*R-(R*SQR(4*R*R-S*S)))
170 LET S = INT(S*100000000 + .5)/100000000
180 LET N = 2*N
190 IF N < 2000 THEN 150
200 END
```

1. A square inscribed in a circle of radius 4 has a side length of $4\sqrt{2}$, or about 5.65685425. RUN the program for $N = 4$, $R = 4$, and $S = 5.65685425$. Values approach 25.1327

2. RUN the program for a square of side length 0.707106781 inscribed in a circle of radius 0.5. Values approach 3.14159

3. What is the length of a side of a regular hexagon inscribed in a circle of radius 4? Of radius 0.5? RUN the program for these initial regular polygons. 4; 0.5

Chapter 9 Summary

Important Terms

Central angle (400)

Centroid (394)

Chord (376)

Circle (375)

Circumcenter (393)

Circumscribed circle (392)

Common tangents (382)

Concentric circles (402)

Concurrent lines (392)

Congruent circles (387)

Degree measure of arcs (401)

Diameter (376)

Exterior of circle (376)

Great circle (378)

Incenter (394)

Incircle (394)

Inscribed angle (406)

Inscribed circle (392)

Intercepted arc (400)

Interior of circle (376)

Major arc (400)

Minor arc (400)

Orthocenter (394)

Point of tangency (377)

Radius (375)

Secant (377)

Semicircle (400)

Small circle (378)

Sphere (377)

Tangent (377)

Tangent circles (383)

Important Ideas

1. Points of a circle are those points in a plane that are a given distance from a given point. (375)

2. The equation for a circle with radius r and center A (h, k) is $(x - h)^2 + (y - k)^2 = r^2$. (375)

3. Points of a sphere are those points in space that are a given distance from a given point. (377)

4. A tangent to a circle is perpendicular to the radius drawn to the point of tangency. (381)

5. Congruent circles are circles with equal radii. (387)

6. A line through the center of a circle and perpendicular to a chord bisects the chord. (387)

7. The perpendicular bisectors of the sides of a triangle are concurrent, as are the angle bisectors. (392–393)

8. If X is on $\overset{\frown}{AB}$, then $m\overset{\frown}{AX} + m\overset{\frown}{XB} = m\overset{\frown}{AXB}$. (401)

9. In a circle, relationships exist between the measures of angles and arcs. (401, 407, 408, 414–415)

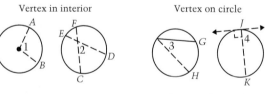

Vertex in interior

Vertex on circle

$m\angle 1 = m\overset{\frown}{AB}$

$m\angle 2 = \frac{1}{2}(m\overset{\frown}{CD} + m\overset{\frown}{EF})$

$m\angle 3 = \frac{1}{2}(m\overset{\frown}{GH})$

$m\angle 4 = \frac{1}{2}(m\overset{\frown}{JK})$

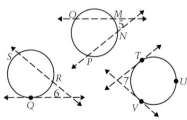

Vertex in exterior

$m\angle 5 = \frac{1}{2}(m\overset{\frown}{OP} - m\overset{\frown}{MN})$

$m\angle 6 = \frac{1}{2}(m\overset{\frown}{QS} - m\overset{\frown}{QR})$

$m\angle 7 = \frac{1}{2}(m\overset{\frown}{TUV} - m\overset{\frown}{TV})$

Chapter 9 Review

Lesson 9-1, page 375

1. $\overleftrightarrow{BD}$ is a _?_. tangent   **2.** $\overleftrightarrow{ED}$ is a _?_. secant   **3.** $\overline{ED}$ is a _?_. chord

4. $\overline{PA}$ is a _?_. radius   **5.** $\overline{CD}$ is a _?_. diameter   **6.** Point D is a _?_. pt. of tangency

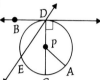

Tell if each statement is *true* or *false.*

7. For a given sphere, the center of a small circle is the center of the sphere. False

8. A line containing exactly one point of a sphere is tangent to the sphere. True

9. The equation of $\odot C$ is $(x - 2)^2 + (y + 8)^2 = 81$. Give the coordinates of C and the radius. (2, −8); 9

Lesson 9-2, page 381

How many common tangents could be drawn to each pair of circles?

10.

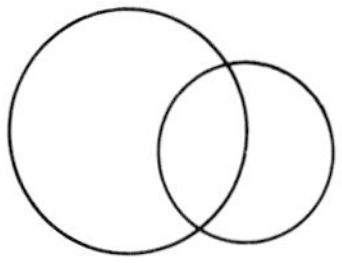

2 external

11.

2 external
2 internal

12.

None

13.

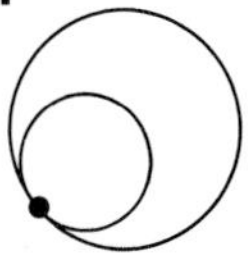

1 external

14. If a radius is drawn to a point of tangency, then the tangent and radius are _?_. 1

Lesson 9-3, page 387

$\overline{AB}$ and $\overline{CD}$ are chords of $\odot P$. $10\sqrt{3} \approx 17.32$

15. $AP = 10$; $PX = 5$; $AB = $ _?_

16. $AB = 24$; $PX = 12$; $PA = $ _?_ $12\sqrt{2} \approx 16.97$

17. If $PX = PY$, then $AB = $ _?_. CD

18. What are congruent circles? Circles with = radii

Lesson 9-4, page 392

Tell if each statement is *always, sometimes,* or *never* true.

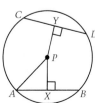

19. The vertices of a polygon inscribed in a circle are in the interior of the circle. Never

20. A circle can be circumscribed about any triangle. Always

21. The circumcenter of a triangle is in its interior. Sometimes

22. The center of the circle inscribed in a triangle is the point of concurrency of its angle bisectors. Always

ANSWERS

Chapter Review

37. Proof: 1. *FG* = *JK* (Given)
2. *m*∠*F* = *m*∠*J* (If 2 inscribed ∠s intercept the same arc on the ⊙, then they are =.) 3. *m*∠*FHG* = *m*∠*JHK* (Vert. ∠s are =.) 4. △*FGH* ≅ △*JKH* (AAS Thm. [1, 2, 3])

Lesson 9-5, page 400

Find the indicated measure.

23. m$\widehat{QR}$ 30   **24.** m$\widehat{STU}$ 170   **25.** m∠*UPQ* 20

26. m∠*SPT* 120   **27.** m$\widehat{UR}$ 50   **28.** m$\widehat{URS}$ 190

29. ∠*QPR* is called a(n) __?__ angle. central

30. Name a major arc. Samples $\widehat{TRS}$; $\widehat{TSQ}$; $\widehat{URS}$

31. State the Arc Addition Postulate. If pt. *P* is on $\widehat{AB}$, then
m$\widehat{AP}$ + m $\widehat{PB}$ = m $\widehat{APB}$

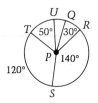

Lesson 9-6, page 406

In the diagram at the right, $\overleftrightarrow{BX}$ is a tangent.

32. If *m*∠*CDE* = 110, then m$\widehat{CAE}$ = __?__. 220

33. Name two equal inscribed angles. ∠*BEC* and ∠*BDC*

34. Name a supplement of ∠*EAC*. ∠*CDE*

35. If $\overline{AC}$ is a diameter, then __?__ is a right angle. ∠*AEC*

36. If *m*∠*XBD* = 70, then m$\widehat{BD}$ = __?__. 140

37. Given: *FG* = *JK*
Prove: △*FGH* ≅ △*JKH*

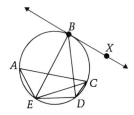

Lesson 9-7, page 414

$\overline{WS}$ and $\overline{WV}$ are tangent segments.

38. m$\widehat{VU}$ = 40; m$\widehat{QR}$ = 75; *m*∠1 = __?__ 57.5

39. m$\widehat{QR}$ = 70; m$\widehat{UT}$ = 32; *m*∠2 = __?__ 19

40. m$\widehat{UT}$ = 15; m$\widehat{TS}$ = 43; m$\widehat{UVQ}$ = 155; *m*∠*QWS* = __?__ 44.5

41. m$\widehat{VR}$ = 120; *m*∠3 = __?__ 120

42. m$\widehat{STV}$ = 130; *m*∠*VWS* = __?__ 50

43. *m*∠1 = 50; m$\widehat{QR}$ = 55; m$\widehat{VU}$ = __?__ 45

44. *m*∠*VWS* = 42; m$\widehat{SRV}$ = __?__ 222

45. *RX* = 16; *XV* = 12; *QX* = 8; *XU* = __?__ 24

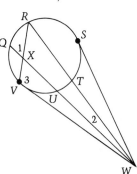

Chapter 9 Test

Decide whether each statement is *true* or *false*. If false, explain why.

1. If $\overline{PA}$ is a radius of $\odot P$ and point Q is in the exterior of $\odot P$, then $PA < PQ$. **True**

2. A secant is a line that contains a chord of a circle. **True**

3. A line that is tangent to a great circle of a sphere is tangent to the sphere. **True**

4. If $\angle A$ is inscribed in a semicircle, then $m\angle A = 180$. **False; $m\angle A = 90$**

5. Two externally tangent circles have exactly two common tangents. **False; the $\odot$s have 2 external and 1 internal tangents.**

6. Two circles are congruent if their radii are equal. **True**

7. All arcs with equal measure have equal corresponding chords. **False; arcs must be from same or $\cong$ $\odot$s.**

8. If X is on $\overset{\frown}{AB}$, then $m\overset{\frown}{AX} + m\overset{\frown}{XB} = m\overset{\frown}{AXB}$. **True**

9. The opposite angles of an inscribed quadrilateral are supplementary. **True**

10. A line that is perpendicular to a chord bisects the chord.

11. The point of concurrency of the perpendicular bisectors of the sides of a triangle is the circumcenter. **True**

12. If $\odot X$ is inscribed in pentagon $ABCDE$, then $\overline{CD}$ is a chord of $\odot X$. **False; $\overleftrightarrow{CD}$ is tangent to $\odot x$.**

13. If $\overline{MN}$ and $\overline{MK}$ are tangent to $\odot W$ at N and K, then $MN = MK$. **True**

10. False; a line $\perp$ to a chord bisects the chord only if the line passes through the center of the $\odot$.

$\overline{AB}$ is a tangent segment in the diagram at the right.

14. $m\overset{\frown}{AC} = 100; \ m\overset{\frown}{AD} = 65; \ m\angle 3 = \underline{\ ?\ }$ **17.5**

15. $m\overset{\frown}{CF} = 85; \ m\overset{\frown}{DE} = 37; \ m\angle 2 = \underline{\ ?\ }$ **24**

16. $m\angle 1 = 43; \ m\overset{\frown}{DE} = 15; \ m\overset{\frown}{CF} = \underline{\ ?\ }$ **71**

17. $m\overset{\frown}{AC} = 80; \ m\angle 4 = \underline{\ ?\ }$ **140**

18. $GE = 6; \ DG = 5; \ FG = 18; \ CG = \underline{\ ?\ }$ **15**

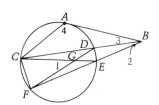

19. Given: $XZ = WY$
Prove: $\overline{XW} \parallel \overline{ZY}$

Chapter Test

19. Proof: 1. $XZ = WY$ (Given)
2. $m\overset{\frown}{XZ} = m\overset{\frown}{WY}$ (If 2 chords of a $\odot$ are =, then the measures of their corr. arcs are =. [1]) 3. $m\angle XWZ = \frac{1}{2}(m\overset{\frown}{XZ})$ and $m\angle YZW = \frac{1}{2}(m\overset{\frown}{WY})$ (The measure of an inscribed $\angle$ is $\frac{1}{2}$ the measure of its intercepted arc.) 4. $\frac{1}{2}(m\overset{\frown}{XZ}) = \frac{1}{2}(m\overset{\frown}{WY})$ (Mult. Prop. [2]) 5. $m\angle XWZ = m\angle YZW$ (Substitution Prop. [3, 4]) 6. $\overline{XW} \parallel \overline{ZY}$ (Alt. int. $\angle$s = $\Rightarrow$ 2 lines $\parallel$. [5])

Cumulative Review   Chapters 7–9

Select the best answer for each item.

1. Solve the proportion for x.

$$\frac{5x + 8}{4} = \frac{9x + 13}{7}$$

A. 3   **B.** 4   **C.** 5   **D.** −5

2. If $\triangle ABC \sim \triangle DEF$, then the perimeter of $\triangle DEF$ is __?__.

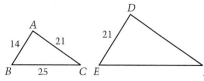

A. 60   **B.** 135   **C.** 90   **D.** 120

3. Besides the information you know from the diagram below, which statement is needed to show that $\triangle ABC \sim \triangle EDC$?

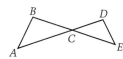

A. $m\angle BCA = m\angle DCE$

B. $AB = DE$

C. $m\angle B = m\angle D$

D. C bisects $\overline{AD}$.

4. If $\overleftrightarrow{DE} \parallel \overleftrightarrow{BC}$, $AB = 12$, $BD = 18$, and $AE = 25$, then $AC =$ __?__.

A. 10

B. $37\frac{1}{2}$

C. 19

D. $17\frac{7}{9}$

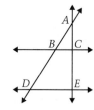

5. To prove $\triangle PQR \sim \triangle STU$ by the SSS Similarity Theorem and $\frac{PQ}{ST} = \frac{QR}{TU}$ is given, show that __?__.

A. $m\angle Q = m\angle T$ **B.** $PR = SU$

C. $\frac{PQ}{QR} = \frac{ST}{SU}$ **D.** $\frac{PR}{SU} = \frac{QR}{TU}$

6. Given: $\triangle ABC \sim \triangle EFG$; $AB = 3x + 5$; $AD = 16$; $EF = 25$; and $EH = 20$. Then $x =$ __?__.

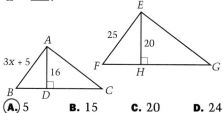

A. 5   **B.** 15   **C.** 20   **D.** 24

7. Sol is 6 feet tall. He casts a 10-foot shadow at the same time that a nearby building casts a 200-foot shadow. The building is __?__ feet tall.

A. 240   **B.** 160   **C.** 120   **D.** 196

8. Given: $\triangle ADC$ with right $\angle D$; $m\angle DBC = 90$. Then $BC =$ __?__.

A. $5\frac{1}{3}$

B. 5

C. 3

D. $6\frac{1}{2}$

9. Which set of numbers can be lengths of sides of a right triangle?

A. 7, 7, 7   **B.** 25, 25, 100

C. 8, 9, 10   **D.** 9, 12, 15

10. The length of a side of an equilateral triangle is 10. The length of a median is __?__.

A. $10\sqrt{3}$ **B.** $5\sqrt{3}$ **C.** $5\sqrt{2}$ **D.** $3\sqrt{10}$

11. $\sin A = \underline{\quad?\quad}$.

A. $\frac{3}{4}$

B. $\frac{3}{5}$ (circled)

C. $\frac{4}{5}$

D. $\frac{4}{3}$

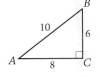

12. If $\sin 50° = .7660$, $\cos 50° = .6428$, and $\tan 50° = 1.1918$, then $BA = \underline{\quad?\quad}$.

A. 8.4

B. 11.9

C. 13.1

D. 15.6 (circled)

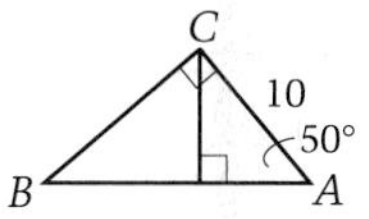

13. If $\overleftrightarrow{AD} \perp \overleftrightarrow{BC}$, and $\overleftrightarrow{AB} \parallel \overleftrightarrow{CD}$, then $AE = \underline{\quad?\quad}$.

A. $8\sqrt{2}$

B. 4

C. $4\sqrt{2}$ (circled)

D. 32

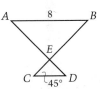

14. Point $P(4, 5)$ is on a circle with center at $Q(1, 1)$. Point $S(-3, 4)$ is $\underline{\quad?\quad}$.

A. On circle R (circled)

B. In the interior of circle R

C. In the exterior of circle R

D. More information is needed.

15. If $\overleftrightarrow{CP}$ is tangent to circle O and $AB = 24$, then $OP = \underline{\quad?\quad}$.

A. 24

B. 20 (circled)

C. 18

D. 28

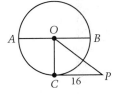

16. If $GE = EF$ and $GB = 7$, $CD = \underline{\quad?\quad}$.

A. 14 (circled)

B. 7

C. 10

D. 3.5

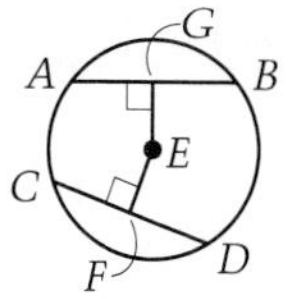

17. A circle has a radius of 5. A square inscribed in this circle has a side of length $\underline{\quad?\quad}$.

A. 5   B. 10   C. $2\sqrt{5}$ D. $5\sqrt{2}$ (circled)

18. If $AB = CD$ and $m\widehat{AB} = 80$, then $m\widehat{BD} + m\widehat{AC} = \underline{\quad?\quad}$.

A. 280

B. 160

C. 200 (circled)

D. 140

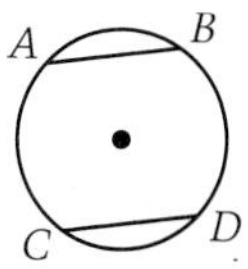

19. In the circle, if $m\widehat{HG} = 15$, then $m\widehat{FE} = \underline{\quad?\quad}$.

A. 55

B. 65 (circled)

C. 25

D. 160

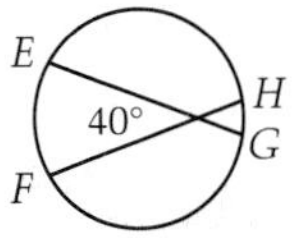

20. In the circle, $AE = \underline{\quad?\quad}$.

A. 2.5 (circled)

B. 5

C. 7.5

D. More information is needed.

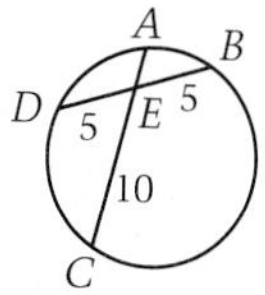

CHAPTER

10

Areas of Polygons and Circles

Chapter Overview

This chapter develops a formal concept of the area of polygonal and circular regions. The chapter begins with the introduction of postulates that describe the basic properties of area, and a formula for the area of a rectangle is established. These postulates are then used to derive formulas for the areas of squares, parallelograms, triangles, trapezoids, rhombuses, kites and regular polygons. The circumference (and area) of a circular region is obtained by applying an intuitive limiting process to the perimeters (and areas) of inscribed regular polygons. The final lesson, on areas of sectors and segments, provides further applications of properties of circles and area.

Problem-solving strategies that involve drawing a diagram and estimating are extremely useful in this chapter.

A **calculator** could be used to solve some exercises in this chapter.

Perspectives

Lesson 10-1 deals with the concept of area as a number assigned to a polygonal region. Because the triangular region is the only one into which all other polygonal regions can be divided, it is used in the definition of polygonal region. The unit square, however, is chosen as the basic unit of area.

Lesson 10-2 presents the formula for the area of a parallelogram by showing that the altitudes form congruent triangles which therefore have equal areas. From Theorem 10-2, the area formula for triangles is easily derived. The special case of the equilateral triangles is considered in Theorem 10-4.

Lesson 10-3 develops the area formulas for three other figures. The formula for the area of a trapezoid is proven by finding the sum of the areas of two triangles.

The formula for a rhombus in Theorem 10-6 may be new to students. The formula for a kite is derived in exactly the same way as that of the rhombus.

Lesson 10-4 explores areas of similar polygons. Review the concept of similarity and related line segments. Corresponding perimeters and altitudes are all proportional to corresponding sides of similar figures but the areas are not in the same ratio.

Lesson 10-5 extends our work with circumscribed and inscribed circles from Chapter 9. Theorem 10-11 provides a method for finding the area of any regular polygon, regardless of the number of sides it has.

Pacing Chart for Chapter 10

Lesson	Objectives	Basic Course	Average \Course	Extended Course
10–1	State basic postulates for area of polygonal regions, and use them to find areas of squares and other rectangles.	1	1	1
10–2	State and apply theorems concerning the areas of regions enclosed by parallelograms and triangles.	1	1	1
10–3	State and apply theorems concerning the area of regions enclosed by trapezoids, rhombuses and kites.	$1\frac{1}{2}$	$1\frac{1}{2}$	$1\frac{1}{2}$
10–4	State and apply theorems concerning areas of similar polygons.	1	1	1
10–5	State and apply relationships with circumscribed and inscribed circles to find areas, perimeters, radii and apothems of regular polygons.	1	1	1
10–6	State and apply theorems concerning the circumference and area of a circle.	1	1	1
10–7	State and apply theorems concerning arc length and areas of sectors and segments of a circle.	2	$1\frac{1}{2}$	$1\frac{1}{2}$
Review		$1\frac{1}{2}$	1	1
Test		1	1	1
Total		11 days	10 days	10 days

Lesson 10-6 applies the formula for the area of a regular polygon using an informal limiting process to derive formulas for the circumference and area of a circle. Areas of regions other than polygons may now be defined by means of limits.

The value and definition of π is fundamental to the development of the circle formulas.

Lesson 10-7 extends the concept of circumference to include that of arc length. Similarly, we use the formula for the area of a circle to derive a formula for the area of a sector. By subtracting the area of a central triangle from that of a sector, we may also compute the area of a segment of a circle.

The theorems in this lesson follow almost intuitively from the circle formulas.

Areas of Polygons and Circles   Chapter 10

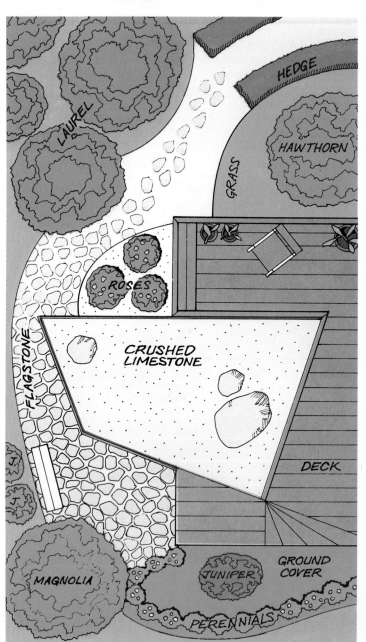

A landscaper needs to spread crushed limestone in the polygonal region indicated on the landscape plan. How can she determine how much limestone is needed?

10-1 Areas of Polygonal Regions

The amount of crushed limestone needed for the region on page 428 depends upon the amount of surface to be covered. You could consider separate regions, some of which are triangular, within the polygonal region.

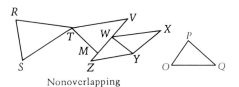

Definition *Triangular Region, Circular Region*

A triangular region consists of a triangle and its interior.
A circular region consists of a circle and its interior.

If the interiors of two coplanar triangles intersect, the two triangular regions *overlap*. *Nonoverlapping* regions have no interior points in common.

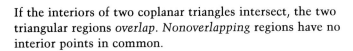

Overlapping   Nonoverlapping

Definition *Polygonal Region*

A polygonal region is a plane figure that is the union of a finite number of coplanar, nonoverlapping triangular regions that intersect at vertices or along sides.

Explain why each of the figures below is a polygonal region.

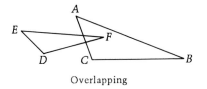

4 triangles   2 triangles   7 triangles

Each figure is the union of a finite number of coplanar, nonoverlapping triangular regions that intersect at vertices or along sides.

Postulate 21 *Area Postulate*

To every polygonal region there corresponds a unique positive number, called the area of the region.

For simplicity, we call the area of a triangular region the area of the triangle, the area of a rectangular region the area of the rectangle, the area of a circular region the area of the circle, and so on.

LESSON 10–1

Resources

Teaching Aid 2, dot paper
Visual Aid 2, dot paper
Teaching Aid 3, grid paper
Visual Aid 3, grid paper
Readiness Worksheet 4
Worksheet 10–1
Extension 10–1
Computer Activities 10–1

OBJECTIVE

State basic postulates for area of polygonal regions, and use them to find areas of squares and other rectangles.

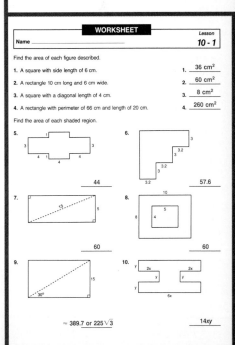

WORKSHEET   Lesson **10 - 1**

Name _____

Find the area of each figure described.

1. A square with side length of 6 cm.
2. A rectangle 10 cm long and 6 cm wide.
3. A square with a diagonal length of 4 cm.
4. A rectangle with perimeter of 66 cm and length of 20 cm.

1. 36 cm²
2. 60 cm²
3. 8 cm²
4. 260 cm²

Find the area of each shaded region.

5. ... 44
6. ... 57.6
7. ... 60
8. ... 60
9. ≈ 389.7 or 225√3
10. 14xy

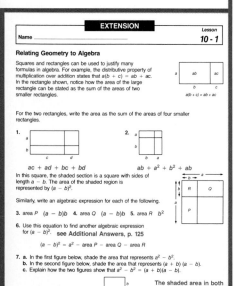

Postulate 22 *Area Postulate for Congruent Triangles*

If two triangles are congruent, then the triangles have equal areas.

In fact, it is true for *any* two congruent polygons or circles that their areas are equal.

The area of a polygonal region may be thought of as the number of square units that exactly fill it. Since the rectangular region at the right is composed of 15 congruent square regions, each with an area of 1 square unit, the area of the rectangle is 15. What is the area of each shaded region below?

□ = 1 sq. unit

a. **b.** **c.** **d.** **e.** **f.**

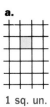 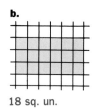 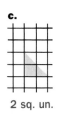 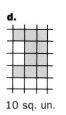 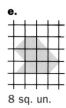 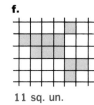

1 sq. un.   18 sq. un.   2 sq. un.   10 sq. un.   8 sq. un.   11 sq. un.

How many 1-inch squares are in each rectangle at the right? How can you find each area without counting the squares? 40; 18; 16; find the product of the dimensions

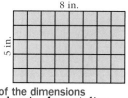

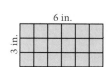

Any side of a rectangle may be selected as its **base**. A line segment perpendicular to that base with its endpoints on the base and the side opposite is an **altitude**. The length of an altitude is the **height** for that base. Postulate 23 gives a formula for the area of a rectangle in terms of its base and height.

Postulate 23 *Area Postulate for Rectangles*

The area A of a rectangle is equal to the product of the length b of a base and the corresponding height h. A = bh

Theorem 10-1 follows directly from Postulate 23. Why? In a square, both b and h equal s, so $A = bh = s(s) = s^2$

Theorem 10-1 *Area of a Square*

The area A of a square is equal to the square of the length s of a side. A = s²

The proof of Theorem 10-1 is left for Exercise 18.

Example 1

A gym floor is to be refinished with polyurethane, a gallon of which covers about 130 square feet. The gym is 108 feet long and 80 feet wide. How many gallons will be needed?

Solution
Divide the area of the floor by 130.

$A = bh$
$= 108(80) = 8,640$ sq. ft. $8,640 \div 130 \approx 66.5$

At least 67 gallons of polyurethane will be needed.

Postulate 24   *Area Addition Postulate*

The area of the union of two or more nonoverlapping polygonal regions is the sum of the areas of the regions.

Example 2

Mr. and Mrs. Gutierrez are having their kitchen floor retiled. How many square feet of flooring will they need?

Solution
They can calculate the areas of A_1, A_2, and A_3. Then, by Postulate 24, they can add these areas.

$A = A_1 + A_2 + A_3$
$= 8(7) + 3(2.5) + 6^2$
$= 56 + 7.5 + 36$
$= 99.5$ sq. ft.

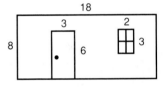

Checking for Understanding

1. Identify the two parts of a triangular region.

2. Draw two congruent triangles on grid paper. Are their areas equal? Explain.

Tell whether each figure is a polygonal region. Explain.

3. Yes   4. Yes   5. No   6. Yes

1. A triangle and its interior.

2. Triangles will vary; the areas are equal by Postulate 22 or by counting square units.

3-6. All but the figure in Ex. 5 can be separated into nonoverlapping triangles that intersect at vertices or along edges.

7. Find the area of rectangle $ABCD$ if $AB = 5$ and $BC = 8$. 40

8. What are two approaches to calculating the area of region **d** on page 430? $3 + 3 + 2(2)$ or $4(3) - 2$

ANSWERS

Written Exercises

18. Given: Square ABCD with sides of length s Prove: Area A of ABCD is $A = s^2$.

Proof: 1. Square ABCD with AB = s (Given) 2. ABCD is a rectangle; AB = BC (Def. of square [1]) 3. Area ABCD = (AB)(BC) (Area Post. for Rectangles [2]) 4. Area of ABCD = s(s) = s^2 (Substitution Prop. [1, 2, 3])

28. Given: Square ABCD with diagonal AC = d Prove: Area A of ABCD = $\frac{1}{2}d^2$

Proof: 1. Square ABCD with AC = d (Given) 2. ABCD is a rectangle; AD = DC (Def. of square [1]) 3. ∠D is a rt. ∠. (Def. of rectangle [2]) 4. $d^2 = (AD)^2 + (DC)^2$ (Pythagorean Thm. [3]) 5. $d^2 = (AD)^2 + (AD)^2 = 2(AD)^2$ (Substitution Prop. [2, 4]) 6. Area ABCD = (AD)(DC) (Area Post. for Rectangles [2]) 7. Area ABCD = (AD)(AD) = $(AD)^2$ (Substitution Prop. [2, 6]) 8. $d^2 = 2$(area ABCD) (Substitution [5, 7]) 9. Area ABCD = $\frac{1}{2}d^2$ (Multiplication Prop. [8])

Review

32. the Pythagorean Theorem

---

9. The area of a square is $24a^2$. Find its perimeter. $8a\sqrt{6}$

10. Find the area of the shaded region at the right. **28**

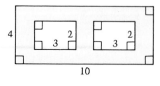

Written Exercises

Set A   Find the area of each rectangle.

1. b = 3
h = 25
75

2. b = 0.25 m
h = 2 m
0.5 m²

3. b = $3\sqrt{2}$ in.
h = $5\sqrt{2}$ in.
30 sq. in.

4. b = r + 2
h = r − 2
$r^2 - 4$

Find the area of each square.

5. s = 11 ft.
121 sq. ft.

6. s = 2.7 cm
7.29 cm²

7. s = $4\sqrt{5}$
80

8. s = $r\sqrt{3b}$
br^2

9. The lengths of the base and altitude of a rectangle are doubled. By what factor is the area multiplied? **4**

10. A rectangular table is 76 cm wide. If its area is 8,664 cm², find its length. **114 cm**

11. How many 4-inch square tiles are needed to cover a rectangular floor 12 ft. 8 in. long and 8 ft. wide? **11. 912 tiles**

12. Jean's seedlings will take up 48 sq. ft. of garden space when they are transplanted. Give three sets of possible whole-number dimensions for the garden.

12. 48′ by 1′; 24′ by 2′; 16′ by 3′; 12′ by 4′; 8′ by 6′

13. 25 bricks

13. How many 6-inch square glass bricks are needed to fill a square window frame with area 900 sq. in.?

Find the area of each shaded region.

14.

25

15.

8

16.
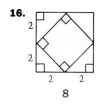
8

17.
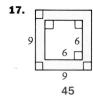
45

18. Prove Theorem 10–1.

Set B   **19.** Find the area of a rectangle if the length of the base is 15 m and the length of a diagonal is 17 m. **120 m²**

Find the area of each rectangle.

20. FIVE for F(1, 3), I(4, 3), V(4, 0), and E(1, 0) **9**

21. BLUE for B(1, 0), L(5, 4), U(4, 5), and E(0, 1) **8**

22. Joy made a quilt with congruent squares. For every 3 squares in length, she allowed 2 squares in width. The area of the quilt squares was 3,456 sq. in. Find the length and the width of this section.
72 in. and 48 in.

23. Find the dimensions (whole numbers) of the largest rectangular garden that can be enclosed by 60 feet of fence. **15 ft. by 15 ft.**

24. The area of a rectangle is 28 cm^2 and its perimeter is 22 cm. Find the dimensions of the rectangle.

25. The area of a rectangle is 75 sq. in. The length is 3 times the width. Find the rectangle's dimensions.

26. The lengths of the base and altitude of a rectangle are tripled. By what factor is the area multiplied? What if the dimensions are multiplied by 4? by n?

27. The length and width of the front-hall carpet at city hall are in the ratio 7:2, and its area is 504 sq. ft. What are the dimensions of the carpet?

24. 7 cm and 4 cm
25. 15 in. and 5 in.
26. 9; 16; n^2
27. 42 ft. and 12 ft.

Set C **28.** Prove: If a diagonal of a square has length d, then the area of the square is $\frac{1}{2}d^2$.

Review **29.** $AB = 12$; $BD = 6$, $BC = 8$; $EB = \underline{\ ?\ }$ **16**

30. $m\widehat{AE} = 84$; $m\widehat{DC} = 58$; $m\angle DBC = \underline{\ ?\ }$ **71**

31. $m\angle EDC = 106$; $m\widehat{EGC} = \underline{\ ?\ }$ **212**

32. Which theorem has been proved in more different ways than any other theorem in geometry?

33. Polygon $LMNO$ is similar to polygon $PQRS$. If $LM = 6$, $NO = 12$, and $RS = 8$, then $PQ = \underline{\ ?\ }$. **4**

Thinking Ahead **34.** Which area is greater, that of rectangle $FECD$ or ▱ $ABCD$? **Neither; their areas are =.**

35. What is the relationship between the areas of $\triangle ADC$ and ▱$ABCD$? **Area $\triangle ADC = \frac{1}{2}$ area ▱$ABCD$**

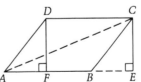

💻 Computer Activities: Drawing and Measuring

1. Draw a parallelogram with no right angles, labeled as shown. Draw $\overline{AE}$ perpendicular to $\overline{BC}$. Measure $\overline{AE}$, $\overline{BC}$, and the area of ▱$ABCD$. Repeat the activity for three more parallelograms. For each parallelogram, what is the relationship among the three numbers?

2. Draw a triangle, with vertices labeled A, B, and C. Draw $\overline{AD}$ perpendicular to $\overline{BC}$. Measure $\overline{AD}$, $\overline{BC}$, and the area of $\triangle ABC$. Repeat the activity for three more triangles. For each triangle what is the relationship among the three numbers?

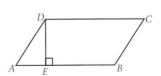

1. AE(BC) = area ▱ABCD
2. $\frac{1}{2}$(AD)(BC) = area △ABC

FOLLOW-UP

More Practice

Use Postulate 22 to define an area function whose domain consists of all polygonal regions and whose range is the set of positive real numbers. Then introduce function notation; for example, $A(\triangle PQR) = 2$ means that the area of triangular region PQR is 2. This will facilitate the writing of proofs throughout the chapter and will emphasize the function relationship.
• **Worksheet 10–1**

Extension

• **Extension 10–1**

Computers

The computer activity in the pupil's book can be completed using *The Geometric Supposer: Quadrilaterals* or *The Geometric preSupposer: Points and Lines.*
• **Computer Activities 10–1**

LESSON 10-2

Resources

Cardboard strips
Index cards
Paper fasteners
Teaching Aid 2, dot paper
Visual Aid 2, dot paper
Readiness Worksheet 5
Worksheet 10-2
Extension 10-2
Computer Activities 10-2
Computer Worksheet 10-2

OBJECTIVE

State and apply theorems concerning the areas of regions enclosed by parallelograms and triangles.

10-2 Areas of Parallelograms and Triangles

The tax on lakefront property in Waushara County is based upon the area of the lot. The Andersons are planning to buy a lot shaped like a parallelogram and want to know what the tax is.

The Area Addition Postulate and the Area Postulates for Rectangles and Congruent Triangles can be used to develop a formula for the area of a parallelogram. As with the rectangle, if one side of a parallelogram is the **base**, a line segment perpendicular to that base with endpoints on the base and the opposite side (or on the lines containing the opposite sides) is the **altitude** for that base. Its length is the **height** h.

Theorem 10-2 *Area of a Parallelogram*

The area A of a parallelogram is equal to the product of the length b of a base and the corresponding height h. A = bh

Given □$ABCD$; base $\overline{AB}$ with length b; altitude $\overline{DE}$ with length h

Prove Area □$ABCD = bh$

Plan for Proof Draw a segment from C perpendicular to $\overrightarrow{AB}$. Quadrilateral $EFCD$ is a rectangle. By the HL Congruence Theorem, $\triangle AED \cong \triangle BFC$. Show $EF = AB = b$. Use the Area Addition Postulate to show that area □$ABCD$ = area rectangle $EFCD = bh$.

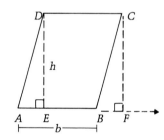

The proof of Theorem 10-2 is left to Exercise 34.

Example 1
Find the area of each parallelogram.

a.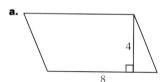

b.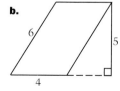

c.

Solution

a. $A = bh$
   $= 8(4)$
   $= 32$

b. $A = bh$
   $= 4(5)$
   $= 20$

c. $A = bh$
   $= 5(3)$
   $= 15$

Example 2

The lake lot the Andersons are considering has the dimensions shown. The tax rate is $0.06 per square foot of land. What is the tax on this lot?

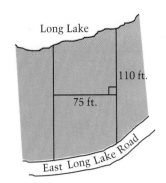

Long Lake

110 ft.

75 ft.

East Long Lake Road

Solution

Multiply the area of the lot by the tax rate.

$A = bh$ $0.06(8,250) = 495.00$
$= 110(75)$
$= 8,250$ sq. ft.

The tax is $495.

Example 3

Find the area of $\square PQRS$ for $P(0, 0)$, $Q(6, 0)$, $R(8, 4)$, $S(2, 4)$.

Solution

Graph the parallelogram and draw an altitude. $ST = 4$ and $PQ = 6$, so $A = bh = 6(4) = 24$.

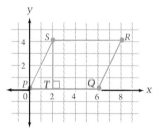

Postulate 22 and Theorem 10-2 can be used to develop a formula for the area of a triangle. Recall that an altitude of a triangle is the segment from a vertex perpendicular to the line containing the opposite side. As with a parallelogram, the length of the altitude is called the **height**.

Theorem 10-3   *Area of a Triangle*

The area A of a triangle is equal to one half the product of the length b of any side and the corresponding height h. $A = \frac{1}{2}bh$

Given $\triangle GBC$; base $\overline{GB}$ of length b; altitude $\overline{CF}$ of length h

Prove   Area $\triangle GBC = \frac{1}{2}bh$

Plan for Proof   Through C, draw $\ell \parallel \overline{GB}$. Locate D on ℓ on the B side of $\overleftrightarrow{GC}$ with $GB = CD$. Draw $\overline{BD}$ to form $\square GBDC$ with $A = bh$. Show $\triangle GBC \cong \triangle DCB$. Then area $\square GBDC = bh = 2(\text{area } \triangle GBC)$. Thus, area $\triangle GBC = \frac{1}{2}bh$.

The proof of Theorem 10-3 is left for Exercise 33.

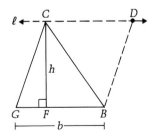

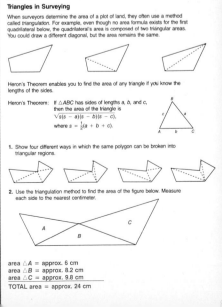

Additional Examples

Example 1

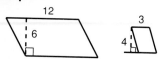

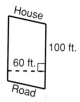

Find the area of each parallelogram. 72; 12; 70

Example 2

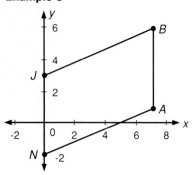

The Nathan's front lawn is a parallelogram with the dimensions
shown above. If sod costs $0.07 a
square foot, how much would it
cost to cover their front yard with
sod? $420

Example 3

Find the area of *JBAN* for *J*(0, 3),
B(7, 6), *A*(7, 1) and *N*(0, −2). 35

Theorem 10-4 applies Theorem 10-3 to equilateral triangles.

Theorem 10-4 *Area of an Equilateral Triangle*

*The area A of an equilateral triangle with side lengths s is equal
to $\frac{s^2}{4}\sqrt{3}$. $A = \frac{s^2}{4}\sqrt{3}$*

Given   Equilateral $\triangle XYZ$ with side length s

Prove   Area $\triangle XYZ = \frac{s^2}{4}\sqrt{3}$

Plan for Draw altitude $\overline{YW}$. $YW = \frac{1}{2}s\sqrt{3}$. Use $A = \frac{1}{2}bh$.
Proof

The proof of Theorem 10-4 is left to Exercise 18.

Example 4
Find the area of each triangle.

a. 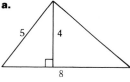   **b.** 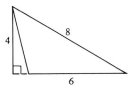   **c.**

Solution

a. $A = \frac{1}{2}bh$
$= \frac{1}{2}(8)(4)$
$= 16$

b. $A = \frac{1}{2}bh$
$= \frac{1}{2}(6)(4)$
$= 12$

c. $A = \frac{s^2}{4}\sqrt{3}$
$= \frac{4^2}{4}\sqrt{3}$
$= 4\sqrt{3}$

Checking for Understanding
In $\square ABCD$, name an altitude corresponding to the given base.

1. Base $\overline{AD}$ $\overline{HA}$, $\overline{CE}$ / $\overline{FD}$ **2.** Base $\overline{DC}$ $\overline{AC}$ **3.** Base $\overline{BC}$ $\overline{AH}$, $\overline{EC}$, $\overline{DF}$

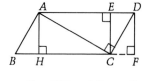

4. Is it possible to find the area of a parallelogram given only
the length of one pair of opposite sides? Explain.

5. How do the areas of the parallelograms *KNIT* and *KNOB*
compare? *KNIT* and *KNUR*? All are =.

6. In the Plan for Proof of Theorem 10-3, why is
$\triangle GBC \cong \triangle DCB$?

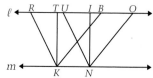

7. In the Plan for Proof of Theorem 10-4, how do you know
that $YW = \frac{1}{2}s\sqrt{3}$?

8. Find the area of a parallelogram and a triangle, each of which
has base of 22 in. and height of 10 in. 220 sq. in.; 110 sq. in.
6. ASA $\cong$ Post. or SAS $\cong$ Post. or SSS $\cong$ Post.
7. The length of an altitude of an equilateral $\triangle$ with sides of
length s is $\frac{1}{2}s\sqrt{3}$. (Thm. 8-7)

Assignment Guide

Basic: 1–18, 39–45
Average: 2–18 (even), 19–33, 39–45
Extended: 2–30 (even), 33–45

Written Exercises

Set A   Find the area of ▱ABCD.

1. $DC = 18$ in.; $DE = 15$ in. **270 sq. in.**

2. $AB = 13$; $DE = 7$ **91**

3. $AB = 12$; $m\angle A = 30$; $AD = 8$ **48**

4. $AB = 15$ cm; $AD = 6\sqrt{2}$ cm; $m\angle A = 45$ **90 cm²**

5. $AB = 2x - 4$; $DE = x - 2$ **2x² − 8x + 8**

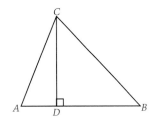

Find the area of △ABC.

6. $AB = 24$ in.; $CD = 9$ in. **108 sq. in.**

7. $AB = 3x - 5$; $CD = x + 5$ **1.5x² + 5x − 12.5**

8. $AB = 18$ cm; $AC = 10$ cm; $m\angle A = 30$ **45 cm²**

9. $AB = 36$; $AC = 12\sqrt{2}$; $m\angle A = 45$ **216**

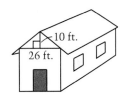

10. Find the area of a right triangular sail. The legs of the triangle measure 6 feet and 9 feet. **27 sq. ft.**

11. If the area of ▱ABCD is 152 sq. in. and its base measures 38 in., what is its height? **4 in.**

12. Find the area of right △ABC with legs $\overline{AC}$ and $\overline{AB}$ if $AC = 11$ and $AB = 16$. **88**

13. Find the area of equilateral △DEF if each side has length $2\sqrt{2}$ yd. **2√3 ≅ 3.46 sq. yd.**

14. Find the area of △KLM with $K(1, 3)$, $L(7, 3)$, and $M(4, -1)$. **12**

15. Find the area of ▱PQRS with $P(0, 1)$, $Q(0, 5)$, $R(-5, 7)$, and $S(-5, 3)$. **20**

16. Bill Rivera is installing siding on a house. The triangular area shown remains to be covered. Bill has 16 strips of siding, each 9 in. by 16 ft. Does he have enough siding? **Yes**

17. Is 75 feet of fencing enough to go along the road in Example 2? Explain.   **No; the side of the ▱ along the road is longer than 75 ft.**

18. Prove Theorem 10-4.

Set B   For each equilateral triangle, find the missing measure.

19. Perimeter $= 8$; $A = \underline{\ \ ?\ \ }$ $\frac{16}{9}\sqrt{3} \cong 3.08$

20. $A = \sqrt{3}$; perimeter $= \underline{\ \ ?\ \ }$ **6**

Example 4

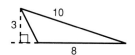

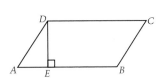

Find the area of each triangle.
6; 12; $9\sqrt{3}$

Error Analysis   Some students may have a difficult time drawing altitudes to bases that are not horizontal. Have students rotate the figure or use an index card to establish perpendicularity. One edge is lined up with the selected base, and the altitude can be drawn along the adjacent edge of the card.

When the altitude of a triangle falls outside the triangle, encourage students to extend the base with a straightedge, and then use the preceding method to find the height.

ANSWERS

Checking for Understanding

4. No; you need to know the length of the altitude to one of the parallel sides.

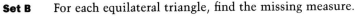

10-2 Areas of Parallelograms and Triangles

Written Exercises

23. No; sample:

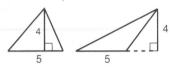

27. $22\frac{1}{2}$ sq. ft.
28. 31.5 sq. ft.
29. 38.25 sq. ft.
30. 45 sq. ft.
31. 38.25 sq. ft.
32. the ▱ with the 90° angle (Exercise 30)

FOLLOW-UP

More Practice

• Worksheet 10–2

Extension

Challenge more capable students to prove that the sum of the distances from any point in the interior of an equilateral triangle to the three sides is equal to the length of an altitude.
• Extension 10–2

Computers

This computer activity can be completed using *The Geometric Supposer: Quadrilaterals* or *Circles.*

   To explore areas of trapezoids and rhombuses, have students use the computer drawing tool to do the following.

   Draw a trapezoid. From one vertex to the base opposite that

Find the area and the perimeter of each parallelogram.

21.

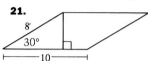

22.

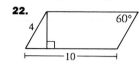

23. Is the converse of Postulate 22 *true*? If *not*, sketch a counterexample.

24. A pennant in the shape of an isosceles triangle is cut from a 24-cm by 16-cm rectangle as shown. How much material is wasted? **192 cm²**

25. Six pennants like the one in Exercise 24 are cut from a 24-cm-wide rectangle as shown. Find the length of the rectangle and the amount of waste.

26. Given: $\ell \parallel m$; $AB = BC$. Compare the areas of triangles ABE, BCE, and ACE.

Sue Kim has two pieces of fencing 9 ft. long and two pieces 5 ft. long. Find the area of the parallelogram with sides of 9 ft. and 5 ft. for each measure of $\angle F$. Use $\sqrt{2} \approx 1.4$ and $\sqrt{3} \approx 1.7$.

27. 30   **28.** 45   **29.** 60   **30.** 90   **31.** 120

32. Which parallelogram encloses the greatest area?

33. Prove Theorem 10-3.

Set C   **34.** Prove Theorem 10-2.

35. Prove: The area of an equilateral triangle whose side is the hypotenuse of a right triangle is equal to the sum of the areas of the equilateral triangles whose sides are the legs.

36. Prove: The diagonals of a parallelogram divide the parallelogram into four triangles with equal areas.

Find the area of each figure.

37. $\triangle FGH$ with vertices $F(0, 0)$, $G(2, 6)$, and $H(7, 7)$ **14**

38. $\square ABCD$ with vertices $A(0, 0)$, $B(5, 5)$, $C(3, 9)$, and $D(-2, 4)$ $10\sqrt{10} = 31.62$

21. $A = 40$; $P = 36$
22. $A = 40$; $P = 20 + \frac{16}{3}\sqrt{3}$
   ≈ 29.24
25. Length: 56 cm; waste: 192 cm²
26. Area $\triangle ABE$ = area $\triangle BCE$
   $= \frac{1}{2}$(area $\triangle ACE$)

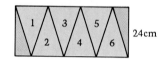

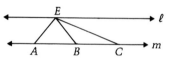

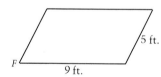

Review **39.** Find the area of a rectangular desk top that measures 30 in. by 60 in. **1,800 sq. in.** **324 cm²**

40. Find the area of a square whose side is 18 cm long.

41. If $\overrightarrow{DA}$ and $\overrightarrow{DC}$ are tangent to $\odot O$, and $m\widehat{ABC} = 290$, then $m\angle ADC = \underline{\ ?\ }$. **110**

42. Find the length of the median of a trapezoid if $b_1 = 8$ and $b_2 = 9$. **$8\frac{1}{2}$**

43. If the measure of the vertex angle of an isosceles triangle is 44, then the measure of an exterior angle adjacent to a base angle is $\underline{\ ?\ }$. **112**

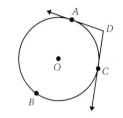

Thinking Ahead **44.** Trace trapezoid $ABCD$. Show how to separate $ABCD$ into rectangles, parallelograms, triangles, or combinations of these polygons to find its area. Discuss your plans with your classmates.

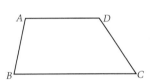

45. Can you find the area of a rhombus if you know the lengths of its diagonals? Explain.

Challenge

The figure at the right is a rectangle made of up ten squares, none of which have the same area. If the areas of A and B are 49 and 144, respectively, find the area of the other eight squares. Is the overall rectangle a square? Explain.

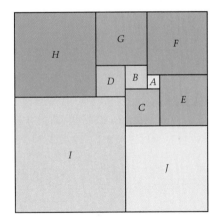

Algebra Review: Solving Quadratic Equations

Solve each equation. You may want to refer back to page 314.

1. $x^2 - 5x - 14 = 0$ **$x = 7$ or -2**   **2.** $x^2 = 169$ **$x = \pm 13$**   **3.** $x^2 + 5x - 1 = 0$ **$x = \frac{-5 \pm \sqrt{29}}{2}$**

4. $x^2 + 12x = 0$ **$x = 0$ or -12**   **5.** $x^2 + x = 6$ **$x = 2$ or -3** **6.** $x^2 - 16x + 64 = 0$ **$x = 8$**

7. $3x^2 - 6x + 2 = 0$ **8.** $x^2 - 36 = 0$ **$x = \pm 6$**   **9.** $2x^2 - 20x + 42 = 0$ **$x = 3$ or 7**
  $x = \frac{3 \pm \sqrt{3}}{3}$

vertex draw a segment perpendicular to the opposite base. Measure the length of that segment; call it h. Measure the lengths of the two bases, find their sum and call it $(b_1 + b_2)$. Calculate the value of $\frac{1}{2}h(b_1 + b_2)$ using the values from your drawing for h and $(b_1 + b_2)$. Measure the area of the trapezoid. Compare the area with your value $\frac{1}{2}h(b_1 + b_2)$. What do you notice? The two values are equal. Repeat this activity for two or three more trapezoids.

Draw a rhombus and its diagonals. What do you know about the angles formed at the intersection of the two diagonals of a rhombus? They are all right angles; therefore, the diagonals are perpendicular to each other. Using what you know about other properties of rhombuses and their diagonals, what must be true about the areas of the four triangles formed by the rhombus and its two diagonals? The four triangles are congruent; therefore, their areas must all be equal. What must be the area of any pair of adjacent triangles in your drawing? Make a conjecture. The area of any pair of adjacent triangles should be $\frac{1}{2}(d_1 \frac{1}{2}d_2)$, or $\frac{1}{4}d_1d_2$. Check this by measuring the area of the large triangle formed by the adjacent pair of right triangles within the rhombus. Now make a conjecture regarding the area of the rhombus in terms of its diagonals. The area should be equal to $2 * \frac{1}{4}d_1d_2$. Now check this by measuring the area of the rhombus. Repeat this activity for two or three more rhombuses.
• **Computer Activities 10-2**
• **Computer Worksheet 10-2**

Excursion: Heron's Theorem

To find the area of a triangular sail given only the lengths of its sides, you can use a formula developed nineteen centuries ago by the Greek mathematician Heron of Alexandria.

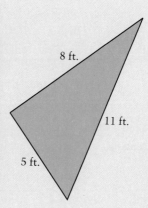

Heron's Theorem
The area of $\triangle ABC$ with side lengths a, b, and c is $\sqrt{s(s-a)(s-b)(s-c)}$, where s is $\frac{1}{2}(a+b+c)$.

Example
Find the area of a triangular sail with sides that measure 5 feet, 8 feet, and 11 feet.

Solution
$s = \frac{1}{2}(a+b+c) = \frac{1}{2}(5+8+11) = 12$
Area $= \sqrt{s(s-a)(s-b)(s-c)}$
$= \sqrt{12(12-5)(12-8)(12-11)}$
$= \sqrt{12(7)(4)(1)}$
$= \sqrt{336} \approx 18.33$ sq. ft.

Find the area of a triangle with the given side lengths.
1. 6, 8, 10 24   **2.** 5, 12, 13 30   **3.** 5, 9, 13   **4.** 9, 17, 21

3. $\frac{9}{4}\sqrt{51} \approx 16.07$

4. $\frac{\sqrt{88,595}}{4} \approx 74.41$

5. Use Heron's Theorem to find the area of an equilateral triangle with sides of length x. $\frac{x^2\sqrt{3}}{4}$

6. Prove Heron's Theorem. Draw altitude $\overline{CD}$ with length h. Use $h^2 = a^2 - x^2 = b^2 - (c-x)^2$ to solve for x in terms of a, b, c. Use this value of x in $h^2 = (a-x)(a+x)$ and factor so that
$$h^2 = \frac{(a+b+c)(-a+b+c)(a-b+c)(a+b-c)}{4c^2}$$
Let $2s = a+b+c$; solve for h. Then, substitute this value into $\frac{1}{2}ch$.

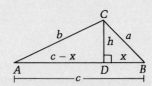

Warm-Up Review

1. A quadrilateral with only one pair of parallel sides is a(n) __?__. Trapezoid
2. If an isosceles right triangle has a hypotenuse 10 units long, what is the length of a leg? $5\sqrt{2}$ units
3. True or false: The diagonals of a rhombus are congruent. False
4. State the formula for the area of a triangle. $A = \frac{1}{2}bh$

10-3 Areas of Other Quadrilaterals

Mrs. Yeh plans to open a craft shop in a large shopping mall. The shop she wants is shaped like a trapezoid. She wants at least 6,400 sq. ft. of floor space. To determine if the shop is large enough, she needs to find the area of a trapezoid.

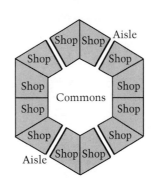

An efficient way to find the area of a trapezoid is to find the sum of the areas of the triangles formed by a diagonal. This method is demonstrated in the Plan for Proof of Theorem 10-5. Its proof is left to Exercise 37. Recall that the bases of a trapezoid are the parallel sides. The altitude is defined here.

Definition   Altitude of a Trapezoid

An altitude of a trapezoid is a segment from any point in one base perpendicular to the line containing the other base. Its length is the height of the trapezoid.

Theorem 10-5   Area of a Trapezoid

The area A of a trapezoid is equal to one half the product of the height h and the sum of the lengths b_1 and b_2 of the bases.
$$A = \frac{1}{2}h(b_1 + b_2)$$

Given   Trapezoid $GBCD$; bases $\overline{GB}$ and $\overline{CD}$ of lengths b_1 and b_2; altitude $\overline{DE}$ of length h

Prove   Area trapezoid $GBCD = \frac{1}{2}h(b_1 + b_2)$

Plan for Proof   Draw $\overline{BD}$ to form $\triangle GBD$ and $\triangle DCB$. From B, draw a segment perpendicular to $\overleftrightarrow{DC}$. Show $BF = DE = h$. Then show area $\triangle GBD = \frac{1}{2}(GB)(DE) = \frac{1}{2}b_1 h$ and area $\triangle DCB = \frac{1}{2}(DC)(BF) = \frac{1}{2}b_2 h$. Then add the areas.

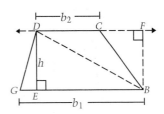

Example 1

The shop Mrs. Yeh wants has the dimensions shown. Is the shop large enough?

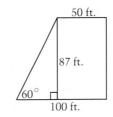

Solution

$A = \frac{1}{2}h(b_1 + b_2)$

  $= \frac{1}{2}(87)(50 + 100)$

  $= 6,525$ sq. ft.

$6,525 > 6,400$ so the shop is large enough.

LESSON 10-3

Resources

Construction paper
Worksheet 10-3
Extension 10-3
💻 Computer Worksheet 10-3

OBJECTIVE

State and apply theorems concerning the area of regions enclosed by trapezoids, rhombuses and kites.

TEACHING NOTES

Introduce the formula for the area of a trapezoid by using **concrete materials** such as a trapezoidal region cut from construction paper. First mark the two bases and the height. Then fold and cut

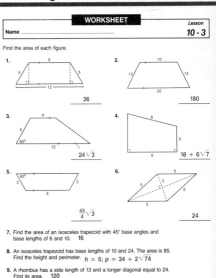

WORKSHEET   Lesson **10-3**

Name _____

Find the area of each figure.

1. _____ 36   2. _____ 180

3. _____ $24\sqrt{3}$ 4. _____ $18 + 6\sqrt{7}$

5. _____ $\frac{45}{4}\sqrt{3}$ 6. _____ 24

7. Find the area of an isosceles trapezoid with 45° base angles and base lengths of 6 and 10. 16

8. An isosceles trapezoid has base lengths of 10 and 24. The area is 85. Find the height and perimeter. $h = 5$; $p = 34 + 2\sqrt{74}$

9. A rhombus has a side length of 13 and a longer diagonal equal to 24. Find its area. 120

10. $AB = 5$; $BE = 3$; $ED = 6$. Find the area. 36

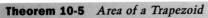
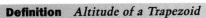

along diagonal $\overline{BD}$, forming the two triangles used in the proof. Thus, it is easy to see that the bases of the trapezoid are the respective bases of the two triangles, and that both triangles share the height of the trapezoid. The proof follows easily.

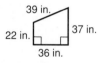

At the end of the lesson, summarize the methods used for proving the various formulas.

Additional Examples

Example 1

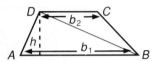

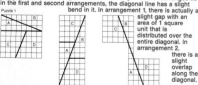

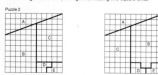
Example 2

If the area of a trapezoid is 40 cm², the height is 5 cm, and one base is 10 cm long, how long is the other base?

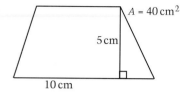

Solution

$A = \frac{1}{2}h(b_1 + b_2)$

$40 = \frac{1}{2}(5)(10 + b_2)$

$40 = 25 + \frac{5}{2}b_2$

$15 = \frac{5}{2}b_2$

$b_2 = 6$ cm

Recall from Chapter 6 that the diagonals of a rhombus are the perpendicular bisectors of each other. In Theorem 10-6, we use the area of the triangles formed by the diagonals to develop a formula for the area of a rhombus. The proof of this theorem is left to Exercise 38.

Theorem 10-6   *Area of a Rhombus*

The area A of a rhombus is equal to one half the product of the lengths d_1 and d_2 of its diagonals. $A = \frac{1}{2}d_1d_2$

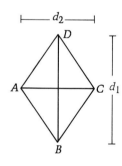

Given   Rhombus $ABCD$ with diagonals $\overline{AC}$ of length d_2 and $\overline{DB}$ of length d_1

Prove   Area rhombus $ABCD = \frac{1}{2}d_1d_2$

Plan for Proof   Consider $\triangle ADB$ and $\triangle CDB$. Since the diagonals of the rhombus are the perpendicular bisectors of each other, area $\triangle ADB = \frac{1}{2}d_1(\frac{1}{2}d_2)$ and area $\triangle CDB = \frac{1}{2}d_1(\frac{1}{2}d_2)$. Then area rhombus $ADCB = \frac{1}{2}d_1(\frac{1}{2}d_2) + \frac{1}{2}d_1(\frac{1}{2}d_2) = \frac{1}{2}d_1(d_2)$.

If exactly one diagonal of a quadrilateral is a perpendicular bisector of the other, the figure is called a *kite.*

The diagonal $\overline{XZ}$ of the kite separates it into two triangles, each with base $\overline{XZ}$ of length d_2 and height $\frac{1}{2}d_1$. The proof that the area of a kite is $A = \frac{1}{2}d_1d_2$ is the same as the proof for the area of a rhombus.

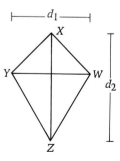

Summary Formulas for the Areas of Quadrilaterals

Rectangle: $A = bh$	Square: $A = s^2$	Parallelogram: $A = bh$
Trapezoid: $A = \frac{1}{2}h(b_1 + b_2)$	Rhombus: $A = \frac{1}{2}d_1d_2$	Kite: $A = \frac{1}{2}d_1d_2$

Assignment Guide

Basic: 1–18, 21, 41–48
Average: 2–18 (even), 19–39, 41–48
Extended: 2–28 (even), 30–48

Checking for Understanding

1. In the Plan for Proof of Theorem 10-6, which diagonal is considered the base of each triangle? **BD**

2. Could you prove Theorem 10-6 by adding the areas of $\triangle ADC$ and $\triangle ABC$? **Yes**

3. Is a rhombus a kite? Explain. **No; in a kite only one diagonal is bisected.**

Find the area of each figure.

4.

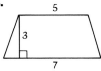

5. $XZ = 12$; $WY = 16$

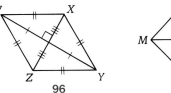

18   96

6. $MO = 18$; $PN = 9$

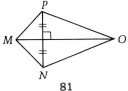

81

Written Exercises

Set A   A trapezoid has base lengths b_1 and b_2, height h, and area A.

1. $b_1 = 6$; $b_2 = 8$; $h = 4$; $A = \underline{?}$ **28**

2. $b_1 = 10$; $b_2 = 15$; $h = 10$; $A = \underline{?}$ **125**

3. $b_1 = 28$; $h = 14$; $A = 364$; $b_2 = \underline{?}$ **24**

4. $b_1 = 8t$; $b_2 = 12t$; $A = 60t^2$; $h = \underline{?}$ **6t**

5. $b_1 = \sqrt{2x}$; $b_2 = 5\sqrt{2x}$; $A = 10\sqrt{2x}$; $h = \underline{?}$ $\frac{10}{3}$

The lengths of the diagonals of a rhombus are given. Find the area of each rhombus.

6. 7.4 cm; 4.3 cm   **7.** $2\sqrt{6}$; $3\sqrt{6}$ **18**
          15.91 cm²

8. $x + 6$; $2x - 1$ **9.** $8 - y$; $8 + y$ **32 − 0.5y²**
$x^2 + 5.5x - 3$

10. Kate and Meg made a paper kite with diagonals 3.5 ft. long and 4 ft. long. How much paper was used? **7 sq. ft.**

11. Find the area of trapezoid $BAND$ for $B(-2, 0)$, $A(2, 0)$, $N(5, 4)$, and $D(-2, 4)$. **22**

Classify each quadrilateral and give its area.

12. $G(-2, 0)$, $I(0, 4)$, $V(5, 4)$, and $E(17, 0)$ **Trapezoid; 48**

13. $T(5, 0)$, $A(8, 6)$, $K(5, 8)$, and $E(2, 6)$ **Kite; 24**

14. $H(-2, -1)$, $E(3, 2)$, $R(-2, 5)$, and $A(-7, 2)$ **Rhombus; 30**

The side of Bob's bunny hutch is shown above. How many square inches of wire mesh will be needed to cover this side of the hutch? **1062 sq. in.**

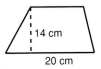

14 cm

20 cm

If the area of a trapezoid is 217 cm, the height is 14 cm and the length of one base is 20 cm, what is the other base? **11 cm**

Error Analysis   Students often have trouble identifying the altitude of a trapezoid if the bases are not horizontal or if one of the legs is perpendicular to the bases. Have students rotate the figure.

EXERCISE NOTES

Exercises 12–14   are easier to solve if students first graph and identify each figure before selecting the formula to be used.

Exercise 33   shows an alternate formula for finding the area of a trapezoid.

15. Estimate the area of North Dakota if its northern and southern borders are 310 and 360 miles long, and they are 210 miles apart. 70,350 sq. mi

310

North Dakota

210

360

16. Wyoming is shaped like a trapezoid. Its northern and southern borders are 345 and 365 miles long, and they are 275 miles apart. Estimate the area.

17. The area of a rhombus is 2,352 sq. in. One diagonal measures 56 in. How long is the other?

18. Given: Kite *ABCD* with area 99; *AC* = 36. Find *BD*.

Set B **19.** Explain how to find the area of a trapezoid given the height and the length of the median.

20. Find the area of a trapezoid if the lengths of its median and altitude are 20 and 15, respectively.

16. 97,625 sq. mi.
17. 84 in.
18. 5.5
19. Multiply the height and the length of the median.
20. 300

Find the area of each figure.

21. Trapezoid *MORE*

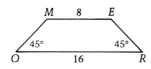

48

22. Trapezoid *TAPE*

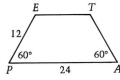

$108\sqrt{3} \approx 187.06$

23. Trapezoid *DESK*

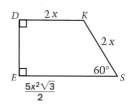

$\frac{5x^2\sqrt{3}}{2}$

24. Kite *STUV*

168

25. Rhombus *PQRS*

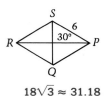

$18\sqrt{3} \approx 31.18$

26. Kite *JKLM*

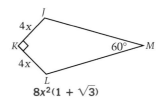

$8x^2(1 + \sqrt{3})$

A hang glider is formed by two congruent isosceles triangles with 45° vertex angles. The glider weighs 35 lb., and the total weight it can carry (including its own) is 1 lb. per sq. ft. of *sail area*, the area of the glider. $112.5\sqrt{2} \approx 159.1$ sq. ft.

27. Find the sail area of the glider.

28. What is the maximum weight possible for a user of the glider? About 124 lb.

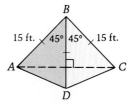

Written Exercises

30.

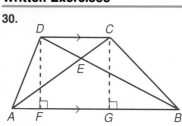

Proof: 1. Trapezoid *ABCD* with $\overline{DC}$ ‖ $\overline{AB}$; $\overline{DB}$ and $\overline{AC}$ intersect at *E*. (Given) 2. Draw lines from pts. *D* and *C* ⊥ to $\overleftrightarrow{AB}$ that intersect $\overline{AB}$ at *F* and *G*, respectively. (Through a pt. not on a given line, there is

29. A rhombus has sides of length 10 and one diagonal of length 16. Find the area of the rhombus. **96**

30. Given: Trapezoid $ABCD$ with $\overline{DC} \parallel \overline{AB}$; $\overline{AC}$ and $\overline{BD}$ intersect at E.
Prove: Area $\triangle ADE$ = area $\triangle BCE$

31. P is the midpoint of $\overline{RE}$. Show that the area of trapezoid $ROVE$ is equal to the area of $\triangle VOS$.

32. The area of a trapezoid is 168 cm². The height is 8 cm. If the length of the longer base is 12 cm more than twice the length of the shorter, what are the base lengths? **10 cm; 32 cm**

33. Prove: The area of a trapezoid is equal to the product of its height and its median.

34. Find the area of the auditorium floor at the right.

To approximate the area of a region with an irregular shape, you can divide it into various polygonal regions. Estimate the area of each state. Dimensions are given in miles.

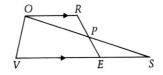

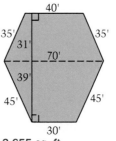

34. 3,655 sq. ft.
35. Texas: 285,075 sq. mi.
36. Tennessee: 41,960 sq. mi.

35.

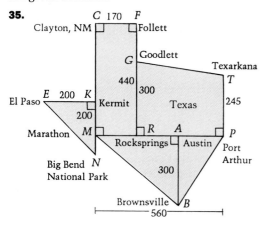

36.

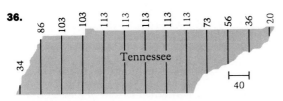

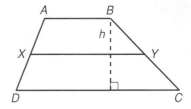

exactly one line $\perp$ to the given line.) 3. $DF = CG$ (The distance between 2 given $\parallel$ lines is constant. [1, 2]) 4. Area $\triangle ADB = \frac{1}{2}(DF)(AB)$; area $\triangle BCA = \frac{1}{2}(CG)(AB)$ (Area of a $\triangle$) 5. Area $\triangle BCA = \frac{1}{2}(DF)(AB)$ (Substitution Prop. [3, 4]) 6. Area $\triangle BCA$ = area $\triangle ADB$ (Substitution Prop. [4, 5]) 7. Area $\triangle BCA$ = area $\triangle BCE$ + area $\triangle AEB$; area $\triangle ADB$ = area $\triangle ADE$ + area $\triangle AEB$ (Area Add. Post.) 8. Area $\triangle BCE$ + area $\triangle AEB$ = area $\triangle ADE$ + area $\triangle AEB$ (Substitution Prop. [6, 7]) 9. Area $\triangle BCE$ = area $\triangle ADE$ (Subtraction Prop. [8])

31. $m\angle RPO = m\angle EPS$ since they are vert. $\angle$s. Because $\overline{OR} \parallel \overline{VS}$, $\angle$s ORP and SEP are alt. int. $\angle$s and their measures are =. Then, since $RP = EP$, $\triangle ORP \cong \triangle SEP$ by the ASA Post. Area $ROVE$ = area $OVEP$ + area $\triangle OPR$ by area add., and area $ROVE$ = area $OVEP$ + area $\triangle SEP$ by substitution. Finally, area $ROVE$ = area $\triangle VOS$ because area $\triangle VOS$ = area $OVEP$ + area $\triangle SEP$.

33. Given: Trap. $ABCD$ with $\overline{AB} \parallel \overline{DC}$, median $\overline{XY}$ and height h
Prove: Area $ABCD = h(XY)$

Proof: 1. Trap. $ABCD$ with $\overline{AB} \parallel \overline{DC}$ has median $\overline{XY}$ and height h. (Given) 2. Area $ABCD = \frac{1}{2}h(AB + CD)$ (Area of a trap [1]) 3. $XY = \frac{1}{2}(AB + CD)$ (Median of a trap. has length = to half the sum of lengths of bases. [1]) 4. Area $ABCD = h(XY)$ (Substitution Prop. [2, 3])

37. Proof: 1. Trap. *GBCD*; bases $\overline{GB}$ and $\overline{CD}$ of lengths b_1, and b_2; altitude $\overline{DE}$ of length h (Given) 2. Draw $\overline{BD}$. (2 pts. determine a line.) 3. Draw $\overline{BF} \perp \overleftrightarrow{DC}$ at F. (Through a pt. not on a given line, there is exactly one line $\perp$ to the given line.) 4. $\overline{GB} \parallel \overline{CD}$ (Def. of trap. [1]) 5. $DE = BF = h$ (Distance between 2 given $\parallel$ lines is constant. [1, 4]) 6. Area $\triangle GBD = \frac{1}{2}(DE)(GB) = \frac{1}{2}hb_1$; area $\triangle DCB = \frac{1}{2}(BF)(DC) = \frac{1}{2}hb_2$ (Area of a $\triangle$ [1, 5]) 7. Area $GBCD$ = area $\triangle GBD$ + area $\triangle DCB$ (Area Add. Post.) 8. Area $GBCD = \frac{1}{2}hb_1 + \frac{1}{2}hb_2 = \frac{1}{2}h(b_1 + b_2)$ (Substitution Prop. [6, 7])

FOLLOW-UP

More Practice

• Worksheet 10-3

Extension

Ask students to verify that the formula for the area of a trapezoid also holds for parallelograms, rectangles and triangles (considering the length of one base to be zero).

Both the Egyptians and the Babylonians found the areas of quadrilaterals by the formula $A = \frac{1}{4}(a + c)(b + d)$, where a, b, c and d are the lengths of consecutive sides. Have students investigate for which quadrilaterals the formula holds. rectangles only

• Extension 10-3

Computers

• Computer Worksheet 10-3

---

37. Prove Theorem 10−5.   **38.** Prove Theorem 10−6.

39. Find the area of the polygon bounded by the x-axis and the lines with equations $y = 2x + 3$, $x = 2$, and $x = 5$. **30**

Set C   **40.** Prove: The segment joining the midpoints of the parallel sides of a trapezoid separates it into two trapezoids that have equal areas.

🔺 **Review**   **41.** Find the area of $\square ABCD$. **108**

42. Find the area of $\triangle AED$. $9\sqrt{10} \approx 28.46$

43. The area of a square is 250 cm². Find its perimeter. $20\sqrt{10} \approx 63.25$ cm

44. Write the following statement in "if . . . then" form. All collies have long hair.

45. In $\square ABCD$ above, if $m\angle B = 9x$ and $m\angle C = 19x + 12$, then $x = \underline{?}$. **6**

44. If a creature is a collie; then it has long hair

Thinking Ahead   **46.** On grid paper, draw two squares, one with side length 4 and the other with side length 8. Compare the areas of the squares.

47. On grid paper, draw two isosceles right triangles, one with side length 6 and the other with side length 3. Compare the areas of the triangles.

48. Find the ratio of the area of $\triangle DEC$ to that of $\triangle ABC$.

🔺 Challenge

Trace $\triangle ABC$. Then construct isosceles $\triangle ABD$ such that area $\triangle ABD$ = area $\triangle ABC$. Construct right $\triangle ABE$ such that area $\triangle ABE$ = area $\triangle ABC$. (HINT: Draw line ℓ through C parallel to $\overline{AB}$.)

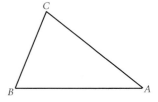

Algebra Review: Equations for Lines in Slope-Intercept Form

Write the equation in slope-intercept form for the line that

1. has slope 2 and contains $A(4, 6)$.

2. has slope -1 and contains $B(0, -5)$. $y = -x - 5$

3. has slope $\frac{2}{3}$ and contains $C(-8, 8)$.

4. has slope 3 and contains $O(0, 0)$. $y = 3x$

5. contains $D(3, -6)$ and $E(1, 0)$.

6. contains $F(-4, -3)$ and $G(4, 5)$. $y = x + 1$

1. $y = 2x - 2$ **3.** $y = \frac{2}{3}x + \frac{40}{3}$ **5.** $y = -3x + 3$

Warm-Up Review

1. Polygons having the same shape are ___?___. Similar
2. The ___?___ of a polygon is the sum of the lengths of its sides. Perimeter
3. The ___?___ Postulate involves finding the sum of the areas of regions that make up a given region. Area Addition
4. Three methods for proving triangles similar are ___?___. SSS; SAS; AA

LESSON 10–4

Resources

Teaching Aid 3, grid paper
Visual Aid 3, grid paper
Worksheet 10–4
Extension 10–4
Quiz 10

10-4 Areas of Similar Polygons

Mr. Fox, the owner of a flower store, wants to enlarge his advertising signs. He pays for the signs by the square inch. What is the ratio of the cost of the larger sign to that of the smaller? How does the ratio of the costs of the signs compare to the ratio of the lengths of corresponding sides of the signs? See below
Do you think that the relationship suggested by your answer is also true for pairs of similar triangles? Yes
2.25 to 1; ratio of costs is square of ratio of lengths.

24"

12"

36"

18"

OBJECTIVE

State and apply theorems concerning areas of similar polygons.

TEACHING NOTES

This lesson may be introduced by having students draw two rectangles on grid paper with dimensions of 3 and 5 and 6 and 10. Ask them to find the ratio of corresponding sides, perimeters and

Theorem 10-7 *Areas of Similar Triangles*

If two triangles are similar, then the ratio of their areas is equal to the square of the ratio of the lengths of any two corresponding sides.

Given $\triangle ABC \sim \triangle XYZ$

Prove $\dfrac{\text{Area } \triangle ABC}{\text{Area } \triangle XYZ} = \left(\dfrac{AB}{XY}\right)^2 = \left(\dfrac{BC}{YZ}\right)^2 = \left(\dfrac{CA}{ZX}\right)^2$

Plan for Proof   Draw altitudes $\overline{BD}$ and $\overline{YW}$, and then express the areas of the triangles as a ratio:

$\dfrac{\text{Area } \triangle ABC}{\text{Area } \triangle XYZ} = \dfrac{\frac{1}{2}(AC)(BD)}{\frac{1}{2}(XZ)(YW)}$. By Theorem 7-8, $\dfrac{BD}{YW} = \dfrac{AC}{XZ}$.

So, $\dfrac{\frac{1}{2}(AC)(BD)}{\frac{1}{2}(XZ)(YW)} = \dfrac{\frac{1}{2}(AC)(AC)}{\frac{1}{2}(XZ)(XZ)} = \left(\dfrac{AC}{XZ}\right)^2$.

Likewise, $\dfrac{\text{area } \triangle ABC}{\text{area } \triangle XYZ} = \left(\dfrac{AB}{XY}\right)^2$ and $\left(\dfrac{BC}{YZ}\right)^2$.

The proof of Theorem 10-7 is left to Exercise 19.

Example 1

Show that $\triangle ABC \sim \triangle RST$, and find the ratio of their areas.

Solution
$\dfrac{AB}{RS} = \dfrac{8}{24} = \dfrac{1}{3}$, $\dfrac{BC}{ST} = \dfrac{6}{18} = \dfrac{1}{3}$, and $\dfrac{CA}{TR} = \dfrac{5}{15} = \dfrac{1}{3}$, so $\triangle ABC \sim \triangle RST$.

$\dfrac{\text{Area } \triangle ABC}{\text{Area } \triangle RST} = \left(\dfrac{1}{3}\right)^2 = \dfrac{1}{9}$

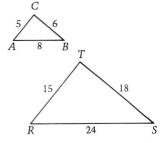

WORKSHEET
Name
Lesson
10-4

1. The area of one rectangle is 36. The area of a similar rectangle is 16. What is the ratio of the perimeters?   1. ___3:2___

2. The ratio of the sides of two similar triangles is 3:5. If the area of the larger triangle is 125, what is the area of the smaller triangle?   2. ___45___

3. Two similar polygons have perimeters 120 and 50. If the area of the smaller polygon is 125, what is the area of the larger polygon?   3. ___720___

4. If ABCD ~ WXYZ, find the area of each figure.   4. ABCD = 28; WXYZ = 63

5. The area of △ACD is 200. What is the area of △ABE?   5. ___72___

6. If the perimeter of DCBA is 48, find x.   6. ___x = 8___

7. If HGFE and DCBA in exercise 6 are similar rectangles, what is the area of HGFE?   7. ___288___

areas. $1:2$; $1:2$; $1:4$ Repeat the exercise using a 9 by 15 rectangle and ask students to form a generalization about ratios of areas. Have them test their generalization by applying Theorem 10–4 to two equilateral triangles.

In some situations, such as that in **Example 2**, it may be more convenient to express the relationship in Theorem 10–8 as $\frac{s_1}{s_2} = \sqrt{\frac{A_1}{A_2}}$ where s_1 and s_2 are the lengths of a pair of corresponding sides, and A_1 and A_2 are the areas of similar polygons.

EXERCISE NOTES

Checking for Understanding Exercises 1–2 and **Exercises 8, 15** and **18** could be done using a calculator.

Exercises 9–10 require students to graph and verify similarity before applying the theorem.

Theorem 10-7 can be applied to similar polygons that are composed of nonoverlapping triangles. For example, you can show that two regular pentagons with side lengths 2 and 3 have areas that are in the ratio $\left(\frac{2}{3}\right)^2$, or $\frac{4}{9}$.

From vertices C and C' draw diagonals $\overline{CE}$, $\overline{CA}$, $\overline{C'E'}$, and $\overline{C'A'}$ to separate the pentagons into triangular regions. $\triangle I \sim \triangle I'$ and $\triangle III \sim \triangle III'$ by the SAS Similarity Theorem.

So $\frac{AC}{A'C'} = \frac{BC}{B'C'} = \frac{2}{3}$ and $\frac{EC}{E'C'} = \frac{DC}{D'C'} = \frac{2}{3}$. Then $\triangle II \sim \triangle II'$. Why? **SSS ~ Thm.**

$\frac{\text{Area I}}{\text{Area I}'} = \frac{\text{area II}}{\text{area II}'} = \frac{\text{area III}}{\text{area III}'} = \left(\frac{2}{3}\right)^2$ by Theorem 10-7.

$\frac{\text{Area I + area II + area III}}{\text{Area I}' + \text{area II}' + \text{area III}'} = \left(\frac{2}{3}\right)^2$ by the Summation Property.

So $\frac{\text{area } ABCDE}{\text{area } A'B'C'D'E'} = \left(\frac{2}{3}\right)^2$ by the Area Addition Postulate.

This analysis suggests the general result in Theorem 10-8, the proof of which omitted.

Theorem 10-8 *Areas of Similar Polygons*

If two polygons are similar, then the ratio of their areas is equal to the square of the ratio of the lengths of any two corresponding sides.

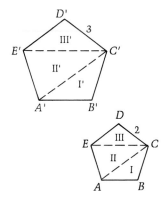

Example 2

Hexagon I is similar to hexagon II, and $\frac{\text{area I}}{\text{area II}} = \frac{1}{16}$. What is the length of side x?

Solution
$\frac{\text{Area I}}{\text{Area II}} = \left(\frac{2}{x}\right)^2 = \frac{4}{x^2}$. Since $\frac{4}{x^2} = \frac{1}{16}$, $x^2 = 64$, and $x = 8$.

Checking for Understanding

1. What is the ratio of the areas of the flower-shop signs?

2. Use 3¢ per sq. in. to verify the ratio of the costs of the signs.

3. The lengths of the corresponding sides of two similar triangles are 3 and 7. What is the ratio of their areas?

4. What is the ratio of the areas of $\triangle MNO$ and $\triangle QRS$? Check by computing the areas. 1:9; 6:54 = 1:9

1. $648:288 = 9:4 = 2.25:1$
2. $19.44:8.64 = 2.25:1$
3. $9:49$

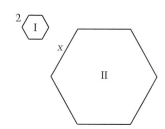

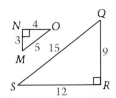

Assignment Guide

Basic: 1–11, 24–33
Average: 2–10 (even), 11–21, 24–33
Extended: 2–14 (even), 15–33

5. The areas of two squares are 64 cm² and 100 cm². What is the ratio of the lengths of their corresponding sides?

$$8:10 = 4:5$$

Written Exercises

Set A Find the ratio of the areas for each pair of similar polygons.

1. 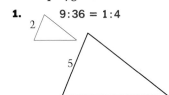 $9:36 = 1:4$

2. 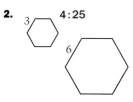 $4:25$

3. If the hexagons in Exercise 2 are regular, compare the ratio of their perimeters to the ratio of their areas.

4. The area of a given triangle is 9 times that of a similar triangle. Find the ratio of the lengths of the corresponding sides of the two triangles. 3:1

5. Given $\triangle ABC \sim \triangle DEF$ with $AB = 18$ in., $DE = 3$ in., and area $\triangle ABC = 72$ sq. in. Find the area of $\triangle DEF$.

6. Find the length of a side of a square whose area is five times the area of a square with side length 6 cm.

7. What is the ratio of the areas of two triangles with corresponding sides of lengths $2\sqrt{3}$ and $6\sqrt{3}$?

8. A sign painter is copying a corporate symbol. The area of a triangle on the letterhead logo is 30 mm² and the length of a side is 6 mm. The length of the corresponding side of the triangle on the sign logo is 75 cm. What is the area of the triangle on the sign? 468, 750 mm² = 4,687.5 cm²

3. Ratio of perimeters is square root of ratio of areas.
5. 2 sq. in.
6. $6\sqrt{5} \approx 13.42$ cm
7. $12:108 = 1:9$

Graph the following pairs of polygons. Can Theorem 10-8 be applied to them? If so, what is the ratio of their areas?

9. $C(0, 0)$, $A(4, 0)$, $S(4, 4)$, $T(0, 4)$ and $I(2, 9)$, $R(9, 9)$, $O(9, 16)$, $N(2, 16)$

10. $F(1, 1)$, $L(6, 1)$, $A(4, 4)$, $P(1, 4)$ and $J(2, 5)$, $A(12, 5)$, $C(8, 11)$, $K(2, 11)$

11. Two squares have side lengths $8x^2$ and $4x$. Find the ratio of their areas. Check by substituting a value for x.

$64x^4:16x^2 = 4x^2:1$; if $x = 2$; $32^2:8^2 = 16:1$

10-4 *Areas of Similar Polygons*

Additional Examples

Example 1

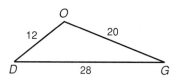

Show that these triangles are similar, and find the ratio of their areas. $\frac{CA}{DO} = \frac{AT}{OG} = \frac{CT}{DG} = \frac{1}{4}$; area $\triangle CAT$/area $\triangle DOG = \frac{1}{16}$

Example 2

Given: pentagon I ~ pentagon II; $\frac{\text{area I}}{\text{area II}} = \frac{1}{6}$
Find *x*. $3\sqrt{6}$

Error Analysis Students may be inclined to use ratios on figures that are not similar. Stress that Theorems 10–7 and 10–8 can only be used with similar polygons.

ANSWERS

Written Exercises

19. Proof: 1. $\triangle ABC \sim \triangle XYZ$ (Given) 2. Draw altitudes $\overline{BD}$ and $\overline{YW}$. (Through a pt. not on a given line, there is exactly one line $\perp$ to the given line.) 3. Area $\triangle ABC = \frac{1}{2}(CA)(BD)$; area $\triangle XYZ = \frac{1}{2}(ZX)(YW)$ (Area of a $\triangle$ [1, 2]) 4. $\frac{\text{Area } \triangle ABC}{\text{Area } \triangle XYZ} = \frac{\frac{1}{2}(CA)(BD)}{\frac{1}{2}(ZX)(YW)}$ (Multiplication Prop. [9]) 5. $\frac{BD}{YW} = \frac{CA}{ZX} = \frac{BC}{YZ} = \frac{AB}{XY}$ (In $\sim \triangle$s, lengths of altitudes from corr. vertices are proportional to lengths of corr. sides. [1]) 6. $\frac{\text{Area } \triangle ABC}{\text{Area } \triangle XYZ} = \frac{\frac{1}{2}(CA)(CA)}{\frac{1}{2}(ZX)(ZX)} = \left(\frac{CA}{ZX}\right)^2$ (Substitution Prop. [4, 5]) 7. $\left(\frac{CA}{ZX}\right)^2 = \left(\frac{BC}{YZ}\right)^2 = \left(\frac{AB}{XY}\right)^2$ (Multiplication Prop. [5]) 8. $\frac{\text{Area } \triangle ABC}{\text{Area } \triangle XYZ} = \left(\frac{AB}{XY}\right)^2 = \left(\frac{BC}{YZ}\right)^2 = \left(\frac{CA}{ZX}\right)^2$ (Substitution Prop. [6, 7])

20.

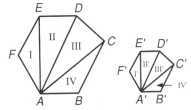

By SAS $\sim$ Thm., $\triangle I \sim \triangle I'$ and $\triangle IV \sim \triangle IV'$. So, $\frac{\text{Area } \triangle I}{\text{Area } \triangle I'} = \left(\frac{FE}{F'E'}\right)^2$. and $\frac{\text{Area } \triangle IV}{\text{Area } \triangle IV'} = \left(\frac{AB}{A'B'}\right)^2$. By def. of $\sim$ polygons, $\frac{ED}{E'D'} = \frac{EF}{E'F'}, \frac{EA}{E'A'} = \frac{EF}{E'F'}, m\angle FED = m\angle F'D'E'$ and $m\angle FEA = m\angle F'E'A'$. Then $\frac{EA}{E'A'} = \frac{ED}{E'D'}$, and by subtraction, $m\angle DEA = m\angle D'E'A'$. Thus, $\triangle I \sim \triangle II$ by SAS $\sim$ Thm., and $\frac{\text{Area } \triangle II}{\text{Area } \triangle II'} = \left(\frac{ED}{E'D'}\right)^2$. Similarly, $\triangle III \sim \triangle III'$ and $\frac{\text{Area } \triangle III}{\text{Area } \triangle III'} = \left(\frac{DC}{D'C'}\right)^2$. Since the hexagons are regular, $AB = CD = ED = EF$ and $A'B' = C'D' = E'D' = E'F'$. So $\frac{AB}{A'B'} = \frac{CD}{C'D'} = \frac{ED}{E'D'} = \frac{EF}{E'F'}$. Hence, $\frac{\text{Area } \triangle I}{\text{Area } \triangle I'} = \frac{\text{Area } \triangle II}{\text{Area } \triangle II'} = \frac{\text{Area } \triangle III}{\text{Area } \triangle III'} = \frac{\text{Area } \triangle IV}{\text{Area } \triangle IV'} = \left(\frac{AB}{A'B'}\right)^2$. By the Summation Prop. of Prop., $\frac{\text{Area } \triangle I + \text{Area } \triangle II + \text{Area } \triangle III + \text{Area } \triangle IV}{\text{Area } \triangle I' + \text{Area } \triangle II' + \text{Area } \triangle III' + \text{Area } \triangle IV'} = \left(\frac{AB}{A'B'}\right)^2$. Finally, by the Area Add.

Set B

12. Two similar triangles have areas 121 cm^2 and 81 cm^2. If a side length of the larger is 22 cm, find the length of the corresponding side of the smaller. **18 cm**

13. The area of one equilateral triangle is 16 times that of another. Find the ratio of their perimeters.

14. The area of a triangle is 9 and its perimeter is $4x - 4$. The area of a similar triangle is 4. Its perimeter is $2x + 6$. Find the perimeter of each triangle.

15. What is the ratio of the areas of two similar TV screens with diagonals 21 in. and 19 in. long?

16. The area of the design on a tablecloth is 2.25 times its area on a matching napkin. What is the ratio of the lengths of a pair of corresponding sides?

17. Find the length of a side of equilateral $\triangle ABC$ that has twice the area of equilateral $\triangle DEF$ if $DE = 8$ ft.

18. A scale drawing of the floor of a convention hall is 11 cm by 30 cm. The actual dimensions are 67.0 m by 182.7 m. Find the ratio of the area of the drawing to that of the actual hall. **1:370,881**

19. Prove Theorem 10-7.

20. Without using Theorem 10-8, show that the ratio of the areas of two regular hexagons is equal to the square of the ratio of the lengths of their corresponding sides. (HINT: Draw diagonals.)

21. Given: $\triangle PQR \sim \triangle TUV$; altitudes $\overline{RS}$ and $\overline{VW}$
Prove: $\dfrac{\text{Area } \triangle PQR}{\text{Area } \triangle TUV} = \left(\dfrac{RS}{VW}\right)^2$

Set C

22. The midpoints of the sides of squares are joined by segments as shown. Find the ratio of the areas of square $WXYZ$ and square $ABCD$. **1:4**

23. In $\triangle ABC$, the height CF is 8, $AB = 16$, and $\overline{DE} \parallel \overline{AB}$. Find DE and GC such that $\triangle CDE$ and trapezoid $ABED$ have equal areas. **$CG = 4\sqrt{2} \approx 5.66$; $DE = 8\sqrt{2} \approx 11.31$**

◆ Review Find the area of each figure in Exercises 24–26.

24. Trapezoid with a height of 7 in. and bases that measure 4 in. and 12 in. **56 sq. in.**

25. Rhombus with diagonals 2.9 cm long and 4.6 cm long

13. $12:3 = 4:1$
14. 48 and 32
15. 441:361
16. 3:2
17. $8\sqrt{2} \approx 11.31$ ft

25. 6.67 cm^2

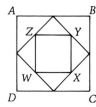

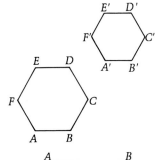

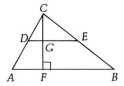

Post., $\frac{\text{Area } ABCDEF}{\text{Area } A'B'C'D'E'F'} =$
$\frac{\text{Area } \triangle I + \text{Area } \triangle II + \text{Area } \triangle III + \text{Area } \triangle IV}{\text{Area } \triangle I' + \text{Area } \triangle II' + \text{Area } \triangle III' + \text{Area } \triangle IV'} =$
$\left(\frac{AB}{A'B'}\right)^2$.

21. Proof: 1. $\triangle PQR \sim \triangle TUV$; altitudes $\overline{RS}$ and $\overline{VW}$ (Given) 2. $\frac{\text{Area } \triangle PQR}{\text{Area } \triangle TUV} = \left(\frac{PQ}{TU}\right)^2$ (Areas of $\sim \triangle$s) 3. $\frac{PQ}{TU} = \frac{RS}{VW}$ (In $\sim \triangle$s, lengths of altitudes from corr. vertices are proportional to lengths of corr. sides. [1]) 4. $\frac{\text{Area } \triangle PQR}{\text{Area } \triangle TUV} = \left(\frac{RS}{VW}\right)^2$ (Substitution Prop. [2, 3])

26. Equilateral triangle with sides 9 m long

26. $\frac{81\sqrt{3}}{4} \approx 35.07 \text{ m}^2$

27. Give the center and radius of a circle whose equation is $(x - 8)^2 + y^2 = 49$. (8, 0); $r = 7$

28. Find the sum of the angle measures in a hexagon. 720

33. If the number of sides is n, the measure of the angle is $\frac{360}{n}$.

Thinking Ahead Trace the regular polygons at the right. Then bisect the angles, extending the bisectors until they just meet. What is the measure of each angle formed at the intersection of the angle bisectors of

29. the triangle? 120   **30.** the square? 90

31. the hexagon? 60   **32.** the octagon? 45

33. For each figure, how does the measure of these angles relate to 360? See above.

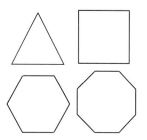

Thinking Ahead

29.

30.

31.

32.

Progress Check

Lesson 10-1, page 429

1. The length of a base and the corresponding height of a rectangle are 15 and 22. Find the area of the rectangle. 330

2. Find the side length of a square with area 169 m². 13 m

3. Given $\triangle ABC \cong \triangle DEF$, what is the ratio of their areas? 1:1

Lesson 10-2, page 434

Find the area of each polygon.

4. A parallelogram with base length 14 and height 24 336

5. $\square ABCD$; $m\angle A = 30$; $AB = 17$; $AD = 12$ 102

6. A right triangle with leg lengths 5 cm and 12 cm 30 cm²

Lesson 10-3, page 441

Find the area of each polygon.

7. Trapezoid $ABCD$; $\overline{AB} \parallel \overline{DC}$; $m\angle A = 60$; $AD = 16$; $AB = 20$; $DC = 10$ $120\sqrt{3} \approx 207.85$

8. A rhombus with diagonal lengths 8 cm and 6 cm 24 cm²

9. Find the area of the game table. 14,536 cm²

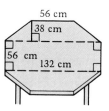

56 cm
38 cm
56 cm
132 cm

Lesson 10-4, page 447

10. $\triangle ABC \sim \triangle DEF$; $\frac{AB}{DE} = \frac{4}{9}$. Find the ratio of the triangles' areas.

11. The ratio of the areas of two similar polygons is 36 to 48. Find the ratio of the lengths of two corresponding sides.

10. 16:81
11. $\sqrt{3}:2 \approx 1.73:2$

LESSON 10-5

Resources

Compass Straightedge
  Teaching Aid 20, circular
  geoboard
Visual Aid 20, circular geoboard
Worksheet 10-5
Extension 10-5
Computer Activities 10-5

OBJECTIVE

State and apply relationships with circumscribed and inscribed circles to find areas, perimeters, radii and apothems of regular polygons.

10-5 Circles and Regular Polygons

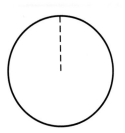 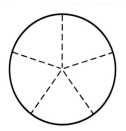 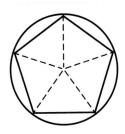 

A graphic designer plans to use a regular pentagon in a company logo. She draws a circle and pencils in a radius. Then she draws five 72° adjacent central angles, marking off five arcs with the same measure. Finally, she draws the chord for each arc. Do you think that a similar procedure can be used to inscribe any regular polygon in a given circle? If so, explain the procedure. Conversely, for any given regular polygon, a circle can be circumscribed about it as stated in Theorem 10-9. The proof of this theorem is omitted.

Yes; draw a circle and draw $\frac{360}{n}$ adjacent central angles, marking of n arcs with the same measure; draw the chord for each arc.

Theorem 10-9

A circle can be circumscribed about any regular polygon.

Given Regular n-gon with vertices $P_1, P_2, P_3, \ldots, P_n$

Prove A circle can be circumscribed about $P_1P_2P_3 \ldots P_n$.

Plan for Proof Draw $\odot O$ through P_1, P_2, and P_3 by applying Theorem 9-7. Draw $\overline{OP_4}$ and radii $\overline{OP_1}$, $\overline{OP_2}$, and $\overline{OP_3}$. Use $m\angle P_1P_2P_3 = m\angle P_2P_3P_4$ and $m\angle 2 = m\angle 3$ to show $m\angle 1 = m\angle 4$. Show $\triangle P_2OP_1 \cong \triangle P_3OP_4$. Since $OP_1 = OP_4$, P_4 lies on $\odot O$. Likewise, show that the remaining vertices $P_5, \ldots, P_n$ lie on $\odot O$.

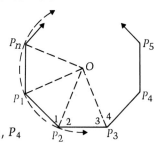

The regular polygon and the circumscribed circle at the right illustrate various parts of a polygon.

The **center** of the polygon is the center of the circumscribed circle. A **radius** of the polygon is a segment from the center to a vertex, or the segment's length. A **central angle** is an angle formed by two radii drawn to the endpoints of a side. The **apothem** is the distance from the center to any side.

What is true about the lengths of all radii of a regular polygon? all apothems? all central angles? They are equal; they are equal; they are equal.

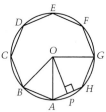

Center: O Radii: $\overline{OA}, \overline{OB}, \overline{OG}$
Central $\angle$s: $\angle AOB, \angle AOG, \angle BOG$
Apothem: $\overline{OP}$

In Lesson 9-4, you found that a circle could be inscribed in any triangle. Is it possible to inscribe a circle in *any* polygon? These diagrams suggest that it *is* possible to inscribe a circle in **No** certain regular polygons.

Square   Hexagon   Octagon

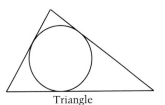

Triangle

Theorem 10-10

A circle can be inscribed in any regular polygon.

The proof of Theorem 10-10 is omitted.

Using the terms defined on page 452, we can develop a formula for the area of a regular polygon. Consider any regular n-gon with side length s, center O, apothem a, perimeter p, and radii $\overline{OP}_1, \overline{OP}_2, \overline{OP}_3, \ldots, \overline{OP}_n$. What kind of triangle is formed by the radii and the sides? The area of each triangle is $\frac{1}{2}as$, and the area of the polygon is $n(\frac{1}{2}as)$, where n is the number of triangles. Then, since $n(\frac{1}{2}as) = \frac{1}{2}a(ns)$, we can give the area of the polygon as $\frac{1}{2}ap$. Why? **Isosceles; $p = ns$**

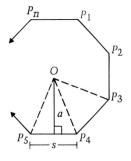

Theorem 10-11, which is to be proved in Exercise 28, formalizes this observation.

Theorem 10-11   *Area of a Regular Polygon*

The area A of a regular polygon is equal to one half the product of the apothem a and the perimeter p. $A = \frac{1}{2}ap$

Example

The floor of the gazebo at the right is shaped like a regular hexagon. Find its area.

Solution

$A = \frac{1}{2}ap$

$\quad = \frac{1}{2}(\frac{1}{2}(10)(\sqrt{3}))(6(10))$

$\quad = \frac{1}{2}(5\sqrt{3})(60)$

$\quad = 150\sqrt{3} \approx 260$ sq. ft.

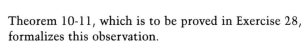

$\frac{1}{2}(10)(\sqrt{3})$

10 ft.

Additional Example

Find the area of this regular pentagon. **385**

Error Analysis Students may confuse the radius of a regular polygon with its apothem. Stress the difference between the terms.

ANSWERS

Checking for Understanding

2. Draw a circle and mark off eight 45° adjacent central angles $\left(\frac{360}{8} = 45\right)$. Draw the chords for the arcs formed by the central angles.
3. Equal central angles have equal arcs and, thus, equal chords form the sides of the pentagon. Because the triangles are congruent (SAS ≅ Post.), the angles of the pentagon are =.
4. The length of an altitude of an equilateral △ with sides of length s is $\frac{1}{2}s\sqrt{3}$.
5. The center of the circle is the intersection of the angle bisectors of the polygon. The radius is the segment from the center to any vertex.

Written Exercises

5. Draw ten adjacent 36° central angles in a circle. Draw the chords for the angles.
6. Draw six adjacent 60° central angles in a circle. Draw the chords for the angles.

Checking for Understanding

1. Why did the graphic designer use central angles of 72 to draw the pentagon for her logo?

2. Using a procedure similar to the one used by the designer, draw a regular octagon.

3. Explain why the pentagon drawn by the designer on page 452 is a regular pentagon.

4. Explain why a in the example is $\frac{1}{2}(80)(\sqrt{3})$.

5. Explain how a circle can be circumscribed about a regular polygon.

6. Find the area of a regular hexagon with perimeter 24 and apothem $2\sqrt{3}$.

7. Describe the relationship between a radius and the apothem in a regular polygon.

Find the measure of a central angle of a regular polygon with the given number of sides.

8. 12 30   **9.** 15a $\frac{24}{a}$

Written Exercises

Set A Find the area of a regular hexagon with apothem a, perimeter p, radius r, and side length s.

1. $s = 12$ **2.** $a = 6$ **3.** $p = 60$ **4.** $r = 5\sqrt{3}$

Use a protractor and a straightedge to draw

5. a regular decagon.   **6.** a regular hexagon.

Find the area of a square inscribed in a circle of radius r when

7. $r = 8$. **128**   **8.** $r = 10$. **200**

For each regular polygon with n sides of length s, find the apothem a; perimeter p; radius r; and area A.

9. $n = 4$; $s = 1$ **10.** $n = 3$; $s = 1$ **11.** $n = 6$; $s = 9$
12. $n = 4$; $s = x$ **13.** $n = 3$; $s = y$ **14.** $n = 6$; $s = z$

15. Find the area of a garden shaped like a regular octagon if each side measures 20 feet and the distance from the center to a side is 24 feet.

Set B **16.** Draw a parallelogram circumscribed about a circle. Is there anything special about the parallelogram? **Its sides are equal.**

---

1. $\frac{360}{n} = \frac{360}{5} = 72$
6. $24\sqrt{3} \approx 41.57$
7. A radius is longer than the apothem.

1. $216\sqrt{3} \approx 374.12$
2. $72\sqrt{3} \approx 124.71$
3. $150\sqrt{3} \approx 259.81$
4. $112.5\sqrt{3} \approx 194.86$

9. $\frac{1}{2}$; 4; $\frac{\sqrt{2}}{2}$; 1
10. $\frac{\sqrt{3}}{6}$; 3; $\frac{\sqrt{3}}{3}$; $\frac{\sqrt{3}}{4}$
11. $4.5\sqrt{3}$; 54; 9; $121.5\sqrt{3}$
12. $0.5x$; $4x$; $0.5x\sqrt{2}$; x^2
13. $\frac{y\sqrt{3}}{6}$; $3y$; $\frac{y\sqrt{3}}{3}$; $\frac{y^2\sqrt{3}}{4}$
14. $0.5z\sqrt{3}$; $6z$; z; $5z^2\sqrt{3}$
15. 1,920 sq. ft.

17. Draw a parallelogram inscribed within a circle. Is there anything special about the parallelogram?

18. The ratio of the lengths of two corresponding sides of two similar polygons is 2:5. Find the ratio of their apothems. **2:5**

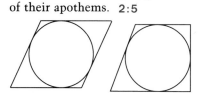

19. A circle can be inscribed in some polygons that are *not* regular. Trace the three quadrilaterals above. Recall the definition of incenter and incircle of a triangle in Lesson 9-4. What is true of the angle bisectors of the quadrilaterals?

20. Trace rectangle *ABCD*. Can you inscribe a circle in it? Why or why not?

21. Given: A regular polygon with center at *O*; side $\overline{AB}$; $\overline{OC} \perp \overline{AB}$ at *C*
Prove: $\overline{OC}$ is the apothem; $\overrightarrow{OC}$ bisects $\angle AOB$; $\overline{OC}$ bisects $\overline{AB}$.

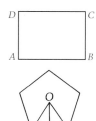

22. Given: Two similar regular polygons
Prove: The ratio of the apothems is equal to the ratio of the lengths of any two corresponding sides.

23. Prove: The ratio of the areas of two similar regular polygons is the square of the ratio of their apothems.

A kaleidoscope is constructed from a circular tube and three congruent glass rectangles as shown.

24. Find the diameter of the tube needed to accommodate the glass rectangles if *s* is 4 cm.

25. The radius of a kaleidoscope is 3 inches. Find *s*.

26. The logo for Circle Electric is at the right. The circle has an inscribed equilateral △*ABC* and a circumscribed equilateral △*XYZ*. Find the ratio of *AB* to *XY* and the ratio of the areas of the triangles.

27. Find the ratio of the areas of an equilateral triangle and a regular hexagon that have the same perimeter.

16.

17.

19.

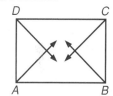

The angle bisectors in each quadrilateral intersect.

20.

No; the angle bisectors of *ABCD* do not intersect.

21. Proof: 1. Reg. poly. has center at *O*; side $\overline{AB}$; $\overline{OC} \perp \overline{AB}$ at *C* (Given) 2. *OC* is the apothem. (Def. of apothem [1]) 3. OA = OB (Radii of the same reg. poly. are =. [1]) 4. $m\angle OAC = m\angle OBC$ (Isos. △ Thm. [3]) 5. $\angle OCA$ and $\angle OCB$ are rt. $\angle$s. (Two $\perp$ lines form 4 rt. $\angle$s. [1]) 6. $m\angle OCA = m\angle OCB$ (All rt. $\angle$s are =. [5]) 7. OC = OC (Reflexive Prop.) 8. △*OCA* ≅ △*OCB* (AAS Thm. [4, 6, 7]) 9. $m\angle AOC = m\angle BOC$; AC = BC (Corr. parts of ≅ △s are =. [8]) 10. $\overrightarrow{OC}$ bisects $\angle AOB$. (Def. of $\angle$ bisector [9]) 11. *C* is midpt. of $\overline{AB}$. (Def. of midpt. [9]) 12. $\overline{OC}$ bisects $\overline{AB}$. (Def. of bisect [11])

FOLLOW-UP

More Practice

• **Worksheet 10–5**

Extension

More capable students may be challenged by using trigonometry to derive a formula for the area of a regular pentagon.

1. Express the apothem a in terms of a side s:

$\tan 36 = \frac{s/2}{a}$, so $a = \frac{s}{2(\tan 36)}$.

2. Substitute $\frac{s}{2(\tan 36)}$ for a in the formula $A = \frac{1}{2}ap$.

$A = \frac{1}{2}\left(\frac{s}{2(\tan 36)}\right)(5s) = \frac{5s^2}{4(\tan 36)}$

Similar methods can be used to find the area of any regular polygon.

• **Extension 10–5**

Computers

The computer activity in the pupil's book can be completed using *The Geometric Supposer: Circles.*

• **Computer Activities 10–5**

Set C **28.** Prove Theorem 10-11.

29. Prove: The area of a regular hexagon with side length s is $\frac{3}{2}s^2\sqrt{3}$.

30. Join the midpoints of the sides of a regular hexagon in order.

Hexagon

a. What kind of polygon is formed?

4:3

b. Find the ratio of the areas of the two polygons.

31. Prove: Given right $\triangle ABC$, the area of a regular hexagon with side length AB is the sum of the areas of the regular hexagons with side lengths AC and BC.

▲ **Review** **32.** $\triangle ABC \sim \triangle KXW$. If $AB = 8$ and $KX = 3$, then the ratio of the area of $\triangle ABC$ to the area of $\triangle KXW$ is __?__.

33. Two similar trapezoids have areas of 64 cm² and 121 cm². If the longer base of the larger trapezoid is 5.5 cm long, find the length of the longer base of the smaller trapezoid.

32. 64:9
33. 4 cm
34. 252

34. The height of a trapezoid is 18 and the length of its median is 14. Find the area.

35. Given: $\overline{AB} \parallel \overline{DE}$; $AB = DE$
Prove: C is the midpoint of $\overline{AE}$.

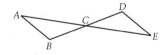

36. How many diagonals does a pentagon have? 5

⏚ **Thinking Ahead** Draw five congruent circles. In each one, inscribe a regular polygon: a triangle, a square, a pentagon, a hexagon, and an octagon. Which has

Octagon

37. the longest side? Triangle **38.** the greatest apothem?

39. the greatest perimeter? **40.** the greatest area?

Octagon   Octagon

41. As the number of sides of a regular polygon increases, the polygon begins to look like a __?__. circle

---

🖳 Computer Activities: Drawing and Measuring

Draw a circle. Measure the radius and the distance around.

1. Find the quotient of the distance around divided by the diameter. 3.14

2. Repeat the activity with ten circles of different sizes. What is the quotient in each case? Compare your quotients with those of your classmates. 3.14

Warm-Up Review

1. A line segment with endpoints the center of a circle and a point of the circle is a(n) __?__.   Radius

2. State the formula for the area of a triangle. $A = \frac{1}{2}bh$

3. State the formula for the area of a regular polygon. $A = \frac{1}{2}ap$

10-6 Circumference and Area of a Circle

A person figuring the amount of fencing needed to enclose a merry-go-round considers the distance around the region to be enclosed. If the region is polygonal, this distance is the *perimeter*. If the region is circular, this distance is the *circumference*.

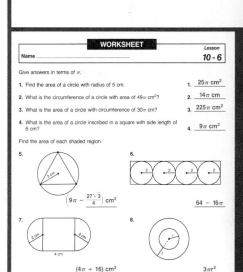

One way to estimate the circumference of a circle is to inscribe regular polygons in the circle. Recall Exercises 37–41 in Lesson 10-5.

As the number of sides of the inscribed polygon is increased the apothem approaches the radius of the circle; the perimeter approaches the circumference of the circle; and the area approaches the area of the circle.

The ***circumference of a circle*** is the *limit* of the perimeters of its inscribed regular polygons as the number of sides increases.

The ***area of a circle*** is the *limit* of the areas of its inscribed regular polygons as the number of sides increases.

Consider two circles with circumferences C and C', radii r and r', and diameters d and d'. Inscribed in the circle are regular n-gons with side lengths s and s', respectively. The limit descriptions given above show that ns approaches C and ns' approaches C' as n gets larger. But all regular n-gons for a given n are similar, and their central angles are parts of similar triangles.

Hence, $\dfrac{ns}{ns'} = \dfrac{s}{s'} = \dfrac{r}{r'} = \dfrac{\frac{1}{2}d}{\frac{1}{2}d'} = \dfrac{d}{d'}$.

For large values of n, $ns \approx C$ and $ns' \approx C'$.

It can be shown that $\dfrac{C}{C'} = \dfrac{d}{d'}$ so $\dfrac{C}{d} = \dfrac{C'}{d'}$.

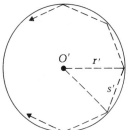

LESSON 10-6

Resources

Cardboard circle
Compass
Protractor
Straightedge
   Teaching Aid 20, circular
      geoboard
Visual Aid 20, circular geoboard
Worksheet 10-6
Extension 10-6
Computer Worksheet 10-6

OBJECTIVE

State and apply theorems concerning the circumference and area of a circle.

WORKSHEET

Name _____   Lesson **10-6**

Give answers in terms of π.

1. Find the area of a circle with radius of 5 cm.   1. 25π cm²

2. What is the circumference of a circle with area of 49π cm²?   2. 14π cm

3. What is the area of a circle with circumference of 30π cm?   3. 225π cm²

4. What is the area of a circle inscribed in a square with side length of 6 cm?   4. 9π cm²

Find the area of each shaded region.

5. $\left(9\pi - \dfrac{27\sqrt{3}}{4}\right)$ cm²

6. $64 - 16\pi$

7. $(4\pi + 16)$ cm²

8. $3\pi r^2$

9. $(36\pi - 54\sqrt{3})$ cm²

10. $25\pi - 24$

Theorem 10-12, which is not proved here, states that the ratio $\frac{C}{d}$ is the same for all circles.

Theorem 10-12

The ratio of the circumference to the diameter of a circle is the same for all circles.

Definition   *Pi (π)*

The ratio of the circumference C of a circle to the diameter d is denoted by π. $\frac{C}{d} = \pi$.

Since π is not a rational number, approximate values such as 3.1416, 3.14, or $\frac{22}{7}$ are commonly used in computation. If you use a calculator, you may use the key for π.

Theorem 10-13 is an immediate consequence of the definition of π.

Theorem 10-13 Circumference of a Circle

The circumference C of a circle is equal to the product of π and the diameter d. $C = \pi d = 2\pi r$

Example 1

Find the circumference of a circle with radius 5 cm. Express your answer in terms of π.

Solution

$$C = 2\pi r$$
$$= 2\pi(5)$$
$$= 10\pi \ cm$$

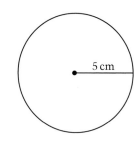

5 cm

Now suppose a regular n-gon is inscribed in circle O. If the perimeter of the polygon is p and the apothem is a, the area of the polygon is $\frac{1}{2}ap$. As the number of sides increases, a approaches r and p approaches C. For large values of n, $\frac{1}{2}ap \approx \frac{1}{2}rC = \frac{1}{2}r(2\pi r)$, or πr^2. As the area of the polygon approaches the area of the circle, it gets close to πr^2. This leads to Theorem 10-14, the proof of which is omitted.

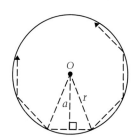

Theorem 10-14   *Area of a Circle*

The area A of a circle is equal to the product of π and the square of the radius r of the circle. $A = \pi r^2$

Assignment Guide

Basic: 1–12, 35–42
Average: 6, 10, 13–31, 35–42
Extended: 2–30 (even), 32–42

Example 2

The diameter of a circular pool is 30 ft. Find its area.

Solution

$A = \pi r^2$
$\quad = 3.14(15)^2$
$\quad \approx 706.5$ sq. ft.

Checking for Understanding

1. To what figure does the word *perimeter* apply? Polygon;
the word *circumference*? circle

2. How is Theorem 10-13 a result of the definition of π?

3. Why can the circumference of a circle be expressed as both
πd and $2\pi r$? $d = 2r$

4. Give a formula for the area of a semicircle. $\frac{\pi r^2}{2}$

Given a circle of radius r, diameter d, circumference C, and
area A, for each given measure, find the other three measures.
Give answers in terms of π.

5. $r = 7$ m   **6.** $C = 18\pi$ cm   **7.** $A = 4\pi$ sq. in.

8. The diameter of the circular region containing the
merry-go-round on page 457 is 50 feet. How much fencing
is needed to enclose the area? $50\pi \approx 157$ ft.

2. $\frac{c}{d} = \pi \Rightarrow C = \pi d$ by the
Mult. Prop.
5. $d = 14m$; $C = 14\pi m$;
$A = 49\pi m^2$
6. $r = 9$ cm; $d = 18$ cm;
$A = 81\pi$ cm^2
7. $r = 2$ in.; $d = 4$ in.;
$C = 4\pi$ in.

Written Exercises

Set A $144\pi \approx 452.16$ cm^2

1. Find the area of a circle with a 24-cm diameter.

2. Find the circumference of a bicycle tire with a
26-in. outside diameter. $26\pi \approx 81.64$ in.

3. Find the area of a circular rug with a radius of 30 cm.

4. How much fringe is needed to go around the edge
of the rug in Exercise 3? $60\pi \approx 188.4$ cm

5. Find the area of a semicircular window with a
radius of 1.2 m. $0.72\pi \approx 2.26$ m^2

6. The area of a circular skating rink is 1,257 m^2.
Find its diameter. 40 m

7. Find the diameter of a circle with circumference 27.

8. Find the radius of a circle with circumference 43 ft.

9. If the radius of a circle is doubled, by what factor is
the circumference multiplied? the area? 2:4
3. $900\pi \approx 2.826$ cm^2 **7.** 8.60   **8.** 6.85 ft.

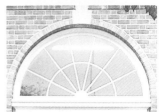

process is used again, the formula for the area of a circle will be readily accepted.

Additional Examples

Example 1
The radius of a bicycle tire is 13 inches. Find a) the exact circumference of the tire and b) the tire's approximate circumference. 26π in.; 81.64 in.

Example 2
If the diameter of a circular tablecloth is 72 inches, find a) its approximate area and b) its exact area. 226.08 sq. in.; 72π sq. in.

Error Analysis   Students are often not alert to whether an exact or approximate answer is requested. When an exact answer is needed, give the result in terms of π. If an approximate answer is adequate, use a rational number for π (usually 3.14 or $3\frac{1}{7}$).

Unless specified, answers involving π will appear both as a multiple of π and as a decimal rounded to the nearest hundredth. As with radicals, encourage students to give both answers.

EXERCISE NOTES

Exercise 16 could be solved with the use of a **calculator**.
Exercise 23 studies ratios of areas in similar figures.
Exercise 31 uses the Distance Formula.
Exercise 33 will be easier if students place radii where they will be useful.

ANSWERS

Written Exercises

12. $8\pi \approx 25.12$; $16\pi \approx 50.24$

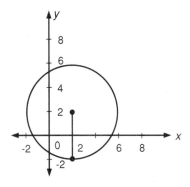

16. The 12-in.-diameter quiche; the smaller one is $0.17 per sq. in., the larger one $0.14 per sq. in.

23. Given: $\odot A$ with radius a; $\odot B$ with radius b Prove: $\frac{\text{Area } \odot A}{\text{Area } \odot B} = \left(\frac{a}{b}\right)^2$
Proof: 1. $\odot A$ with radius a; $\odot B$ with radius b (Given) 2. Area $\odot A$ $= \pi a^2$; area $\odot B = \pi b^2$ (Area of a $\odot$ [1]) 3. $\frac{\text{Area } \odot A}{\text{Area } \odot B} = \frac{\pi a^2}{\pi b^2}$ (Division Prop. [2]) 4. $\frac{\text{Area } \odot A}{\text{Area } \odot B} = \frac{a^2}{b^2} = \left(\frac{a}{b}\right)^2$ (Multiplication Prop. [3])

24. $150\sqrt{3} \approx 259.81$; 60

26. $\frac{\text{Area 4-inch pipe}}{\text{Area 1-inch pipe}} = \frac{16}{1}$; 16 1-inch pipes

27. $100\pi - 192 \approx 122$ sq. in.

31.

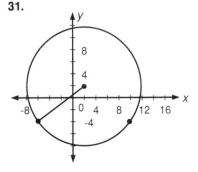

10. By what factor must the radius of a circle be multiplied to make its area 9 times as large? 3

11. Which has the greater area, the bottom of an 11-inch square frying pan or of a 12-inch-diameter round frying pan? How much greater? 11-in. squares; 7.96 sq. in.

12. On a set of axes, draw a circle with center (2, 2) and containing the point (2, −2). Find its circumference and its area. $8\pi \approx 25.12$; $16\pi \approx 50.24$

Set B Find the ratio of the circumferences and the areas of two circles with the given radii.

13. $r_1 = 1$, $r_2 = 4$ **14.** $r_1 = 2$, $r_2 = 5$
1:4; 1:16   2:5; 4:25

15. Estimate the length of a cable if it lies in five 3-ft.-diameter coils. $15\pi \approx 47.1$ ft.

16. A caterer charges $10.95 for a 9-inch-diameter quiche and $15.95 for a 12-inch-diameter quiche. Which is the better buy? Why?

17. Air moved by a fan depends upon the area covered by its blades, how many fans with 12-in.-diameter blades move as much air as one with 30-in.-diameter blades? 7 fans

Find the area of each shaded region.

18.   **19.**   **20.**   **21.**

$144 - 36\pi \approx 30.96$ $18\pi \approx 56.52$ $16 - 4\pi \approx 3.44$ $27\pi \approx 84.78$
                              $AB = 12$

22. Which has the greater area, a square with perimeter 20 or a circle with circumference 20? circle

23. Prove: The ratio of the areas of two circles is equal to the square of the ratio of their radii.

24. Find the area and the perimeter of a regular hexagon inscribed in a circle with circumference 20π.

25. How many feet does a 26-inch-diameter wheel cover in 100 revolutions? 680.33 ft.

26. The amount of water a pipe carries depends on the area of its opening—the cross section. How does the cross-sectional area of a 4-in.-diameter pipe compare to that of a 1-in. pipe? How many 1-in. pipes carry the same amount of water as a 4-in. pipe?

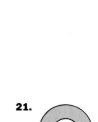

27. The design for a stained-glass window is shown at the right. How much red glass will be needed?

16"
12"

28. Find the circumference of a circle circumscribed about a square with side length 16. **$16\pi\sqrt{2} \approx 71.05$**

29. Find the area and the circumference of a circle circumscribed about an equilateral triangle with side length $3x$. **$9.42 x^2$; $6.28\sqrt{3}x \approx 10.88x$**

27. $100\pi - 192 \approx 122$ sq. in.

30. The shaded area in the figure at the right is 36 cm². If $OC = 6$, find OA.

31. On a set of axes, draw a circle with center $(2, 2)$ and containing point $(-6, -4)$. Find its circumference and its area in terms of π.

30. $\sqrt{36 + \frac{36}{\pi}} \approx 6.89$ cm   **31.** 20π; 100π

Set C

32. Find the circumference of a circle inscribed in a rhombus with diagonal lengths 12 and 16. **$9.6\pi \approx 30.14$**

33. Given a square, prove that the area of the circumscribed circle is twice the area of the inscribed circle.

34. Find the circumference of a circle inscribed in an isosceles trapezoid with base lengths 8 and 20. **$4\pi\sqrt{10} \approx 39.71$**

◆ Review

35. Draw a regular octagon inscribed in a circle.

36. Find the area and perimeter of a regular hexagon with an 8-inch side. **48 in.; $96\sqrt{3} \approx 166.28$ sq. in.**

37. $\triangle GDA \sim \triangle PMT$, $DA = 6$, $MT = 9$, and the area of $\triangle GDA$ is 144. Find the area of $\triangle PMT$. **324**

38. A ramp 16 ft. long rises 6 ft. vertically. Use trigonometric ratios to find the measure of the angle the ramp makes with level ground. **22**

39. If $JK \parallel PQ \parallel WV$, then $QV = \underline{}$. **20**

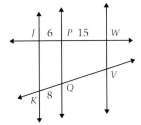
J 6 P 15 W
K 8 Q V

Thinking Ahead In each exercise, find the length of $\overset{\frown}{AB}$.

40.

B
A
6

$3\pi \approx 9.42$

41.

B
A
6

$1.5\pi \approx 4.71$

42.

B
A
6

$2\pi \approx 6.28$

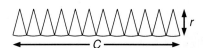

ANSWERS

Using Logo

8. Alternate program:

```
TO CIRCLE :AREA
MAKE "R SQRT (:AREA/
  3.1416)
REPEAT 360 [FD :R *
  0.01745 RT 1]
END
```

Using Logo: Drawing Circles

The Logo turtle can be taught to draw circles in the same manner as it draws regular polygons.

1. The procedure POLYGON has been used previously to draw any regular polygon with :N as the variable for the number of sides and :SIDE as the variable for the side length.

```
TO POLYGON :N :SIDE
REPEAT :N (FD :SIDE RT 360/ :N)
END
```

Use POLYGON to draw each of these regular polygons:

a. Octagon with side length 24 — Use POLYGON 8 24

b. 16-sided polygon with side length 24 — Use POLYGON 16 24

c. 16-sided polygon with side length 12 — Use POLYGON 16 12

d. 32-sided polygon with side length 12 — Use POLYGON 32 12

2. What conjecture can you make about the number of sides and the side length of the polygons that are more circular in appearance?

As the number of sides increases and the side length decreases, the polygons appear to be more circular.

3. Revise POLYGON as follows so that the second input is :PERIMETER:

```
TO POLYGON :N :PERIMETER
REPEAT :N (FD :PERIMETER/ :N RT 360/ :N)
END
```

Use POLYGON to draw a 36-sided polygon with perimeter 180.

Type POLYGON 36 180

4. Compute the circumference of a circle with radius 50. (Use 3.14 for π.) Use POLYGON to draw a 48-sided polygon with a perimeter equal to the circumference of the circle.

Type POLYGON 48 314

5. Use POLYGON to draw a 360-sided polygon with a perimeter equal to the circumference of a circle with radius 50.

Type POLYGON 360 314

6. The procedure CIRCLE uses a 360-sided polygon to approximate a circle with radius :R

```
TO CIRCLE :R
REPEAT 360 (FD :R " .01745 RT 1)
END
```

Type CIRCLE 60

Use CIRCLE to draw a "circle" with radius 60.

7. Explain how the value .01745 that is used in CIRCLE was computed. (Use 3.1416 for π.)

$\frac{2\pi}{360} = \frac{2(3.1416)}{360} = 0.01745$

8. Revise CIRCLE so that the input variable is the area of a circle.

```
TO CIRCLE :AREA
REPEAT 360[FD(SQRT(:AREA/3.1416))*0.01745 RT 1]
END
```

Warm-Up Review

1. The shortest path of a circle between two points on the circle is a(n) __?__. Minor arc
2. State two formulas for the circumference of a circle. $C = \pi d$; $C = 2\pi r$
3. State the formula for the area of a circle. $A = \pi r^2$
4. Find the measure of a central angle that intercepts a 120-degree arc. 120

10-7 Areas of Sectors and Segments of a Circle

The circle graph at the right shows how Southville's annual budget is allocated. Each budget item is represented by a sector of the circle.

Definition *Sector of a Circle*

A sector of a circle is a region bounded by two radii and either the major arc or the minor arc that is intercepted.

The sector formed by $\overarc{AB}$ is shaded. The sector formed by $\overarc{AKB}$ is unshaded.

In the circle graph, the measure of the central angle of the sector representing Roads is 60. The Roads sector accounts for $\frac{60}{360}$, or $\frac{1}{6}$, of the budget. The Parks sector has a central angle with measure 30; it accounts for $\frac{30}{360}$, or $\frac{1}{12}$, of the budget.

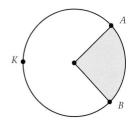

How can you find the length of an arc of a circle? Recall that the degree measure of an arc is the same as that of its central angle. The length of an arc of a circle is a portion of the circumference of the circle. The following theorem, given without proof, establishes the procedure for finding the length of an arc.

Theorem 10-15

In a circle of radius r, the ratio of the length s of an arc to the circumference C of the circle is the same as the ratio of the arc measure m to 360. $\dfrac{s}{C} = \dfrac{m}{360}$ *or* $s = \dfrac{m}{360}(2\pi r)$

Example 1

Chicago and Paris lie on a great circle of the earth. The measure of the arc from Chicago to Paris is 60. Find the arc distance between the two cities. The radius of the earth is about 4,000 miles.

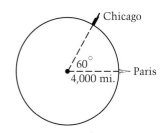

Solution

$$s = \frac{m}{360}(2\pi r)$$
$$= \frac{60}{360}(2\pi)(4,000)$$
$$= \frac{1}{6}(8,000\pi)$$
$$\approx 4,189 \text{ miles}$$

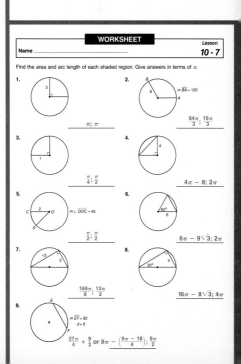

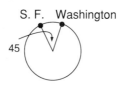
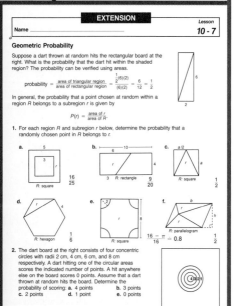

Similarly, the area of a sector is a portion of the area of the total circle. Theorem 10-16, also given without proof, shows the procedure for finding the area of a sector of a circle.

Theorem 10-16   *Area of a Sector of a Circle*

In a circle of radius r, the ratio of the area of a sector to the area A_C of the circle is the same as the ratio of the arc measure m to A_S 360.

$$\frac{A_S}{A_C} = \frac{m}{360} \text{ or } A_S = \frac{m}{360}(\pi r^2)$$

Example 2

A lawn sprinkler waters a lawn as shown. Find the area of the watered portion of the lawn.

Solution

The watered portion of the lawn is a sector of a circle with radius 15 m.

$$A = \frac{m}{360}(\pi r^2)$$
$$= \frac{120}{360}\pi(15)^2$$
$$= \frac{1}{3}\pi(225) \approx 236 \text{ m}^2$$

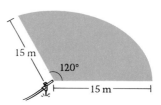

In circle O, the shaded portion is a segment of the circle.

Definition   *Segment of a Circle*

A segment of a circle is a region bounded by a chord and either the major arc or the minor arc that is intercepted.

The area of the segment formed by $\overset{\frown}{AB}$ is found by subtracting the area of $\triangle AOB$ from the area of the sector bounded by $\overset{\frown}{AB}$. How would you find the area of the unshaded major arc segment? Subtract the area of the minor arc segment from the area of the circle.

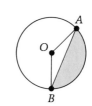

Example 3

Find the area of a drop leaf of a round table with a 120-cm diameter. Each drop leaf has an arc measure of 90.

Solution

Since the diameter is 120 cm, r = 60 cm.

Area of sector $= \frac{90}{360}\pi(60)^2 \approx 2{,}827$

Area of $\triangle AOB = \frac{1}{2}(60)(60) = 1{,}800$

Area of drop leaf $\approx 2{,}827 - 1{,}800 \approx 1{,}027 \text{ cm}^2$

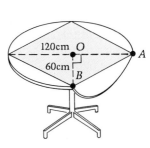

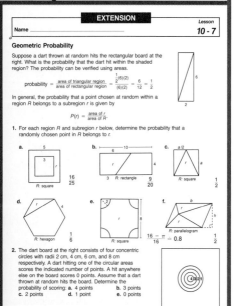

Assignment Guide

Basic: 1–10, 27–31
Average: 2–10 (even), 11–27, 28–31
Extended: 2–10 (even), 11–31

Checking for Understanding

In Exercises 1-3, what fraction of the circular region is tinted?
Find the area of each tinted region.

1.
45°
5

2.
120°
2

3.
75°
4

4.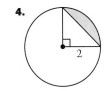
2

5.
3 120°

6. The Southville budget allows 25% for Fire and Police Protection. What size is the central angle for that sector? **90°**

7. Describe two ways to find the area of the tinted region at the right.

8. In a circle of radius 4, $m\widehat{AB} = 30$. Find the length of $\widehat{AB}$.
$\frac{2}{3}\pi \approx 2.09$

Written Exercises

Set A   In each exercise, find the arc length $\widehat{AB}$.

1.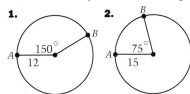
150°
A   B
12

2.
B
75°
A
15

3.
A
30°
B
20

4.
270°
A
6
B

Find the area of each tinted region.

5.
60° 10

6.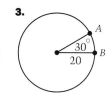
s° n

7.
4

8.
60°
6

9. In a circle with radius 16, find the arc measure and the area of the sector whose arc length is 25.1.

10. If the arc measure is 120 and the area of its sector is 27π, what is the radius of the circle? **9**
9. 90; $64\pi \approx 200.96$

measure of the arc from San Francisco to Washington is 45. Find the arc distance between the two cities, given that the radius of the earth is about 4000 miles. 1000π mi., or about 3140 mi.

Example 2
A hand fan forms a 120-degree angle when unfolded. If one side of the fan is 12 cm long, about how much material is needed to cover the fan? 150.7 cm²

Example 3

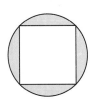

The circle graph shown is being enlarged so that the diameter of the new graph is 10 inches. Find the approximate area of the shaded section after it is enlarged. 19.6 sq. in.

Error Analysis Students often use incorrect formulas for finding arc lengths and the area of sectors because they try to memorize the equations. Encourage students to think of the length of an arc as a fractional part of the circle's circumference and the area of a sector as a fractional part of the circle's area. When viewed in this manner, students could simply write the appropriate proportion to solve a problem of either type.

EXERCISE NOTES

Exercise 30 should be explained or completed before assigning **Exercise 31**.

ANSWERS

Written Exercises

1. $10\pi \approx 31.4$
2. $\frac{25}{4}\pi \approx 19.63$
3. $\frac{10}{3}\pi \approx 10.47$
4. $3\pi \approx 9.42$
5. $\frac{50}{3}\pi \approx 52.33$
6. $\frac{\pi s n^2}{360}$
7. $4\pi - 8 \approx 4.56$
8. $6\pi - 9\sqrt{3} \approx 3.25$
13. $56\pi \approx 175.84$
14. $\frac{50}{3}\pi \approx 52.33$
15. $64\pi - 48\sqrt{3} \approx 117.82$
16. $64\pi - 96\sqrt{3} \approx 34.68$
17. $36\pi - 36 \approx 77.04$
18. $49\pi - 49 \approx 104.86$
19. $30\pi + 9\sqrt{3} \approx 109.79$
20. $24\pi - 18\sqrt{3} \approx 44.18$
21. $\frac{65}{9}\pi \approx 22.68$
22. $\frac{35}{3}\pi \approx 36.63$
23. $2\pi \approx 6.28$
25. Let $AB = 2c$, $BC = 2a$ and $CA = 2b$. Area of semicircle on $\overline{AB} = \frac{1}{2}\pi c^2$; area of semicircle on $\overline{AC} = \frac{1}{2}\pi b^2$; area of semicircle on $\overline{BC} = \frac{1}{2}\pi a^2$. Area of two shaded regions = (area of semicircle on $\overline{AC}$ + area of semicircle on $\overline{BC}$) − (area of semicircle on $\overline{AB}$ − area $\triangle ABC$). Since area $\triangle ABC = \frac{1}{2}(2a)(2b) = 2ab$, area of shaded regions = $\frac{1}{2}\pi b^2 + \frac{1}{2}\pi a^2 - (\frac{1}{2}\pi c^2 - 2ab) = \frac{1}{2}\pi(b^2 + a^2 - c^2) + 2ab$. By the Pythagorean Thm., $b^2 + a^2 = c^2$, so $b^2 + a^2 - c^2 = 0$, and area of shaded regions = $0 + 2ab$ = area $\triangle ABC$.

Set B

11. Find the area of the free-throw region in this basketball court.

12. Find the area of the ice rink. $m\ \overset{\frown}{AC} = 90$

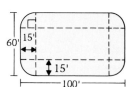

11. $228 + 18\pi \approx 284.52$ sq. ft.
12. $5,100 + 225\pi \approx 5,806.5$ sq. ft.

Find the area of each tinted region.

13.

14.

15.

 $\triangle ABC$ is equilateral.

16.

 $PQRSTU$ is a regular hexagon.

17.

18.

19.

20.

Find the length of $\overset{\frown}{AC}$.

21.

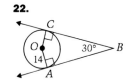

22.

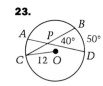

23.

24. Equilateral $\triangle ABC$ with apothem 5 is inscribed in circle O. Find the area of the shaded segment. $\frac{100}{3}\pi - 25\sqrt{3} \approx 61.37$

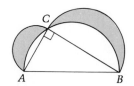

Set C

25. $\triangle ABC$ is inscribed in a semicircle and semicircles are drawn on its legs. Show that the area of $\triangle ABC$ equals the sum of the areas of the two shaded regions.

26. A belt is stretched over two pulleys whose radii are 10 and 50. The distance between the centers of the two pulleys is 80. Find the length of the belt. $1{,}300\pi + 80\sqrt{3} \approx 4{,}220.56$

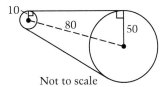

10

80

50

Not to scale

 Review   **27.** π is the ratio of __?__ to __?__.   circumference; diameter

28. Find the circumference and area of a circle whose diameter is 12. $12\pi \approx 37.68$; $36\pi \approx 113.04$

29. Find the area of a square inscribed in a circle whose radius is 5.   **50**

30. Find h in the figure shown.   **6**

31. What does it mean to say: "$\odot A \cong \odot O$"?

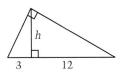

h

3   12

$\odot A$ and $\odot O$ have = radii

FOLLOW-UP

More Practice

• **Worksheet 10–7**

Extension

Ask students to prove that the area of a semicircle constructed on the hypotenuse of a right triangle is equal to the sum of the areas of the semicircles constructed on the legs.

• **Extension 10–7**

Progress Check

Lesson 10-5, Page 452
1. How would you draw a regular nonagon?

2. Given a regular hexagon with side length 6, find the apothem a, perimeter p, radius r, and area A.

3. The perimeter of a regular polygon is 48 in. and its area is 216 sq. in. Find the length of the apothem.   **9 in.**

1. Draw nine adjacent 40° central angles in a circle. Draw the chords for the angles.

2. $3\sqrt{3} \approx 5.20$; 36; 6; $54\sqrt{3} \approx 93.53$

Lesson 10-6, Page 457
4. The circumference of a circle is 37 cm. Find its diameter to the nearest centimeter.   **12 cm**

5. Find the area of a circle inscribed in a square with side length 22. Give your answer in terms of π. 242π

6. As an automobile tire with diameter 27 inches makes 200 revolutions, what distance does it travel?
$5{,}400\pi \approx 16{,}956$ in. $\approx 1{,}413$ ft.

Lesson 10-7, Page 463
7. Find the arc length and the area of a sector of a circle if the arc measure is 135 and the radius is 14. $\frac{21}{2}\pi \approx 32.97$; $\frac{147}{2}\pi \approx 230.79$

Find the area of each tinted region.

8.

12

9.

4   4
4

8. $108\pi \approx 339.12$

9. $\frac{8}{3}\pi - 4\sqrt{3} \approx 1.45$

Chapter 10 Summary

Important Terms

Altitude of a parallelogram (434)
Altitude of a rectangle (430)
Altitude of a trapezoid (441)
Altitude of a triangle (435)
Apothem of a regular polygon (452)
Arc length (463)
Area (429)
Base of a parallelogram (434)

Base of a rectangle (430)
Center of a regular polygon (452)
Central angle of a regular polygon (452)
Circumference of a circle (457)
Height of a parallelogram (434)
Height of a rectangle (430)
Height of a trapezoid (441)

Height of a triangle (435)
Kite (442)
Pi (π) (458)
Polygonal region (429)
Radius of a regular polygon (452)
Sector of a circle (463)
Segment of a circle (464)
Triangular region (429)

Important Ideas

1. A polygonal region may be separated into a finite number of nonoverlapping triangular regions that intersect at vertices or along sides. (429)

2. If two triangles are congruent, then they have equal areas. (429)

3. Areas of nonoverlapping polygonal regions may be added to find the area of the union of the regions. (431)

4. These are formulas for areas of polygons:

   Rectangle: $A = bh$ (430)

   Parallelogram: $A = bh$ (434)

   Equilateral triangle: $A = \frac{s^2}{4}\sqrt{3}$ (436)

   Rhombus: $A = \frac{1}{2}d_1 d_2$ (442)

   Regular polygon: $A = \frac{1}{2}ap$ (453)

   Square: $A = s^2$ (430)

   Triangle: $A = \frac{1}{2}bh$ (435)

   Trapezoid: $A = \frac{1}{2}h(b_1 + b_2)$ (441)

   Kite: $A = \frac{1}{2}d_1 d_2$ (442)

5. The ratio of the areas of two similar polygons is the square of the ratio of the lengths of any two corresponding sides. (448)

6. For any circle, the ratio of the circumference to the diameter is the constant π. (458)

7. These formulas involve circles:

   Circumference: $C = 2\pi r$ (458)

   Arc length: $s = \frac{m}{360}(2\pi r)$ (463)

   Area: $A = \pi r^2$ (458)

   Area of sector: $A = \frac{m}{360}(\pi r^2)$ (464)

   Area of a segment bounded by a minor arc:
   A = area of the sector − area of the triangle (464)

Chapter 10 Review

Lesson 10-1, Page 429
1. Find the area of a rectangle with base length 15 and height 13. 195

2. Find the area of a square with side length $2\sqrt{3}$. 12

3. Find the area of a square with diagonal length $8\sqrt{2}$. 64

Lesson 10-2, Page 434
Find the area of each triangle or parallelogram.

4.
6
4
12

5.
11
9
49.5

6.
5   5
5
$6.25\sqrt{3} \approx 10.83$

7.
14
21
294

8.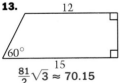
30°
15
12
90

9.
45°
$10\sqrt{2}$
24
240

10. Find the area of a right triangle whose legs have lengths 20 and 25. 250

11. Find the area of a parallelogram with base length 35 and altitude of length 10. 350

Lesson 10-3, Page 441
Find the area of each polygon.

12.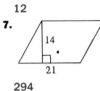
7
4
6
35

13.
12
60°
15
$\frac{81}{2}\sqrt{3} \approx 70.15$

14.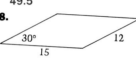
25
14
336

15. A kite whose diagonals have lengths 12 and 24 144

16. A rhombus with diagonal lengths 10 and 17 85

17. A trapezoid with a median of length 25 and height 14 350

18. Trapezoid $XYZW$ with bases $\overline{XY}$ and $\overline{ZW}$; $m\angle X = 30$; $XW = 30$; $XY = 35$; $ZW = 10$ 337.5

19. A trapezoid with height 2 and base lengths 3 and 4 7

Lesson 10-4, Page 447

20. Two similar regular pentagons have side lengths in the ratio of 7 to 10. What is the ratio of their perimeters? the ratio of their areas? 7:10; 49:100

21. The ratio of the areas of two similar polygons is 81 to 25. A side length of the larger is 14. Find the corresponding side length of the smaller. $7\frac{7}{9}$

22. $\triangle ABC \sim \triangle XYZ$, area $\triangle ABC = 2$(area $\triangle XYZ$), and $XY = 10$. Find AB. $10\sqrt{2} \approx 14.14$

Lesson 10-5, Page 452

Find the area of each regular polygon. **23.** 696 **24.** $216\sqrt{3} \approx 374.12$ **25.** 196

23.

24.

25.

26. Find the apothem of a regular pentagon with area 690 and side length 20. 13.8

Lesson 10-6, Page 457

27. Find the radius and area of a circle with circumference 12π. 6; $36\pi \approx 113.04$

28. Find the area and the circumference of a circle with radius 9. $81\pi \approx 254.34$; $18\pi \approx 56.52$

29. Find the area of a circle circumscribed about a square with side length 8. $32\pi \approx 100.48$

30. Find the area of the region bounded by concentric circles with radii of 9 and 11. $40\pi \approx 125.6$

31. The area of a circle is 289π. Find the radius and circumference. 17; $34\pi \approx 106.76$

Lesson 10-7, Page 463

Find the area of each tinted region.

32.

33.

32. $\frac{25}{2}\pi \approx 39.25$
33. $24\pi - 36\sqrt{3} \approx 13.01$

34. Find the arc length and area of a sector of a circle if the arc measure is 80 and the radius is 6. $\frac{8}{3}\pi \approx 8.37$ $8\pi \approx 25.12$

Chapter 10 Test

Find the area of each figure.

1.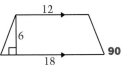

2.

3.

4.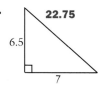
$433.5\sqrt{3} \approx 750.84$

5.
440

6.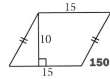
150

7.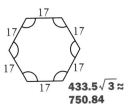
90

8.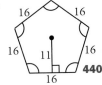
72

9.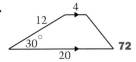
$784\pi \approx 2{,}461.76$

10. A kite with diagonals measuring 12 and 16

11. A rhombus with diagonals measuring 10 and 15

12. A square with diagonals measuring $9\sqrt{2}$

13. An equilateral triangle with side length 10

14. A trapezoid with median of length 30 and height 12

15. A rectangle with side length 7 and diagonal length 25

16. Find the radius of a regular hexagon of side length 9.

17. Find the area of a regular hexagon of side length 15.

18. Two similar polygons have areas of 36 cm² and 121 cm². Find the ratio of the lengths of corresponding sides.

19. Find the circumference and area for a circle of radius 12.

20. A and B are on $\odot O$; $OA = 8$; $m\widehat{AB} = 60$. Find the length of $\widehat{AB}$, the area of its sector, and the area of its segment.

21. Find the height of a rectangle with an area of 221 cm² and a base length of 13 cm.

10. 96
11. 75
12. 81
13. $25\sqrt{3} \approx 43.30$
14. 360
15. 168
16. 9
17. $337.5\sqrt{3} \approx 584.57$
18. 6:11
19. $24\pi \approx 75.36$; $144\pi \approx 452.16$
20. $\frac{8}{3}\pi \approx 8.37$; $\frac{32}{3}\pi \approx 33.49$; $\frac{32}{3}\pi - 16\sqrt{3} \approx 5.78$
21. 17 cm

CHAPTER 11

Solids

Chapter Overview

The world we live in is three-dimensional; it is therefore important to extend our study of geometry to three-dimensional figures. In this chapter we study lateral area, total area and volume of prisms, cylinders, pyramids, cones and spheres.

The demand for numerical computation in this topic provides an excellent opportunity to use a **calculator**.

Perspectives

Lesson 11-1 defines a polyhedron as a surface; it is therefore "hollow" and encloses a region of space. When we study lateral and total area, we are concerned with the polygonal faces. When we consider volume, we are measuring the region enclosed by the faces.

Lesson 11-2 introduces the concepts of lateral area and total area of a prism, with emphasis on application. Encourage students to draw oblique prisms with a right section and a cross section.

Lesson 11-3 defines a solid polyhedron as the union of a polyhedron with its interior. A measure of solid polyhedrons is volume, which can be found by counting unit cubes. The formula $V = Bh$ is introduced to eliminate the counting of cubes.

Lesson 11-4 derives formulas for area and volume of a cylinder from those of prisms by using an intuitive limiting process.

In problems involving a rational approximation for pi, using a **calculator** eliminates arithmetic errors and allows students to concentrate on the process.

Lesson 11-5 develops area formulas for a regular pyramid and the volume formula for all pyramids. Lateral area of nonregular pyramids is simply the sum of the areas of the triangular faces.

Pacing Chart for Chapter 11

Lesson	Objectives	Basic Course	Average Course	Extended Course
11–1	Define polyhedron, prism and related terms; determine the length of diagonals.	1	1	1
11–2	Compute the lateral and total area of prisms.	1	1	1
11–3	Compute the volume of a prism.	1	1	1
11–4	Compute the area and volume of cylinders.	1	2	$1\frac{1}{2}$
11–5	Compute the area and volume of pyramids.	1	2	$1\frac{1}{2}$
11–6	Compute the area and volume of cones.	1	2	$1\frac{1}{2}$
11–7	Compute the area and volume of spheres.	1	2	$1\frac{1}{2}$
Review		1	1	1
Test		1	1	1
Total		9 days	13 days	11 days

Lesson 11–6 points out the fact that the formulas for pyramids and cones are related like the formulas for prisms and cylinders. If students are made aware of these similarities, they will have fewer formulas to remember.

Lesson 11–7 presents the formulas for area and volume of a sphere. As with other problems involving rational approximations of pi, the problems in this lesson afford an opportunity for students to use a **calculator**.

ANSWERS

1. square

2. triangles; triangles; rectangles; circles

3. yes; yes

4. likenesses: pair of parallel bases; differences: blue/green has no vertices, edges or faces and shape of base is different from red/yellow

5. likenesses: both have 5 faces, some triangular, some rectangular; differences: pink/purple has one less edge and one less vertex and only one base

Solids

Chapter 11

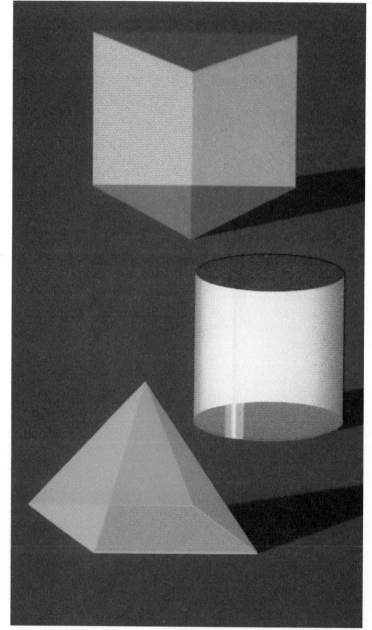

1. What shape is the green region?
2. What shape are the dark purple regions? the turquoise regions? the light purple regions? the red regions?
3. Do the red regions appear to be parallel? the dark purple regions?
4. How are the red/yellow and the purple figures alike? How are they different?
5. How are the purple and the green/turquoise figures alike? How are they different?

11-1 Polyhedrons and Prisms

In a plane, polygons are formed by intersecting line segments. In space, *polyhedrons* are formed by intersecting polygonal regions. A polyhedron is the three-dimensional counterpart of a polygon.

Which of the figures in the computer graphic on page 472 are polyhedrons? Which are not? Explain your answers.

The purple figure and the turquoise/green figure are polyhedrons because they are formed by intersecting polygonal regions. The red/yellow figure is not a polyhedron because it is formed by circles and a curved surface.

LESSON 11-1

Resources

Teaching Aid 23, rectangular prisms
Visual Aid 23, rectangular prisms
Teaching Aid 24, triangular prisms
Visual Aid 24, triangular prisms
Readiness Worksheet 6
Worksheet 11–1
Extension 11–1

Definition *Polyhedron*

A polyhedron is a figure formed by four or more noncoplanar polygonal regions which enclose a part of space.

The space enclosed is the *interior* of the polyhedron. The word polyhedron is commonly used to designate the *solid* which includes the interior portion as well as the surface of the figure.

The polygonal region *KMRQ* is a *face* of the polyhedron at the right. The intersection of two faces, such are $\overline{NM}$, is an *edge*. The intersection of three edges in a point such as *I* is a *vertex*.

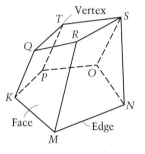

OBJECTIVES

Define polyhedron, prism and related terms; determine the length of diagonals.

Definition *Prism*

A prism is a polyhedron with two congruent faces contained in parallel planes. All other faces are parallelograms.

In the prism at the right, the congruent faces *ABCDE* and *A'B'C'D'E'* are *bases*. The parallelograms *A'B'BA*, *B'C'CB*, and so on, included between the parallel planes are *lateral faces*. The line segments $\overline{AA'}$, $\overline{BB'}$, and so on, are *lateral edges*.

What appears to be true regarding the lateral edges of the prism? Your answer should suggest Theorem 11-1, the proof of which is omitted. They are equal and parallel.

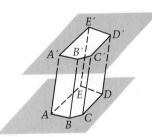

Theorem 11-1

The lateral edges of a prism are equal and parallel.

What appears to be true regarding the bases of the prism? Your answer should suggest Theorem 11-2, which is to be proved for a right rectangular prism in Exercise 18.

They are contained in parallel planes, and have equal areas since they are congruent polygons.

Theorem 11-2

The bases of a prism have equal areas.

WORKSHEET
Lesson 11-1
Name _____

Match each prism with one and only one of the statements.

g 1. triangular prism
a 2. cube
f 3. oblique prism
d 4. parallelepiped
c 5. regular hexagonal prism
h 6. right prism
e 7. pentagonal prism
b 8. right rectangular prism

a. All the faces are squares.
b. The bases are rectangles.
c. The bases are regular hexagons.
d. All the faces are parallelograms.
e. The bases are pentagons.
f. The lateral edges are not perpendicular to the planes of the bases.
g. The bases are triangles.
h. The lateral edges are perpendicular to the planes of the bases.

A prism has *e* edges, *f* faces, and *v* vertices, and each base has *s* sides. Find the missing values.

	e	f	v	s
9.	12	6	8	4
10.	18	8	12	6
11.	39	15	26	13
12.	33	13	22	11
13.	9	5	6	3

Tell whether each statement is *always*, *sometimes*, or *never* true.

14. The bases of a prism have equal area. always
15. The height of a prism is the length of a lateral edge. sometimes
16. The bases of a prism are contained in parallel planes. always
17. The lateral faces of a prism are rectangles. sometimes
18. Four edges intersect to form each vertex of a prism. never
19. Every cube is a right rectangular prism. always
20. Every pentagonal prism is an oblique prism. never

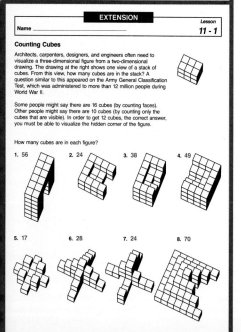

A segment from a point in one base perpendicular to the plane of the other base is an **altitude** of the prism. The length of the altitude is the **height** of the prism. A prism is a **right prism** if the lateral edges are perpendicular to the planes of the bases. Otherwise, the prism is an **oblique prism**.

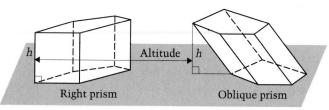

Right prism   Oblique prism

A prism is named by the shape of its base.

 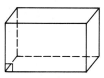

Triangular prism   Right rectangular prism   Pentagonal prism

Which of the prisms above are right? oblique? **Rectangular and pentagonal prisms; triangular prism**

A **regular prism** is a right prism whose bases are regular polygons. A **cube** is a regular prism in which all faces are squares. A **parallelepiped** is a prism in which all faces are parallelograms. Is a cube a parallelepiped? Is a rectangular prism a parallelepiped? **Yes; yes**

  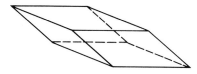

Regular hexagonal prism   Cube   Parallelepiped

A right rectangular prism, such as the prism at the right, is commonly called a **rectangular solid**. The vertices C and E, which are not on the same face, are **opposite vertices**. Name two other opposite vertices. The line segment AG, which joins two opposite vertices, is a **diagonal**. Every rectangular solid has four diagonals. How do they appear to compare in length? **Equal**

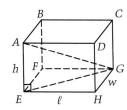

The three dimensions of the solid are referred to as length ℓ, width w, and height h.

opp vertices: **B, H; A, G; F, D**

Assignment Guide

Basic: 1–13, 26–32
Average: 2–12 (even), 13–18, 21–25, 26–32
Extended: 2–18 (even), 19–32

Theorem 11-3 relates the dimensions of a solid and the length of its diagonal.

Theorem 11-3

The length d of a diagonal of a rectangular solid with length ℓ, width w, and height h is $\sqrt{\ell^2 + w^2 + h^2}$. $d = \sqrt{\ell^2 + w^2 + h^2}$

Given   Rectangular solid with bases *ABCD* and *EFGH*

Prove $AG = \sqrt{\ell^2 + w^2 + h^2}$

Plan for   Since $\triangle AEG$ and $\triangle EHG$ are right triangles, $EG^2 =$
Proof $\ell^2 + w^2$ and $AG^2 = AE^2 + EG^2$. Substitute h for AE and $\ell^2 + w^2$ for EG^2 to show $AG^2 = \ell^2 + w^2 + h^2$. Then $AG = \sqrt{\ell^2 + w^2 + h^2}$.

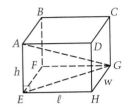

The proof of Theorem 11-3 is requested in Exercise 25.

Example

Find the length of the diagonal of a box whose dimensions are 12 in., 8 in., and 4 in.

Solution

$d = \sqrt{\ell^2 + w^2 + h^2}$
$d = \sqrt{12^2 + 8^2 + 4^2}$
$d = \sqrt{144 + 64 + 16}$
$d = \sqrt{224} = 4\sqrt{14}$

The diagonal of the box measures $4\sqrt{14}$ inches.

Checking for Understanding

1. How many faces does a pentagonal prism have? 7

2. What is the least number of faces a prism can have? 5

3. What is the least number of faces a polyhedron can have? 4

4. If a prism has nine faces, how many sides does its base have? 7

5. How many faces does an octagonal prism have? 10

6. How many edges does an octagonal prism have? 24

7. How many pairs of bases does a right rectangular prism have? 3

ANSWERS

Written Exercises

9. Given: Prism with bases *PQRSTU* and *P'Q'R'S'T'U'* Prove: $\overline{RT} \parallel \overline{R'T'}$ Proof: 1. Prism with bases *PQRSTU* and *P'Q'R'S'T'U'* (Given) 2. Draw $\overline{RT}$ and $\overline{R'T'}$. (2 pts. determine a line.) 3. $\overline{RR'} \parallel \overline{TT'}$; $RR' = TT'$ (Lateral edges of a prism are = and ∥. [1, 2]) 4. *RR'T'T* is a ▱. (A quad with 1 pr. opp. sides = and ∥ is a ▱. [3]) 5. $\overline{RT} \parallel \overline{R'T'}$ (Opp. sides of a ▱ are ∥. [4])

12. Proof: 1. Rt. rect. prism with bases *ABCD* and *A'B'C'D'* (Given) 2. *ABCD* is a rectangle. (Def. of rectangular prism [1]) 3. *ABCD* is a ▱. (Def. of rectangle [2]) 4. *AA'D'D* is a ▱. (Def. of prism [1]) 5. *AB* = *CD*; *AA'* = *DD'* (Opp. sides of a ▱ are =. [3, 4]) 6. $\overline{AA'}$ and $\overline{DD'}$ are ⊥ to plane of ▱*ABCD*. (Def. of rt. prism [1]) 7. $\overline{AA'} \perp \overline{AB}$; $\overline{DD'} \perp \overline{DC}$ (Def. of line ⊥ to a plane [6]) 8. ∠*BAA'* and ∠*CDD'* are rt. ∠s. (2 ⊥ lines form 4 rt. ∠s. [7]) 9. m∠*BAA'* = 90; m∠*CDD'* = 90 (Def. of rt. ∠ [8]) 10. m∠*BAA'* = m∠*CDD'* (Substitution Prop. [9]) 11. △*BAA'* ≅ △*CDD'* (SAS Post. [5, 10]) 12. *BA'* = *CD'* (Corr. parts of ≅ △s are =. [11])

13. Proof: 1. Rt. rect. prism with bases *ABCD* and *A'B'C'D'* (Given) 2. *ABCD* and *A'B'C'D'* are rectangles. (Def. of rect. prism [1]) 3. ∠*BCD* and ∠*B'A'D'* are rt. ∠s. (Def. of rectangle [2]) 4. m∠*BCD* = m∠*B'A'D'* (All rt. ∠s are =. [3]) 5. *ABCD* and *A'B'C'D'* are ▱s. (Def. of rectangle [2]) 6. *CD* = *AB*; *BC* = *AD* (Opp. sides of a ▱ are =. [5]) 7. *ABB'A'* and *CDD'C'* are ▱s. (Def. of prism [1]) 8. *AB* = *A'B'*; *AD* = *A'D'* (Opp. sides of a ▱ are =. [7]) 9. *CD* = *A'B'*; *BC* = *A'D'* (Transitive Prop. [6, 8]) 10. △*BDC* ≅ △*D'B'A'* (SAS Post. [4, 9])

Written Exercises

Set A Each prism has *e* edges, *f* faces, and *v* vertices. The base of each prism has *s* sides. Find the missing items.

1. *e* = 15; *f* = 7; *v* = 10
2. *s* = 9; *f* = 11; *e* = 27
3. *s* = 10; *f* = 12; *v* = 20
4. *s* = 12; *e* = 36; *v* = 24

1. *s* = 5 **2.** *v* = 18 **3.** *e* = 30 **4.** *f* = 14

Given the parallelepiped at the right with *BC* = 10, *AB* = 8, and *BF* = 6, find each measure.

5. *AE* 6 **6.** *EH* 10 **7.** *CD* 8 **8.** *DH* 6

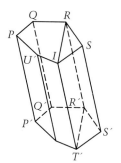

9. Given: Prism with bases *PQRSTU* and *P'Q'R'S'T'U'* Prove: $\overline{RT} \parallel \overline{R'T'}$

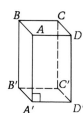

10. Find the length of the diagonal of a rectangular solid that has length 10 in., width 5 in., and height 3 in. $\sqrt{134} \approx 11.58$ in.

11. Find the length of the diagonal of a cube whose edges measure 20 cm. $20\sqrt{3} \approx 34.64$ cm

Given: Right rectangular prism with bases *ABCD* and *A'B'C'D'*

12. Prove: *A'B* = *D'C*
13. Prove: △*BDC* ≅ △*D'B'A'*

Set B **14.** If each base of a prism has *n* sides, find the number of faces, edges, and vertices of the prism.

14. Faces: *n* + 2 edges: 3*n* vertices: 2*n*

15. How many sides does each base of a prism have if the prism has *m* vertices? $\frac{1}{2}m$

16. A diagonal of a cube is 6 cm. Find the length of an edge. $2\sqrt{3}$

17. Derive a formula for the diagonal of a cube.

17. *e* = length of edge $d = \sqrt{e^2 + e^2 + e^2} = \sqrt{3e^2} = e\sqrt{3}$

18. Prove Theorem 11-2 for a right rectangular prism.

Given: Parallelepiped with bases *ABCD* and *A'B'C'D'*

19. Prove: *AB'* = *DC'*
20. How do you know that $\overline{D'B}$ intersects $\overline{DB'}$?
21. Prove: $\overline{D'B}$ bisects $\overline{DB'}$ (HINT: Draw $\overline{DB}$ and $\overline{D'B'}$.)

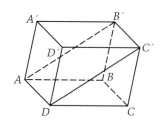

Given: Right prism with bases $ABCDE$ and $A'B'C'D'E'$; $\overline{MM'} \parallel \overline{DD'}$

22. M is the midpoint of $\overline{AB}$; M' is the midpoint of $\overline{A'B'}$.
Prove: $\overline{MD} = \overline{M'D'}$

23. $\overline{MM'}$ is perpendicular to $ABCDE$.
Prove: $\overline{MD} = \overline{M'D'}$

24. The dimensions of a carton shaped like a rectangular solid are 18 in., 24 in., and 40 in. Find the maximum length of ski poles that fit in the carton. **50 in**

25. Prove Theorem 11-3.

▲ **Review**

26. Find the area of the tinted region. $\frac{40\pi}{3} \approx 41.87$

27. Find the length of $\overset{\frown}{AB}$. $\frac{4\pi}{3} \approx 4.19$

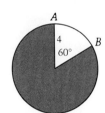

28. Find the ratios of the circumferences and the areas of two circles whose radii are 7 and 10. **7:10; 49:100**

29. Define *great circle* and *small circle of a sphere*.

30. From which set(s) of information can you conclude that $\triangle JMD \sim \triangle XYC$? **a, b**

a. $m\angle M = m\angle Y$; $m\angle J = m\angle X$

b. $\triangle XYC \cong \triangle JMD$

c. $m\angle D = m\angle C$; $\frac{JM}{XY} = \frac{JD}{YC} = \frac{MD}{XC}$

d. $\frac{JM}{XY} = \frac{MD}{YC}$

≡ **Thinking**
▼ **Ahead**

For each prism, draw a pattern that can be folded to form the prism. Then find the total area of the faces.

31. Rectangular solid

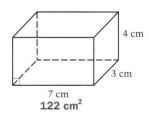

4 cm
3 cm
7 cm
122 cm²

32. Right triangular prism

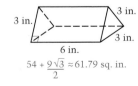

3 in.
3 in.
3 in.
6 in.
$\frac{54 + 9\sqrt{3}}{2} \approx 61.79$ sq. in.

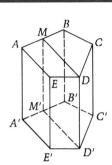

18. See diagram for Exercises 12–13. Given: Rt. rect. prism with bases $ABCD$ and $A'B'C'D'$ Prove: Area $ABCD$ = area $A'B'C'D'$ Proof: 1. Rt. rect. prism with bases $ABCD$ and $A'B'C'D'$ (Given) 2. Draw $\overline{BD}$ and $\overline{B'D'}$. (2 pts. determine a line.) 3. $ADD'A'$, $ABB'A'$, $BCC'B'$ and $CDD'C'$ are $\square$s. (Def. of prism [1]) 4. $AD = A'D'$; $AB = A'B'$; $BC = B'C'$; $CD = C'D'$ (Opp. sides of a $\square$ are =. [3]) 5. $\angle A$, $\angle A'$, $\angle C$ and $\angle C'$ are rt. $\angle$s. (Def. of rect. prism [1]) 6. $m\angle A = m\angle A'$; $m\angle C = m\angle C'$ (All rt. $\angle$s are =. [5]) 7. $\triangle ABC \cong \triangle A'B'C'$; $\triangle BCD \cong \triangle B'C'D'$ (SAS Post. [4, 6]) 8. Area $\triangle ABC$ = area $\triangle A'B'C'$; area $\triangle BCD$ = area $\triangle B'C'D'$ (Area Post. for $\cong \triangle$s [7]) 9. Area $\triangle ABC$ + area $\triangle BCD$ = area $\triangle A'B'C'$ + area $\triangle B'C'D'$ (Addition Prop. [8]) 10. Area $ABCD$ = area $\triangle ABC$ + area $\triangle BCD$; area $A'B'C'D'$ = area $\triangle A'B'C'$ + area $\triangle B'C'D'$ (Area Add. Post.) 11. Area $ABCD$ = area $A'B'C'D'$ (Substitution Prop. [9, 10])

FOLLOW-UP

More Practice

• **Worksheet 11–1**

Extension

A diagonal of a polyhedron is a segment joining any two vertices not in the same face. Ask students to consider the minimum number of faces a polyhedron may have in order to have at least one diagonal. **6 faces** Have more capable students investigate the relationship between the number of faces and the number of diagonals.

• **Extension 11–1**

Warm-Up Review

1. Find the area of a parallelogram with height 5 and base 15. 75
2. State the formula for the area of a regular polygon. $A = \frac{1}{2}ap$
3. Find the area of a triangle with base 10 and height 6. 30
4. Find the area of a regular hexagon with side measure of 6. $54\sqrt{3}$

LESSON 11–2

Resources

Teaching Aid 23, rectangular prisms
Visual Aid 23, rectangular prisms
Teaching Aid 24, triangular prisms
Visual Aid 24, triangular prisms
Worksheet 11–2
Extension 11–2
Computer Worksheet 11–2

OBJECTIVE

Compute the lateral and total area of prisms.

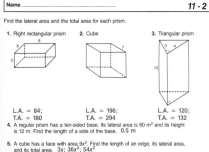

WORKSHEET Lesson 11-2

Name _____

Find the lateral area and the total area for each prism.

1. Right rectangular prism   2. Cube   3. Triangular prism

L.A. = 84;   L.A. = 196;   L.A. = 120;
T.A. = 180   T.A. = 294   T.A. = 132

4. A regular prism has a ten-sided base. Its lateral area is 60 m² and its height is 12 m. Find the length of a side of the base. 0.5 m

5. A cube has a face with area 9x². Find the length of an edge, its lateral area, and its total area. 3x; 36x²; 54x²

For each right rectangular prism, h is the length of a lateral edge; s_1 is the length of one side of the base; p is the perimeter of the base. Fill in the missing chart values.

	h	s_1	p	L.A.	T.A.
6.	5	7	18	90	118
7.	10	3	12	120	138
8.	2	2	8	16	24
9.	24	1	6	144	148
10.	4	10	34	136	276

11-2 Areas of a Prism

The aquarium shown is shaped like a regular hexagonal prism. The pattern could be folded to form a model of the aquarium with its top. To find the total surface area of the aquarium with its top, we must find the area of the lateral faces and the area of the bases.

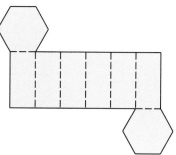

Definition *Lateral and Total Areas of a Prism*

The lateral area L.A. of a prism is the sum of the areas of its lateral faces. The total area T.A. of a prism is the sum of its lateral area and the areas of its two bases.

When a plane intersects all of the lateral faces of a prism the polygonal region formed is a *section* of the prism.

Definition *Cross Section of a Prism*

A cross section of a prism is a section parallel to the bases of the prism.

ABCDE is a cross section of the prism at the right.

Definition *Right Section of a Prism*

A right section of a prism is a section perpendicular to the lateral edges of the prism.

RSTUV is a right section of the prism at the right. $\overline{RS}$, $\overline{ST}$, $\overline{TU}$, $\overline{UV}$, and $\overline{VR}$ are perpendicular to the lateral edges.

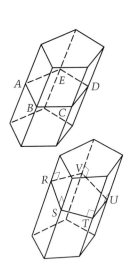

Theorem 11-4, the proof of which is omitted, gives a formula for finding the lateral area of a prism. This formula uses the length of a lateral edge and the perimeter of a right section of the prism. A Plan for Proof is given for a pentagonal prism.

Theorem 11-4   *Lateral Area of a Prism*

The lateral area L.A. of a prism is the product of the length ℓ of a lateral edge and the perimeter p of a right section of the prism. L.A. = ℓp

Given   Prism with bases $FGHKL$ and $F'G'H'K'L'$ and right section $ABCDE$

Prove   L.A. = ℓp where ℓ is the length of a lateral edge and p is the perimeter of $ABCDE$

Plan for Proof   Each lateral face is a parallelogram. Show that the height of each parallelogram is the length of the corresponding side of the right section. Then show that the sum of the areas of the lateral faces $\ell h_1 + \ell h_2 + \ell h_3 + \ell h_4 + \ell h_5 = \ell(h_1 + h_2 + h_3 + h_4 + h_5) = \ell p$. Thus, L.A. = ℓp.

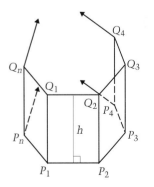

The formula for finding the lateral area of a right prism is given in Theorem 11-5, which follows directly from Theorem 11-4. A paragraph proof is given.

Theorem 11-5   *Lateral Area of a Right Prism*

The lateral area of a right prism is the product of the length of a lateral edge h and the perimeter p of the base. L.A. = hp

Given   A right prism with bases $P_1, P_2, P_3, \ldots, P_n$ and $Q_1, Q_2, Q_3, \ldots, Q_n$; length of a lateral edge $P_1Q_1, = h$; and perimeter p

Prove   L.A. = hp

Proof   Since all lateral faces of a prism are parallelograms, each lateral face of a right prism is a rectangle. Why? The area of rectangle $P_1P_2Q_2Q_1$ is $h(P_1P_2)$. The area of each of the other lateral faces can be represented similarly. Thus, L.A. = $h(P_1P_2 + P_2P_3 + P_3P_4 + \ldots + P_nP_1)$ and L.A. = hp. Lateral edges are ⊥ to the base, forming rt. ∠s and thus rectangles.

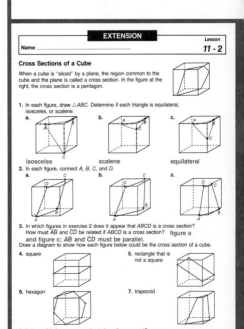

Additional Example

A right prism has a right triangular base, with legs 5 and 12. One lateral edge has length 4. Find the lateral area and the total area. L.A. = 120; T.A. = 180

Error Analysis   Because students' experience with oblique prisms is limited, the following errors are likely to occur:
1. Confusion of base with right section.
2. Confusion of length of lateral edge with perpendicular distance between bases.
3. Failure to realize all lateral edges are equal.
Correct the first two errors by exaggerating obliqueness and the third by reviewing properties of a parallelogram.

EXERCISE NOTES

Exercise 9   develops a formula for lateral and total area of a cube.
Exercise 16   can be solved by using the formula from **Exercise 9**.
Exercise 21   involves the properties of the diagonals of a rhombus and the Pythagorean Theorem.
Exercise 23   uses ratios of a 30-60-90 triangle.

Example

Find the lateral area and the total area of a regular octagonal prism with lateral edge of length 3 m, base sides of length 2 m, and apothem of each base approximately 2.4 m.

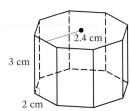

Solution

$$L.A = hp \qquad B = \text{area of base} \qquad T.A. = L.A. + 2B$$

$$\begin{aligned} &= 3(16) & &= \tfrac{1}{2}ap & &\approx 48 + 2(19.2) \\ &= 48 \text{ m}^2 & &\approx \tfrac{1}{2}(2.4)(16) & &\approx 86 \text{ m}^2 \\ & & &\approx 19.2 \text{ m}^2 \end{aligned}$$

Checking for Understanding

1. In a right prism, a cross section is also a _?_ section.   right

Find the lateral area of each prism.

2.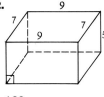

160

3.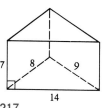

217

4.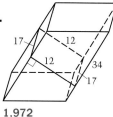

1,972

5. The edge of a cubical cardboard box measures 7 in. Find the total area of cardboard in the box. **294 sq. in.**

6. The total area of a right prism is 2,500 cm² and its lateral area is 2,000 cm². What is the area of a base of the prism? **250 cm²**

7. The perimeter of a right section of a prism is 16 cm and the lateral area is 80 cm². How long is each lateral edge? **5 cm**

Written Exercises

Set A   Find the lateral area of each prism.

1.

800

2.

252

3. A right prism with height 6 cm and perimeter of each base 12 cm **72 cm**

4. The height of the aquarium pictured on page 478 is 18 in. Each side of a base measures 7 in. What is the lateral area of the aquarium? **756 sq. in**

Find the total area of each prism.

5.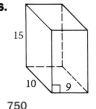
12
10 10 8
12
592

6.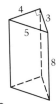
15
10 9
750

7.
4 3
5
8
108

Find the lateral and total areas for each prism.

8. A cube whose edge measures 5 m **100 m²; 150 m²**

9. A cube whose edge has length *e* **4 e²; 6e²**

10. A cube whose base has perimeter 24 cm **144 cm²; 216 cm²**

11. A cube whose base has perimeter 8x **16x²; 24x²**

12. A right prism with the perimeter of each square base 48 in. and height 10 in. **480 sq. in; 768 sq. in.**

13. A right prism whose bases are squares 15 in. on each side and whose height is 24 in. **1,440 sq. in.; 1,890 sq. in.**

14. A right section of an oblique pentagonal prism has edges 7 in., 8 in., 9 in., 10 in., and 12 in. long. A lateral edge is 11 in. long. Find the lateral area. **506 sq. in.**

15. Find the total area of a rectangular darkroom 8 m long and 5 m wide if the ceiling is 3 m above the floor. **158 m²**

16. A dining room has the shape of a hexagonal prism. Find the area to be painted if the walls are to be painted. Allow 76 sq. ft. for doors and windows. **332 sq. ft.**

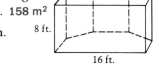
5 ft. 7 ft. $5\frac{1}{2}$ ft.
9 ft. 9 ft.
8 ft.
16 ft.

Set B **17.** The lateral area of a cube is 196 sq. in. How long is an edge of the cube? **7 in.**

18. Each base of a jewelry box that is shaped like a regular prism is a pentagon with sides of 8 cm. The altitude measures 16 cm. Find the lateral area. **640 cm²**

19. Find the amount of glass needed to build this regular octagonal terrarium: each side of a base measures 10 cm and the apothem is 12 cm; the height of the terrarium is 30 cm. It has a top. **3,360 cm²**

20. Find the total surface area of the aquarium on
page 478. Include the top of the aquarium
(See Exercise 4.) **1,010.62 sq. in.**

21. Each base of a right prism is a rhombus with
diagonals measuring 10 in. and 24 in. The height
of the prism is 15 in. Find the lateral area. **780 sq. in.**

22. The total area of a right prism is 210 cm². Each
base of the prism is a square 5 cm on a side. Find
the height of the prism. **8 cm**

23. Find the lateral area and total area of the right
prism shown. Its bases are isosceles trapezoids.

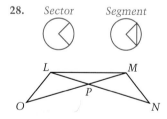

Set C　**24.** Find the total area of wrapping paper needed to
cover a regular hexagonal gift box: each side of
a base measures 7 cm; the height of the box is 16 cm.

25. The ratio of the lengths of the edges of two cubes
is 3 to 1. What is the ratio of their total areas? **9:1**

23. 1,248 + 192√3 ≈
1,580.55;
1,580.55 + 104√3 ≈
1,760.69
24. 672 + 147√3 ≈
926.61 cm²

◆ **Review**　**26.** If a prism has ten faces, each base is a(n) __?__.
octagon

27. Find the length of the diagonal of a rectangular
box that measures 5 ft. by 11 ft. by 12 ft.
√290 ≈ 17.03 ft.

28. Draw two circles. In one, shade a sector. In the
other, shade a segment.

28. *Sector*　*Segment*

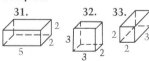

29. Given: *m∠NLM = m∠OML; LN = MO*
Prove: *△NLM ≅ △OML*

30. *KQST* is inscribed in a circle, *m∠K = 2x + 5*, and
m∠S = 8x − 25. Find *m∠K*. **45**

Samples:

≋ **Thinking**　Draw a rectangular solid that will hold the given
▼ **Ahead**　number of cubes, each with edge length of 1 unit.

31. 20　　　　**32.** 18　　　　**33.** 12

31.　32.　33.

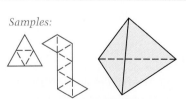

Challenge

Draw a pattern that can be folded to form
each polyhedron. The one on the left is made
up of four equilateral triangles, while the
one on the right is composed of eight
equilateral triangles.

Samples:

Excursion: Regular Polyhedrons

A polyhedron is *regular* if its faces are congruent regular polygons that form equal dihedral angles along its edges. These polyhedrons are known as *Platonic solids*, because Plato (429–348 B.C.) described them so fully in his writings. The five possible regular polyhedrons are shown below.

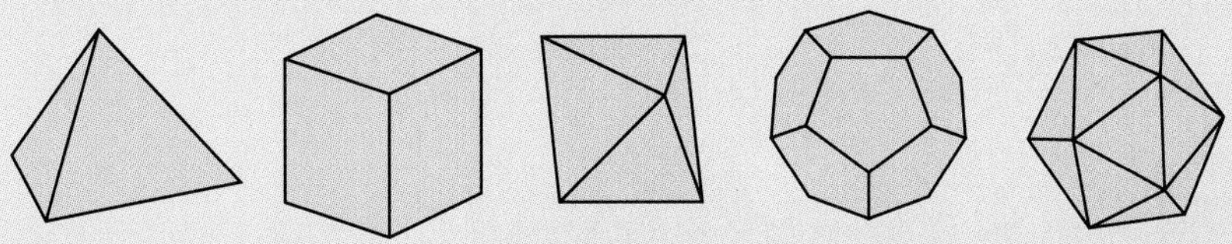

Tetrahedron   Hexahedron   Octahedron   Dodecahedron   Icosahedron

For each polyhedron,

1. what is the number of polygons that intersect at each vertex? 3; 3; 4; 3; 5

2. what is the sum of the measures of all the face angles at each vertex?

   180; 270; 240; 324; 300

3. What must be true of the sum of the measures of all the face angles at each vertex of a regular polyhedron? Why?

   3. Sum must be <360; otherwise if Sum = 360, face ∠s would be coplanar

4. Which regular polygons can be faces of regular polyhedrons? Why?

   4. Equilateral triangles, squares, regular pentagons; since at least 3 face ∠s meet at a vertex, the sum of their measures could be less than 360.

5. In a table, list the number of faces F, vertices V, and edges E in a tetrahedron, a hexahedron, an octahedron, a dodecahedron, and an icosahedron. How are F, V, and E related? $F + V = E + 2$

The Swiss mathematician Leonhard Euler (1707–1783) generalized the relationship in the following theorem: In *any* polyhedron, $F + V = E + 2$.

Verify Euler's Theorem for each polyhedron.

6.

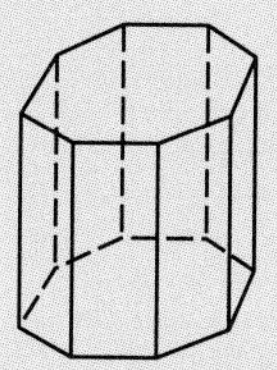

7.

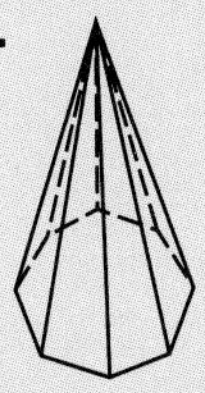

8.

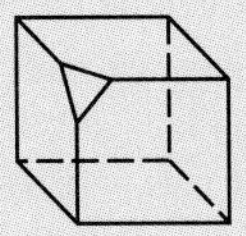

9. Verify Euler's Theorem for a prism whose bases are n-sided polygons.

10. Verify Euler's Theorem for a pyramid whose base is an n-sided polygon.

5.

	F	V	E
Tetrahedron	4	4	6
Hexahedron	6	8	12
Octahedron	8	6	12
Dodecahedron	12	20	30
Icosahedron	20	12	30

6. $F + V = E + 2$
   $10 + 16 = 24 + 2$,
   $26 = 26$

7. $F + V = E + 2$
   $9 + 9 = 16 + 2$, $18 = 18$

8. $F + V = E + 2$
   $7 + 10 = 15 + 2$,
   $17 = 17$

9. $F + V = E + 2$
   $(n + 2) + (2n) = (3n) + 2$, $3n + 2 = 3n + 2$

10. $F + V = E + 2$
    $(n + 1) + (n + 1) = (2n) + 2$, $2n + 2 = 2n + 2$

Warm-Up Review

1. What type of figure is a lateral face of an oblique prism? Parallelogram
2. What type of figure is a lateral face of a right prism? Rectangle
3. Which faces of a prism are always in parallel planes? Bases
4. Find the area of a regular pentagon if one side is 8 and the apothem is 5.5. 110
5. Find the area of an equilateral triangle with a side of 6 in. $9\sqrt{3}$ in., or 15.6 in.

LESSON 11–3

Resources

Congruent cubes
  Teaching Aid 23, rectangular
    prisms
  Visual Aid 23, rectangular
    prisms
  Teaching Aid 24, triangular
    prisms
  Visual Aid 24, triangular prisms
Worksheet 11–3
Extension 11–3
  Computer Activities 11–3

OBJECTIVE

Compute the volume of a prism.

WORKSHEET   Lesson **11-3**

Name _____

1. A prism has a base with an area of 45 cm² and an altitude of 13 cm. Find the volume of the prism. 585 cm³

2. A rectangular prism has a volume of 240 cu. ft. The length of one side of the base is 3 ft. and the height is 16 ft. Find the area of the base and the length of the other side of the base. 15 sq. ft.; 5 ft.

3. A cube has a volume of 1331 m³. Find the length of an edge. 11 m

4. A garage floor is 9 ft. by 15 ft. A new concrete floor 6 in. deep is being poured. The amount of concrete needed is ___?___ or ___?___.   67½ cu. ft.; 116,640 cu. in. or 2⅕ cu. yd.

Find the area of a base and the volume of each of these right prisms.

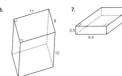

5.	6.	7.
B = 30	B = 99	B = 51.2
V = 810	V = 1188	V = 128

8. A regular hexagonal prism has a base with area 162 m² and a height of 8 m. The volume of the prism is ___?___. If the height is increased to 12 m, the volume is increased by ___?___.   1296 m³; 648 m³

9. A side of the square base of a solid metal pole is 8 cm and the height of the pole is 20 cm. The metal's mass is 5 g/cm³. Find the volume and total mass of the pole. 1280 cm³; 6400 g

10. The volume of a rectangular prism is 2340 cu. ft. A base is 5 ft. by 13 ft. Find its height. 36 ft.

11-3 Volume of a Prism

Barbara Wilson is trying to decide which refrigerator to buy. To determine which one occupies more space, she associates a number with each.

UPRIGHT FREEZER
64" high
32" wide
27" deep

CHEST FREEZER
35" high
59" wide
30" deep

Postulate 25 *Volume Postulate*

To every solid polyhedron there corresponds a unique positive real number called the volume of the polyhedron.

Suppose a cube whose edge is one unit long is used as the unit of volume. Then the volume of a polyhedron is the number of these cubes that exactly fill the interior of the polyhedron.

How many cubes are in a horizontal layer of the rectangular solid at the right? How many layers are there? How could you find its volume? Your answer should suggest Postulate 26.

12; 5 layers; 5 × 12 = 60

Postulate 26 *Volume of a Rectangular Solid*

The volume V of a rectangular solid is the product of base B and height h. $V = Bh$

The formula in Postulate 26 can be restated as $V = \ell wh$. Why?
We can substitute $\ell(w)$ for area of the
rectangular base.

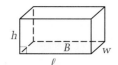

Are the sheets of paper in the stack at the right congruent? **Yes**
Your answer suggests Theorem 11-6, the proof of which
is omitted.

Theorem 11-6   *Area of a Cross Section*

All cross sections of a prism have equal area.

The stacks of paper below contain the same number of
congruent sheets. Do the polyhedrons suggested by the two **Yes**
stacks have the same volume? If we let a single sheet of paper
represent a cross section of each stack, then at every level the
cross sections have the same area. Bonaventura Cavalieri
(1598–1647), an Italian mathematician, used this idea to
compare the volumes of two solids.

Postulate 27   *Cavalieri's Principle*

***Given a plane and two solids, if every plane parallel to this
plane that intersects one of the solids also intersects the other so
that each pair of cross sections formed have the same areas, then
the solids have the same volume.***

The prisms at the right have the same height and bases of the
same area. Use Cavalieri's Principle to compare their volumes.
Are the volumes equal? Your answer should agree with **Yes**
Theorem 11-7. The proof of this theorem is omitted.

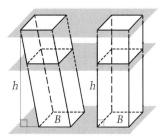

TEACHING NOTES

Develop Postulate 27 by using
concrete materials such as a box
of congruent cubes. Students
should soon see that to find volume we can count the cubes in
one layer and multiply by the
number of layers.

Prove Theorem 11–6 by drawing diagonals from one vertex of a
cross section and corresponding
diagonals in one base. Show that
the area of the cross section is
the same as the area of the base.

Stress Theorem 11–7.

Additional Example

Find the volume of a right triangular prism if its height is 12 and the
bases are equilateral triangles
with side length 3. $27\sqrt{3}$

EXTENSION

Name _____   *Lesson* **11 - 3**

Volume and Surface Area of Boxes

A manufacturer of boxes plans to make open-topped boxes by cutting squares
from sheets of cardboard measuring 10 inches by 7 inches.

If the manufacturer cuts larger squares from the corners, the box will be deeper,
but the base will be smaller.

The manufacturer plans to make three different sizes of boxes as follows:
Box 1 will have $\frac{1}{4}$ square inch $\left(\frac{1}{2} \times \frac{1}{2}\right)$ cut from each corner. Box 2 will have
1 square inch (1 × 1) cut from each corner. Box 3 will have 4 square inches
(2 × 2) cut from each corner.

1. Complete the chart below to determine which box will have the greatest volume. **Box 2**

	length (ℓ)	width (w)	height (h)	volume (V)
Box 1	9	6	$\frac{1}{2}$	27
Box 2	8	5	1	40
Box 3	6	3	2	36

2. Complete the chart below to determine which box will have the least surface area. **Box 3**

	area of side (ℓh)	area of side (ℓh)	area of end (wh)	area of end (wh)	area of bottom (ℓw)	total surface area
Box 1	$4\frac{1}{2}$	$4\frac{1}{2}$	3	3	54	69
Box 2	8	8	5	5	40	66
Box 3	12	12	6	6	18	54

3. The manufacturer can purchase precut patterns for the boxes at a cost of $0.03 per
square inch. The manufacturer wants to find the box that is most economical. To do this,
the manufacturer finds the cost per cubic inch. The formula is as follows:

$$\text{cost per cubic inch} = \frac{\text{surface area} \times \text{cost per square inch}}{\text{volume}}$$

Which box is most economical, Box 1, Box 2, or Box 3? **Box 3**

EXERCISE NOTES

Exercises 17 and **18** illustrate the water displacement technique for measuring the volume of irregular solids.

Theorem 11-7 *Volume of a Prism*

The volume V of a prism is the product of the area B of a base and the height h. V = Bh

Given A prism with base area B and height h

Prove $V = Bh$

Plan for Consider a rectangular solid that has bases in the same
Proof planes as those of the given prism and has base area B. The areas of all cross sections are equal, including the base. The volume of the rectangular solid is Bh. By Cavalieri's Principle the two solids have the same volume. Thus, the volume of the given prism is Bh.

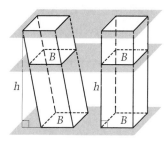

Example
Find the volume of this regular pentagonal prism.

Solution
$$B = \tfrac{1}{2}ap \qquad\qquad V = Bh$$
$$= \tfrac{1}{2}(5.5)(40) \qquad\quad = 110(5)$$
$$= 110 \text{ cm}^2 \qquad\qquad = 550 \text{ cm}^3$$

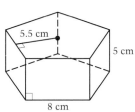

Checking for Understanding

1. Find the volume of a prism with height 5 cm and area of base 24 cm². 120 cm³

2. Find the volume of the prism at the right. 1,728 cu. yd.

Tell whether each of the following statements is *always*, *sometimes*, or *never* true.

3. If the volumes of two rectangular solids are equal, then their total areas are equal. Sometimes

4. If the total areas of two cubes are equal, then their volumes are equal. Always

5. Refer to the freezers in the photo on page 484. Which freezer takes up more space? The chest freezer

6. The area of the base of a prism is 12 cm². If the volume of the prism is 156 cm³, what is its height? 13 m

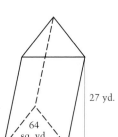

Assignment Guide

Basic: 1–10, 23–28
Average: 2–6 (even), 8–18, 23–28
Extended: 2–10 (even), 11–28

7. The base of a prism is 8 in. long and 9 in. wide. If the volume of the prism is 288 cu. in., what is its height? **4 in.**

Written Exercises

Set A   Find the volume of each prism.

1.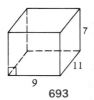
7
11
9
693

2.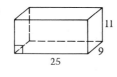
11
9
25
2,475

3.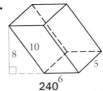
10
8
5
6
240

4. Find the volume of a right pentagonal prism with a base area of 3.5 sq. yd. and a height of 9 yd.
31.5 cu. yd.

5. The base of a right prism is a square and its height is 12 cm. If the volume is 588 cm³, how long is one side of the base? **7 cm**

6. About how many cubic feet of sand can be placed in the pickup truck shown at the right?
80 cu. ft.

8'
4'
2' 6"

7. How many cubic meters of concrete will be needed for a patio 12 m long, 10 m wide, and 10 cm deep? **12 m³**

Set B   Find the volume of each prism.

8.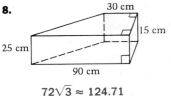
30 cm
15 cm
25 cm
90 cm
72√3 ≈ 124.71

9.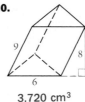
26 cm
31 cm
10 cm
22,500 cm³

10.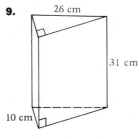
9
8
6
3,720 cm³

11. Find the weight of a wooden beam 4 in. by 12 in. by 8 ft. if the wood weighs 46 lb. per cu. ft. **122⅔ lb.**

Written Exercises

19. Given: Cube with edge e
Prove: Volume of cube = e^3
Proof: 1. Cube with edge e (Given)
2. Cube is a rect. solid. (Def. of cube) 3. Volume of cube = ℓwh (Vol. of rect. solid) 4. $\ell = w = h = e$ (Def. of cube [1]) 5. Volume of cube = $e \cdot e \cdot e = e^3$ (Substitution Prop. [3, 4])

12. What is the effect on the volume of a cube when the length of each edge is doubled? tripled?   **12.** 2^3 = 8 times as great 3^3 = 27 times as great

13. Find the weight of an iron post shaped like a right square prism if each side of each base is 10 cm and the height is 1.3 m. Iron weighs 7 g/cm^3. **91,000g**

14. A water tank shaped like a right rectangular prism measures 6 ft. by 8 ft. by 10 ft. How many gallons of water will it hold? (1 cu. ft. ≈ 7.5 gal.) **3,600 gal**

15. A packaging company wants to design a shipping box shaped like a rectangular solid that has the greatest possible volume with the least possible area. If the desired volume is 64 cu. in., what would the dimensions be for the box to have the least area? **4 in. by 4 in. by 4 in.**

16. A board foot is a piece of lumber 1 ft. by 1 ft. by 1 in. How many board feet are there in a board 8 in. by $\frac{3}{4}$ in. by 10 ft.? **5 board feet**

17. The container at the right, a cube 18 in. on each edge, is half full of water. What is the volume of water in the container? **2,916 cu. in.**

18. A stone is placed in the container of water. The water level rises 2 in. What is the volume of the stone?
3,564 cu. in.; 648 cu. in.

Set C **19.** Prove that the volume of a cube with edge e is e^3.

20. If the number of cubic inches in the volume of a certain cube equals the number of square inches in its total area, what is the length of an edge of the cube? **6 in.**

21. A tinsmith wishes to make a rectangular tank to hold 16 cu. ft. of water. If no cover is used, how many square feet of material will be needed if the base is a square and the height of the tank is 2 ft.?

22. A cube measures 2 in. on each side. By what number must the length of a side be multiplied to double the volume of the cube?
21. $8 + 16\sqrt{2} \approx 30.63$ sq. ft.   **22.** $\sqrt[3]{2}$

Review

23. In a $\underline{?}$ prism, a cross section is a right section. right

24. The height of a right prism is 10 and the perimeter of each base is 82. Find the lateral area. 820

25. List as many properties of the bases of a prism as you can.

26. Give the ratios for sin Y, cos Y, and tan Y.

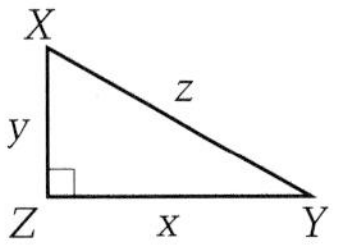

27. Find the area of an equilateral triangle whose perimeter is 4. $\frac{4\sqrt{3}}{9} \approx 0.77$

Thinking Ahead

28. Consider the container at the right. How would you find the lateral area? the total area? the volume?

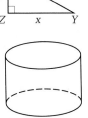

Computer Activities: Drawing and Measuring

1. Draw two congruent circles and a rectangle whose length is the same as the circumference of each circle. If you combine the three figures by matching the two lengths with the circumferences of the circles to form a solid, what would the solid look like? Right cylinder
2. Use paper and pencil to draw a diagram of the solid.
3. Find the total area of the solid. Answers will vary

1.

2.

Algebra Review: Equations for Lines

1. If two nonvertical lines are parallel, then their slopes are $\underline{?}$. equal
2. If two nonvertical and nonhorizontal lines are perpendicular, then their slopes are $\underline{?}$. negative reciprocals of each other

Write the equation in slope-intercept form for the line that

3. contains $A(2, -3)$ and is parallel to the line with equation $y = 4x - 1$. $y = 4x - 11$
4. contains $B(0, 5)$ and is parallel to the line with equation $2x + 5y = 10$. $y = \frac{-2}{5}x + 5$
5. contains $C(\frac{1}{2}, 3)$ and is perpendicular to the line with equation $y = -\frac{3}{4}x + 2$. $y = \frac{4}{3}x + \frac{7}{3}$
6. is the perpendicular bisector of the segment with endpoints $D(-1, 4)$ and $E(2, 1)$. (HINT: Use the Midpoint Formula.) $y = x + 2$

Review

25. contained in ∥ planes; are ≅ polygonal regions; have = areas; have = perimeters
26. $\sin Y = \frac{y}{z}$; $\cos Y = \frac{x}{z}$; $\tan Y = \frac{y}{x}$

Thinking Ahead

28. find the area of the curved surface; add the areas of the two bases to the lateral area; multiply the area of a base times the height of the cylinder.

FOLLOW-UP

More Practice

- **Worksheet 11-3**

Extension

Similar polyhedrons may be defined as those that have
1. the same number of faces.
2. faces similar to each other in corresponding locations.
3. equal corresponding polyhedral angles.

Have students examine ratios of volumes in similar polyhedrons. They are proportional to cubes of corresponding edges.

- **Extension 11-3**

Computers

The computer activity in the pupil's book can be completed using *The Geometric Supposer: Circles* or *GeoDraw*.

- **Computer Activities 11-3**

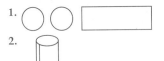

Warm-Up Review

1. Find the circumference of a circle with radius 4. 8π, or 25.12
2. Find the area of a circle with radius 4. 16π, or 50.24
3. True or false: The bases of a prism have equal area. True
4. The length of an altitude is the ___?___ of the prism. Height
5. State the formula for lateral area of a right prism. L.A. = hp

LESSON 11–4

Resources

Construction paper
Cylinders
　Teaching Aid 27, cylinders
　Visual Aid 27, cylinders
Worksheet 11–4
Extension 11–4
　Computer Activities 11–4
　Computer Worksheet 11–4
Quiz 11

OBJECTIVE

Compute the area and volume of cylinders.

11-4 Areas and Volume of a Cylinder

Tin cans, hot water heaters, and refinery storage tanks all suggest cylinders.

Definition *Cylinder*

A cylinder is a figure formed by two congruent circular regions contained in parallel planes along with all segments having an endpoint on each circle and parallel to the line joining the centers of the circles.

Many properties of a cylinder correspond to those of a prism. The parallel circular regions of a cylinder are its **bases**. The segment joining centers of the circles is the **axis** of the cylinder. The terms *altitude*, *height*, and *cross section* are defined similarly for prisms and cylinders.

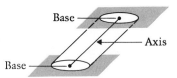

In a right prism, the lateral edges are perpendicular to the planes of the bases. Similarly, in a **right cylinder** the axis of the cylinder is perpendicular to the planes of the bases. Otherwise, the cylinder is an **oblique cylinder**.

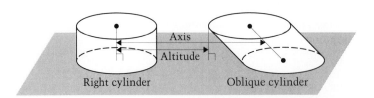

Right cylinder　　Oblique cylinder

WORKSHEET　　Lesson 11-4

Name _____

Tell whether each statement is *always*, *sometimes*, or *never* true.

1. The bases of a cylinder lie in parallel planes. **always**
2. The lateral area of a right cylinder is the area of a rectangle. **always**
3. The axis of a cylinder is a lateral edge. **never**
4. The axis of a cylinder has the same measure as its height. **sometimes**
5. The lateral area of a cylinder is equal to the product of the radius of the base and the height. **never**
6. The volume of a cylinder is equal to the product of the area of the base and the height. **always**
7. An oblique cylinder has its axis perpendicular to its bases. **never**
8. A right cylinder has a base with radius 5 cm and a height of 19 cm. Find the following, giving answers in terms of π.

$B = \underline{25\pi}$; L.A. $= \underline{190\pi}$; T.A. $= \underline{240\pi}$; $V = \underline{475\pi}$

9. Two cylindrical tanks are being built. Tank X is 15 m tall and the base has a radius of 12 m. Tank Y is 12 m tall and the base has a diameter of 30 m. Fill in the values. Use 3.14 for π.

	Tank X	Tank Y
B	452.16 m²	706.5 m²
L.A.	1130.4 m²	1130.4 m²
T.A.	2034.72 m²	2543.4 m²
V	6782.4 m³	8478 m³

10. Find the following for the right cylinder shown. Use 3.14 for π.

L.A. $= \underline{251.2 \text{ m}^2}$
T.A. $= \underline{653.12 \text{ m}^2}$
$V = \underline{1004.8 \text{ m}^3}$

To find the area and volume of a cylinder, consider regular prisms inscribed in a cylinder.

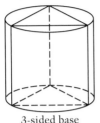
3-sided base

6-sided base

8-sided base

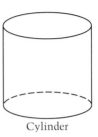
Cylinder

As the number of edges in each base of the prism is increased, the shape of the prism approaches the shape of a cylinder as a limit. It follows then that the formulas for the lateral area, total area, and volume of a cylinder are similar to those for a prism.

Theorem 11-8 gives the formula for the lateral area of a right cylinder. Its proof is omitted.

Theorem 11-8   *Lateral Area of a Right Cylinder*

The lateral area L.A. of a right cylinder is the product of the circumference C of a base and the height h. L.A. = Ch = $2\pi rh$

A convenient way to remember how to find the lateral area of a right cylinder is to consider a model such as the salt container pictured below. If the bases are removed and the model is cut along the dashed line and flattened out, the lateral area of the model is the area of the rectangle.

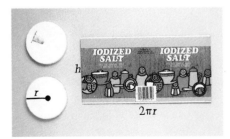

The total area T.A. of a cylinder is the sum of its lateral area and the areas of its two bases. T.A. = L.A. + 2B = $2\pi rh + 2\pi r^2$

11-4 *Areas and Volume of a Cylinder*

TEACHING NOTES

To introduce this lesson, use **concrete materials** in the shape of cylinders, such as coffee cans. What shapes are needed to cover the cans? two circles and a rectangle How do the dimensions of the rectangle compare with the dimensions of the lateral area of a cylinder? length = circumference of base; width = height of cylinder

Point out the similarities between prisms and cylinders. The formula for the lateral area of a cylinder is the same as that for a prism, except perimeter is replaced by circumference.

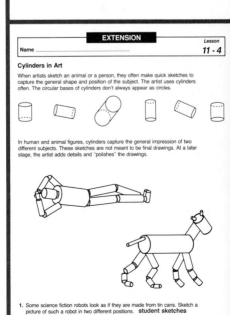

Additional Examples

Example 1
If the diameter of the base is 6 in. and its height is 8 in., find the approximate area of the cardboard needed to make a cylindrical oatmeal box. 207.2 sq. in.

Example 2
How many cubic inches of oatmeal will the above cylinder hold? 226.1 cu. in.

Error Analysis
Students are often not aware of when an approximate answer is appropriate and when the answer should be left in terms of pi. In general, encourage the former unless otherwise specified.

Answers found by using the π key on a calculator will be slightly different than answers found by using 3.14 for π.

Exercises 7 and **8** could be solved with the use of a **calculator.**

Exercises 16 and **17** show the relationship between volumes of similar cylinders and related heights and radii.

Exercise 18 involves inscribed polygons and 30-60-90 triangles.

Exercises 24–26 could be solved by making models of the prism and pyramid.

Example 1
About how much tin is needed to make a tennis-ball can 20.1 cm high with a base whose radius is 3.4 cm?

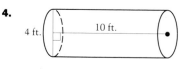

Solution

$$L.A. = 2\pi rh$$
$$\approx 2(3.14)(3.4)(20.1)$$
$$\approx 429.2 \text{ cm}^2$$

$$B = \pi r^2$$
$$\approx 3.14(3.4)^2$$
$$\approx 36.3 \text{ cm}^2$$

$$T.A. = L.A. + 2B$$
$$\approx 429.2 + 2(36.3)$$
$$\approx 501.8 \text{ cm}^2$$

The proof of Theorem 11-9, which relies upon Cavalieri's Principle, is omitted.

Theorem 11-9 *Volume of a Cylinder*

The volume V of a cylinder is the product of the area B of a base and the height h. $V = Bh = \pi r^2 h$

Example 2
What is the volume of the can described in Example 1?

Solution

$$V = Bh$$
$$\approx 36.3(20.1)$$
$$\approx 729.6 \text{ cm}^3$$

Checking for Understanding
1. How are a cylinder and a prism similar? How are they different?

Find the lateral area, the total area, and the volume for each right cylinder. Give answer in terms of π.

2. Radius of base 6 cm; height 8 cm

3.

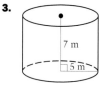

7 m

5 m

4.

4 ft.   10 ft.

5. Find the volume of an oblique cylinder whose base has radius 3 and whose height measures 6. $V = 54\pi \approx 169.56$

6. Find the height of a cylinder whose volume is 200 cm³ and whose base has diameter of 12 cm. $\frac{50}{9\pi} \approx 1.77$ cm

7. Are the volumes of the two cylinders shown at the bottom of page 490 the same? Why or why not?

8. What is the important difference between the hypotheses of Theorems 11-8 and 11-9?

1. Both have parallel, congruent bases, the lateral surface of a prism is formed of parallelograms, while the lateral surface of a cylinder is curved.
2. 96π cm²; 168π cm²; 288π cm³
3. 70π m²; 120π m²; 175π m³
4. 90π sq. ft.; 130.5π sq. ft.; 202.5π cu. ft.
7. If the bases have equal area; yes; because the heights are equal.
8. Thm. 11-8 requires the cylinder to be a *right* cylinder. Thm. 11-9 does not.

Assignment Guide

Basic: 1–10, 19–26
Average: 2–8 (even), 9–17, 19–26
Extended: 2–8 (even), 9–26

Written Exercises

Set A   For Exercises 1–6, give answers in terms of π.

Find the lateral area, the total area, and the volume of each right cylinder.

1.

2.

3. Radius of base a; height 3 $6\pi a$; $6\pi a + 2\pi a^2$; $3\pi a^2$

4. Diameter of base $12d$; height $2d$ $24\pi d^2$; $96\pi d^2$; $72\pi d^3$

Find the volume of each oblique cylinder.

5.

6.

1. 40π sq. ft.; 52.5π sq. ft.; 50π cu. ft.
2. 170π cm^2; 220π cm^2; 425π cm^3
5. 200π cu. in
6. 24π cm^3

For Exercises 7–13, all cylinders are right.

7. Find the weight of a cylindrical marble column 2.5 ft. in diameter and 27 ft. high. (1 cu. ft. $\approx$ 154 lb.) 20,400 lb.

8. How many gallons of water can be held by a cylindrical tank 2.5 ft. in diameter and 8 ft. deep? (1 cu. ft. $\approx$ 7.5 gal.) **294.38 gal.**

Set B   Find the lateral area, the total area, and the volume of each cylinder. Give answers in terms of π.

9. Circumference of base 18π; height 7

10. Circumference of base $8x\pi$; height $5x$

11. How many cubic feet of water can be held in 144 ft. of pipe whose internal diameter is 2 in.? **3.14 cu. ft.**

12. How many cubic feet of gas will a pipeline hold if it is 1,000 mi. long with a diameter of 2 ft.?

13. A cylindrical tank has an 18-in. diameter and a 20-in. height. It is half full of water. How much more water will be needed to raise the water level by 8 in.? **2,034.72 cu. in.**

9. 126π; 288π; 567π
10. $40\pi x^2$; $72\pi x^2$; $80\pi x^3$
12. 16,579,200 cu. ft.

ANSWERS

Written Exercises

16.

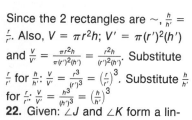

Since the 2 rectangles are $\sim$, $\frac{h}{h'} = \frac{r}{r'}$. Also, $V = \pi r^2 h$; $V' = \pi (r')^2(h')$ and $\frac{V}{V'} = \frac{\pi r^2 h}{\pi (r')^2(h')} = \frac{r^2 h}{(r')^2(h')}$. Substitute $\frac{r}{r'}$ for $\frac{h}{h'}$: $\frac{V}{V'} = \frac{r^3}{(r')^3} = \left(\frac{r}{r'}\right)^3$. Substitute $\frac{h}{h'}$ for $\frac{r}{r'}$: $\frac{V}{V'} = \frac{h^3}{(h')^3} = \left(\frac{h}{h'}\right)^3$

22. Given: $\angle J$ and $\angle K$ form a linear pr.; $\angle Q$ is a complement of $\angle K$. Prove: $m\angle J > 90$

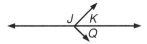

Proof: Either $m\angle J > 90$ or $m\angle J \not> 90$. Assume $m\angle J \not> 90$. Then $m\angle J \le 90$. Since $\angle J$ and $\angle K$ form a lin. pr., $m\angle J + m\angle K = 180$ and $m\angle J = 180 - m\angle K$. Substituting and simplifying, we have $180 - m\angle K \le 90$, or $m\angle K \ge 90$. But this contradicts the fact that $\angle K$ and $\angle Q$ are complements, that is, that $m\angle Q + m\angle K = 90$. Thus our assumption that $m\angle J \not> 90$ must be false and $m\angle J > 90$ is true.

FOLLOW-UP

More Practice

• Worksheet 11–4

Extension

Have students make a model of an oblique cylinder. Investigate the following.
1. What is the shape of the lateral surface? **parallelogram**

---

14. How many square meters of tin will be used to make 50 cylindrical air-conditioning pipes, each 18 cm in diameter and 90 cm long? **25.43 m²**

15. How many ounces of liquid will the cup hold? (1.8 cu. in. $\approx$ 1 oz.) **16.12 oz.**

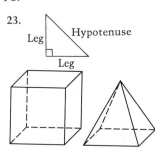

16. If two similar rectangles are revolved about corresponding sides as axes, the two cylinders generated are called *similar cylinders of revolution*. Show that the ratio of the volumes of the cylinders is the same as the cube of the ratio of the heights or the cube of the ratio of the radii: $\frac{V}{V'} = \left(\frac{h}{h'}\right)^3 = \left(\frac{r}{r'}\right)^3$

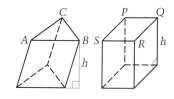

17. Use the result from Exercise 16 to compare the volumes of two similar cylinders, one with height 9 and radius 3 and the other with height 6 and radius 2. **27:8**

Set C **18.** A regular triangular prism with a base perimeter of $6\sqrt{3}$ cm and a height of 25 cm is inscribed in a right cylinder. Find the total area of the cylinder. **$108\pi \approx 339.12$ cm²**

▲ Review **19.** $\triangle ABC$ and $\square PQRS$ have equal areas. How do the volumes of the prisms compare? **Equal**

20. Find the volume of a rectangular solid whose dimensions are 6 by 8 by 13. **624**

21. Find the total area of the solid in Exercise 20. **460**

22. Given that $\angle J$ and $\angle K$ form a linear pair and that $\angle Q$ is a complement of $\angle K$, prove indirectly that $m\angle J > 90$.

23. Draw a right isosceles triangle and identify the hypotenuse and the legs.

23.

≡ Thinking Ahead The cube and the pyramid at the right have congruent bases and equal heights.

24. Which figure appears to have greater area? greater volume? **Cube; cube**

25. Estimate the ratio of the total area of the pyramid to that of the prism. **Answers will vary.**

26. Estimate the ratio of the volume of the pyramid to that of the prism. **Answers will vary.**

💻 Computer Activities: Drawing and Measuring

1. Draw a pattern for a polyhedron whose base is an equilateral triangle and whose three sides are congruent isosceles triangles. How must the altitude of a side compare to the apothem of the base? **The altitude must be greater than the apothem.**

2. Draw a pattern for a polyhedron whose base is a square and whose four sides are congruent isosceles triangles. Can the triangles have any right angles? How must the altitude of a side compare to the apothem of the base? **No; the altitude must be greater than the apothem.**

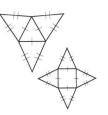

Progress Check

Lesson 11-1, page 473

1. A prism has 11 lateral faces. How many sides does each base of the prism have? **11**

2. A base of a prism has nine sides. How many edges does the prism have? **27**

3. Find the length of a diagonal of a rectangular solid whose dimensions are 8 cm, 5 cm, and 3 cm. $7\sqrt{2} \approx$ **9.90 cm**

Lesson 11-2, page 478

4. Find the lateral area of a right triangular prism if each base has edges 6 in., 14 in., and 18 in. and its height is 24 in. **912 sq. in.**

5. A right prism has a lateral area of 240 cm² and a height of 12 cm. What is the perimeter of a base? **20 cm**

6. A regular right prism has a height of 25 cm and hexagonal bases with perimeters of 90 cm. Find the total area of the prism. $675\sqrt{3} + 2,250 \approx$ **3,419.13 cm²**

Lesson 11-3, page 484

7. Find the volume of a rectangular solid whose dimensions are 6 cm by 4 cm by 8 cm. **192 cm³**

8. The volumes of two cubes are in the ratio of 8 to 27. What is the ratio of the lengths of their edges? **2:3**

9. Find the volume of a right prism with height 7 in. and area of each base 35 sq. in. **245 cu. in.**

Lesson 11-4, page 490

10. A right cylindrical container has a height of 14 mm. The area of a base is 135 mm². Find the volume of the container. **1,890 mm³**

11. An oblique cylinder has a height of 28 in. and a base with radius of 8 in. What is the volume? $1,792\pi \approx$ **5,626.88 cu. in.**

12. A right cylinder has a lateral area of 2,480 cm² and a height of 16 cm. What is the radius of a base? $\frac{77.5}{\pi} \approx$ **24.68 cm**

---

2. How do the dimensions of the lateral surface relate to those of the cylinder? *B* = circumference of base; *h* = height of cylinder

This activity also shows that the formulas for a right cylinder work for an oblique cylinder as well.

• **Extension 11-4**

Computers

The computer activity in the pupil's book can be completed using *The Geometric preSupposer: Points and Lines, The Geometric Supposer: Triangles* or *Quadrilaterals,* or *GeoDraw.*
• **Computer Activities 11-4**
• **Computer Worksheet 11-4**

ANSWERS

Using BASIC

4.
```
105 PRINT "WHAT IS THE
    VOLUME?"
106 INPUT V
107 LET H = V/(3.1416 *
    R ∧ 2
```
5.4 cm and 4.3 cm

5. Since $354 = 2\pi r^2 + 2\pi rh$, $h = \frac{354 - 2\pi r^2}{2\pi r}$.
```
100 REM MAXIMIZING VOLUME
    OF A CLOSED CAN
110 PRINT "WHAT ARE
    INITIAL RADIUS AND
    INCREMENT SEPARATED
    BY A COMMA"
120 INPUT R , I
130 PRINT "RADIUS"; TAB
    (9); "HEIGHT"; TAB
    (27); "VOLUME"
140 FOR J = 1 TO 10
150 LET H = (354 - 2 *
    3.1416 * R ∧ 2)/(2 *
    3.1416 * R)
160 LET V = 3.1416 * R ∧ 2
    * H
170 PRINT R; TAB(7); H;
    TAB(25); V
180 LET R = R + I
190 NEXT J
200 END
```
4.3 cm radius; 8.8 cm height (greatest volume is about 511.3 cm³)

Using BASIC: Optimization and Container Design

In order to minimize production costs, a container manufacturer needs to design a 236-ml cylindrical can that requires the least amount of metal possible. What should the dimensions of the can be? A 236-cm³ can holds 236 ml.

Since $V = \pi r^2 h = 236$, $h = \frac{236}{\pi r^2}$.

The height of the can depends upon its radius, and its total area depends upon the height and the radius (T.A. $= 2\pi rh + 2\pi r^2$). You can test various values of the radius to find which corresponding total area is least. The following program uses systematic trial and error in looking for a pattern. It lets you choose where to begin a table and the size of the step, or *increment*, to use in the table. The sample run shows the results for an initial radius of 1 cm and an increment of 1 cm.

```
100 REM MINIMIZING T.A. OF CLOSED CAN
110 PRINT "ENTER INITIAL RADIUS AND
    INCREMENT"
120 PRINT "SEPARATED BY A COMMA";
130 INPUT R,I
140 PRINT "RADIUS";TAB(9);"HEIGHT";
150 PRINT TAB(27);"T.A."
160 FOR J=1 TO 10
170 LET H=236/(3.1416*R^2)
180 LET TA=2*3.1416*R*H+2*3.1416*R^2
190 PRINT R;TAB(7);H;TAB(25);TA
200 LET R=R+I
210 NEXT J
220 END
```

```
RUN
ENTER INITIAL RADIUS AND
INCREMENT SEPARATED BY A COMMA?1,1
RADIUS    HEIGHT              T.A.
1         75.1209575          478.2832
2         18.7802394          261.1328
3         8.34677306          213.882133
4         4.69505984          218.5312
5         3.0048383           251.48
6         2.08669326          304.861867
7         1.53308076          375.305372
8         1.17376496          461.1248
9         .927419228          561.383645
10        .751209575          675.52
```

1. What is the optimal length for the radius? **3 cm**

2. RUN the program with different values to find the ideal radius of a can to the nearest millimeter (0.1 cm). **33 mm or 3.3 cm**

3. Change one number in one line of the program so that you can use it to find optimal dimensions for a can of automotive motor oil ($V = 946$ ml).

4. Change the original program so that the user can input the volume of the can whose total area is to be minimized. What are the optimal dimensions for 1,000-ml and 500-ml cans? **5.4 cm; 4.3 cm**

5. Write a program that will help determine the dimensions of a cylindrical can that will yield the greatest possible volume for 354 cm² of metal (total area). **4.3 cm radius, 8.8 cm height**

3. Line 170: Change 236 to 946; optimal radius = 5.3 cm

11-5 Areas and Volume of a Pyramid

Monumental structures shaped like pyramids were built in many parts of the world. The most famous are located in Egypt and Mexico. The Egyptian pyramid pictured at the right is located southwest of Cairo, Egypt. It was built as a tomb for Khufu and is included as one of the Seven Wonders of the Ancient World.

Definition   *Pyramid*

A pyramid is a polyhedron formed by a polygonal region in a plane ℛ, a point P not in plane ℛ, and the triangular regions formed by joining the vertices of the polygonal region with P.

The **base** of a pyramid is the polygonal region, and the **vertex** is the point not in the plane. The **altitude** is the segment from the vertex perpendicular to the plane of the base. The length of the altitude is the **height** of the pyramid. As with a prism, a pyramid is named by the shape of its base.

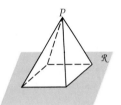

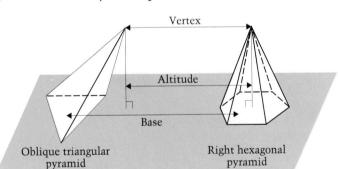

Oblique triangular pyramid

Right hexagonal pyramid

A **regular pyramid** has a regular polygon for a base, and its altitude passes through the center of the base. The **slant height** of a regular pyramid is the height of any lateral face.

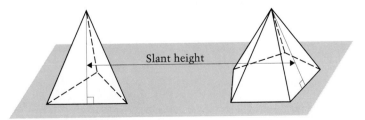

Slant height

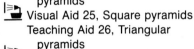

LESSON 11–5

Resources

Models of pyramids and prisms
  Teaching Aid 25, Square pyramids
  Visual Aid 25, Square pyramids
  Teaching Aid 26, Triangular pyramids
  Visual Aid 26, Triangular pyramids
Worksheet 11–5
Extension 11–5

OBJECTIVE

Compute the area and volume of pyramids.

Visualization is important in introducing this lesson. Use models to explain the difference between lateral edge, slant height and altitude. Point out that slant height is only defined for regular pyramids.

Stress the concept of lateral area of a regular pyramid rather than the formula for Theorem 11–11.

To demonstrate Theorem 11–12, use a pyramid and prism of the same base and height and ask students how many pyramids of sand it will take to fill the prism.

Additional Examples

Example 1
Find the lateral area of a regular square pyramid if both its lateral edge and an edge of the base are 10. $100\sqrt{3}$

EXTENSION

Name _____

Lesson **11 - 5**

3-D Puzzles

The patterns on this page can be used to form solid figures. To make copies, draw or trace the pattern onto another sheet of paper. Make sure that sides marked by the same number of slashes are equal in length. Glue the paper to cardboard or construction paper before cutting.

1. Make three copies of this figure and fold them to make three pyramids. Then combine the pyramids to make a cube. **student construction**

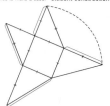

2. Use the pattern to make four solids and then combine them to form a tetrahedron. **student construction**

What appears to be true about the lateral faces of a regular pyramid? Your answer should suggest Theorem 11-10, which is to be proved in Exercise 10. They appear to be isosceles △s

Theorem 11-10

The lateral faces of a regular pyramid are congruent isosceles triangles.

The slant height and the perimeter of the base of a regular pyramid can be used in a formula for its lateral area.

Theorem 11-11   *Lateral Area of a Regular Pyramid*

The lateral area L.A. of a regular pyramid is one half the product of the slant height s and the perimeter p of the base.
$$L.A. = \tfrac{1}{2}sp$$

Given A regular pyramid with vertex V and base $P_1P_2P_3\ldots P_n$; slant height s; and perimeter p

Prove $L.A. = \tfrac{1}{2}sp$

Proof By definition all lateral faces of a pyramid are triangles. In a regular pyramid the triangles are all congruent. The area of $\triangle VP_1P_2$ is $\tfrac{1}{2}s(P_1P_2)$.
Thus, $L.A. = \tfrac{1}{2}s(P_1P_2 + P_2P_3 + \ldots + P_nP_1) = \tfrac{1}{2}sp$.

The total area T.A. of a pyramid is the sum of the lateral area and the area of the base. $T.A. = L.A. + B$

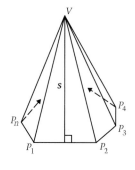

Example 1
Given a regular hexagonal pyramid with base 4 in. on a side and length of a lateral edge 8 in., find the lateral area of the pyramid.

Solution
Use the Pythagorean Theorem.

$s^2 = 8^2 - 2^2 \qquad p = 6(4) \qquad L.A. = \tfrac{1}{2}sp$

$\quad = 60 \qquad\qquad = 24 \qquad\quad = \tfrac{1}{2}(2\sqrt{15})(24)$

$s = 2\sqrt{15} \qquad\qquad\qquad\qquad = 24\sqrt{15} \approx 92.95$ sq. in.

The volume of a pyramid can be found by relating it to a prism with a congruent base and the same height. In the figure at the right, the volume of the pyramid is $\tfrac{1}{3}$ the volume of the prism. This is stated formally in Theorem 11-12. The proof is omitted.

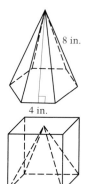

Assignment Guide

Basic: 1–9, 23–29
Average: 1–16, 23–29
Extended: 2–10 (even), 11–29

Theorem 11-12 *Volume of a Pyramid*

The volume V of a pyramid is one third the product of the area B of the base and the height h. $V = \frac{1}{3}Bh$

Example 2
Given a regular triangular pyramid with base edge 12 cm and height 18 cm, find the volume of the pyramid.

Solution

$B = \frac{e^2}{4}\sqrt{3}$ $\qquad V = \frac{1}{3}Bh$

$\quad = \frac{(12)^2}{4}\sqrt{3}$ $\qquad = \frac{1}{3}(36\sqrt{3})(18)$

$\quad = 36\sqrt{3}$ $\qquad = 216\sqrt{3}$ cm^3

Checking for Understanding

1. Can a rhombus be the base of a regular pyramid? Explain.

2. How does the height of a regular pyramid compare with the length of a lateral edge? with the slant height? Explain.

Find the lateral area, the total area, and the volume of each regular pyramid.

3.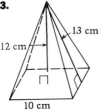
12 cm · 13 cm · 10 cm

4.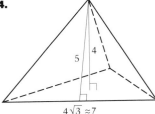
5 · 4 · $4\sqrt{3} \approx 7$

Written Exercises

Set A Find the lateral area, the total area, and the volume of each regular pyramid.

1.
4 in. · 5 in. · 3 in.

2.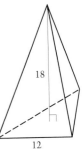
5 · 10 · $5\sqrt{3}$ · 10

3. Estimate the volume of the pyramid at the top of page 497 if it has a square base covering over 13 acres and a height of over 450 ft. (1 acre = 43,560 sq. ft.)

18 · 12

1. Yes, if the rhombus is a square

2. The height is less than both a lateral edge and the slant height. The shortest segment from a pt. to a plane is the length of the perpendicular segment.

3. 260 cm^2; 360 cm^2; 400 cm^3

4. $30\sqrt{3} \approx 51.96$; $42\sqrt{3} \approx 72.75$; $16\sqrt{3} \approx 27.71$;

1. 60 sq. in.; 96 sq. in.; 48 cu. in.

2. 300; 300 + $15\sqrt{3} \approx$ 559.81

3. 85,000,000 cu. ft.

Example 2
Find the volume of a pyramid whose base is a right triangle with legs 5 and 12, and whose height is 9. 90

Error Analysis The height, slant height and lateral edge of a regular pyramid are easily confused. Use physical models to correct this error.

EXERCISE NOTES

Exercises 11–15 give students an opportunity to visualize dividing a solid into parts.

Exercises 18–21 introduce the term "frustum."

Exercises 28 and 29 could be done as a **group activity**. Have students make models of a cone and cylinder and compare areas and volumes.

ANSWERS

Written Exercises

10. Given: Regular pyramid with vertex V; base $P_1P_2P_3 \ldots P_n$; slant ht. s; perimeter P Prove: $\triangle P_1VP_2, \triangle P_2VP_3, \ldots, \triangle P_nVP_1$ are isosceles $\triangle$s; $\triangle P_1VP_2 \cong \triangle P_2VP_3 \cong \ldots \cong \triangle P_nVP_1$

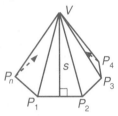

Proof: 1. Reg. pyramid with vertex V; base $P_1P_2P_3 \ldots P_n$; slant ht. s; perimeter P (Given) 2. $P_1V = P_2V = \ldots = P_nV$ (Def. of reg. pyramid [1]) 3. $\triangle P_1VP_2, \triangle P_2VP_3, \ldots, P_nVP_1$ are isosceles $\triangle$s. (Def. of isos. $\triangle$ [2]) 4. $P_1P_2P_3 \ldots P_n$ is a reg. polygon (Def. of reg. pyramid [1]) 5. $P_1P_2 = P_2P_3 = \ldots = P_nP_1$ (Def. of reg. polygon [4]) 6. $\triangle P_1VP_2 \cong \triangle P_2VP_3 \cong \ldots \cong \triangle P_nVP_1$ (SSS Post. [2, 5])
11. Yes; the bases of a prism have equal areas.
12. Yes; the height of each pyramid equals the height of the prism; yes, by Cavaliere's Principle.
13. Yes; each is half of the same rectangle.
14. Yes; the height of each is the distance from C to the plane containing $\square XYBA$; yes, by Cavaliere's Principle.
15. Exercises 11–14 show that the volumes of the three pyramids are equal and their sum equals the volume of the prism. Therefore, the volume of each pyramid is one-third the volume of the prism.

4. Find the volume of a pyramid with height 45 in. and rectangular base 13 in. by 10 in. **1,950 cu. in.**

5. Find the amount of material needed to make a tent shaped like a regular square pyramid if each side of the floor is to be 12 ft. and the height is to be 8 ft. **384 sq. ft.**

6. Find the length of each lateral edge in Exercise 5. **$2\sqrt{34} \approx 11.66$ ft.**

7. Find the lateral and the total areas for a regular square pyramid if each side of the base is 36 m and the length of each lateral edge is 30 m. **1,728 m^2; 3,024 m^2**

8. Find the perimeter of the base of a regular pyramid with slant height 9 cm and lateral area 94.5 cm^2. **21 cm**

9. Find the slant height of a regular pentagonal pyramid with lateral area 120 cm^2 and base 6 cm on a side. **8 cm**

Set B **10.** Prove Theorem 11-10.

The triangular prism in I at the right has been separated into three triangular pyramids. The three pyramids are shown separately in II, III, and IV. For Exercises 11 and 12, consider II and III. For Exercises 13 and 14, consider III and IV. Explain each answer.

11. Do $\triangle XYZ$ and $\triangle ABC$ have the same area?

12. Let $\triangle XYZ$ and $\triangle ABC$ be the bases of the pyramids in figures II and III respectively. Do the pyramids have the same height? the same volume?

13. Do $\triangle AXB$ and $\triangle YBX$ have the same area?

14. Let $\triangle AXB$ and $\triangle YBX$ be the bases of the pyramids in figures III and IV respectively. Do the pyramids have the same height? the same volume?

15. Explain how Exercises 11-14 help to verify Theorem 11-12.

16. Find the total area of a right pyramid whose base is a rectangle 10 in. by 8 in. and whose height is 5 in. **$80 + 10\sqrt{41} + 8\sqrt{50} \approx 200.60$ sq. in.**

I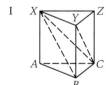

II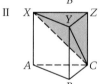

III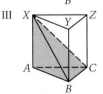

IV

FOLLOW-UP

Set C

17. A pyramid is formed by joining the midpoints of three edges of a cube that have a common vertex. Each edge of the cube has length e. Find the volume of the pyramid. $\frac{e^3}{48}$

e

A *frustum* of a pyramid is the part of the pyramid between its base and a cross section parallel to the base. The figure at the right is a regular square pyramid with the frustum shaded. $A'B'C'D'$ is parallel to the base and bisects each lateral edge.

18. What is the area of square $A'B'C'D'$? **16**

19. $ABB'A'$ is a lateral face of the frustum. What type of figure is it? What is its area? **Trapezoid; $12\sqrt{13}$**

20. What is the volume of the pyramid? **256**

21. What is the volume of the frustum of the pyramid? **224**

22. Find the lateral area of the regular square pyramid at the right. **544**

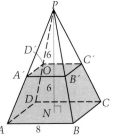

▲ **Review**   A right cylinder has a radius of 6 m and a height of 13 m.

23. Find the total area.   24. Find the volume.

23. $228\pi \approx 715.92$ m^2
$468\pi \approx 1,469.52$ m^2

25. The base of a prism is a right triangle whose legs are 16 in. long and 20 in. long. The height of the prism is 12 in. Find the volume. **1,920 cu. in.**

26. In a __?__ triangle, the length of the hypotenuse is $\sqrt{2}$ times the length of a leg. **Right isosceles**

27. In which quadrilaterals are the diagonals equal? **Rectangles; isosceles trapezoids**

≡ **Thinking Ahead**   28. Suppose you have models of a cone and a cylinder that have equal radii and heights. If both models have open tops and you fill the cone with sand and dump the sand into the cylinder, how many cones of sand do you think would be required to fill the cylinder? **Answers will vary; 3**

29. Draw a pattern that could be used to make a model of a cone.

29.
Sample:

FOLLOW-UP

More Practice
• Worksheet 11–5

Extension

Have students investigate finding the lateral area of a frustum of a pyramid. It follows from the area of a trapezoid that L.A. $= \frac{1}{2}s(p + p')$, where p and p' are perimeters of the bases and s is the slant height of the frustum.
• Extension 11–5

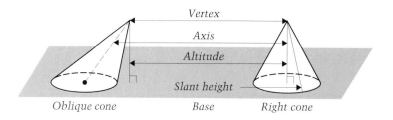

11-6 Areas and Volume of a Cone

A prism and a cylinder are alike
in that they each have two
congruent bases contained in
parallel planes. A pyramid and a
cone are alike in that they each
have only one base. The bases of
prisms and pyramids are
polygonal regions, while the
bases of cylinders and cones are
circular regions.

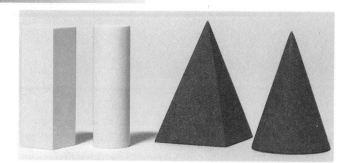

Definition   *Cone*

A cone is a figure formed by a circular region, a point V not in
the plane of the circle, and all segments joining a point of the
circle to V.

The parts of a cone are similar to those of a pyramid. The
circular region is the **base** of the cone, and the **vertex** is the
point not in the plane. The points of the cone not in the base
form the **lateral surface** of the cone.

The **altitude** of a cone is the segment from the vertex
perpendicular to the plane of the base. The length of the
altitude is the **height** of the cone. The segment from the vertex
to the center of the base is the **axis** of the cone. If the axis is
perpendicular to the base, the cone is a **right cone**. Otherwise,
it is an **oblique cone**. The **slant height** of a right cone is the
length of a segment from the vertex to a point of the circle.

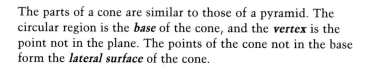

Vertex

Axis

Altitude

Slant height

Oblique cone   *Base*   *Right cone*

To find the areas and volume of a cone, consider regular pyramids inscribed in a cone.

   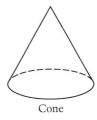

| 4-sided base | 6-sided base | 8-sided base | Cone |

As the number of edges in the base of the pyramid is increased, the shape of the pyramid approaches the shape of a cone as a limit. It follows that the formulas for the lateral area, the total area, and the volume of a cone are similar to those for a pyramid.

Theorem 11-13 *Lateral Area of a Right Cone*

The lateral area L.A. of a right cone is one half the product of the circumference C of its base and its slant height s.
L.A. = $\frac{1}{2}Cs = \pi rs$

The total area T.A. of a right cone is the sum of its lateral area and the area of its base. T.A. = L.A. + B = $\pi rs + \pi r^2$

Theorem 11-14 *Volume of a Cone*

The volume V of a cone is one third the product of the area B of its base and its height h. $V = \frac{1}{3}Bh = \frac{1}{3}\pi r^2 h$

The proofs of Theorems 11-13 and 11-14 are omitted.

Example
The funnel section of the storage bin is shaped like a right cone. Its diameter is 10 ft. and its height is 8 ft. Find the lateral area and the volume of the funnel section.

Solution
Use the Pythagorean Theorem.

$s^2 = 5^2 + 8^2$ L.A. = πrs $V = \frac{1}{3}\pi r^2 h$

$\quad = 89$ $\approx 3.14(5)(9.43)$ $\approx \frac{1}{3}(3.14)(5^2)(8)$

$s \approx 9.43$ ≈ 148.05 sq. ft. ≈ 209.33 cu. ft.

dents to guess how many cones of sand will fill the cylinder.

Point out that the lateral surfaces of a prism are plane figures, whereas the lateral surface of a cylinder is a curved surface. The same relationship exists between a pyramid and a cone.

When rational approximations for pi are used in examples, a **calculator** will make computational errors less likely.

Additional Example

A paper conical drinking cup has a diameter of 12 cm and a height of 8 cm.
(a) Find the slant height of the cone. 10 cm
(b) Find the area of paper needed to make the cup. 188.4 cm^2
(c) Find the number of cubic centimeters of water the cup will hold. 301.44 cm^3

EXTENSION

Name _____   Lesson 11-6

Conic Sections

When a line e is rotated in space about a second fixed line a that it intersects, the resulting surface is a *right circular cone*. Any position of e is called an *element* and the fixed line a is called the *axis*. Notice that the cone has two bases.

When a cone is intersected by a plane, the resulting curve is called a *conic section*, as illustrated in the following figures.

Parabola   Circle   Ellipse   Hyperbola

1. Which conic section is formed when the plane is perpendicular to the axis? **circle**

2. Which conic section is formed when the plane is parallel to the axis and passes through both bases? **hyperbola**

3. Which conic section is formed when the plane is not perpendicular to the axis and not parallel to an element of the cone? **ellipse**

4. Which two conic sections can be formed by a plane that is parallel to an element of the cone? **parabola; hyperbola**

5. Draw a sketch to show how a plane might intersect a cone at only one point.

6. Draw a sketch to show how a plane might intersect a cone to form a conic section of two intersecting lines.

7. Form a cone from a sheet of paper. Carefully outline a conic section onto the cone, using the figures above as a guide. Unfold the paper. What happened to the outline? **Answers will vary.**

5.   6.

EXERCISE NOTES

Exercises 6, 8–11 and **15–17** could be solved with the use of a **calculator**.

Exercises 12 and **13** show the relationship between volume and linear measure of similar solids.

ANSWERS

Written Exercises

1. 15π; 24π; 12π
2. 128π; 192π; $\frac{512\pi\sqrt{3}}{3}$
3. 135π; 216π; 324π
4. $25\pi\sqrt{5}$; $25\pi + 25\pi\sqrt{5}$; $\frac{250\pi}{3}$
5. $3\pi\sqrt{17}$; $3\pi + 3\pi\sqrt{17}$; $4\pi\sqrt{3}$

Checking for Understanding

Find the lateral area, the total area, and the volume of each right cone. Give answers in terms of π.

1.

2.

1. 65π; 90π; 100π
2. 136π; 200π; 320π

3. The volume of a right cone is 960π. If the radius of the cone is 8, find the height. **45**

4. The height of the cylindrical section of the bin on page 503 is 18 ft. Find the total volume of the cylinder and funnel. **1,622.33 cu. ft.**

Written Exercises

Set A Find the lateral area, the total area, and the volume of each right cone. Give answers in terms of π.

1.   **2.**   **3.**   **4.**   **5.**

6. Find the volume of the oblique cone at the right. $64\pi \approx 200.96$

7. A right cone and a right cylinder both have radii 6 and height 15. Find the ratio of their volumes without actually calculating the two volumes. **1:3**

8. The lateral area of a right cone is 384 sq. in. If the radius of the cone is 8 in., find the slant height. $\frac{48}{\pi} \approx 15.28$ in.

Set B **9.** How many square meters of material are in a right conical tent 5 m in diameter and 2.5 m height? The tent is made with a floor. **47.38 m²**

10. The area of the base of a right cone is 144π cm² and the height is 5 cm. Find the lateral area.

11. A teepee has a lateral area of 94.2 sq. ft. If the slant height is 10 ft., find the height of the teepee.

10. $156\pi \approx 489.84$ cm² **11.** 9.54 ft.

12. A right cone generated by a right triangle as it revolves about one of its legs is called a *cone of revolution*. Find the ratio of the lateral areas generated by the cones at the right. **6:4**

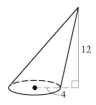

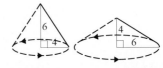

13. Two similar right triangles are revolved about corresponding legs to generate two similar cones of revolution. Show that the ratio of the volumes of the two cones is the cube of the ratio of the heights:
$$\frac{V_1}{V_2} = \left(\frac{h_1}{h_2}\right)^3$$

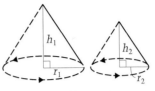

14. A frustum of a cone is the part of the cone between its base and a cross section parallel to the base. The figure at the right is a right cone with the frustum shaded. Find the volume of the frustum. **1,248π ≈ 3,918.72**

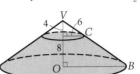

Set C **15.** A semicircular piece of paper whose radius is 8 in. is rolled into a conical drinking cup. Disregarding overlap, what is the volume of the cup?

16. The legs of a right triangle measure 15 in. and 20 in. The triangle is revolved about its hypotenuse forming the two conical surfaces. Find the total lateral area of the surfaces formed.
500π ≈ 1,570 sq. in.

17. A right cone is inscribed in a regular triangular pyramid all of whose edges measure 6 in. Find the volume of the cone. **2π√6 ≈ 15.38 cu. in.**

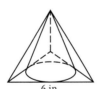

 Review **18.** Find the volume of a regular triangular pyramid with a base edge of 8 m and a height of 14 m.
224√3 ≈ 387.98 m³

19. Find the total area of a regular square pyramid whose height is 10 and whose base perimeter is 48.
144 + 48√34 ≈ 423.89

20. Draw an oblique cylinder.

21. Given: m∠1 = m∠7
Prove: m∠12 = m∠16

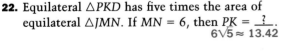

22. Equilateral △PKD has five times the area of equilateral △JMN. If MN = 6, then PK = _?_.
6√5 ≈ 13.42

 Thinking Ahead **23.** Find the volume of the tennis-ball can.

24. Estimate the volume of each tennis ball.
23. $\frac{3}{4}\pi d^3$ **24.** Answers will vary; a little less than $\frac{\pi d^3}{4}$

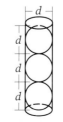

13. $\frac{V_1}{V_2} = \frac{\frac{1}{3}(\pi r_1{}^2)h_1}{\frac{1}{3}(\pi r_2{}^2)h_2} = \frac{r_1{}^2 h_1}{r_2{}^2 h_2} = \left(\frac{r_1}{r_2}\right)^2\left(\frac{h_1}{h_2}\right)$

Since the △s are similar, $\frac{r_1}{r_2} = \frac{h_1}{h_2}$.
Substitute in the equation above:
$\frac{V_1}{V_2} = \left(\frac{h_1}{h_2}\right)^2\left(\frac{h_1}{h_2}\right) = \left(\frac{h_1}{h_2}\right)^3$

15. $\frac{64\pi\sqrt{3}}{3} \approx 116.02$ cu. in.

Review

20. Sample:

21. Proof: 1. m∠1 = m∠7 (Given)
2. m∠5 = m∠7 (Vertical angles are =.) 3. m∠1 = m∠5 (Substitution Prop. [1, 2]) 4. a ∥ b (Corr. ∠s = ⇒ 2 lines ∥. [3]) 5. m∠12 = m∠16 (2 lines ∥ ⇒ corr. ∠s =. [4])

Warm-Up Review

1. State the formula for the area of a circle. $A = \pi r^2$
2. The set of all points equidistant from a given point forms a(n) __?__. Sphere
3. The line segment formed by connecting the center and a point on a circle is its __?__. Radius

---

LESSON 11–7

Resources

Worksheet 11–7
Extension 11–7

Computer Worksheet 11–7
Algebra Review 11
Chapter 11 Test, Form I
Chapter 11 Test, Form II
Chapter 11 Test, Form III

OBJECTIVE

Compute the area and volume of spheres.

TEACHING NOTES

To begin this lesson, review definitions relating to the sphere such as "great circle."

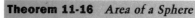

WORKSHEET   *Lesson* **11-7**

Name _____

Match each sphere element with one and only one of the descriptions.

__d__ 1. radius of a sphere
__c__ 2. small circle of a sphere
__b__ 3. diameter of a sphere
__e__ 4. great circle of a sphere
__a__ 5. a sphere

a. The set of all points in space that are a given distance from a given point
b. A segment that contains the center and has its endpoints on the sphere
c. The intersection of a sphere and a plane containing an interior point of the sphere but not the center
d. A segment determined by the center and a point on the sphere
e. The intersection of a sphere and a plane containing the center of the sphere

6. A sphere has a radius of 5. Find the area and the volume of the sphere. Use 3.14 for π. **314; 523.33**

7. The area of a sphere is 576π. The radius of the sphere is __?__. In terms of π, the volume of the sphere is __?__. **12; 2304π**

8. A sphere has a diameter of 2 m. Find the volume and the area of the sphere. Use 3.14 for π. **4.19 m³; 12.56 m²**

A sphere has a radius of 6. A cylinder has the same radius with a height of 6. Find the missing values. Give answers in terms of π.

		T.A.	V
9.	Sphere	144π	288π
10.	Cylinder	144π	216π

11. The volume of a sphere is 972π. The radius is __?__. The area of the sphere is __?__. (Give answer in terms of π.) **9; 324π**

12. The radius of a sphere is 0.3. Find the area and the volume of the sphere in terms of π. **.36 π; .036 π**

11-7 Area and Volume of a Sphere

Recall from Chapter 9 that in space, the counterpart of a circle is a sphere. Theorems 11-15 and 11-16 give formulas for computing the volume and the area of a sphere. Proofs of these theorems are omitted.

Theorem 11-15 *Volume of a Sphere*

The volume V of a sphere of radius r is $\frac{4}{3}\pi r^3$. $V = \frac{4}{3}\pi r^3$

Example 1

The planet Mars is roughly a sphere whose radius is approximately 3,400 km. Find the volume of Mars.

Solution

$V = \frac{4}{3}\pi r^3$

$\approx \frac{4}{3}(3.14)(3,400)^3$

$\approx 164,550,000,000$ km³

To find the formula for the area of a sphere, begin with the formula for its volume. Consider a solid sphere with center Q and radius r. Imagine that the sphere is made up of solids resembling pyramids. Each "pyramid" has vertex Q and height r. One such pyramid is shown. The volume of each pyramid is $\frac{1}{3}Br$, where B is the area of the base. The volume of the sphere is the sum of the volumes of the pyramids.

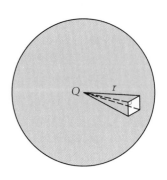

$\frac{4}{3}\pi r^3 = \frac{1}{3}B_1 r + \frac{1}{3}B_2 r + \frac{1}{3}B_3 r + \ldots + \frac{1}{3}B_n r$

$= \frac{1}{3}r(B_1 + B_2 + B_3 + \ldots + B_n)$

Dividing both sides of this equation by $\frac{1}{3}r$ results in the following equation: $4\pi r^2 = B_1 + B_2 + B_3 + \ldots + B_n$.
The area of the sphere—the sum $B_1 + B_2 + B_3 + \ldots + B_n$— is $4\pi r^2$.

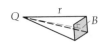

Theorem 11-16 *Area of a Sphere*

The area A of a sphere of radius r is $4\pi r^2$. $A = 4\pi r^2$

Assignment Guide

Basic: 1–20, 32–36
Average: 2–14 (even), 15–29, 32–36
Extended: 2–20 (even), 21–36

Example 2

Echo I, the first communications satellite, was a large spherical plastic balloon with a thin metal coating. Its diameter was 100 ft. Find its area and its volume.

Solution

$A = 4\pi r^2$
$\approx 4(3.14)(50)^2$
$\approx 31,400$ sq. ft.

$V = \frac{4}{3}\pi r^3$
$\approx \frac{4}{3}(3.14)(50)^3$
$\approx 523,333$ cu. ft.

Checking for Understanding 3. 400π cm²

Give answers for Exercises 1–3 in terms of π.

1. Find the volume of a sphere whose radius is 5 m. $\frac{500\pi}{3}$ m³

2. Find the volume of a sphere whose diameter is 12 in. 288π cu. in.

3. Find the area of a sphere whose diameter is 20 cm.

4. Find the area of Mars. 145,193,600 km²

5. Recall that a great circle of a sphere has its center at the center of the sphere. How does the area of a great circle compare to the area of the sphere?
Area great circle = $\frac{1}{4}$ area of sphere

1. 64π m²; $\frac{256}{3}\pi$ m³
2. $19,600\pi$ cm²; $\frac{1,372,000\pi}{3}$ cm³
3. 324π sq. in.; 972π cu. in.
4. 1.44π m²; 0.288π m³
5. $3,600\pi$ sq. ft.; $36,000\pi$ cu. ft.
6. 484π sq. in.; $\frac{5,324\pi}{3}$ cu. ft.
7. $100\pi t^2$; $\frac{500\pi t^3}{3}$
8. $36\pi k^2$; $36\pi k^3$

Written Exercises

Set A Find the area and the volume of each sphere in terms of π.

1. $d = 8$ m **2.** $r = 70$ cm **3.** $r = 9$ in.

4. $d = 1.2$ m **5.** $d = 60$ ft. **6.** $d = 22$ in.

7. $r = 5t$ **8.** $r = 3k$

Given a sphere with radius r, diameter d, area A, volume V, and a great circle of circumference C, find the four items not given in terms of π.

9. $A = 2,916\pi$ **10.** $C = 28\pi$ **11.** $V = 288\pi$

12. $A = 1,936\pi$ **13.** $C = 172\pi$ **14.** $V = \frac{4}{3}\pi$

To help students remember the area formula, point out that the area of a sphere is exactly four times the area of a great circle. Some students may find it easier to visualize a hemisphere as twice the area of a great circle.

Additional Examples

Example 1
Find the area of a volleyball that has a diameter of 10 in. 100π sq. in., or ≈ 314 sq. in.

Example 2
Find the volume of the given volleyball. 166.7π cu. in., or ≈ 523.33 cu. in.

Error Analysis Students may forget the formula for the volume of a sphere. Point out that volume equals area times $\frac{1}{3}r$, or $\frac{r}{3}$.

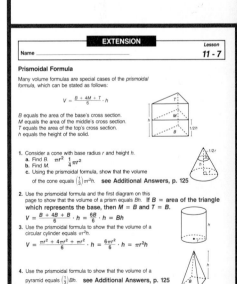

EXTENSION

Lesson 11-7

Name _____

Prismoidal Formula

Many volume formulas are special cases of the *prismoidal formula*, which can be stated as follows:

$$V = \frac{B + 4M + T}{6} \cdot h$$

B equals the area of the base's cross section.
M equals the area of the middle's cross section.
T equals the area of the top's cross section.
h equals the height of the solid.

1. Consider a cone with base radius r and height h.
   a. Find B. πr^2 $\frac{1}{4}\pi r^2$
   b. Find M.
   c. Using the prismoidal formula, show that the volume of the cone equals $\left(\frac{1}{3}\right)\pi r^2 h$. **see Additional Answers, p. 125**

2. Use the prismoidal formula and the first diagram on this page to show that the volume of a prism equals Bh. If B = area of the triangle which represents the base, then $M = B$ and $T = B$.
   $V = \frac{B + 4B + B}{6} \cdot h = \frac{6B}{6} \cdot h = Bh$

3. Use the prismoidal formula to show that the volume of a circular cylinder equals $\pi r^2 h$.
   $V = \frac{\pi r^2 + 4\pi r^2 + \pi r^2}{6} \cdot h = \frac{6\pi r^2}{6} \cdot h = \pi r^2 h$

4. Use the prismoidal formula to show that the volume of a pyramid equals $\left(\frac{1}{3}\right)Bh$. **see Additional Answers, p. 125**

5. Use the prismoidal formula to show that the volume of a sphere with radius r is given by $V = \left(\frac{4}{3}\right)\pi r^3$.
   $B = 0; T = 0;$
   $M = \pi r^2; h = 2r;$
   $V = \frac{0 + 4\pi r^2 + 0}{6} \cdot 2r = \frac{8\pi r^3}{6} = \frac{4\pi r^3}{3}$

Written Exercises

9. $r = 27$; $d = 54$; $V = 26,244\pi$; $C = 54\pi$

10. $r = 14$; $d = 28$; $A = 784\pi$; $V = \frac{10,976\pi}{3}$

11. $r = 6$; $d = 12$; $A = 144\pi$; $C = 12\pi$

12. $r = 22$; $d = 44$; $V = \frac{42,592\pi}{3}$; $C = 44\pi$

13. $r = 86$; $d = 172$; $A = 29,584\pi$; $V = \frac{2,544,224\pi}{3}$

14. $r = 1$; $d = 2$; $A = 4\pi$; $C = 2\pi$

27. Given: Sphere I with $r = a$; sphere II with $r = b$ Prove: $\frac{V_I}{V_{II}} = \left(\frac{a}{b}\right)^3$ Proof: 1. Sphere I with $r = a$; sphere II with $r = b$ (Given) 2. V_I = Volume of sphere I = $\frac{4}{3}\pi a^3$; V_{II} = Volume of sphere II = $\frac{4}{3}\pi b^3$ (Volume of sphere = $\frac{4}{3}\pi r^3$ [1]) 3.

$\frac{V_I}{V_{II}} = \frac{\frac{4}{3}\pi a^3}{\frac{4}{3}\pi b^3} = \frac{a^3}{b^3} = \left(\frac{a}{b}\right)^3$ (Multiplica-

tion Prop. and algebra [2])

28. Given: Sphere I with $r = a$; sphere II with $r = b$ Prove: $\frac{A_I}{A_{II}} = \left(\frac{a}{b}\right)^2$ Proof: 1. Sphere I with $r = a$; sphere II with $r = b$ (Given) 2. A_I = area sphere I = $4\pi a^2$; A_{II} = area sphere II = $4\pi b^2$ (Area of sphere = $4\pi r^2$) 3. $\frac{A_I}{A_{II}} = \frac{4\pi a^2}{4\pi b^2} = \frac{a^2}{b^2} = \left(\frac{a}{b}\right)^2$ (Multiplication Prop. and algebra [2])

15. A soccer ball has a diameter of 22 cm. Find its area and its volume.

16. The earth is roughly a sphere whose radius is approximately 4,000 miles. Find its area and its volume.

17. The area of a sphere is 1,516 cm². What is the area of a great circle of the sphere? **379 cm²**

18. Two spheres have radii 5 m and 8 m. What is the ratio of their areas? their volumes? **25:64; 125:512**

19. The silo pictured is a right cylinder capped with a hemisphere (half a sphere). The height of the cylinder is 48 ft. and its diameter is 16 ft. Find the total volume. **10,717.87 cu. ft.**

20. How do the volumes of the cone and sphere pictured at the right compare?
Volume of cone = $\frac{1}{2}$ volume of sphere.

Set B **21.** A spherical water tank is 40 feet in diameter. How many gallons of water can be stored in the tank? (1 cu. ft. ≈ 7.5 gal.) **251,200 gal.**

22. One gallon of paint covers about 300 sq. ft. How many gallons will be needed to give the tank one coat of paint? **17 gal.**

23. Find the volume of a sphere whose area is 180 m². **227.92 m³**

24. The areas of two spheres are in the ratio of 81 to 4. Find the ratio of their diameters. **9:2**

25. The ratio of the volumes of two spheres is 8 to 27. What is the ratio of their radii? **2:3**

26. A sphere is inscribed in a cylinder. Compare the surface area of the sphere to the lateral area of the cylinder. **Equal**

27. Prove: The volumes of two spheres have the same ratio as the cubes of the radii.

28. Prove: The areas of two spheres have the same ratio as the squares of their radii.

29. A steel marble of radius $\frac{1}{2}$ in. weighs 2 ounces. How much would a steel wrecking ball of radius 2 ft. weigh? **221,184 oz. or 13,824 lb.**

15. $A = 484\pi \approx 1{,}519.76$ cm²
$V = \frac{5{,}324\pi}{3} \approx 5{,}572.45$ cm³

16. 200,960,000 sq. mi.
267,950,000,000 cu. mi.

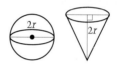

Set C   **30.** An inflated spherical balloon has a radius of 15 cm. If more air is added and the radius increases by 3 cm, what will be the increase in volume of the balloon? **$3{,}276\pi \approx 10{,}286.64$ cm^3**

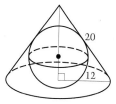

31. Find the radius of the sphere inscribed in the right cone pictured. **6**

$4\pi\sqrt{65} \approx 101.26$ cm^2

▲ Review   **32.** Find the lateral area of the right cone.

33. Find the volume of the right cone. **$\frac{112\pi}{3} \approx 117.23$ cm^3**

34. A prism and a pyramid have congruent bases and equal heights. How do their volumes compare?

35. Inscribed $\angle A$ and central $\angle Q$ both intercept $\overset{\frown}{XY}$. $m\angle A = \underline{\ ?\ }$ $(m\angle Q).$ $\frac{1}{2}$ **34.** Vol. prism = 3 times vol of pyramid

36. For the following statements, complete the missing conclusion and draw a Venn diagram. All trapezoids are quadrilaterals. *WXYZ* is a trapezoid, so $\underline{\ ?\ }$. *WXYZ* is a quadrilateral.

Progress Check

Lesson 11-5, page 497

1. Find the lateral area of a regular hexagonal pyramid with base 8 in. on a side and length of each lateral edge 11 in. $24\sqrt{105} \approx 245.93$ sq. in.

The base of a regular pyramid is a square 14 m on a side. Its height is 24 m.

2. Find the total area. **896 m^2**   **3.** Find the volume. **1,568 m^3**

Lesson 11-6, page 502

A right cone has radius 3 ft. and height 4 ft.

4. Find the lateral area.   **5.** Find the volume.
$15\pi \approx 47.10$ sq. ft. $12\pi \approx 37.68$ cu. ft.

6. Find the total area of a right cone with diameter 5 m and height 3 m. $\frac{5\pi\sqrt{61}}{4} + \frac{25\pi}{4} \approx 50.28$ m^2

Lesson 11-7, page 506

7. Find the volume of a sphere whose diameter is 6 m.
$36\pi \approx 113.04$ m^3

8. Find the area of a sphere whose radius is 13 ft.

9. Find the volume and the area of a basketball with diameter 9.6 in. **463.01 cu. in.; 289.38 sq. in.**

8. $676\pi \approx 2{,}122.64$ cu. ft.

FOLLOW-UP

More Practice

• **Worksheet 11-7**

Extension

Just as three noncollinear points determine a circle, four non-collinear points determine a sphere. It follows that a sphere may be circumscribed about any tetrahedron. Have students determine in which types of solids a sphere can always be inscribed.

• **Extension 11-7**

Computers

• **Computer Worksheet 11-7**

Chapter 11 Summary

Important Terms

Altitude (474, 490, 497, 502)
Axis (490, 502)
Bases (473, 490, 497, 502)
Cavalieri's Principle (485)
Cone (502)
Cross section (478, 490)
Cube (474)
Cylinder (490)
Diagonal of a rectangular solid (474)
Edge of a polyhedron (473)
Face of a polyhedron (473)
Height (474, 490, 497, 502)

Interior of a polyhedron (473)
Lateral area of a prism (478)
Lateral edge of a prism (473)
Lateral face of a prism (473)
Lateral surface of a cone (502)
Oblique solids (474, 490, 497, 502)
Parallelepiped (474)
Polyhedron (473)
Prism (473)
Pyramid (497)
Rectangular solid (474)

Regular solids (474, 483, 497)
Right solids (474, 490, 497, 502)
Right section (478)
Section (478)
Slant height (497, 502)
Solid (473)
Sphere (506)
Total area (478)
Vertex of a solid (473, 497, 502)
Volume (484)

Important Ideas

1. A polyhedron is a figure formed by four or more noncoplanar polygonal regions, which enclose a part of space. (473)

2. These are formulas for lateral area of a solid:
   Prism: L.A. = ℓp (479)
   Right prism: L.A. = hp (479)
   Right cylinder: L.A. = $Ch = 2\pi rh$ (491)
   Regular pyramid: L.A. = $\frac{1}{2}sp$ (498)
   Right cone: L.A. = $\frac{1}{2}Cs = \pi rs$ (503)

3. These are formulas for total area of a solid:
   Prism: T.A. = L.A. + $2B$ (480)
   Cylinder: T.A. = L.A. + $2B = 2\pi rh + 2\pi r^2$ (491)
   Pyramid: T.A. = L.A. + B (498)
   Right cone: T.A. = L.A. + $B = \pi rs + \pi r^2$ (503)

4. These are formulas for volume of a solid:
   Rectangular solid: $V = Bh = \ell wh$ (484)
   Prism: $V = Bh$ (486)
   Cylinder: $V = \pi r^2 h$ (492)
   Pyramid: $V = \frac{1}{3}Bh$ (499)
   Cone: $V = \frac{1}{3}Bh = \frac{1}{3}\pi r^2 h$ (503)

5. These are formulas for area and volume of a sphere: (506)
   $A = 4\pi r^2$
   $V = \frac{4}{3}\pi r^3$

Chapter 11 Review

Lesson 11-1, Page 473

1. Each base of an oblique prism has nine sides. How many faces of the prism are parallelograms? **9**

2. A prism has 22 vertices. How many sides does each base of the prism have? **11**

3. A prism has 16 faces. How many edges does it have? **42**

4. How many faces of a regular hexagonal prism are rectangles? **6**

5. Find the length of a diagonal of a rectangular solid whose dimensions are 14 in., 12 in., and 15 in.
$\sqrt{565} \approx 23.77$ **in.**

Lesson 11-2, Page 478

6. The perimeter of a base of a right prism is 3 m. The length of a lateral edge is 4 m. Find the lateral area. **12 m²**

Find the lateral area and the total area of each prism.

7. Rectangular solid

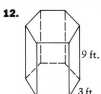
35 in.
48 in.
60 in.

8. Right prism; regular hexagonal base

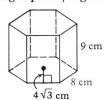
9 cm
8 cm
4√3 cm

7. 7,560 sq. in.; 13,320 sq. in.
8. 432 cm²; 432 + 192√3 ≈ 764.55 cm²

9. Find the total area of a cube whose base has a perimeter of 28 cm. **294 cm²**

10. The total area of a right prism is 592 cm² and the lateral area is 352 cm². What is the area of a base of the prism?
120 cm²

Lesson 11-3, Page 484

11. Find the volume of an oblique rectangular prism if each base measures 12 in. by 8 in. and the height is 18 in.
1,728 cu. in.

Find the volume of each regular prism.

12.

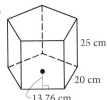
9 ft.
3 ft.

13.

25 cm
20 cm
13.76 cm

14.

3 m
5 m

12. 121.5√3 ≈ 210.44 cm³
13. 17,200 cm³
14. $\frac{45\sqrt{3}}{4}$ ≈ 19.49 m³

Lesson 11-4, Page 490

Find the lateral area, the total area, and the volume of each right cylinder. Give answers in terms of π.

15.

16.

17.

18. The circumference of a base of a right cylinder is 55 cm. Its height is 10 cm. What is its lateral area? **550 cm²**

Lesson 11-5, Page 497

Find the lateral area, the total area, and the volume for each regular pyramid.

19.

20.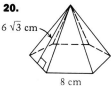

21.

Lesson 11-6, Page 502

Find the lateral area, the total area, and the volume for each right cone.

22.

23.

24.

25. Find the height of a right cone whose volume is 924 cm³ and whose base has a radius of 14 cm. $h \approx 4.5$ cm

Lesson 11-7, Page 506

26. Find the area and the volume of a sphere whose radius is 7 ft.

27. The circumference of a great circle is 16π m. Find the area and the volume of the sphere. Give answers in terms of π.

28. Find the volume of a basketball with diameter 9.56 in.

15. 24π sq. in.; 56π sq. in.; 48π cu. in.
16. 140π cm²; 190π cm²; 350π cm³
17. 63π sq. ft.; 87.5π sq. ft.; 110.25π cu. ft
19. $100\sqrt{5} \approx 223.61$ sq. in.; $100 + 100\sqrt{5} \approx 323.61$ sq. in.; $\frac{1,000}{3} \approx 333.33$ cu. in.
20. $144\sqrt{3} \approx 249.42$ cm²; $240\sqrt{3} \approx 415.69$ cm²; $192\sqrt{5} \approx 429.33$ cm³
21. $108\sqrt{3} \approx 187.06$ cm²; $144\sqrt{3} \approx 249.42$ cm²; $144\sqrt{2} \approx 203.65$ cm³
22. $5\pi\sqrt{61} \approx 122.62$ sq. in.; $5\pi\sqrt{61} + 25\pi \approx 201.12$ sq. in.; $50\pi \approx 157.00$ cu. in.
23. $36\pi\sqrt{481} \approx 2,479.16$ cm² $36\pi\sqrt{481} + 324\pi \approx 3,496.52$ cm²; $4,320\pi \approx 13,564.80$ cm³
24. $17\sqrt{145}\pi \approx 642.78$ cm²; $17\sqrt{145}\pi + 145\pi \approx 1,098.08$ cm²; $580\pi \approx 1,821.20$ cm³

26. $A = 615.44$ sq. ft.; $V = 1,436.03$ cm³
27. 256π m²; $\frac{2,048\pi}{3}$ m³
28. 457.25 cu. in.

Chapter 11 Test

1. How many faces does a pentagonal prism have? 7

Find the lateral area, the total area and the volume of each right
solid. The pyramids have regular polygonal bases. For cones
and cylinders, give answers in terms of π.

2.

13 in.

4 in.

7 in.

3.

5 cm

8 cm

4.

13 cm

5 cm

2. 286 sq. in.; 342 sq. in.;
   364 cu. in.
3. 80π cm²; 130π cm²;
   200π cm³
4. 65π cm²; 90π cm²;
   100π cm³
5. 240 cm²; 384 cm²; 384 cm³
6. $18\sqrt{127} \approx 202.85$ sq. in.;
   $18\sqrt{127} + 54\sqrt{3} \approx 296.38$ sq. in.;
   $180\sqrt{3} \approx 311.77$ cu. in.

5.
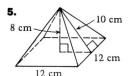
8 cm

10 cm

12 cm

12 cm

6.

10 in.

6 in.

7. The dimensions of a rectangular solid are 8 in., 10 in., and
12 in. Find its total area and its volume. 592 sq. in.; 960 cu. in.

8. Find the length of a diagonal of the rectangular solid in
Item 7. $2\sqrt{77} \approx 17.55$ in.

9. Find the volume of a regular triangular prism whose height
is 6 ft. and whose bases have sides measuring 9 ft.

9. $\frac{243\sqrt{3}}{2} \approx 210.44$ cu. ft.

10. The total area of a cube is 216 cm². Find the volume. 216 cm³

11. Find the area and the volume of a sphere whose radius is 4 cm.

11. $64\pi \approx 200.96$ cm²;
$\frac{256\pi}{3} \approx 267.95$ cm³

12. The area of a sphere is 832 sq. in. What is the area of a
great circle of the sphere? 208 sq. in.

13. A right cone has a volume of 4,500 m³. If the radius of its
base is 12 m, find its height. 29.86 m

14. A sphere has an area of 9,850 sq. ft. What is its radius? $\approx$ 28 ft.

CHAPTER

12

Transformations

Chapter Overview

In this chapter, transformations are used to organize and unify the important concepts of congruence, similarity and symmetry. The role of transformations as a problem-solving tool is also studied.

Line reflections are introduced as the basic building block of all isometries. After a definition of point reflections, translations and rotations are defined as composites of two line reflections.

Dilations are introduced as transformations that are not isometries but that do preserve shape. A similarity transformation is defined as a composite of a dilation and an isometry.

A major application of our work with transformations in this chapter is to redefine congruence and similarity.

Perspectives

Lesson 12–1 defines line and point reflections in terms of the postulates and definitions we have already studied. Triangle congruence is used to show that both types of reflections are isometries.

Lesson 12–2 suggests that certain properties are invariant under a line reflection. The properties that are preserved are developed in this lesson for all isometries. This approach has two advantages:

The proofs are easier for isometries in general than for specific transformations.

For transformations developed later, we need only prove that they preserve distance, and the other properties will follow immediately.

Orientation is discussed as a property that is not preserved under every isometry.

Lesson 12–3 applies line reflections to various real-world problems. Many problems involve minimizing distance. **Problem-solving strategies** should be used when needed.

Lesson 12–4 defines a translation as a composite of reflections over two parallel lines. A translation is an isometry and thus possesses all the properties of an isometry.

In this lesson, we allow a line to be parallel to itself. When the two lines of reflection for a translation coincide, the translation becomes the identity transformation.

Lesson 12–5 defines a rotation as a composite of two reflections over intersecting lines. If the lines coincide, the rotation has a magnitude of zero; that is, it is the identity transformation. If the lines are perpendicular, the magnitude of rotation is 180. Therefore, a point reflection is a special case of rotation.

Lesson 12–6 shows that symmetry is applicable in terms of finding geometric concepts in real-world situations. Using the transformations we have already defined, we can give precise definitions to our intuitive notions of symmetry.

Pacing Chart for Chapter 12

Lesson	Objectives	Basic Course	Average Course	Extended Course
12–1	Find images of points under line reflections and point reflections.	1	1	2
12–2	State and apply properties of isometries.	1	1	2
12–3	Apply properties of reflections to problem-solving situations.	1	2	2
12–4	State and apply properties of translations.	1	$1\frac{1}{2}$	2
12–5	State and apply properties of rotations.	1	2	2
12–6	Examine various figures for point, line and rotational symmetry.	1	1	2
12–7	Use isometries to extend the concept of congruence.	1	$1\frac{1}{2}$	2
12–8	Find the images of figures under dilations.	1	2	2
12–9	State and apply properties of dilations.	1	2	2
12–10	Use similarity transformations to extend the concept of similarity.	1	2	2
Review		1	1	2
Test		1	1	1
Total		12 days	18 days	23 days

Lesson 12–7 gives legitimacy and precision to Euclid's concept of congruence in terms of superposition. Once Theorem 12–9 establishes that there is a unique isometry that maps a geometric figure onto a congruent one, we can redefine congruence in terms of isometries.

Theorem 12–10 establishes the line reflection as the fundamental building block of all isometries.

Lesson 12–8 introduces dilations, which give students experience with a type of transformation that does not preserve distance. The use of concrete materials such as a pantograph gives students real-world experience with dilations.

Lesson 12–9 determines which properties of the other types of transformations are shared by dilations.

Although dilations do not preserve distance, they do preserve ratios of distances.

Lesson 12–10 redefines similarity using similarity transformations. This lesson begins with a definition of similarity transformation.

Theorem 12–16, the fundamental theorem of similarity transformations, establishes that a similarity transformation is completely determined by three noncollinear points and their images.

Transformations

Chapter 12

Mauritz Escher, the Dutch artist (1898–1972), produced many patterns like the one shown here. He called this type of drawing a "regular division of the plane."

An interesting aspect of such a drawing is that it suggests various ways to "move" one figure of the plane onto another.

1. Suppose a mirror is placed on line ℓ. If Crab I is reflected "through" the mirror, on which crab would its image land?

2. Imagine that Crab II can spin about point A. Through what fraction of a complete circular path would Crab II rotate before it coincides with Crab III?

3. Could Crab III coincide with Crab IV if it slides along line ℓ?

4. Describe a way to "move" one of the light-colored crabs onto one of the dark crabs.

Warm-Up Review

1. A line perpendicular to a segment at its midpoint is a(n) __?__. Perpendicular bisector
2. If M is the midpoint of $\overline{AB}$, then A, M and B are collinear and __?__. $AM = MB$
3. Two triangles are congruent if two sides and the __?__ of one are equal
   to the corresponding parts of the other. Included angle
4. What is the name given to the statement in Exercise 3? SAS Postulate

12-1 Reflections and Other Transformations

Suppose a plane containing rectangle $ABCD$ could be stretched like a sheet of rubber, as shown. The "stretched" vertices are marked on the plane as A', B', C', and D'. In this way each point P of the plane is associated with a unique point P'. Such a correspondence is a transformation.

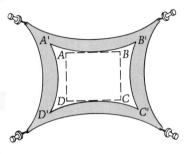

Definition   *Transformation of a Plane*

A transformation of a plane is a one-to-one correspondence between the points of the plane and themselves.

A transformation is also called a *mapping*. Above, A is mapped onto A'. A' is called the *image* of A. A is the *preimage* of A'.

The Plexiglas "mirror" pictured at the right provides another example of a transformation. The mirror can be used to pair points with their reflected images.

Suppose the mirror is placed along a line ℓ. The images of A and B are A' and B', respectively. How do you think ℓ is related to the segments $\overline{AA'}$ and $\overline{BB'}$?
⊥ bisector
What is the image of a point on ℓ?
Itself
Your observations should suggest the next definition.

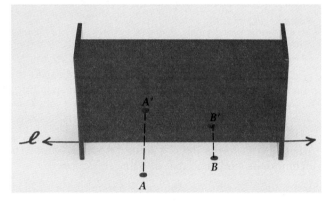

Definition   *Reflection Over a Line*

In a plane, a reflection over a line ℓ is a transformation that maps each point P of the plane onto a point P' as follows:
*   *If P is not on ℓ, then ℓ is the perpendicular bisector of $\overline{PP'}$.*
*   *If P is on ℓ, then P' coincides with P (written $P = P'$).*

ℓ is called the *line of reflection*. P' is called the *reflection image* of P. What is the reflection image of P'? Why?   P; because ℓ is
⊥ bisector of $\overline{P'P}$

A transformation *preserves* distance if and only if the distance between two points is equal to the distance between their images.

Definition   *Isometry*

An isometry is a transformation that preserves distance.

LESSON 12–1

Resources

Plexiglas mirror
Ruler
Teaching Aid 5, graphs
Visual Aid 5, graphs
Worksheet 12–1
Extension 12–1
Computer Activities 12–1

OBJECTIVE

Find images of points under line reflections and point reflections.

TEACHING NOTES

To introduce the concept of a line reflection, use **concrete materials** like transparent mirrors. By lining

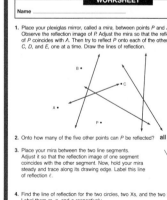

WORKSHEET   Lesson
Name _____   **12 - 1**

1. Place your plexiglas mirror, called a *mira*, between points P and A, below. Observe the reflection image of P. Adjust the mira so that the reflection image of P coincides with A. Then try to reflect P onto each of the other points, B, C, D, and E, one at a time. Draw the lines of reflection.

2. Onto how many of the five other points can P be reflected?   **all 5**

3. Place your mira between the two line segments. Adjust it so that the reflection image of one segment coincides with the other segment. Now, hold your mira steady and trace along its drawing edge. Label this line of reflection ℓ.

4. Find the line of reflection for the two circles, two Xs, and the two squares. Label them m, n, and o respectively.

up the mirror with the line of reflection, students can directly sight the correct position of A'. Have them do more complex reflections, such as the vertices of a scalene triangle.

A point reflection can be done by using a ruler. Lightly trace the line containing A and the center of reflection O. Measure $\overline{OA}$ and locate A' the same distance on the other side of O.

Additional Examples

Example 1

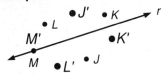

Find the images of J, K, L and M over t.

Do you think the "stretch" transformation on page 515 is an isometry? For example, does $AD = A'D'$? **No, no**

Does reflection over a line preserve distance? In each case of a line reflection shown below, does $PQ = P'Q'$? **Yes**   Yes

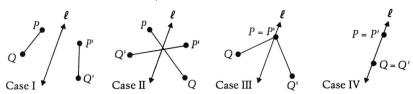

Case I   Case II   Case III   Case IV

Theorem 12-1

A line reflection is an isometry.

Given   A reflection over ℓ maps P onto P' and Q onto Q'.

Prove $PQ = P'Q'$

Plan for **Case I** P and Q are on the same side of ℓ.
Proof   Draw $\overline{PP'}$ and $\overline{QQ'}$ intersecting ℓ in M and N as shown. Draw $\overline{MQ}$ and $\overline{MQ'}$. Show $\triangle MNQ \cong \triangle MNQ'$. Show $\triangle PQM \cong \triangle P'Q'M'$. Use corresponding parts.

The proof of Theorem 12-1 Cases I–IV, is left to Exercises 9–12.

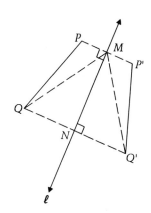

Another transformation is a point reflection. Notice that its definition is similar to that of a line reflection.

Definition   *Reflection Through a Point*

In a plane, a reflection through a point O is a transformation that maps each point P of the plane onto a point P' as follows:
• *If P does not coincide with O, then O is the midpoint of $\overline{PP'}$.*
• *If P coincides with O, then $P' = P$.*

A rotation through half a complete circular path about point O maps a point onto its image.

In the diagram, a reflection through point O maps P onto P' and Q onto Q'. What is the image of P'? Why?   **P; because O is the midpoint of $\overline{P'P}$**
A point reflection is also called a ***half-turn***. Why do you think this is so? Point O is called the ***center*** of the half-turn. **See right.**

Do you think $PQ = P'Q'$? How could you show it? **Yes**
Show $\triangle POQ \cong \triangle P'O'Q'$ and use corresponding parts.

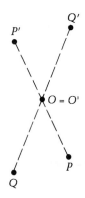

Theorem 12-2

A point reflection is an isometry.

The proof of Theorem 12-2 is requested in Exercises 13–15.

Assignment Guide

Basic: 1–8, 20–28
Average: 1–15, 20–28
Extended: 1–28

Suppose each point of the plane is its own image. Is this correspondence a transformation? Why?   **Yes, it is a one-to-one correspondence between the points and themselves.**

Definition   *Identity Transformation*

The identity transformation is the transformation that maps each point of the plane onto itself.

Checking for Understanding

1. Is the identity transformation an isometry? Explain. **Yes; it preserves distance.**

A transformation maps A onto B and E onto F.

2. Name the image of A. **B**   **3.** Name the preimage of B. **A**

4. Name the image of E. **F**   **5.** Does $AE = BF$? **Not necessarily**

6. A line reflection over ℓ appears to map S onto $\underset{C}{\underline{\ ?\ }}$ and W onto $\underline{\ ?\ }$. **W**

7. A point reflection through W appears to map D onto $\underset{C}{\underline{\ ?\ }}$ and W onto $\underline{\ ?\ }$. **W**

8. The identity transformation maps C onto $\underset{C}{\underline{\ ?\ }}$, D onto $\underset{D}{\underline{\ ?\ }}$, S onto $\underset{S}{\underline{\ ?\ }}$, and W onto $\underline{\ ?\ }$. **W**

Given only P and its image P', how can you find

9. the line of reflection if $P \neq P'$? if $P = P'$?

10. the center of a half-turn if $P \neq P'$? if $P = P'$?
Find the midpt. of PP'; P is the center.

9. Find the $\perp$ bisector of $\overline{PP'}$; a unique line of reflection cannot be found because it is any one of infinitely many lines through P.

Written Exercises

Set A   **1.** Trace line ℓ and points X, Y, and Z. Draw the reflection images of X, Y, and Z over ℓ.

2. Trace points X, Y, and Z. Draw the reflection images of X, Y, and Z through point Z.

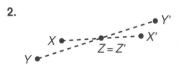

For each exercise, graph points $A(5, 0)$, $B(0, -4)$, and $C(-3, 4)$. Draw and give the coordinates of the images of A, B, and C under

3. a reflection over the x-axis. $A'(5, 0)$, $B'(0, 4)$, $C'(-3, -4)$

4. a reflection over the y-axis. $A'(-5, 0)$, $B'(0, -4)$, $C'(3, 4)$

5. a reflection through the origin, $O(0, 0)$.

6. the identity transformation. $A'(5, 0)$, $B'(0, 4)$, $C'(3, -4)$
    5. $A'(-5, 0)$, $B'(0, 4)$, $C'(3, -4)$

Example 2

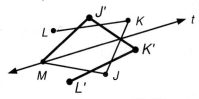

Find the reflections of $\overline{LK}$, $\overline{MJ}$ and $\overline{KJ}$ over t.

Example 3

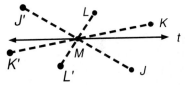

Find the reflections of L, K and J through M.

Error Analysis   Students sometimes have difficulty understanding the concept of a fixed point. For example, under a reflection over line k, every point on k is its own image; these points are said to remain fixed. Use examples involving fixed points so that students become accustomed to the idea.

ANSWERS

Written Exercises

1.

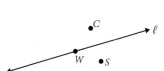

2.

FOLLOW-UP

More Practice

• Worksheet 12–1

Extension

Ask students to find the following images.

1. (2, 0) under a reflection over the line $x = 5$ (8, 0)

2. (−1, 3) under a reflection over the line $x = 3$ (7, 3)

3. (a, b) under a reflection over the line $x = k$ (2k − a, b)

Extension 12–1

Computers

This computer activity can be completed using *The Geometric preSupposer: Points and Lines*, *The Geometric Supposer: Triangles* or *Circles*, or *GeoDraw*.

To give students experience with Theorems 12–5 and 12–6, have students do the following.

Draw any triangle and any line or segment outside the triangle. Reflect the triangle over that line. Measure the sides and angles of the two triangles. What is true about the corresponding angles of the two triangles? They are equal. What is true about the two triangles? They are congruent.

Repeat the activity several times, each time beginning with a different triangle. What seems to be true about the angles formed by the reflection of any three points over a line? What seems to be true about the two triangles so formed? They are equal; they are congruent.

• **Computer Activities 12–1**

Set B   Trace points X and Y for each exercise.

7. Draw line ℓ so that Y is the reflection image of X over ℓ. Describe the method you used.

8. Draw point O so that X is the image of Y under a half-turn about O. Describe the method you used.

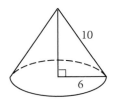

Use the Given, Prove, and appropriate diagram from page 516 to prove Theorem 12-1 for each case.

9. Case I   **10.** Case II   **11.** Case III   **12.** Case IV

Prove Theorem 12-2 for each case shown.

13. Case I   **14.** Case II   **15.** Case III

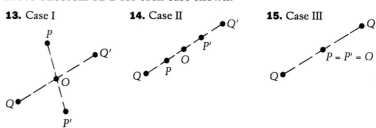

Set C   Determine the coordinates of the reflection image of any point P (x, y)

16. over the y-axis. (−x, y)   **17.** over the x-axis. (x, −y)

18. through $O(0, 0)$.   **19.** through $A(3, 0)$.

18. (−x, −y)   **19.** (6 − x, −y)

▲ Review   The diameter of a sphere is 18 cm.

20. Find the area. 324 π cm²   **21.** Find the volume. 972π cm³

22. Find the volume of the cone shown at the right.

23. A trapezoid has $\frac{?}{2}$ parallel sides called the $\frac{?}{\text{bases}}$.

24. State the HL Congruence Theorem.

22. 120 π

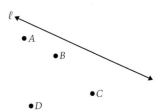

≡ Thinking Ahead   Trace the diagram. Draw A', B', C', and D', the reflection images of A, B, C, and D, respectively, over ℓ.

25. Are A, B, and C collinear? What appears to be true about A', B', and C'? Yes; they are collinear

26. If E is on $\overleftrightarrow{AB}$, where do you think the image of E is?

27. If F is between B and C, where do you think the image of F is? Between B' and C'

28. Draw $\angle DAB$ and $\angle D'A'B'$. Compare their measures.

26. On $\overleftrightarrow{A'B'}$ **28.** m∠DAB = m∠D'A'B'

12-2 Properties of Isometries

The line reflection image of $\triangle TUV$ is marked behind a Plexiglas mirror.

Are T, S, and V collinear? Are the reflection images of T, S, and V collinear? We say that a mirror reflection *preserves* collinearity of points. Is S between T and V? What is the position of S'? A mirror reflection also preserves betweenness of points. *Yes; yes; yes; between T' and V'*

These properties hold for all line and point reflections. Do you think they hold for the identity transformation? Theorem 12-3 states that these properties hold for *all* isometries. *Yes*

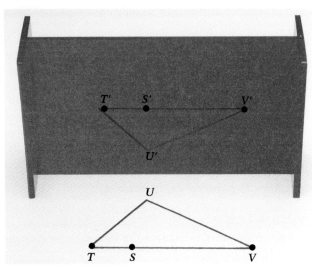

Theorem 12-3

An isometry preserves collinearity and betweenness of points.

Given Collinear points A, B, and C, with A', B', and C' their images under an isometry; B is between A and C.

Prove A', B', and C' are collinear; B' is between A' and C'.

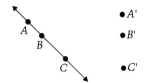

Plan for Proof Use the definition of isometry to show $AB = A'B'$, $BC = B'C'$, and $AC = A'C'$. Since B is between A and C, $AB + BC = AC$. Then, by substitution, $A'B' + B'C' = A'C'$; and A', B', and C' are collinear with B' between A' and C'.

Proof

Statements	Reasons
1. A', B', and C' are the images of A, B, and C under an isometry.	1. Given
2. $AB = A'B'$; $BC = B'C'$; $AC = A'C'$	2. Def. of isometry [1]
3. B is between A and C.	3. Given
4. $AB + BC = AC$	4. Segment Addition Post. [3]
5. $A'B' + B'C' = A'C'$	5. Substitution Prop. [2, 4]
6. A', B' and C' are collinear, and B' is between A' and C'.	6. Points A, B, and C are collinear and B is between A and C if $AB + BC = AC$. [5]

LESSON 12-2

Resources

Plexiglas mirror
Teaching Aid 5, graphs
Visual Aid 5, graphs
Teaching Aid 29, reflections
Visual Aid 29, reflections
Worksheet 12-2
Extension 12-2

OBJECTIVE

State and apply properties of isometries.

TEACHING NOTES

Begin this lesson with an example of a reflection. Ask students to make observations in the original figure and its image regarding the

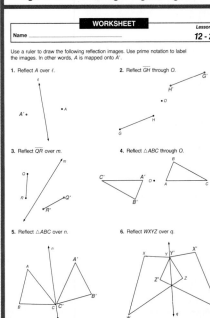

following:
1. Collinearity.
2. Betweenness.
3. Angle measure.
4. Triangle congruence.
5. Orientation.

Only the first four are preserved.

An important implication of the theorems of this lesson is that the image of any polygon under an isometry is a congruent polygon. The image of a polygon must be named in the same order as in the preimage.

Additional Examples

Example 1

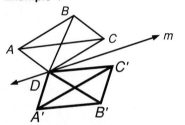

Theorem 12-3 suggests that isometries map lines onto lines, rays onto rays, and segments onto segments. This is formalized in Theorem 12-4. Its proof is omitted.

Theorem 12-4

If an isometry maps A onto A′ and B onto B′, then the image of $\overleftrightarrow{AB}$ is $\overleftrightarrow{A'B'}$, the image of $\overrightarrow{AB}$ is $\overrightarrow{A'B'}$, and the image of $\overline{AB}$ is $\overline{A'B'}$.

Since an angle is defined in terms of rays, the image of an angle under an isometry is another angle. What do you think is the image of a triangle? Under an isometry, what do you think can be said about an angle and its image? a triangle and its image? A△; ≅; ≅

Theorem 12-5

An isometry preserves angle measure.

Theorem 12-6

Under an isometry, a triangle and its image are congruent.

Theorems 12-5 and 12-6 are to be proved in Exercises 29 and 30.

Theorems 12-3 and 12-4 suggest that the reflection image of any polygon can be drawn by joining the images of consecutive vertices, as shown at the right. What do the definition of isometry and Theorem 12-5 suggest about a polygon and its image? They are congruent.

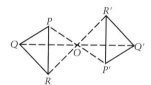

Observe that for *EFGH*, the *orientation* from E to F to G to H is clockwise. However, the orientation from E′ to F′ to G′ to H′ is counterclockwise. We say that a line reflection *reverses* orientation. But a point reflection *preserves* orientation.

Summary Isometries

Isometries preserve	Isometries map
• Distance	• A line onto a line
• Collinearity	• A ray onto a ray
• Betweenness	• A segment onto a segment
• Angle measure	• A triangle onto a congruent triangle

Assignment Guide

Basic: 1–20, 32–40
Average: 2–10 (even), 11–30, 32–40
Extended: 2–18 (even), 19–40

Checking for Understanding

1. The identity transformation __?__ orientation. **preserves**

2. Do the theorems in this lesson hold for all line reflections? all point reflections? the identity transformation? Explain.

Describe the minimum set of points that must be reflected to find the reflection image of each figure.

3. Line 2 **4.** Ray 2 **5.** Segment 2 **6.** Angle 3 **7.** Trapezoid 4

2. Yes; yes; yes. The theorems had for all isometries. All three of these transformations are isometries.
4. ∠DAB   **5.** △DCB
9. ∠DOA   **10.** △CDA

Written Exercises

Set A For each figure, name the reflection image over line ℓ.

1. A D   **2.** $\overline{DC}$ $\overline{AB}$ **3.** $\overline{AC}$ $\overline{DB}$ **4.** ∠ADC   **5.** △ABC

For each figure, name the reflection image through O.

6. A C   **7.** $\overline{AB}$ $\overline{CD}$ **8.** $\overline{AC}$ $\overline{CA}$ **9.** ∠BOC   **10.** △ABC

An isometry maps U onto U′, V onto V′, and W onto W′?

11. What is the orientation of △UVW? **Counterclockwise**

12. What is the orientation of △U′V′W′? **Counterclockwise**

13. Can △U′V′W′ be the image of △UVW under a line of reflection? Explain. **No; line reflections reverse orientation**

A reflection through point O maps P onto S and Q onto R. Explain why each statement is true.

14. PO = OS   **15.** PQ = SR
16. m∠PQR = m∠SRQ   **17.** $\overleftrightarrow{PQ} \parallel \overleftrightarrow{RS}$
18. △SRO ≅ △PQO   **19.** The image of $\overrightarrow{QP}$ is $\overrightarrow{RS}$.
20. If X is on $\overleftrightarrow{PQ}$, then the image of X is on $\overleftrightarrow{SR}$.

Set B For each exercise, draw △ABC with coordinates A(2, 4), B(4, 1), and C(0, 2). Draw the image of △ABC under the reflection described.

21. Over the x-axis   **22.** Over the y-axis

23. Over the line with equation x = 2

24. Through the origin O(0, 0)

25. Trace ABCD and line ℓ. Draw the reflection image of ABCD over ℓ.

26. Trace ABCD and point E. Draw the reflection image of ABCD through E.

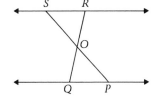

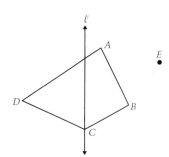

Draw the reflection images of △ABC, △BCD and ABCD over line m.

Example 2

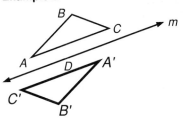

Draw the reflection image of △ABC through D.

Error Analysis Students may have difficulty understanding the concept of orientation. Try drawing curved arrows through the vertices in the order they are named.

It should be clear that a counter-clockwise orientation maps onto one that is clockwise, so orientation is not preserved.

ANSWERS

Written Exercises

14. by def. of pt. reflection and def. of midpt.
15. by Thm. 12–2 (A pt. reflection is an isometry.) and def. of isometry
16. by Thm. 12–2 (A pt. reflection is an isometry.) and Thm. 12–5 (Isometries preserve ∠ measure.)
17. m∠PQR = m∠SRQ (see Ex. 16) and alt. int. ∠s ⇒ lines ∥

27. If $\ell \perp m$, they meet to form a rt. ∠. Since isometries preserve ∠ meas., ℓ' and m' meet to form a rt. ∠. Hence, $\ell' \perp m'$.

28. Suppose ℓ' and m' intersect in a pt. X. Then there is a pt. A on ℓ that maps onto X. There is also a pt. B on m that maps onto X. Since $\ell \parallel m$, $A \neq B$. But this contradicts the fact that an isometry is a transformation, which is a one-to-one correspondence. Thus, $\ell' \parallel m'$.

FOLLOW-UP

More Practice

• Worksheet 12–2

Extension

Have students find the images of the following points under a reflection in the line $x = 5$.

1. $A(2, 4)$ $A'(8, 4)$
2. $B(0, 0)$ $B'(10, 0)$
3. $C(-1, -2)$ $C'(11, -2)$

Then ask students to verify that the following properties are preserved.

1. Distance using Distance Formula, $AB = A'B' = \sqrt{20}$; $BC = B'C' = \sqrt{5}$; $AC = A'C' = \sqrt{45}$
2. Collinearity, slope of $\overleftrightarrow{AB} =$ slope of $\overleftrightarrow{BC} = 2$, so A, B and C are collinear; slope of $\overleftrightarrow{A'B'} =$ slope of $\overleftrightarrow{B'C'} = -2$, so their images are collinear

• Extension 12–2

An isometry maps ℓ onto ℓ' and m onto m'. Explain why each statement is true.

27. If $\ell \perp m$, then $\ell' \perp m'$.

28. If $\ell \parallel m$, then $\ell' \parallel m'$.

29. Prove Theorem 12-5.

30. Prove Theorem 12-6.

Set C **31.** Trace this diagram in which X' is the reflection image of X over n. Using only a straightedge, locate the reflection image of Y.

▲ Review **32.** Define *transformation*.   **33.** Define *isometry*.

34. Find the volume of a sphere whose radius is 11 m.

35. Line ℓ is a(n) __?__ to $\odot O$ and $\odot P$. tangent

36. In $\triangle ABC$, $m\angle C = 90$, $AB = 8$, and $BC = 2$. Find AC.

34. $1774\frac{2}{3}\pi m^3$ **36.** $2\sqrt{15}$

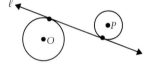

≣ Thinking Ahead **37.** Trace the diagram at the right. Draw B', the reflection image of B over ℓ.

38. Draw $\overline{AB'}$. Label X, the intersection of $\overline{AB'}$ and ℓ.

39. Why does $AX + XB = AX + XB'$?

40. Work with a partner. Can you find a point Y on ℓ for which $AY + YB < AX + XB$? Explain.

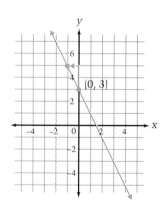

Algebra Review: Graphing the Line for an Equation

Example

Graph the line whose equation is $2x + y = 3$.

Solution

Write the equation in slope-intercept form, $y = mx + b$.

$2x + y = 3$, so $y = -2x + 3$.

Since the y-intercept b is 3, graph the point whose coordinates are $(0, 3)$. The slope m is *negative* 2, so from the point at $(0, 3)$, move *up* 2 units and to the *left* 1 unit. (For a positive slope, move *up* and to the *right*.) Mark this point and draw the line.

Graph each line on a separate grid.

1. $y = 3x + 1$ **2.** $y = \frac{1}{2}x - 4$ **3.** $y = 3$

4. $x = 5$ **5.** $y - 4x = 0$ **6.** $2x + 3y = 6$

Warm-Up Review

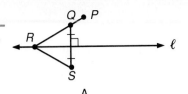

1. If two sides of a triangle have lengths 5 and 12, find the range of possible lengths for the third side. $7 < x < 17$
2. What theorem is applied in Exercise 1? Triangle Inequality Theorem
3. Name the image of Q under a reflection over line ℓ. S
4. True or false: $QR = SR$. True

A

12-3 Applications of Reflections

Reflections have useful applications in art, engineering, science, and sports, as illustrated by these examples.

Example 1

Two farms A and B are to be connected by separate wires to a transformer on a main power line ℓ. Where should the transformer be located so that the minimum amount of wire will be needed?

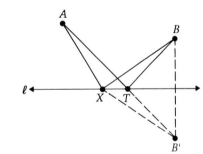

Solution

Find B', the reflection image of B over ℓ, as shown. Locate the transformer T at the intersection of $\overline{AB'}$ and ℓ. Then $AT + TB$ is the minimum amount of wire needed.

To see why, suppose the transformer were located at some other point X on ℓ, as shown in the second diagram. Then, by Theorem 12-1, $XB = XB'$ and $TB = TB'$. So $AX + XB = AX + XB'$ and $AT + TB = AT + TB'$. But $AX + XB' > AT + TB'$. Why? So $AX + XB > AT + TB$.
By the △ Inequality Thm.

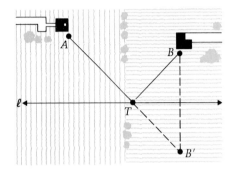

Example 2

Where should you aim to make a hole-in-one on the miniature golf green shown at the right?

Solution

Visualize H', the reflection image of H over k. Aim for the point P where $\overline{BH'}$ intersects k.

Since the ball hits the side and *rebounds* at the same angle, P must be located so that $m\angle 1 = m\angle 3$. We can show that Vert ∠s
$m\angle 1 = m\angle 2$. How? Also, $m\angle 2 = m\angle 3$. are =
Why? So, $m\angle 1 = m\angle 3$, as desired.
∠2 is the reflection image of ∠3 over k
Could you bounce the ball off two sides to make a hole-in-one? Yes

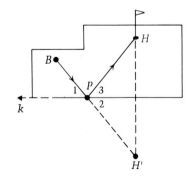

LESSON 12-3

Resources

Teaching Aid 31, reflections in a rectangle
Visual Aid 31, reflections in a rectangle
Teaching Aid 32, applications of reflections
Visual Aid 32, applications of reflections
Worksheet 12-3
Extension 12-3
Computer Activities 12-3
Computer Worksheet 12-3

OBJECTIVE

Apply properties of reflections to problem-solving situations.

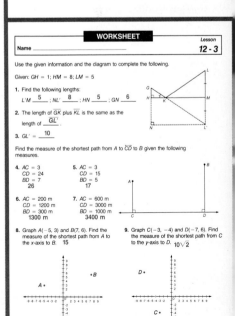

Assignment Guide

Basic: 1–12, 18–25
Average: 1–16, 18–25
Extended: 1–25

TEACHING NOTES

Begin this lesson with a discussion of **Example 1**. Help students learn to use reflections to simplify problems.

Example 3 uses the **problem-solving strategy** of working backwards. First find the point that the ball aims at to make its last bounce and work back from there, continuing to use reflections.

Additional Examples

Example 1

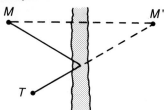

A camper leaves his tent *T*, goes to the stream for water and then

EXTENSION

Name ______________________ *Lesson* *12-3*

Magic Squares

In a *magic square,* the sum of each row, column, and diagonal is the same. Also, no number is repeated. The magic square at the right appeared in a painting by Albrecht Dürer (1471–1528), a famous artist. The *magic sum* is 34.

16	3	2	13
5	10	11	8
9	6	7	12
4	15	14	1

1. The oldest known magic square appeared on a Chinese tablet 4,000 years ago. According to legend, an ancient emperor spotted the pattern on the back of a tortoise. Translate the magic square pattern into corresponding numerals. 4, 9, 2; 3, 5, 7; 8, 1, 6

2. If you reverse the numbers in all the rows or columns of a magic square, a different magic square is formed. Each square below is based on the magic square from the Dürer painting. Complete each square and verify that it is a magic square. Magic sum is still 34.

13	2	3	16
8	11	10	5
12	7	6	9
1	14	15	4

4	15	14	1
9	6	7	12
5	10	11	8
16	3	2	13

3. Magic squares can also be transformed into other magic squares by adding, subtracting, multiplying, or dividing all the numbers by any constant nonzero value. Transform the ancient Chinese magic square by first adding 4 to each number and then dividing by 2. Show the results as simplified fractions. Then verify that the new square is another magic square. $4, \frac{13}{2}, 3; \frac{7}{2}, \frac{9}{2}, \frac{11}{2}; 6, \frac{5}{2}, 5$; magic sum is $13\frac{1}{2}$

4. An even more amazing type of magic square is a bordered magic square. In this type of magic square, the square remains magic when the outer border is removed. Verify that both the large square and the inside square are magic. Magic sum of large square is 65; magic sum of small square is 39.

21	1	2	22	19
23	**16**	**9**	**14**	3
6	**11**	**13**	**15**	20
8	**12**	**17**	**10**	18
7	25	24	4	5

5. In this magic square, two borders can be removed. Verify that three different magic squares occur in the figure. Magic sum of largest square is 175; magic sum of inner 5 × 5 square is 125; magic sum of center 3 × 3 square is 75.

46	1	2	3	42	41	40
45	35	13	14	32	31	5
44	34	**28**	**21**	**26**	16	6
7	17	**23**	**25**	**27**	33	43
12	20	**24**	**29**	**22**	30	38
11	19	37	36	18	15	39
10	49	48	47	8	9	4

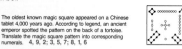

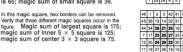

Example 3

On the billiard table shown at the right, where should you aim so that the cue ball at *C* hits three sides and then hits the ball at *R*?

Solution

Let R_1 be the reflection image of R over ℓ; R_2, the reflection image of R_1 over m; and R_3, the reflection image of R_2 over n. Aim the cue ball for V, the point where $\overline{CR_3}$ intersects n. Reasoning as in Example 2, you can show $m\angle 1 = m\angle 3$, $m\angle 4 = m\angle 6$, and $m\angle 7 = m\angle 9$.

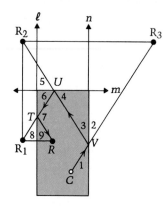

Checking for Understanding

Refer to Example 3 above. Explain why each statement is true.

1. $m\angle 1 = m\angle 2$ **2.** $m\angle 1 = m\angle 3$ **3.** $m\angle 4 = m\angle 6$
4. $m\angle 7 = m\angle 9$ **5.** $TR_1 = TR$ **6.** $UR_1 = UR_2$
7. The distance the cue ball travels is equal to CR_3.

Tell how to find each point on $\overleftrightarrow{AB}$ at the right.

8. Point *P*, such that $CP + PF$ is as small as possible
9. Point Q, such that $CQ + QD$ is as small as possible
10. Point *R*, such that $m\angle CRA = m\angle DRB$

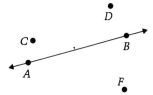

Written Exercises

Set A **1.** A pumping station *P* is to be built to pump water to towns *S* and *T* such that the minimum amount of pipe will be needed. Trace the diagram. Locate point *P* along the river.

For each exercise, trace the diagram at the right. Show how to determine the path of a cue ball at *C* so that it bounces off the given sides and then hits the ball at *R*.

2. Side 1 **3.** Side 4 **4.** Side 1, and then side 2
5. Side 1, then side 2, and then side 3
6. Side 3, then side 1, and then side 2

For each exercise, trace the diagram at the right. Show how to determine the path of a ball at *B* so that a hole in one is made after the ball bounces off

7. 1 side. **8.** 2 sides. **9.** 3 sides.

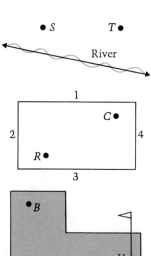

10. A laser beam emitted from point X is to be received by a measuring device at Y upon reflection from a flat surface ℓ. Trace the diagram. At what point on ℓ should the beam be aimed? Explain.

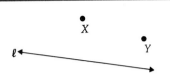

Strip (or *frieze*) patterns, as shown at the right, are used in architecture and interior decorating.

11. Trace and complete the upper frieze pattern by finding images of the fish under repeated reflections over the given lines.

12. Trace and complete the lower frieze pattern by finding images of repeated reflections through the given points.

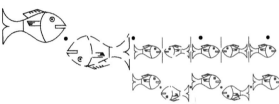

Set B **13.** Commercial artists use a device similar to the one shown at the right for drawing mirror images. $AP = PB = BP' + P'A$. The joints pivot freely as A and B slide along ℓ. As P traces out a figure, P' traces out its reflection image. Why does this work?

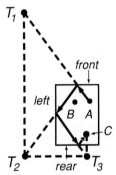

For a canoe race, contestants begin at A, paddle to any point on the shoreline, and end at B. Trace the diagram at the right.

14. Show how to determine the point on the shore to which you should paddle.

15. Find the length of the shortest route to the nearest ten meters. **1080 m**

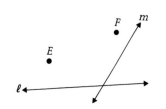

16. In a vacuum tube, an electron sent from E is to be aimed at ℓ so that it reflects from ℓ to m and finally to F. Trace the diagram at the right and show how to determine the path of the electron.

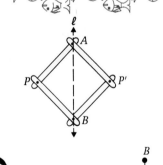

heads for the mess tent M to start breakfast. What is his shortest path?

Example 2

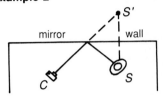

At what point on the mirror wall should the camera C be aimed to photograph the subject S?

Example 3

In a game of handball, player A wants to hit the ball off the front wall so that it rebounds off the left and rear walls and gets to position C. At what point on the front wall should he aim?

Error Analysis When solving an application problem involving minimal distance, students may choose any point on the line instead of understanding that it is important to find the reflection of the final point. Then work backwards to find the correct line segments.

526

FOLLOW-UP

More Practice

• Worksheet 12–3

Extension

Challenge students to find two line reflections that are equivalent to a point reflection. An example is given below, but solutions are not unique.

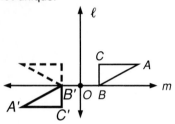

A reflection over *l* followed by a reflection over *m* is equivalent to a half-turn about *O*.

• Extension 12–3

Computers

The computer activity in the pupil's book can be completed using *The Geometric preSupposer: Points and Lines, The Geometric Supposer: Triangles* or *GeoDraw*.

Note: If you are using *The Geometric Supposer* or *The Geometric preSupposer*, students will have to simulate a line by drawing an initial segment that would not intersect the triangle even if it were extended in either direction. Students *will* be able to draw a "draft line" parallel to the initial segment. In both *The Geometric Supposer* and *GeoDraw*, a line must be defined by two points in order to reflect an image over it.

• Computer Activities 12–3
• Computer Worksheet 12–3

Set C 17. Hailey University plans to build a hockey rink (*H*) on Ash Street, an intramural building (*I*) on Vine Avenue, and a gymnasium (*G*) on 6th Street. All the buildings are to be connected by tunnels. Trace the diagram and show where to locate the buildings so that the total length of the tunnels is as short as possible. Explain your solution.

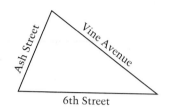

▲ **Review** 18. Isometries preserve _?_, _?_, _?_, and _?_.

19. Line reflections do not preserve _?_. orientation

20. Name three isometries.

21. The measures of two supplementary angles are in the ratio of 2 to 7. Find the measures of the angles.

22. Find the sum of the angle measures of a nonagon.
21. 40; 140   22. 1260

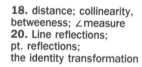

18. distance; collinearity, betweeness; ∠measure
20. Line reflections; pt. reflections; the identity transformation

Thinking Ahead 23. Trace the diagram at the right. Draw $\triangle A_1B_1C_1$, the reflection image of $\triangle ABC$ over *l*. Then draw $\triangle A'B'C'$, the reflection image of $\triangle A_1B_1C_1$ over *m*.

24. How do *l* and *m* appear to be related? Parallel

25. Study $\triangle ABC$ and $\triangle A'B'C'$ in your drawing. Describe a single physical motion that would move $\triangle ABC$ onto $\triangle A'B'C'$. sliding

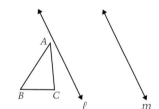

💻 **Computer Activities: Drawing and Measuring**

1. Draw a scalene triangle and a line that does not intersect the triangle. Reflect the triangle over the line. Draw a second line parallel to the first that does not intersect the reflected image of the triangle over the second line.

2. Repeat Exercise 1 with several other sets of parallel lines and triangles.

3. Draw two intersecting lines and a scalene triangle as shown. Reflect the triangle over one of the lines. Then reflect the image over the other line. If the reflected image of the triangle or the reflection of that image intersects one of the lines, modify your drawing so that neither image is intersected by a line.

4. Repeat Exercise 3 with several other sets of intersecting lines and triangles.

5. When the reflection lines are parallel, how is the *position* of the second reflection image related to that of the original triangle?

6. When the reflection lines intersect, how is the *position* of the second reflection image related to that of the original triangle?

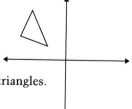

12-4 Translations

The photograph shows two parallel mirrors generating a repeating pattern. Figure 1 is the mirror reflection of a cardboard triangle placed between the mirrors. Figure 2 is the reflection image of Figure 1.

The result of two successive mirror reflections is called the composite of the reflections. This idea can be applied to any two transformations.

Figure 2

Figure 1

Definition *Composite of Transformations*

Let F and G be transformations. The composite of F and G is the transformation which maps each point P onto a point P′ as follows:

• *First P is mapped onto P_1 under transformation F.*
• *Then P_1 is mapped onto P′ under transformation G.*

The diagram at the right shows the image of $\triangle ABC$ under a composite of two line reflections: reflection over ℓ and then reflection over m. Notice that $\ell \parallel m$ and that it appears that $\triangle ABC$ "slides" onto $\triangle A'B'C'$. The definition below gives a mathematical description of the physical motion of sliding.

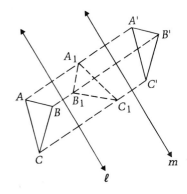

Definition *Translation*

A translation is a composite of two reflections over two parallel lines.

In the diagram, $AB = A_1B_1$ and $A_1B_1 = A'B'$ because line reflections are isometries. Thus, $AB = A'B'$. This suggests Theorem 12-7. Its proof is requested in Exercise 13.

12-4 *Translations*

527

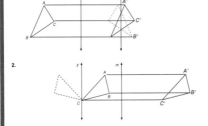

not find the lines of reflection to find the image of a given point. Discuss the method used in **Example 1**.

Have students prove some of the properties of a translation. Discuss the similarities and differences between translations and reflections.

Additional Examples

Example 1

If a translation maps A onto A', find the image of B. Complete parallelogram $AA'B'B$

Theorem 12-7

A translation is an isometry.

It follows that translations share all the properties of isometries:

- Distance, collinearity, betweenness, and angle measure are preserved.
- A line maps onto a line, a ray onto a ray, a segment onto a segment, and a triangle onto a congruent triangle.

Other properties of translations are suggested by the diagram at the right.

How do $\overleftrightarrow{AC}$ and $\overleftrightarrow{A'C'}$ seem to be related? $\overleftrightarrow{AB}$ and $\overleftrightarrow{A'B'}$? **∥; ∥**

What appears to be true about $\overline{AA'}$, $\overline{BB'}$, and $\overline{CC'}$? AA', BB', and CC'? **They are ∥. They are =.**

How is $\overline{AA'}$ related to ℓ and m? **It is twice the distance.**

How does AA' compare with the distance between ℓ and m?

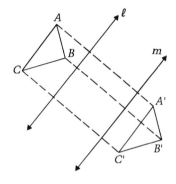

These additional properties of translations are listed below. (For the rest of this chapter, in order to simplify the statements of properties, we will extend our definition of parallel lines to include: Every line is parallel to itself.)

Under a translation that maps A onto A' and B onto B':
- $\overleftrightarrow{AB} \parallel \overleftrightarrow{A'B'}$
- $\overline{AA'} \parallel \overline{BB'}$
- $AA' = BB'$
- $\overline{AA'}$ is perpendicular to each of the parallel lines of reflection that define the translation
- AA' is twice the distance between the parallel lines of reflection that define the translation.

The constant distance AA' is called the ***magnitude*** of the translation.

Example 1

A translation maps R onto R'. Find the image of S.

Solution

Draw the parallelogram having S, R, and R' as three of its vertices, and $\overline{RR'}$ as a side. S' is the fourth vertex.

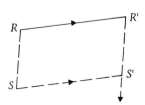

Assignment Guide

Basic: 1–7, 17–22
Average: 1–12, 17–22
Extended: 1–22

Example 2

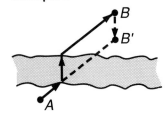

Example 2

Two campsites, A and B, are separated by a river. Where should a bridge, perpendicular to the river banks, be located so that the route connecting the sites is as short as possible?

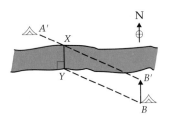

Solution

Use a translation with magnitude the width of the river and direction per pendicular to the banks of the river. Let B' be the image of B under the translation. Let X be the intersection of $\overline{AB'}$ with the north bank. Locate the bridge at X.

Exercise 8 explores why the route from A to X to Y to B is the shortest way from A to B via a bridge.

Checking for Understanding

Name the image of each figure under the composite: reflection over j and then reflection over k.

1. X A
2. $\overline{YZ}$ $\overline{BC}$
3. $\angle XZY$ $\angle ACB$
4. $\triangle XYZ$ $\triangle ABC$

5. Refer to the diagram on page 527. Would the image of $\triangle ABC$ still be $\triangle A'B'C'$ if the composite were changed to: reflection over m and then reflection over ℓ? **No**

6. Refer to the last two properties on page 528. Are these properties also true for $\overline{BB'}$ and BB'? Explain.

7. Does a translation reverse or preserve orientation? **Preserve**

8. Draw lines ℓ, m, and $\overleftrightarrow{AB}$ with $\ell \parallel m$ and $\overleftrightarrow{AB} \perp \ell$. Draw the image of $\overleftrightarrow{AB}$ under the composite: reflection over ℓ and then reflection over m.

9. Suppose we had not extended our definition of parallel lines. Which properties of translations would not hold for the translation in Exercise 8? $\overleftrightarrow{AB} \parallel \overleftrightarrow{A'B'}$, $\overline{AA'} \parallel \overline{BB'}$
6. Yes, true for any pt. and its image

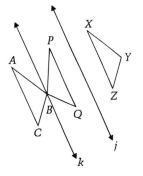

Written Exercises

Set A
1. Trace points X, Y, and Z at the right. Find the image of Z under a translation that maps X onto Y.

2. Graph points $S(2, 2)$, $T(-2, 3)$, $U(0, -2)$, and $V(3, -4)$. Find the images of S, T, U, and V under a translation that maps $W(-4, -3)$ onto $W'(-2, -2)$.

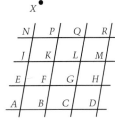

In the tessellation at the right, a translation maps A onto F. Find the image of

3. E. **K** **4.** K. **Q** **5.** $\overline{AE}$. $\overline{FK}$ **6.** $\angle EJK$. **7.** $\square BCGF$.

$\angle KPQ$ $\square GHML$ $\angle EJK$

2. $S'(4, 3)$, $T'(0, 4)$, $U'(2, -1)$, $V'(5, -3)$

While running an obstacle course, Gloria must cross a strip of mud to get from A to B. To spend as little time in the mud as possible, she decides to cut across perpendicular to the strip of mud. What is her shortest path from A to B?

Error Analysis Some students may tend to draw a reflection over one line or draw a reflection and then a translation when only a translation is required. Point out that a translation consists of two consecutive reflections over a pair of parallel lines.

ANSWERS

Checking for Understanding

8.

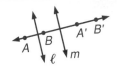

Written Exercises

1.

8.

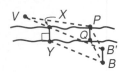

Both *XYBB'* and *PQBB'* are □s
(Opp. sides = and ∥). So *AX + XY
+ YB = AX + XB' + B'B* and *AP
+ PQ + QB = AP + PB' + B'B*.
By the △ Inequality Thm., *AX +
XB' < AP + PB'*, so *AX + XB' +
B'B < AP + PB' + B'B*. Thus, by
substitution, *AX + XY + YB < AP
+ PQ + QB*.

9.

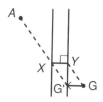

$\overline{XY}$ represents the crosswalk.

10. Sample:

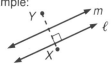

FOLLOW-UP

More Practice

• **Worksheet 12–4**

Extension

Have students try the following
problems.
1. Find the image of (4, −2) under
a translation that maps (−1, 6)
onto (2, 2). (7, −6)
2. Find the image of (x, y) under a
translation that maps (a, b) onto
(c, d). (x + c − a, y + d − b)
• **Extension 12–4**

Computers

• **Computer Worksheet 12–4**

Set B   **8.** Trace the diagram in Example 2. Mark any other
point *P* on the north bank and draw bridge $\overline{PQ}$.
Show that *AX + XY + YB < AP + PQ + QB*.
(HINT: Find equal distances in □*XYBB'* and □*PQBB'*,
and apply the Triangle Inequality Theorem.)

9. A school plans to build a crosswalk over Grant
Street perpendicular to the sides of the street.
Trace the diagram and show how to find the
location of the crosswalk so the route from the
auditorium *A* to the gym *G* is as short as possible.

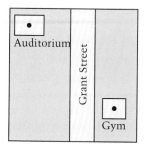

10. Trace points *X* and *Y* in Exercise 1. Use the
properties of translations to draw lines *ℓ* and *m* so
that *Y* is the image of *X* under the composite:
reflection over *ℓ* and then reflection over *m*.

11. Are the two lines you drew in Exercise 10 the only
ones that will work?   **No**

12. In the wallpaper print shown at the right, the
arrows suggest that the flowers can be translated
onto flowers congruent to themselves. Find a
similar example of a wallpaper or fabric print.
Answers will vary.

Set C   **13.** Prove Theorem 12-7.

Given: A translation maps *A* onto *A'* and *B* onto *B'*.

14. Prove: $\overline{AB} \parallel \overline{A'B'}$

15. Prove: $\overline{AA'} \parallel \overline{BB'}$ and *AA' = BB'*

16. Find the coordinates of the image of *P(x, y)* under
a translation that maps *O(0, 0)* onto *A(a, b)*.
(x + a, y + b)

◆ **Review**   Trace the diagram at the right.

17. Draw point *G* on *n* such that *HG + GK* is as small
as possible.

18. Why is *HG + GK < HE + EK* for any other point *E* on *n*?

19. Under an isometry, a triangle and its image are ___?___.
19. ≅
20. Define *secant*.   **21.** Draw a regular hexagon.
20. A line that intersects a ⊙ in 2 pts.

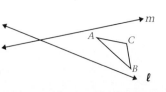

≡ **Thinking** **22.** Trace the diagram at the right. Draw △*A'B'C'*, the
 Ahead   image of △*ABC* under the composite: Reflection
over *ℓ* and then reflection over *m*. Describe a
single motion that would move △*ABC* onto △*A'B'C'*.
Rotation

12-5 Rotations

The composite of two reflections over parallel lines is a translation. Consider now the composite of two reflections over intersecting lines.

In the diagram at the right, a reflection over ℓ maps $\triangle ABC$ onto $\triangle A_1B_1C_1$, and a reflection over m maps $\triangle A_1B_1C_1$ onto $\triangle A'B'C'$.

Notice that if the triangles were on a turntable with center at P, $\triangle ABC$ could be rotated to the position of $\triangle A'B'C'$.

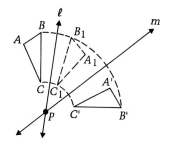

Definition   *Rotation*

A rotation is the composite of two reflections over two intersecting lines.

The point of intersection of the two lines is called the **center of the rotation**. The direction of the rotation can be either clockwise or counterclockwise. $\triangle ABC$ above was rotated in a clockwise direction about center P.

In the diagram above, $AB = A_1B_1$ and $A_1B_1 = A'B'$. Why? Thus, $AB = A'B'$. This suggests Theorem 12-8. Its proof is requested in Exercise 19. A line reflection is an isometry.

Theorem 12-8

A rotation is an isometry.

It follows that rotations share all the properties of isometries:
- Distance, collinearity, betweenness, and angle measure are preserved.
- A line maps onto a line, a ray onto a ray, a segment onto a segment, and a triangle onto a congruent triangle.

A counterclockwise rotation with center P is shown at the right. Trace the diagram. Draw and measure $\angle APA'$, $\angle BPB'$, and $\angle CPC'$. How are these measures related? They are equal.

Measure the acute angle formed by ℓ and m. How does this measure compare with those found above? $\frac{1}{2}$

Your observations should agree with the properties of rotations listed on the next page.

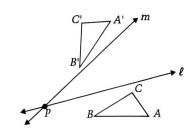

LESSON 12-5

Resources

Compass
Transparencies
   Teaching Aid 30, rotations
   Visual Aid 30, rotations
Worksheet 12-5
Extension 12-5
Quiz 12

OBJECTIVE

State and apply properties of rotations.

TEACHING NOTES

Use the following **activity** to help students visualize rotations.
1. Have the same triangle drawn on two separate transparencies

WORKSHEET

Name _____   Lesson 12-5

A rotation is a composite of two reflections over two intersecting lines. As with a translation, a rotation is a single transformation, even though two lines are involved.

In each case, reflect the point first over ℓ, and then over m. Label the image of the second reflection A', B', C', and D', respectively.

1.   2.

3.   4.

A has now been rotated about P, the intersection of the two lines, while B has been rotated about X, C has been rotated about Q, and D has been rotated about Y. Using a protractor, find the magnitude of each rotation.

5. $m\angle APA'$ 120°   6. $m\angle BXB'$ 90°

7. $m\angle CQC'$ 180°   8. $m\angle DYD'$ 50°

Using a ruler, find the following to the nearest tenth of a centimeter.

9. AP 2.0 cm   10. $A'P$ 2.0 cm   11. BX 2.2 cm   12. $B'X$ 2.2 cm

13. CQ 1.8 cm   14. $C'Q$ 1.8 cm   15. AA' 3.4 cm   16. BB' 3.2 cm

17. In each case, was the point rotated about the intersection of the two lines in a clockwise or counterclockwise direction? clockwise

18. What else did you observe? Answers will vary.

and place both on the projector so that the triangles coincide.
2. Place a compass point at the desired center of rotation and turn the top transparency.
3. Locate and draw the two lines of reflection.
  Explain that the lines intersect at the center of rotation.

Additional Examples

Example 1

Find the image of P under a clockwise rotation about O of magnitude 90.

Under a rotation with center P that maps A onto A' and B onto B' (such that P is not on $\overline{AA'}$ or $\overline{BB'}$):
- $m\angle APA' = m\angle BPB'$
- $m\angle APA'$ is twice the measure of the acute angle formed by the intersecting lines of reflection that define the rotation.

The measure of $\angle APA'$ is called the **magnitude** of the rotation. If P lies on $\overline{AA'}$, the magnitude is 180 and the intersecting lines are perpendicular. In this case, the rotation is simply a half-turn, or point reflection, as shown at the right.

How do $\overleftrightarrow{AB}$ and $\overleftrightarrow{A'B'}$ appear to be related? While a line is parallel to its image under a translation, the same is true for a rotation only when the rotation is a half-turn. They are ∥

Example
Find the image of X under a clockwise rotation with center O and magnitude 135.

Solution
Draw $\overrightarrow{OX}$, and then a ray that forms a 135° angle with $\overrightarrow{OX}$ in a clockwise direction. Locate X' on this new ray so that $OX' = OX$. Then X' is the rotation image of X.

Checking for Understanding
1. The magnitude of a rotation is greater than __?__ and less than __?__. 0; 180

2. If $j \perp k$, then a reflection over j followed by a reflection over k is equivalent to a __?__. half-turn (or pt. reflection)

3. If the lines of reflection are not given, what information is needed to determine the rotation image of a given point?

4. Does a rotation preserve or reverse orientation? Preserve

Under what conditions is the composite of two line reflections the given transformation?

5. A translation   **6.** A rotation

7. The identity transformation

8. The composite of a clockwise rotation with center P, magnitude 70, and __?__ is the identity transformation.

3. The center; the magnitude, and the direction
5. The lines of reflection are ∥.
6. The lines of reflection intersect
7. The lines of reflection coincide
8. clockwise rotation with center P, magnitude 70

Assignment Guide

Basic: 1–9, 13–18, 22–27
Average: 1–18, 21–27
Extended: 1–27

Written Exercises

Set A   Refer to the regular hexagon at the right.

A rotation with center O maps A onto C.

1. Name the image of B. **D**   **2.** Name the image of $\overline{DE}$. **FA**

3. Give the magnitude and direction of this rotation.
120; clockwise

A rotation with center O maps E onto D.

4. Name the image of O. **O**   **5.** Name the image of ∠EFA. **∠DEF**

6. Give the magnitude and direction of this rotation.
6. 60; counterclockwise

7. Name the image of $\overline{AB}$ under a half-turn about O.
DE

8. Trace point R and $\overline{ST}$. Draw the image of $\overline{ST}$ under a 120° counterclockwise rotation about R.

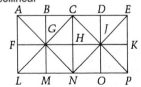

9. Graph A(2, 2), B(−2, 3), C(0, −2), and D(3, −4). Find the images of A, B, C, and D under a clockwise rotation with center O(0, 0) and magnitude 90. **9. A′(2, −2); B′(3, 2); C′(−2, 0); D′(−4 −3)**

Set B   **10.** Trace points O, X, and X′ from the Example on page 532. Use the properties of rotations to draw lines ℓ and m so that X′ is the image of X under the composite: reflection over ℓ and then reflection over m. Are ℓ and m the only lines that work? **No**

Under a half-turn with center H, points J and K are mapped onto J′ and K′, respectively.

11. $\overrightarrow{JK}$ __?__ $\overrightarrow{J'K'}$ ∥   **12.** When do $\overrightarrow{JK}$ and $\overrightarrow{J'K'}$ coincide?
12. When J, K and H are collinear

In this tessellation with isosceles right triangles, name an isometry that maps **Samples are given.**

13. △LFG onto △ABG.   **14.** △HJN onto △HJN.

15. △ABG onto △CDJ.   **16.** △LFG onto △AFG.

17. △CHG onto △NHJ.   **18.** △LFG onto △GFA.

Set C   **19.** Prove Theorem 12-8.

20. Prove: The composite of two reflections over perpendicular lines is a half-turn.

21. Find the coordinates of the image of P(x, y) under a 90° clockwise rotation with center O(0, 0).
(y, −x)

13. 90° clockwise rotation about G
14. Identity transformation
15. Translation that maps A onto C
16. Reflection over $\overleftrightarrow{FG}$
17. Half-turn about H
18. 90° counterclockwise rotation about F

Example 2

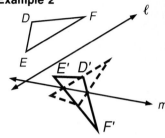

Rotate △DEF over ℓ and m. Locate △D′E′F′.

Error Analysis   Given a center of rotation, a direction and a magnitude, students are often not aware that we can find the image of any point under the rotation without using the intersecting lines of reflection. This will be clarified with practice.

ANSWERS

Written Exercises

8.

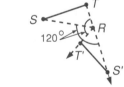

9.

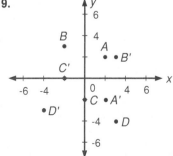

More Practice

• Worksheet 12–5

Extension

Have students do problems like **Exercise 21** for the following rotations and ask them to guess the coordinate rule for each.
1. Clockwise 90 about (0, 0) $(x, y) \rightarrow (y, -x)$
2. Counterclockwise 90 about (0, 0). $(x, y) \rightarrow (-y, x)$
3. 180 about (0, 0) $(x, y) \rightarrow (-x, -y)$
• Extension 12–5

ANSWERS

Progress Check

7. Draw U', the reflection image of U over $\overleftrightarrow{VW}$. Draw $\overline{TU'}$. P is the intersection of $\overline{TU'}$ and $\overleftrightarrow{VW}$.
8. Locate Q as P was located in Exercise 7.
9. A translation "slides" a figure. A translation is a composite of two reflections over parallel lines.
10.

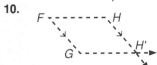

11. A rotation "turns" a figure. A rotation is a composite of two reflections over intersecting lines.
12.

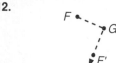

◆ **Review** A translation maps A onto A' and B onto B'.
22. $\overrightarrow{AB} \underline{\ ?\ } \overleftrightarrow{A'B'}$. ∥   **23.** $AA' \underline{\ ?\ } BB'$ =

24. A golf ball G is aimed at H', the reflection image of H over ℓ. Why does $m\angle 1 = m\angle 3$? $m\angle 1 = m\angle 2$ (vert.$\angle$s) and $m\angle 2 = m\angle 3$(isometry)
A circle has a radius of 9 cm.

25. Find its area.   **26.** Find the length of a 30° arc.
$81\,\pi$ cm² or about 254.3 cm²   **26.** $1.5\,\pi$ cm or about 4.7 cm

≡ **Thinking Ahead** **27.** Work with a partner. Describe a characteristic common to all three figures at the right. Draw another figure that shares this characteristic.

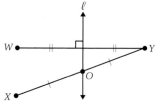

Progress Check

Lesson 12-1, page 515
1. Can two points have the same image under a transformation? No
2. The image of Y under a line reflection over ℓ is $\underline{\ ?\ }$. W
3. The image of Y under a half-turn about O is $\underline{\ ?\ }$. X

Lesson 12-2, page 519
An isometry maps A, B, and C onto A', B', and C', respectively.
4. If $AB = 14$, then $A'B' = \underline{\ ?\ }$. 14   **5.** $\triangle ACB \cong \underline{\ ?\ }$ $\triangle A'C'B'$
6. The image of $\overleftrightarrow{AB}$ is $\underline{\ ?\ }$. $\overleftrightarrow{A'B'}$

Lesson 12-3, page 523
Explain how to locate the specified point on $\overleftrightarrow{VW}$.
7. Point P such that $m\angle TPV = m\angle UPW$
8. Point Q such that $TQ + QU$ is minimal

Lesson 12-4, page 527
9. Describe a translation. Then define it mathematically.
10. Trace F, G and H. A translation maps F onto G. Draw the image of H.

Lesson 12-5, page 531
11. Describe a rotation. Then define it mathematically.
12. Trace F and G. Draw the image of F under a counterclockwise rotation with center G and magnitude 90.

Warm-Up Review

1. What is the image of C under a reflection over line ℓ? A
2. What is the image of C under a reflection over line m? D
3. What is the image of C under a reflection through point O? A
4. What is the image of C under a 90-degree clockwise rotation about O? D
5. What is the image of E under a reflection over line m? E

LESSON 12–6

Resources

Teaching Aid 5, graphs
Visual Aid 5, graphs
Worksheet 12–6
Extension 12–6

12-6 Symmetry

The property of symmetry is illustrated by the dogface butterfly and the harlequin beetle pictured. Observe that each figure coincides roughly with its reflection image over ℓ.

Definition   *Line Symmetry*

A plane figure has line symmetry if and only if there is a line ℓ such that the figure coincides with its reflection image over ℓ. Line ℓ is called a line of symmetry or a symmetry line for the figure.

We can show that the perpendicular bisector of the base of an isosceles triangle is a symmetry line for the triangle. Since $AB = AC$, A is on the perpendicular bisector of $\overline{BC}$. Why? So, by the definition of line reflection, reflection over $\overleftrightarrow{AD}$ maps A onto A and B and C onto each other. Thus, $\triangle ABC$ is its own image under a reflection over $\overleftrightarrow{AD}$. So $\overleftrightarrow{AD}$ is a symmetry line.

In a plane the locus of points equidistant from two given points is the ⊥ bisector of the segment joining the two points.

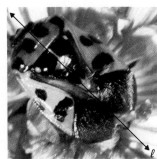

Example 1

Draw the symmetry lines, if any, of a rectangle.

Solution

A rectangle has two lines of symmetry—the perpendicular bisectors of the sides. ℓ and m at the right are the lines of symmetry.

Designs and symbols often exhibit symmetry. Which of the symbols at the right exhibit line symmetry? The first two.

The third symbol exhibits point symmetry which is defined next.

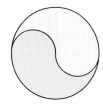

OBJECTIVE

Examine various figures for point, line and rotational symmetry.

TEACHING NOTES

Introduce line symmetry by using a paper-folding **activity**. Have students explore figures that include more than one line of symmetry.

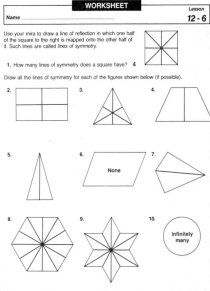

WORKSHEET   Lesson 12-6

Name _____

Use your mira to draw a line of reflection in which one half of the square to the right is mapped onto the other half of it. Such lines are called *lines of symmetry*.

1. How many lines of symmetry does a square have? 4

Draw all the lines of symmetry for each of the figures shown below (if possible).

2.   3.   4.

5.   6. None   7.

8.   9.   10. Infinitely many

11. Which figures exhibit point symmetry? (List figure numbers.) 1, 2, 3, 8, 9, and 10

12. Which figures exhibit rotational symmetry? (List figure numbers.) 1, 2, 3, 8, 9, and 10

Every creased line that folds half the figure onto itself is a line of symmetry.

When discussing point symmetry, point out that a point reflection is a 180-degree rotation. Thus, to determine point symmetry, rotate the figure 180 degrees clockwise or counterclockwise. It has point symmetry if it looks exactly the same. Rotational symmetry of other magnitudes can be treated in the same way.

Additional Examples

Example 1

Draw all the symmetry lines of a square.

Definition *Point Symmetry*

A plane figure has point symmetry if and only if there is a point P such that the figure and its image coincide under a reflection through P.

The diagonals of a parallelogram bisect each other.

The properties of a parallelogram suggest that a parallelogram has point symmetry. The diagonals of $\square ABCD$ bisect each other at P. Why? Therefore, A and C are the images of each other, as are B and D under a reflection through P. Hence, the images of $\overline{AB}$, $\overline{BC}$, $\overline{CD}$, and $\overline{DA}$ are $\overline{CD}$, $\overline{DA}$, $\overline{AB}$, and $\overline{BC}$, respectively. So a reflection through P maps $\square ABCD$ onto itself. We can say, then, that $\square ABCD$ has point symmetry about P.

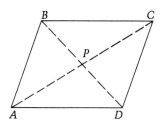

Point symmetry is a special case of rotational symmetry.

Definition *Rotational Symmetry*

A plane figure has rotational symmetry if and only if there is a rotation such that the figure and its image coincide under the rotation.

Example 2

Does each figure at the right have rotational symmetry? If so, give the magnitude and direction of each rotation that maps the figure onto itself.

Solution

Both figures have rotational symmetry. In the left figure, a rotation of magnitude 120, either clockwise or counterclockwise, maps the figure onto itself. For the right figure, rotations of magnitude 90 and 180, in both directions, map the figure onto itself.

Checking for Understanding

Refer to Example 2. Does either figure exhibit

1. line symmetry?   **2.** point symmetry?

3. How many symmetry lines does a circle have? Describe them.

4. Does a circle have rotational symmetry? If so, how many distinct rotations map the circle onto itself?

5. If a figure has two or more lines of symmetry, must it have rotational symmetry? Explain.

1. Yes, the right one.
2. Yes, the right one.
3. Infinitely many; any line containing the center.
4. Yes; infinitely many
5. Yes, the composite of reflections over any two lines of symmetry is a rotation

Assignment Guide

Basic: 1–15, 30–35
Average: 1–24, 30–35
Extended: 1–35

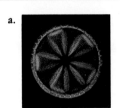
a.

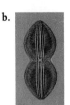
b.

c.

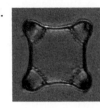
d.

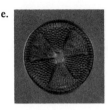
e.

Refer to the pictures above of *diatoms*. Diatoms are single-celled sea plants. Which pictures exhibit the given type of symmetry?

6. Line symmetry   **7.** Point symmetry   **8.** Rotational symmetry
a, b, c, d, e   b, d   a, b, d, e

Written Exercises

Set A   For each figure below:
   a. Determine the number of symmetry lines.
   b. Determine if the figure has point symmetry.
   c. Determine if the figure has rotational symmetry. If it does, state the magnitude and direction of each rotation that maps the figure onto itself.

1. a. 5; b. No; c. Yes: 72 and 144 in both directions
2. a. 0; b. No; c. Yes: 120 in both directions
3. a. 1; b. No; c. No
4. a. 8; b. Yes; c. Yes: 45, 90, 135, 180 in both directions
5. a. 5; b. No; c. Yes: 72 and 144 in both directions
6. a. 4; b. Yes; c. Yes: 90 and 180 in both directions
7. a. 0; b. Yes; c. Yes: 180 in both directions
8. a. 6; b. Yes; c. Yes: 60, 120, 180 in both directions

1.

2.

3.

4.

5.

6.

7.

8.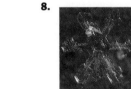

9.    **10.**    **11.**   **12.**

Refer to the alphabet as it is printed at the right.

13. The letter A has a *vertical* symmetry line. List the other letters that have vertical symmetry lines.

14. The letter E has a *horizontal* symmetry line. List the other letters that have horizontal symmetry lines. B, C, D, H, I, O, X

15. List the letters that have point symmetry. H, I, N, O, S, X, Z

13. H, I, M, O, T, U, V, W, X, Y

Z A B C D E F
G H I J K L M
N O P Q R S T
U V W X Y Z A

Example 2

(a)   (b)

Does each of these figures have rotational symmetry? If so, give the magnitude and direction of each rotation that maps the figure onto itself. (a) yes, 120 either way; (b) yes, 90 and 180 either way

Error Analysis   Students often mistakenly state that a figure with point symmetry has line symmetry. Let them try many fold lines to convince them that it does not.

ANSWERS

Written Exercises

9. 2; yes; yes, 180 in both directions
10. 1; no; no
11. infinitely many; yes; yes, 180 in both directions
12. 1; no; no

FOLLOW-UP

More Practice

• Worksheet 12–6

Extension

Our everyday experience gives many examples of various types of symmetry. Have students find examples of point, line and rotational symmetry in the following.
1. Trademarks.
2. Corporate logos.
3. National flags.
• Extension 12–6

Set B Draw a figure that satisfies the given conditions. If impossible, write *not possible*.

Samples:

16.

17.

18.

16. A triangle with both line and rotational symmetries

17. A triangle with only line symmetry

18. A quadrilateral with four symmetry lines

19. A quadrilateral with line symmetry but no rotational symmetry

19.

21.

20. An angle with no lines of symmetry Impossible

21. A pentagon with no rotational symmetry

22. A figure with rotational symmetry, magnitude 45

22.

23. A figure with rotational symmetry, magnitude 13

24. Prove that the perpendicular bisector of a side of a rectangle is a symmetry line for the rectangle.
23. Impossible

Set C A figure contains the point $P(a, b)$. Give the coordinates of another point on the figure if the figure has the symmetry described below.

25. the y-axis as a line of symmetry $(-a, b)$

26. the x-axis as a line of symmetry $(a, -b)$

27. Point symmetry about $O(0, 0)$ $(-a, -b)$

28. How many symmetry lines does a regular n-gon have?
n

29. How many distinct rotations map a regular n-gon onto itself? $n - 1$

preserve

▲ Review **30.** Define *rotation*.   **31.** Rotations ___?___ orientation.

32. A translation maps $A(2, -6)$ onto $B(1, -2)$. Find the coordinates of the image of $C(3, 4)$. $(2, 8)$

33. Find the distance between A and B in Exercise 32. $\sqrt{17}$

34. Prove indirectly: If $m\angle 1 = 49$, then $\angle 1$ is not an obtuse angle.
30. A rotation is the composite of 2 reflections over 2 intersecting lines.

≡ Thinking Ahead **35.** Do you think there is an isometry that maps Flower A onto Flower B? If so, is this isometry a line reflection? a point reflection? a translation? a rotation? Explain your thinking.

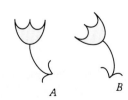

A B

12-7 A Second Look at Congruence

Theorem 12-6 states that under an isometry a triangle and its image are congruent. Now consider the converse of Theorem 12-6. If two triangles are congruent, do you think that an isometry can be found that maps one of the triangles onto the other?

Study the congruent triangles shown at the right. A method for finding a composite of line reflections that maps $\triangle ABC$ onto $\triangle A'B'C'$ can be specified as follows.

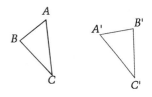

1. Let ℓ_1 be the perpendicular bisector of $\overline{AA'}$. Then $\triangle A'B_1C_1$ is the reflection image of $\triangle ABC$ over ℓ_1.

   If $B_1 = B'$ and $C_1 = C'$, then ℓ_1 is the only line of reflection needed. If $B_1 \neq B'$, then find a second line of reflection as follows.

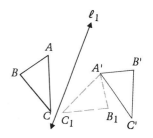

2. Let ℓ_2 be the perpendicular bisector of $\overline{B_1B'}$. Then $\triangle A'B'C_2$ is the reflection image of $\triangle A'B_1C_1$ over ℓ_2.

   If $C_2 = C'$, then ℓ_1 and ℓ_2 are the only lines of reflection needed. If not, then find a third line.

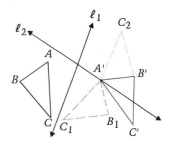

3. Let ℓ_3 be the perpendicular bisector of $\overline{C_2C'}$. Then $\triangle A'B'C'$ is the reflection image of $\triangle A'B'C_2$ over ℓ_3.

Thus, the composite of reflections over ℓ_1, then over ℓ_2, and then over ℓ_3 maps $\triangle ABC$ onto $\triangle A'B'C'$. This composite is an isometry. Why? In Exercise 13, you are asked to prove that this isometry is unique. These ideas are summarized in Theorem 12-9, the converse of Theorem 12-6.

Each line reflection is an isometry.

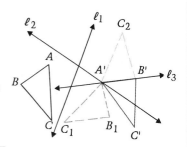

Theorem 12-9

In a plane, if $\triangle ABC \cong \triangle A'B'C'$, then there is a unique isometry that maps $\triangle ABC$ onto $\triangle A'B'C'$.

LESSON 12-7

Resources

Compass
Protractor
Straightedge
Teaching Aid 29, reflections
Visual Aid 29, reflections
Teaching Aid 30, rotations
Visual Aid 30, rotations
Worksheet 12-7
Extension 12-7
Computer Activities 12-7

OBJECTIVE

Use isometries to extend the concept of congruence.

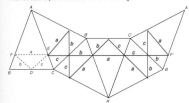
We can now give a definition of congruence which applies to all geometric figures in a plane.

Definition *Congruent Figures*

Two plane figures are congruent if and only if there is an isometry that maps one figure onto the other.

In the Escher drawing at the right, II and III are reflection images of each other through point A. Hence, they are congruent. Also, I and III are congruent because a translation maps one figure onto the other.

Theorem 12-9 guarantees that if two plane figures are congruent, there is a unique isometry that maps one figure onto the other. The method for specifying this isometry, as shown for triangles on page 539, suggests the striking result expressed in Theorem 12-10. The proof of this theorem is omitted.

Theorem 12-10

Every isometry can be expressed as a composite of at most three line reflections.

Checking for Understanding

1. If $\triangle ABC \cong \triangle DEF$ by the definition in Chapter 5, are the triangles also congruent by the new definition? Explain.

2. If $\triangle ABC \cong \triangle DEF$ by the new definition, are the triangles also congruent by the definition in Chapter 5? Explain.

Assignment Guide

Basic: 1–8, 18–21
Average: 1–12, 14–21
Extended: 1–21

An isometry maps noncollinear points P, Q, and R onto P', Q', and R', respectively. Explain why each statement is true.

3. $PQ = P'Q'$ **4.** $\overline{PQ} \cong \overline{P'Q'}$

5. $m\angle PQR = m\angle P'Q'R'$ **6.** $\angle PQR \cong \angle P'Q'R'$

Consider a composite of seven line reflections.

7. Is this composite an isometry? Explain.

8. Does this composite reverse or preserve orientation?

9. Can this composite be expressed as a composite of three line reflections? two line reflections? Explain.

10. $\triangle ABC \cong \triangle A'B'C'$, and the two triangles have the same orientation. Why must $\triangle A'B'C'$ be the image of $\triangle ABC$ under either a translation or a rotation?

Refer to $\triangle ABC$ and $\triangle A'B'C'$ on page 539.

11. Are ℓ_1, ℓ_2, and ℓ_3, the only lines of reflection that map $\triangle ABC$ onto $\triangle A'B'C'$? Explain.

12. If there does exist a second set of lines of reflection that maps $\triangle ABC$ onto $\triangle A'B'C'$, is the composite of reflections over these three lines a different isometry than the composite of reflections over ℓ_1, ℓ_2, and ℓ_3? Explain.

3. By def. of isometry
4. By def. of $\cong$ figures
5. An isometry preserves $\angle$meas.
6. By def. of $\cong$ figures
7. Yes; each line reflection is an isometry, so any given distance is preserved.
9. Yes; no; since the orientation is reversed, the composite can be expressed as either one line reflection or a composite of 3 line reflections. (One line reflection can be expressed as a composite of 3 line reflections over the same line.)
12. No; by Thm. 12-9, the isometry is unique.

EXERCISE NOTES

Checking for Understanding
Exercise 10 assumes triangles ABC and $A'B'C'$ do not coincide.
   Exercise 11 shows how three noncollinear points and their images determine the unique isometry that maps any figure onto a congruent one.

ANSWERS

Checking for Understanding

1. Yes; by Thm. 12–9, there is an isometry that maps $\triangle ABC$ onto $\triangle DEF$. So $\triangle ABC \cong \triangle DEF$ by the new definition.
2. Yes; by the new definition, an isometry maps $\triangle ABC$ onto $\triangle DEF$. Since an isometry preserves distance and $\angle$ measure, $AB = DE$, $AC = DF$, $BC = EF$, $m\angle A = m\angle D$, $m\angle B = m\angle E$ and $m\angle C = m\angle F$. Hence, $\triangle ABC = \triangle DEF$ by the definition in Chapter 5.
10. By Thm. 12–10, the isometry that maps $\triangle ABC$ onto $\triangle A'B'C'$ can be expressed as a composite of 3 or fewer line reflections. Since orientation is preserved, the isometry is the composite of 2 line reflections. If the 2 lines of reflection are ∥, it is a translation. If they intersect, it is a rotation.
11. No; the first line of reflection drawn could have been the ⊥ bisector of $\overline{BB'}$ or $\overline{CC'}$.

Written Exercises

Set A   The figures in each exercise are congruent. Decide which of these isometries appear to map one figure onto the other: line reflection (L), rotation (R), half-turn (H), translation (T), or a composite of three line reflections (C).

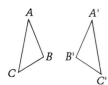

2.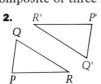

3.

4.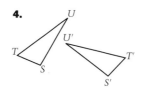

5.

6.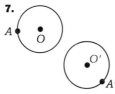

7.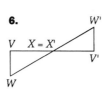

8.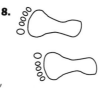

1. L   **2.** H or R   **3.** T   **4.** C

5. R   **6.** H or R   **7.** L   **8.** C

Written Exercises

11.

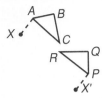

12. Sample:

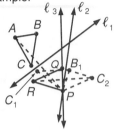

Computer Activities

1.

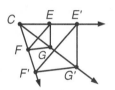

Yes; no; there is a one-to-one correspondence between the pts. and themselves, but distance is not preserved.

Set B Refer to the Escher drawing on page 540.

9. Study one of the points where the tails of three of the figures meet. What is the magnitude of the rotation that maps one of these figures onto another? 120

10. A 60° rotation maps some figures onto neighboring figures. Describe the center point of this rotation.
Point is at meeting of right fins.

Trace the diagram at the right.

11. An isometry maps $\triangle ABC$ onto $\triangle PQR$. Draw the image of X under this isometry.

12. Draw appropriate lines to map $\triangle ABC$ onto $\triangle PQR$ under a composite of reflections over the lines.

Set C **13.** Prove indirectly that the isometry in Theorem 12-9 is unique. (HINT: Assume that there are two distinct isometries that map $\triangle ABC$ onto $\triangle A'B'C'$. Let P' be the image of a point P under the first isometry, and let P^* be the image of P under the second isometry.)
2; the lines containing the diagonals

◆ Review **14.** A rhombus has _?_ symmetry lines. Describe them.

15. Draw a design that has rotational symmetry.

16. Trace the diagram at the right. Draw the image of $\overline{JK}$ under a 75° clockwise rotation about Q.

17. Can a triangle have side lengths 8, 12, and 20? Explain.

18. Find the volume of a cube with total area 1,350 cm². 3,375 cm³

≋ Thinking Graph $\triangle ABC$ with vertices $A(0, 0)$, $B(3, 7)$, and $C(-2, 9)$.
▽ Ahead On the same grid, draw triangles whose vertices have

19. coordinates 3 times the coordinates of A, B, and C.

20. coordinates $\frac{1}{2}$ the coordinates of A, B, and C.

21. Is the correspondence between $\triangle ABC$ and each other triangle a transformation? an isometry? Explain.

15. Sample:

17. No, by the △ Inequality Thm. the sum of the lengths of any 2 sides > the length of the third side. 8 + 12 ≯ 20.

19. $A_1(0, 0)$, $B_1(9, 21)$, $C_1(-6, 27)$

20. $A'(0, 0)$, $B'\left(\frac{3}{2}, \frac{7}{2}\right)$, $C'\left(-1, \frac{9}{2}\right)$

21. Yes; no; there is a one-to-one correspondence between pts. and themselves, but distance is not preserved.

💻 Computer Activities: Drawing and Measuring

1. Draw $\triangle ABC$ and locate point D in its exterior. Then draw $\overrightarrow{DA}$ containing E such that $DE = 2DA$, $\overrightarrow{DB}$ containing F such that $DF = 2DB$, and $\overrightarrow{DC}$ containing G such that $DG = 2DC$. Draw $\triangle EFG$. Is the correspondence between $\triangle ABC$ and $\triangle EFG$ a transformation? an isometry? Explain.

2. Repeat the activity using a multiplier other than 2.
Answers will vary.

12-8 Dilations

Cartographers, or map makers, often need to alter the size but not the shape of a map. They sometimes use a pantograph like the one shown below. The rods are hinged so that $PQRS$ is always a parallelogram, and C, P, and P' are always collinear.

The pantograph is fastened down at C. As a pointer at P traces the shape of the map, a pencil at P' draws the same shape enlarged in size.

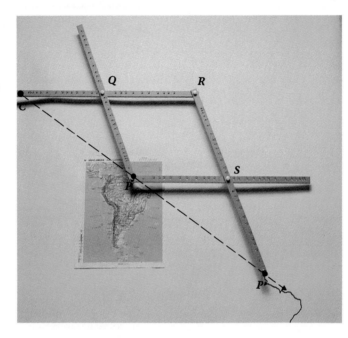

In every position of the pantograph, $\triangle CPQ \sim \triangle CP'R$, so $\dfrac{CR}{CQ} = \dfrac{CP'}{CP}$. If $\dfrac{CR}{CQ} = 2$, then $\dfrac{CP'}{CP} = 2$ and $CP' = 2(CP)$.

Thus, the pantograph can be used to set up a one-to-one correspondence which pairs any point P on the plane with an image point P'.

This correspondence can be interpreted in mathematical terms as a transformation of the plane.

Definition   *Dilation*

Let C be a point and k a positive real number. A dilation is a transformation that maps each point of the plane onto an image point as follows:
- *C is its own image.*
- *For any point P other than C, the image of P is the point P' on $\overrightarrow{CP}$ for which $CP' = k(CP)$*

C is called the **center** and k the **scale factor** of the dilation. The diagrams on the next page illustrate the definition.

12-8 *Dilations*

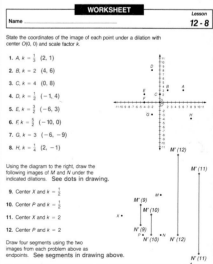

countries. Discuss the definition of a dilation.

As a construction **activity**, have students try sketches and perform dilations with a compass and straightedge.

Additional Example

Find dilations for $\triangle ABC$ with points $A(4, 0)$, $B(8, 2)$ and $C(6, 4)$ under the following conditions.

(a) Center at $(0, 0)$ and $k = 3$
$A'(12, 0)$, $B'(24, 6)$; $C'(18, 12)$

(b) Center at $(-5, 7)$ and $k = 1$
identity-original coordinates

(c) Center at $(3, 2)$ and $k = \frac{1}{2}$
$A'(3.5, 1)$, $B'(5.5, 2)$,
$C'(4.5, 3)$

Error Analysis

Unless they are given experience with scale factors less than one, students tend to think of dilations only in terms of enlargement. Be sure to include examples of dilations that are reductions.

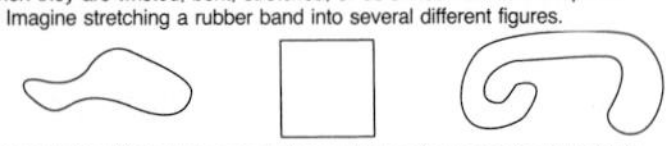

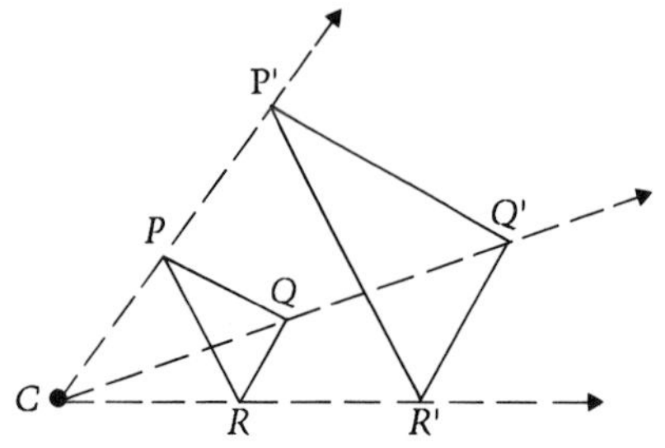

Center C; scale factor 2 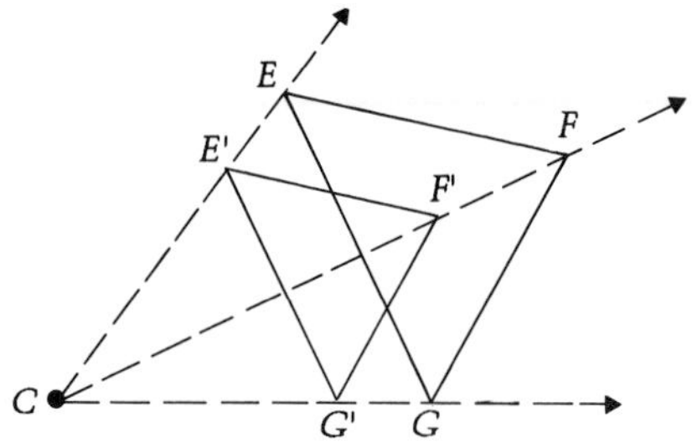   Center C; scale factor $\frac{3}{4}$

The diagrams suggest that a dilation preserves shape.

If $k > 1$, the dilation is an ***enlargement***.

If $k < 1$, the dilation is a ***reduction***.

If $k = 1$, the dilation is simply the identity transformation. Why?
Each point of the plane is mapped onto itself.

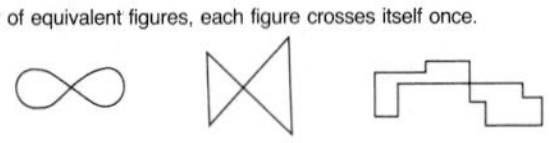

The diagram at the right illustrates an enlargement with center C and scale factor 3.

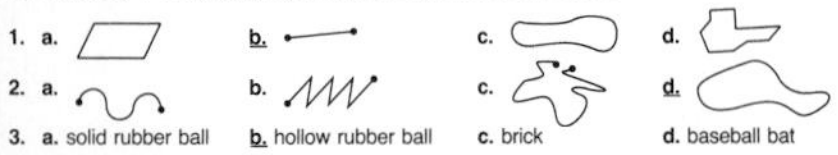

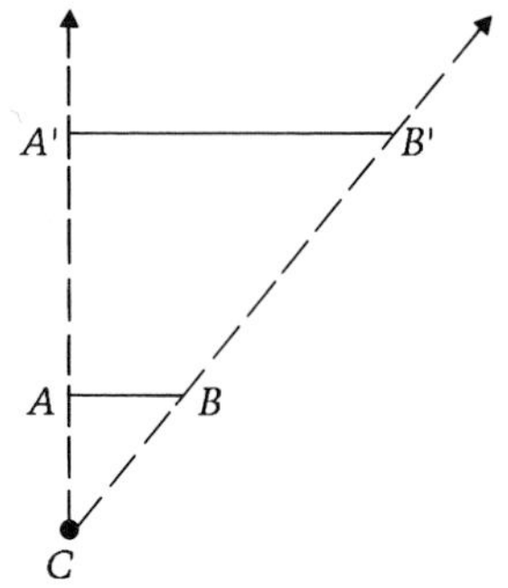

By definition $CA' = 3(CA)$, and $CB' = 3(CB)$. So $\frac{CA'}{CA} = 3 = \frac{CB'}{CB}$.

Since $m\angle ACB = m\angle A'CB'$, it follows that $\triangle ACB \sim \triangle A'CB'$. Why?
By SAS ~ Thm.
So $\frac{A'B'}{AB} = 3$ or $A'B' = 3(AB)$.

This idea is generalized in the next theorem. Its proof is left to Exercise 11.

Theorem 12-11

If a dilation with center C and scale factor k maps A onto A' and B onto B', then A'B' = k(AB).

Checking for Understanding

1. Under what circumstances is a dilation an isometry? Explain.

2. What is the scale factor of the dilation illustrated by the pantograph on page 543? **2**

3. Suppose the pointer and the pencil of the pantograph are interchanged. Compare the size of the map drawn by the pencil to the size of the map traced by the pointer, and state the scale factor of this dilation. $\frac{1}{2}$

1. When $k = 1$. If $k > 1$, the distance between two pts. in the image is greater than the corr. distance in the preimage. If $k < 1$, the distance in the image is less.

Assignment Guide

Basic: 1–8, 13–20
Average: 1–10, 12–20
Extended: 1–20

1.
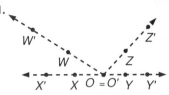

Name the image of *A* under a dilation with center *O* and scale factor *k*. Then state whether the dilation is an enlargement, a reduction, or the identity transformation.

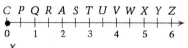

4. $k = 2$ *V*   **5.** $k = 1$ *A*   **6.** $k = \frac{1}{2}$ *Q*   **7.** $k = \frac{3}{4}$ *R*   **8.** $k = \frac{5}{2}$

9. Under a(n) __?__ the image is *farther* from the center than is the preimage, and under a(n) __?__ the image is *closer* to the center than is the preimage. **enlargement; reduction**

4. Enlargement
5. Identify Transformation
6–7. Reductions
8. Enlargement

2.
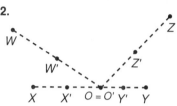

Written Exercises

Set A   For each exercise, trace the diagram at the right. Draw the image of each point under a dilation with center *O* and the scale factor given below.

   1. 2   **2.** $\frac{1}{2}$ **3.** 3   **4.** 0.25   **5.** $1\frac{1}{3}$ **6.** 1

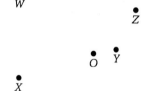

Set B   A dilation with center *C* and scale factor *k* maps *A* onto *A'* and *B* onto *B'*. For each exercise, draw a sketch and find the missing value.

   7. $CB = 12$; $CB' = 4$; $k = $ __?__ $\frac{1}{3}$
   8. $CB = 7$; $CB' = 7$; $k = $ __?__ 1
   9. $CA = 3$; $AA' = 9$; $k = $ __?__ 4
   10. $A'B' = 14$; $k = 2$; $AB = $ __?__ 7

Set C   **11.** Prove Theorem 12-11.

   12. Find the coordinates of the image of $P(x, y)$ under a dilation with center $O(0, 0)$ and scale factor *k*.
   (kx, ky)

▲ Review   **13.** Give two definitions of *congruent triangles*. Yes

   14. Is a composite of ten line reflections an isometry?

   15. Draw a hexagon with exactly one symmetry line.

   16. What is a *centroid?*   **17.** What is an *apothem?*

≡ Thinking Ahead   Graph $P(-2, 2)$, $Q(4, 5)$, $R(6, -2)$ and $S(2, 4)$.

   18. Find P', Q', R', and S', the images of *P*, *Q*, *R*, and *S*, respectively, under a dilation with center $O(0, 0)$ and scale factor 2.

   19. Draw $\triangle PQR$ and $\triangle P'Q'R'$. Where is *S?* Where is *S'?*

   20. What appears to be true about $\angle PQR$ and $\angle P'Q'R'$? $\triangle PQR$ and $\triangle P'Q'R'$?

13. (1) Two △s are ≅ if and only if there is a correspondence between the vertices of each pair of corr. sides and each pair of corr. ∠s are =. (2) Two △s are ≅ if and only if there is an isometry that maps one △ onto the other.

15. Sample:

11. The pt. of concurrency of the medians of a △
17. The distance from the center of a reg. polygon to each side

19. Between *P* and *Q*; between *P'* and *Q'*.
20. They are =; they are ~.

FOLLOW-UP

More Practice

• Worksheet 12–8

Extension

The following classic problem is difficult to solve without using a dilation.

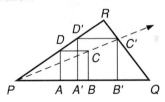

Given $\triangle PQR$, draw a square with one side on $\overline{PQ}$, a vertex on $\overline{PR}$ and another vertex on $\overline{QR}$. Draw any square with one side on $\overline{PQ}$ and a vertex on $\overline{PR}$. Draw $\overline{PC}$, intersecting $\overline{QR}$ at C'. Use a dilation with center *P* and scale factor $\frac{PC'}{PC}$ to find other vertices.

• Extension 12–8

Computers

• Computer Worksheet 12–8

LESSON 12-9

Resources

Worksheet 12-9
Extension 12-9

OBJECTIVE

State and apply properties of dilations.

TEACHING NOTES

Choose several examples like **Exercises 1-8** as an **activity** to introduce this lesson. After the drawings are done, ask students to make observations about what properties are preserved under a dilation.

When discussing Theorem 12-13, stress that it also guarantees

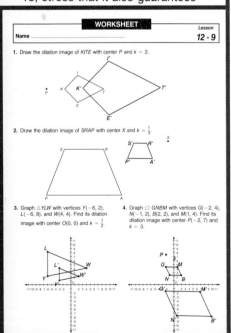

12-9 Properties of Dilations

A photographic enlargement can be viewed geometrically as a dilation with $k > 1$. Does the enlargement above appear to preserve collinearity? betweenness? angle measure? **Yes; yes; yes**

Theorem 12-12

A dilation preserves collinearity and betweenness of points.

Given Collinear points A, B and C with B between A and C; A', B', and C' the images of A, B, and C, respectively, under a dilation with center O and scale factor k.

Prove A', B', and C' are collinear; B' is between A' and C'.

Plan for Proof Use the Segment Addition Postulate and the Multiplication Property to get $k(AB) + k(BC) = k(AC)$. Using Theorem 12-11, substitute to show $A'B' + B'C' = A'C'$. Then this implies collinearity and betweenness by Theorem 5-13.

The next theorem follows from Theorem 12-12.

Theorem 12-13

If a dilation maps A onto A' and B onto B', then the image of $\overleftrightarrow{AB}$ is $\overleftrightarrow{A'B'}$, then the image of $\overrightarrow{AB}$ is $\overrightarrow{A'B'}$, and the image of $\overline{AB}$ is $\overline{A'B'}$.

Note that while a dilation maps a segment onto a segment, the image and preimage are equal in length only when the scale factor is 1.

Theorems 12-12 and 12-13 are not proved.

Assignment Guide

Basic: 1–19, 31–38
Average: 2–14 (even), 15–27, 31–38
Extended: 2–18 (even), 19–38

Compare the next two theorems to Theorems 12-5 and 12-6 involving isometries. Exercises 24 and 25 ask for Plans for Proof. Their proofs are omitted.

Theorem 12-14

A dilation preserves angle measure.

Theorem 12-15

Under a dilation, a triangle and its image are similar.

Recall that under a translation or a half-turn (point reflection), a line is parallel to its image. This is also true for dilations, as illustrated by the diagram at the right.

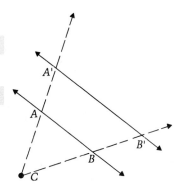

Checking for Understanding

A dilation with center C and scale factor 5 maps P onto P', Q onto Q', and R onto R'.

1. $CP = 3$; $CP' = \underline{?}$ 15   **2.** $CR' = 25$; $CR = \underline{?}$ 5

3. $QR = 6$; $Q'R' = \underline{?}$ 30   **4.** $P'R' = 20$; $PR = \underline{?}$ 4

5. If Q is between P and R, then $\underline{?}$ is between $\underline{?}$ and $\underline{?}$.

6. What is the image of $\overline{PQ}$? $\overrightarrow{RP}$? $\overleftrightarrow{QR}$? $\angle RPQ$? $\triangle PQR$?

7. If $m\angle PQR = 70$, then $m\angle P'Q'R' = \underline{?}$. 70

8. $\triangle QRP \underline{?} \triangle Q'R'P' \sim$ **9.** $\overline{PR} \parallel \underline{?}$ and $\overline{QR} \parallel \underline{?}$. $P'R'$; $Q'R'$

10. Explain how to find the image of any polygon under this dilation. Through each vertex V, draw $\overrightarrow{CV}$. On $\overrightarrow{CV}$ draw V' such that $CV' = 5(CV)$. Join the image vertices in the same order as their preimages are joined.

Written Exercises

Set A   For each exercise, trace $\triangle ABC$ and point O. Draw the image of $\triangle ABC$ under the indicated dilation.

     1. Center O and scale factor 2

     2. Center O and scale factor $\frac{1}{2}$

     3. Center A and scale factor $\frac{1}{3}$

     4. Center A and scale factor 3

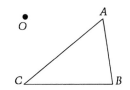

12-9 *Properties of Dilations*   547

---

that the images of an angle and a polygon under a dilation are an angle and a polygon, respectively.

Error Analysis   Students may have difficulty remembering the properties of dilations. Compare the properties of dilations with the other types of transformations and note similarities and differences.

ANSWERS

Written Exercises

1.

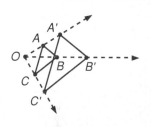

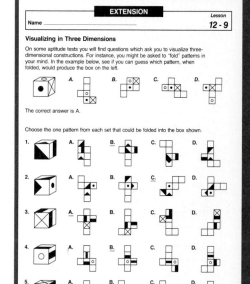

5.

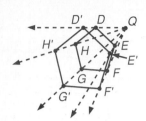

6.

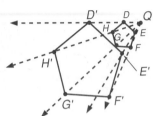

7.

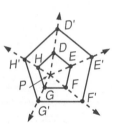

8.

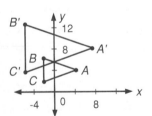

15.

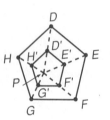

16.

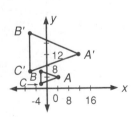

For each exercise, trace *DEFGH*, point *P*, and point *Q*. Draw the image of *DEFGH* under the indicated dilation.

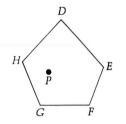

5. Center *Q* and scale factor $\frac{3}{2}$

6. Center *Q* and scale factor 2.5

7. Center *P* and scale factor $\frac{1}{2}$

8. Center *P* and scale factor 2

A dilation with center *C* and scale factor $\frac{3}{4}$ maps *X* onto *X'*, *Y* onto *Y'*, and *Z* onto *Z'*.

9. $CX = 8$; $CX' = \underline{\ ?\ }$ 6   **10.** $YZ = 20$; $Y'Z' = \underline{\ ?\ }$ 15

11. $X'Z' = 3$; $XZ = \underline{\ ?\ }$ 4   **12.** $CY' = 9$; $CY = \underline{\ ?\ }$ 12

13. $m\angle YZX = 55$; $m\angle Y'Z'X' = \underline{\ ?\ }$ 55

14. $\triangle X'Z'Y' \underline{\ ?\ } \triangle XZY \sim$

For each exercise, graph $\triangle ABC$ with vertices *A*(4, 4), *B*(−2, 6), and *C*(−2, 2). Find the image of $\triangle ABC$ under a dilation with center *O*(0, 0) and scale factor *k*.

15. $k = 2$ **16.** $k = 3$ **17.** $k = 0.5$ **18.** $k = 1$

19. Does a dilation preserve orientation? Yes

15. A'(8, 8), B'(−4, 12), C'(−4, 4)
16. A'(12, 12), B'(−6, 18), C'(−6, 6)
17. A'(2, 2), B'(−1, 3), C'(−1, 1)
18. A'(4, 4), B'(−2, 6), C'(−2, 2)

Set B   Trace the diagram at the right.

20. Find the center of the dilation that maps *A* onto *A'* and *B* onto *B'*.

21. Find the scale factor of the dilation in Exercise 20.   3

22. Is there a dilation that maps *A* onto *A'* and *C* onto *C'*? Explain.

23. Trace the diagram at the right. A dilation that maps *K* onto *K'* has its center on *m*. Find the image of *J* under this dilation.

24. Write a Plan for Proof for Theorem 12-14.

25. Write a Plan for Proof for Theorem 12-15.

At the right, $\overline{QR} \parallel \overline{ST}$. Find the center and scale factor of the dilation that maps

26. $\triangle PQR$ onto $\triangle PST$. P; $\frac{3}{2}$ **27.** $\triangle PST$ onto $\triangle PQR$. P; $\frac{2}{3}$

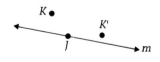

22. No; $\overleftrightarrow{AC} \nparallel \overleftrightarrow{A'C'}$. (or if Q is the pt. of intersection of $\overleftrightarrow{AA'}$ and $\overleftrightarrow{CC'}$, $\frac{QA'}{QA} \neq \frac{QC'}{QC}$.

Set C **28.** Prove that under a dilation, a line and its image are parallel.

A dilation maps ℓ and m onto ℓ' and m', respectively.

29. Prove that if ℓ and m are perpendicular, then ℓ' and m' are perpendicular.

30. Prove that if ℓ and m are parallel, then ℓ' and m' are parallel.

▲ Review **31.** If $AB = 18$ and $A'B' = 6$, find the scale factor of a dilation that maps A onto A' and B onto B'. $\frac{1}{3}$

32. When is a dilation an enlargement? a reduction?

33. Explain why a composite of eleven line reflections is equivalent to either a single line reflection or a composite of three line reflections.

34. $\angle 1$ and $\angle 2$ are vertical angles. If $m\angle 1 = 7x + 4$ and $m\angle 2 = 12x - 11$, then x = ?. 3

35. Find the distance across the lake if $JK = 30$ m, $KO = 35$ m, $MO = 140$ m, and $\overline{JK} \parallel \overline{MN}$. 120m

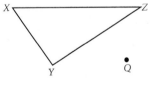

Thinking Ahead **36.** Trace $\triangle XYZ$ and point Q. Draw $\triangle X_1Y_1Z_1$, the image of $\triangle XYZ$ under a dilation with center Q and scale factor 3.

37. Draw $\triangle X'Y'Z'$, the image of $\triangle X_1Y_1Z_1$ in Exercise 36 under a 135° clockwise rotation about Q.

38. Study $\triangle XYZ$ and $\triangle X'Y'Z'$. What appears to be true? **38.** They are ~.

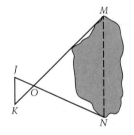

32. When the scale factor > 1; when the scale factor < 1

33. This composite is equivalent to a composite of 3 or fewer line reflections, by Thm. 12-10. Of those possible, only a single line reflection or composite of 3 reverse orientation, as does a composite of 11 line reflections.

Challenge

The words printed at the right exhibit line symmetry.

1. Print another word that has a horizontal symmetry line.

2. Print another word that has a vertical symmetry line.

3. Print a complete sentence that has either a horizontal or a vertical symmetry line.
Samples: **1.** ODD **2.** HIT **3.** HE KICKED DEE.

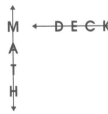

---

29. Given: A dilation maps ℓ and m onto ℓ' and m', respectively; $\ell \perp m$ Prove: $\ell' \perp m'$

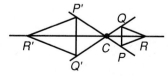

Proof: 1. A dilation maps ℓ and m onto ℓ' and m', respectively; $\ell \perp m$. (Given) 2. $m\angle 1 = m\angle 2$ (A dilation preserves $\angle$ meas. [1]) 3. $\angle 1$ is a rt. $\angle$. (2 $\perp$ lines form 4 rt. $\angle$s. [1]) 4. $m\angle 1 = 90$ (Def. of rt. $\angle$ [3]) 5. $m\angle 2 = 90$ (Substitution Prop. [2, 4]) 6. $\angle 2$ is a rt. $\angle$. (Def. of rt. $\angle$ [5]) 7. $\ell' \perp m'$ (Def. of $\perp$ lines [6])

FOLLOW-UP

More Practice

- **Worksheet 12-9**

Extension

Dilations do not preserve orientation if we include negative scale factors. If $k < 0$, $CA' = k(CA)$ and CA and CA' are opposite rays. A dilation with $k = -2$ is shown below.

Ask students to experiment with various dilations having negative scale factors.
- **Extension 12-9**

LESSON 12–10

Resources

Teaching Aid 5, graphs
Visual Aid 5, graphs
Worksheet 12–10
Extension 12–10
Algebra Review 12
Chapter 12 Test, Form I
Chapter 12 Test, Form II
Chapter 12 Test, Form III

OBJECTIVE

Use similarity transformations to extend the concept of similarity.

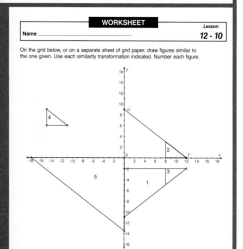

WORKSHEET

Lesson 12 - 10

Name

On the grid below, or on a separate sheet of grid paper, draw figures similar to the one given. Use each similarity transformation indicated. Number each figure.

1. Line reflection over $y = -1$

2. Dilation ($k = .333$) with center T

3. Line reflection over $y = -1$ and dilation ($k = .333$) with center T

4. Dilation ($k = .333$) with center U and translation over line $x = -1$ and then over $x = -8$

5. Dilation ($k = 1.5$) with center S and reflection over $y = -x$ and then $y = x$

12-10 A Second Look at Similarity

In this Escher print, some of the reptiles are congruent. Others are similar but of various sizes.

I can be mapped onto II by a dilation with center C.

Can I be mapped onto III by a dilation alone? Notice that a **No** composite of a dilation and a rotation does map I onto II. A dilation with center C maps I onto III. Then a rotation about C maps II onto III. Such a composite is called a similarity transformation.

Definition *Similarity Transformation*

A similarity transformation is a composite of a dilation and an isometry.

A dilation alone or an isometry alone is itself a similarity transformation as illustrated in the following example.

Example
For the Escher print above, what similarity transformation maps I onto II? II onto III?

Solution
I is mapped onto II by just a dilation with center C. This is equivalent to the *dilation* followed by the identity transformation (the *isometry*).

II is mapped onto III by just a rotation about C. This is equivalent to a *dilation* with $k = 1$ (the identity transformation) followed by the rotation (the *isometry*).

Compare the next theorem with Theorem 12-9 (page 539).

Theorem 12-16

In a plane, if △ABC ~ △A'B'C', then there is a unique similarity transformation that maps △ABC onto △A'B'C'.

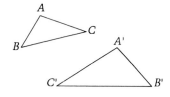

Given △ABC ~ △A'B'C'

Prove **Part I** There is a similarity transformation that maps △ABC onto △A'B'C'.

Part II This transformation is unique.

Plan for Proof **Part I** Show that under a composite of a dilation and an isometry, △ABC can be mapped onto △A'B'C'.

Let $\frac{A'B'}{AB} = \frac{B'C'}{BC} = \frac{A'C'}{AC} = k$.

Let the image of △ABC under a dilation with center A and scale factor k be △AB₁C₁. Show △AB₁C₁ ≅ △A'B'C'. Use Theorem 12-9 to show there is an isometry that maps △AB₁C₁ onto △A'B'C'. Finally, show that the composite of these two mappings is a similarity transformation that maps △ABC onto △A'B'C'.

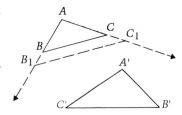

Part II Show uniqueness indirectly.

We can now give a general definition of similarity.

Definition *Similar Figures*

Two plane figures are similar if and only if there is a similarity transformation that maps one figure onto the other.

Checking for Understanding

1. If △ABC ~ △DEF by the definition in Chapter 7, are the triangles also similar by the new definition? Explain.

2. If △ABC ~ △DEF by the new definition, are the triangles also similar by the definition in Chapter 7? Explain.

Is each property preserved by all similarity transformations? Explain your answers.

3. Distance No   **4.** Angle measure Yes   **5.** Collinearity Yes

6. Parallelism Yes   **7.** Betweenness Yes   **8.** Orientation No

1. Yes; by Thm. 12-16, there is a similarity transformation that maps △ABC onto △DEF. So △ABC ~ △DEF by the new definition.
2. Yes; by the new definition, a similarity transformation maps △ABC onto △DEF. By Thm. 12-11, DE = k(AB), DF = k(AC), and EF = k(BC). So $\frac{DE}{AB} = \frac{DF}{AC} = \frac{BC}{EF}$. By Thm. 12-5 and Thm. 12-14, m∠A = m∠D, m∠B = m∠E, and m∠C = m∠F. So, △ABC ~ △DEF.

TEACHING NOTES

To motivate the need for the definition of similarity transformation, ask the following questions.
1. How are a triangle and its image under a dilation related? similar
2. Given two similar triangles, is there always a dilation that maps one onto the other? no
3. Do you think that there is *some* transformation that maps one onto the other? This should lead to the definition.

Error Analysis The name "similarity transformation" may lead some students to believe that there is circularity involved in the redefinition of similarity. Point out that the concept of similarity transformation is in no way dependent on the concept of similarity; it is defined strictly in terms of transformations.

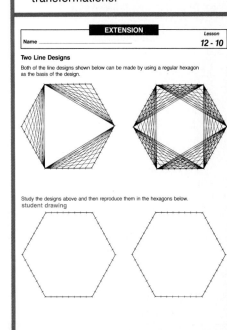

Assignment Guide

Basic: 1–12, 18–22
Average: 1–15, 18–22
Extended: 1–22

ANSWERS

Written Exercises

3. It is the composite of a dilation with $k = 1$ and an isometry, the line reflection.

4. It is the composite of a dilation with $k > 1$ and an isometry, the identity transformation.

5. It is the composite of a dilation with $k = 1$ and an isometry, the translation.

6. It is the composite of a dilation with $k < 1$ and an isometry, the identity transformation.

7. It is the composite of a dilation with $k = 1$ and an isometry, the rotation.

8. It is the composite of a dilation with $k = 1$ and an isometry, the identity transformation.

9. Sample: a dilation with center $(4, 0)$ and $k = \frac{1}{2}$, followed by a 90° counterclockwise rotation about the origin

10. Sample: a dilation with center $(0, 0)$ and $k = \frac{3}{4}$, followed by a reflection over the y-axis

11. Sample: a dilation with center $(0, 4)$ and $k = 2$, followed by a translation 5 units in the neg. direction along the y-axis

12. Sample: a dilation with any center and $k = 1$, followed by a 90° counterclockwise rotation about $(2\frac{1}{2}, -2\frac{1}{2})$

15. Let $\odot R_1$ have radius r_1 and $\odot R_2$ have radius r_2. Then a similarity transformation that is the composite of a dilation with $k = \frac{r_2}{r_1}$ followed by an isometry will map $\odot R_1$ onto $\odot R_2$.

16.

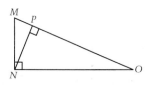

Written Exercises

Set A   For each pair of similar figures, find the scale factor of a dilation that maps I onto a figure congruent to II.

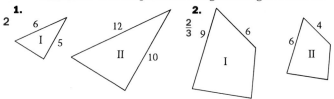

Explain why each transformation is a similarity transformation.

3. Line reflection   **4.** Enlargement

5. Translation   **6.** Reduction

7. Rotation   **8.** Identity transformation

Set B   Refer to the graph at the right. Specify a similarity transformation that maps

9. △I onto △II.   **10.** △I onto △III.

11. △II onto △IV.   **12.** △I onto △IV.

Refer to the Escher print on page 550.

13. What is the scale factor of the dilation that maps I onto II? **2**

14. What is the magnitude and direction of the rotation that maps II onto III? **90, clockwise**

15. Explain why any two circles are similar.

Set C   A transformation maps each point $A(x, y)$ of the coordinate plane onto $B(x + 2y, y)$.

16. Graph the rectangle with vertices $O(0, 0)$, $P(3, 0)$, $Q(3, 2)$, and $R(0, 2)$. Draw the image of $OPQR$.

17. Is this mapping a similarity transformation? Why? **No; ∠meas. is not preserved.**

▲ Review   **18.** Name three properties preserved by all dilations.

19. Under a dilation, a triangle and its image are _?_. ~

20. Under a dilation, is any point its own image? Explain.

21. How many faces does an octagonal pyramid have? **9**

22. Name three similar triangles at the right.

16. $O'(0, 0)$; $P'(3, 0)$; $Q'(7, 2)$; $R'(4, 2)$

18. Any three: ∠ meas., collinearity, betweenness, parallelism, perpendicularity, orientation

20. Yes, the center. For $k = 1$, all pts.

Progress Check

Lesson 12-6, page 535

Draw a triangle with

1. line symmetry, but no rotational symmetry.

2. rotational symmetry.

1. **2.**

Lesson 12-7, page 539

3. Under what conditions are two plane figures congruent?

4. Every isometry can be expressed as ___?___.
at most 3 line reflections

3. If one is the image of the other under an isometry.

Lesson 12-8, page 543

For each exercise, trace X, Y, Z, and C. Draw the image of X, Y, and Z under a dilation with center C and scale factor k.

5. $k = 3$ **6.** $k = \frac{3}{4}$ **7.** $k = 1$

Lesson 12-9, page 546

8. Trace X, Y, Z, and C. Draw $\triangle XYZ$. Then draw $\triangle X'Y'Z'$, the image of $\triangle XYZ$ under a dilation with center C and scale factor 2.5.

9. In Exercise 8, if $XY = 12$, then $X'Y' = $ ___?___. 30

Lesson 12-10, page 550

10. Under what conditions are two figures similar?

11. Explain why a rotation is a similarity transformation.
It is the composite of a dilation with $k = 1$ followed by an isometry, the rotation.

10. If one is the image of the other under a similarity transformation

Challenge

Which types of transformations are illustrated in the Kuba textile shown? Reflection, translation, rotation

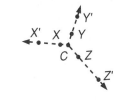

ANSWERS

Excursion

1.

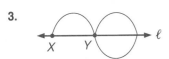

2.

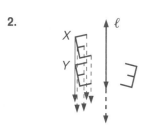

3.

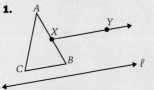

Excursion: Glide Reflections

In this Escher pattern, do you think that bird B is the image of bird A under a line reflection? a point reflection? a translation? a rotation? No; no; no; no

Bird A can be mapped onto bird B by a composite of a translation and a reflection as follows:

First, translate bird A from X to Y as shown at the right. Its image is bird A'.

Then reflect bird A' over ℓ.

This composite is called a *glide reflection*. Notice that the line of reflection ℓ is parallel to the direction of the translation, indicated by $\overrightarrow{XY}$. Do you think a glide reflection is an isometry? Why? Yes; both the translation and line reflection are isometries.

Trace each diagram. Draw the image of the figure under the glide reflection that is a composite of a translation from X to Y followed by a reflection over ℓ.

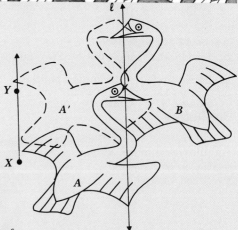

1.

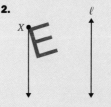

2.

3.

Using Logo: Isometries in a Coordinate Plane

The procedure AXES clears the computer screen and draws a coordinate axis. The procedure FLAG can be used to draw a flag for which the bottom of the flag's staff is at the location set by the variable :XY.

```
TO AXES
CS PD HT
SETPC 1
SETPOS [-140 0]
SETPOS [139 0]
HOME
SETPOS [0 120]
SETPOS [1 -119]
HOME
END
```

```
TO FLAG :XY
SETPC 5
PU
SETPOS :XY
SETH 0
PD
FD 40
REPEAT 2 [RT 120 FD 20]
END
```

1. Use AXES to draw a coordinate axes. Do FLAG (20 30). On the same axes, use FLAG to draw flags at (50, −65), (−28, −75), and (−34, 0).

2. Use the Logo editor to change the command SETH 0 to SETH 45 in FLAG. Do AXES, and then draw a flag at (40, 20). What is the function of the command SETH?

3. Erase the flags from the screen using AXES. Use FLAG (20 30) 0 to draw a flag. Use the editor to change the command RT 120 to RT −120 in FLAG. Do FLAG (20 30) 0 again. What is the effect of the change?

4. Revise the two lines in FLAG shown to include a variable :O for orientation.

```
TO FLAG :XY :H :O
REPEAT 2 [RT 120" :O FD 20]
```

   Draw a flag at (60, −42) with a heading of 0 and orientation 1. Draw a second flag at (30, −42) with a heading of 0 and orientation −1. What happens if you use integers other than 1 and −1 for :O?

5. Draw flags for each pair of inputs and name the isometry that maps the first flag onto the second flag:
   a. (50 45) 50 1 and (50 45) 230 1
   b. (40 −20) 60 1 and (−40 −20) −60 −1
   c. (−80 55) 70 −1 and (−20 −50) 70 −1
   d. (−50 20) 350 1 and (50 −20) 190 1

6. Do AXES, then do FLAG (−40 30) 0 −1. Use FLAG to draw the image of that flag under each of these reflections:
   a. over the x-axis
   b. over the y-axis
   c. over the line: y = x

7. Write a procedure HALFTURN that calls the procedure FLAG to draw both a flag and its image under a half-turn. Use the bottom of the flag's staff as the center of the half-turn.

8. Write a procedure REFLECTION that calls the procedure FLAG to draw both a flag and its reflection over the x-axis.

Using Logo

1. Use FLAG [50 −65], FLAG [−28 −75] and FLAG [−34 0].
2. sets the heading for the staff of the flag
3. The second flag is a reflection of the first over its staff.
4. Use FLAG [60 −42] 0 1; then FLAG [30 −42] 0 −1 :O cannot be a multiple of 3. Other multiples can be used. −1, 2, −4, 5, −7, 8 and so on all have the same effect as −1; 1, −2, 4, −5, 7, −8 and so on all have the same effect as 1.
5a. point reflection
b. line reflection
c. translation
d. point reflection
6a. FLAG [−40 −30] 180 1
b. FLAG [40 30] 0 1
c. FLAG [40 −30] 180 −1

7.
```
TO HALFTURN :XY :H :O
  FLAG :XY :H :O
  MAKE "H :H + 180
  FLAG :XY :X :O
END
```

8.
```
TO REFLECTION :XY :H :O
  FLAG :XY :H :O
  MAKE "H :H + 180
  MAKE "O −1*:O
  MAKE "X FIRST :XY
  MAKE "Y LAST :"XY
  MAKE "XY LIST :X −1*:Y
  FLAG :XY :H :O
END
```

Chapter 12 Summary

Important Terms

Composite of transformations (527)
Congruent figures (540)
Dilation (543)
Enlargement (544)
Half-turn (516)
Identity transformation (517)
Isometry (515)
Line symmetry (535)
Magnitude of a rotation (532)
Magnitude of a translation (528)
Point symmetry (536)

Reduction (544)
Reflection over a line (515)
Reflection through a point (516)
Rotation (531)
Rotational symmetry (536)
Scale factor of a dilation (543)
Similar figures (551)
Similarity transformation (550)
Symmetry line (535)
Transformation (515)
Translation (527)

Important Ideas

1. A transformation is a one-to-one correspondence between the points of a plane and themselves. (515)

2. Isometries are transformations that preserve distance. (515)

3. All isometries preserve distance, collinearity, betweenness, and angle measure. (520)

4. Line reflections, point reflections (half-turns), the identity transformation, translations, and rotations are all isometries. (516–517, 528, 531)

5. A figure may have line symmetry, point symmetry, rotational symmetry, or combinations of these. (535–536)

6. Two plane figures are congruent if and only if there is an isometry that maps one figure onto the other. (540)

7. Every isometry is equivalent to a composite of three or fewer line reflections. (540)

8. A dilation with scale factor k is an enlargement if $k > 1$, a reduction if $k < 1$, or the identity transformation if $k = 1$. (544)

9. Enlargements and reductions preserve collinearity, betweenness, and angle measure, but not distance. (546–547)

10. Two plane figures are similar if and only if there is a similarity transformation, a composite of a dilation and an isometry, that maps one figure onto the other. (550–551)

Chapter 12 Review

Lesson 12-1, Page 515

A' and B' are the reflection images of A and B, respectively, over line ℓ.

1. Name the image of B'. B

2. How is ℓ related to $\overline{AA}'$?

X' and Y' are the reflection images of X and Y, respectively, through point O.

3. Name the image of X'. X

4. How is O related to $\overline{YY}'$?

Explain when a given point is its own image under

5. a line reflection.

6. a point reflection.

7. the identity transformation.   **2.** ℓ is the $\perp$ bisector of $\overline{AA}'$.   **4.** O is the midpt. of $\overline{YY}$:   **5.**
When the pt. is on the line of reflection   **6. When the pt. is the
half-turn (pt. reflection)**   **7.** Every pt. is its own image.

Lesson 12-2, Page 519

An isometry maps X, Y, and Z onto X', Y', and Z', respectively.

8. The image of $\overleftrightarrow{XZ}$ is __?__. $\overleftrightarrow{X'Z'}$

9. $m\angle XZY = 32$; $m\angle X'Z'Y' = $ __?__ 32

10. If Z is between X and Y, then __?__ is between __?__ and __?__. Z'; X'; Y'

Lesson 12-3, Page 523

11. A hockey player at A passes the puck to his teammate at B, first bouncing it off $\overline{FG}$. Find the path of the puck. Explain your solution.

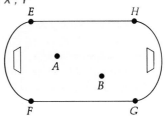

Lesson 12-4, Page 527

Refer to the tessellation with squares at the right. A translation maps A onto F. Name the image of each figure.

12. Point B G   **13.** Point L Q   **14.** $\overline{AB}$ FG   **15.** $\overrightarrow{BF}$ GL

16. $\angle FBC$ **17.** $\angle BGC$ **18.** $\triangle FGC$ **19.** $\square BCGF$
  $\angle LGH$ $\angle GMH$ $\triangle LMH$ $\square GHML$

Lesson 12-5, Page 531

Refer to the tessellation with squares at the right. A rotation about F maps K onto E. Name the image of each figure.

20. Point B G   **21.** $\overline{GC}$ KL   **22.** $\angle EFB$ $\angle BFG$ **23.** $\square CDHG$ $\square LPOK$

24. What are the magnitude and direction of the rotation in Exercises 20–23? 90, counterclockwise

N	O	P	Q
J	K	L	M
E	F	G	H
A	B	C	D

11.

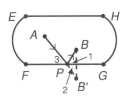

Draw B', the reflection image of B over $\overline{FG}$. Aim for P, the intersection of $\overline{AB'}$ and $\overline{FG}$. $m\angle 1 = m\angle 2$ because an isometry preserves $\angle$ meas., and $m\angle 2 = m\angle 3$ because vert. $\angle$s are =. So $m\angle 1 = m\angle 3$ and it follows that the puck will travel to B after bouncing off $\overline{FG}$ at P.

Lesson 12-6, Page 535

Refer to the figures named below.

a. Segment   b. Isosceles trapezoid
c. Regular pentagon   d. Equilateral triangle
e. Parallelogram   f. Regular hexagon

25. How many lines of symmetry does each figure have?

26. Which figures have point symmetry? *a, e, f*

27. Which figures have rotational symmetry? *a, c, d, e, f*
     25. a. 2; b. 1; c. 5; d. 3; e. 0; f. 6

Lesson 12-7, Page 539

28. No more than __?__ line reflections are needed to express any isometry. 3

What is the least number of line reflections that appear to be needed to map I onto II? **29.** 1   **30.** 2

29.

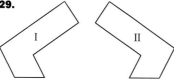

30.

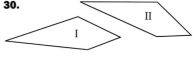

Lesson 12-8, Page 543

X' and Y' are the images of X and Y, respectively, under a dilation with center C and scale factor 1.5.

31. $CX = 8$; $CX' = $ __?__ 12   **32.** $X'Y' = 18$; $XY = $ __?__ 12

33. Is any point its own image under this dilation? Explain.
     Yes, the center C
34. Does a dilation ever map every point onto itself? Explain.
     Yes; if $k = 1$ the dilation is the identity transformation.

Lesson 12-9, Page 546

35. A triangle and its image under a dilation are __?__ . ~

At the right, $\overline{VW} \parallel \overline{ST}$. Specify the center and scale factor of a dilation that maps

36. $\triangle UVW$ onto $\triangle UST$. $u; \frac{4}{3}$ **37.** $\triangle UST$ onto $\triangle UVW$. $u; \frac{3}{4}$

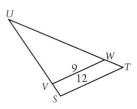

Lesson 12-10, Page 552

38. Name three properties preserved by all similarity transformations. Betweenness; collinearity; ∠measure

39. At the right, $\triangle ABC$ and $\triangle CDE$ are equilateral. Specify a similarity transformation that maps $\triangle ACB$ onto $\triangle DCE$.
Composite of a dilation with center C and $k = \frac{1}{3}$ with a 60° counterclockwise rotation about C.

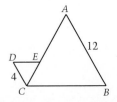

Chapter 12 Test

Tell whether each statement is *true* or *false*. If false, explain.

1. Isometries preserve angle measure. True

2. If A' and B' are the images of A and B, respectively, under an isometry, then $AA' = BB'$.

3. The image of a square under a dilation is a square. True

4. The composite of a dilation and a rotation is a similarity transformation. True

5. A figure with rotational symmetry has line symmetry.

6. If $\triangle ABC \cong \triangle XYZ$ and the triangles have the same orientation, then either a rotation or a translation maps $\triangle ABC$ onto $\triangle XYZ$. True

7. Under a translation, a line is parallel to its image. True

8. All isometries preserve angle measure. True

9. Under any dilation, a segment and its image have different lengths. False; if $k = 1$, distance is preserved.

2. False; if A and B are not the same distance from a line of reflection, then $AA' \neq BB'$.

5. False; consider the letter "s", which has rotational symmetry but no line symmetry.

Refer to this tessellation with equilateral triangles.

10. Name the reflection image of $\overline{FG}$ over $\overleftrightarrow{FB}$. $\overline{FA}$

11. A translation maps A onto F. Name the image of $\angle LGM$. $\angle RMS$

12. State the magnitude and direction of a rotation about M that maps N onto G. 120, clockwise

13. Name the image of $\triangle LMG$ under a half-turn about G. $\triangle CBG$

14. Name the image of $\triangle QCT$ under a dilation with center C and scale factor $\frac{2}{3}$. $\triangle LCN$

15. Specify a similarity transformation that maps $\triangle ABF$ onto $\triangle BES$.

16. Jim, at point J, needs to get water at the river on the way to his campsite at C. Trace the diagram at the right and draw the shortest possible route.

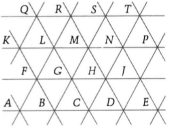

15. Sample: The composite of a dilation with center A and $k = 3$, and then a translation that maps A onto B.

Draw the figure described. If impossible, write *not possible*.

17. A quadrilateral with rotation symmetry but no line symmetry

18. A triangle with exactly two lines of symmetry Not possible

16.

17.

CHAPTER 13

Coordinates and Vectors

Chapter Overview

This chapter concentrates on the coordinate model. Proofs of the formulas for midpoints and distance are given, and the concepts are extended to three dimensions.

A formal definition of the slope of a line is used to develop the skill of writing the equation of a line that fits specific conditions. Coordinate proofs are introduced and practiced.

The basic concepts of vectors are introduced, and the necessary skills in addition, subtraction and scalar multiplication of vectors are developed. These skills are then applied in vector proofs.

The closing lesson compares the synthetic, transformation, coordinate and vector methods of proof in geometry.

Perspectives

Lesson 13-1 reviews plotting points, calculating distance and finding midpoints. It also develops the corresponding skills and formulas for points in space. Then the proofs for the Distance and Midpoint formulas are presented.

Lesson 13-2 reviews and formally defines the slope of a nonvertical line. The definition of slope is then used to generate the equation of the line.

This lesson also reviews slopes of parallel and perpendicular lines.

The equation for a circle is introduced.

Lesson 13-3 introduces coordinate methods of proving theorems, using the formulas and concepts developed in the coordinate model. Much emphasis is given to the subskills of judicious placement of the figure on coordinate axes and selection of appropriate coordinates for vertices.

Lesson 13-4 introduces the basic concepts of vectors. Vectors are defined as directed segments, and the concept of a position vector provides an immediate tie with coordinates.

The Distance Formula is used to find the magnitude of any vector, and the trigonometric ratios are used to find the angle of direction.

Pacing Chart for Chapter 13

Lesson	Objectives	Basic Course	Average Course	Extended Course
13–1	Plot points, and find and use distances and midpoints in both two and three dimensions.	1	2	2
13–2	Write an equation of a line (or circle) in standard form; graph the equation of a line (or circle).	1	2	2
13–3	Place specific types of geometric figures on coordinate axes; write coordinate proofs.	1	2	2
13–4	Name and draw vectors; find the magnitude and direction angle of a given vector.	1	2	2
13–5	Draw and calculate sums and differences of vectors.	1	2	2
13–6	Draw and compute scalar multiples of vectors.	1	2	2
13–7	Write proofs using vectors.	1	2	2
13–8	Write the proof of a theorem using transformation, coordinate, synthetic and vector methods.	1	2	2
Review		1	1	2
Test		1	1	1
Cumulative Review and Test		3	3	3
Total		13 days	21 days	22 days

Lesson 13–5 introduces the sum of two vectors geometrically as the diagonal of the vector parallelogram. We then show that the algebraic definition follows; that is, if $u = (a, b)$ and $v = (c, d)$, then $u + v = (a + c, b + d)$. Vector subtraction is defined in terms of addition of the opposite.

Problems involving resultant vectors are solved using horizontal and vertical components. The trigonometric ratios and the Pythagorean Theorem play an important role in this lesson.

Lesson 13–6 develops the skills and concepts associated with scalar multiplication.

Lesson 13–7 explores techniques for using vectors as an alternate vehicle for proof. Vectors are especially useful in proving theorems involving midpoints and diagonals, where one vector can be expressed in terms of others.

Lesson 13–8 serves as a retrospective study of geometric proof.

CHAPTER OPENER

Each line of longitude is a great circle, the largest circle that can be drawn over the surface of the globe. These great circles are all the same size, and all pass through both poles. Their centers are a common single point at the center of the core of the earth.

Each line of latitude is a circle parallel to the equator (every point on a particular circle is equidistant from the equator). These circles have no points in common. The equator is a line of latitude and a great circle, but as one moves farther from the equator, the circles representing the lines of latitude become smaller.

ANSWERS

1. Bermuda
2. (340° Longitude, 50° North Latitude)

Coordinates and Vectors

Chapter 13

One of the oldest coordinate systems in the world is a system used to locate positions on the surface of the earth. A place was located by its *latitude*, the number of degrees north or south of the equator, and by its *longitude*, the number of degrees east of a given great circle through the North and South Poles. The map pictured here, drawn by the Dutch cartographer Claes Janszoon Visscher in 1652, includes part of the east coast of North America, the British Isles, and parts of Spain and Africa. The southern coast of England is located near these coordinates: (30° Longitude, 50° North Latitude).

1. Identify the island whose coordinates are approximately (330° Longitude, 30° North Latitude).

2. Give the approximate coordinates of the island called Terra Nova, which is shown near the coast of North America.

Warm-Up Review

1. What are the coordinates of a point 2 units to the right of the y-axis and 3 units below the x-axis? (2, −3)
2. The point of intersection of the axes is called the __?__. Origin
3. Find the distance from P(1, −1) to Q(4, 3). 5
4. What equation describes the points on the x-axis? $y = 0$

13-1 Coordinate Systems

Notice the similarity between locating a place on the earth's surface and locating a point on the coordinate plane. On the earth's surface, a place is located according to its position east or west of the *prime meridian*, a great circle passing through Greenwich, England, and the North and South Poles, and north or south of the equator. A point on a coordinate plane is located with respect to whether it is right or left of the y-axis and above or below the x-axis.

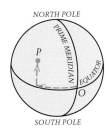

Recall how the 2-dimensional coordinate model was constructed in Lesson 1-8 and used throughout this book. The x-axis and y-axis are perpendicular number lines that intersect at the origin, a point that corresponds to 0 on both lines. A point A is located by an ordered pair of real numbers (−2, 3). The x-coordinate, −2, indicates A is located 2 units left of the y-axis, and the y-coordinate, 3, indicates that A is 3 units above the x-axis. A similar system is used to locate a point in space.

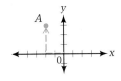

A point in space can be described by an **ordered triple** of real numbers, (x, y, z).

The x-, y-, and z-axes in a 3-dimensional coordinate system are perpendicular to each other at the origin. The axes determine the xy-, xz-, and yz-coordinate planes. It is customary in mathematics to place the x- and y-axes on a horizontal plane, with the z-axis perpendicular to this plane as illustrated. The x-coordinate of a point is its directed distance from the yz-plane; the y-coordinate, the directed distance from the xz-plane; and the z-coordinate, the directed distance from the xy-plane.

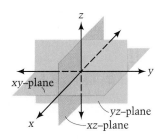

To locate the point A(3, 5, 4) begin at the origin and move 3 units along the positive x-axis to (3, 0, 0). From there, move 5 units to the right from the xz-plane to the point with coordinates (3, 5, 0). Finally, move 4 units up from the xy-plane to the point A(3, 5, 4).

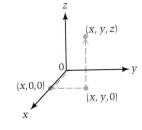

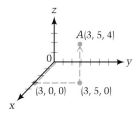

TEACHING NOTES

Introduce this lesson by comparing longitude and latitude with the rectangular coordinate system in the plane. Use a globe to locate points in a spherical coordinate system.

Using the classroom as an example, ask students what would be necessary to describe a location in space. Point out that we must specify distance from the front (or back) wall, distance from the right (or left) wall and distance from the floor (or ceiling). Then introduce the *x*-, *y*- and *z*-axes.

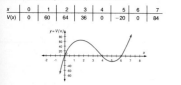

Example 1

Graph the following points. Draw a different diagram for each point.

a. $P(-1, 3)$ **b.** $Q(-1, 3, 0)$ **c.** $R(-1, 3, 4)$

Solution

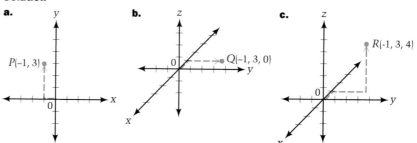

In our coordinate model, the Distance Formula provides an interpretation of the distance between two points in a plane. As you can see below, this formula is a consequence of the Pythagorean Theorem.

Let $A(x_1, y_1)$ and $B(x_2, y_2)$ be any two points in the coordinate plane. To find AB, draw a vertical line through B and a horizontal line through A to form a right triangle $\triangle ABC$. By the definition of distance between two points on a horizontal line and on a vertical line, $AC = |x_2 - x_1|$ and $BC = |y_2 - y_1|$. Then by the Pythagorean Theorem, $AB^2 = AC^2 + BC^2$. Substitute for AC and BC, and solve for AB.

$$AB^2 = (|x_2 - x_1|)^2 + (|y_2 - y_1|)^2$$
$$AB^2 = (x_2 - x_1)^2 + (y_2 - y_1)^2$$
$$AB = \sqrt{(x_2 - x_1)^2 + (y_2 - y_1)^2}$$

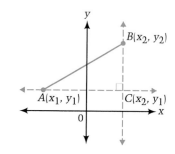

Theorem 13-1 *The Distance Formula*

If the coordinates of points P and Q are (x_1, y_1) and (x_2, y_2), respectively, then the distance between them is given by the formula: $PQ = \sqrt{(x_2 - x_1)^2 + (y_2 - y_1)^2}$.

The Distance Formula in three dimensions is analogous to the distance formula for two dimensions.

If the coordinates of points P and Q are (x_1, y_1, z_1) and (x_2, y_2, z_2), respectively, then the distance between them is given by this formula: $PQ = \sqrt{(x_2 - x_1)^2 + (y_2 - y_1)^2 + (z_2 - z_1)^2}$.

Study the coordinates in the diagram at the right. The Pythagorean Theorem can be used to find PQ. In $\triangle PQR$, $(PQ)^2 = (PR)^2 + (QR)^2$, and in $\triangle PSR$, $(PS)^2 + (SR)^2 = (PR)^2$. Substituting for $(PR)^2$ in the first equation gives $(PQ)^2 = (PS)^2 + (SR)^2 + (QR)^2$. Since $\overline{PS}$, $\overline{SR}$, and $\overline{QR}$ are each parallel to one of the axes, you know $PS = |x_2 - x_1|$, $SR = |y_2 - y_1|$, and $QR = |z_2 - z_1|$.

Then $(PQ)^2 = |x_2 - x_1|^2 + |y_2 - y_1|^2 + |z_2 - z_1|^2$

$(PQ)^2 = (x_2 - x_1)^2 + (y_2 - y_1)^2 + (z_2 - z_1)^2$

$PQ = \sqrt{(x_2 - x_1)^2 + (y_2 - y_1)^2 + (z_2 - z_1)^2}$

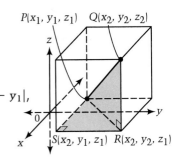

The Midpoint Formula which was introduced in Chapter 1 can also be derived.

Theorem 13-2   *The Midpoint Formula*

If the coordinates of points P and Q are $(x_1, y_1,)$ and (x_2, y_2), respectively, then the midpoint M of PQ has coordinates
$$\left(\frac{x_1 + x_2}{2}, \frac{y_1 + y_2}{2}\right).$$

Case I   Let $\overline{PQ}$ be a horizontal line segment with $P(x_1, y_1)$ and $Q(x_2, y_1)$. Let $x_1 < x_2$ and let M be the midpoint of $\overline{PQ}$. Then the x-coordinate of M is $x_1 + PM$.

$x_1 + PM = x_1 + \frac{1}{2}PQ$

$x_1 + PM = x_1 + \frac{1}{2}(x_2 - x_1) = \frac{1}{2}x + \frac{1}{2}x_2 = \frac{x_1 + x_2}{2}$

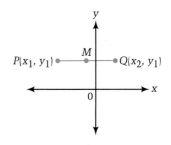

Case II   By a similar argument you can show that if $\overline{PQ}$ is a vertical segment, then the y-coordinate of M is $\frac{y_1 + y_2}{2}$.

Case III If $\overline{PQ}$ is neither vertical nor horizontal, to find the coordinates of M, draw the horizontal and vertical segments shown at the right.

Since $\overline{MR} \parallel \overline{QT}$, $\triangle PMR \sim \triangle PQT$ and R is the midpoint of $\overline{PT}$. Therefore, R has coordinates $\left(\frac{x_1 + x_2}{2}, y_1\right)$. Similarly, $\triangle QSM \sim \triangle QTP$ and S is the midpoint of $\overline{TQ}$. Therefore, S has coordinates $\left(x_2, \frac{y_1 + y_2}{2}\right)$. M has the same x-coordinate as R and the same y-coordinate as S.

The coordinates of M are $\left(\frac{x_1 + x_2}{2}, \frac{y_1 + y_2}{2}\right)$.

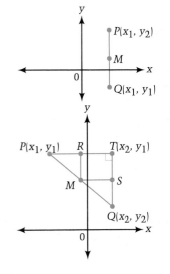

Additional Examples

Example 1
Graph the following points. Draw a different diagram for each point.
(a) $A(2, -4)$

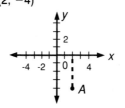

(b) $B(2, -4, 0)$

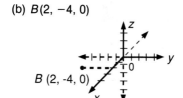

(c) $C(2, -4, 3)$

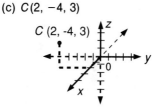

Example 2
Given: $G(-2, 1, 1)$ and $I(2, -5, 13)$ Find GI 14 and H, the midpoint of $\overline{GI}$ $H(0, -2, 7)$. Then find GH and HI to verify that H is equidistant from G and I. both 7

Error Analysis Students often have trouble visualizing and drawing two-dimensional representations of three dimensions. When introducing the three-dimensional coordinate system, use **concrete materials** such as straws to represent the axes so that students can see what is being drawn on paper.

ANSWERS

Checking for Understanding

4. Use the Distance Formula to show all 3 sides are =.

5. For pts. A, B and C show that the slope of $\overleftrightarrow{AB}$ = the slope of $\overleftrightarrow{AC}$ or use the Distance Formula and Seg. Add. Post. to show that $AB + BC = AC$.

Written Exercises

1.

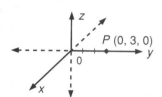

2.

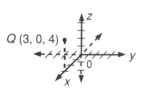

3.

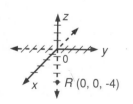

The Midpoint Formula for a segment in three dimensions is also similar to its two-dimensional counterpart. Its derivation is left to Exercise 24.

For points $P(x_1, y_1, z_1)$ and $Q(x_2, y_2, z_2)$, the midpoint M of $\overline{PQ}$ has coordinates $\left(\dfrac{x_1 + x_2}{2}, \dfrac{y_1 + y_2}{2}, \dfrac{z_1 + z_2}{2}\right)$.

Example 2

Given: $A(5, -1, 6)$ and $C(9, 7, -2)$. Find AC and the coordinates of B, the midpoint of $\overline{AC}$. Then find AB and BC to verify that B is equidistant from A and B.

Solution

$AC = \sqrt{(9-5)^2 + [7-(-1)]^2 + (-2-6)^2}$

$\quad = \sqrt{4^2 + 8^2 + (-8)^2}$

$\quad = 12$

The coordinates of B are $\left(\dfrac{9+5}{2}, \dfrac{7+(-1)}{2}, \dfrac{-2+6}{2}\right) = (7, 3, 2)$.

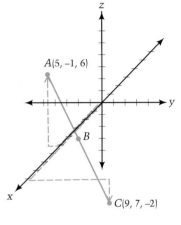

Using the Distance Formula, we have

$AB = \sqrt{(7-5)^2 + [3-(-1)]^2 + (2-6)^2}$

$\quad = \sqrt{2^2 + 4^2 + (-4)^2}$

$\quad = 6$

$BC = \sqrt{(9-7)^2 + (7-3)^2 + (-2-2)^2}$

$\quad = \sqrt{2^2 + 4^2 + (-4)^2}$

$\quad = 6$

Since $AB = BC = 6$, B is equidistant from A and C.

Checking for Understanding

For each pair of points P and Q, find PQ and the coordinates of M, the midpoint of $\overline{PQ}$.

1. $P(3, -1)$; $Q(-2, -3)$ $\sqrt{29}$; $(\frac{1}{2}, -2)$ **2.** $P(6, -6, 1)$; $Q(2, 10, 1)$ $4\sqrt{17}$; $(4, 2, 1)$

3. If A has coordinates $(5, 3)$, find the coordinates of B so that $M(6, 4)$ is the midpoint of $\overline{AB}$. $(7, 5)$

4. Explain how you could show that a triangle is equilateral given the coordinates of its vertices.

5. Explain how you could show that three points are collinear given the coordinates of the three points.

Written Exercises

Set A   Graph the following points. Draw a different diagram
for each point.

1. $P(0, 3, 0)$ **2.** $Q(3, 0, 4)$ **3.** $R(0, 0, -4)$

4. $S(2, 3, 4)$ **5.** $T(-2, 3, 4)$ **6.** $U(2, -3, 4)$

For a segment with the given endpoints, find the length
of the segment and the coordinates of its midpoint.

7. $A(3, 4, 2)$; $B(6, -2, 8)$ **8.** $C(-1, -4, -8)$; $D(1, 4, 8)$

9. $E(2, 4, 1)$; $F(5, -3, 7)$ **10.** $G(6, 2, 8)$; $H(-3, 4, -2)$

Show that $\triangle ABC$ is the type of triangle indicated.

11. $A(7, 2, 0)$; $B(7, 10, 0)$; $C(2, 6, 7)$; isosceles

12. $A(2, 2, 0)$; $B(6, 8, 0)$; $C(2, 2, -10)$; right

13. $A(6, -5, 6)$; $B(6, -5, 0)$; $C(0, -5, 6)$; isosceles
and right

Use the Distance Formula to determine if $ABCD$
is a parallelogram.

14. $A(4, 0, 4)$; $B(0, 6, 4)$; $C(0, 7, 0)$; $D(4, 1, 0)$ Yes

15. $A(2, -1, 3)$; $B(-4, -1, 3)$; $C(-5, 5, -2)$; $D(2, 4, -2)$ No

16. $A(3, -1, 2)$; $B(-2, 2, 2)$; $C(-2, 3, 0)$; $D(3, 1, 0)$ No

Set B   Find the midpoint of $\overline{JK}$.

17. $J(10, -4u)$; $K(2v, 6)$ $(5 + V, 3 - 2u)$

18. $J(7a, -b, -2c)$; $K(a, b, c)$ $(4a, 0, \frac{-c}{2})$

Given: $P(1, 1, 1)$; $Q(2, -3, -7)$; $R(-1, 9, 17)$;
$S(3, -7, -15)$

19. Are P, Q, and R collinear? Explain your answer. Yes; $PQ + PR = QR$

20. Are P, Q, and S collinear? Explain your answer. Yes; $PQ + QS = PS$

21. Show that the quadrilateral with vertices $S(0, 0)$,
$T(b, 0)$, $A(b + c, d)$, and $R(c, d)$ is a parallelogram.

22. Given the points $A(30, 0, 0)$, $B(0, 0, 40)$, and
$C(0, 25, 40)$, find the coordinates of D if $ABCD$
is a parallelogram. Use the Distance Formula
to show that D is the fourth vertex. D (30, 25, 0);
$AD = BC = 25$; $AB = DC = 50$

23. Show how you would derive the y-coordinate
of M in Case II of Theorem 13-2.

4.

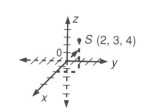

5.

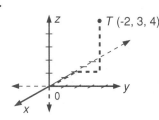

6.

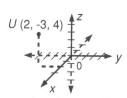

7. $AB = 9$; $(\frac{9}{2}, 1, 5)$

8. $CD = 18$; $(0, 0, 0)$

9. $EF = \sqrt{94}$; $(\frac{7}{2}, \frac{1}{2}, 4)$

10. $GH = \sqrt{185}$; $(\frac{3}{2}, 3, 3)$

11. $AB = BC = 3\sqrt{10}$

12. $AB = 2\sqrt{13}$; $AC = 10$; $BC = 2\sqrt{38}$; Since $AB^2 + AC^2 = BC^2$, $\triangle ABC$ is a rt. $\triangle$.

13. Since $AB = AC = 6$, $\triangle ABC$ is isos.; since $AB^2 + AC^2 = BC^2$, $\triangle ABC$ is a rt. $\triangle$.

21. $RA = \sqrt{b^2 + 0^2} = |b| = ST$; slope of $\overline{RA}$ is 0; slope of $\overline{ST}$ is 0. So, $RA = ST$ and $\overline{RA} \parallel \overline{ST}$. Therefore, $STAR$ is $\square$. (If 2 sides of quad. are = and $\parallel$, then quad. is a $\square$.)

23. $y_1 + \frac{1}{2}QP = y_1 + \frac{1}{2}(y_2 - y_1) = \frac{1}{2}y_1 + \frac{1}{2}y_2 = \frac{y_1 + y_2}{2}$

24. (Use the first diagram on page 563.)

Let T be the midpt. of $\overline{PR}$. From the Midpt. Formula for a plane, T is $\left(\frac{x_1 + x_2}{2}, \frac{y_1 + y_2}{2}, z_1\right)$. If M is the midpt. of $\overline{PQ}$, then $\overline{MT}$ joins the midpts. of 2 sides of $\triangle PRQ$. So, $\overline{MT} \parallel \overline{RQ}$, $\overline{MT} \perp \overline{PR}$ and $MT = \frac{1}{2}RQ$. Therefore, $MT = z_1 + \frac{1}{2}(z_2 - z_1) = \frac{z_1 + z_2}{2}$ and m is $\left(\frac{x_1 + x_2}{2}, \frac{y_1 + y_2}{2}, \frac{z_1 + z_2}{2}\right)$.

26.

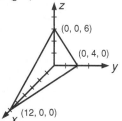

FOLLOW-UP

More Practice

- **Worksheet 13–1**

Extension

The xy-, xz- and yz-planes separate space into eight areas known as *octants*. Because they are not easily numbered, we may denote an octant by the signs of the coordinates of its points. For example, the +, −, + octant contains points whose x- and z-coordinates are positive, and whose y-coordinates are negative.

Have students draw a three-dimensional coordinate system and label each octant.

- **Extension 13–1**

Computers

- **Computer Activities 13–1**
- **Computer Worksheet 13–1**

Set C   **24.** Draw a diagram and explain how to derive the formula for the midpoint of a segment in a three-dimensional coordinate system.

In three-dimensional space $1x + 3y + 2z = 12$ is an equation of a plane. $(12, 0, 0)$; $(0, 4, 0)$; $(0, 0, 6)$

25. Determine the points of intersection of this plane with the x-, y-, and z-axes, respectively.

26. Draw the lines of intersection of this plane and the xy-, yz-, and xz-planes, respectively.

◆ Review   **27.** What is a similarity transformation?

28. Under what circumstances are any two plane figures similar?

29. Trace $LMNOP$ and point C. Draw the image of $LMNOP$ under a dilation with center C and scale factor 2.5.

30. How many faces and edges does a pentagonal prism have?

31. Use a calculator or the table on page 617 to find $m\angle X$ to the nearest degree if $\tan X = 1.3270$.   **53**

Thinking Ahead   **32.** What is the slope of $\overleftrightarrow{AB}$? $\frac{3}{4}$

33. Write an equation for $\overleftrightarrow{AB}$. $y = \frac{3}{4}x + 3$

34. How is $\triangle AOB$ related to $\triangle BDC$? Explain.

35. If point C has coordinates (x, y), what are the coordinates of point D? $(x, 3)$

36. Write a proportion involving the term $\frac{y - 3}{x - 0}$.

37. Write an equation for $\overleftrightarrow{BC}$. $y = \frac{3}{4}x + 3$

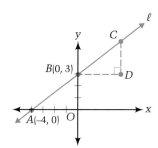

⌨ **Computer Activities: Drawing and Measuring**

1. Graph each equation and describe the graph.

   a. $y = x + 7$ **b.** $y = x^2 + 7$ **c.** $y = x^3 + 7$ **d.** $y = 3x + 1$
   e. $y = 2x^2 - 1$ **f.** $y = -3x^3$ **g.** $y = -x^2$ **h.** $y = -x^3 + 2$

What is the graph of an equation in the form

2. $y = mx + b$?   **3.** $y = mx^2 + b$?   **4.** $y = mx^3 + b$?

5. What conjectures can you make about the graphs of these equations?

Warm-Up Review

1. What is the slope of the line whose equation is $y = 2x - 3$? 2
2. If two lines are parallel, their slopes are ___?___. Equal
3. What is the slope of a line perpendicular to the line whose equation is $y = 2x - 3$? $-\frac{1}{2}$
4. What is the x-coordinate of a point on the y-axis? 0

13-2 Equations for Lines and Circles

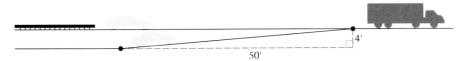

The *grade* of a road is a measure of its steepness. It is the ratio, expressed as a percent, of the vertical distance (rise) between two points to the horizontal distance (run) between the points. For example, a car driven up the ramp above moves 4 feet up and 50 feet to the right.

$$\frac{\text{rise}}{\text{run}} = \frac{4}{50} = 0.08 \text{ or the ramp has a grade of } 8\%.$$

The ratio of the rise to the run is also used to measure the steepness of a line or segment in the coordinate plane. You should recognize this ratio as the slope of a line.

Definition *Slope*

The slope m of a nonvertical line that contains two points $P(x_1, y_1)$ and $Q(x_2, y_2)$ is $m = \dfrac{y_2 - y_1}{x_2 - x_1}$.

Example 1

Find an equation of the line that contains $A(-2, 1)$ and $B(2, 3)$.

Solution

$m = \dfrac{y_2 - y_1}{x_2 - x_1} = \dfrac{3 - 1}{2 - (-2)} = \dfrac{1}{2}$

AA ~ Post.

Let $P(x, y)$ be another point on $\overleftrightarrow{AB}$. Then $\triangle ACB \sim \triangle BDP$. Why?

So we know $\dfrac{y - 3}{x - 2} = \dfrac{1}{2}$, which can be rewritten as $y - 3 = \dfrac{1}{2}(x - 2)$.

This equation describes every point $P(x, y)$ on $\overleftrightarrow{AB}$. If a point is on $\overleftrightarrow{AB}$, then its coordinates satisfy the equation. Conversely, a point must be on $\overleftrightarrow{AB}$ if its coordinates satisfy the equation.

This procedure provides an alternate form for the equation of a line as given in Theorem 13-3.

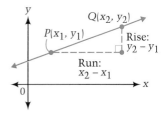

LESSON 13-2

Resources

- Teaching Aid 3, grid paper
- Visual Aid 3, grid paper
- Teaching Aid 5, graphs
- Visual Aid 5, graphs
- Worksheet 13-2
- Extension 13-2
- Computer Activities 13-2

OBJECTIVES

Write an equation of a line (or circle) in standard form; graph the equation of a line (or circle).

TEACHING NOTES

To begin this lesson, review the meaning of the slope of a line by

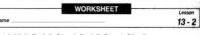

using either or both of the following common notations:

$$m = \frac{y_2 - y_1}{x_2 - x_1} \quad \text{or} \quad m = \frac{\triangle y}{\triangle x}$$

Point out that $\triangle x$ and $\triangle y$ are *directed* segments rather than lengths.

Compare the standard, point-slope and slope-intercept forms of the same equation of a line. Discuss when each form should be used.

Additional Examples

Example 1
Find the equation of the line that contains $P(3, -1)$ and $Q(4, -4)$.
$y = -3x + 8$

Example 2
(a) Write an equation of the line that contains $C(1, -2)$ and $W(2, -6)$. $y + 2 = -4(x - 1)$, or $y = -4x + 2$
(b) Give the y-intercept of the line. 2

EXTENSION

Name _____ Lesson **13-2**

Equations for Conic Sections

You have already seen how it is possible to describe any line with an equation. It is also possible to describe conic sections with equations. A conic section is formed when a plane is passed through a right circular cone.

In the figures below, the x- and y-axes lie in the shaded planes. In the equations, h, k, and p are constants.

The equation of a parabola can be written in more than one way. Two different parabolas might be defined as follows:
$(x - h)^2 = p(y - k)$
$(y - k)^2 = p(x - h)$

Parabola

The general equation of a circle is as follows:
$\frac{(x - h)^2}{a^2} + \frac{(y - k)^2}{a^2} = 1, a \neq 0$

Circle

In the general equation of an ellipse, a and b are also constants.
$\frac{(x - h)^2}{a^2} + \frac{(y - k)^2}{b^2} = 1, a \neq b \neq 0$

Ellipse

A common form for the equation for a hyperbola is as follows:
$\frac{(x - h)^2}{a^2} - \frac{(y - k)^2}{b^2} = \pm 1, a \neq b \neq 0$

Hyperbola

Tell if each equation is the equation of a parabola, a circle, an ellipse, or a hyperbola.

1. $\frac{(x - 3)^2}{9} + \frac{(y + 1)^2}{4} = 1$ ellipse

2. $\frac{(x - 1)^2}{9} + \frac{(y - 2)^2}{9} = 1$ circle

3. $\frac{(y - 2)^2}{25} - \frac{(x - 3)^2}{16} = 1$ hyperbola

4. $\frac{(x + 4)^2}{25} + \frac{(y + 4)^2}{25} = 1$ circle

5. $(y - 2)^2 = 8(x + 1)$ parabola

6. $(x + 3)^2 = -12(y + 1)$ parabola

7. $(x + 2)^2 = 24(y + 3)$ parabola

8. $(y + 3)^2 = -12(x + 5)$ parabola

Theorem 13-3

The graph of the equation $y - y_1 = m(x - x_1)$ is the nonvertical line ℓ that has slope m and contains $P(x_1, y_1)$.

Part I Prove that all points on ℓ satisfy the equation.

Given Nonvertical line ℓ through $P(x_1, y_1)$ with slope m; $Q(x_2, y_2)$ is on ℓ.

Prove The coordinates of Q satisfy $y - y_1 = m(x - x_1)$.

Proof **Case I** P and Q coincide.
Then $x_1 = x_2$ and $y_1 = y_2$, so $x_2 - x_1 = 0$ and $y_2 - y_1 = 0$. Thus, $y_2 - y_1 = m(x_2 - x_1)$.

Case II P and Q are distinct.
Then $x_1 \neq x_2$.
By definition, $m = \frac{y_2 - y_1}{x_2 - x_1}$. So $y_2 - y_1 = m(x_2 - x_1)$.

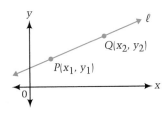

Part II Prove that all points that satisfy the equation are on ℓ.

Given Any point T whose coordinates satisfy $y - y_1 = m(x - x_1)$

Prove T is on the nonvertical line ℓ through $P(x_1, y_1)$ with slope m.

Proof Let (x_3, y_3) be the coordinates of T. Suppose T is *not* on ℓ. Then a vertical line through T will intersect ℓ in a point $S(x_4, y_4)$, where $x_3 = x_4$, but $y_3 \neq y_4$.
$m = \frac{y_4 - y_1}{x_4 - x_1}$, so $y_4 = m(x_4 - x_1) - y_1$.
Substitution gives $y_4 = m(x_3 - x_1) + y_1$ and $y_3 \neq m(x_3 - x_1) + y_1$. But this contradicts the Given. We conclude that T is on ℓ.

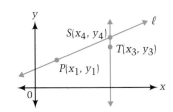

An equation of a line in the form $y - y_1 = m(x - x_1)$ is said to be in *point-slope form*.

Note, if line ℓ has slope m and y-intercept b (That is, it contains $(0, b)$.), then by Theorem 13-3, its equation is $y - b = m(x - 0)$, or $y = mx + b$. This is the *slope-intercept form* of an equation that characterized an equation of a line in our coordinate model. Theorem 13-4 follows directly from Theorem 13-3.

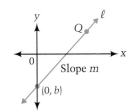

Theorem 13-4

The graph of the equation $y = mx + b$ is the nonvertical line with slope m and y-intercept b.

Example 2
Write an equation of the line which contains $S(3, -5)$ and $T(5, 7)$. Give the y-intercept of the line.

Solution

Find the slope of the line: $m = \dfrac{y_2 - y_1}{x_2 - x_1} = \dfrac{7 - (-5)}{5 - 3} = 6.$

Next use the point-slope form of an equation of a line and the coordinates of either S or T. Using T gives $y - 7 = 6(x - 5)$. This is one solution for the equation.

To find the y-intercept, either write the equation in slope-intercept form, or let $x = 0$ in the equation and solve for y. Using the first method gives:

$y - 7 = 6(x - 5)$

$y - 7 = 6x - 30$

$\quad y = 6x - 23$

Therefore, the y-intercept is -23.

Definition   *Linear Equation in Standard Form*

A linear equation in x and y is an equation that can be written in the form Ax + By = C, where A, B, and C are integers and A and B are not both zero.

The equation of the line in Example 2 written in standard form is $6x - y = 23$, where $A = 6$, $B = -1$, and $C = 23$. It is also in standard form when it is written $-6x + y = -23$, where $A = -6$, $B = 1$, and $C = -23$.

Theorem 13-5

The graph of an equation in x and y is a line if and only if the equation is a linear equation.

Part I   Any line can be described with a linear equation.

Given   Any line ℓ

Prove   There is an equation for ℓ of the form $Ax + By = C$ with A and B not both zero.

Proof   **Case I** ℓ is vertical.
Then it has an equation $x = C$, which is the form $(1)x + (0)y = C$.

Case II ℓ is nonvertical.
Then it has slope m and intersects the y-axis in some point $(0, b)$. By Theorem 13-4, ℓ has an equation $y = mx + b$, or $(m)x + (-1)y = -b$.

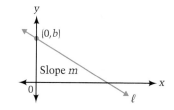

Example 3
Write an equation for the line tangent to a circle at point $R(b, 8)$ where $b < 0$ if the circle has center $O(1, 8)$ and radius 4. $x = -3$

Error Analysis   Students may confuse the three forms of equations of lines. Point out that the standard form involves integers, the point-slope form involves points and the slope, and the slope-intercept form involves the slope and y-intercept. When the directions do not ask for a specific form, students may use any form if they have the right information.

Part II   The graph of any linear equation is a line.

Given   An equation $Ax + By = C$ with A and B not both zero

Prove   The graph of $Ax + By = C$ is a line ℓ.

Proof   **Case I** $B = 0$

Then $Ax = C$, or $x = \frac{C}{A}$. The graph of this equation is a vertical line.

Case II $B \neq 0$

Then solving $Ax + By = C$ for y gives $y = -\frac{A}{B}x + \frac{C}{B}y$.

By Theorem 13-4, the graph of this equation is a line ℓ with slope $-\frac{A}{B}$ and y-intercept $\frac{C}{B}$.

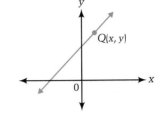

In our coordinate model, we interpreted parallel lines as lines with equal slopes. This fact can now be established by using similar triangles. The proof of Theorem 13-6 is required in Exercise 34.

Theorem 13-6

Two nonvertical lines are parallel if and only if they have equal slopes.

We interpreted perpendicular lines in our coordinate model as lines whose slopes are negative reciprocals of each other. This fact can also be established within our system. The proof of Theorem 13-7 is omitted.

Theorem 13-7

Two nonvertical lines are perpendicular if and only if the slope m_1 of one line is the negative reciprocal of the slope m_2 of the other line. $m_1 = -\dfrac{1}{m_2}$, or $m_1 m_2 = -1$

Once the Distance Formula has been established as a theorem within our system, we can also establish the **standard form for an equation of a circle.**

Let $P(x, y)$ be any point on the circle with center $A(h, k)$ and radius r. Then $AP = \sqrt{(x - h)^2 + (y - k)^2}$. Since $AP = r$, we have $\sqrt{(x - h)^2 + (y - k)^2} = r$, or $(x - h)^2 + (y - k)^2 = r^2$. This establishes Theorem 13-8.

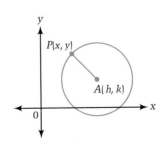

Theorem 13-8

The equation of a circle with center (h, k) and radius r is
$(x - h)^2 + (y - k)^2 = r^2$.

Example 3

Write an equation for the line tangent to a circle at point $P(-4, a)$ where $a > 0$ if the circle has center $C(-4, 2)$ and radius r.

Solution

The coordinates of P must satisfy $(x + 4)^2 + (y - 2)^2 = 9$. Thus, $(-4 + 4)^2 + (a - 2)^2 = 9$ or $a - 2 = \pm\sqrt{9}$. Therefore, $a = 5$ or $a = -1$. Since $a > 0$, $a = 5$. Since $\overleftrightarrow{CP} \perp \ell$ at P (Why?), the slopes of $\overleftrightarrow{CP}$ and ℓ are negative reciprocals of each other. The slope of $\overleftrightarrow{CP}$ is undefined. Therefore, the slope of ℓ is 0. Since ℓ is a horizontal line containing $P(-4, 5)$, its equation is $y = 5$.

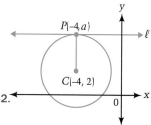

Checking for Understanding

Given $A(4, -3)$ and $B(6, -2)$ on line ℓ

1. What is the slope of ℓ? $\frac{1}{2}$

2. Write the equation of line ℓ in point-slope form, slope-intercept form, and standard form.

> **2.** $y + 3 = \frac{1}{2}(x - 4)$;
> $y = \frac{1}{2}x - 5$;
> $x - 2y = 10$

3. What are the x- and y-intercepts of ℓ? 10; −5

4. What is the slope of any horizontal line? 0

5. What is the slope of any vertical line? Undefined

6. Describe how all lines with positive slopes slant when graphed on a coordinate plane. Upward to the right

7. Describe how all lines with negative slopes slant when graphed on a coordinate plane. Downward to the right.

8. What is the equation of the circle in Example 3?
$(x + 4)^2 + (y - 2)^2 = 9$

Written Exercises

Set A Write the equations of each line in both point-slope form and slope-intercept form for the line containing

1. $A(3, 5)$; $B(2, 3)$.   **2.** $C(-6, -3)$; $D(2, -3)$.

3. $E(-5, 8)$; $F(-5, -6)$.   **4.** $G(0, 3)$; $H(4, 0)$.

> **1.** $y - 3 = 2(x - 2)$
> $y = 2x - 1$
> **2.** $y + 3 = 0(x - 2)$;
> $y = x - 3$
> **3.** $x = -5$
> **4.** $y - 0 = -\frac{3}{4}(x - 4)$;
> $y = -\frac{3}{4}x + 3$

Find the slope and the x- and y-intercepts of the line with the given equation. Graph each equation.

5. $3x - 5y = 10$ **6.** $x + 3y = -12$ **7.** $3x + y = 3$
    $\frac{3}{5}; \frac{10}{3}; -2$ $-\frac{1}{3}; -12; -4$ $-3; 1; 3$

EXERCISE NOTES

Exercises 12 and **13** may be done as a **group activity**.
Exercise 23 uses the **problem-solving strategy** of guess-and-check.
Exercises 35–37 provide a review of the definitions of special segments in a triangle.

ANSWERS

Written Exercises

5.

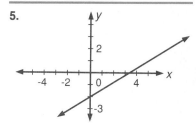

6.

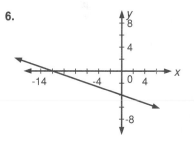

7.

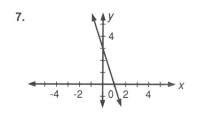

12.

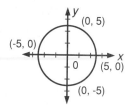

13.

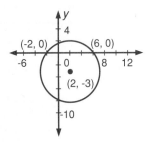

15. Slope of $\overleftrightarrow{PQ}$ = slope of $\overleftrightarrow{RS}$ = $-\frac{1}{4}$. Since slopes are =, the lines are ∥.

16. Slope of $\overleftrightarrow{RS}$ = $-\frac{1}{4}$ = m_1; slope of $\overleftrightarrow{RU}$ = 4 = m_2. Since m_1m_2 = −1, the lines are ⊥.

17. By the Distance Formula, SE = ND = $\sqrt{34}$ and SD = EN = $2\sqrt{34}$. Since both pairs of opp. sides are =, SEND is a ▱.

18. Slope of $\overleftrightarrow{EN}$ = $-\frac{5}{3}$ and slope of $\overleftrightarrow{ND}$ = $\frac{3}{5}$. Since the product of the slopes is −1, $\overleftrightarrow{EN} \perp \overleftrightarrow{ND}$. Thus, ∠END is a rt. ∠ and △END is a rt. △.

19. SN = ED = $\sqrt{170}$

31. QT = $y_2 - y_1$; PT = $x_2 - x_1$; SU = $y_4 - y_3$; RU = $x_4 - x_3$; $\frac{y_2 - y_1}{x_2 - x_1} = \frac{y_4 - y_3}{x_4 - x_3}$

34. *Part I* Given: Nonvertical lines ℓ and k with slopes m_1 and m_2, respectively; $\ell \parallel k$ Prove: m_1 = m_2

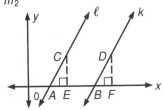

Write an equation in standard form for

8. the line that contains $P(3, 2)$ and is parallel to the line whose equation is $-x + 2y = 6$.

9. the line that has y-intercept 4 and is perpendicular to the line whose equation is $-8x + 9y = -2$.

10. the line that is the perpendicular bisector of the segment whose endpoints are $A(-6, 5)$ and $B(8, -2)$.

11. the line that is perpendicular to the line whose equation is $y = 1$ and contains $P(15, 1)$

Find the radius and center of the circle with the given equation. Graph the equation. Is point P on the circle?

12. $x^2 + y^2 = 25$; $P(0, 0)$

13. $(x - 2)^2 + (y + 3)^2 = 25$; $P(-3, -3)$

14. The Federal Highway Commission recommends a maximum grade of 12% for a road. What is the maximum vertical rise for a section of road covering 100 feet of horizontal distance? **12 ft.**

Using the graph at the right, show that

15. $\overleftrightarrow{PQ} \parallel \overleftrightarrow{RS}$. **16.** $\overleftrightarrow{RS} \perp \overleftrightarrow{RU}$.

Given: $S(-5, 5)$; $E(0, 8)$; $N(6, -2)$; $D(1, -5)$

17. Show that SEND is a parallelogram.

18. Show that △END is a right triangle.

19. Show that the diagonals of SEND are equal.

Set B Write an equation for the line that

20. contains the origin and is parallel to the line whose equation is $y = -5x - 9$. $y = -5x$

21. contains $B(-2, 4)$ and is perpendicular to the line whose equation is $y - 1 = -\frac{3}{5}(x + 6)$.

22. has slope 5 and contains the midpoint of the segment joining $A(3, 8)$ and $B(-5, -2)$.

21. $y - 4 = \frac{5}{3}(x + 2)$ **22.** $y - 3 = 5(x + 1)$

Find n so that $\overleftrightarrow{AB}$ has the given slope.

23. $A(5, -2)$, $B(-4, n)$; slope 0 −2

24. $A(n + 1, n)$, $B(n - 1, 1)$; slope $\frac{1}{2}$ 2

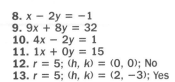

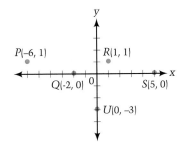

8. $x - 2y = -1$
9. $9x + 8y = 32$
10. $4x - 2y = 1$
11. $1x + 0y = 15$
12. $r = 5$; $(h, k) = (0, 0)$; No
13. $r = 5$; $(h, k) = (2, -3)$; Yes

25. Write an equation of the circle with center $B(-2, 8)$ and radius 5.

26. Write an equation of the circle whose center is the origin and which contains the point $Q(8, 15)$.

27. Does the point $P(4, -3)$ lie on the circle with center $A(-4, 3)$ and radius 7? Explain.

Given: $P(x_1, y_1)$, $Q(x_2, y_2)$, $R(x_3, y_3)$, and $S(x_4, y_4)$ are on line k; $\overleftrightarrow{PT}$ and $\overleftrightarrow{RU}$ are horizontal lines; $\overleftrightarrow{QT}$ and $\overleftrightarrow{SU}$ are vertical lines.

28. Why is $m\angle QPT = m\angle SRU$?

29. Why is $\triangle PTQ \sim \triangle RUS$? AA~Post.

30. $\dfrac{QT}{PT} = \dfrac{?}{?} \dfrac{SU}{RU}$

31. Write each of the distances in Exercise 30 using the coordinates of the points. Then rewrite the proportion.

Set C

32. Are $X(4, 3)$, $Y(-2, -9)$, and $Z(7, 9)$ collinear? Yes

33. $\triangle DEF$ has vertices $D(-2, -5)$, $E(4, -3)$, and $F(2, 7)$. Write an equation of the line passing through the midpoints of $\overline{DE}$ and $\overline{DF}$. Show that this line is parallel to $\overleftrightarrow{EF}$. $y = -5x + 1$; slope of EF is -5

34. Write a paragraph proof of Theorem 13-6.

Given: $A(-4, 0)$, $B(4, 8)$, and $C(6, -3)$. Write an equation in standard form for each line described.

35. Each line containing a median of $\triangle ABC$.

36. Each line containing an altitude of $\triangle ABC$.

37. The perpendicular bisector of each side of $\triangle ABC$.

38. Graph the circle with equation $x^2 - 10x + y^2 - 6y = 30$.

▲ Review Given: $\overline{ST}$ has endpoints $S(2, -1, 4)$ and $T(0, 5, -2)$.

39. Find ST. $2\sqrt{19}$

40. Find the coordinates of the midpoint of $\overline{ST}$. $(1, 2, 1)$

41. Explain why a dilation with scale factor 3 is a similarity transformation. SSS~Thm.

25. $(x + 2)^2 + (y - 8)^2 = 25$
26. $x^2 + y^2 = 289$
27. No; $AP = 10$ which: is >7.
28. Since $\overleftrightarrow{RU} \parallel \overleftrightarrow{PT}$ these corres. $\angle$s are $=$.

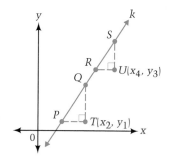

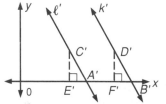

case iii

Proof: *Case I* If ℓ and k are parallel to the x-axis, each line has slope zero. Then $m_1 = m_2$. *Case II* ℓ and k intersect the x-axis and have positive slopes. Let A and B, respectively, be the points of intersection with the x-axis. Let C and D be points on each line on the same side of the x-axis. Draw $\overline{CE}$ and $\overline{DF}$ $\perp$ to the x-axis. Since $\triangle AEC \sim \triangle BFD$ by the AA $\sim$ Post., $\dfrac{CE}{DF} = \dfrac{AE}{BF}$ or $\dfrac{CE}{AE} = \dfrac{DF}{BF}$. Since $\dfrac{CE}{AE} = m_1$ and $\dfrac{DF}{BF} = m_2$, we conclude $m_1 = m_2$ by the Substitution Prop. *Case III* ℓ and k intersect the x-axis and have negative slopes. Then by an argument as in Case II, $m_1 = -\dfrac{C'E'}{A'E'}$ and $m_2 = -\dfrac{D'F'}{B'F'}$. So, $m_1 = m_2$.

Part II Given: Nonvertical lines ℓ and k with slopes m_1 and m_2, respectively; $m_1 = m_2$ Prove: $\ell \parallel k$ Proof: *Case I* If $m_1 = m_2 = 0$, then ℓ and k are both $\parallel$ to the x-axis. Thus they are $\parallel$ to each other. *Case II* $m_1 = m_2 \neq 0$. Choose A, B, C, D, E and F as in Part I, Case II. (Use the diagram given in Part I, Case II.) Then since $m_1 = m_2$, using the Substitution Prop. gives $\dfrac{CE}{AE} = \dfrac{DF}{BF}$. $\angle CEA$ and $\angle DFB$ are rt. $\angle$s. Thus, by SAS $\sim$ Thm., $\triangle CEA \sim \triangle DFB$ and $m\angle CAE = m\angle DBF$. Therefore, $\ell \parallel k$. (Corres. $\angle$s $= \Rightarrow$ lines $\parallel$.)
35. $7x + 6y = 24$; $5x - 18y = -20$; $19x - 6y = 28$
36. $x + y = 3$; $2x - 11y = -8$; $10x - 3y = 16$
37. $x + y = 4$; $4x - 22y = -35$; $20x - 6y = 29$
38. circle with center at $(5, 3)$ and radius 8

Thinking Ahead

44. $A(0, 0)$; $B\left(\frac{a}{2}, \frac{a}{2}\sqrt{3}\right)$; $C(a, 0)$; $AB = BC = AC = a$

45. $A(0, 0)$; $B(a, a\sqrt{3})$; $C(2a, 0)$; $AB = BC = AC = 2a$

FOLLOW-UP

More Practice

• **Worksheet 13-2**

Extension

When a linear equation is written in the form
$$\frac{x}{a} + \frac{y}{b} = 1$$
it can be shown that the x- and y-intercepts are a and b, respectively. This is known as the intercept form of the equation. Have students write some of the equations in the exercises in this form. Then have them graph the equations using intercepts.
• **Extension 13-2**

Computers

Note: The activity in the pupil's book cannot be completed using a function grapher that uses $f(x)$ notation.
• **Computer Activities 13-2**

---

42. Find the lateral area, the total area, and the volume of the right cylinder. Give your answers in terms of π.
360π; 522π; 1620π

43. If plane E cuts parallel planes G and H in lines ℓ and m, how many points do ℓ and m have in common?
None

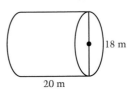

18 m

20 m

 Thinking Ahead **44.** Give the coordinates of the vertices of equilateral $\triangle ABC$. Use the distance formula to show that $\triangle ABC$ is equilateral.

45. Change the coordinates of M to $(a, 0)$. Find the coordinates of the vertices. Use the Distance Formula to verify that $\triangle ABC$ is equilateral.

46. Which set of coordinates of $\triangle ABC$ were easier to compute with in the Distance Formula? **Exercise 45**

47. Suppose B is on the y-axis. How could you name the coordinates of the vertices?

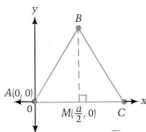

47. A $(-a, 0)$; $B(0, a\sqrt{3})$; C $(a, 0)$

💻 Computer Activities: Graphing

Graph all of the following equations on the same set of axes.

1. Graph line ℓ, whose equation is $y - 3x = -2$ and line ℓ_2 whose equation is $2y + x = 10$.

2. Add the equations to find $\ell_1 + \ell_2$ and graph the resulting equation.

3. Multiply both sides of the equation for ℓ_2 by 3 and add this result to the equation for ℓ_1 to find $\ell_1 + 3\ell_2$. Graph $\ell_1 + 3\ell_2$.

4. Multiply both sides of the equation for ℓ_1 by -2 and add this result to the equation for ℓ_2 to find $(-2)\ell_1 + \ell_2$. Graph the resulting equation.   They all intersect at pt. $P(2, 4)$.

5. What do you notice about the lines graphed above?

6. Which two lines immediately give you the coordinates of the point of intersection of ℓ_1 and ℓ_2?
$\ell_1 + 3\ell_2$; $(-2)\ell_1 + \ell_2$

Algebra Review: Graphing Systems of Linear Equations

Using a separate coordinate grid for each exercise, graph each pair of equations and describe the intersection of the lines. Then solve the exercises algebraically.

1. $x = 0$; $y = -5$; a point
2. $x = 3$; $y = 12$; a point
3. No solution, the lines are ∥.

1. $y = 3x - 5$
$2x + 3y = -15$

2. $y - 8 = \frac{2}{3}(x + 3)$
$3y - 4x = 24$

3. $y + 3x = -4$
$y + 2 = -3(x - 1)$

1. Express in simplest form the distance from $O(0, 0)$ to $P(x, y)$. $\sqrt{x^2 + y^2}$
2. Express in simplest form the slope of the line containing $A(a, b)$ and $B(c, d)$. $(d - b)/(c - a)$
3. Write an equation of the line containing $O(0, 0)$ and $R(3, 6)$. $y = 2x$
4. True or false: All sides of a rhombus are equal. True

13-3 Proofs Using Coordinates

Given $W(1, 0)$, $X(4, 0)$, $Y(4, 4)$, and $Z(1, 4)$, you can show that the diagonals of rectangle $WXYZ$ are equal by using the Distance Formula. By using variables for the coordinates of a rectangle, you can prove that the diagonals of any rectangle are equal.

Example 1

Prove that the diagonals of a rectangle are equal.

Solution

Given   Rectangle $OPQR$

Prove $OQ = PR$

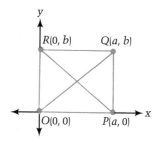

Let the sides of the rectangle have nonzero measures of a and b. Place the coordinate axes so that one vertex of the rectangle, say O, is at the origin, and another vertex, say P, is on the x-axis. Then the coordinates of the vertices are $O(0, 0)$, $P(a, 0)$, $Q(a, b)$, and $R(0, b)$. By the Distance Formula, we have

$OQ = \sqrt{(a - 0)^2 + (b - 0)^2}$ and $PR = \sqrt{(0 - a)^2 + (b - 0)^2}$
$OQ = \sqrt{a^2 + b^2}$ $PR = \sqrt{a^2 + b^2}$

Since OQ and PR have the same length, $OQ = PR$.

Note that in labeling the coordinates of rectangle $OPQR$, we must assume $a \neq b$. Labeling the rectangle as shown at the right assumes that the figure is a square.

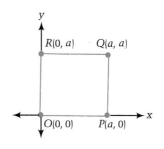

Also note in Example 1 that the placement of the axes with respect to $OPQR$ is important.

Suppose we choose rectangle $EFGH$ to represent any rectangle and place the coordinate axes as shown. Use the Distance Formula to show $EG = FH$. Note that this placement of the axes complicated use of the Distance Formula.
$EG = \sqrt{(t - r)^2 + (u - s)^2}$; $FH \sqrt{(t - r)^2 + (s - u)^2}$
but since $(u - s)^2 = (s - u)^2$, $FH = EG$

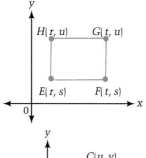

Why is it inconvenient to place the coordinate axes as shown in the diagram at the right?   It complicates the use of the Dinstance Formula

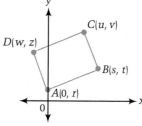

Is it possible to position the axes as shown in Example 1 for every rectangle? Why? Yes; the axes are $\perp$ and form a rt. $\angle$, and therefore, translate on to a rt. $\angle$ of a rectangle.

LESSON 13-3

Resources

Worksheet 13-3
Extension 13-3

OBJECTIVES

Place specific types of geometric figures on coordinate axes; write coordinate proofs.

TEACHING NOTES

Begin this lesson with exercises that develop the **proof subskills** of drawing necessary proof diagrams and writing the "Given" and "Prove" parts of a proof. In the case of coordinate proofs, this involves placement on the axes and selection of coordinates.

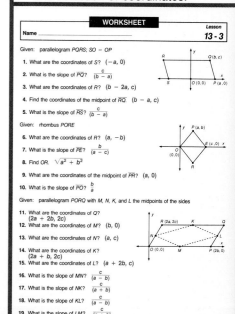

In proofs that involve midpoints, it is wise to choose coordinates such as $(2a, 2b)$ rather than (a, b) for the vertices. Demonstrate both methods to give students an appreciation of the algebraic ease of the former.

Additional Examples

Example 1

Prove that the diagonals of a parallelogram bisect each other.

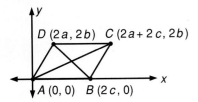

Let $A(0, 0)$, $B(2c, 0)$, $C(2a + 2c, 2b)$ and $D(2a, 2b)$. The midpoints of both $\overline{AC}$ and $\overline{BD}$ are $(a + c, b)$.

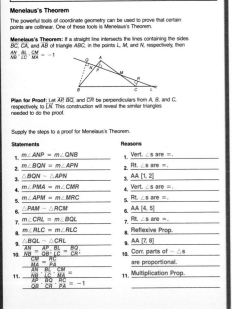

Example 2

Place the coordinate axes in a convenient position with respect to an isosceles triangle.

Solution

For isosceles $\triangle JOB$, place the axes as shown. Choose $2a$ for the x-coordinate of J to avoid fractions in computation. The x-coordinate of B is a since B has the same x-coordinate as M, the midpoint of $\overline{OJ}$.

You can also place the coordinate axes so tht M is at $(0, 0)$. What could you label the coordinates of $\triangle UVW$? This placement uses the symmetry of an isosceles triangle to place each vertex on one of the axes.

Samples: $U(a, 0)$; $V(-a, 0)$; $W(0, b)$

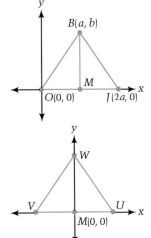

Example 3

Use the coordinate method of proof to prove that if the diagonals of a rhombus are equal, then the rhombus is a square.

Solution

Given   Rhombus $OPQR$ with $OQ = PR$

Prove $OPQR$ is a square.

Since $OPQR$ is a rhombus, $\overline{OP} \parallel \overline{RQ}$ and $OP = RQ$. Place the coordinate axes so that three vertices, O, P, and R, have coordinates $(0, 0)$, $(c, 0)$, and (a, b), respectively. Then the fourth vertex Q must have coordinates $(a + c, b)$. Since $OQ = PR$, $\sqrt{(a + c - 0)^2 + (b - 0)^2} = \sqrt{(a - c)^2 + (b - 0)^2}$ Simplifying this equation gives $4ac = 0$. Since P is not the origin, $c \neq 0$. Then a must be zero. If $a = 0$, then R is on the y-axis, $\overline{OP} \perp \overline{OR}$, and rhombus $OPQR$ is a square.

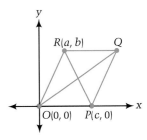

Summary   Placing a Coordinate System Relative to a Polygon

Place the coordinate axes so that a vertex is at the origin and the nonnegative portion of the x-axis contains a side of the polygon.

If the polygon has a right angle, position the axes so that the sides of the right angle lie on the x- and y-axes.

Place the x- or y-axes so that it contains any axis of symmetry.

Use an expression such as $2a$ instead of a simple variable a if symmetry or midpoints are involved.

The next example shows how a coordinate method can be used to prove statements involving distance and lengths of segments.

Example 4

Prove that the medians of a triangle are concurrent in a point whose distance from each vertex is two thirds of the length of the median containing that vertex.

Solution

Given: $\triangle MNO$; A, B, and C are the midpoints of $\overline{MN}$, $\overline{NO}$, and $\overline{OM}$, respectively.

Prove: *Part I* There is a point D which lies on $\overleftrightarrow{AO}$, $\overleftrightarrow{BM}$, and $\overleftrightarrow{CN}$.

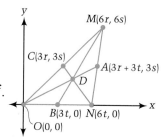

$$\text{Part II} \quad \frac{DO}{AO} = \frac{DM}{BM} = \frac{DN}{CN} = \frac{2}{3}$$

Place the coordinate axes as shown. Let the vertices of the scalene triangle be $M(6r, 6s)$, $N(6t, 0)$, and $O(0, 0)$. Why are these vertices a convenient choice? Then the midpoints are $A(3r + 3t, 3s)$, $B(3t, 0)$, and $C(3r, 3s)$. **2 and 3 are factors of 6.**

Part I Write an equation for each median.

Line	Slope	Equation in point-slope form
$\overleftrightarrow{AO}$	$\dfrac{s}{r + t}$	$y - 0 = \left(\dfrac{s}{r + t}\right)(x - 0)$
$\overleftrightarrow{BM}$	$\dfrac{2s}{2r - t}$	$y - 0 = \left(\dfrac{2s}{2r - t}\right)(x - 3t)$
$\overleftrightarrow{CN}$	$\dfrac{s}{r - 2t}$	$y - 0 = \left(\dfrac{s}{r - 2t}\right)(x - 6t)$

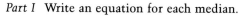

Find the intersection of $\overleftrightarrow{AO}$ and $\overleftrightarrow{BM}$ by substitution.

$$\left(\frac{s}{r + t}\right)(x - 0) = \left(\frac{2s}{2r - t}\right)(x - 3t)$$

Solving for x, $x = 2r + 2t$.

Substitute this value for x in the equation for $\overleftrightarrow{AO}$ to find $y = 2s$. So $D(2r + 2t, 2s)$ lies on $\overleftrightarrow{AO}$ and $\overleftrightarrow{BM}$.

Substitute the coordinates of D in the equation for $\overleftrightarrow{CN}$.

$$(2s) = \left(\frac{s}{r - 2t}\right)[(2r + 2t) - 6t]$$

$$= \left(\frac{s}{r - 2t}\right)[2(r - 2t)]$$

$$= 2s$$

Since the coordinates of D satisfy the equation, D lies on $\overleftrightarrow{CN}$. Therefore, there is a point D which lies on $\overleftrightarrow{AO}$, $\overleftrightarrow{NO}$, and $\overleftrightarrow{CN}$.

The proof of Part II is left to Exercise 15.

Example 2
Place the coordinate axes in a convenient position with respect to a right triangle. $C(0, 0)$, $A(a, 0)$ and $B(0, b)$

Example 3
Use the coordinate method of proof to prove that if the diagonals of a parallelogram are equal, then the parallelogram is a rectangle.

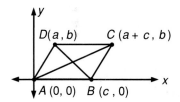

Let $A(0, 0)$, $B(c, 0)$, $C(a + c, b)$ and $D(a, b)$. Because $AC = BD$,
$$\sqrt{(a + c)^2 + b^2} = \sqrt{(a - c)^2 + b^2}, \text{ so } a = 0.$$

Assignment Guide

Basic: 1–16, 27–37
Average: 1–20, 27–37
Extended: 2–10 (even), 11–37

Error Analysis When choosing coordinates, be sure students do not forget what they are trying to prove. For example, in **Example 3** we cannot choose $R(0, b)$ because we would be assuming the conclusion is true.

ANSWERS

Written Exercises

15. Proof: Let the vertices have coordinates $M(6r, 6s)$, $N(6t, 0)$ and $O(0, 0)$. The midpts. are $A(3r + 3t, 3s)$, $B(3t, 0)$ and $C(3r, 3s)$. From Part I, $D(2r + 2t, 2s)$ lies on $\overleftrightarrow{AO}$, $\overleftrightarrow{BM}$ and $\overleftrightarrow{CN}$. By the Distance Formula:

$DO = \sqrt{(2r + 2t - 0)^2 + (2s - 0)^2}$
$\quad = 2\sqrt{(r + t)^2 + s^2};$
$AO = \sqrt{(3r + 3t - 0)^2 + (3s - 0)^2}$
$\quad = 3\sqrt{(r + t)^2 + s^2};$
$DM = \sqrt{(2r + 2t - 6r)^2 + (2s - 6s)^2}$
$\quad = 2\sqrt{(t - 2r)^2 + (2s)^2};$
$BM = \sqrt{(3t - 6r)^2 + (0 - 6s)^2}$
$\quad = 3\sqrt{(t - 2r)^2 + (2s)^2};$
$DN = \sqrt{(2r + 2t - 6t)^2 + (2s - 0)^2}$
$\quad = 2\sqrt{(r - 2t)^2 + s^2};$
$CN = \sqrt{(3r - 6t)^2 + (3s - 0)^2}$
$\quad = 3\sqrt{(r - 2t)^2 + s^2}.$
Thus, $\frac{DO}{AO} = \frac{DM}{BM} = \frac{DN}{CN} = \frac{2}{3}$

16. Given: Isosceles trap. $ABCD$; $AD = BC$ Prove: $AC = BD$

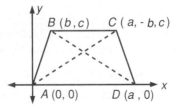

Proof: Place the coordinate axes on $ABCD$ so that A coincides with the origin and $\overline{AD}$ falls on the positive x-axis. Let the coordinates of D be $(a, 0)$. Since $ABCD$ is isos.,

Checking for Understanding

Find the coordinates of each point whose coordinates are not given.

1. Rectangle $EFGO$

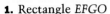
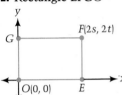

2. Equilateral $\triangle MNO$

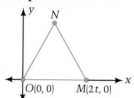

3. Isosceles trapezoid DEFG; $DO = EO$

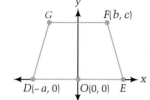

1. $E(2s, 0)$; $G(0, 2t)$
2. $N(t, t\sqrt{3})$
3. $E(a, o)$; $G(-b, c)$

$OPQR$ is a parallelogram.

4. What are the coordinates of Q? $(a + b, c)$

5. What are the slopes of $\overline{RO}$ and of $\overline{PQ}$? $\frac{c}{a}$

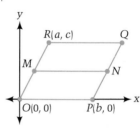

If M and N are midpoints of $\overline{RO}$ and $\overline{PQ}$, respectively,

6. what are the coordinates of M and N? $\left(\frac{a}{2}, \frac{c}{2}\right)$; $\left(\frac{a + 2b}{2}, \frac{c}{2}\right)$

7. what is the slope of $\overline{MN}$? 0

8. Given: Isosceles trapezoid $MNOP$ with $P(2a, 0)$, $O(0, 0)$, $N(2b, 2c)$, and $\overline{OP} \parallel \overline{MN}$. Find the coordinates of M. $(2a - 2b, 2c)$

Written Exercises

Set A Find the coordinates of each point whose coordinates are not given.

1. Square $OFGH$

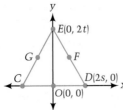

2. Equilateral $\triangle RST$

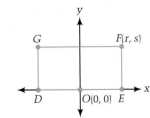

3. $CE = DE$, $GC = GE$, $FD = FE$, $CO = DO$

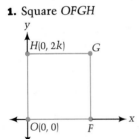
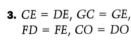

4. Rectangle $DEFG$; $DO = EO$

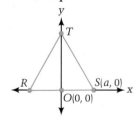

1. $F(2k, 0)$ $G(2k, 2k)$
2. $R(-a, 0)$; $T(0, a\sqrt{3})$
3. $C(-2s, 0)$; $F(s, t)$ $G(-s, t)$
4. $D(-r, 0)$; $E(r, 0)$; $G(-r, s)$

5. Coordinate axes are placed on square $ABCD$ so that the y-axis bisects $\overline{AB}$ and $\overline{CD}$, and the x-axis bisects $\overline{BC}$ and $\overline{DA}$. Assign coordinates to A, B, C, and D.

6. Coordinate axes are placed on rectangle $DEFG$ so that the midpoint of $\overline{EF}$ is on the x-axis and the midpoint of $\overline{FG}$ is on the y-axis. Assign coordinates to the vertices.

Given: Trapezoid $ROCK$ with $R(2, 3)$, $O(0, 0)$, $C(6, 0)$, and $K(5, 3)$.

7. Find the coordinates of the midpoints of the sides.

8. Find the slope of the median of trapezoid $ROCK$. 0

9. Write the equation of the line joining the midpoints of the bases. $y = 6(x - 3)$

10. Compare the length of the median with the lengths of the bases. $RK + OC = 9$; Length of median $= \frac{9}{2}$

Given: Isosceles $\triangle PQR$ with $R(0, b)$ and $\overline{PQ}$ on the x-axis

11. If $PR = RQ$, assign coordinates to P and Q.

12. If $m\angle RPQ = 90$, find the coordinates of P and Q.

13. Given: $\square OBCD$ with $O(0, 0)$, $B(s, 0)$, and $C(t, u)$. Find the coordinates of D. $(t - s, u)$

14. Given: $\square EFGH$ with $\overline{EF}$ parallel to the x-axis and diagonals that intersect at the origin; $F(c, -b)$; $G(a, b)$. Find the coordinates of E and H. $E(-a, -b)$ $H(-c, b)$

15. Prove Part II of Example 4.

Prove each of the statements in Exercises 16–23 by coordinate methods.

16. The diagonals of an isosceles trapezoid are equal.

Set B　**17.** If the diagonals of a parallelogram are equal, then the parallelogram is a rectangle.

18. The segments joining the midpoints of consecutive sides of a rectangle form a rhombus.

19. The lines containing the altitudes of a triangle are concurrent.

20. The perpendicular bisectors of the sides of a triangle are concurrent.

5. Sample:
$A(-a, a)$;
$B(a, a)$;
$C(a, -a)$;
$D(-a, -a)$
6. Sample:
$D(-a, b)$;
$E(a, b)$;
$F(a, -b)$;
$G(-a, -b)$;
7. $\overline{RO}$: $(1, \frac{3}{2})$;
$\overline{OC}$: $(3, 0)$;
$\overline{CK}$: $(\frac{11}{2}, \frac{3}{2})$;
$\overline{KR}$: $(\frac{7}{2}, 3)$

11. Samples:
$P(-a, 0)$; $Q(a, 0)$
12. Samples:
$P(0, 0)$; $Q(b, 0)$

the coordinates of B and C are (b, c) and $(a - b, c)$. By the Distance Formula, $AC =$
$\sqrt{(a - b - 0)^2 + (c - 0)^2} =$
$\sqrt{(a - b)^2 + c^2}$ and $BD =$
$\sqrt{(a - b)^2 + (0 - c)^2} =$
$\sqrt{(a - b)^2 + c^2}$. Thus, $AC = BD$ by the Substitution Prop.

17. Given: $\square ABCD$; $AC = BD$
Prove: $ABCD$ is a rectangle.

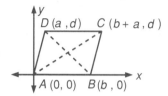

Proof: Place the coordinate axes on $\square ABCD$ so that $A(0, 0)$, $B(b, 0)$, $C(b + a, d)$ and $D(a, d)$. By the Distance Formula, $AC =$
$\sqrt{(b + a)^2 + d^2}$ and $BD =$
$\sqrt{(b - a)^2 + d^2}$. Since $AC = BD$,
$\sqrt{(b + a)^2 + d^2} =$
$\sqrt{(b - a)^2 + d^2}$, or $-a = a$. This is true if and only if $a = 0$. Therefore, $\overline{AD} \perp \overline{AB}$ and $\angle A$ is a rt. $\angle$. Thus, $\angle C$, $\angle D$ and $\angle B$ are also rt. $\angle$s. (Opp. $\angle$s of a $\square$ are $=$, and int. $\angle$s on same side of transversal are supp.) So $ABCD$ is a rectangle.

18. Given: Rectangle $ABCD$ with M, N, P, Q the midpts. of its sides
Prove: $MNPQ$ is a rhombus.

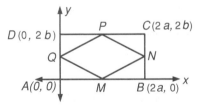

Proof: Place the coordinate axes so that $\angle A$ is at $(0, 0)$ and AB is on the positive x-axis. Let the coordinates of B be $(2a, 0)$. Then C and D have coordinates $(2a, 2b)$ and $(0, 2b)$, respectively. By the Midpt. Formula, the midpts. are $M(a, 0)$, $N(2a, b)$, $P(a, 2b)$ and $Q(0, b)$. Then by the Distance Formula, $MN = NP = PQ = QM = \sqrt{a^2 + b^2}$.

21. Given: Rhombus *ABCD* Prove:
$\overline{AC} \perp \overline{BD}$

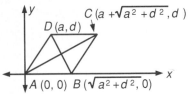

Proof: Place the coordinates axes on *ABCD* so that $\overline{AB}$ falls on the *x*-axis, with *A* at the origin; then *A*(0, 0). Let *D* have coordinates (*a*, *d*). By the Pythagorean Theorem and the definition of a rhombus, the other vertices are $B(\sqrt{a^2 + d^2}, 0)$ and $C(a + \sqrt{a^2 + d^2}, d)$. Slope m_1 of $\overline{AC} = \frac{d}{a + \sqrt{a^2 + d^2}}$. Slope m_2 of $\overline{BD} = \frac{d}{a - \sqrt{a^2 + d^2}}$. Since $m_1 m_2 = -1$, $\overline{AC} \perp \overline{BD}$.

22. Given: Quad. *WXYO*; $\overline{WY}$ and $\overline{OX}$ bisect each other. Prove: *WXYO* is a ▱.

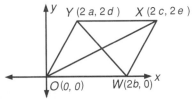

Proof: Place the coordinate axes so that *O*(0, 0) and $\overline{OW}$ falls on the *x*-axis. Let the other vertices be *W*(2*b*, 0), *X*(2*c*, 2*e*) and *Y*(2*a*, 2*d*). By the Midpt. Formula, the midpt. of $\overline{OX}$ is $M_1(c, e)$ and the midpt. of $\overline{WY}$ is $M_2(a + b, d)$. Since the diags. bisect each other, $M_1 = M_2$, so $a + b = c$ and $d = e$. Slope $\overline{XY} = \frac{e - d}{c - a} = 0 =$ slope $\overline{OW}$. Thus, $\overline{XY} \parallel \overline{OW}$. Slope $\overline{XW} = \frac{2e}{2(c - b)} = \frac{d}{a} =$ slope $\overline{OY}$. Thus, $\overline{XW} \parallel \overline{OY}$. Therefore, *OWXY* is a ▱.

23. Given: Rhombus *ABCD*; *M*, *N*, *O* and *P* are midpts. of $\overline{AB}$, $\overline{BC}$, $\overline{CD}$ and $\overline{DA}$, respectively. Prove: *MNOP* is a rectangle.

Set C

21. The diagonals of a rhombus are perpendicular.

22. If the diagonals of a quadrilateral bisect each other, then the quadrilateral is a parallelogram.

23. The segments joining the midpoints of consecutive sides of a rhombus form a rectangle.

Given a cube with the coordinates of its vertices as shown in the diagram

24. Find $\overline{EC}$. $a\sqrt{3}$

25. Prove: $EC = BF = AG = HD$

26. Find the coordinates of the midpoints of $\overline{EC}$, $\overline{BF}$, $\overline{AG}$, and $\overline{HD}$. What can you conclude about these segments?

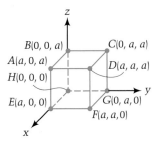

▲ Review Given: *A*(2, 6) and *B*(−1, 4)

27. What is the slope of $\overleftrightarrow{AB}$? $\frac{2}{3}$

28. Write the equation of $\overleftrightarrow{AB}$ in point-slope form.

29. The vertices of △*DEF* are *D*(−1, 2, −2), *E*(2, 3, 0), and *F*(0, 4, −1). If △*DEF* isosceles? Yes

30. In ⊙*O*, find $m\angle 1$ and $m\angle 2$. 33; 47

31. The area of a rectangle is 180 cm² and the length is 5 times the width. Find its length and width. 30; 6

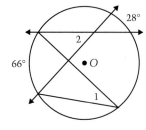

≡ Thinking Ahead

32. The directed line segment $\overline{AB}$ describes a transformation of the plane. Using this directed line segment, find the images of points *D*, *E*, and *F*. Draw the image of △*DEF*.

33. What kind of transformation is described by the directed line segment $\overline{AB}$? Translation

34. What is the image of △*DEF* under the transformation described by the directed line segment $\overline{GH}$?

35. Draw a directed line segment with one endpoint at the origin that would describe the same transformation as the directed line segment $\overline{GH}$.

36. Draw a directed line segment with one endpoint at *T*(−7, 3) that would describe the same transformation as the directed line segment $\overline{AB}$.

37. What is the measure of the angle that the directed line segment in Exercise 35 makes with the nonnegative *x*-axis? What is the length of the segment? 34; $\sqrt{13}$

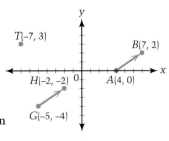

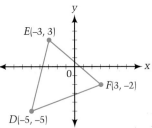

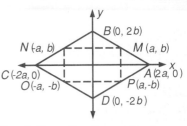

Proof: Since the diagonals of a rhombus are ⊥ and bisect each other, place the coordinate axes on the rhombus so that its diags. lie on the axes. Then $A(2a, 0)$, $B(0, 2b)$, $C(-2a, 0)$ and $D(0, -2b)$ are the vertices. Midpt. of $\overline{AB}$ is $M(a, b)$; midpt. of $\overline{BC}$ is $N(-a, b)$; midpt. of $\overline{CD}$ is $O(-a, -b)$; midpt. of $\overline{DA}$ is $P(a, -b)$. Since the slopes of $\overline{MN}$ and $\overline{OP}$ are 0, $\overline{MN} \parallel \overline{OP}$. Since the slopes of $\overline{NO}$ and $\overline{MP}$ are undefined, $\overline{NO} \parallel \overline{MP}$. So $MNOP$ is a ▱. Further, $\overline{MN} \perp \overline{MP}$; $\overline{MP} \perp \overline{OP}$; $\overline{OP} \perp \overline{NO}$; and $\overline{NO} \perp \overline{MN}$. So $\angle MNO$, $\angle NOP$, $\angle OPM$ and $\angle PMN$ are rt. $\angle$s. Therefore, $▱MNOP$ is a rectangle.

Progress Check

Lesson 13-1, page 561

For a segment with the given endpoints, find the length of the segment and the coordinates of its midpoint.

1. $X(-2, 3)$, $Y(4, -5)$ 10; $(1, -1)$ **2.** $A(3, 0, -2)$, $B(-2, 5, 2)$ $\sqrt{66}$; $(\frac{1}{2}, \frac{5}{2}, 0)$

3. The vertices of $\triangle ABC$ are $A(4, -2)$, $B(2, 4)$, and $C(0, -3)$. Is $\triangle ABC$ a right triangle? No

Lesson 13-2, page 567

Given: $C(1, 2)$, $D(-4, 5)$, $E(-4, 7)$, and $F(5, 4)$

4. Find the slope of a line parallel to $\overleftrightarrow{CD}$. $-\frac{3}{5}$

5. Find the slope of a line perpendicular to $\overleftrightarrow{EF}$. 3

Write an equation of the line that

6. contains $A(-7, 9)$ and has slope $\frac{2}{3}$. $y - 9 = \frac{2}{3}(x + 7)$

7. has slope $\frac{-5}{6}$ and y-intercept -4. $y = -\frac{5}{6}x - 4$

8. contains $C(-3, 5)$ and $D(7, -4)$. $y - 5 = -\frac{9}{10}(x + 3)$

9. What is the x-intercept of the line with slope 3 through the point $P(-1, 6)$? -3

10. Find the slope and y-intercept of the line whose equation is $2x + 3y = 9$. Graph the equation. $-\frac{2}{3}$; 3

11. Find the x- and y-intercepts of the line with equation $-3x + 5y = 15$. Graph the equation. -5; 3

12. Write an equation in standard form of the line that contains $E(5, -3)$ and is perpendicular to the line whose equation is $-2x + 9y = 18$. $9x + 2y = 39$

13. Find the center and radius of a circle whose equation is $(x - 2)^2 + (y + 5)^2 = 16$. Graph the equation. $(2, -5)$; 4

Lesson 13-3, page 575

Given: Right $\triangle ABC$; $\angle BCA$ is a right angle; B has coordinates (p, q).

14. Find the coordinates of A and C. $(0, 0)$; $(P, 0)$

15. Find the slope of $\overleftrightarrow{AB}$. $\frac{q}{p}$

16. What is the slope of a line that is perpendicular to $\overleftrightarrow{AB}$? $-\frac{p}{q}$

17. Find the coordinates of D if $\angle BAD$ is a right angle. $(p, -\frac{p^2}{q})$

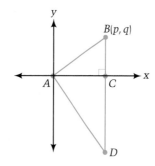

FOLLOW-UP

More Practice

• Worksheet 13–3

Extension

The following proof shows the power of coordinate proofs: If a segment joins the midpoints of two sides of a triangle, then it is parallel to the third side, and its length is half the length of the third side.

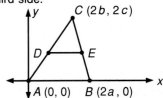

Let $A(0, 0)$, $B(2a, 0)$ and $C(2b, 2c)$. Then midpoints of $\overline{AC}$ and $\overline{BC}$ are $D(b, c)$ and $E(a + b, c)$. Slopes of $\overleftrightarrow{DE}$ and $\overleftrightarrow{AB}$ are both 0, $AB = 2a$ and $DE = a$.

• Extension 13–3

LESSON 13-4

Resources

- Teaching Aid 18, square root table
- Visual Aid 18, square root table
- Teaching Aid 19, trigonometric ratios
- Visual Aid 19, trigonometric ratios
- Worksheet 13-4
- Extension 13-4
- Quiz 13

OBJECTIVES

Name and draw vectors; find the magnitude and direction angle of a given vector.

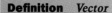

WORKSHEET — Lesson 13-4

Name _____

1. Draw $\overrightarrow{QR}$ if $|\overrightarrow{QR}| = 4$ and the direction angle is 120°.
2. Draw $\overrightarrow{TP}$ equal to $\overrightarrow{QR}$.
3. Draw $\overrightarrow{TS}$ equal to $-\overrightarrow{QR}$.
4. Find the magnitude of $\overrightarrow{k} = (12, -5)$. 13
5. Find the direction angle of $\overrightarrow{a} = (2, 2)$. 45°
6. Find the magnitude of $\overrightarrow{DE}$ given $D(6, -3)$ and $E(2, 0)$. 5

Check the statements that are ALWAYS true.

_____ 7. A vector is a directed line.
✓ 8. The length of a vector is called its *magnitude*.
✓ 9. A vector that has a magnitude of 0 is called a zero vector.
_____ 10. The magnitude of a vector is the distance from the origin to the terminal point of the vector.
_____ 11. Two vectors are equal if they have the same magnitude.
✓ 12. For $\overrightarrow{AB}$, A is the initial point and B is the terminal point.

Find the magnitude to the nearest tenth and the direction angle to the nearest degree for each vector. Draw the vector, measure the magnitude, and measure the direction angle with a protractor.

13. $\overrightarrow{a} = (1, 3)$
magnitude = 3.2
direction angle = 72°
measured magnitude = 3.2
measured direction angle = 72°

14. $\overrightarrow{k} = (4, 2)$
magnitude = 4.5
direction angle = 27°
measured magnitude = 4.5
measured direction angle = 27°

13-4 Vectors and Coordinates

If a plane leaving Chicago travels at 250 miles per hour, you can determine how far it will fly in 4 hours. However, you cannot know where it will be in 4 hours unless you know the direction of its flight. Vectors are used to express physical quantities that have both length and direction.

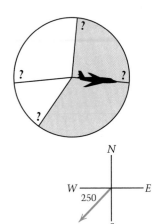

The diagram at the right represents the path of the plane flying southwest at 250 miles per hour. It is a line segment with an arrowhead at one endpoint to indicate its direction. This representation leads to the definition of a vector.

Definition *Vector*

A vector is a directed line segment.

There are many ways to denote a vector. In this text, we will use two notations. Sometimes we will use a "half arrow" over a bold lowercase letter, $\overrightarrow{v}$, which is read "vector v."

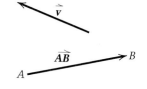

We will also use a half arrow over the uppercase letters of the endpoints of the segment, with the direction of the vector indicated by the direction of the half arrow. $\overrightarrow{AB}$ is read "vector AB" with the direction going from A to B.

For any $\overrightarrow{AB}$, A is the *initial point* and B is the *terminal point*. The length of a vector is called its *magnitude*. The magnitude of $\overrightarrow{AB}$ is the distance between its endpoints and is written $|\overrightarrow{AB}|$. The magnitude of $\overrightarrow{v}$ is written $|\overrightarrow{v}|$.

For every vector $\overrightarrow{v}$, there is a vector $-\overrightarrow{v}$, called the *opposite* of $\overrightarrow{v}$, that has the same magnitude as $\overrightarrow{v}$ but the opposite direction. A vector that has a magnitude of 0 is called a *zero vector* and written $\overrightarrow{0}$.

Definition *Equal Vectors*

Two vectors are equal if and only if they have the same magnitude and direction.

In the diagram at the right, $\overrightarrow{PQ}$ and $\overrightarrow{RS}$ are equal vectors. $\overrightarrow{PQ}$ and $\overrightarrow{XY}$ are not equal because they have different magnitudes. $\overrightarrow{PQ}$ and $\overrightarrow{FG}$ are not equal because they have different directions.

Does $\overrightarrow{PQ} = \overrightarrow{QP}$? Does $|\overrightarrow{PQ}| = |\overrightarrow{QP}|$? No; yes

Vectors can be translated to any location in a plane as long as the direction and magnitude remain the same. If a vector is placed so that its initial point coincides with the origin in a coordinate plane, the vector is said to be **standard position**. The vector is also called a **position vector**. In the diagram, $\overrightarrow{OP}$ is in standard position.

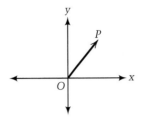

When a vector $\overrightarrow{OP}$ is in standard position, it can be thought of as an ordered pair of real numbers (x, y) where x and y are th coordinates of the terminal point. It is written $\overrightarrow{OP} = (x, y)$.

When a vector $\vec{v}$ is in standard position, the angle that the vector makes with the nonnegative portion of the x-axis is called the **direction angle** of $\vec{v}$.

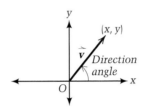

Example 1
Draw $\overrightarrow{OQ}$ if $|\overrightarrow{OQ}| = 5$ and the direction angle is 135°.

Solution
Use a protractor to measure and draw the direction angle. Then locate Q so that $OQ = 5$. Draw an arrowhead at Q.

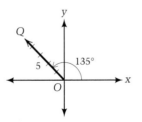

When a vector is given in standard position, you can calculate the magnitude by using the Pythagorean Theorem. You can also find the direction angle by using trigonometric ratios.

Example 2
Find the magnitude and direction angle of $\vec{u} = (4, 5)$.

Solution
Locate $(4, 5)$ and draw $\vec{u}$. Let T be the terminal point of $\vec{u}$. Draw $\overline{TS}$ perpendicular to the x-axis at S. Then $OS = 4$ and $ST = 5$. Why? Use the Pythagorean Theorem to find $\overline{OT}$.

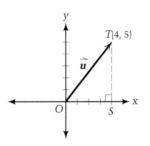

$$OS^2 + ST^2 = OT^2$$
$$4^2 + 5^2 = OT^2$$
$$41 = OT^2$$
$$\sqrt{41} = OT$$
$$6.4 \approx OT$$

Def. of distances between two pts. on a horizontal line and vertical line.

Since you know the lengths of the sides opposite and adjacent to $\angle TOS$, use the tangent ratio.

$$\tan \angle TOS = \frac{5}{4} = 1.25$$

Using a calculator or the table of trigonometric ratios on page 617, you find that $m\angle TOS \approx 51$. Therefore, the magnitude of $\vec{u}$ is about 6.4 and its direction angle is about 51°.

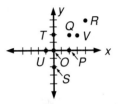

Assignment Guide

Basic: 1–10, 14–17, 20–25
Average: 1–17, 20–25
Extended: 1–25

Additional Examples

Example 1
Draw $\overrightarrow{OR}$, if $|\overrightarrow{OR}| = 3$ and the direction angle is 60.°

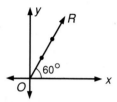

Example 2
Find the magnitude and direction angle for $\overrightarrow{w} = (-1, 3)$. $\sqrt{10} \approx$ 3.2; 108°

Example 3
Find the magnitude of $\overrightarrow{AB}$ with endpoints $A(4, -2)$ and $B(-4, 2)$. $\sqrt{80} \approx 8.9$

Error Analysis   Students often confuse vectors, which have magnitude and direction, with rays, which have direction but may be extended indefinitely. Encourage students to make their "half arrows" distinct.

ANSWERS

Written Exercises

4. Samples: $\overrightarrow{u} = \overrightarrow{v} = \overrightarrow{w}$

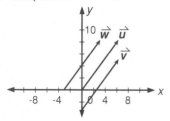

You can find the magnitude of any vector, regardless of its position in the coordinate plane, by using the Distance Formula.

Example 3
Find the magnitude of $\overrightarrow{PQ}$ with endpoints $P(-3, 5)$ and $Q(7, -4)$.

Solution
To find the distance between points P and Q, substitute their coordinates in the Distance Formula.

$$|\overrightarrow{PQ}| = \sqrt{(x_2 - x_1)^2 + (y_2 - y_1)^2}$$
$$= \sqrt{(-3 - 7)^2 + (5 - (-4))^2}$$
$$= \sqrt{181}$$
$$|\overrightarrow{PQ}| \approx 13.5$$

Checking for Understanding
1. Explain how a ray differs from a vector.

2. What are the coordinates of the zero vector? (0, 0)

3. If two vectors are equal, are they always parallel? Explain.

4. If $\overrightarrow{u}$ and $\overrightarrow{v}$ are collinear and $|\overrightarrow{u}| = |\overrightarrow{v}|$, does $\overrightarrow{u} = \overrightarrow{v}$?

5. Draw a vector equal to $-\overrightarrow{w}$.

Written Exercises 1. $\overrightarrow{c} = \overrightarrow{e}$; $\overrightarrow{f} = \overrightarrow{h}$
Set A   1. Name all pairs of equal vectors.

2. Name all pairs of opposite vectors.
$\overrightarrow{c}, \overrightarrow{d}$; $\overrightarrow{e}, \overrightarrow{d}$; $\overrightarrow{a}, \overrightarrow{b}$

3. Draw a vector to illustrate a velocity of 55 miles per hour going directly northeast.

4. Draw two vectors equal to $\overrightarrow{u} = (6, 8)$.

5. Draw $\overrightarrow{a}$ if $|\overrightarrow{a}| = 2$ and the direction angle is 25°.

Find the magnitude and direction angle for each vector.

6.
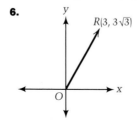

7.
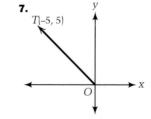

---

1. Given $\overleftrightarrow{PQ}$, $\overrightarrow{PQ}$ includes $\overline{PQ}$ and all pts. S such that Q lies between P and S. $\overline{PQ}$ is a directed line segment
3. Yes; a line is parallel to itself.
4. No; they could have opposite directions.
5.

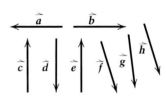

3. Sample:
6. 6; 60
7. $5\sqrt{2}$; 135

5.
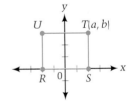

8. Find the magnitude of $\overrightarrow{OP}$ = (5, 12). **13**

9. Find the magnitude of $\overrightarrow{MN}$ if M(1, 3) and N(7, −6). **3√13**

Set B Find the magnitude to the nearest tenth and the angle of direction to the nearest degree for each vector.

10. $\vec{u}$ = (2, 5) **11.** $\vec{v}$ = (−3, 5) **12.** $\vec{w}$ = (−10, 1)

13. Find $|\overrightarrow{RS}|$ if R(−6, −2) and S(−9, 5). **7.6**

10. 5.4; 68°
11. 5.8; 121°
12. 10.0; 174°

Are the following pairs of vectors opposites of one another? Explain why or why not.

14. $\vec{a}$ = (2, 4); $\vec{b}$ = (4, 2) **15.** $\vec{c}$ = (1, 3); $\vec{d}$ = (−1, 3)
16. $\vec{u}$ = (−3, 5); $\vec{v}$ = (3, −5) **17.** $\vec{w}$ = (−2, −1); $\vec{z}$ = (1, 2)

14. No; $\vec{a}$ and $\vec{b}$ have the same magnitude but not opposite directions.
15. No; $\vec{c}$ and $\vec{d}$ have the same magnitude but not opposite directions.
16. Yes; $\vec{u}$ and $\vec{v}$ have the same magnitude but opposite directions.
17. No; $\vec{w}$ and $\vec{v}$ have the same magnitude but not opposite directions.

Set C Suppose we define the direction angle of a vector in standard position to be positive when the angle formed suggests a counterclockwise motion from the nonnegative part of the x-axis to the vector. The direction angle is considered negative when moving clockwise to the vector.

18. Name a positive and negative direction angle for $\vec{u}$ = (1, √3). **60°; −300°**

19. Name a positive and negative direction angle for $-\vec{u}$ in Exercise 18. **240°; −120°**

△ Review **20.** In rectangle RSTU, what are the coordinates of point S? point R? point U? **(a, 0); (−a, 0); (−a, b)**

21. Given: Trapezoid CDEF with vertices C(−4, 0), D(4, 0), E(3, 3), and F(−3, 3). Find the coordinates of the midpoints of the legs. $\left(-\frac{7}{2}, \frac{3}{2}\right), \left(\frac{7}{2}, \frac{3}{2}\right)$

22. Write the equation of $\overleftrightarrow{GH}$ in slope-intercept form for G(−3, 0) and H(2, 10). **y = 2x + 6**

23. Give an "if . . . then" statement for the Venn diagram.

24. Give the converse, the inverse, and the contrapositive of the conditional in Exercise 23.

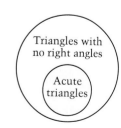

Review

23. If a triangle is an acute triangle, then it has no right angle.
24. *Converse*: If a triangle has no rt. angle, then it is an acute triangle.
Inverse: If a triangle is not an acute triangle, then it has a right angle.
Contrapositive: If a triangle has a right angle, then it is not an acute triangle.

FOLLOW-UP

More Practice
• **Worksheet 13–4**

Extension

Show that for points P(a, b) and Q(c, d), the position vector that is equal to $\overrightarrow{PQ}$ is (c − a, d − b).
Have students find the position vector equal to $\overrightarrow{AB}$ for each of the following:
1. A(2, 3), B(5, 7). (3, 4)
2. A(6, 2), B(1, 7). (−5, 5)
3. A(−3, 5), B(2, −6). (5, −11)
4. A(2, −4), B(0, 0). (−2, 4)
• **Extension 13–4**

Thinking Ahead **25.** In the diagram at the right, $\overrightarrow{OP}$ and $\overrightarrow{PQ}$ illustrate a portion of the path of a cruise ship during two 2-hour trips. What vector would represent the result or sum of the four-hour cruise? $\overrightarrow{OQ}$

1. If opposite sides of a quadrilateral are equal, then the quadrilateral is a(n) ___?___. Parallelogram
2. In vector $\overline{AB}$, A is called the ___?___ point. Initial
3. If v = (6, 8), find $|v|$. 10

LESSON 13–5

Resources

Teaching Aid 18, square root table
Visual Aid 18, square root table
Teaching Aid 19, trigonometric ratios
Visual Aid 19, trigonometric ratios
Worksheet 13–5
Extension 13–5

OBJECTIVE

Draw and calculate sums and differences of vectors.

13-5 Sums and Differences of Vectors

The sum of two vectors is a vector. You can write the sum of $\vec{u}$ and $\vec{v}$ as $\vec{u} + \vec{v}$, or you can use one letter $\vec{w}$ where $\vec{w} = \vec{u} + \vec{v}$.

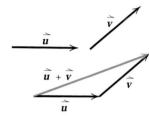

To draw the vector $\vec{u} + \vec{v}$, place the initial point of $\vec{v}$ on the terminal point of $\vec{u}$. Then the vector with the same initial point as $\vec{u}$ and the same terminal point as $\vec{v}$ is the vector $\vec{u} + \vec{v}$.

Another way to draw $\vec{u} + \vec{v}$ is to use the **parallelogram rule.** Place the vectors so that their initial points coincide. Then translate $\vec{u}$ so that its initial point maps onto the terminal point of $\vec{v}$. Translate $\vec{v}$ so that its initial point coincides with the terminal point of $\vec{u}$. The vectors and their translations complete a parallelogram. The vector with the same initial point as $\vec{u}$ and $\vec{v}$ that coincides with the diagonal of the parallelogram is the same vector sum that is shown in the first method.

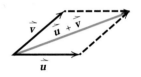

The vector $\vec{u} + \vec{v}$ is called the **resultant** of $\vec{u}$ and $\vec{v}$. Each of the vectors $\vec{u}$ and $\vec{v}$ is a **component** of the vector $\vec{u} + \vec{v}$.

There are infinitely many pairs of components for a given vector. Because trigonometric ratios are defined for right triangles, the most useful components of a given vector are its vertical and horizontal components. In both diagrams at the right, OR is the horizontal component of $\overline{OP}$. $\overline{OQ}$ and $\overline{RP}$ are both vertical components of $\overline{OP}$. Why does $\overline{OQ} = \overline{RP}$?
They have the same magnitude and direction.

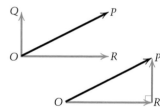

Example 1
Find (x, y) if $\vec{v}$ = (x, y), $|\vec{v}|$ = 10, and the direction angle is 35°.

Solution
Draw $\vec{v}$ so that $|\vec{v}|$ = 10. Let $\overline{OR}$ and $\overline{RP}$ be its horizontal and vertical components. Use the sine and cosine ratios to find RP and OR.

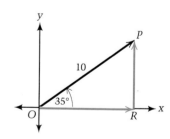

$$\sin 35° = \frac{RP}{10} \qquad \cos 35° = \frac{OR}{10}$$
$$10 \sin 35° = RP \qquad 10 \cos 35° = OR$$
$$10(0.5736) \approx RP \qquad 10(0.8191) \approx OR$$
$$5.7 \approx RP \qquad 8.2 \approx OR$$

Therefore, $\vec{v} \approx$ (8.2, 5.7).

The difference of two vectors is a vector. The vector $\vec{u} - \vec{v}$ equals $\vec{u} + (-\vec{v})$.

Example 2
Draw $\vec{u} + \vec{v}$ and $\vec{u} - \vec{v}$.

Solution
The diagram at the right shows $\vec{u} + \vec{v}$ using the parallelogram rule.

To find $\vec{u} - \vec{v}$, first draw $-\vec{v}$ which is a vector with magnitude equal to $\vec{v}$ but with direction opposite to that of $\vec{v}$.

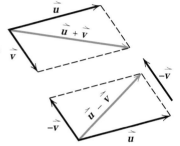

The diagram at the right shows $\vec{u} + (-\vec{v})$ or $\vec{u} - \vec{v}$ using the parallelogram rule.

Example 3
How does a wind blowing due east at 30 mph affect the speed and direction of an airplane traveling due north at 150 mph? What is the actual direction and rate of the plane?

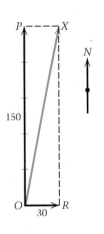

Solution
Draw $\overrightarrow{OP}$ such that $|\overrightarrow{OP}| = 150$ and its direction is due north. Draw $\overrightarrow{OR}$ so that its initial point coincides with the initial point of $\overrightarrow{OP}$, $|\overrightarrow{OR}| = 30$, and its direction is due east.

If the plane were flying in still air, it would actually be flying 150 mph due north. There would be no wind to help the plane go faster or to slow the plane down. A wind blowing due east at 30 mph will cause the plane to go east of north and the actual speed of the plane will increase. The resultant of $\overrightarrow{OP}$ and $\overrightarrow{OR}$ is the actual speed and direction of the plane. Draw $\overrightarrow{OX} = \overrightarrow{OP} + \overrightarrow{OR}$.

By the Pythagorean Theorem, $|\overrightarrow{OX}| \approx 153$.
Since $\tan \angle ROX = \frac{150}{30}$, $m\angle ROX \approx 79$.

Therefore, the wind causes the plane to go about 11° east of north, or its direction angle is actually around 79°. The speed of the plane increases to 153 mph.

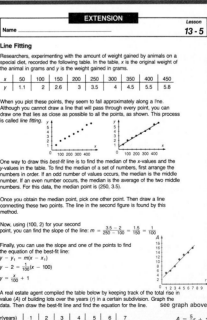

Example 2
Draw $\vec{a} + \vec{b}$ and $\vec{a} - \vec{b}$.

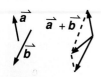

Example 3
The Huntington River flows south at a rate of 5 mph. A speedboat heads east across the river at a speed of 30 mph. What is the actual speed and direction of the boat? 30.4 mph; 9 degrees south of east

Example 4
In the diagram, $\vec{a} = (x_1, y_1)$, $\vec{b} = (x_2, y_2)$ and $\vec{c} = \vec{a} - \vec{b}$.

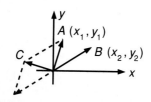

Find the coordinates of the endpoint of $\vec{c}$. $(x_1 - x_2, y_1 - y_2)$

Example 5
A plane flies at an air speed of 250 mph, heading 30 degrees north of west. The wind is blowing 10 degrees west of due north at 20 mph. Find the actual speed and direction of the plane. 263.3 mph; 33 degrees north of west

Error Analysis   Students often have difficulty drawing an accurate diagram of vectors when two directions are involved. Point out that 30° west of north is not the same as 30° north of west. Draw diagrams that illustrate the difference between these directions.

Example 4
In the diagram at the right $\overrightarrow{OA} = (x_1, y_1)$, $\overrightarrow{OB} = (x_2, y_2)$, and $\overrightarrow{OC} = \overrightarrow{OA} + \overrightarrow{OB}$. Find the coordinates of the terminal point of $\overrightarrow{OC}$.

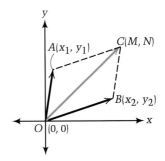

Solution
Let the coordinates of C be (M, N). In $\square OACB$, the slope of $\overrightarrow{OA}$ equals the slope of $\overrightarrow{BC}$, and the slope of $\overrightarrow{AC}$ equals the slope of $\overrightarrow{OB}$. The equations below represent the equalities of these slopes.

$$\frac{y_1 - 0}{x_1 - 0} = \frac{N - y_2}{M - x_2} \qquad \frac{N - y_1}{M - x_1} = \frac{y_2 - 0}{x_2 - 0}$$

Solving both equations for N gives the following:

$$\frac{y_1}{x_1}(M - x_2) + y_2 = N \qquad N = \frac{y_2}{x_2}(M - x_1) - y_1$$

The Substitution Property yields the following equation:

$$\frac{y_1}{x_1}(M - x_2) + y_2 = \frac{y_2}{x_2}(M - x_1) + y_1$$

Solving this equation for M gives $M = x_1 + x_2$.

Subsitute $x_1 + x_2$ for M in either of the original equations.

Then $N = y_1 + y_2$.

Therefore, $\overrightarrow{OC} = (x_1 + x_2, y_1 + y_2)$.

Example 4 leads to the definition of vector addition using the coordinate form of vectors.

Definiton   *Vector Addition*
For every pair of vectors $\vec{u} = (x_1, y_1)$ and $\vec{v} = (x_2, y_2)$, $\vec{u} + \vec{v} = (x_1 + x_2, y_1 + y_2)$.

This definition of vector addition along with the Pythagorean Theorem and the trigonometric ratios will help you to solve problems like the one given in the next example.

Example 5

A plane is flown at 200 miles per hour due northeast. A wind is blowing 15° north of east at 20 miles per hour. What is the actual speed and direction of the plane?

Solution

On a coordinate plane, draw $\overrightarrow{OQ}$ to represent the motion of the airplane, and $\overrightarrow{OP}$ to represent the wind. Why is the direction angle for the airplane equal to 45°? Let $\overrightarrow{OR} = \overrightarrow{OQ} + \overrightarrow{OP}$. We want to find $|\overrightarrow{OR}|$ and $m\angle MOR$.

First, find the horizontal and vertical components of $\overrightarrow{OQ}$ and $\overrightarrow{OP}$. $\triangle OAQ$ is a 45-45-90 triangle with hypotenuse of length 200. Therefore, $OA = AQ = 100\sqrt{2} \approx 141.4$ and $\overrightarrow{OQ} \approx (141.4, 141.4)$.

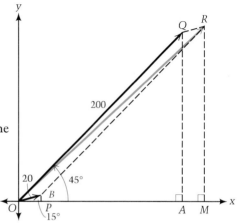

Due northeast means the plane is the same number of degrees east of north as it is north of east.

For $\triangle OBP$, the hypotenuse is 20 and $m\angle BOP = 15$. Use the sine and cosine ratios to find BP and OB.

$$\sin 15° = \frac{BP}{20} \qquad \cos 15° = \frac{OB}{20}$$

Solving these equations gives $BP \approx 5.2$ and $OB \approx 19.3$. Therefore, $\overrightarrow{OP} \approx (19.3, 5.2)$.

By the definition of vector addition, $\overrightarrow{OR} \approx (141.4 + 19.3, 141.4 + 5.2)$ or $(260.7, 146.6)$.

Using the Pythagorean Theorem gives $|\overrightarrow{OR}| \approx 299.1$.

Use the tangent ratio to find $m\angle MOR$. Since $\tan \angle MOR = \frac{146.6}{260.7}$, we know $m\angle MOR \approx 29$.

The actual speed of the airplane is about 299 miles per hour and its direction angle is about 29°.

Checking for Understanding

1. What does $\vec{u} + (-\vec{u})$ equal? $\vec{o}$

2. Draw any two nonzero vectors. Show that the Commutative Property for Addition is true for these vectors.

3. Explain why $(\vec{u} + \vec{v}) + \vec{w}$ is a vector.

4. Copy $\vec{u}$, $\vec{v}$, and $\vec{w}$ given at the right and draw $(\vec{u} + \vec{v}) + \vec{w}$. Then draw $\vec{u} + (\vec{v} + \vec{w})$. Compare these two vectors. What property seems to be true?

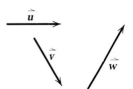

ANSWERS

Checking for Understanding

2. Sample:

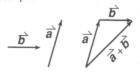

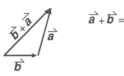

$\vec{a} + \vec{b} = \vec{b} + \vec{a}$

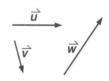

3. Since $(\vec{u} + \vec{v})$ is a vector, and the sum of two vectors is a vector, $(\vec{u} + \vec{v}) + \vec{w}$ is a vector.

4.

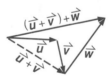

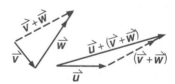

Since $(\vec{u} + \vec{v}) + \vec{w} = \vec{u} + (\vec{v} + \vec{w})$, the Associative Property of Addition seems to be true.

5. $|\vec{u} + \vec{v}| = 12$

6. $|\vec{a} + \vec{b}| = 7$

Written Exercises

1.

2.

3.

4.

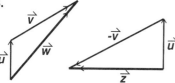

5.

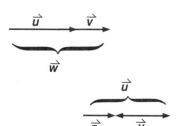

6.

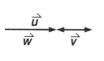

Assignment Guide

Basic: 1–15, 30–40
Average: 2–14 (even), 16–26, 30–40
Extended: 6, 10, 13–15, 17, 21, 23, 24, 26–40

5. Draw $\vec{u} + \vec{v}$. What is $|\vec{u} + \vec{v}|$? 12

6. Draw $\vec{a} + \vec{b}$. What is $|\vec{a} + \vec{b}|$? 7

7. Find (x, y) if $\vec{w} = (x, y)$, $|\vec{w}| = 100$, and the direction angle for $\vec{w}$ is 60°. (50, 50√3) ≈ (50, 86.6)

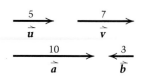

Written Exercises

Set A   Copy each diagram and draw $\vec{w} = \vec{u} + \vec{v}$ and $\vec{z} = \vec{u} - \vec{v}$.

1.
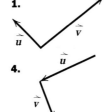

2.
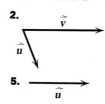

3.
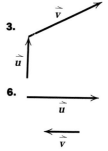

4.
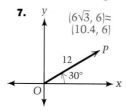

5.
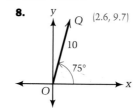

6.
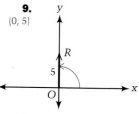

Find the ordered pair that names each vector.

7. (6√3, 6)≈ (10.4, 6)

8. (2.6, 9.7)

9. (0, 5)

10. (−5.1, 6.1)

11. (−99.6, 8.7)

12. (2, 0)

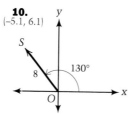

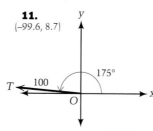

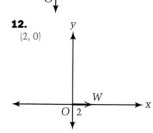

For Exercises 13–15, draw vectors to represent both the given information and the resultant.

13. At an airport, a passenger hurrying to catch his plane runs at a rate of 4 mph on a moving sidewalk that is going in the same direction at 3 mph. How fast is the passenger actually moving? 7 mph

14. A group of campers is canoeing upstream at a rate of 5 mph. The river current is 2 mph. What is the actual rate and direction of the canoes? 3 mph

15. A pilot is flying a plane due north at 250 mph. A wind is blowing due west at 10 mph. What is the actual speed and direction angle of the plane?

Set B Copy the three vectors given at the right. Then draw

16. $\vec{u} + \vec{v} + \vec{w}$ **17.** $\vec{u} + \vec{v} - \vec{w}$

18. Draw diagrams that show $|\vec{a} + \vec{b}| = |\vec{a}| + |\vec{b}|$.

19. When does $|\vec{a} + \vec{b}| = |\vec{a}| + |\vec{b}|$?

20. In Example 4, show how to solve the equation for M.

21. In Example 4, show the substitution for M into one of the original equations and solve for N.

22. In Example 5, show how the Pythagorean Theorem is used to get $|\overrightarrow{OR}| \approx 299.1$.

23. Use the definiton of vector addition with coordinates to write a paragraph proof of the Commutative Property for Addition: For any vectors $\vec{a}$ and $\vec{b}$, $\vec{a} + \vec{b} = \vec{b} + \vec{a}$.

For each diagram, add the vectors. Then for each resultant vector, find (a) the coordinates of the terminal point, (b) the magnitude, and (c) the direction angle.

24.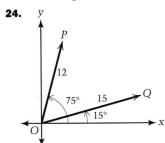

25.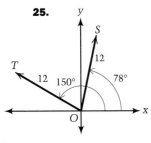

26. A plane is flown at 250 mph at an angle of direction equal to 60°. A wind is blowing at 15 mph with an angle of direction equal to 20°. What is the acutal speed and direction angle of the plane?
About 261.6 mph at 57°

Set C **27.** Find the actual speed and direction of a plane traveling due northwest at 150 mph if a wind is blowing due northeast at 30 mph.
153 mph; 124°

15. $|\overrightarrow{OP}| = 250.2$ mph
Since $\theta \approx 88°$, the plane's actual direction is about 2° west of north, or its direction angle is about 92°.

16.

17.

18. Sample: $|\vec{a}| + |\vec{b}| = |\vec{a} + \vec{b}|$

19. When $\vec{a} \parallel \vec{b}$, and $\vec{a}$ and $\vec{b}$ have the same direction, $|\vec{a}| + |\vec{b}| = |\vec{a} + \vec{b}|$. It is also true if $\vec{a}$ or $\vec{b}$ or both are the zero vector.

20.
$$\frac{y_1}{x_1}(M - x_2) + y_2 = \frac{y_2}{x_2}(M - x_1) + y_1$$
$$x_2y_1(M - x_2) + x_1x_2y_2 = x_1y_2(M - x_1) + x_1x_2y_1$$
$$x_2y_1M - x_2^2y_1 + x_1x_2y_2 = x_1y_2M - x_1^2y_2 + x_1x_2y_1$$
$$x_2y_1M - x_1y_2M = x_1x_2y_1 - x_1^2y_2 + x_2^2y_1 - x_1x_2y_2$$
$$(x_2y_1 - x_1y_2)M = x_1(x_2y_1 - x_1y_2) + x_2(x_2y_1 - x_1y_2)$$
$$(x_2y_1 - x_1y_2)M = (x_1 + x_2)(x_2y_1 - x_1y_2)$$
$$M = x_1 + x_2$$

28.

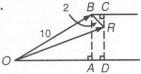

$AB = 5$ and $OA = 5\sqrt{3}$ by 30-60-90 △ Thm. and $BC = RC = \sqrt{2}$ by the 45-45-90 △ Thm. There-fore, $OD = 5\sqrt{3} + \sqrt{2}$ and $RD = 5 - \sqrt{2}$. So, $\tan \angle ROD = \frac{5 - \sqrt{2}}{5\sqrt{3} + \sqrt{2}}$ $\approx \frac{3.6}{10.1} \approx 0.3564$. Thus, $m\angle ROD \approx 20$. By the Pythagorean Thm. $|\vec{OR}| = \sqrt{(3.6)^2 + (10.1)^2} \approx 10.7$ The wake changes the angle of direction to 20° and increases its speed to 10.7 mph.

29. Given: Any vectors, $\vec{a}$, $\vec{b}$ and $\vec{c}$ Prove: $(\vec{a} + \vec{b}) + \vec{c} = \vec{a} + (\vec{b} + \vec{c})$ Proof: Let $\vec{a} = (a_1, a_2)$, $\vec{b} = (b_1, b_2)$ and $\vec{c} = (c_1, c_2)$ where a_1, a_2, b_1, b_2, c_1 and c_2 are real num-bers. (A vector can be translated in plane to a position vector.) By definition of vector addition $(\vec{a} + \vec{b}) = (a_1 + b_1, a_2 + b_2)$ and $(\vec{a} + \vec{b}) + \vec{c} = ([a_1 + b_1] + c_1, [a_2 + b_2] + c_2)$. Similarly, $\vec{b} + \vec{c} = (b_1 + c_1, b_2 + c_2)$ and $\vec{a} + (\vec{b} + \vec{c}) = (a_1 + [b_1 + c_1], a_2 + [b_2 + c_2])$. But, since the Associative Proper-ty of Addition is true for all real numbers, $(\vec{a} + \vec{b}) + \vec{c} = \vec{a} + (\vec{b} + \vec{c})$.

FOLLOW-UP

More Practice

• Worksheet 13-5

Extension

Suppose P, Q, R and S are non-collinear, and $\vec{PQ} + \vec{RS} = (0, 0)$.
1. What do we know about $\vec{PQ}$ and $\vec{RS}$? $|\vec{PQ}| = |\vec{RS}|$, and their directions are opposite.
2. What can we conclude about quadrilateral $PQRS$? It is a paral-lelogram.
Challenge students to put these arguments together into a rough vector proof.
• Extension 13-5

28. A sailboat is crossing a lake at 10 knots in a northeasterly direction of 30° from the shore. The wake from another boat has a force of 2 knots and it comes from the northwest at an angle of 45° that it makes with the opposite shore. How will the wake move the sailboat and affect its speed?

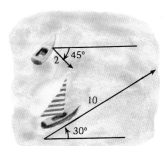

29. Use the definition of vector addition to prove the Associative Property for Addition: For any vectors $\vec{a}$, $\vec{b}$, and $\vec{c}$, $(\vec{a} + \vec{b}) + \vec{c} = \vec{a} + (\vec{b} + \vec{c})$.

◆ Review **30.** Draw $\vec{a}$, $\vec{b}$, and $\vec{c}$, such that $\vec{a} = \vec{b}$ and $\vec{c} = -\vec{a}$.

31. Find the magnitude to the nearest tenth and the angle of direction for $\vec{u} = (-1, 4)$. $\sqrt{17}$; 104

32. How would you label the vertices of a rectangle if you placed the coordinate plane on it so that the intersection of its diagonals coincided with the origin?

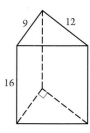

33. Find the total area of the right prism. 684

34. Marie placed her ruler on a sheet of notebook paper. The top two lines of the paper crossed the ruler at the 3-inch and 4-inch marks, respectively. Which line crossed the 6-inch mark? Explain.

Thinking Ahead Given: $\vec{u} = (4, 3)$

35. Find the coordinates of the terminal point of $\vec{v}$ which is twice as long as $\vec{u}$ and in the same direction. (8, 6)

36. Find the coordinates of a vector $\vec{w}$ with the same magnitude as $\vec{u}$ but in the opposite direction. $(-4, -3)$

37. Consider the vectors $\vec{p} = (12, 9)$ and $\vec{q} = (-8, -6)$. How are their respective directions and magnitudes related to those of $\vec{u}$?

Make a conjecture about the length and direction of a vector with terminal point $(4k, 3k)$ with respect to $\vec{u}$

38. When $k > 0$.   **39.** when $k < 0$.   **40.** when $k = 0$.

Challenge

Show that if P_1, P_2, P_3, P_4, and P_5 are arbitrary points in a coordinate plane, then $\vec{P_1P_2} + \vec{P_2P_3} + \vec{P_3P_4} + \vec{P_4P_5} + \vec{P_5P_1} = \vec{0}$.

13-6 Multiples of Vectors

If $\vec{v}$ represents a force in some direction, then $3\vec{v}$ represents a force acting in the same direction with 3 times the magnitude of $\vec{v}$. Geometrically, $3\vec{v}$ is a vector that is 3 times as long as $\vec{v}$ and has the same direction.

Definition   *Multiple of Vectors*

If k is a real number and $\vec{v}$ is a vector, then $k\vec{v}$ is a vector that has a magnitude equal to $|k|\,|\vec{v}|$ and has the same direction as $\vec{v}$ if k is positive or the opposite direction of $\vec{v}$ if k is negative. If $k = 0$, then $k\vec{v}$ is the zero vector.

The number k is called a *scalar* and the vector $k\vec{v}$ is called a *scalar multiple of $\vec{v}$*. The vector $k\vec{v}$ is also referred to as the scalar product of k and $\vec{v}$.

Since $|k|\,|\vec{v}| = |k\vec{v}|$, you can use either form as the magnitude of the vector kv.

Example 1
Given vector $\vec{v}$ at the right, draw $2\vec{v}$, $-2\vec{v}$, $\frac{1}{2}\vec{v}$, and $-\frac{1}{3}\vec{v}$.

Solution

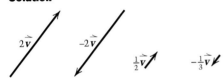

Here are some fundamental properties of the operation of multiplying vectors by scalars.

For any scalars k and r and vectors $\vec{u}$ and $\vec{v}$:

$1\vec{v} = \vec{v}$

$(-1)\vec{v} = -\vec{v}$

$k(\vec{u} + \vec{v}) = k\vec{u} + k\vec{v}$

$(k + r)\vec{v} = k\vec{v} + r\vec{v}$

LESSON 13-6

Resources

Teaching Aid 18, square root table
Visual Aid 18, square root table
Teaching Aid 19, trigonometric ratios
Visual Aid 19, trigonometric ratios
Worksheet 13-6
Extension 13-6
Computer Worksheet 13-6

OBJECTIVE

Draw and compute scalar multiples of vectors.

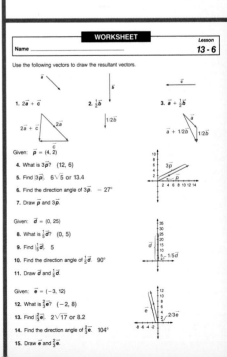

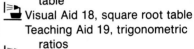

TEACHING NOTES

Use the following **activity** to introduce the definition of scalar multiplication.

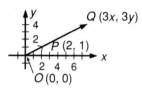

1. Given $O(0, 0)$ and $P(2, 1)$, draw $\overrightarrow{OP}$.
2. If $\overrightarrow{OP} = (x, y)$, find x and y.
   2; 1
3. Find $|\overrightarrow{OP}|$. $\sqrt{5} \approx 2.2$
4. Find the direction angle of $\overrightarrow{OP}$. 27°
5. Let $\overrightarrow{OQ} = (3x, 3y)$. Draw $\overrightarrow{OQ}$.
6. Find $|\overrightarrow{OQ}|$. $\sqrt{45} = 3\sqrt{5} \approx 6.7$
7. Find the direction angle of $\overrightarrow{OQ}$. 27°

Students should easily see that (kx, ky) has a magnitude of k times that of (x, y), and its direction angle is the same.

Matrices

A *matrix* (plural: matrices) is a sequence of elements arranged in rows and columns. Matrices have a surprising variety of applications to everyday situations. They are used extensively in business, science, and social science, as well as in mathematics. The matrix at the left below represents the runs scored by two teams in each inning of a baseball game. The matrix at the right represents the sales of three stores over a three-year period.

A matrix with m rows and n columns is said to have dimensions $m \times n$.

A column matrix has one column. A row matrix has one row. [3 6 8] A square matrix has the same number of rows and columns.

Matrices can be used to represent polygons. The polygon shown below has vertices at $(-2, 1)$, $(0, 4)$, $(3, 4)$, and $(5, 0)$.

The vertices can be represented as follows:

You can combine these into one matrix.

1. Give the dimensions for the two matrices at the top of this page. $2 \times 9; 3 \times 3$
2. Give the dimensions for the column matrix, the row matrix, and the square matrix near the middle of this page. $4 \times 1; 1 \times 3; 2 \times 2$
3. Name the vertices for the polygon represented by $\begin{bmatrix} 0 & 1 & 3 & 5 \\ 2 & 4 & 8 & 0 \end{bmatrix}$. (0, 2), (1, 4), (3, 8), (5, 0)
4. How many elements are there in a 3×5 matrix? 15
5. Give an example of a matrix that can show the points scored in each quarter by two teams in a basketball game. Answers will vary.

In Example 2, we will consider a scalar multiple of a vector in standard position.

Example 2
Given $\vec{v} = (3, 1)$, draw $3\vec{v}$ in standard position. Then find $|3\vec{v}|$, the direction angle for $3\vec{v}$, and the coordinates of the terminal point of $3\vec{v}$.

Solution
Draw both $\vec{v}$ and $3\vec{v}$ in standard position. What do you know about the direction angle for $3\vec{v}$? It is the same as $\vec{v}$

Since $\tan \angle POS = \frac{1}{3} \approx 0.3333$, $m\angle POS \approx 18$.

By either the Pythagorean Theorem or the Distance Formula, $|\vec{v}| = \sqrt{10}$. Therefore, $|3\vec{v}| = 3\sqrt{10}$.

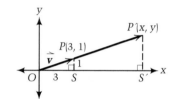

There are several ways to find x and y when $3\vec{v} = (x, y)$. The method given below uses a system of equations. Equation (1) is the result of applying the Pythagorean Theorem with $\triangle P'OS'$ and equation (2) uses similar triangles POS and $P'OS'$.

(1) $x^2 + y^2 = (3\sqrt{10})^2$

(2) $\frac{1}{3} = \frac{y}{x}$

Solving for x in equation (2) gives $x = 3y$ and substituting for x in equation (1) gives $(3y)^2 + y^2 = (3\sqrt{10})^2$.

Solving for y yields $y = 3$. Substituting in equation (2) gives $x = 9$. Therefore, $3\vec{v} = (9, 3)$.

Notice that $3\vec{v} = ((3)3, (3)1)$ when $\vec{v} = (3, 1)$. This example has shown the following definition of scalar multiples.

Definition *Scalar Multiple of $\vec{v}$*

For any real number k and vector $\vec{v} = (x, y)$, a scalar multiple of $\vec{v}$ is defined as $k\vec{v} = (kx, ky)$.

Example 3
If $\vec{u} = (x, y)$, what is $(-1)\vec{u}$?

Solution
$(-1)\vec{u} = (-1)(x, y) = ((-1)x, (-1)y) = (-x, -y)$

Assignment Guide

Basic: 1–15, 23–30
Average: 1–20, 23–30
Extended: 1–30

Example 4

If $\vec{v} = (-4, 1)$, what is $3\vec{v}$? Draw $3\vec{v}$. What is $|3\vec{v}|$? Find the direction angle of $3\vec{v}$.

Solution

By definition of scalar multiple, if $\vec{v} = (-4, 1)$, then $3\vec{v} = 3(-4, 1) = (-12, 3)$.

To draw $3\vec{v}$, locate the point $P(-12, 3)$ on the coordinate plane and draw the vector from the origin to the point P.

Use the Distance Formula to get $|3\vec{v}| = 3\sqrt{17}$.

The tangent ratio gives $m\angle 1 \approx 14$. Therefore, the direction angle of $3\vec{v}$ is about 166°. Why? By def. of ∠ of direction, it is the ∠whose sides are the rays containing the vector and the nonnegative x-axis.

Checking for Understanding

Copy the vectors $\vec{u}$, $\vec{v}$, and $\vec{w}$ and then draw the following vectors.

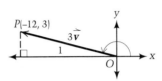

1. $3\vec{u}$ 2. $\frac{3}{2}\vec{v}$
3. $-\vec{v}$ 4. $3\vec{u} - 2\vec{u}$
5. $-\frac{1}{2}\vec{w}$ 6. $\vec{v} + 2\vec{u}$
7. $\vec{v} + 2\vec{u} - \vec{w}$ 8. $3(\vec{v} + \vec{w})$

9. If $\overrightarrow{OP} = (\sqrt{2}, \sqrt{2})$, what is $2(\overrightarrow{OP})$? Draw $2(\overrightarrow{OP})$. What is $|2(\overrightarrow{OP})|$? What is the direction angle of $2(\overrightarrow{OP})$?

Written Exercises

Set A Copy the vectors $\vec{u}$, $\vec{v}$, and $\vec{w}$, and then draw the following vectors.

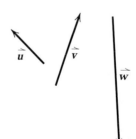

1. $4\vec{u}$ 2. $-2\vec{v}$
3. $\frac{2}{3}\vec{w}$ 4. $4\vec{u} - 2\vec{v}$
5. $2(\vec{v} + \vec{w})$ 6. $\vec{v} - \vec{u} + \vec{w}$

Given: $\vec{a} = (2, 2\sqrt{3})$

7. What is $5\vec{a}$?   8. Draw $5\vec{a}$.   9. Find $|5\vec{a}|$. 20
10. Find the direction angle of $5\vec{a}$. 60°

Given: $\vec{b} = (5, 12)$

11. What is $\frac{1}{2}\vec{b}$?   12. Draw $\frac{1}{2}\vec{b}$.   13. What is $|\frac{1}{2}\vec{b}|$? 6.5
14. Find the direction angles of $\frac{1}{2}\vec{b}$. 67°

Additional Examples

Example 1

Given vector $\vec{u}$, draw the following.

(a) $3\vec{u}$ (b) $-3\vec{u}$
(c) $\frac{2}{3}\vec{u}$ (d) $-\frac{1}{2}\vec{u}$

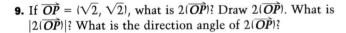

Example 2

Given $\vec{a} = (2, 5)$, find the following.

(a) $|2\vec{a}|$ $2\sqrt{29} \approx 10.8$
(b) the direction angle of $2\vec{a}$ 68°
(c) the coordinates of the terminal point of $2\vec{a}$ (4, 10)

Example 3

If $\vec{b} = (x, y)$, what is $2\vec{b}$?   (2x, 2y)

Example 4

Given: $\vec{v} = (-2, 3)$
(a) What is $2\vec{v}$?   (−4, 6)
(b) What is $|2\vec{v}|$? $2\sqrt{13} \approx 7.2$
(c) Find the direction angle of $2\vec{v}$ 124°

Error Analysis When working with vectors with negative horizontal or vertical components, students often find the correct direction angle but fail to write the final answer in relation to the positive side of the x-axis. Point out that drawing diagrams should correct this error.

ANSWERS

Written Exercises

15. (6, 6); $6\sqrt{2} \approx 8.46$; 45°

16. (−5, 3); $\sqrt{34} \approx 5.83$; 149°

17. (10, 16); $2\sqrt{89} \approx 18.87$; 58°

18. (−8, 6); 10; 143°

19. Since $\vec{u} + \vec{v} = (x_1 + x_2, y_1 + y_2)$, $k(\vec{u} + \vec{v}) = (kx_1 + kx_2, ky_1 + ky_2)$.

20. $(k + r)\vec{v} = k\vec{v} + r\vec{v} = k(x, y) + r(x, y) = (kx, ky) + (rx, ry) = (kx + rx, ky + ry)$

FOLLOW-UP

More Practice

• **Worksheet 13–6**

Extension

Use the following **activity** to explore the criteria for perpendicularity of vectors in terms of their magnitudes.

1. Draw vectors $\vec{a}$ and $\vec{b}$ with a common initial point.

2. Draw $\vec{a} + \vec{b}$ and $\vec{a} - \vec{b}$.

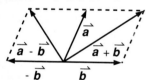

3. How do the two quadrilaterals that have $\vec{b}$ and $-\vec{b}$ as sides relate? congruent parallelograms

4. How do $|\vec{a} + \vec{b}|$ and $|\vec{a} - \vec{b}|$ relate to these quadrilaterals? They are the lengths of the diagonals.

5. Under what circumstances is $|\vec{a} + \vec{b}| = |\vec{a} - \vec{b}|$? If the quadrilaterals are rectangles; i.e., if $\vec{a} \perp \vec{b}$

• **Extension 13–6**

Computers

• **Computer Worksheet 13–6**

Set B For each vector $\vec{v} = (x, y)$ and scalar k given below, find (a) $k\vec{v}$, (b) $|k\vec{v}|$, and (c) the direction angle of $k\vec{v}$.

15. $\vec{a} = (1, 1)$; 6

16. $\vec{b} = (-15, 9)$; $\frac{1}{3}$

17. $\vec{c} = (5, 8)$; 2

18. $\vec{d} = (4, -3)$; −2

19. If $\vec{u} = (x_1, y_1)$ and $\vec{v} = (x_2, y_2)$, and k is a scalar, what is $k(\vec{u} + \vec{v})$?

20. If $\vec{v} = (x, y)$ and k and r are scalars, what is $(k + r)\vec{v}$?

Set C **21.** Draw a diagram that illustrates the following statement and explain why the statement is true: If $\vec{a}$, $\vec{b}$, $\vec{c}$, and $\vec{d}$ are position vectors with coplanar terminal points A, B, C, and D, respectively, and if $\vec{b} - \vec{a} = \vec{c} - \vec{d}$, then $ABCD$ is a parallelogram.

22. Given nonzero position vectors $\vec{u}$ and $\vec{v}$, and a position vector $\vec{w}$ whose terminal point is the midpoint of the segment joining the terminal points of $\vec{u}$ and $\vec{v}$, express $\vec{w}$ in terms of $\vec{u}$ and $\vec{v}$. $\vec{w} = \frac{1}{2}(\vec{u} + \vec{v})$

◆ Review **23.** Trace $\vec{p}$ and $\vec{q}$. Then draw $\vec{r} = \vec{p} + \vec{q}$ and $\vec{s} = \vec{p} - \vec{q}$.

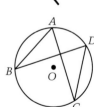

24. What ordered pair names $\vec{t}$ if its magnitude is 12 and its direction angle is 45°? $(6\sqrt{2}, 6\sqrt{2}) \approx (8.49, 8.49)$

25. Find the magnitude of $\overrightarrow{GH}$ if $G(-2, 3)$ and $H(5, 5)$. $\sqrt{53} \approx 7.28$

26. Two similar pentagons have areas of 64 sq. in. and 121 sq. in. If the perimeter of the larger pentagon is 33 in., what is the perimeter of the smaller pentagon? 24 in.

27. Given: $\odot O$ with $m\widehat{AB} = m\widehat{DC}$
Prove: $\triangle AEB \cong \triangle DEC$

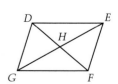

⇩ Thinking Ahead Quadrilateral $DEFG$ is a parallelogram. Complete each statement.

28. $\overrightarrow{EF} + \frac{1}{2}\overrightarrow{FD} = \underline{\quad?\quad}$. $\overrightarrow{EH}$

29. $\frac{1}{2}\overrightarrow{GE} + \frac{1}{2}\overrightarrow{DF} = \underline{\quad?\quad}$. $\overrightarrow{GH}$

30. $\overrightarrow{FG} + \overrightarrow{GD} + \overrightarrow{DH} = \underline{\quad?\quad}$. $\overrightarrow{FH}$

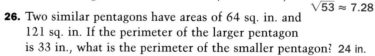

13-7 Proofs Using Vectors

Vectors provide another way to prove statements in geometry. Before we use vectors in proofs, we need to mark diagrams.

Example 1

Given parallelogram $PQRS$ with its diagonals, use the parallelogram rule and the definition of vector sum to denote the vectors on the diagram.

Solution

Since we know that the opposite sides of a parallelogram are equal and parallel, we can think of them as vectors that have the same magnitude and direction. We will choose $\overrightarrow{PQ} = \overrightarrow{SR}$ and $\overrightarrow{QR} = \overrightarrow{PS}$. The parallelogram rule gives $\overrightarrow{PS} + \overrightarrow{PQ} = \overrightarrow{PR}$. Using the definition of vector sum, we can mark $\overrightarrow{QS}$ so that $\overrightarrow{PQ} + \overrightarrow{QS} = \overrightarrow{PS}$, or we can mark $\overrightarrow{SQ}$ so that $\overrightarrow{PS} + \overrightarrow{SQ} = \overrightarrow{PQ}$. We will mark the diagram as $\overrightarrow{QS}$. Then we also have $\overrightarrow{PQ} = \overrightarrow{PS} - \overrightarrow{QS}$ and $\overrightarrow{QS} = \overrightarrow{PS} - \overrightarrow{PQ}$. Why? Subtraction Prop.

Suppose that we are also given that the diagonals intersect at T. Then we will choose $\overrightarrow{QT}$, $\overrightarrow{TS}$, $\overrightarrow{PT}$, and $\overrightarrow{TR}$. Give some vector sums and differences using this notation.
Samples: $\overrightarrow{PQ} + \overrightarrow{QT} = \overrightarrow{PT}$; $\overrightarrow{QT} + \overrightarrow{TR} = \overrightarrow{QR}$

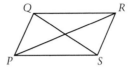

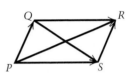

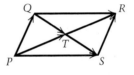

Example 2

Find x in terms of the given vectors.

a.

b.

c.

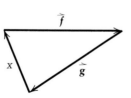

Solution

a. By definition of vector sum, $x = \vec{a} + 2\vec{b}$.

b. By definition of vector sum, $x + 2\vec{d} = 3\vec{c}$, or $x = 3\vec{c} - 2\vec{d}$.

c. If x had the opposite direction, we would have $\vec{f} + \vec{g} = x$. Therefore, $\vec{f} + \vec{g} = -x$, or $x = \vec{f} - \vec{g}$. Note that this diagram is an example of a zero vector, $\vec{f} + \vec{g} + (-\vec{f} - \vec{g}) = \vec{0}$.

After you have marked vectors on a diagram, you can use them to prove statements as shown in Example 3.

13-7 *Proofs Using Vectors*   597

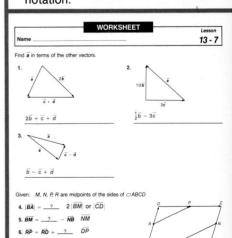

Additional Examples

Example 1

Given □WXYZ with midpoints L, M, N and P of $\overline{WX}$, $\overline{XY}$, $\overline{YZ}$ and $\overline{ZW}$, respectively, denote vectors on the diagram.

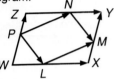

Choose $\overrightarrow{WX} = \overrightarrow{ZY}$ and $\overrightarrow{WZ} = \overrightarrow{XY}$. Then $\overrightarrow{LM} = \frac{1}{2}\overrightarrow{WX} + \frac{1}{2}\overrightarrow{XY}$, etc.

Example 2

Find x in terms of the given vectors.

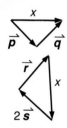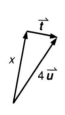

Example 3

Prove that the diagonals of a parallelogram bisect each other.

Solution

Given: □ABCD

Prove: $\overline{AC}$ and $\overline{BD}$ bisect each other.

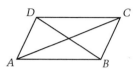

Since ABCD is a parallelogram, $\overrightarrow{AD} = \overrightarrow{BC}$ and $\overrightarrow{AB} = \overrightarrow{DC}$.

Part I Let M be the midpoint of $\overline{AC}$. Then $AM = MC$ and $\overrightarrow{AM} = \overrightarrow{MC}$.

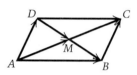

$$\overrightarrow{DM} + \overrightarrow{MC} = \overrightarrow{DC} \qquad \overrightarrow{AM} + \overrightarrow{MB} = \overrightarrow{AB}$$
$$\overrightarrow{DM} = \overrightarrow{DC} - \overrightarrow{MC} \qquad \overrightarrow{MB} = \overrightarrow{AB} - \overrightarrow{AM}$$
$$\overrightarrow{DM} = \overrightarrow{AB} - \overrightarrow{AM}$$

Therefore, $\overrightarrow{DM} = \overrightarrow{MB}$ and $DM = MB$. Since $\overrightarrow{DM}$ and $\overrightarrow{MB}$ are equal vectors, and have the point M in common, they must be collinear and M is the midpoint of $\overline{DB}$.

Part II Let M be the midpoint of $\overline{DB}$. Then $DM = MB$ and $\overrightarrow{DM} = \overrightarrow{MB}$.

$$\overrightarrow{AM} = \overrightarrow{AD} + \overrightarrow{DM} \qquad \overrightarrow{MC} = \overrightarrow{MB} + \overrightarrow{BC}$$
$$\overrightarrow{AM} = \overrightarrow{BC} + \overrightarrow{MB} \qquad \overrightarrow{MC} = \overrightarrow{BC} + \overrightarrow{MB}$$

Then $\overrightarrow{AM} = \overrightarrow{MC}$ and $AM = MC$. Since point M is common to both vectors $\overrightarrow{AM}$ and $\overrightarrow{MC}$ are collinear and M is the midpoint of $\overline{AC}$.

Parts I and II prove that $\overline{AC}$ and $\overline{BD}$ intersect each other at their midpoints. Therefore, $\overline{AC}$ and $\overline{BD}$ bisect each other.

We can also prove this theorem using the coordinate notation for vectors. Let $\overrightarrow{AB} = (a, 0)$ and $\overrightarrow{AD} = (b, c)$. Then $\overrightarrow{AC} = \overrightarrow{AB} + \overrightarrow{AD} = (a, 0) + (b, c) = (a + b, c)$.

Part I Let M be the midpoint of $\overline{AC}$. Then $\overrightarrow{AM} = \left(\frac{a+b}{2}, \frac{c}{2}\right)$.

$$\overrightarrow{DM} = \overrightarrow{AM} - \overrightarrow{AD} \qquad \overrightarrow{MB} = \overrightarrow{AB} - \overrightarrow{AM}$$
$$\overrightarrow{DM} = \left(\frac{a+b}{2}, \frac{c}{2}\right) - (b, c) \qquad \overrightarrow{MB} = (a, 0) - \left(\frac{a+b}{2}, \frac{c}{2}\right)$$
$$\overrightarrow{DM} = \left(\frac{a-b}{2}, -\frac{c}{2}\right) \qquad \overrightarrow{MB} = \left(\frac{a-b}{2}, -\frac{c}{2}\right)$$

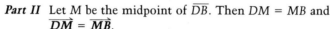

Then $\overrightarrow{DM} = \overrightarrow{MB}$ and $DM = MB$. The vectors are collinear and M is the midpoint of $\overline{DB}$.

Part II of this proof using the coordinate form for vectors is left to Exercise 11.

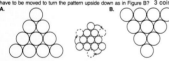

Assignment Guide

Basic: 1–8, 14–20
Average: 1–11, 14–20
Extended: 1–20

Checking for Understanding

Given: E is the midpoint of the diagonal $\overline{AC}$ of $\square ABCD$.

1. Express $\overrightarrow{BE}$ in terms of $\overrightarrow{DC}$ and $\overrightarrow{AE}$. $\overrightarrow{BE} = \overrightarrow{AE} - \overrightarrow{DC}$

2. Express $\overrightarrow{AE}$ in terms of $\overrightarrow{AB}$ and $\overrightarrow{BC}$. $\overrightarrow{AE} = \frac{1}{2}(\overrightarrow{AB} + \overrightarrow{BC})$

3. If R is the midpoint of $\overline{PQ}$, explain why $\overrightarrow{PR} = \frac{1}{2}\overrightarrow{PQ}$ is true. Could $\overrightarrow{RP} = \frac{1}{2}\overrightarrow{QP}$?

Refer to the proof using the coordinate notation for vectors in Example 3 to answer the following questions.

4. In the diagram, the terminal point of $\overrightarrow{DM}$ is $M\left(\frac{a+b}{2}, \frac{c}{2}\right)$.
Explain what $\overrightarrow{DM} = \left(\frac{a-b}{2}, -\frac{c}{2}\right)$ means in the proof.

5. Express $\overrightarrow{MC}$ in standard form.

Since $\overrightarrow{AM} = \overrightarrow{MC}$, $\overrightarrow{MC} = \left(\frac{a+b}{2}, \frac{c}{2}\right)$

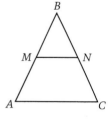

Written Exercises

Set A

1. Use the definition of vector addition to denote vectors on isosceles $\triangle ABC$ if $AB = BC$ and M and N are the midpoints of $\overline{AB}$ and $\overline{BC}$, respectively.

2. Explain how you could show that $2\overrightarrow{MN} = \overrightarrow{AC}$ for the diagram in Exercise 1.

3. In isosceles $\triangle ABC$, $|\overrightarrow{AB}| = |\overrightarrow{BC}|$. Does $\overrightarrow{AB} = \overrightarrow{BC}$? No

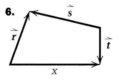

Find x in terms of the given vectors.

4.

5.

6.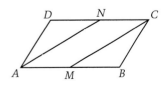

7. Draw a diagram and explain why the triangle formed by $\vec{u}$, $\vec{v}$, and $\vec{u} + \vec{v}$ is similar to the triangle formed by $k\vec{u}$, $k\vec{v}$, and $k\vec{u} + k\vec{v}$.

8. Given $\square ABCD$ with N the midpoint of $\overline{DC}$ and M the midpoint of $\overline{AB}$, use vectors to prove $AMCN$ is a parallelogram.

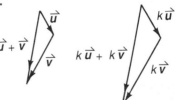

(a) $x = \vec{p} + \vec{q}$; (b) $x = -2\vec{s} - \vec{r}$; (c) $x = 4\vec{u} - \vec{t}$

Error Analysis Students may have difficulty expressing a vector as a difference of two others. Encourage them to write a sum first and then use simple vector algebra.

3. $\overrightarrow{PR} + \overrightarrow{RQ} = \overrightarrow{PQ}$ and $\overrightarrow{PR} = \overrightarrow{RQ} \Rightarrow \overrightarrow{PR} + \overrightarrow{PR} = \overrightarrow{PQ}$ or $\overrightarrow{PR} = \frac{1}{2}\overrightarrow{PQ}$; yes

4. It means that if $\overrightarrow{DM}$ were in standard position, its terminal point would have those coordinates.

ANSWERS

Written Exercises

1.

2. Since $\overrightarrow{MB} + \overrightarrow{BN} = \overrightarrow{MN}$, $2\overrightarrow{MB} + 2\overrightarrow{BN} = 2\overrightarrow{MN}$. By def. of midpt., $\overrightarrow{AM} = \overrightarrow{MB}$ and $\overrightarrow{BN} = \overrightarrow{NC}$. The definition of vector addition gives $\overrightarrow{AM} + \overrightarrow{MB} = \overrightarrow{AB}$ and $\overrightarrow{BN} + \overrightarrow{NC} = \overrightarrow{BC}$. Substituting, $\overrightarrow{MB} + \overrightarrow{MB} = \overrightarrow{AB}$ and $\overrightarrow{BN} + \overrightarrow{BN} = \overrightarrow{BC}$, or $2\overrightarrow{MB} = \overrightarrow{AB}$ and $2\overrightarrow{BN} = \overrightarrow{BC}$. Thus, $\overrightarrow{AB} + \overrightarrow{BC} = 2\overrightarrow{MN}$ by substituting in the first step.

4. $x = 3\vec{p} + 2\vec{q}$

5. $x = \vec{b} - \vec{a}$

6. $x = \vec{r} - \vec{s} + \vec{t}$

7.

Since $\frac{\vec{u}}{k\vec{u}} = \frac{\vec{v}}{k\vec{v}} = \frac{\vec{u} + \vec{v}}{k\vec{u} + k\vec{v}} = \frac{1}{k}$, the $\triangle$s are $\sim$ by SSS $\sim$ Thm.

9. Given: △ABC with D the midpt. of $\overline{AB}$ and E the midpt. of $\overline{AC}$
Prove: $DE = \frac{1}{2}BC$ and $\overline{DE} \parallel \overline{BC}$

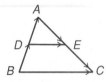

Proof: By def. of midpt. $\overrightarrow{DA} = \frac{1}{2}\overrightarrow{BA}$ and $\overrightarrow{AE} = \frac{1}{2}\overrightarrow{AC}$. Then $\overrightarrow{DE} = \overrightarrow{DA} + \overrightarrow{AE} = \frac{1}{2}\overrightarrow{BA} + \frac{1}{2}\overrightarrow{AC} = \frac{1}{2}(\overrightarrow{BA} + \overrightarrow{AC}) = \frac{1}{2}\overrightarrow{BC}$. By def. of = vectors, $\overline{DE} \parallel \overline{BC}$ and $DE = \frac{1}{2}BC$.

FOLLOW-UP

More Practice

• **Worksheet 13–7**

Extension

$\vec{u}$ is perpendicular to $\vec{v}$ if and only if $|\vec{u} + \vec{v}| = |\vec{u} - \vec{v}|$. Use this fact to prove that the diagonals of a rhombus are perpendicular.

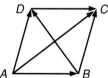

Given: rhombus ABCD with $\overrightarrow{AB} = \overrightarrow{DC}$ and $\overrightarrow{AD} = \overrightarrow{BC}$. Then $\overrightarrow{AC} = \overrightarrow{AB} + \overrightarrow{BC}$ and $\overrightarrow{BD} = \overrightarrow{BC} + \overrightarrow{CD}$.
Therefore,
$|\overrightarrow{AC} + \overrightarrow{BD}| = |2\overrightarrow{BC} + \overrightarrow{AB} + \overrightarrow{CD}|$
$= |2\overrightarrow{BC}|$ and
$|\overrightarrow{AC} - \overrightarrow{BD}| = |\overrightarrow{AB} - \overrightarrow{CD}|$
$= |2\overrightarrow{AB}|$
Because $|\overrightarrow{AB}| = |\overrightarrow{BC}|$, $\overrightarrow{AC}$ is perpendicular to $\overrightarrow{BD}$.

• **Extension 13–7**

Set B **9.** Use vectors to prove the following statement: If a segment joins the midpoint of two sides of a triangle, then it is parallel to the third side, and its length is one half the length of the third side.

10. Use vectors to prove that the figure formed by joining the midpoints of the sides of a rhombus in order is a parallelogram.

11. Prove Part II of Example 3 using the coordinate notation for vectors.

Set C **12.** Use vectors to prove that if a line segment joins the midpoints of the nonparallel sides of a trapezoid, then it is parallel to both of the bases and its length is equal to one half the sum of the lengths of the bases.

13. Use vectors to prove that if a line segment joins the midpoints of the two diagonals of a trapezoid, then it is parallel to the bases and its length is equal to one half the difference of the lengths of the bases.

▲ **Review** **14.** List the steps in the Proof-Writing Process.

15. What is in your inventory of geometric facts?

16. What is the slope of a line parallel to a line whose equation is $4x - 8y = 15$? $\frac{1}{2}$

17. What are the x- and y-intercepts of the line with equation $y + 2 = -3(x - 6)$? $\frac{16}{3}$; 16

18. If $|\overrightarrow{XY}| = |\overrightarrow{YZ}|$, does $\overrightarrow{XY} = \overrightarrow{YZ}$? Explain.

≡ **Thinking** **19.** In this lesson you learned to prove a statement
▽ **Ahead** using vectors. What other methods of proof have you studied in this text? What forms did you use when you wrote your proofs?

20. Describe how you might prove the following statement: If a line segment joins the midpoints of two sides of a triangle, then it is parallel to the third side and its length equals one half the length of the third side. **Answers will vary.**

19. Synthetic method; Transformation method; Coordinate method; two column form or paragraph form

13-8 Proof Techniques Revisited

In the development of this course in geometry, you have generally used synthetic proofs. A **synthetic proof** is a method of proof that allows you to make conclusions based on reasoning from a combination of assumed and established propositions which we called postulates and theorems. These postulates were independent of a coordinate system.

Your proofs have been written in two-column form or in paragraph form. You have used transformations and vectors in your proofs. You have also been introduced to analytic geometry when you used coordinates and algebraic methods to prove a statement.

This lesson re-examines the familiar synthetic proof and proofs that use transformations, coordinates, and vectors. The following example illustrates how each of these methods can be used to prove the same statement.

Example

Use four different methods of proof to prove the following statement: If a line segment joins the midpoints of two sides of a triangle, then it is parallel to the third side and its length equals one half the length of the third side.

Given: $\triangle ABC$ with X and Y the midpoints of $\overline{AC}$ and $\overline{BC}$
Prove: $\overline{XY} \parallel \overline{AB}$ and $XY = \frac{1}{2} AB$.

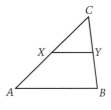

Solution

Vector Method of Proof

Given: $\triangle ABC$ with X and Y the midpoints of $\overline{AC}$ and $\overline{BC}$
Prove: $\overline{XY} \parallel \overline{AB}$ and $XY = \frac{1}{2} AB$.

X and Y are midpoints, so $\overrightarrow{AX} = \overrightarrow{XC} = \frac{1}{2}\overrightarrow{AC}$ and $\overrightarrow{CY} = \overrightarrow{YB} = \frac{1}{2}\overrightarrow{CB}$.
Also, by definition of vector sum, $\overrightarrow{AC} + \overrightarrow{CB} = \overrightarrow{AB}$. Then the following argument is valid:

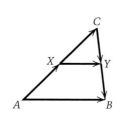

$\overrightarrow{XC} + \overrightarrow{CY} = \overrightarrow{XY}$ *Definition of vector sum*
$\frac{1}{2}\overrightarrow{AC} + \frac{1}{2}\overrightarrow{CB} = \overrightarrow{XY}$ *Substitution Property*
$\frac{1}{2}(\overrightarrow{AC} + \overrightarrow{CB}) = \overrightarrow{XY}$
$\quad\quad \frac{1}{2}\overrightarrow{AB} = \overrightarrow{XY}$ *Substitution Property*

Therefore, $XY = \frac{1}{2} AB$ by the definition of magnitude and distance between two points. Since $\overrightarrow{XY}$ is a scalar multiple of $\overrightarrow{AB}$, $\overline{XY} \parallel \overline{AB}$.

LESSON 13–8

Resources

Worksheet 13–8
Extension 13–8
Algebra Review 13
Chapter 13 Test, Form I
Chapter 13 Test, Form II
Chapter 13 Test, Form III
Cumulative Test Chapters 7–13,
    Form I
Cumulative Test Chapters 7–13,
    Form II
Practice for Standardized
    Tests 4

OBJECTIVE

Write the proof of a theorem using synthetic, transformation, coordinate and vector methods.

TEACHING NOTES

Use a **group activity** to discuss the advantages and disadvantages of each type of geometric proof. Divide the class into four groups, and have each group use a different method of proof for the **Example**. Have each group present its view on the method they used.

Error Analysis Some students use simple physical cues to distinguish one type of proof from another. Point out that any type of proof can be written in either two-column or paragraph form.

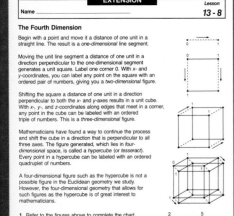

Transformation Method of Proof

Given: $\triangle ABC$ with X and Y the midpoints of $\overline{AC}$ and $\overline{BC}$

Prove: $\overline{XY} \parallel \overline{AB}$ and $XY = \frac{1}{2} AB$.

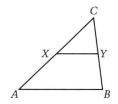

Statements	Reasons
1. $\triangle ABC$ with X the midpt. of $\overline{AC}$ and Y the midpt. of $\overline{BC}$	1. Given
2. $CX = XA$; $CY = YB$	2. Def. of midpt. [1]
3. $CX + XA = CA$; $CY + YB = CB$	3. Seg. Add. Post.
4. $CX + CX = CA$, or $2\ CX = CA$; $CY + CY = CB$, or $2CY = CB$	4. Substitution Prop. [2, 3]
5. There is a dilation with center C and scale factor 2 that maps X onto A and Y onto B.	5. Def. of dilation [4]
6. C is its own image.	6. Def. of dilation
7. $\triangle XYC \sim \triangle ABC$	7. Under a dilation, a $\triangle$ and its image are $\sim$. [5, 6]
8. $m\angle CYX = m\angle CBA$	8. Corres. $\angle$s of $\sim \triangle$s are $=$. [7]
9. $\overline{XY} \parallel \overline{AB}$	9. $=$ corres. $\angle$s $\Rightarrow$ 2 lines $\parallel$. [8]
10. $AB = 2XY$	10. If a dilation with center C and scale factor k maps A onto A' and B onto B', then $A'B' = k(AB)$. [5]
11. $XY = \frac{1}{2}AB$	11. Multiplication Prop. [10]

Coordinate Method of Proof

Given: $\triangle ABC$ with X and Y the midpoints of $\overline{AC}$ and $\overline{BC}$

Prove: $\overline{XY} \parallel \overline{AB}$ and $XY = \frac{1}{2} AB$.

Place coordinate axes on $\triangle ABC$ so that A coincides with the origin and B lies on the x-axis. Let the coordinates be $A(0, 0)$, $B(a, 0)$, and $C(b, c)$.

By the Midpoint Formula, the coordinates of X and Y are $\left(\frac{b}{2}, \frac{c}{2}\right)$ and $\left(\frac{a+b}{2}, \frac{c}{2}\right)$.

By the Distance Formula, $AB = a$ and $XY = \left|\frac{a+b}{2} - \frac{b}{2}\right| = \frac{1}{2}a$.

Substituting for a gives $XY = \frac{1}{2}AB$.

$\overline{XY} \parallel \overline{AB}$ because $\overline{XY}$ and $\overline{AB}$ are horizontal lines whose slopes equal 0.

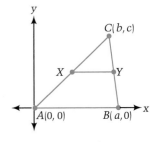

Synthetic Method of Proof

Given: △ABC with X and Y the midpoints of $\overline{AC}$ and $\overline{BC}$

Prove: $\overline{XY} \parallel \overline{AB}$ and $XY = \frac{1}{2} AB$.

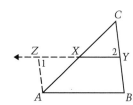

Statements	Reasons
1. △ABC, X the midpt. of $\overline{AC}$, Y the midpt. of $\overline{BC}$	1. Given
2. Locate Z on $\overrightarrow{YX}$ so that ZY = 2 XY.	2. Seg. Construction Post.
3. Draw $\overline{AZ}$.	3. 2 pts. deter. a line.
4. $m\angle ZXA = m\angle YXC$	4. Vert. ∠s are =.
5. AX = XC; BY = YC	5. Def. of midpt. [1]
6. ZX + XY = ZY	6. Seg. Add. Post.
7. ZX + XY = 2 XY	7. Substitution Prop. [2, 6]
8. ZX = XY	8. Add. Prop. [7]
9. △ZXA ≅ △YXC	9. SAS ≅ Post. [4, 5, 8]
10. AZ = CY; m∠1 = m∠2	10. Corres. Parts of ≅ △s are =. [9]
11. AZ = BY	11. Substitution Prop. [5, 10]
12. $\overline{AZ} \parallel \overline{BY}$	12. = alt. int. ∠s ⇒ 2 lines ∥. [10]
13. ABZX is a ▱.	13. Opp. sides = and ∥ ⇒ quad. is ▱. [11, 12]
14. $\overline{XY} \parallel \overline{AB}$	14. Def. of a ▱ [13]
15. ZY = AB	15. Opp. sides of ▱ are =. [13]
16. 2XY = AB	16. Substitution Prop. [2, 15]
17. XY = $\frac{1}{2}$AB	17. Multiplication Prop. [16]

Checking for Understanding

1. Name four methods of geometric proof. Synthetic, transformations; Coordinates, Vectors

2. Write the Transformation Method of Proof given in the Example in paragraph form.

3. Which of the four methods of proof given in the example appears to be the easiest? Why? Vector or coordinate; there are less steps in proof.

4. Write a Synthetic Method of Proof for the statement given in the Example, but use the SAS Similarity Theorem and write your proof in paragraph form.

5. Suppose points X and Y in the example were such that $CX = \frac{1}{3}CA$ and $CY = \frac{1}{3}CB$. What conclusions could you draw? Which method(s) of proof would most easily generalize to this new situation?

EXERCISE NOTES

Exercises 1–13 could be used as **group activities**.

ANSWERS

Checking for Understanding

2. Proof: Since X and Y are midpts., 2CX = CA and 2CY = CB. Under the dilation with center C and scale factor 2, the image of X is A and the image of Y is B. C is its own image. Thus, △XYC ~ △ABC. (Under a dilation, a △ and its image are ~.) Because ∠CYX and ∠CBA are = corres. ∠s, $\overline{XY} \parallel \overline{AB}$. AB = 2XY (If a dilation with center C and scale factor k maps A onto A′ and B onto B′, then A′B′ = kAB.), or XY = $\frac{1}{2}$AB.

4. Given: △ABC with X the midpt. of $\overline{AC}$ and Y the midpt. of $\overline{BC}$

Prove: XY = $\frac{1}{2}$AB and $\overline{XY} \parallel \overline{AB}$

Proof: Since X and Y are midpts., CA = 2CX and CB = 2CY. Therefore, $\frac{CX}{CA} = \frac{CY}{CB} = \frac{1}{2}$. Since $m\angle C = m\angle C$, △CXY ~ △CAB by the SAS ~ Thm. By def. of ~ △s, $\frac{XY}{AB} = \frac{1}{2}$, or XY = $\frac{1}{2}$AB. ∠CYX and ∠CBA are = corres. ∠s and therefore $\overline{XY} \parallel \overline{AB}$.

5. XY = $\frac{1}{3}$AB; synthetic Proof using SAS ~ Thm., vector Proof or transformation Proof

Assignment Guide

Basic: 1–4, 8, 14–18
Average: 1–9, 14–18
Extended: 3–18

Written Exercises

1a. SAS ≅ Post.

b.

c.

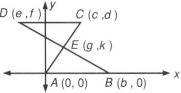

d. reflection through E, or a half-turn about E **e.** *Synthetic Method of Proof*: 1. E is the midpt. of $\overline{BD}$ and $\overline{AC}$. (Given) 2. $BE = ED$; $AE = EC$ (Def. of midpt. [1]) 3. $m\angle AEB = m\angle DEC$ (Vert. ∠s are =.) 4. $\triangle AEB \cong \triangle CED$ (SAS ≅ Post. [2, 3]) *Vector Method of Proof*: Since E is the midpt. of $\overline{BD}$ and $\overline{AC}$, $BE = ED$ and $CE = EA$. So $\overrightarrow{BE} = \overrightarrow{ED}$ and $\overrightarrow{CE} = \overrightarrow{EA}$. By the def. of vector addition, $\overrightarrow{BA} = \overrightarrow{BE} + \overrightarrow{EA}$ and $\overrightarrow{CD} = \overrightarrow{CE} + \overrightarrow{ED}$. By substitution, $\overrightarrow{BA} = \overrightarrow{ED} + \overrightarrow{CE}$. So $\overrightarrow{BA} = \overrightarrow{CD}$ and $BA = CD$. Therefore, $\triangle AEB \cong \triangle CED$ by the SSS ≅ Post.
Coordinate Method of Proof: Place the coordinate axes on the diagram so that $\overline{AB}$ lies on the x-axis and A is at the origin. Assign coordinates as shown on the diagram. Since E is the midpt. of $\overline{BD}$, $BE = ED$ and $(g, k) = \left(\frac{b+e}{2}, \frac{f}{2}\right)$; and since E is also the midpt. of $\overline{AC}$, $AE = EC$ and $(g, k) = \left(\frac{c}{2}, \frac{d}{2}\right)$. Therefore, $b + e = c$ and $f = d$. Then $DC = \sqrt{(c - e)^2 + (d - f)^2} = \sqrt{b^2 + 0^2} = b = AB$. Thus, the △s are ≅ by the SSS ≅ Post.
Transformation Method of Proof: Since E is the midpt. of $\overline{AC}$ and $\overline{BD}$ under a reflection through E,

---

Written Exercises

Set A   Answer a–e for Exercises 1 and 2.

    a. Which of the triangle congruence postulates would you use to prove the triangles congruent for a synthetic method of proof?

    b. Trace the diagram and show how you would mark it for a vector method of proof.

    c. Place coordinate axes on the diagram and give the coordinates for each of the vertices to use in a coordinate method of proof.

    d. What kind of transformation can be used to prove the statement?

    e. Choose a method of proof and prove the given statement. Which method did you use? Compare your proof with the proofs of other students in class. Which method was used most often?

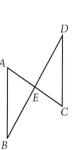

1. Given: E is the midpoint of $\overline{BD}$ and $\overline{AC}$.
    Prove: $\triangle ABE \cong \triangle CDE$

2. Given: Diameters $\overline{FH}$ and $\overline{IG}$ in $\odot O$
    Prove: $FGHI$ is a parallelogram.

Set B   Use four different methods to prove the statement in

3. Exercise 1.   **4.** Exercise 2.

Prove the following statements using two different methods.

5. The diagonals of a parallelogram bisect each other.

6. If the diagonals of a quadrilateral bisect each other, then the quadrilateral is a parallelogram.

7. The segments joining the midpoints of the adjacent sides of a quadrilateral form a parallelogram.

8. Prove by using the synthetic and coordinate methods. The length of the median of the hypotenuse of a right triangle is one half the length of the hypotenuse.

9. Prove by using the synthetic and transformation methods.
    Given: $\odot T \cong \odot Q$; $m\angle RTQ = m\angle SQT$
    Prove: $m\angle R = m\angle S$

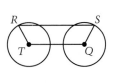

Set C   For Exercises 10–12, use two different methods of proof.

10. Given: $\triangle RBC$ with median $\overline{RM}$; $\overline{EF} \parallel \overline{BC}$
    Prove: $\overline{RM}$ bisects $\overline{EF}$.

11. If a line divides two sides of a triangle proportionally, then it is parallel to the third side.

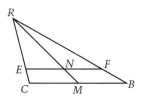

12. Given: *GHJK* and *PQJO* are parallelograms with
GH = 3*PQ* and *HJ* = 3 *QJ*
Prove: *G*, *P*, and *J* are collinear.

13. Use four different methods of proof.

Given: $\overline{RV}$ and $\overline{US}$ bisect each other;
$\overline{SW}$ and $\overline{VT}$ bisect each other.
Prove: *RTWU* is a parallelogram.

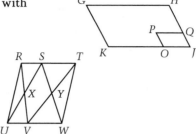

▲ **Review**   Given quadrilateral *ABCD*,

14. draw a diagram using vectors.

15. prove that $\overrightarrow{AB} + \overrightarrow{BC} + \overrightarrow{CD} = \overrightarrow{AD}$.

Define each term.

16. *Scalar multiple* **17.** *Equilateral* **18.** *Regular polygon*

16. If *k* is a real number and
v is a vector, $\overrightarrow{kv}$ is a scalar
multiple of $\overrightarrow{v}$.
17. Having equal sides
18. A polygon having equal
sides and equal angles

the image of *A* is *C*, the image of
B is *D* and the image of *E* is *E*.
Thus, the image of △*ABE* is
△*CDE*. Since a reflection through
a pt. is an isometry, *AB* = *CD*, *AE*
= *CE* and *BE* = *DE*. Therefore, the
△s are ≅ by SSS ≅ Post.
2a. SAS ≅ Post.
b.

c.

Progress Check

Lesson 13-4, page 582
1. Find the magnitude and direction angle for $\overrightarrow{v}$ = (−5, 8).
$\sqrt{89} \approx 9.43$; 122°

Lesson 13-5, page 586
2. Find (x, y) if $\overrightarrow{u}$ = (x, y), $|\overrightarrow{u}|$ = 2, and the direction angle is 75°.
(0.52, 1.93)
3. A plane is flying due north at 300 mph. A wind is blowing
at 10 mph with an angle of direction equal to 30°. What is
the actual speed and direction angle of the plane?
305.12 mph; 88°

Lesson 13-6, page 593
4. If $\overrightarrow{w}$ = (−5, 1), draw $2\overrightarrow{w}$ in standard position. Find $|2\overrightarrow{w}|$, the
direction angle for $2\overrightarrow{w}$, and the coordinates of the terminal
point of $2\overrightarrow{w}$. 10.20; 169°; (−10, 2)

Lesson 13-7, page 597
5. Use vectors to prove the following:
Given: $\dfrac{AX}{DX} = \dfrac{BX}{CX} = 3$
Prove: △*ABX* ~ △*DCX*

Lesson 13-8, page 601
6. Use the transformation and coordinate methods of proof.

Given: $\overline{EG}$ is the perpendicular bisector of $\overline{FH}$.
Prove: △*EFG* ≅ △*EHG*

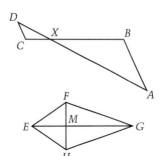

EXCURSION

ANSWERS

Excursion

1. $A(2, 30°)$; $B(1, 45°)$; $C(3, 90°)$; $D(2, 135°)$; $E(1, 180°)$; $F(2, 240°)$; $G(3, 300°)$; $H(2, 330°)$
2. $A(\sqrt{3}, 1)$; $B(\frac{\sqrt{2}}{2}, \frac{\sqrt{2}}{2})$; $C(0, 3)$; $D(-\sqrt{2}, \sqrt{2})$; $E(-1, 0)$; $F(-1, -\sqrt{3})$; $G(\frac{3}{2}, -\frac{3\sqrt{3}}{2})$; $H(\sqrt{3}, -1)$
3. $R(13, 67°)$
4. $S(9.43, 238°)$

Excursion: Polar Coordinates

Another important coordinate system that is used to locate points in a plane is the *polar coordinate system*. The plane consists of a fixed point O, called the origin or *pole*, and a ray, called the *polar axis* with endpoint at O. To locate a point P, other than the pole, draw $\overline{OP}$. Let r be the distance from O to P. Let θ be the angle that $\overline{OP}$ makes with the polar axis. We define θ as an angle measured from the polar axis to $\overline{OP}$ in a counterclockwise direction. Then any point P in the polar coordinate system has coordinates (r, θ). The point Q has coordinates (2, 45°).

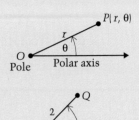

The points A through H are drawn on a polar grid. In the polar coordinate system, notice that when you move in a counterclockwise direction the polar axis to a segment, say $\overline{OF}$, the angle formed may have a measure greater than or equal to 180.

1. Write the polar coordinates of each point in the diagram.

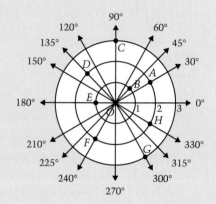

Place the polar coordinate system in a rectangular coordinate system (the xy-plane) so that the pole coincides with the origin and the polar axis coincides with the nonnegative x-axis. Then a point P can be located by using either its rectangular coordinates (x, y) or its polar coordinates (r, θ).

Draw a perpendicular from P to the x-axis determining right △PQO. We define the trigonometric ratios as follows:

For $P(r, θ)$, $r \neq 0$, $\sin θ = \frac{y}{r}$, $\cos θ = \frac{x}{r}$, and $\tan θ = \frac{y}{x}$.

To change a point P from polar to rectangular coordinates, use the sine ratio to find y and the cosine ratio to find x.

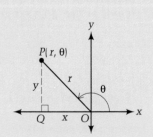

To change a point P from rectangular to polar coordinates, use the Pythagorean Theorem to find r. Then use one of the trigonometric ratios to find θ.

2. Find the rectangular coordinates of each point A through H.

Find the polar coordinates of

3. $R(5, 12)$.   **4.** $S(-5, -8)$.

💻 Using BASIC: Perpendiculars to Lines

```
100 REM PERPENDICULAR FROM P NOT ON LINE AB
110 PRINT "ENTER X,Y COORDINATES OF A,B,"
120 PRINT "AND P IN THAT ORDER, WITH COMMAS."
130 INPUT XA, YA, XB, YB, XP, YP
140 IF XA = XB THEN 210
150 IF YA = YB THEN 270
160 LET MAB = (YA-YB)/(XA-XB)
170 LET MPQ = -1/MAB
180 LET XQ = (MAB*XA-YA-MPQ*XP+YP)/(MAB-MPQ)
190 LET YQ = MAB*(XQ-XA)+YA
200 GO TO 290
210 IF YA<>YB THEN 240
220 PRINT"A AND B MUST BE DISTINCT POINTS."
230 GO TO 110
240 LET XQ=XA
250 LET YQ=YP
260 GO TO 290
270 LET XQ=XP
280 LET YQ=YA
290 PRINT "FOOT OF PERPENDICULAR FROM P"
300 PRINT "TO LINE AB IS (";XQ;",";YQ;")."
310 END
```

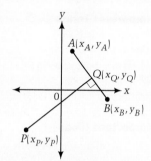

Using BASIC

1. $m_{AB} = \frac{Y_A - Y_B}{X_A - X_B}$; $m_{PQ} = -\frac{1}{m_{AB}}$

2. $Y = m_{AB}(X - X_A) + Y_A$; $Y = m_{PQ}(X - X_P) + Y_P$

6. Add these lines:

```
310 LET D = SQR (ABS (XP -
    XQ) ^ 2 + ABS (YP - YQ) ^
    2);
320 PRINT ""DISTANCE FROM
    P TO AB IS''; D
330 LET YZ = SQR (ABS (XA -
    XB) ^ 2 + ABS (YA - YB) ^
    2)
340 LET A = .5 * YZ * D
350 PRINT "AREA OF TRIAN-
    GLE XYZ IS''A;
360 END
```

If the coordinates of three points, A, B, and P, are known, then the program above can be used to locate the perpendicular from P to $\overleftrightarrow{AB}$. Let Q be the intersection of $\overleftrightarrow{AB}$ and the perpendicular through P, and let m_{AB} and m_{PQ} be the slopes of $\overleftrightarrow{AB}$ and $\overleftrightarrow{PQ}$, respectively.

1. What is m_{AB}? m_{PQ}?

2. What are the equations of $\overleftrightarrow{AB}$ and $\overleftrightarrow{PQ}$ in point-slope form?

To find x_Q substitute one equation into the other and solve for x. This gives the formula for x_Q used in line 180. Then use x_Q in one of the original equations to find y_Q. This gives the formula in line 190.

Given a triangle with vertices $X(6, 8)$, $Y(4, 2)$, and $Z(11, 4)$.

3. Find W and V so that $\overline{WX}$ and $\overline{VY}$ are altitudes of $\triangle XYZ$.

4. Compute the area of $\triangle XYZ$. 18.9 sq. units

5. Repeat Exercises 3 and 4 for $X(0, 3)$, $Y(-12, 0)$, and $Z(4, -2)$.

6. Revise the program to compute the area of $\triangle XYZ$.

   3. (7.4, 3.0); (7.7, 6.6)
   5. W(−0.5, −1.4); V(−3.2, 7.0); 35.4 sq. units

Chapter Review

6a.

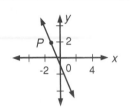

b.

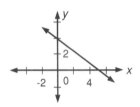

7.

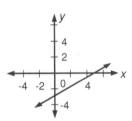

16. Given: $\square ABCD$ with diags. $\overline{AC}$ and $\overline{BD}$ Prove: $\overline{AC}$ and $\overline{BD}$ bisect each other.

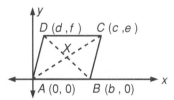

Proof: Place the coordinate plane on $\square ABCD$ so that A coincides with the origin and $\overline{AB}$ lies on the x-axis. Let the coordinates of A, B, C and D be $(0, 0)$, $(b, 0)$, (c, e) and (d, f), respectively. By def. of $\square$, $\overline{DC} \parallel \overline{AB}$ so the slope of $\overline{DC}$ = the slope of $\overline{AB}$ which = 0 since both are horizontal lines. Then $\frac{e - f}{c - d} = 0$ and $e = f$. Also, $\overline{AD} \parallel \overline{BC}$, so their slopes are =. Thus $\frac{f}{d} = \frac{f}{c - b}$, so $d = c - b$ or $c = b + d$.

Chapter 13 Summary

Important Terms

Component (586)
Direction angle (583)
Distance Formula (562)
Magnitude (582)
Midpoint Formula (563)

Opposite vector (582)
Parallelogram Rule (586)
Point-slope form (568)
Resultant (586)
Scalar multiple (593)

Slope-intercept form (568)
Standard form of circle (570)
Standard form of a line (569)
Standard position (583)
Vector (582)

Important Ideas

1. The distance between point $P(x_1, y_1, z_1)$ and $Q(x_2, y_2, z_2)$ is
$PQ = \sqrt{(x_2 - x_1)^2 + (y_2 - y_1)^2 + (z_2 - z_1)^2}$. (562)

2. The midpoint of $\overline{PQ}$ for $P(x_1, y_1, z_1)$ and $Q(x_2, y_2, z_2)$ has coordinates $\left(\frac{x_1 + x_2}{2}, \frac{y_1 + y_2}{2}, \frac{z_1 + z_2}{2}\right)$. (563)

3. *Point-slope form:* An equation of the line containing $P(x_1, y_1)$ with slope m is $y - y_1 = m(x - x_1)$. A point is on the line if and only if its coordinates satisfy the equation. (568)

4. *Slope-intercept form:* An equation of the line with slope m and y-intercept b is $y = mx + b$. (568)

5. *Standard form:* The graph of an equation is a line if and only if the equation can be written in the form $Ax + By = C$, where A, B, and C are integers and A and B are not both zero. (569)

6. The equation of a circle with center (h, k) and radius r is $(x - h)^2 + (y - k)^2 = r^2$. (571)

7. To prove a theorem by a coordinate method, place coordinate axes on the given geometric figure in a position which simplifies the work. (576)

8. A vector is a directed line segment. The magnitude of $\vec{u}$ is the distance between its initial and terminal points, written $|\vec{u}|$. (582)

9. The sum of two vectors $\vec{u}$ and $\vec{v}$ is the vector $\vec{u} + \vec{v}$. The difference of the vectors is the vector $\vec{u} - \vec{v}$ which equals $\vec{u} + (-\vec{v})$. (586–587)

10. If k is a real number and $\vec{v}$ is a vector, then $k\vec{v}$ is a vector that has a magnitude equal to $|k| \, |\vec{v}|$ and has the same direction as $\vec{v}$ if $k > 0$ or the opposite direction of $\vec{v}$ if $k < 0$. If $k = 0$, then $k\vec{v} = 0$. (593)

11. A statement may be proved by using a synthetic method, vector method, coordinate method, or transformational method. These methods of proof may be written in two-column form or paragraph form. (601–603)

Chapter 13 Review

Lesson 13-1, page 561

1. Find the midpoint and the length of the segment whose endpoints are $G(-1, 0, 1)$ and $H(3, -2, 7)$. (1, −1, 4)

2. Show that $C(2, 3, 3)$ is equidistant from $B(1, 1, 5)$ and $D(4, 4, 1)$. Is C the midpoint of $\overline{DB}$? CB = CD = 3; no

Lesson 13-2, page 567

3. Find the slope of the line through the given points.

  a. $A(-2, -4)$; $B(5, 3)$ 1   **b.** $C(3, 8)$; $D(3, 11)$ undefined

4. What is the slope of a line perpendicular to the y-axis? 0

5. Are $\overleftrightarrow{AB}$ and $\overleftrightarrow{CD}$ parallel, or perpendicular, or neither?

  a. $A(8, 6)$, $B(0, 3)$, $C(5, 3)$, $D(2, 11)$ ⊥

  b. $A(4, 7)$, $B(-5, 0)$, $C(-16, 4)$, $D(-7, 11)$ ∥

6. Write an equation of the line described. Graph Items a and b.

  a. The line that contains $P(-1, 2)$ and has slope -3 y − 2 = −3(x +1)

  b. The line that has y-intercept 4 and slope $-\frac{3}{4}$ $y = -\frac{3}{4}x + 4$

  c. The line that contains $A(-1, 6)$ and $B(3, -2)$ y − 6 = −2(x + 1)

  d. The line that contains $D(3, -2)$ and is parallel to the graph of $y = \frac{2}{3}x - 5$ $y + 2 = \frac{2}{3}(x - 3)$

  e. The line that has y-intercept -2 and is perpendicular to the line whose equation is $y - 4 = -2(x + 5)$ $y = \frac{1}{2}x - 2$

7. Find the slope and y-intercept of the line whose equation is $3x - 5y = 15$. Graph the equation. $\frac{3}{5}$; −3

8. Write an equation in standard form of the line that:

  a. contains $K(-3, 2)$ and is perpendicular to the line whose equation is $5x + 3y = 9$. 3x − 5y = −19

  b. contains $G(6, -3)$ and is parallel to the graph of $3y - 4x = 9$. 4x − 3y = 33

  c. has x-intercept 3 and is perpendicular to the line whose equation is $-4x - 2y = 3$. x − 2y = 3

9. Find the center and radius of the circle whose equation is $(x + 2)^2 + (y - 3)^2 = 121$. (−2, 3); 11

10. Write an equation for the circle with center $(3, -1)$ and radius 9.
$(x - 3)^2 + (y + 1)^2 = 81$

Let X be the midpt. of $\overline{BD}$. Then X has coordinates $\left(\frac{b + d}{2}, \frac{f}{2}\right)$. Let X' be the midpt. of $\overline{AC}$. Then X' has coordinates $\left(\frac{c}{2}, \frac{e}{2}\right) = \left(\frac{b + d}{2}, \frac{f}{2}\right)$. So $X = X'$ and the diags. bisect each other.

24.

Proof: Since $\overrightarrow{AC}$ and $\overrightarrow{BD}$ have the same direction and $AC = BD$, $\overrightarrow{AC} = \overrightarrow{BD}$. Also, since $\overrightarrow{AF} \parallel \overrightarrow{BE}$ and $AF = BE$, $\overrightarrow{AF} = \overrightarrow{BE}$. Then $\overrightarrow{CF} = -\overrightarrow{AC} + \overrightarrow{AF} = -\overrightarrow{BD} + \overrightarrow{AF} = \overrightarrow{DB} + \overrightarrow{BE} = \overrightarrow{DE}$. So $\overrightarrow{CF} = \overrightarrow{DE}$ and $\overrightarrow{CF} \parallel \overrightarrow{DE}$.

25. Given: Equilateral $\triangle ABC$ with medians $\overline{AE}$, $\overline{BF}$ and $\overline{CD}$ Prove: AE = BF = CD

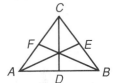

Synthetic Method: 1. Equilateral $\triangle ABC$ with medians $\overline{AE}$, $\overline{BF}$ and $\overline{CD}$ (Given) 2. AB = BC = CA (Def. of equilateral △ [1]) 3. $\frac{1}{2}AB = \frac{1}{2}BC = \frac{1}{2}CA$ (Mult. Prop. [2]) 4. D, E and F are midpts. of $\overline{AB}$, $\overline{BC}$ and $\overline{CA}$, respectively. (Def. of median [1]) 5. AD = DB; BE = EC; CF = FA (Def. of midpt. [4]) 6. AD + DB = AB; BE + EC = BC; CF + FA = CA (Seg. Add. Post.) 7. AD + AD = AB; BE + BE = BC; CF + CF = CA, or 2AD = AB; 2BE = BC; 2CF = CA (Substitution Prop. [5, 6]) 8. AD = $\frac{1}{2}AB$; BE = $\frac{1}{2}BC$; CF = $\frac{1}{2}CA$ (Mult. Prop. [7]) 9. AD = BE = CF (Substitution Prop. [3, 8]) 10. $\triangle ABC$ is equiangular. (An equilateral △ is equiangular. [1]) 11. $m\angle CAD = m\angle ABE = m\angle BCF$ (Def. of equiangular △ [10]) 12. $\triangle CAD \cong \triangle ABE \cong \triangle BCF$ (SAS ≅ Post. [2,

9, 10]) 13. $CD = AE = BF$ (Corres. parts of $\cong \triangle$s are =. [12])

Vector Method: By def. of median, D, E and F are midpts. By def. of midpt. and vector addition, $\overrightarrow{CD} = \overrightarrow{CA} + \overrightarrow{AD} = \overrightarrow{CA} + \frac{1}{2}\overrightarrow{AB}$, $\overrightarrow{AE} = \overrightarrow{AB} + \overrightarrow{BE} = \overrightarrow{AB} + \frac{1}{2}\overrightarrow{BC}$ and $\overrightarrow{BF} = \overrightarrow{BC} + \overrightarrow{CF} = \overrightarrow{BC} + \frac{1}{2}\overrightarrow{CA}$. Since $\triangle ABC$ is equilateral, $AB = BC = CA$ and $|\overrightarrow{AB}| = |\overrightarrow{BC}| = |\overrightarrow{CA}|$. And since the medians of an equilateral $\triangle$ are also altitudes, $\triangle ABE$, $\triangle BCF$ and $\triangle CAD$ are rt. $\triangle$s. Therefore, by the Pythagorean Thm.,
$|\overrightarrow{CD}|^2 = |\overrightarrow{CA}|^2 + |\frac{1}{2}\overrightarrow{AB}|^2$
$= |\overrightarrow{CA}|^2 + \frac{1}{4}|\overrightarrow{AB}|^2$,
$|\overrightarrow{AE}|^2 = |\overrightarrow{AB}|^2 + |\frac{1}{2}\overrightarrow{BC}|^2$
$= |\overrightarrow{CA}|^2 + \frac{1}{4}|\overrightarrow{AB}|^2$, and
$|\overrightarrow{BF}|^2 = |\overrightarrow{BC}|^2 + |\frac{1}{2}\overrightarrow{CA}|^2$
$= |\overrightarrow{CA}|^2 + \frac{1}{4}|\overrightarrow{AB}|^2$.
Thus, $CD = AE = BF$.

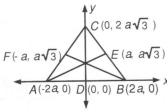

Coordinate Method: Place the coordinate axes so that D coincides with the origin and $\overline{AB}$ lies on the x-axis. Since D is the midpt. of $\overline{AB}$, $AD = DB$. Let the coordinates of A and B be $(-2a, 0)$ and $(2a, 0)$, respectively. Since the medians of an equilateral $\triangle$ are also altitudes, $\overline{CD} \perp \overline{AB}$ and C falls on the y-axis. Also, in rt. $\triangle ACD$, $AC = 4a$, $AD = 2a$ and $CD = 2a\sqrt{3}$. Thus, the coordinates of C are $(0, 2a\sqrt{3})$. Using the Midpt. Formula gives $E(a, a\sqrt{3})$ and $F(-a, a\sqrt{3})$. Then by the Distance Formula, $AE = \sqrt{(-2a - a)^2 + (0 - a\sqrt{3})^2} = 2a\sqrt{3}$ and $BF = \sqrt{(-a - 2a)^2 + (a\sqrt{3} - 0)^2} = 2a\sqrt{3}$. Thus, $CD = AE = BF$.

Lesson 13-3, page 575
Given: Equilateral $\triangle FGH$

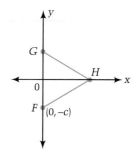

11. Find the coordinates of G and H. $G(0, C)$; $H(C\sqrt{3}, 0)$

12. Find the slope of a line that is perpendicular to $\overleftrightarrow{GH}$. $\sqrt{3}$

Given: $\square OPQR$ with $O(0, 0)$, $P(2t, 0)$, and $R(2s, 2z)$

13. Find the slope of $\overleftrightarrow{OR}$. $\frac{z}{s}$

14. Find the coordinates of point Q. $(2s + 2t, 2z)$

15. Find the coordinates of the midpoint of $\overline{PQ}$. $(s + 2t, z)$

16. Prove: The diagonals of a parallelogram bisect each other.

Lesson 13-4, page 582
Find the magnitude and direction angle for $\vec{t}$ if

17. $\vec{t} = (5, 2)$.   **18.** $\vec{t} = (\sqrt{3}, 1)$.   **19.** $\vec{t} = (-1, \sqrt{3})$.
$\sqrt{29} \approx 5.39$; 22°   2; 30°   2; 120°

Lesson 13-5, page 586
Find (x, y) if $\vec{v} = (x, y)$, $|\vec{v}| = 10$, and the direction angle is

20. 40°. $(7.66, 6.43)$ **21.** 140°. $(-7.66, 6.43)$

22. A plane is flying 80° north of east at 275 mph. A wind is blowing from the west at 15 mph. What is the actual speed and direction angle of the plane? 277.99 mph; 77°

Lesson 13-6, page 593
23. If $\vec{u} = (-8, 4)$, draw $\frac{1}{2}\vec{u}$ in standard position. Find $|\frac{1}{2}\vec{u}|$, the direction angle for $\frac{1}{2}\vec{u}$, and the coordinates of the terminal point of $\frac{1}{2}\vec{u}$. $\sqrt{20} \approx 4.47$; 153°; $(-4, 2)$

Lesson 13-7, page 597
24. Use vectors for the following proof.
Given: $\overline{AF} \parallel \overline{BE}$; $AF = BE$; $AC = BD$
Prove: $\overline{CF} \parallel \overline{DE}$

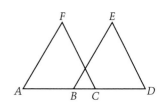

Lesson 13-8, page 601
25. Use two methods of proof to prove that the medians of an equilateral triangle are equal.

Chapter 13 Test

1. Given: $P(-4, 3, 0)$ and $Q(4, -5, 4)$. Find PQ and the coordinates of the midpoint of $\overline{PQ}$. **12; (0, −1, 2)**

2. Given: $A(2, 3)$, $B(1, 5)$, $C(6, 5)$, $D(4, 8)$. Are $\overleftrightarrow{AB}$ and $\overleftrightarrow{CD}$ parallel, perpendicular, or neither? **Neither**

3. Given: $E(2, 1)$, $F(7, 3)$, $G(6, 7)$, $H(1, 5)$. Show that $EFGH$ is a parallelogram. **$\overline{EF} \parallel \overline{GH}$: slope $\overline{EF}$ = slope $\overline{GH}$ = $\frac{2}{5}$; $\overline{FG} \parallel \overline{EH}$; slope $\overline{FG}$ = slope $\overline{EH}$ = −4**

4. Find the value of x such that the line through $U(x, 0)$ and $V(-3, 5)$ will have slope $-\frac{2}{5}$. **$-\frac{31}{2}$**

5. Write and equation in point-slope form of the line through $P(-3, 4)$ with slope $-\frac{3}{5}$. **$y -4 = -\frac{3}{5}(x + 3)$**

6. Write an equation in slope-intercept form of the line containing $A(-2, 3)$ and $B(4, -1)$. **$y = -\frac{2}{5}x + \frac{5}{3}$**

7. Write an equation in standard form of the line through $P(2, -1)$ that is perpendicular to the line whose equation is $2x + 3y = 7$. **$3x − 2y = 8$**

8. Write an equation in slope-intercept form for the line that is the perpendicular bisector of the segment whose endpoints are $A(-3, 5)$ and $B(0, -1)$. **$y = \frac{1}{2}x + \frac{11}{4}$**

9. What are the center and radius of the circle whose equation is $(x − 9)^2 + (y + 16)^2 = 64$? **(9, −16); 8**

Given: $\overline{OB} \parallel \overline{CD}$ and $OB = CD$

10. What are the coordinates of C? **(r + s, t)**

11. What is the slope of a line perpendicular to $\overleftrightarrow{BC}$? **$-\frac{s}{t}$**

12. Prove: $\overline{BC} \parallel \overline{DO}$ and $\overline{BC} = \overline{DO}$

13. Find the magnitude and direction angle for $\vec{v} = (8, 4)$. **$2\sqrt{20} \approx 8.94$, 27°**

14. Find the coordinates of the terminal point for $\vec{u}$ in standard position if $|\vec{u}| = 8$ and its direction angle is 50°. **(5.14, 6.13)**

15. If $\vec{u} = (3, 5)$ and $\vec{v} = (-4, 6)$, find the coordinates of $\vec{u} + \vec{v}$. What is the direction angle for $\vec{u} + \vec{v}$? **(−1, 11); 95°**

16. Use two different methods of proof to prove the following statement: If the diagonals of a quadrilateral bisect each other, then the quadrilateral is a parallelogram.

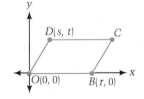

Transformation Method: In an equilateral $\triangle$, medians are also altitudes, so $\overline{CD} \perp \overline{AB}$ and $\overline{AE} \perp \overline{CB}$. Under a reflection over $\overleftrightarrow{CD}$, the images of C, B and $\overline{CB}$ are C, A and $\overline{CA}$. Similarly, under a reflection over $\overleftrightarrow{AE}$, the images of A, B and $\overline{AB}$ are A, C and $\overline{AC}$. Since a line reflection preserves distance, collinearity and betweenness of points, if E' is the image of E, then E' is on $\overline{CA}$ with $CE' = CE = \frac{1}{2}CA$. Thus $E' = F$ since $CF = \frac{1}{2}CA$, and the image of $\overline{AE}$ is $\overline{BF}$. Therefore, $AE = BF$. Using a similar argument with the reflection over $\overleftrightarrow{AE}$, $BF = CD$. Therefore, $AE = BF = CD$.

Chapter Test

12. Given: $\overline{OB} \parallel \overline{CD}$; $OB = CD$
Prove: $\overline{BC} \parallel \overline{DO}$; $BC = DO$ Proof:
Place the coordinate axes on $DCBO$ so that O coincides with the origin and $\overline{OB}$ lies on the x-axis. Let the coordinates of B and D be $(r, 0)$ and (s, t). Since $\overline{OB} \parallel \overline{CD}$, C has coordinates $(r + s, t)$. Then the slope of $\overline{BC} = \frac{t}{s} =$ the slope of $\overline{DO}$ and $\overline{BC} \parallel \overline{DO}$. By the Distance Formula, $BC = \sqrt{s^2 + t^2} = OD$.

Cumulative Review   Chapters 7–13

Select the best answer for each item.

1. In the proportion, x = ___?___ .

$$\frac{4x + 3}{7} = \frac{3x + 1}{5}$$

A. 5   **B.** −2   **C.** 7   **D.** 8

2. If quadrilateral *ABCD* ~ quadrilateral *EFGH*, find the perimeter of *EFGH*.

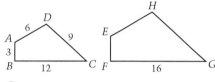

A. 40   **B.** 30   **C.** 24   **D.** 22½

3. If $\overline{ST} \parallel \overline{PQ}$, then which statement is false?

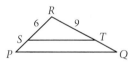

A. $\frac{RT}{TQ} = \frac{RS}{SP}$ **B.** $\frac{RS}{RP} = \frac{RT}{RQ}$

C. $\frac{RS}{TQ} = \frac{RT}{SP}$ **D.** $\frac{RS}{RT} = \frac{SP}{TQ}$

4. The perimeters of two equilateral triangles are in the ratio of 3 to 5. If the median of the larger triangle is 20, then the median of the smaller is ___?___ .

A. 10   **B.** 12   **C.** 18   **D.** 33⅓

5. Given: △ABC ~ △XYZ; *AB* = 8; *XY* = 12; *AC* = 4x − 4; and *XZ* = 3x + 6. Then x = ___?___ .

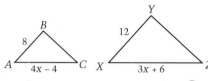

A. $\frac{2}{3}$ **B.** 0   **C.** 2   **D.** 4

6. A flagpole is 32 feet tall. It casts an 8-foot shadow at the same time that a post casts a 6-foot shadow. The post is ___?___ feet tall.

A. 7   **B.** 8   **C.** 24   **D.** 30

7. If *ABCD* is a rectangle, *DA* = ___?___ .

A. 20   **B.** 21   **C.** 23   **D.** 9

8. The length of the altitude of an equilateral triangle is $6\sqrt{3}$. The length of a side is ___?___ .

A. $6\sqrt{3}$ **B.** 6   **C.** 18   **D.** 12

9. The length of a leg of an isosceles right triangle is 8 cm. The length of the hypotenuse is ___?___ cm.

A. $8\sqrt{2}$ **B.** 16   **C.** 64   **D.** $16\sqrt{2}$

10. If $\cos B = \frac{5}{13}$, then $\sin B = \underline{}$.

  A. $\frac{13}{5}$ **B.** $\frac{13}{12}$ **C.** $\frac{5}{13}$ **D.** $\frac{12}{13}$

11. If $\sin 25° = .4226$ and $\cos 25° = .9063$, then $EF = \underline{}$.

  A. 9.1

  B. 4.2

  C. 23.7

  D. 11.0

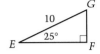

12. In $\odot O$, $\overleftrightarrow{AB}$ is called a $\underline{}$.

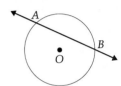

  A. Tangent   **B.** Diameter

  C. Chord   **D.** Secant

13. Circles A and B are externally tangent. If the radius of $\odot A$ is 12 and $AB = 13$, then the radius of $\odot B$ is $\underline{}$.

  A. 1   **B.** 5

  C. 25   **D.** Not enough information

14. If $AB = CD$, find EF.

  A. 6   **B.** 8   **C.** 10   **D.** $2\sqrt{41}$

15. In $\odot M$, $AB = AC$. If $m\widehat{AB} = 150$, then $m\widehat{BC} = \underline{}$.

  A. 105

  B. 75

  C. 150

  D. 60

16. If $m\widehat{AB} = 100$ and $\overline{AC} \perp \overline{BD}$, then $m\widehat{CD} = \underline{}$.

  A. 60

  B. 80

  C. 90

  D. 100

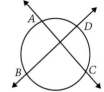

17. If circle O has a radius of 8 and $AC = 4$, find AB.

  A. 12

  B. 4

  C. $4\sqrt{5}$

  D. 16

18. The area of a rectangle is 48 cm², and the perimeter is 28 cm. The lengths of the sides are $\underline{}$ and $\underline{}$.

  A. 6; 8   **B.** 3; 16

  C. 4; 12   **D.** $3\sqrt{2}$; $8\sqrt{2}$

19. The area of a rhombus is 48, and one of its diagonals has a length of 8. The length of the other diagonal is __?__.

(A.) 12 **B.** 8 **C.** 6 **D.** 3

20. A trapezoid has median 10 and area 300. Its altitude has length __?__.

(A.) 30 **B.** 15 **C.** $\sqrt{30}$ **D.** 3

21. If $\triangle ABC \sim \triangle DEF$, and $\frac{AC}{DF} = \frac{1}{4}$, then $\frac{\text{area } \triangle ABC}{\text{area } \triangle DEF} = $ __?__.

A. $\frac{1}{4}$ **B.** $\frac{1}{8}$ **(C.)** $\frac{1}{16}$ **D.** $\frac{1}{12}$

22. The diameter of a circle with area 121π is __?__.

A. 11 **B.** 11π **C.** 121 **(D.)** 22

22. The radius of a circle is 6. If the arc that intercepts a central angle has measure 60, then the area of the sector is __?__.

(A.) 6π **B.** 12π **C.** 2π **D.** 36π

24. Each lateral face of an oblique prism is a __?__.

A. Rectangle **B.** Triangle
(C.) Parallelogram **D.** Trapezoid

25. The total area of this right circular cylinder is __?__.

A. 150π
(B.) 350π
C. 300π
D. $3,000\pi$

26. A regular pyramid has a triangular base 6 inches on a side. Its slant height is 5 inches. Its lateral area is __?__ square inches.

A. 30
(B.) 45
C. 60
D. 90

27. The slant height of a right circular cone is 15 cm and the diameter of the base is 20 cm. The lateral area of the cone is __?__.

(A.) 150π
B. 250π
C. 300π
D. 700π

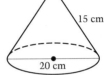

28. The area of a great circle of a sphere is 400π m^2. The area of the sphere is __?__ m^2.

A. 400π **B.** $10,666.67\pi$
(C.) $1,600\pi$ **D.** 533.33π

29. Reflections do not necessarily preserve __?__.

A. Distance
B. Angle measure
C. Betweenness of points
(D.) Orientation of points

30. $A'B'$ is an isometry of $\overline{AB}$ provided __?__.

(A.) $A'B' = AB$ **B.** $\overleftrightarrow{A'B'} \parallel \overleftrightarrow{AB}$
C. $A'A = B'B$ **D.** $\overline{AB} \perp \overline{A'B'}$

31. The shortest path from A to B by way of line ℓ is __?__.

A.

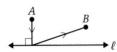

B.

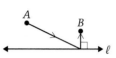

(C.)

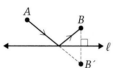

D.

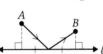

32. If $\ell \parallel m$, then the composite of the reflections over ℓ and then m is a(n) __?__.

(A.) Translation

B. Half-turn

C. Rotation

D. Identity transformation

33. A rectangle has __?__ lines of symmetry.

A. One

(B.) Two

C. Four

D. Zero

34. A dilation centered at P maps S onto S' and T onto T'. If $PS = 10$, $PS' = 5$, and $PT' = 18$, then $PT = $ __?__.

A. 9   **B.** 23   **C.** 13   **(D.)** 36

35. $\overleftrightarrow{AB}$ contains points $A(1, 1)$ and $B(3, 7)$. The slope of a line perpendicular to $\overleftrightarrow{AB}$ is __?__.

A. 3   **B.** -3 **C.** $\frac{1}{3}$ **(D.)** $-\frac{1}{3}$

36. The equation of line ℓ is $7x - 5y = 2$. An equation of a line parallel to ℓ is __?__.

A. $14x - 10y = 4$ **B.** $10x - 14y = 7$

(C.) $14x - 10y = 0$ **D.** $5x - 7y = 2$

37. The equations of two lines are $3x - 2y = 3$ and $4x - 3y = 2$. The coordinates of the point of intersection of these lines are __?__.

(A.) $(5, 6)$ **B.** $(2, 2)$

C. $(3, 3)$ **D.** $(1, 0)$

38. If $\overrightarrow{OP}$ has endpoints $O(1, 3)$ and $P(4, 0)$, then $|\overrightarrow{OP}| = $ __?__.

A. 3   **B.** 1   **C.** 4   **(D.)** 5

39. If $\vec{v}$ has direction $60°$, $\frac{1}{2}\vec{v}$ has direction __?__.

A. $20°$ **B.** $30°$ **(C.)** $60°$ **D.** $120°$

40. Given $3\vec{v}$ and $5\vec{u}$, $x = $ __?__.

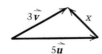

A. $5\vec{u} - 3\vec{v}$ **B.** $3\vec{v} + 5\vec{u}$

(C.) $3\vec{v} - 5\vec{u}$ **D.** $-3\vec{v} - 5\vec{u}$

■ Squares and Square Roots

n	n^2	$\sqrt{n}$	n	n^2	$\sqrt{n}$	n	n^2	$\sqrt{n}$	n	n^2	$\sqrt{n}$
1	1	1.000	51	2601	7.141	101	10,201	10.050	151	22,801	12.288
2	4	1.414	52	2704	7.211	102	10,404	10.100	152	23,104	12.329
3	9	1.732	53	2809	7.280	103	10,609	10.149	153	23,409	12.369
4	16	2.000	54	2916	7.348	104	10,816	10.198	154	23,716	12.410
5	25	2.236	55	3025	7.416	105	11,025	10.247	155	24,025	12.450
6	36	2.449	56	3136	7.483	106	11,236	10.296	156	24,336	12.490
7	49	2.646	57	3249	7.550	107	11,449	10.344	157	24,649	12.530
8	64	2.828	58	3364	7.616	108	11,664	10.392	158	24,964	12.570
9	81	3.000	59	3481	7.681	109	11,881	10.440	159	25,281	12.610
10	100	3.162	60	3600	7.746	110	12,100	10.488	160	25,600	12.649
11	121	3.317	61	3721	7.810	111	12,321	10.536	161	25,921	12.689
12	144	3.464	62	3844	7.874	112	12,544	10.583	162	26,244	12.728
13	169	3.606	63	3969	7.937	113	12,769	10.630	163	26,569	12.767
14	196	3.742	64	4096	8.000	114	12,996	10.677	164	26,896	12.806
15	225	3.873	65	4225	8.062	115	13,225	10.724	165	27,225	12.845
16	256	4.000	66	4356	8.124	116	13,456	10.770	166	27,556	12.884
17	289	4.123	67	4489	8.185	117	13,689	10.817	167	27,889	12.923
18	324	4.243	68	4624	8.246	118	13,924	10.863	168	28,224	12.961
19	361	4.359	69	4761	8.307	119	14,161	10.909	169	28,561	13.000
20	400	4.472	70	4900	8.367	120	14,400	10.954	170	28,900	13.038
21	441	4.583	71	5041	8.426	121	14,641	11.000	171	29,241	13.077
22	484	4.690	72	5184	8.485	122	14,884	11.045	172	29,584	13.115
23	529	4.796	73	5329	8.544	123	15,129	11.091	173	29,929	13.153
24	576	4.899	74	5476	8.602	124	15,376	11.136	174	30,276	13.191
25	625	5.000	75	5625	8.660	125	15,625	11.180	175	30,625	13.229
26	676	5.099	76	5776	8.718	126	15,876	11.225	176	30,976	13.266
27	729	5.196	77	5929	8.775	127	16,129	11.269	177	31,329	13.304
28	784	5.292	78	6084	8.832	128	16,384	11.314	178	31,684	13.342
29	841	5.385	79	6241	8.888	129	16,641	11.358	179	32,041	13.379
30	900	5.477	80	6400	8.944	130	16,900	11.402	180	32,400	13.416
31	961	5.568	81	6561	9.000	131	17,161	11.446	181	32,761	13.454
32	1024	5.657	82	6724	9.055	132	17,424	11.489	182	33,124	13.491
33	1089	5.745	83	6889	9.110	133	17,689	11.533	183	33,489	13.528
34	1156	5.831	84	7056	9.165	134	17,956	11.576	184	33,856	13.565
35	1225	5.916	85	7225	9.220	135	18,225	11.619	185	34,225	13.601
36	1296	6.000	86	7396	9.274	136	18,496	11.662	186	34,596	13.638
37	1369	6.083	87	7569	9.327	137	18,769	11.705	187	34,969	13.675
38	1444	6.164	88	7744	9.381	138	19,044	11.747	188	35,344	13.711
39	1521	6.245	89	7921	9.434	139	19,321	11.790	189	35,721	13.748
40	1600	6.325	90	8100	9.487	140	19,600	11.832	190	36,100	13.784
41	1681	6.403	91	8281	9.539	141	19,881	11.874	191	36,481	13.820
42	1764	6.481	92	8464	9.592	142	20,164	11.916	192	36,864	13.856
43	1849	6.557	93	8649	9.644	143	20,449	11.958	193	37,249	13.892
44	1936	6.633	94	8836	9.695	144	20,736	12.000	194	37,636	13.928
45	2025	6.708	95	9025	9.747	145	21,025	12.042	195	38,025	13.964
46	2116	6.782	96	9216	9.798	146	21,316	12.083	196	38,416	14.000
47	2209	6.856	97	9409	9.849	147	21,609	12.124	197	38,809	14.036
48	2304	6.928	98	9604	9.899	148	21,904	12.166	198	39,204	14.071
49	2401	7.000	99	9801	9.950	149	22,201	12.207	199	39,601	14.107
50	2500	7.071	100	10,000	10.000	150	22,500	12.247	200	40,000	14.142

▪▪ Tangents, Sines, and Cosines

$m\angle A$ in degrees ▪	tan A ▪	sin A ▪	cos A ▪	$m\angle A$ in degrees ▪	tan A ▪	sin A ▪	cos A ▪
1	.0175	.0175	.9998	46	1.0355	.7193	.6947
2	.0349	.0349	.9994	47	1.0724	.7314	.6820
3	.0524	.0523	.9986	48	1.1106	.7431	.6691
4	.0699	.0698	.9976	49	1.1504	.7547	.6561
5	.0875	.0872	.9962	50	1.1918	.7660	.6428
6	.1051	.1045	.9945	51	1.2349	.7771	.6293
7	.1228	.1219	.9925	52	1.2799	.7880	.6157
8	.1405	.1392	.9903	53	1.3270	.7986	.6018
9	.1584	.1564	.9877	54	1.3764	.8090	.5878
10	.1763	.1736	.9848	55	1.4281	.8192	.5736
11	.1944	.1908	.9816	56	1.4826	.8290	.5592
12	.2126	.2079	.9781	57	1.5399	.8387	.5446
13	.2309	.2250	.9744	58	1.6003	.8480	.5299
14	.2493	.2419	.9703	59	1.6643	.8572	.5150
15	.2679	.2588	.9659	60	1.7321	.8660	.5000
16	.2867	.2756	.9613	61	1.8040	.8746	.4848
17	.3057	.2924	.9563	62	1.8807	.8829	.4695
18	.3249	.3090	.9511	63	1.9626	.8910	.4540
19	.3443	.3256	.9455	64	2.0503	.8988	.4384
20	.3640	.3420	.9397	65	2.1445	.9063	.4226
21	.3839	.3584	.9336	66	2.2460	.9135	.4067
22	.4040	.3746	.9272	67	2.3559	.9205	.3907
23	.4245	.3907	.9205	68	2.4751	.9272	.3746
24	.4452	.4067	.9135	69	2.6051	.9336	.3584
25	.4663	.4226	.9063	70	2.7475	.9397	.3420
26	.4877	.4384	.8988	71	2.9042	.9455	.3256
27	.5095	.4540	.8910	72	3.0777	.9511	.3090
28	.5317	.4695	.8829	73	3.2709	.9563	.2924
29	.5543	.4848	.8746	74	3.4874	.9613	.2756
30	.5774	.5000	.8660	75	3.7321	.9659	.2588
31	.6009	.5150	.8572	76	4.0108	.9703	.2419
32	.6249	.5299	.8480	77	4.3315	.9744	.2250
33	.6494	.5446	.8387	78	4.7046	.9781	.2079
34	.6745	.5592	.8290	79	5.1446	.9816	.1908
35	.7002	.5736	.8192	80	5.6713	.9848	.1736
36	.7265	.5878	.8090	81	6.3138	.9877	.1564
37	.7536	.6018	.7986	82	7.1154	.9903	.1392
38	.7813	.6157	.7880	83	8.1443	.9925	.1219
39	.8098	.6293	.7771	84	9.5144	.9945	.1045
40	.8391	.6428	.7660	85	11.4301	.9962	.0872
41	.8693	.6561	.7547	86	14.3007	.9976	.0698
42	.9004	.6691	.7431	87	19.0811	.9986	.0523
43	.9325	.6820	.7314	88	28.6363	.9994	.0349
44	.9657	.6947	.7193	89	57.2900	.9998	.0175
45	1.0000	.7071	.7071				

■■ Symbols and Abbreviations

▲

$\angle APB$	angle with vertex P (25)	$m\widehat{AB}$	measure of arc AB in degrees (401)
a	apothem (452)	$\widehat{AB}$	minor arc with endpoints A and B (400)
$\approx$	is approximately equal to (43)	(x, y)	ordered pair of numbers (41)
A	area (430)	$\parallel$	is parallel to (61)
B	area of base of a solid (480)	$\nparallel$	is not parallel to (152)
b	base of a polygon (430)	$\square$	parallelogram (239)
$\odot R$	circle with center R (375)	p	perimeter of a polygon (453)
C	circumference of a circle (457)	$\perp$	is perpendicular to (34)
$\cong$	is congruent to (191)	$\not\perp$	is not perpendicular to (152)
$\not\cong$	is not congruent to (191)	π	pi (458)
$\leftrightarrow$	corresponds to (191)	$\mathcal{R}$	plane named by letter $\mathcal{R}$ (6)
$\cos A$	cosine of angle A with measure of $\angle A$ given in degrees (357)	T	point named by letter T (5)
		$P_1P_2 \ldots P_n$	polygon with n vertices, P_1, $P_2, \ldots, P_n$ (452)
cm^3	cubic centimeter (486)		
PQ	distance between points P and Q; length of $\overline{PQ}$ (19)	$\overrightarrow{RT}$	ray with endpoint R that contains point T (14)
h	height; length of altitude (434)	$\overline{RT}$	segment with endpoints R and T (14)
$\Rightarrow$	implies (65)	$\sim$	is similar to (292)
L.A.	lateral area (478)	$\sin A$	sine of angle A with measure of $\angle A$ given in degrees (357)
d	length of diameter (376)		
r	length of radius (375)	m	slope of nonvertical line (60)
s	length of a side of a regular polygon (453); length of a side of a square (430); length of an arc of a circle (463); slant height of a solid (497)	cm^2	square centimeter (432)
		$\tan A$	tangent of angle A with measure of $\angle A$ given in degrees (357)
		T.A.	total area (478)
$\overleftrightarrow{AB}$	line containing points A and B (5)	$\triangle ABC$	triangle with vertices A, B, and C (166)
$\overset{\frown}{AQB}$	major arc of circle with endpoints A and B; point Q is on arc (400)	$\vec{v}$	vector v (582)
		V	volume (484)
$m\angle C$	measure of angle C in degrees (26)		

Postulates and Theorems

☐ **Chapter 1** *Introduction to Geometry*

Postulate 1 *Points Postulate*
A line contains at least two points. A plane contains at least three noncollinear points. Space contains at least four noncoplanar, noncollinear points. (10)

Postulate 2 *Line Postulate*
Two points are contained in one and only one line. (10)

Postulate 3 *Plane Postulate*
Three noncollinear points are contained in one and only one plane. (10)

Postulate 4 *Flat Plane Postulate*
If two points are contained in a plane, then the line through them is contained in the same plane. (11)

Postulate 5 *Plane Intersection Postulate*
If two planes intersect, then they intersect in a line. (11)

Postulate 6 *Ruler Postulate*
For every pair of points, there is a unique positive real number that gives the distance between the two points. (19)

Postulate 7 *Segment Construction Postulate*
On any ray, there is exactly one point at a given distance from the endpoint of the ray. (19)

Postulate 8 *Segment Addition Postulate*
If point P is between points A and B, then $AP + PB = AB$. (20)

Postulate 9 *Midpoint Postulate*
A segment has exactly one midpoint. (20)

Postulate 10 *Protractor Postulate*
For every angle there is a unique real number r, called its degree measure, such that $0 < r < 180$. (26)

Postulate 11 *Angle Construction Postulate*
Let $\mathcal{H}_1$ be a half-plane with edge $\overleftrightarrow{PA}$. There is exactly one ray PB with B in $\mathcal{H}_1$ such that $\angle APB$ has a given measure. (26)

Postulate 12 *Angle Addition Postulate*
If B is in the interior of $\angle APC$, then $m\angle APB + m\angle BPC = m\angle APC$. (26)

Postulate 13 *Angle Bisector Postulate*
An angle has exactly one bisector. (27)

Postulate 14 *Supplement Postulate*
The angles in a linear pair are supplementary. (33)

☐ **Chapter 3** *Proof in Geometry*

Theorem 3–1
If two lines intersect, then they intersect in one and only one point. (101)

Theorem 3–2
A line and a point not on the line are contained in one and only one plane. (101)

Theorem 3–3
Two intersecting lines lie in one and only one plane. (101)

Theorem 3–4
Supplements of equal angles are equal. (107)

Theorem 3–5
Supplements of the same angle are equal. (109)

Theorem 3–6
Complements of equal angles are equal. (110)

Theorem 3–7
Complements of the same angle are equal. (110)

Theorem 3–8
Vertical angles are equal. (116)

Theorem 3–9
If one angle of a linear pair is a right angle, then the other angle is also a right angle. (117)

Theorem 3–10
If the angles in a linear pair are equal, then the lines containing their sides are perpendicular. (123)

Theorem 3–11
Two perpendicular lines intersect to form four right angles. (126)

Theorem 3–12
All right angles are equal. (126)

☐ **Chapter 4**   *Parallel Lines and Planes*

Postulate 15 *Parallel Lines Postulate*
Two coplanar lines cut by a transversal are parallel if and only if a pair of corresponding angles are equal. (139)

Theorem 4–1
If a transversal is perpendicular to one of two parallel lines, then it is perpendicular to the other. (140)

Theorem 4–2
In a plane, if two lines are perpendicular to the same line, then they are parallel. (140)

Theorem 4–3
If two parallel lines are cut by a transversal, then alternate interior angles are equal. (2 Lines ∥ ⇒ alt. int. ∠s =.) (144)

Theorem 4–4
If two lines are cut by a transversal so that a pair of alternate interior angles are equal, then the lines are parallel. (Alt. int. ∠s = ⇒ lines ∥.) (144)

Theorem 4–5
If two parallel lines are cut by a transversal, then interior angles on the same side of the transversal are supplementary. (2 lines ∥ ⇒ int. ∠s on the same side supp.) (145)

Theorem 4–6
If two lines are cut by a transversal so that a pair of interior angles on the same side of the transversal are supplementary, then the lines are parallel. (Int. ∠s on the same side supp. ⇒ lines ∥.) (145)

Theorem 4–7
Through a point not on a given line, there is exactly one line parallel to the given line. (155)

Theorem 4–8
In a plane, if two lines are parallel to the same line, then they are parallel to each other. (156)

Theorem 4–9
In a plane, through a point on a given line, there is exactly one line perpendicular to the given line. (157)

Theorem 4–10
In a plane, a segment has exactly one perpendicular bisector. (157)

Theorem 4–11
Through a point not on a given line, there is exactly one line perpendicular to the given line. (157)

Theorem 4–12
If two planes are perpendicular to the same line, then the planes are parallel. (162)

Theorem 4–13
If two parallel planes are cut by a third plane, then the lines of intersection are parallel. (163)

Theorem 4–14
The sum of the measures of the angles of a triangle is 180. (170)

Theorem 4–15
If two angles of one triangle are equal to two angles of another triangle, then the remaining angles are equal. (170)

Theorem 4–16
The acute angles of a right triangle are complementary. (170)

Theorem 4–17
Each angle of an equiangular triangle has measure 60. (170)

Theorem 4–18
The measure of an exterior angle of a triangle is equal to the sum of the measures of its remote interior angles. (171)

Theorem 4–19
The measure of an exterior angle of a triangle is greater than the measure of either of its remote interior angles. (171)

Theorem 4–20
The sum of the measures of the angles of a convex polygon of n sides is $(n - 2)180$. (180)

Theorem 4–21
The sum of the measures of the exterior angles of a convex polygon, one angle at each vertex, is 360. (181)

☐ Chapter 5 *Congruent Triangles*

Theorem 5–1
Congruence of triangles is reflexive, symmetric, and transitive. (192)

Postulate 16 *SSS Congruence Postulate*
If three sides of one triangle are equal to the corresponding parts of another triangle, then the triangles are congruent. (195)

Postulate 17 *SAS Congruence Postulate*
If two sides and the included angle of one triangle are equal to the corresponding parts of another triangle, then the triangles are congruent. (196)

Postulate 18 *ASA Congruence Postulate*
If two angles and the included side of one triangle are equal to the corresponding parts of another triangle, then the triangles are congruent. (196)

Theorem 5–2 *AAS Congruence Theorem*
If two angles and the side opposite one of the angles in one triangle are equal to the corresponding parts of another triangle, then the triangles are congruent. (200)

Theorem 5–3 *Isosceles Triangle Theorem*
If two sides of a triangle are equal, then the angles opposite those sides are equal. (220)

Theorem 5–4
If two angles of a triangle are equal, then the sides opposite those angles are equal. (221)

Theorem 5–5
An equiangular triangle is also equilateral. (221)

Theorem 5–6
An equilateral triangle is also equiangular. (221)

Theorem 5–7 *HL Congruence Theorem*
If the hypotenuse and a leg of one right triangle are equal to the corresponding parts of another right triangle, then the triangles are congruent. (222)

Theorem 5–8
If the lengths of two sides of a triangle are unequal, then the measures of the angles opposite those sides are unequal in the same order. (225)

Theorem 5–9
If the measures of two angles of a triangle are unequal, then the lengths of the sides opposite those angles are unequal in the same order. (225)

Theorem 5–10 *Triangle Inequality Theorem*
The sum of the lengths of any two sides of a triangle is greater than the length of the third side. (226)

Theorem 5–11 *Hinge Theorem*
If two sides of one triangle are equal to two sides of another triangle and the included angles are unequal, then the lengths of the third sides are unequal in the same order. (226)

Theorem 5–12
If two sides of one triangle are equal to two sides of another triangle and the lengths of the third sides are unequal, then the measures of the angles included between the equal sides are unequal in the same order. (227)

Theorem 5–13
If $AB + BC = AC$, then points A, B, and C are collinear and B is between A and C. (230)

Theorem 5–14
The perpendicular segment from a point to a line is the shortest segment from the point to the line. (231)

Theorem 5–15
The perpendicular segment from a point to a plane is the shortest segment from the point to the plane. (231)

☐ Chapter 6 *Quadrilaterals*

Theorem 6–1
Both pairs of opposite sides of a parallelogram are equal. (239)

Theorem 6–2
Both pairs of opposite angles of a parallelogram are equal. (240)

Theorem 6–3
The diagonals of a parallelogram bisect each other. (240)

Theorem 6–4
The distance between two given parallel lines is constant. (241)

Theorem 6–5
If two sides of a quadrilateral are parallel and equal, then the quadrilateral is a parallelogram. (244)

Theorem 6–6
If both pairs of opposite sides of a quadrilateral are equal, then the quadrilateral is a parallelogram. (244)

Theorem 6–7
If the diagonals of a quadrilateral bisect each other, then the quadrilateral is a parallelogram. (245)

Theorem 6–8
A parallelogram is a rectangle if and only if its diagonals are equal. (249)

Theorem 6–9
A parallelogram is a rhombus if and only if its diagonals are perpendicular. (250)

Theorem 6–10
A parallelogram is a rhombus if and only if each diagonal bisects a pair of opposite angles of the parallelogram. (250)

Theorem 6–11
If a segment joins the midpoints of two sides of a triangle, then it is parallel to the third side, and its length is one half the length of the third side. (255)

Theorem 6–12
If three or more parallel lines cut off equal segments on one transversal, then they cut off equal segments on every transversal. (256)

Theorem 6–13
The median of a trapezoid is parallel to the bases and its length is one half the sum of the lengths of the bases. (261)

Theorem 6–14
Each pair of base angles of an isosceles trapezoid are equal. (262)

Theorem 6–15
The diagonals of an isosceles trapezoid are equal. (263)

Theorem 6–16
In a plane, the locus of points equidistant from two given points is the perpendicular bisector of the segment joining the two points. (273)

Theorem 6–17
The locus of points equidistant from two given points is the plane perpendicular to and bisecting the segment joining the given points. (274)

Theorem 6–18
In a plane, the locus of points equidistant from the sides of an angle is the bisecting ray of the angle, excluding its endpoint. (274)

Theorem 6–19
If a line is perpendicular to each of two intersecting lines at their point of intersection, then it is perpendicular to the plane containing the two lines. (275)

☐ Chapter 7 *Similarity*

Theorem 7–1
The perimeters of two similar polygons are proportional to the lengths of any pair of corresponding sides. (293)

Postulate 19 *AA Similarity Postulate*
If two angles of one triangle are equal to two angles of another triangle, then the triangles are similar. (297)

Theorem 7–2
Similarity of triangles is reflexive, symmetric, and transitive. (298)

Theorem 7–3
If a line parallel to one side of a triangle intersects the other two sides, then it divides them proportionally. (302)

Theorem 7–4
If three parallel lines intersect two transversals, then the parallel lines divide the transversals proportionally. (303)

Theorem 7–5 *SAS Similarity Theorem*
If an angle of one triangle is equal to an angle of a second triangle, and if the lengths of the sides including these angles are proportional, then the triangles are similar. (310)

Theorem 7-6 *SSS Similarity Theorem*
If the lengths of the sides of one triangle are proportional to the lengths of the sides of a second triangle, then the triangles are similar. (311)

Theorem 7-7
In similar triangles, the lengths of bisectors of corresponding angles are proportional to the lengths of corresponding sides. (316)

Theorem 7-8
In similar triangles, the lengths of altitudes from corresponding vertices are proportional to the lengths of corresponding sides. (316)

Theorem 7-9
In similar triangles, the lengths of medians from corresponding vertices are proportional to the lengths of corresponding sides. (316)

Theorem 7-10
The bisector of an angle of a triangle divides the opposite side into two segments whose lengths are proportional to the lengths of the two sides adjacent to the segments. (317)

☐ **Chapter 8** *Right Triangles*

Theorem 8-1
If an altitude is drawn to the hypotenuse of a right triangle, then the new triangles formed are similar to the given triangle and to each other. (331)

Theorem 8-2
The length of the altitude to the hypotenuse of a right triangle is the geometric mean of the lengths of the segments into which the altitude separates the hypotenuse. (332)

Theorem 8-3
If the altitude to the hypotenuse is drawn in a right triangle, then the length of either leg is the geometric mean of the lengths of the hypotenuse and the segment on the hypotenuse which is adjacent to that leg. (332)

Theorem 8-4 *Pythagorean Theorem*
In a right triangle, the square of the length of the hypotenuse is equal to the sum of the squares of the lengths of the legs. (338)

Theorem 8-5
If the sum of the squares of the lengths of two sides of a triangle is equal to the square of the length of the third side, then the triangle is a right triangle. (339)

Theorem 8-6
In a 30-60-90 triangle, the length of the hypotenuse is twice the length of the shorter leg, and the length of the longer leg is $\sqrt{3}$ times the length of the shorter leg. (346)

Theorem 8-7
The length of an altitude of an equilateral triangle with sides of length s is $\frac{1}{2}s\sqrt{3}$. (347)

Theorem 8-8
In a 45-45-90 triangle, the length of the hypotenuse is $\sqrt{2}$ times the length of a leg. (347)

Theorem 8-9
In a right $\triangle ABC$ with right $\angle C$, $(\sin A)^2 + (\cos A)^2 = 1$. (359)

☐ **Chapter 9** *Circles*

Theorem 9-1
A line that lies in the plane of a circle and contains an interior point of the circle is a secant. (377)

Theorem 9-2
In a plane, a line is tangent to a circle if and only if it is perpendicular to a radius drawn to the point of tangency. (381)

Theorem 9-3
Segments drawn tangent to a circle from an exterior point are equal. (381)

Theorem 9-4
If a line through the center of a circle is perpendicular to a chord, then it bisects the chord. (387)

Theorem 9-5
In the same circle or in congruent circles, two chords have the same length if and only if they are the same distance from the center(s) of the circle(s). (388)

Theorem 9–6
The perpendicular bisectors of the sides of a triangle are concurrent in a point equidistant from the vertices of the triangle. (392)

Theorem 9–7
A circle can be circumscribed about any triangle. (393)

Theorem 9–8
The angle bisectors of a triangle are concurrent in a point equidistant from the sides of the triangle. (393)

Theorem 9–9
A circle can be inscribed in any triangle. (394)

Postulate 20 *Arc Addition Postulate*
If P is on AB, then $m\overset{\frown}{AP} + m\overset{\frown}{PB} = m\overset{\frown}{APB}$. (401)

Theorem 9–10
In the same circle or in congruent circles, two minor arcs have equal measures if and only if their chords have the same length. (401)

Theorem 9–11
The measure of an inscribed angle is one half the measure of its intercepted arc. (407)

Theorem 9–12
If two inscribed angles intercept the same arc or arcs of equal measure, then the angles are equal. (408)

Theorem 9–13
If an angle is inscribed in a semicircle, then it is a right angle. (408)

Theorem 9–14
If a quadrilateral is inscribed in a semicircle, then the opposite angles are supplementary. (408)

Theorem 9–15
The measure of an angle formed by a tangent and a secant that intersect at the point of tangency is one half the measure of the intercepted arc. (408)

Theorem 9–16
The measure of an angle formed by two secants that intersect in the interior of a circle is one half the sum of the measures of the arcs intercepted by the angle and its vertical angle. (414)

Theorem 9–17
The measure of an angle formed by two secants, a secant and tangent, or two tangents that intersect in the exterior of a circle is one half the difference of the measures of the intercepted arcs. (415)

Theorem 9–18
If two chords intersect in a circle, then the product of the lengths of the segments on one chord is equal to the product of the lengths of the segments on the other. (416)

□ **Chapter 10**   *Areas of Polygons and Circles*

Postulate 21 *Area Postulate*
To every polygonal region there corresponds a unique positive number called the area of the region. (429)

Postulate 22 *Area Postulate for Congruent Triangles*
If two triangles are congruent, then the triangles have equal areas. (430)

Postulate 23 *Area Postulate for Rectangles*
The area A of a rectangle is equal to the product of the length b of a base and the corresponding height h. $A = bh$ (430)

Theorem 10–1 *Area of a Square*
The area A of a square is equal to the square of the length s of a side. $A = s^2$ (430)

Postulate 24 *Area Addition Postulate*
The area of the union of two or more nonoverlapping polygonal regions is the sum of the areas of the regions. (431)

Theorem 10–2 *Area of a Parallelogram*
The area A of a parallelogram is equal to the product of the length b of a base and the corresponding height h. $A = bh$ (434)

Theorem 10–3 *Area of a Triangle*
The area A of a triangle is equal to one half the product of the length b of any side and the corresponding height h. $A = \frac{1}{2}bh$ (435)

Theorem 10–4 *Area of an Equilateral Triangle*
The area A of an equilateral triangle with side lengths s is equal to $\frac{s^2}{4}\sqrt{3}$. $A = \frac{s^2}{4}\sqrt{3}$ (436)

Theorem 10–5 *Area of a Trapezoid*
The area A of a trapezoid is equal to one half the product of the height h and the sum of the lengths b_1 and b_2 of the bases. $A = \frac{1}{2}h(b_1 + b_2)$ (441)

Theorem 10–6 *Area of a Rhombus*
The area A of a rhombus is equal to one half the product of the lengths d_1 and d_2 of its diagonals. $A = \frac{1}{2}d_1d_2$ (442)

Theorem 10–7 *Areas of Similar Triangles*
If two triangles are similar, then the ratio of their areas is equal to the square of the ratio of the lengths of any two corresponding sides. (447)

Theorem 10–8 *Areas of Similar Polygons*
If two polygons are similar, then the ratio of their areas is equal to the square of the ratio of the lengths of any two corresponding sides. (448)

Theorem 10–9
A circle can be circumscribed about any regular polygon. (452)

Theorem 10–10
A circle can be inscribed in any regular polygon. (453)

Theorem 10–11 *Area of a Regular Polygon*
The area A of a regular polygon is equal to one half the product of the apothem a and the perimeter p. $A = \frac{1}{2}ap$ (453)

Theorem 10–12
The ratio of the circumference to the diameter of a circle is the same for all circles. (458)

Theorem 10–13 *Circumference of a Circle*
The circumference C of a circle is equal to the product of π and the diameter d. $C = \pi d = 2\pi r$. (458)

Theorem 10–14 *Area of a Circle*
The area A of a circle is equal to the product of π and the square of the radius r of the circle. $A = \pi r^2$ (458)

Theorem 10–15
In a circle of radius r, the ratio of the length s of an arc to the circumference C of the circle is the same as the ratio of the arc measure m to 360. $\frac{s}{C} = \frac{m}{360}$, or $s = \frac{m}{360}(2\pi r)$ (463)

Theorem 10–16 *Area of a Sector of a Circle*
In a circle of radius r, the ratio of the area A_s of a sector to the area A_c of the circle is the same as the ratio of the arc measure m to 360. $\frac{A_s}{A_c} = \frac{m}{360}$, or $A_s = \frac{m}{360}(\pi r^2)$ (464)

☐ Chapter 11 *Solids*

Theorem 11–1.
The lateral edges of a prism are equal and parallel. (473)

Theorem 11–2
The bases of a prism have equal areas. (473)

Theorem 11–3
The length d of a diagonal of a rectangular solid with length ℓ, width w, and height h is $\sqrt{\ell^2 + w^2 + h^2}$. $d = \sqrt{\ell^2 + w^2 + h^2}$ (475)

Theorem 11–4 *Lateral Area of a Prism*
The lateral area L.A. of a prism is the product of the length ℓ of a lateral edge and the perimeter p of a right section of the prism. L.A. $= \ell p$ (479)

Theorem 11–5 *Lateral Area of a Right Prism*
The lateral area of a right prism is the product of the length of a lateral edge h and the perimeter p of the base. L.A. $= hp$ (479)

Postulate 25 *Volume Postulate*
To every solid polyhedron there corresponds a unique positive real number called the volume of the polyhedron. (484)

Postulate 26 *Volume of a Rectangular Solid*
The volume V of a rectangular solid is the product of its base B and height h. $V = Bh$ (484)

Postulate 27 *Cavalieri's Principle*
Given a plane and two solids, if every plane parallel to this plane that intersects one of the solids also intersects the other so that each pair of cross sections formed have the same area, then the solids have the same volume. (485)

Theorem 11–6
All cross sections of a prism have equal areas. (485)

Theorem 11–7 *Volume of a Prism*
The volume V of a prism is the product of the area B of a base and the height h. $V = Bh$ (486)

Theorem 11–8 *Lateral Area of a Right Cylinder*
The lateral area L.A. of a right cylinder is the product of the circumference C of a base and the height h. L.A. $= Ch = 2\pi rh$ (491)

Theorem 11–9 *Volume of a Cylinder*
The volume V of a cylinder is the product of the area B of a base and the height h. $V = Bh = \pi r^2 h$ (492)

Theorem 11–10
The lateral faces of a regular pyramid are congruent isosceles triangles. (498)

Theorem 11–11 *Lateral Area of a Regular Pyramid*
The lateral area L.A. of a regular pyramid is one half the product of the slant height s and the perimeter p of the base. L.A. $= \frac{1}{2}sp$. (498)

Theorem 11–12 *Volume of a Pyramid*
The volume V of a pyramid is one third the product of the area B of the base and the height h. $V = \frac{1}{3}Bh$ (499)

Theorem 11–13 *Lateral Area of a Right Cone*
The lateral area L.A. of a right cone is one half the product of the circumference C of its base and its slant height s. L.A. $= \frac{1}{2}Cs = \pi rs$ (503)

Theorem 11–14 *Volume of a Cone*
The volume V of a cone is one third the product of the area B of its base and its height h.
$V = \frac{1}{3}Bh = \frac{1}{3}\pi r^2 h$ (503)

Theorem 11–15 *Volume of a Sphere*
The volume V of a sphere of radius r is $\frac{4}{3}\pi r^3$
$V = \frac{4}{3}\pi r^3$ (506)

Theorem 11–16 *Area of a Sphere*
The area A of a sphere of radius r is $4\pi r^2$
$A = 4\pi r^2$ (506)

□ **Chapter 12** *Transformations*

Theorem 12–1
A line reflection is an isometry. (516)

Theorem 12–2
A point reflection is an isometry. (516)

Theorem 12–3
An isometry preserves collinearity and betweenness of points. (519)

Theorem 12–4
If an isometry maps A onto A' and B onto B', then the image of $\overleftrightarrow{AB}$ is $\overleftrightarrow{A'B'}$, the image of $\overrightarrow{AB}$ is $\overrightarrow{A'B'}$, and the image of $\overline{AB}$ is $\overline{A'B'}$. (520)

Theorem 12–5
An isometry preserves angle measure. (520)

Theorem 12–6
Under an isometry, a triangle and its image are congruent. (520)

Theorem 12–7
A translation is an isometry. (528)

Theorem 12–8
A rotation is an isometry. (531)

Theorem 12–9
In a plane, if $\triangle ABC \cong \triangle A'B'C'$, then there is a unique isometry that maps $\triangle ABC$ onto $\triangle A'B'C'$. (539)

Theorem 12–10
Every isometry can be expressed as a composite of at most three line reflections. (540)

Theorem 12–11
If a dilation with center C and scale factor k maps A onto A' and B onto B', then $A'B' = k(AB)$. (544)

Theorem 12–12
A dilation preserves collinearity and betweenness of points. (546)

Theorem 12–13
If a dilation maps A onto A' and B onto B', then the image of $\overleftrightarrow{AB}$ is $\overleftrightarrow{A'B'}$, the image of $\overrightarrow{AB}$ is $\overrightarrow{A'B'}$, and the image of $\overline{AB}$ is $\overline{A'B'}$. (546)

Theorem 12–14
A dilation preserves angle measure. (547)

Theorem 12–15
Under a dilation, a triangle and its image are similar. (547)

Theorem 12–16
In a plane, if $\triangle ABC \sim \triangle A'B'C'$, then there is a unique similarity transformation that maps $\triangle ABC$ onto $\triangle A'B'C'$. (551)

☐ **Chapter 13** *Coordinates and Vectors*

Theorem 13–1 *The Distance Formula*
If the coordinates of points P and Q are (x_1, y_1) and (x_2, y_2), respectively, then the distance between them is given by the formula: $PQ = \sqrt{(x_2 - x_1)^2 + (y_2 - y_1)^2}$. (562)

Theorem 13–2 *The Midpoint Formula*
If the coordinates of points P and Q are (x_1, y_1) and (x_2, y_2), respectively, then the midpoint M of $\overline{PQ}$ has coordinates $\left(\frac{x_1 + x_2}{2}, \frac{y_1 + y_2}{2}\right)$. (563)

Theorem 13–3
The graph of the equation $y - y_1 = m(x - x_1)$ is the nonvertical line ℓ that has slope m and contains $P(x_1, y_1)$. (568)

Theorem 13–4
The graph of the equation $y = mx + b$ is the nonvertical line with slope m and y-intercept b. (568)

Theorem 13–5
The graph of an equation in x and y is a line if and only if the equation is a linear equation. (569)

Theorem 13–6
Two nonvertical lines are parallel if and only if they have equal slopes. (570)

Theorem 13–7
Two nonvertical lines are perpendicular if and only if the slope m_1 of one line is the negative reciprocal of the slope m_2 of the other line. $m_1 = -\frac{1}{m_2}$, or $m_1 m_2 = -1$ (570)

Theorem 13–8
The equation of a circle with center (h, k) and radius r is $(x - h)^2 + (y - k)^2 = r^2$. (571)

Glossary

Acute angle An angle whose measure is less than 90. (32)

Acute triangle A triangle with three acute angles. (166)

Adjacent angles Two coplanar angles with a common side and no common interior points. (33)

Affirming the hypothesis Establishing that the hypothesis is true in a particular case. (71)

Alternate interior angles In the diagram, transversal *t* cuts lines *ℓ* and *m*. ∠3 and ∠5, ∠4 and ∠6 are pairs of alternate interior angles. (61)

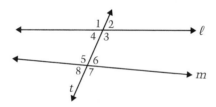

Altitude of a cone The segment from the vertex perpendicular to the plane of the base. (502)

Altitude of a cylinder See *altitude of a prism*. (490)

Altitude of a parallelogram A segment perpendicular to the base with endpoints on the base and the opposite side (or on the lines containing them). (434)

Altitude of a prism A segment from a point in one base perpendicular to the plane of the other base. The length of the altitude is the *height* of the prism. (474)

Altitude of a pyramid The segment from the vertex perpendicular to the plane of the base. (497)

Altitude of a rectangle A segment perpendicular to a base with its endpoints on that base and the side opposite. (430)

Altitude of a trapezoid A segment from any point in one base perpendicular to the line containing the other base. (441)

Altitude of a triangle The segment from any vertex of the triangle perpendicular to the line containing the opposite side. (217)

Angle The union of two noncollinear rays which have the same endpoint. The rays are called the *sides* of the angle and their common endpoint is the *vertex*. (25)

Angle bisector of a triangle The segment from any vertex of the triangle to the opposite side on the ray bisecting the angle. (217)

Angle inscribed in a circle An angle whose vertex is on the circle and whose sides contain chords of the circle. (406)

Apothem of a regular polygon The distance from the center to each side. (452)

Area of a circle The limit of the areas of its inscribed regular polygons. (457)

Area of a polygonal region A unique positive number which corresponds to the polygonal region. (429)

Argument The logical reasoning that leads to a conclusion. (71)

Auxiliary line A line introduced to aid in the proof of a theorem. (155)

Axis of a cone The segment from the vertex to the center of the base of the cone. (502)

Axis of a cylinder The segment joining the centers of its bases. (490)

Base angle of an isosceles triangle See *isosceles triangle*. (167)

Base of a cone See *cone*. (502)

Base of a cylinder See *cylinder*. (490)

Base of an isosceles triangle See *isosceles triangle*. (167)

Base of a parallelogram Any side of the parallelogram. (434)

Base of a prism A face in one of the parallel planes. (473)

Base of a pyramid See *pyramid*. (497)

Base of a rectangle Any side of the rectangle. (430)

Base of a trapezoid One of the parallel sides of the trapezoid. (261)

Bisector of an angle Ray $\overrightarrow{PB}$ is the bisector of $\angle APC$ if and only if B is in the interior of $\angle APC$ and $m\angle APB = m\angle BPC$. (27)

Bisector of a segment A set of points whose intersection with the segment is the midpoint of the segment. (20)

■

Center of a circle See *circle*. (21)

Center of a dilation See *dilation*. (543)

Center of a regular polygon The center of its circumscribed circle. (452)

Center of a rotation See *rotation*. (531)

Central angle of a circle An angle in the plane of the circle whose vertex is the center of the circle. (400)

Central angle of a regular polygon An angle formed by two radii drawn to the endpoints of one side. (452)

Centroid of a triangle Point of concurrency of the medians of the triangle. (394)

Chord A segment whose endpoints lie on a circle. (376)

Circle The set of coplanar points at a given distance from a given point in the plane. The given point is called the *center*. (375)

Circumference of a circle The limit of the perimeters of the inscribed regular polygons. (457)

Circumcenter of a triangle The point of concurrency of the perpendicular bisectors of the sides of the triangle. (393)

Circumscribed circle A circle is circumscribed about a polygon which the vertices of the polygon lie on the circle. The polygon is *inscribed in the circle*. (392)

Collinear points Points that are contained in one line. (5)

Common external tangent A common tangent that does not intersect the segment joining the centers of the circles. (382)

Common internal tangent A common tangent that intersects the segment joining the centers of the circles. (382)

Common tangent A line that is tangent to each of two coplanar circles. (382)

Complementary angles Two angles whose measures have a sum of 90. (32)

Component When two vectors $\vec{A}$ and $\vec{B}$ are added to get $\vec{A} + \vec{B}$, each of the vectors $\vec{A}$ and $\vec{B}$ is a component of the vector $\vec{A} + \vec{B}$. (586)

Composite of two transformations Let F and G be transformations. The composite of F and G is the transformation which maps each point P onto a point P' as follows: First, P is mapped onto P_1 under F. Then P_1 is mapped onto P' under G. (527)

Concentric circles Coplanar circles with the same center. (402)

Conclusion The "then" clause of a conditional statement. (65)

Concurrent lines Two or more lines that intersect in a single point. The point is the *point of concurrency*. (392)

Conditional statement A statement of the form "If p, then q." (65)

Cone A figure formed by a circular region, a point V not in the plane of the circle, and all segments joining a point of the circle to V. The circular region is the *base* of the cone. The point V is the *vertex*. (502)

Congruent circles Circles with equal radii. (387)

Congruent figures Two plane figures are congruent if and only if there is an isometry that maps one figure onto the other. (191, 540)

Congruent triangles Two triangles in which there is a correspondence between the vertices such that each side and each angle is equal to its corresponding side or angle. (191)

Conjecture A statement that seems to be true. (60)

Consecutive angles of a polygon Two angles such that the same side of the polygon is contained in a side of each angle. (175)

Consecutive sides of a polygon Two sides with a common endpoint. (175)

Contrapositive A statement formed from the original statement by negating the hypothesis and the conclusion and then interchanging them. (85)

Converse A statement formed by interchanging the hypothesis and the conclusion of the original statement. (83)

Convex polygon A polygon such that each line that contains a side of the polygon contains no points in the interior of the polygon. (175)

Coordinate plane The set of all ordered pairs (x, y) of real numbers. The coordinate plane contains two perpendicular number lines, the *x-axis* and the *y-axis*, that intersect at the origin. (41)

Coplanar points (lines) Points (lines) that are contained in one plane. (6)

Corresponding angles In the diagram, transversal t cuts lines ℓ and m. ∠1 and ∠5, ∠2 and ∠6, ∠3 and ∠7, ∠4 and ∠8 are pairs of corresponding angles. (61)

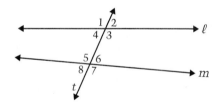

Cosine ratio In right △ABC with acute ∠A:
$$\cos A = \frac{\text{length of side adjacent } \angle A}{\text{length of hypotenuse}} \quad (357)$$

Counterexample A statement or diagram that shows that a given statement is not always true. (21)

Cross section of a prism A section parallel to the bases of the prism. (478)

Cube A prism in which all faces are squares. (474)

Cylinder A figure formed by two congruent circular regions contained in parallel planes along with all segments having an endpoint on each circle and parallel to the line joining the centers of the circles. The parallel circular regions are the *bases* of the cylinder. (490)

■

Deductive reasoning The use of logical principles to draw conclusions. (77)

Degree measure of a major arc 360 minus the measure of the corresponding minor arc. (401)

Degree measure of a minor arc The measure of its central angle. (401)

Degree measure of an angle The unique real number r that corresponds to the angle such that $0 < r < 180$. (26)

Degree measure of a semicircle The degree measure of a semicircle is 180. (401)

Diagonal of a polygon A segment joining two nonconsecutive vertices of the polygon. (176)

Diagonal of a rectangular solid See *rectangular solid*. (474)

Diameter of a circle A segment that contains the center and has its endpoints on the circle. Also the length of this segment. (376)

Diameter of a sphere A segment that contains the center and has its endpoints on the sphere. (377)

Dihedral angle The union of two noncoplanar half-planes with a common edge, together with the common edge. (39)

Dilation Let C be a point and k a positive real number. A dilation is a transformation that maps each point of the plane onto an image point as follows: C is its own image. For any point P other than C, the image of P is the point P′ on $\overrightarrow{CP}$ for which CP′ = k(CP). C is the *center* and k is the *scale factor* of the dilation. (543)

Direction angle When a vector P is in standard position, the angle that the vector makes with the nonnegative portion of the x-axis is called the direction angle. (583)

Distance between two parallel lines The length of a segment drawn from any point on one line perpendicular to the other line. (241)

Distance between two points A unique positive real number that corresponds to the pair of points. (19)

Distance from a point to a line (plane) not containing the point The length of the perpendicular segment from the point to the line (plane). (231)

◼

Edge of a polyhedron See *polyhedron*. (473)

Enlargement A dilation in which the scale factor is greater than 1. (544)

Equal angles Angles that have the same measure. (27)

Equal segments Segments that have the same length. (20)

Equiangular polygon A polygon in which all the angles are equal. (176)

Equiangular triangle A triangle with three equal angles. (167)

Equilateral polygon A polygon in which all the sides are equal. (176)

Equilateral triangle A triangle with three equal sides. (167)

Exterior angle of a triangle An angle which forms a linear pair with one of the angles of the triangle. (171)

Exterior angles In the diagram, transversal *t* cuts lines ℓ and *m*. $\angle 1$, $\angle 2$, $\angle 7$, and $\angle 8$ are exterior angles. (61)

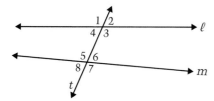

Exterior of a circle The set of points in the plane whose distance from the center is greater than the radius. (376)

Exterior of an angle The set of points in the plane which do not belong to the interior of the angle or to the angle itself. (25)

Exterior of a polygon The set of points in the plane which do not belong to the polygon or its interior. (175)

Externally tangent circles Two tangent circles such that the segment joining the centers of the circles intersects the tangent line. (383)

◼

Face of a polyhedron See *polyhedron*. (473)

◼

Geometric mean The positive number *x* such that $\frac{a}{x} = \frac{x}{b}$ where *a* and *b* are two positive real numbers. (332)

Great circle of a sphere The intersection of a sphere and a plane containing the center of the sphere. (378)

◼

Half-turn See *reflection through point O*. (516)

Height of a cone The length of its altitude. (502)

Height of a parallelogram for a given base The length of an altitude. (434)

Height of a prism The length of its altitude. (474)

Height of a pyramid The length of its altitude. (497)

Height of a rectangle for a given base The length of an altitude. (430)

Height of a trapezoid The length of its altitude. (441)

Height of a triangle The length of its altitude. (435)

Hypotenuse The side opposite the right angle in a right triangle. (166)

Hypothesis The "if" clause of a conditional statement. (65)

◼

Identity transformation The transformation that maps each point of the plane onto itself. (517)

Image If *A* is mapped onto *A'*, *A'* is called the image of *A*. *A* is the *preimage* of *A'*. (515)

Incenter of a triangle The point of concurrency of the angle bisectors of the triangle. The inscribed circle is the *incircle*. (394)

Incircle of a triangle See *incenter of a triangle*. (394)

Included angle An included angle for two sides of a triangle is an angle whose rays contain the two sides of the triangle. (192)

Included side An included side for two angles of a triangle is a side whose endpoints are the vertices of the angles. (192)

Indirect reasoning The process of forming a conclusion by assuming the alternative and proving it to be false by contradiction of a known fact. (149)

Inductive reasoning The process of forming a conclusion based upon examination of several specific cases. (53)

Inscribed angle An angle whose vertex is on a circle and whose sides contain chords of the circle. (406)

Inscribed circle A circle is inscribed in a polygon when the sides of the polygon are tangent to the circle. The polygon is *circumscribed about the circle.* (392)

Intercepted arc An arc whose endpoints lie on different sides of an angle and whose other points lie in the interior of the angle. (400)

Interior angles In the diagram, transversal t cuts lines ℓ and m. $\angle 3$, $\angle 4$, $\angle 5$, and $\angle 6$ are interior angles. (61)

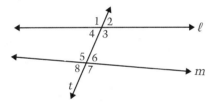

Interior angles on the same side of the transversal In the diagram above, $\angle 4$ and $\angle 5$, $\angle 3$ and $\angle 6$ are pairs of interior angles on the same side of the transversal. (61)

Interior of a circle The set of points in a plane whose distance from the center is less than the radius. (376)

Interior of an angle The interior of $\angle APB$ is the intersection of two half-planes: the side of $\overleftrightarrow{PA}$ containing B and the side of $\overleftrightarrow{PB}$ containing A. (25)

Interior of a polygon The intersection of the interiors of its angles. (175)

Internally tangent circles Two tangent circles such that the segment joining the centers of the circles does not intersect the tangent line. (383)

Intersection of two sets The set of elements that the two sets have in common. (6)

Inverse A statement formed from the original statement by negating both the hypothesis and the conclusion. (85)

Isometry A transformation that preserves distance. (515)

Isosceles trapezoid A trapezoid whose legs are equal. (262)

Isosceles triangle A triangle with at least two equal sides. In an isosceles triangle, the equal sides are the *legs;* the third side is the *base.* The angle opposite the base is the *vertex angle.* The angles opposite the equal sides are the *base angles.* (167)

■

Kite A quadrilateral such that exactly one diagonal is the perpendicular bisector of the other. (442)

■

Lateral area of a prism The sum of the areas of its lateral faces. (478)

Lateral edge of a prism The intersection of two lateral faces of the prism. (473)

Lateral face of a prism A face of the prism other than a base. (473)

Lateral surface of a cone The points of a cone not in the base. (502)

Leg of an isosceles triangle See *isosceles triangle.* (166)

Leg of a right triangle One of the sides that is not the hypotenuse of the right triangle. (166)

Leg of a trapezoid One of the nonparallel sides of the trapezoid. (261)

Length of an arc In a circle of radius r, the ratio of the length s of an arc to the circumference C of the circle is the same as the ratio of the arc measure m to 360. (463)

Length (linear measure) of a segment The distance between its endpoints. (19)

Line of symmetry See *line symmetry.* (535)

Line parallel to a plane A line and a plane are parallel if and only if they do not intersect. (162)

Line perpendicular to a plane A line and a plane that intersect are perpendicular if and only if every line in the given plane which passes through the point of intersection is perpendicular to the given line. (162)

Line symmetry A plane figure has line symmetry if and only if there is a line ℓ such that the figure coincides with its reflection image over ℓ. Line ℓ is a *line of symmetry* or a *symmetry line* for the figure (535)

Linear equation An equation that can be written in the form $Ax + By = C$, with A and B not both zero and A, B, and C real numbers. (569)

Linear pair of angles A pair of adjacent angles whose noncommon sides are opposite rays. (33)

Locus The set of all points, and only those points, that satisfy a given condition. (268)

■

Magnitude of a rotation If a rotation with center P maps A onto A', then the measure of $\angle APA'$ is the magnitude of the rotation. (532)

Magnitude of a translation The constant distance AA' is the magnitude of the translation. (528)

Magnitude of a vector The length of the vector. (582)

Major arc of a circle The set of points on the circle that lie on a central angle or in the exterior of the central angle. (400)

Mapping See *transformation*. (515)

Median of a trapezoid The segment joining the midpoints of the legs of the trapezoid. (261)

Median of a triangle The segment from any vertex of the triangle to the midpoint of the opposite side. (217)

Midpoint of a segment A point S is the midpoint of segment $\overline{RT}$ if and only if R, S, and T are collinear and $RS = ST$. (20)

Minor arc of a circle The set of points on the circle that lie on a central angle or in the interior of the central angle. (400)

■

Negation The negation of a statement p is "not p." (84)

Noncollinear points Points that are not contained in one line. (5)

Noncoplanar points (lines) Points (lines) that are not contained in the same plane. (6)

■

Oblique cone A cone in which the axis is not perpendicular to the base. (502)

Oblique cylinder A cylinder in which the axis is not perpendicular to the planes of the bases. (490)

Oblique prism A prism in which the lateral edges are not perpendicular to the planes of the bases. (474)

Obtuse angle An angle whose measure is greater than 90. (32)

Obtuse triangle A triangle with an obtuse angle. (166)

Opposite rays Rays $\overrightarrow{AB}$ and $\overrightarrow{AC}$ are opposite rays if points A, B, and C are collinear and A is between B and C. (14)

Opposite vector For every vector $\vec{v}$, there is a vector $-\vec{v}$, called the opposite of $\vec{v}$, that has the same magnitude as $\vec{v}$ but the opposite direction. (582)

Opposite vertices of a rectangular solid See *rectangular solid*. (474)

Orthocenter of a triangle Point of concurrency of the lines containing the altitudes of the triangle. (394)

■

Parallel lines Lines which are coplanar and do not intersect. (61)

Parallel planes Planes that do not intersect. (162)

Parallelepiped A prism in which all faces are parallelograms. (474)

Parallelogram A quadrilateral in which both pairs of opposite sides are parallel. (239)

Perimeter of a polygon The sum of the lengths of its sides. (176)

Perpendicular bisector of a segment A line which is perpendicular to the segment and contains its midpoint. (34)

Perpendicular lines Lines that intersect to form a right angle. (34)

Pi (π) The ratio of the circumference of a circle to the diameter. (458)

Platonic solids Five regular polyhedrons which Plato described fully in his writings: tetrahedron, hexahedron, octahedron, dodecahedron, and icosahedron. (483)

Point reflection See *reflection through point O*. (515)

Point symmetry A plane figure has point symmetry if and only if there is a point P such that the figure and its image coincide under a reflection through P. (536)

Point of tangency See *tangent to a circle*. (377)

Polygon The union of three or more coplanar segments such that each segment intersects exactly two other segments, one at each endpoint, and no two intersecting segments are collinear. (175)

Polygonal region A plane figure formed by the union of a finite number of coplanar, nonoverlapping triangular regions. (429)

Polyhedron A figure formed by four or more noncoplanar polygonal regions which enclose a part of space. The enclosed space is the *interior* of the polyhedron. A *solid polyhedron* is the union of a polyhedron and its interior. Each polygon is a *face* of the polyhedron. The intersection of two faces is an *edge* of the polyhedron. The intersection of three or more edges is a *vertex* of the polyhedron. (473)

Postulate A statement that is assumed to be true. (10)

Preimage See *image*. (515)

Prism A polyhedron with two congruent polygonal faces contained in parallel planes. These faces are called the *bases* of the prism. The other faces are called *lateral faces*. (473)

Proof A deductive argument in which each step follows from the previous ones by affirming the hypothesis. (95)

Proportion An equation which states that two or more ratios are equal. (287)

Pyramid A polyhedron formed by a polygonal region in a plane R, a point P not in plane R, and the triangular regions formed by joining the vertices of the polygonal region with P. The polygonal region is the *base* of the pyramid. (497)

Quadrant The x- and y- axes separate the points of the coordinate plane not on the axes into four regions called quadrants. (46)

Quadrilateral A polygon with four sides. (176)

Radius of a circle A segment determined by the center and a point on the circle. Also the length of this segment. (375)

Radius of a regular polygon A segment from the center to a vertex. (452)

Radius of a sphere A segment determined by the center and a point on the sphere. (377)

Ratio A number which represents the comparison or relationship of two numbers. (287)

Ray A ray $\overrightarrow{RT}$ is the set of points containing $\overline{RT}$ and all points S such that T lies between R and S. (14)

Rectangle A parallelogram with four right angles. (249)

Rectangular solid A right rectangular prism. Vertices which are not on the same face are *opposite vertices*. The line segment which joins two opposite vertices is a *diagonal*. (474)

Reduction A translation in which the scale factor is less than 1. (544)

Reflection over line ℓ A transformation that maps each point P of the plane onto a point P' as follows: If P is not on ℓ, then ℓ is the perpendicular bisector of PP'. If P is on ℓ, then P' coincides with P. ℓ is the *line of reflection*. P' is the *reflection image* of P. (515)

Reflection through point O A transformation that maps each point P of the plane onto a point P' as follows: If P does not coincide with O, then O is the midpoint of PP'. If P coincides with O, then $P' = P$. A point reflection is also called a *half-turn*. (516)

Regular polygon A convex polygon which is both equiangular and equilateral. (176)

Regular polyhedron A polyhedron whose faces are congruent regular polygons that form equal dihedral angles along its edges. (483)

Regular prism A right prism whose bases are regular polygons. (474)

Regular pyramid A pyramid which has a regular polygon for a base, and whose altitude passes through the center of the base. (497)

Remote interior angles of a triangle The two angles of a triangle which are not adjacent to a given exterior angle. (171)

Resultant The sum of two vectors $\vec{u}$ and $\vec{v}$ is a vector, $\vec{u} + \vec{v}$, called the resultant of $\vec{u}$ and $\vec{v}$. (586)

Rhombus A parallelogram with four equal sides. (249)

Right angle An angle whose measure is 90. (32)

Right cone A cone in which the axis is perpendicular to the base. (502)

Right cylinder A cylinder in which the axis is perpendicular to the planes of the bases. (490)

Right prism A prism in which the lateral edges are perpendicular to the planes of the bases. (474)

Right section of a prism A section perpendicular to the lateral edges of the prism. (478)

Right triangle A triangle with a right angle. The side opposite the right angle is the *hypotenuse*. The other two sides are the *legs*. (166)

Rotation A composite of two reflections over two intersecting lines. The point of intersection of the two lines is the *center of the rotation*. (531)

Rotational symmetry A plane figure has rotational symmetry if and only if there is a rotation such that the figure and its image coincide under the rotation. (536)

■

Scalar See *scalar multiple of a vector*. (593)

Scalar multiple of a vector If k is a real number and $\vec{v}$ is a vector, then $k\vec{v}$ is a vector that has magnitude equal to $|k| \, |\vec{v}|$ and has the same direction as $\vec{v}$ if k is positive or the opposite direction of $\vec{v}$ if k is negative. If $k = 0$, then $k\vec{v}$ is the *zero vector*. The number k is a *scalar*. The vector $k\vec{v}$ is a scalar multiple of $\vec{v}$, or *scalar product* of k and $\vec{v}$. (593)

Scale factor See *dilation*. (543)

Scalene triangle A triangle with no two sides equal. (167)

Secant A line that intersects a circle in two points. (377)

Section of a prism The polygonal region formed when a plane intersects all of the lateral faces of a prism. (478)

Sector of a circle A region bounded by two radii and either the major arc or the minor arc that is intercepted. (463)

Segment A segment $\overline{RT}$ is the set of points containing R, T, and all the points between R and T. (14)

Segment of a circle A region bounded by a chord and either the major arc or the minor arc that is intercepted. (464)

Semicircle The set of points which includes the endpoints of a diameter and the points of the circle in a given half-plane formed by the line containing the diameter. (400)

Sides of an angle See *angle*. (25)

Similar convex polygons Convex polygons for which there is a correspondence between their vertices such that the corresponding angles are equal and the lengths of corresponding sides are proportional. (292)

Similarity Two plane figures are similar if and only if there is a similarity transformation that maps one figure onto the other. (292, 551)

Similarity transformation A composite of a dilation and an isometry. (550)

Sine ratio In right $\triangle ABC$ with acute $\angle A$:
$$\sin A = \frac{\text{length of side opposite } \angle A}{\text{length of hypotenuse}} \quad (357)$$

Skew lines Two lines that are not coplanar. (66)

Slant height of a regular pyramid The length of the altitude of any lateral face from the vertex of the pyramid. (497)

Slant height of a right cone The length of a segment from the vertex to a point of the circle. (502)

Slope of a line The slope, m, of a nonvertical line that contains two points $P(x_1, y_1)$ and $Q(x_2, y_2)$ is:
$$m = \frac{y_2 - y_1}{x_2 - x_1}. \quad (60, 567)$$

Small circle of a sphere The intersection of a sphere and a plane containing an interior point of the sphere, but not containing the center. (378)

Solid polyhedron The union of a polyhedron and its interior. (473)

Space The set of all points. (5)

Sphere The set of all points in space that are a given distance from a given point. The given point is the *center* of the sphere. (377)

Square A rectangle with four equal sides. (249)

Standard position of a vector If a vector is placed so that its initial point coincides with the origin in a coordinate plane, the vector is in standard position. (583)

Statement A sentence that is either true or false but not both. (65)

Straightedge An unmarked ruler. (24)

Supplementary angles Two angles whose measures have a sum of 180. (32)

Symmetry line See *line symmetry*. (535)

Synthetic proof A method of proof in which conclusions are drawn based on the combination of definitions, postulates, and theorems. (601)

Tangent circles Two coplanar circles that are tangent to the same line at the same point. (383)

Tangent ratio In right $\triangle ABC$ with acute $\angle A$:

$$\tan A = \frac{\text{length of side opposite } \angle A}{\text{length of side adjacent to } \angle A} \quad (357)$$

Tangent ray A ray which is a subset of a tangent line and which contains the point of tangency. (377)

Tangent segment A segment which is a subset of a tangent line and which contains the point of tangency. (377)

Tangent to a circle A line in the plane of the circle that intersects the circle in exactly one point. The point of the intersection is called the *point of tangency*. (377)

Tessellation An arrangement of polygonal shapes that completely covers a plane surface without overlapping and without leaving gaps. (184)

Theorem A statement that is proved. (95)

Total area of a prism The sum of its lateral area and the areas of its two bases. (478)

Transformation of a plane A one-to-one correspondence between the points of the plane and themselves. Also called a *mapping*. (515)

Translation A composite of two reflections over two parallel lines. (527)

Transversal A line which intersects two coplanar lines in two distinct points. (61)

Trapezoid A quadrilateral with exactly one pair of opposite sides parallel. (261)

Triangle The union of three segments determined by three noncollinear points. (166)

Triangular region The union of a triangle and its interior. (429)

Unequal in the same order For real numbers a, b, c, and d: a and b are unequal in the same order as c and d if (1) $a > b$ and $c > d$, or (2) $a < b$ and $c < d$. (225)

Vector A directed line segment. (582)

Vertex angle of an isosceles triangle See *isosceles triangle*. (167)

Vertex of an angle The common endpoint of the rays which are its sides. (25)

Vertex of a polyhedron See *polyhedron*. (473)

Vertical angles Two angles whose sides form two pairs of opposite rays. (34)

Volume of a solid polyhedron A unique positive real number which corresponds to the solid polyhedron. (484)

x-axis See *coordinate plane*. (41)

x-intercept The x-coordinate of the point of intersection of a line and the x-axis. (42)

y-axis See *coordinate plane*. (41)

y-intercept The y-coordinate of the point of intersection of a line and the y-axis. (42)

Zero vector See *scalar multiple of a vector*. (593)

Answers to Selected Exercises

Chapter 1

Pages 2–4

Written Exercises **1.** c; octagon **3.** a; triangle
5. Yes; measure them. **7.** Provides more spaces
17. 30 **18.** 13 **19.** 288 **20.** 4 **21.** Earth
measure **22.** logical reasoning

Pages 7–9

Written Exercises **1.** A, G, B, or F, G, D
3. G **5.** Sample: A, G, B, F **7.** B **9.** Plane
11. Point **13.** Line
15. **19.**

23. 0, 1, 3, 4, 5, or 6 **25a.** 15 **b.** 21 **c.** 28
d. 66 **27.** $x + n - 1$ **31.** Samples: Ring, plate,
wheel **32.** Samples: Flag, door, stamp

Pages 11–13

Written Exercises **1.** line **3.** plane **5.** $\overrightarrow{PQ}$
7. Plane Post. **9.** Plane Intersection Post.
11. always **13.** sometimes **15.** Line Post.
17. Plane Post. **19.** Points Post. **21.** They are
the same line. **23.** Planes $\mathcal{E}$ and $\mathcal{H}$ intersect in
line ℓ. **28.** Point, line, plane **31.** Lines
contained in one plane
Algebra Review **1.** $x = 7$ **3.** $x = 0.5$
5. $x = 14$ **7.** $x = 45$ **9.** $x = 2$

Pages 16–18

Written Exercises **1.** Sample: $\overline{AC}$ and $\overline{DE}$
3. $\overline{BC}$ and $\overline{BD}$ **5.** $\overline{CE}$ **7.** $\overline{DE}$ and $\overline{DC}$ (or $\overline{DB}$ or
$\overline{DA}$) **9.** $\overrightarrow{CA}$ **11.** $\mathcal{H}_1$ and $\mathcal{H}_2$ **13.** $\overleftrightarrow{BC}$
19.  **21.**

23. Ray **25.** Line **27.** Same **29.** 6; 20; 30
31. d **33.** 28 segments **35.** 378 lines
36. Postulates **37.** 1 **38.** $\overrightarrow{XY}, \overrightarrow{YX}, m$
39. noncoplanar **40.** Appearance of figures can
be misleading.

Pages 21–23

Written Exercises **1.** 6 **3.** 12 **5.** 9 **7.** Starting
at one end of the pipe, measure the length
desired. There is only one place on the pipe the
given distance from the end. **9a.** 35 yd. **b.** Seg.
Add. Post. **11.** Ruler Post. **13.** Midpt. Post.
19. 6 **21.** Seg. Construction Post. **23.** Any pt.
on $\overline{X_1X_2}$ **25.** Any pt. on $\overline{X_2X_3}$ **28.** Segment
29. 1 **30.** Sample: floor tile

Pages 27–30

Written Exercises **1.** $\angle DEG, \angle GED$ **3.** $\angle 1$,
$\angle 2, \angle 3, \angle DEH, \angle GEF$ **5.** D or F **7.** No; rays
are collinear. **9.** $m\angle 1 = m\angle 2$ **11.** APC
13. BPC **15.** 28 **17.** $2x$ **19.** 150; Angle Add.
Post.
21. **25.**

27. 60; 30 **31.** In Post. 10, change "degree" to
"mil" and "$0 < r < 180$" to "$0 < r < 3,200$".
Post. 11-13 remain the same. **33.** 1,600; 2,400
37. 190 **38.** bisector **40.** No; different
endpoints **41.** Sometimes **42.** Always

Pages 35–37

Written Exercises **1.** $\angle ABC, \angle BAD$ **3.** Any 10
of these 11 $\angle$s: $\angle ADP, \angle PDC, \angle DCP, \angle PCB$,
$\angle CBP, \angle PBA, \angle BAP, \angle PAD, \angle DPC, \angle BPA$,
$\angle DCB$ **9.** 85 **11.** 52 **13.** $90 - x$ **15.** 149
17. 105 **19.** $180 - 2x$ **21.** Not adjacent; no
common side **23.** Not adjacent; no common
side **25.** 140 **27.** 90 **29.** Right **31.** Right; $\angle 1$
and $\angle 2$ form a lin. pr. so they are supp. $\angle$s.
33. 4 **35.** Acute or complementary **37.** $m\angle A =$
72; $m\angle B = 18$ **39.** 140 **41.** $\angle 1$ is a rt. $\angle$.
$m\angle 1 + m\angle 2 = 180$. Since $m\angle 2 = 90$,
$m\angle 1 = 90$. **43.** 65 **45.** No; rays must be
noncollinear. **46.** 2 **47.** No; only if D, X, and E
are collinear. **48.** Neither **49.** a line

Pages 45–46

Written Exercises **1.** (2, 1) **3.** (2, 0) **5.** M
7. Q **9.** $y = 2$ **11.** $x = -4$ for $-2 \le y \le 2$

13. $y = \frac{1}{2}x$ **15.** 4.1 **17.** 2.2 **19.** $(0.5, -1.5)$
21. $(1, 0.5)$ **23.** Line **25.** Line **27.** Point
29. $y = -\frac{1}{3}x + 1$ and $0 \leq x \leq 3$ **31.** $(y = x + 1$
and $x \geq 0)$ or $(y = -\frac{1}{3}x + 1$ and $x \geq 0)$
33. $y > x + 1$ **35.** $(-3, 0)$ **37.** $(8, 7)$ **39.** III
41. IV **43.** $y > 0$ **45.** $\frac{0 - b}{m}$ **51.** 46

Chapter 1 Review, Pages 49–50
1. Samples: Box, book **2.** Samples: Doorstop,
ramp **5.** $T, A, R,$ or S, U, R **6.** Sample: S, U, R, Q
7. Sample: T, A, S **8.** False; only if noncollinear
9. True; by Flat Plane Post. **10.** False; a line
11. D, E **12.** $\overrightarrow{PS}, \overrightarrow{PT}$ **13.** 2 **14.** 11 **15.** 22
17. $\angle RYS, \angle RYT, \angle RYV, \angle SYT, \angle SYV, \angle TYV$
18. T **19.** V **20.** 117 **21.** 45 **22.** $\angle DEB$
23. $\angle DEA, \angle ABE,$ OR $\angle ECD$ **24.** Samples: $\angle A,$
$\angle D, \angle CED$ **25.** Sample: $\angle BEC, \angle CED$
26. Sample: $\angle ABE, \angle CBE$ **27.** Sample: $\angle AEB,$
$\angle BED; \angle AEC, \angle CED$ **28.** $\angle ABE, \angle EBC; \angle BCE,$
$\angle ECD$ **29.** 45 **30.** 90 **31.** 2 **32.** 12.1
33. $(1.5, -3.5)$ **34.** $y = x$

Chapter 2

Pages 55–57
Written Exercises **1.** Sample: Upon entering a
street which experience has shown to be heavily
used by children on bicycles, a driver will
decrease the speed of his car. **5.** The $\perp$
bisectors intersect in a single pt. **7.** 1, 2, 8, 16
9. 3, 7, 12, 9; 3, 5, 8, 8; 5, 2
13. To determine the number of times the ball
will hit the sides of a 4-by-n table, find the
reduced form of the ratio $4:n$. If $a:b$ is the
reduced form, the ball will hit the sides
$(a + b - 2)$ times. **18.** 10 **19.** $(2, 4)$ **20.** $x = 7;$
$m\angle Q = 47; m\angle R = 43$ **21.** Collinear pts. are
pts. contained in one line. **22.** 26
Algebra Review **1.** $y = -2x + 3$ **3.** $y = x - 7$
5. $y = \frac{3}{5}x + 2$

Pages 63–64
Written Exercises **1.** It is the $\perp$ bisector of
$\overline{AB}$. **3.** By measuring the two segs. into which
this pt. divides $\overline{ST}$. **5.** corr. $\angle$s **7.** corr. $\angle$s
9. not $=$ **11.** Sample: $\overrightarrow{SR} \perp \overrightarrow{RU}; \overrightarrow{SX} \perp \overrightarrow{ST};$
$\overrightarrow{TW} \perp \overrightarrow{TU}$ **15.** 0; $(0, b)$ **17.** Some **19.** If two $\parallel$
lines are cut by a transversal, then the alt. int.
$\angle$s formed are $=$. **21.** (1) Measure $\angle$s. (2) Use
tracing paper. **22.** The process of forming a

conclusion based upon examination of several
specific cases **23.** To develop laws of motion
based upon conclusions from several pendulum
experiments **24.** $y = -1$

Pages 67–69
Written Exercises **1.–7.** Hypothesis underlined
once; conclusion underlined twice **1.** If a
student passes the exam, then he will graduate.
3. If 2 line segs. intersect, then they lie in a
plane. **5.** If a figure is a $\triangle$, then it has 3 sides.
7. If $\angle$s are adj. $\angle$s, then they have a common
side. **11.** If a figure is a square, then it is a
4-sided figure. **13.** If one is a resident of Texas,
then one is a resident of the United States.
25. If 3 pts. are noncollinear, then they are
contained in 1 and only 1 plane. **27.** If 2 $\angle$s
form a lin. pr., then they are supp. $\angle$s.
32. They are $=$; they are $=$. **33.** The sum of the
lengths of two sides of a triangle is greater than
the length of the third side. **34.** If a patient
exhibits several symptoms of an illness, then the
doctor might draw a conclusion based upon the
specific symptoms in forming a diagnosis of the
patient's condition. **35.** C **36.** 90
Algebra Review **1.** $2c$ **3.** $14m^2n^5$ **5.** a^4b^3
7. $-12x^6y^2z^6$

Pages 73–75
Written Exercises
3. Yes; $m\angle 1 + m\angle 2 = 90$ **5.** Yes; $(8)(2) =$
$(3 + 5)(2)$ **7.** No **9.** No conclusion **11.** No
conclusion **13.** $\angle 1$ is supp. to $\angle 2$. **15.** No
conclusion **17.** $x - 5 = 32$ **19.** $\overrightarrow{AB}$ and $\overrightarrow{AC}$ are
noncollinear rays. **21.** If B is in the interior of
$\angle APC$, then $m\angle APB + m\angle BPC = m\angle APC$.
22. If a figure is an $\angle$, then it is a plane figure.
24. A line which intersects 2 coplanar lines in 2
distinct pts. **25.** If 2 pts. are contained in a
plane, then the line through them is contained
in the same plane. **26.** 13

Pages 79–82
Written Exercises **1.** Repair or replace the
clock. **3.** If $\overrightarrow{AB}$ bisects $\overline{CD}$ at pt. M, then $CD =$
MD. **5.** If it rains, then I will be grounded.
7. If a student is 16 years old before September
1, then he or she will have extra money.
9. 1. $\angle Q$ and $\angle R$ are rt. $\angle$s; 90; 90 2. Protractor
3. Add. **11.** Since we are using real numbers, it
follows from the Reflexive Prop. that $2 = 2$.
Since $-3x + 2 > 14$ and $2 = 2$, it follows from

the Subtraction Prop. that $-3x + 2 - 2 > 14 - 2$, or $-3x > 12$. Since we are using real numbers, it follows that $-3 = -3$. Since $-3x > 12$ and $-3 = -3$, it follows from the Div. Prop. that $\frac{-3x}{3} < \frac{12}{-3}$, or $x < -4$. **13.** Since $QM = RM$, and assuming Q, R, and M are collinear and distinct, it follows from the def. of the midpt. of a seg. that M is the midpt. of $\overline{QR}$. Assuming H is not on $\overleftrightarrow{QR}$, and M is the intersection of $\overrightarrow{HM}$ and $\overleftrightarrow{QR}$, it follows from the def. of a seg. bisector that line $\overleftrightarrow{HM}$ bisects $\overline{QR}$. **15.** (i) If the storm ends, then Mr. Hogan will get home by 4:00 P.M. (h) If Mr. Hogan gets home by 4:00 P.M., then he and Mrs. Hogan will attend a school meeting tonight. (d) If Mr. and Mrs. Hogan have to attend a meeting tonight, then they will take a taxi. **16.** $0 < x < 180$ **17.** Def. of comp. ∠s **20.** $y = 45$; 45 and 135

Pages 86–88
Written Exercises **1.** Sometimes **3.** Always **5.** Always **7.** Converse: If I swim in salt water, then I swim in the Atlantic. (false) Inverse: If I do not swim in the Atlantic, then I do not swim in salt water. (false) Contrapositive: If I do not swim in salt water, then I do not swim in the Atlantic. (true) **9.** Converse: If 2 ∠s do not have a common side, then they are not adj. ∠s. (true) Inverse: If 2 ∠s are adj. ∠s, then they have a common side. (true) Contrapositive: If 2 ∠s have a common side, then they are adj. ∠s. (true) **15.** Converse: $r \Rightarrow not\ p$ Inverse: $p \Rightarrow not\ r$ **17.** If 2 ∠s are supp. ∠s, then the sum of their measures is 180. If the sum of the measures of 2 ∠s is 180, then the ∠s are supp. ∠s. **19.** An ∠ is a rt. ∠ if and only if its measure is 90. **21.** 2 ∠s are comp. ∠s if and only if the sum of their measures is 90. **23.** If $p \Rightarrow q$ and $q \Rightarrow r$, then $p \Rightarrow r$. **24.** If $a = b$, then a may replace b in any equation or inequality. **25.** q is true. **26.** ∠GHE **27.** ∠EHD

Chapter 2 Review, Pages 91–92
1. 14, 30 **2.** $n^2 + (n - 1)^2 + \ldots + 1^2$; inductive **3.** The seg. joining the midpt. of two sides of a triangle is ‖ to and half as long as the third side.

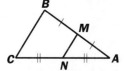

4. skew **5.** ∠4 and ∠6; ∠3 and ∠5 **6.** ∠1 and ∠5; ∠2 and ∠6; ∠4 and ∠8; ∠3 and ∠7 **7.–9.** Hypothesis underlined once; conclusion underlined twice **7.** If 3AB = 90, then AB = 30. **8.** If your dog eats Barko, he'll stay happy and healthy. **9.** Two angles are equal if they are vertical angles. **10.** If a student is in senior mathematics, then he is also in physics. **11.** If 2 ∠s form a linear pair, then they are supp. ∠s. **12.** If 2 circles intersect, then they intersect in at most 2 pts. **13.** If it rains, then the principal is in a bad mood. **14.** $m∠1 + m∠2 > 180$ **15.** ∠X and ∠Y are rt. ∠s. **16.** No conclusion **17.** $r \parallel s$ **18.** No conclusion **19.** Seg. Add. Post. **20.** Symmetric Prop. **21.** Division Prop. **22.** Subtraction Prop. **23.** If the noncommon sides of two adj. ∠s are ⊥, then the sum of the measures of the ∠s is 90. **24.** Converse: If $\overleftrightarrow{KB}$ bisects $\overline{JH}$, then $JK = KH$. Inverse: If $JK \neq KH$, then $\overleftrightarrow{KB}$ does not bisect $\overline{JH}$. Contrapositive: If $\overleftrightarrow{KB}$ does not bisect $\overline{JH}$, then $JK \neq KH$. **25.** Converse: If it is not summer, then it snows. Inverse: If it does not snow, then it is summer. Contrapositive: If it is summer, then it does not snow. **26.** Converse: If $m∠1 = m∠2$, then ∠1 and ∠2 are complements of the same ∠. Inverse: If ∠1 and ∠2 are not complements of the same ∠, then $m∠1 \neq m∠2$. Contrapositive: If $m∠1 \neq m∠2$, then ∠1 and ∠2 are not complements of the same ∠. **27.** If an ∠ is acute, then its measure is less than 90. If the measure of an ∠ is less than 90, then the ∠ is acute.

Chapter 3

Pages 98–99
Written Exercises **1.** 1. Given; 2. Given; 4. Substitution Prop. [1, 3] **3.** 1. ∠A is a rt. ∠; 2. Given; 3. $m∠A = 90$; 4. Substitution Prop.; 5. ∠B is a rt. ∠; Def. of rt. ∠ [4] **5.** 1. By hypothesis, R is between P and O; 2. $p \Rightarrow q$: If point P is between pts. A and B, then $AP + PB = AB$ (Seg. Add. Post.). p: R is between P and O. q: $PR + RO = PO$; 3. $q \Rightarrow r$. For all real numbers a, $a = a$ (Reflexive Prop.). q: RO is a real number. r: $RO = RO$; 4. $r \Rightarrow s$: For all real numbers a, b, c, and d, if $a = b$ and $c = d$, then $a - c = b - d$ (Subtraction Prop.). r: $PR + RO = PO$ and $RO = RO$ s: $PR = PO - RO$

7. *Proof:* 1. ∠*A* is a rt ∠. (Given) 2. *m*∠*A* = 90 (Def. of rt. ∠ [1]) 3. ∠*B* is obtuse. (Given) 4. *m*∠*B* > 90 (Def. of obtuse ∠ [3]) 5. *m*∠*B* > *m*∠*A* (Substitution Prop. [2, 4]) **8.** If it is November, then it is Thanksgiving Day. False **9.** If it is not November, then it is not Thanksgiving Day. True. **10.** For all real numbers *a*, *a* = *a*. **11.** $\overrightarrow{YW}$; $\overrightarrow{YZ}$ **12.** *U*

Pages 104–106
Written Exercises 1. c
5. Samples:

(*m*∠*ABG* = 120) or

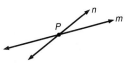

9. Thm. 3-3 **11.** Thm. 3-1
19. *Given:* Lines *m* and *n* intersect at *P. Prove:* *m* and *n* are contained in one and only one plane.
21. True **23.** True **25.** True
28. Diagram; Given; Prove; Proof **29.** Given
30. $\overrightarrow{PB}$ is the bisector of ∠*APC* if and only if *B* is in the interior of ∠*APC* and *m*∠*APB* = *m*∠*BPC*. **31.** The set of all points **32.** 40
Algebra Review 1. *d* = 595 mi. **3.** *F* = 95°

Pages 110–114
Written Exercises 1. *C* is the midpt. of $\overline{AB}$.
3. ∠1 and ∠2 are supp. **5.** $\overrightarrow{BD}$ bisects ∠*ABC*.
7. Yes; the conclusion from this reason is that 2 ∠s are =. **9.** No; the conclusion from this reason is that 2 ∠s are supp. **11.** e, a, b, d, c
13. Statements: a, d, b, e, c; Reasons: i or j, f [1], g [2], i or j, h [3, 4] **19.** Definitions; postulates, properties of real numbers, theorems, and Given
20. The process of forming a conclusion based upon examination of several specific cases
21. If you are 15 years old, you are a teenager.
Algebra Review 1. *m* = 2; *n* = 2 **3.** *x* = 4; *y* = 3 **5.** $a = \frac{19}{5}$; $b = \frac{24}{5}$ **7.** *r* = −3; *s* = 2

Pages 118–120
Written Exercises 1. 70 **3.** 110 **5.** 105 **7.** *k* ⊥ *ℓ* **9.** Decreased by 10 **11.** 78; 78 **13.** 140; 40
15. Samples: *m*∠*FOD* = 90; *m*∠*DOP* = *m*∠*POF*; *m*∠*DOP* = 45; *m*∠*POF* = 45 **17.** Samples: *m*∠*DOF* > 90; *m*∠*DOP* = *m*∠*POF*; *m*∠*DOP* + *m*∠*POF* = *m*∠*DOF*; *m*∠*DOP* + *m*∠*POF* > 90
19. Samples: ∠*WOX* is a rt. ∠; *m*∠*WOX* = 90;

m∠*ZOY* = *m*∠*WOX*; *m*∠*ZOY* = 90 **21.** a, c, b or c, a, b **23.** Sample: *Plan for Proof:* Show that *m*∠1 + *m*∠2 = 90 by using the def. of rt. ∠s, the Angle Add. Post. and Substitution Prop. Then use the def. of complementary ∠s.
25. Sample: *Plan for Proof:* Use def. of rt. ∠, Angle Add. Post., and Substitution Prop. to show *m*∠1 + *m*∠2 = 90 and *m*∠3 + *m*∠4 = 90. Use def. of comp. ∠s and Thm. 3-6 to show *m*∠1 = *m*∠3. **27.** x = 94, y = 8; *m*∠1 = 118; *m*∠2 = 62; *m*∠3 = 118 **29.** x = 5; y = −6; *m*∠1 = 47; *m*∠2 = 133; *m*∠3 = 47 **31.** *Proof:* 1. ∠1 is a rt. ∠; ∠1 and ∠2 are lin. pr. (Given) 2. ∠1 and ∠2 are supp. (Supp. Post. [1]) 3. *m*∠1 + *m*∠2 = 180 (Def. of supp. ∠s [2]) 4. *m*∠1 = 90 (Def. of rt. ∠ [1]) 5. *m*∠2 = 90 (Subtraction Prop. [3, 4]) 6. ∠2 is a rt. ∠. (Def. of rt. ∠ [5])
33. Yes **34.** No **35.** ∠*UVT* and ∠*SVW* are vert. ∠s; *T*, *V*, and *S* are collinear; *V* is between *T* and *S*.

Pages 124–125
Written Exercises 1. ∠3 is a rt. ∠; ∠4 is a rt. ∠. **3.** ∠*EBA* is a rt. ∠; *m*∠*DEB* = *m*∠*EBF*; *m*∠*EBA* = 90; *m*∠*DBE* + *m*∠*EBF* = *m*∠*DBF*
5. *m*∠3 = 90 and *m*∠4 = 90; ∠3 and ∠4 are rt. ∠s. **7.** *m*∠*ABE* = *m*∠*CBE* and *m*∠*DBE* = *m*∠*FBE* **9.** *Plan for Proof:* Since ∠*GPK* is a rt. ∠, ∠3 is a rt. ∠ by Thm. 3-9. Since ∠3 is a rt. ∠, ∠4 is a rt. ∠ by Thm. 3-9. Since ∠3 and ∠4 are rt. ∠s, their measures are 90. Then by the Substitution Prop., *m*∠3 = *m*∠4. **11.** *Plan for Proof:* Use the def. of an ∠ bisector to show that *m*∠*DBE* = *m*∠*EBF*. From the diagram ∠*EBC* and ∠*EBA* form a lin. pr. Use Thm. 3-9 to show that ∠*EBA* is a rt. ∠. Then use the def. of a rt. ∠ and the Substitution Prop. to show that *m*∠*EBC* = *m*∠*EBA*. Use the Subtraction Prop. to show that *m*∠*EBC* − *m*∠*EBF* = *m*∠*EBA* − *m*∠*DBE*. By the ∠ Add. Post. *m*∠*ABD* + *m*∠*DBE* = *m*∠*EBA* and *m*∠*EBF* + *m*∠*CBF* = *m*∠*EBC*. Then by the Subtraction Prop. *m*∠*ABD* = *m*∠*EBA* − *m*∠*DBE* and *m*∠*CBF* = *m*∠*EBC* − *m*∠*EBF*. Then use the Substitution Prop. to show that *m*∠*ABD* = *m*∠*CBF*. **13.** *Proof:* 1. ∠1 = ∠4 (Given) 2. ∠1 = ∠2 (Vertical ∠s are =.) 3. ∠2 = ∠4 (Substitution Prop. [1, 2]) 4. *m*∠4 = *m*∠5 (Vertical ∠s are =.) 5. *m*∠2 = *m*∠5 (Transitive Prop. [3, 4]) **15.** *Given:* Line *ℓ* and point *P* not on line *ℓ. Prove:* *ℓ* and *P* lie in a plane. *Proof:* 1. *P* is not on line *ℓ.* (Given) 2. Let *A* and *B* be

any two pts. on ℓ. (A line contains at least 2 pts.) **3.** ℓ is the only line that contains both A and B. (2 pts. are contained in exactly one line.) **4.** A, B, and P are noncollinear. (Def. of noncollinear) **5.** A, B, and P are contained in exactly one plane, say $\mathcal{K}$ (3 noncoll. pts. determine a plane). **6.** ℓ is contained in $\mathcal{K}$ (Flat Plane Post.) **7.** P and ℓ are contained in one and only one plane $\mathcal{K}$, (Steps 5 and 6) **16.** 72; 108

Pages 128–129

Written Exercises   1. If 2 $\angle$s are = and supp., then they are both rt. $\angle$s.   **3.** If an $\angle$ is obtuse, then its measure is greater than the measure of any acute $\angle$.   **5.** If $\angle A$ is acute, then the measure of the complement of $\angle A$ is less than the measure of the supplement of $\angle A$.

7.

9.
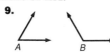

Given: $m\angle 1 = m\angle 2$; $\angle 1$ and $\angle 2$ are supp. *Prove:* $\angle 1$ and $\angle 2$ are rt. $\angle$s.

Given: $\angle A$ is acute; $\angle B$ is obtuse. *Prove:* $m\angle B > m\angle A$

13. *Plan for Proof:* Use the def. of supp. $\angle$s to show that $m\angle 1 + m\angle 2 = 180$. Then use the Substitution Prop. to show that $2(m\angle 1) = 180$ and $2(m\angle 2) = 180$. Then use the Div. Prop. to show that $m\angle 1 = 90$ and $m\angle 2 = 90$. By the def. of a rt. $\angle$, $\angle 1$ and $\angle 2$ are rt. $\angle$s.   **15.** *Plan for Proof:* Use the def. of an acute $\angle$ to show that $m\angle A < 90$. Then use the def. of an obtuse $\angle$ to show that $m\angle B > 90$. Then use the Transitive Prop. to state that $m\angle B > m\angle A$.   **19.** *Proof:* 1. $\angle 1$ and $\angle 2$ are supp. (Given) 2. $m\angle 1 + m\angle 2 = 180$ (Def. of supp. $\angle$s [1]) 3. $m\angle 1 = m\angle 2$ (Given) 4. $m\angle 1 + m\angle 1 = 180$ or $2(m\angle 1) = 180$; $m\angle 2 + m\angle 2 = 180$ or $2(m\angle 2) = 180$ (Substitution Prop. [2, 3]) 5. 2 = 2 (Reflexive Prop.) 6. $m\angle 1 = 90$; $m\angle 2 = 90$ (Div. Prop. [4, 5]) 7. $\angle 1$ and $\angle 2$ are rt. $\angle$s. (Def. of rt. $\angle$ [6]) **21.** *Proof:* 1. $\angle B$ is obtuse. (Given) 2. $m\angle B > 90$ (Def. of obtuse $\angle$ [1]) 3. $\angle A$ is acute. (Given) 4. $m\angle A < 90$ or $90 > m\angle A$ (Def. of acute $\angle$ [3]) 5. $m\angle B > m\angle A$ (Transitive Prop. [2, 4]) **25.** *Given:* $m\angle 1 = m\angle 5$ *Prove:* $m\angle 2 = m\angle 6$; $m\angle 3 = m\angle 7$; $m\angle 4 = m\angle 8$

Proof: 1. $m\angle 1 = m\angle 5$ (Given) 2. $\angle 1$ and $\angle 2$ are supp.; $\angle 5$ and $\angle 6$ are supp. (Supp. Post.) 3. $m\angle 2 = m\angle 6$ (Supp. of = $\angle$s are =. [1, 2]) 4. $m\angle 1 = m\angle 4$; $m\angle 2 = m\angle 3$; $m\angle 5 = m\angle 8$; $m\angle 6 = m\angle 7$ (Vert. $\angle$s are =.) 5. $m\angle 3 = m\angle 7$; $m\angle 4 = m\angle 8$ (Substitution Prop. [1, 3, 4]) **29.** *Given:* Line ℓ and pt. P not on ℓ *Prove:* ℓ and P lie in a plane.

Proof: 1. Line ℓ and pt. P not on ℓ (Given) 2. ℓ contains at least 2 pts. A and B (Pts. Post.) 3. P, A, and B are noncollinear (Def. noncollinear pts.) 4. P, A, and B lie in a plane (3 noncollinear pts. lie in 1 and only 1 plane) 5. ℓ and P lie in a plane (Flat Plane Post.) **31.** B is the midpt. of $\overline{JK}$; $JB = BK$ **32.** *Proof:* 1. $\overrightarrow{XZ}$ bisects $\angle WXU$ (Given) 2. $m\angle 1 = m\angle 2$ (Def. $\angle$ bisector [1]) 3. $\overrightarrow{XT}$ bisects $\angle VXY$ (Given) 4. $m\angle 3 = m\angle 4$ (Def. $\angle$ bisector [3]) 5. $m\angle 1 = m\angle 3$ (Given) 6. $m\angle 2 = m\angle 4$ (Substitution Prop. [2, 4, 5])

Chapter 3 Review, Pages 133–134

1. 1. $m\angle 1 + m\angle 2 + m\angle 3 = 180$; 2. Supplement Post.; 3. Def. of supp. $\angle$s [2]; 4. Substitution Prop. [1, 3]; 5. $m\angle 3 = m\angle 3$; 6. $m\angle 1 + m\angle 2 = m\angle 4$
6. b, f, e, a, d, c or b, f, e, d, a, c **7.** Def. of $\perp$ lines; Thms. 3-10, 3-11 **8.** Def. of lin. pr. of $\angle$s; Supplement Post.; Thms. 3-9, 3-10 **9.** Sample: $m\angle 3 = m\angle 4$; M is the midpt. of $\overline{GN}$, $GM = NI$
10. Sample: $GM = MN$, $MN = NI$, $GM = NI$
11. $\angle 1$ is a rt. $\angle$; $m\angle 1 = m\angle 2$ **12.** $m\angle 1 = 90$; $\angle 2$ is a rt. $\angle 2$ **13.** *Plan for Proof:* Since $\angle ABC$ is a rt. $\angle$, $\angle 1$ and $\angle 2$ are complementary. By the def. of comp. $\angle$s, $m\angle 1 + m\angle 2 = 90$. Use Thm. 3-8 to show that $m\angle 1 = m\angle 3$. Then use the Substitution Prop. to state $m\angle 3 + m\angle 2 = 90$. By the def. of comp. $\angle$s, $\angle 3$ and $\angle 2$ are comp.   **14.** $m\angle 2 = m\angle 3$; $m\angle 2 = m\angle 5$ **15.** $m\angle 2 = m\angle 5$; $m\angle 1 = m\angle 6$ **16.** $m\angle 2 = m\angle 5$; $m\angle 1 = m\angle 4$ **17.** $m\angle 2 + m\angle 6 = 180$; $m\angle 1 = m\angle 5$
18. A is the midpt. of $\overline{SQ}$; $AS = AQ$ **19.** A is the midpt. of $\overline{SQ}$; $\overline{RD}$ bisects $\overline{SQ}$.   **20.** If 2 vert. $\angle$s are supp., then their sides are $\perp$.

21.
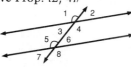
22. *Given:* $\angle 1$ and $\angle 2$ are supp. *Prove:* $m \perp n$
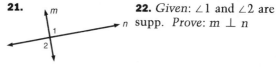

23. *Plan for Proof*: Use the def. of supp. ∠s to show that $m\angle 1 + m\angle 2 = 180$. Then use Thm. 3-8 to show that $m\angle 1 = m\angle 2$. Using the Substitution Prop. gives $2(m\angle 1) = 180$. Then use the Div. Prop. to show that $m\angle 1 = 90$. Use the def. of a rt. ∠ to state that ∠1 is a rt. ∠. By the def. of ⊥ lines, $m \perp n$ **24.** *Proof*: 1. ∠1 and ∠2 are supp. (Given) 2. $m\angle 1 + m\angle 2 = 180$ (Def. of supp. ∠ [1]) 3. $m\angle 1 = m\angle 2$ (Vert. ∠s are =.) 4. $m\angle 1 + m\angle 1 = 180$ or $2(m\angle 1) = 180$ (Substitution Prop. [2, 3]) 5. $2 = 2$ (Reflexive Prop.) 6. $m\angle 1 = 90$ (Div. Prop. [4, 5]) 7. ∠1 is a rt. ∠. (Def. of rt. ∠. [6]) 8. $m \perp n$ (Def. of ⊥ [7])

Chapter 4

Pages 141–143
Written Exercises **1.** 102 **3.** 78 **5.** $m \parallel n$
7. Thm. 4-2 **9.** $-\frac{5}{8}$ **13.** *Proof*: 1. $\overleftrightarrow{BC} \parallel \overleftrightarrow{DE}$ (Given) 2. $m\angle 1 = m\angle 3$ (Lines $\parallel \Rightarrow$ corres. ∠s =. [1]) 3. $m\angle 1 = m\angle 2$ (Given) 4. $m\angle 2 = m\angle 3$ (Substitution Prop. [2, 3]) **15.** 120; 60; 120 **17.** $x = 63$; $m\angle 1 = m\angle 2 = 90$ **19a.** $y = 3x - 5$; **b.** $y = -5x + 3$; **c.** $y = 3x + 6$; $a \parallel c$; slopes are =. **21.** 0 **23.** $-\frac{1}{3}$ **25.** *Proof*: 1. Coplanar lines n, m, and t; $n \perp t$; $m \perp t$ (Given) 2. ∠1 and ∠2 are rt. ∠s. (2 ⊥ lines form 4 rt. ∠s. [1]) 3. $m\angle 1 = m\angle 2$ (All rt. ∠s are =. [2]) 4. $n \parallel m$ (Corres. ∠s = ⇒ lines ∥. [3]) **27.** Yes **29.** Align the carpenter's square so that one edge is ∥ to the level shelf. Then the vertical edge is ⊥ to the level shelf. Align the new shelf so that it is ⊥ to the vertical edge of the carpenter's square. It will be ∥ to the first shelf by Thm. 4-2. **33.** *Given*: ∠ABE and ∠EBC form a lin. pr.; $\overrightarrow{BD}$ bisects ∠ABE, $\overrightarrow{BF}$ bisects ∠EBC *Prove*: $\overrightarrow{BD} \perp \overrightarrow{BF}$ **34.** (See diagram for Exercise 33.) *Proof*: 1. ∠ABE and ∠EBC form a linear pair; $\overrightarrow{BD}$ bisects ∠ABE; $\overrightarrow{BF}$ bisects ∠EBC (Given) 2. ∠ABE and ∠EBC are supp. (Supp. Post. [1]) 3. $m\angle ABE + m\angle EBC = 180$ (Def. of supp. ∠s [2]) 4. $m\angle ABD = m\angle 1$; $m\angle CBF = m\angle 2$ (Def. of ∠ bisector [1]) 5. $m\angle ABE = m\angle ABD + m\angle 1$; $m\angle EBC = m\angle CBF + m\angle 2$ (Angle Add. Post.) 6. $m\angle ABE = m\angle 1 + m\angle 1 = 2(m\angle 1)$; $m\angle EBC = m\angle 2 + m\angle 2 = 2(m\angle 2)$ (Substitution Prop. [4, 5]) 7. $2(m\angle 1) + 2(m\angle 2) = 180$ (Substitution

Prop. [3, 6]) **8.** $\frac{1}{2} = \frac{1}{2}$ (Reflexive Prop.) **9.** $m\angle 1 + m\angle 2 = 90$ (Mult. Prop. [7, 8]) **10.** $m\angle 1 + m\angle 2 = m\angle DBF$ (Angle Add. Post.) **11.** $m\angle DBF = 90$ (Substitution Prop. [9, 10]) **12.** ∠DBF is a rt. ∠. (Def. of rt. ∠ [11]) **13.** $\overrightarrow{BD} \perp \overrightarrow{BF}$ (Def. of ⊥ lines [12]) **35.** $m\angle 1 + m\angle 2 = 90$; $m\angle ABC = 90$

Pages 146–148
Written Exercises **1.** 75 **3.** 70 **5.** $k \parallel \ell$ (Thm. 4-4) **7.** None **9.** $m \parallel n$ (Thm. 3-8, Thm. 4-6) **11.** None **13.** ∠1 and ∠3 are corr. ∠s; by Post. 15, corr. ∠s = ⇒ ∥ lines. **15.** Thm. 4-2, Thm. 4-4, Thm. 4-6 **17.** *Proof*: 1. $\ell \parallel m$ (Given) 2. $m\angle 1 = m\angle 4$ (Lines ∥ ⇒ corres. ∠s =. [1]) 3. $m\angle 1 = m\angle 2$ (Given) 4. $m\angle 2 = m\angle 4$ (Substitution Prop. [2, 3])
21. *Given*: Lines ℓ and m are cut by transversal t; $\ell \parallel m$ *Prove*: ∠1 and ∠2 are supp; ∠3 and ∠4 are supp.

Proof: 1. Lines ℓ and m are cut by trans. t; $\ell \parallel m$ (Given) 2. $m\angle 1 = m\angle 3$; $m\angle 2 = m\angle 4$ (Lines ∥ ⇒ alt. int. ∠s =. [1]) 3. ∠1 and ∠4 are supp.; ∠2 and ∠3 are supp. (Supp. Post.) 4. $m\angle 1 + m\angle 4 = 180$; $m\angle 2 + m\angle 3 = 180$ (Def. of supp. [3]) 5. $m\angle 1 + m\angle 2 = 180$; $m\angle 3 + m\angle 4 = 180$ (Substitution Prop. [2, 4]) 6. ∠1 and ∠2 are supp.; ∠3 and ∠4 are supp. (Def. of supp. ∠s [5]) **23.** *Proof*: 1. $\overleftrightarrow{BC} \parallel \overleftrightarrow{EF}$ (Given) 2. $m\angle 2 = m\angle 4$ (Lines ∥ ⇒ corres. ∠s =. [1]) 3. $m\angle 1 + m\angle 4 = 180$ (Given) 4. $m\angle 1 + m\angle 2 = 180$ (Substitution Prop. [2, 3]) 5. ∠1 and ∠2 are supp. ∠s. (Def. of supp. [4]) 6. $\overleftrightarrow{BA} \parallel \overleftrightarrow{ED}$ (Int. ∠s on the same side supp. ⇒ lines ∥. [5]) **25.** *Proof*: 1. $\overleftrightarrow{HJ} \parallel \overleftrightarrow{ML}$ (Given) 2. $m\angle 7 = m\angle 8$ (Lines ∥ ⇒ corres. ∠s =. [1]) 3. $\overleftrightarrow{HG} \parallel \overleftrightarrow{KL}$ (Given) 4. $m\angle 5 = m\angle 7$ (Lines ∥ ⇒ corres. ∠s =. [3]) 5. $m\angle 5 = m\angle 8$ (Transitive Prop. [2, 4]) **27.** $x = 4$; $m\angle 3 = m\angle 5 = 24$ **29.** $x = -9$ or $x = 8$. When $x = -9$, $m\angle 3 = 99$ and $m\angle 6 = 81$. When $x = 8$, $m\angle 3 = 81$ and $m\angle 6 = 132$.
33. *Given*: $\ell \parallel m$; $\overrightarrow{BP}$ bisects ∠ABC; $\overrightarrow{CQ}$ bisects ∠BCD. *Prove*: $\overrightarrow{BP} \parallel \overrightarrow{CQ}$

Proof: 1. $\ell \parallel m$; $\overrightarrow{BP}$ bisects ∠ABC; $\overrightarrow{CQ}$ bisects ∠BCD. (Given) 2. $m\angle 1 = m\angle 2$; $m\angle 3 = m\angle 4$ (Def. of ∠ bisector [1]) 3. $m\angle ABC = m\angle 1 + m\angle 2$; $m\angle BCD = m\angle 3 + m\angle 4$ (Angle Add.

Post.) **4.** $m\angle ABC = m\angle 2 + m\angle 2 = 2(m\angle 2)$;
$m\angle BCD = m\angle 3 + m\angle 3 = 2(m\angle 3)$ (Substitution
Prop. [2, 3]) **5.** $m\angle ABC = m\angle BCD$ (Lines $\parallel \Rightarrow$
alt. int. $\angle$s =. [1]) **6.** $2(m\angle 2) = 2(m\angle 3)$
(Substitution Prop. [4, 5]) **7.** 2 = 2 (Reflexive
Prop.) **8.** $m\angle 2 = m\angle 3$ (Div. Prop. [6, 7])
9. $\overrightarrow{BP} \parallel \overrightarrow{CQ}$ (Alt. int. $\angle$s = $\Rightarrow$ lines $\parallel$. [8])
35. 130 **36.** 2 **37.** $m\angle A = m\angle E$; $\angle D$ and $\angle B$
are rt. $\angle$s; $AC = CE$ **38.** $p \Rightarrow r$ **39.** Given

Pages 152–154
Written Exercises 1. Thm. 3-1 **3.** Thm. 3-3
5. No; an acute $\angle$ is an $\angle$ whose measure is
between 0 and 90, and $0 < 63 < 90$.
7. Thursday, January 30 **9.** P and ℓ lie in only 1
plane. **11.** $\mathcal{E}$ and $\mathcal{H}$; Pts.; P; Q; R **13.** P and ℓ lie
in 2 or more planes; false **15.** *Proof:* Either
$m\angle 1 = m\angle 4$ or $m\angle 1 \neq m\angle 4$. Suppose that
$m\angle 1 = m\angle 4$. Then since $\angle 1$ and $\angle 4$ are =
corres. $\angle$s, $\ell \parallel m$. But this contradicts the given
fact that $\ell \not\parallel m$. Therefore, the assumption that
$m\angle 1 = m\angle 4$ is false. We conclude that $m\angle 1 \neq$
$m\angle 4$. **17.** *Proof:* Either the waterfall exists in
the real world, or the waterfall cannot exist in
the real world. Suppose that the waterfall does
exist in the real world. Then an object in the
water at the top of the waterfall would float
down the falls and up the course to the top of
the falls. Thus, the water flows uphill. This
defies the law of gravity. Therefore, the
assumption that the waterfall exists in the real
world is false, and we conclude that the waterfall
cannot exist in the real world. **21.** *Given:* ℓ and
m intersect at pt. P. *Prove:* ℓ and m lie in only
one plane. *Proof:* Either ℓ and m lie in only one
plane, or ℓ and m lie in two or more planes.
Suppose that ℓ and m lie in two or more planes.
Then by the Points Post., there is a pt. other
than P, say A, on ℓ, and a pt. other than P, say B,
on m. Since ℓ and m intersect at P, we know
that A, B, and P are noncollinear. Then there are
3 noncollinear points in two or more planes. But
this contradicts the Plane Post. Therefore, the
assumption that ℓ and m lie in two or more
planes is false. We conclude that ℓ and m lie in
only one plane. **23.** 12 **24.** Show: two corr. $\angle$s
=; two alt. int. $\angle$s =; two int. $\angle$s on the same
side of a trans. supp.; a trans. is $\perp$ to each of
two given lines; the lines are coplanar and do
not intersect. **25.** Thm. 4-1 and Thm. 4-2
26. 38 **27.** 1

Algebra Review 1. $y = 2x - 1$ **3.** $y = -1x + 4$
5. $y = -3x + 2$ **7.** $y = \frac{2}{3}x - \frac{7}{3}$

Pages 158–160
Written Exercises 1. Given **3.** $\angle$ Construction
Post. **5.** Def. of $\perp$ lines [4] **7.** Thm. 4-11
9. Thm. 4-7 **11.** *Proof:* 1. $p \parallel r$; $m\angle 1 = m\angle 2$
(Given) 2. $p \parallel q$ (Alt. int. $\angle$s = $\Rightarrow$ lines $\parallel$. [1])
3. $q \parallel r$ (In a plane, 2 lines $\parallel$ to same line are $\parallel$ to
each other. [1, 2]) **13.** lines in $\mathcal{H}$ through $P \perp \ell$
15. 90; 90 **17.** two or more lines in $\mathcal{H}$ through P
$\perp$ to ℓ **19.** No **21.** No **25.** *Given:* t, ℓ, and m
are coplanar; t intersects ℓ at A; $\ell \parallel m$ *Prove:* t
intersects m *Proof:* Since t and m are coplanar,
either $t \parallel m$ or t intersects m. Suppose $t \parallel m$.
Then t and ℓ both contain A and t and ℓ are both
parallel to m. This contradicts the fact that
through a pt. not on a given line, there is one
and only one line $\parallel$ the given line. So the
assumption that $t \parallel m$ is false. We conclude that
t and m intersect. Samples: **27.** $y = -x + 7$
29. $y = -\frac{1}{3}x$ **31.** $y = -\frac{1}{2}x$ **33.** $y = \frac{7}{5}x + 1$ **35.** 90
37. *Proof:* 1. $\overrightarrow{PQ} \parallel \overrightarrow{ST}$
(Given) 2. Draw $\overrightarrow{RX} \parallel$
$\overrightarrow{ST}$ (Through a pt.
not on a given line,

there is exactly 1 line $\parallel$ to the given line.) 3. $\overrightarrow{RX}$
$\parallel \overrightarrow{PQ}$ (In a plane, if 2 lines are $\parallel$ to the same line,
they are $\parallel$ to each other. [1, 2]) 4. $m\angle QRS =$
$m\angle 2 + m\angle 3$ (Angle Add. Post.) 5. $m\angle 1 =$
$m\angle 2$; $m\angle 3 = m\angle 4$ (2 lines $\parallel \Rightarrow$ alt. int. $\angle$s =. [2,
3]) 6. $m\angle QRS = m\angle 1 + m\angle 4$ (Substitution
Prop. [4, 5]) **41.** Yes
42. *Given:* P and Q on $\overrightarrow{SP}$

Prove: $SP \neq SQ$
Proof: Either $SP = SQ$ or $SP \neq SQ$. Suppose $SP =$
SQ. Then there are 2 pts. on ray $\overrightarrow{SP}$ that are the
same distance from S. This contradicts the Seg.
Const. Post. which states that on any ray, there
is exactly one pt. at a given distance from the
endpt. of the ray. Thus, the assumption that SP
$= SQ$ is false. We conclude $SP \neq SQ$. **43.** 75
44. If 2 $\angle$s are $\neq$, then they are not vert. $\angle$s;
true. **45.** 10; 40; 40

Pages 164–165
Written Exercises 1. $j \parallel k$ **3.** None **5.** $\mathcal{E} \parallel \mathcal{F}$; j
$\parallel k$; $n \perp j$; $n \perp m$; $n \perp k$; $n \perp \ell$ **7.** Infinitely
many **9.** 30 **11.** Thm. 4-4 **13.** 18 cm
21. *Proof:* 1. $n \perp \mathcal{H}$ at P; $\mathcal{H} \parallel \mathcal{K}$ (Given) 2. Let A

be a point on n different from P. (A line contains at least two points.) 3. Let Q be any point of $\mathcal{K}$. (A plane contains at least 3 noncollinear points.) 4. Let $\mathcal{E}$ be the plane determined by A, P, and Q. (3 noncollinear pts. lie in exactly one plane.) 5. Plane $\mathcal{E}$ intersects plane $\mathcal{H}$ in a line through P; call it ℓ. Plane $\mathcal{E}$ intersects plane $\mathcal{K}$ in a line through Q; call it m. (Plane Intersection Post.) 6. Plane $\mathcal{E}$ contains $\overleftrightarrow{AP}$ (line m). (Flat Plane Post.) 7. m is in $\mathcal{E}$; ℓ is in $\mathcal{E}$. (Def. of intersection [5, 6]) 8. $\overleftrightarrow{AP} \perp \ell$ (Def. of line $\perp$ to plane [1]) 9. $\ell \parallel m$ (If two $\parallel$ planes are cut by a third plane, the lines of intersection are $\parallel$. [1, 5]) 10. $\overleftrightarrow{AP}$ intersects m. (In a plane, if a line intersects one of two $\parallel$ lines, it intersects the other. [6, 7, 8, 9]) 11. $\overleftrightarrow{AP}$ (line n) intersects $\mathcal{K}$. (Def. of intersection and steps 5 and 10) **23.** No; Thm. 4-7 **24.** 1 **25.** $\angle Y$ is acute or rt. **26.** 19; 78; 78 **27.** $\perp$
Algebra Review 1. 5 **3.** $\sqrt{41}$ **5.** 3

Pages 168–169
Written Exercises
9. They intersect in a single point. **11.** Proof: 1. $\overleftrightarrow{AB} \parallel \overleftrightarrow{CD}$; $\overleftrightarrow{AC} \perp \overleftrightarrow{CD}$ (Given) 2. $\overleftrightarrow{AC} \perp \overleftrightarrow{AB}$ (If a trans. is $\perp$ to one of 2 $\parallel$ lines, it is $\perp$ to the other. [1]) 3. $\angle CAB$ is a rt. $\angle$. (Def. $\perp$ lines [2]) 4. $\triangle ABC$ is a rt. triangle. (Def. rt. triangle [3]) **13.** Equilateral **15.** Given: $\triangle ABC$ Prove: $\triangle ABC$ cannot have 2 rt. $\angle$s. Proof: Either a $\triangle$ cannot have 2 rt. $\angle$s or it can have 2 rt. $\angle$s. Suppose $\triangle ABC$ has 2 rt. $\angle$s., $\angle B$ and $\angle C$. Then $\overleftrightarrow{AB} \perp \overleftrightarrow{BC}$ and $\overleftrightarrow{AC} \perp \overleftrightarrow{BC}$. Thus, there are 2 lines through A perpendicular to $\overleftrightarrow{BC}$. This contradicts the fact that in a plane, through a pt. not on a given line, there is one and only one line $\perp$ to the given line. Thus, the assumption that $\triangle ABC$ has 2 rt. $\angle$s is false. We conclude that $\triangle ABC$ cannot have 2 rt. $\angle$s. **17.** Sometimes **21.** Line m is $\perp$ to every intersection of m and $\mathcal{T}$. **22.** $j \parallel k$ **23.** $y = -4x + 11$ **24.** When they are coplanar **25.** $\left(\frac{3}{2}, \frac{3}{2}\right)$

Pages 172–174
Written Exercises 1. $m\angle QRP = 30$
3. $m\angle QPR = 90$; $m\angle QRP = 37$ **5.** $m\angle QPR = 80$; $m\angle Q = 70$; $m\angle QRP = 30$ **7.** Thm. 4-19
9. Given: $\triangle ABC$ is a rt. triangle; $\angle C$ is a rt. $\angle$. Prove: $\angle A$ and $\angle B$ are comp. Proof: 1. $\triangle ABC$ is a rt. triangle; $\angle C$ is a rt. $\angle$. (Given) 2. $m\angle C = 90$ (Def. rt. $\angle$ [1]) 3. $m\angle A + m\angle B + m\angle C = 180$ (Sum

of meas. of $\angle$s of a $\triangle$ = 180. [1]) **4.** $m\angle A + m\angle B + 90 = 180$ (Substitution Prop. [2, 3]) 5. $90 = 90$ (Reflexive Prop.) 6. $m\angle A + m\angle B = 90$ (Subtraction Prop. [4, 5]) 7. $\angle A$ and $\angle B$ are comp. (Def. comp. $\angle$s [6]) **11.** Proof: 1. $\triangle HGJ$ is a rt. triangle with rt. $\angle$ at G; $\triangle MJK$ is a rt. triangle with rt. $\angle$ at K (Given) 2. $\angle H$ and $\angle GJH$ are comp.; $\angle M$ and $\angle KJM$ are comp. (The acute $\angle$s of a rt. $\triangle$ are comp. [1]) 3. $m\angle H + m\angle GJH = 90$; $m\angle M + m\angle KJM = 90$ (Def. of comp. $\angle$s [2]) 4. $m\angle GJH > 0$; $m\angle KJM > 0$ (Protractor Post.) 5. $m\angle H < 90$; $m\angle M < 90$ (Def. of $a > b$ [3, 4]) **13.** Proof: 1. $\triangle ABC$ with rt. $\angle$ at B (Given) 2. $m\angle B = 90$ (Def. rt. $\angle$ [1]) 3. $m\angle CAD > m\angle B$ (The meas. of an ext. $\angle$ of $\triangle$ is greater than either of its remote interior $\angle$s.) 4. $m\angle CAD > 90$ (Substitution Prop. [2, 3]) 5. $\angle CAD$ is obtuse. (Def. obtuse $\angle$ [4]) **17.** They are converses of each other. **19.** 125
21. Given: $\triangle ABC$ with ext. $\angle 1$
Prove: $m\angle 1 = m\angle B + m\angle C$
Proof: 1. $\triangle ABC$ with ext. $\angle 1$ (Given) 2. $\angle 1$ and $\angle 2$ form a linear pair. (Def. of ext. $\angle$ [1]) 3. $\angle 1$ and $\angle 2$ are supp. (Supp. Post. [2]) 4. $m\angle 1 + m\angle 2 = 180$ (Def. of supp. $\angle$s [3]) 5. $m\angle B + m\angle C + m\angle 2 = 180$ (Sum of meas. of $\angle$s of $\triangle$ = 180. [1]) 6. $m\angle 1 + m\angle 2 = m\angle B + m\angle C + m\angle 2$ (Substitution Prop. [4, 5]) 7. $m\angle 2 = m\angle 2$ (Reflexive Prop.) 8. $m\angle 1 = m\angle B + m\angle C$ (Subtraction. Prop. [6, 7]) **23.** Proof: 1. $\overleftrightarrow{CD} \perp \overleftrightarrow{AB}$; $m\angle A = m\angle B$ (Given) 2. $\angle CDA$ and $\angle CDB$ are rt. $\angle$s. (Two $\perp$ lines intersect to form 4 rt. $\angle$s. [1]) 3. $m\angle CDA = m\angle CDB$ (All rt. $\angle$s are =. [2]) 4. $m\angle ACD = m\angle BCD$ (If 2 $\angle$s of a $\triangle$ = 2 $\angle$s of another $\triangle$, the third $\angle$s are =. [1, 3]) 5. $\overrightarrow{CD}$ bisects $\angle ACB$ (Def. $\angle$ bisector [4]) **29.** Thm. 4-18 **33.** $\angle D$ **34.** scalene **35.** $\parallel$
36. $\angle FAB$ and $\angle ABE$; $\angle FAC$ and $\angle CBE$; $\angle FBD$ and $\angle DBE$ **37.** If an object is a moon (hyp.), then it revolves around a planet (concl.).

Pages 177–179
Written Exercises 1. A, B, C, D, E, F **3.** $\overline{AB}$, $\overline{BC}$, $\overline{CD}$, $\overline{DE}$, $\overline{EF}$, and $\overline{AF}$ **5.** $\angle A$, $\angle B$, $\angle C$, $\angle D$, $\angle E$, $\angle F$ **7.** 135 **9.** $9x$ **11.** Convex; equiangular **13.** Nonconvex; equilateral **15.** 0, 1, 3, 4, 5, 7; 0, 2, 9, 14, 20, 35 **17.** $\frac{n(n-3)}{2}$ **21.** $x = 25$, perimeter = 102 **23.** Regular pentagon is formed.

24. *Proof:* Either $m\angle B < 90$ or $m\angle B > 0$ or $m\angle B = 90$. Suppose $m\angle B > 90$. Then since $m\angle C > 90$ and $m\angle A > 0$, $m\angle A + m\angle B + m\angle C > 90 + 90 + 0$ by the Add. Prop. Thus, $m\angle A + m\angle B + m\angle C > 180$. This contradicts the fact that the sum of the meas. of the $\angle$s of a $\triangle = 180$. The assumption that $m\angle B > 90$ is false. Next suppose that $m\angle B = 90$. Then since $m\angle C > 90$ and $m\angle A > 0$, $m\angle A + m\angle B + m\angle C > 180$ by the Add. Post. Again this contradicts the fact that the sum of the meas. of the $\angle$s of a $\triangle = 180$. Thus, it is false that $m\angle C = 90$. Since $m\angle B \not> 90$ and $m\angle B \neq 90$, we conclude that $m\angle B < 90$. **25.** 12 **26.** No **27.** The Prove

Pages 182–183
Written Exercises **1.** 360 **3.** 1,080 **5.** Since the measures of the $\angle$s of a regular polygon are $=$, the measure of each $\angle$ = (the sum of the measures of the $\angle$s of the polygon) ÷ (the number of $\angle$s). **7.** $128\frac{4}{7}$ **11.** 6

15. 6 **17.** 15 **19.** 9 **21.** 12 **23.** 36
25. *Given:* Any convex hexagon $ABCDEF$ *Prove:* At least one angle of $ABCDEF$ has a measure of 120 or more. *Proof:* Either a convex hexagon has at least one angle with measure greater than or equal to 120 or it has no angles with measures greater than or equal to 120. Suppose every angle of $ABCDEF$ has a measure less than 120. Then $m\angle A < 120, m\angle B < 120, \ldots,$ $m\angle F < 120$ and by the Addition Prop. $m\angle A + m\angle B + \ldots + m\angle F < 720$. This contradicts the fact that the sum of the measures of the angles of any convex hexagon is $(6 - 2)180 = 720$. Thus, the assumption is false. We conclude that at least one angle of $ABCDEF$ has a measure of 120 or more. **26.** 256 **27.** 14 **28.** 68
29. Segment **30.** *Given:* Lines ℓ and m are skew lines. *Prove:* ℓ and m do not intersect. *Proof:* Either ℓ and m intersect or ℓ and m do not intersect. Suppose ℓ and m intersect. Then ℓ and m are coplanar since two intersecting lines determine a plane. This contradicts the definition of skew lines which states that skew lines are noncoplanar. Therefore, the assumption that ℓ and m intersect is false. We conclude that ℓ and m do not intersect.

Chapter 4 Review, Pages 187–188
1. 80 **2.** 90 **3.** ∥ **4.** 120 **5.** 180 **6.** Thm. 4-3
7. Def. of ∥ lines **8.** Either Wayne scored at least three goals in one of the two hockey games, or

he scored less than three goals in each game. Suppose he scored less than three goals in each game. Then he scored two or fewer goals in each game. Therefore, in two games, Wayne scored four or fewer goals. But this contradicts the given information that Wayne scored five goals in two hockey games. Therefore, the assumption that he scored less than three goals in each game is false, and we conclude that Wayne scored at least three goals in one of the two hockey games.
9. Line Post. **10.** 1 **11.** 1 **12.** Sample: $y = \frac{1}{2}x$
13. Always **14.** Sometimes **15.** Never **16.** Never
20. $\sqrt{(-1 - 1)^2 + (-1 - 1)^2} = 2\sqrt{2};$
$\sqrt{(-3 - (-1))^2 + (3 - (-1))^2} = 2\sqrt{5};$
$\sqrt{(-3 - 1)^2 + (3 - 1)^2} = 2\sqrt{5};$ 2 sides $= \Rightarrow \triangle$ is isosceles. **21.** 105 **22.** 110 **23.** 60 **24.** A $\triangle$ can have at most one rt. $\angle$, or sum of $\angle$ measures > 180. **25.** $\overline{AC}, \overline{BD}$ **26.** $AB = BC = CD = DA;$ $m\angle A = m\angle B = m\angle C = m\angle D$ **27.** $AB + BC + CD + AD$ **30.** $(n - 2)180$ **31.** 60 **32.** 108

Chapter 5

Pages 193–194
Written Exercises **1.** $PA = TE; PS = TL; AS = EL$ **3.** $\overline{PS}$ **5.** Yes **7.** No **9.** True **11.** True
13. $AB = CB; AE = CD; BE = BD; m\angle A = m\angle C;$ $m\angle ABE = m\angle CBD; m\angle AEB = m\angle CDB$
15. $AB = CB; AD = CE; BD = BE; m\angle A = m\angle C;$ $m\angle ABD = m\angle CBE; m\angle ADB = m\angle CEB$
17. *Given:* $\triangle ABC$ *Prove:* $\triangle ABC \cong \triangle ABC$
Proof: 1. $\triangle ABC$ (Given)
2. $AB = AB; BC = BC;$
$AC = AC; m\angle A = m\angle A; m\angle B = m\angle B; m\angle C = m\angle C$ (Reflexive Prop.) 3. $\triangle ABC \cong \triangle ABC$ (Def. of $\cong \triangle$s (2)) **21.** Yes **23.** *Proof:* 1. $\triangle ABC \cong \triangle CBA$ (Given) 2. $AB = CB$ (Corr. parts of $\cong \triangle$s are $=$. (1)) 3. $\triangle ABC$ is isos. (Def. of isos. $\triangle$ (2))
25. *Given:* $\triangle ABC \cong \triangle DEF;$ $\triangle ABC$ is scalene.
Prove: $\triangle DEF$ is scalene.
Proof: Either (1) $\triangle DEF$ is scalene or (2) $\triangle DEF$ is not scalene. Suppose $\triangle DEF$ is not scalene. Then at least 2 sides of $\triangle DEF$ are $=$; say $DE = EF$. Since $\triangle ABC \cong \triangle DEF$ and corr. parts of $\cong \triangle$s are $=$, it follows that $AB = DE$ and $BC = EF$. So, by substitution, $AB = BC$. But this contradicts the fact that $\triangle ABC$ is scalene. Thus, the assumption that $\triangle DEF$ is not scalene is false. We conclude that $\triangle DEF$ is scalene. **26.** 120 **27.** 5 **28.** 12

29. If 2 ∠s are = and complementary, then each has a measure of 45.

Pages 197–199
Written Exercises 1. *AR; RT; AT* **3.** m∠*O* = m∠*R*; m∠*W* = m∠*T* **5.** m∠*O* = m∠*A*; m∠*W* = m∠*T* **7.** By SSS Post. (*AB* = *CB* = *AD* = *CD*; *OA* = *OC*; *OB* = *OD*) **9.** Given; Given; *AC* = *AC*; SAS Post. **11.** *Proof:* 1. *AD* = *CB*; *AB* = *CD* (Given) 2. *AC* = *CA* (Reflexive Prop.) 3. △*ABC* ≅ △*CDA* (SSS Post. [1, 2]) **15.** ∠*M*, ∠*F*; ∠*N*, ∠*G*; ∠*P*, ∠*H* **17.** *Proof:* 1. m∠*A* = m∠*D*; *B* is midpt. of *AD*. (Given) 2. *AB* = *DB* (Def. of midpt. [1]) 3. m∠*ABC* = m∠*DBE* (Vert. ∠s are =.) 4. △*ABC* ≅ △*DBE* (ASA Post. [1, 2, 3]) **21.** *Proof:* 1. *RS* = *RP*; m∠*FRO* = m∠*PRO* (Given) 2. *OR* = *OR* (Reflexive Prop.) 3. △*PRO* ≅ △*SRO* (SAS Post. [1, 2]) **23.** *Proof:* 1. *PM* = *PN*; m∠*MPR* = m∠*NPR* (Given) 2. *PR* = *PR* (Reflexive Prop.) 3. △*MRP* ≅ △*NRP* (SAS Post. [1, 2]) **27.** *Proof:* 1. *DC* ⊥ *H*; △*ABC* is equilateral. (Given) 2. *AC* = *BC* (Def. of equilateral △ [1]) 3. *DC* ⊥ *AC*; *DC* ⊥ *BC* (Def. of line ⊥ plane [1]) 4. ∠*ACD* and ∠*BCD* are rt. ∠s. (2 ⊥ lines form 4 rt. ∠s. [3]) 5. m∠*ACD* = m∠*BCD* (All rt. ∠s are =. [4]) 6. *CD* = *CD* (Reflexive Prop.) 7. △*ACD* ≅ △*BCD* (SAS Post. [2, 5, 6]) **30.** ∠*N* **31.** 360 **32.** x = 8 **33.** 134

Pages 202–204
Written Exercises 1. *N*; *D* **3.** *AN*; *ED* or *TN*; *RD* **5.** *BC* ⊥ *AD*; 2 ⊥ lines form 4 rt. ∠s [1]; m∠*ACB* = m∠*DCB*; Reflexive Prop.; Given; AAS Thm. **7.** *Proof:* 1. m∠*A* = m∠*D*; *AB* = *DC* (Given) 2. m∠*AOB* = m∠*DOC* (Vert. ∠s are =.) 3. △*AOB* ≅ △*DOC* (AAS Thm. [1, 2]) **9.** *Proof:* 1. *PT* bisects ∠*IPQ*; m∠*I* = m∠*Q* (Given) 2. m∠*IPT* = m∠*QPT* (Def. of ∠ bisector [1]) 3. *PT* = *PT* (Reflexive Prop.) 4. △*TIP* ≅ △*TQP* (AAS Thm. [1, 2, 3]) **11.** *Proof:* 1. m∠*P* = m∠*S*; m∠*Q* = m∠*T*; *QR* = *TU* (Given) 2. m∠*R* = m∠*U* (If 2 ∠s of 1 △ are = to 2 ∠s of another △, then remaining ∠s are =. [1]) 3. △*PQR* ≅ △*STU* (ASA Post. [1, 2]) **13.** *Proof:* 1. *RT* bisects ∠*SRW* and ∠*STW*. (Given) 2. m∠*SRT* = m∠*WRT*; m∠*STR* = m∠*WTR* (Def. of ∠ bisector [1]) 3. *RT* = *RT* (Reflexive Prop.) 4. △*RST* ≅ △*RWT* (ASA Post. [2, 3]) **17.** *Proof:* 1. m∠*PQS* = m∠*PRS*; ∠*QSP* and ∠*RSP* are rt. ∠s. (Given) 2. m∠*QSP* = m∠*RSP* (All rt. ∠s are =. [1]) 3. *PS* = *PS* (Reflexive Prop.) 4. △*PQS* ≅

△*PRS* (AAS Thm. [1, 2, 3]) **19.** For the other end, mark the midpoint *B'* of *R'S'*. Then, cut ∠*R'B'A'* and ∠*S'B'C'* equal to ∠*RBA* and ∠*SBC*. Since *B'* is the midpoint of *R'S'*, *R'B'* = *S'B'*. m∠*R* = m∠*S*, because all rt. ∠s are =, and △*B'R'A'* ≅ △*B'S'C* by the ASA Post. **23.** *Proof:* 1. *EB* ⊥ *AC*; *AD* ⊥ *EC*; *AC* = *EC* (Given) 2. ∠*CBE* and ∠*CDA* are rt. ∠s. (2 ⊥ lines form 4 rt. ∠s. [1]) 3. m∠*CBE* = m∠*CDA* (All rt. ∠s are =. [2]) 4. m∠*C* = m∠*C* (Reflexive Prop.) 5. △*CAD* ≅ △*CEB* (AAS Thm. [1, 3, 4]) **24.** ASA Post. **25.** *AC*, *RK* **26.** △*SQP* **28.** (−8, 7)
Algebra Review 1. x < 31 **3.** g ≥ 99 **5.** x ≤ 24 **7.** m ≤ 3

Pages 207–209
Written Exercises 1. *Proof:* 1. *WZ* = *YZ*; m∠1 = m∠2 (Given) 2. *XZ* = *XZ* (Reflexive Prop.) 3. △*XWZ* ≅ △*XYZ* (SAS Post. [1, 2]) 4. m∠3 = m∠4 (Corr. parts of ≅ △s are =. [3]) **5.** *Proof:* 1. *PK* = *NM*; *KL* = *ML*; rt. ∠s at *K* and *M* (Given) 2. m∠*K* = m∠*M* (All rt. ∠s are =. [1]) 3. △*PKL* ≅ △*NML* (SAS Post. [1, 2]) 4. *PL* = *NL* (Corr. parts of ≅ △s are =. [3]) **9.** *Proof:* 1. *AB* = *CD*; m∠2 = m∠3 (Given) 2. *AC* = *CA* (Reflexive Prop.) 3. △*ABC* ≅ △*CDA* (SAS Post. [1, 2]) 4. m∠1 = m∠4 (Corr. parts of ≅ △s are =. [3]) 5. *AD* ∥ *CB* (Alt. int. ∠s = ⇒ lines ∥. [4]) **13.** △*CED* ≅ △*CAB* by SAS Post. *DE* = *BA*, m∠*CED* = m∠*CAB*, and m∠*CDA* = m∠*CBA* because corr. parts of ≅ △s are =. **15.** Since ∠*C* and ∠*A* are rt. ∠s, m∠*C* = m∠*A*. Also, m∠*CBP* = m∠*ABP'*, and *CB* = *AB*. So △*CBP* ≅ △*ABP'* by ASA Post., and *CP* = *AP'* because corr. parts of ≅ △s are =. **17.** *Proof:* 1. *QR* = *NS*; *MR* = *PS*; m∠*QRM* = m∠*NSP* (Given) 2. *RS* = *SR* (Reflexive Prop.) 3. *QR* + *RS* = *NS* + *SR* (Addition Prop. [1, 2]) 4. *QR* + *RS* = *QS*; *NS* + *SR* = *NR* (Seg. Add. Post.) 5. *QS* = *NR* (Substitution Prop. [3, 4]) 6. ∠*MRN* and ∠*QRM* are supp. ∠s; ∠*PSQ* and ∠*NSP* are supp. ∠s. (Supplement Post.) 7. m∠*MRN* = m∠*PSQ* (Supplements of = ∠s are =. [1, 6]) 8. △*MRN* ≅ △*PSQ* (SAS Post. [1, 5, 7]) 9. m∠1 = m∠2 (Corr. parts of ≅ △s are =. [8]) **18.** *Proof:* 1. ∠*B* and ∠*D* are rt. ∠s; *C* is the midpt. of *BD*; m∠*A* = m∠*E* (Given) 2. m∠*B* = m∠*D* (All rt. ∠s are =. [1]) 3. *BC* = *DC* (Def. of midpt. [1]) 4. △*ABC* ≅ △*EDC* (AAS Thm. [1, 2, 3] **19.** Yes; by SAS Post. **20.** SSS **21.** Definitions **22.** 21

Pages 212–213
Written Exercises 1. *Proof:* 1. $m\angle UXY =$ $m\angle UZY$; $\overrightarrow{YU}$ bisects $\angle XYZ$. (Given) 2. $m\angle XYU$ $= m\angle ZYU$ (Def. of $\angle$ bisector [1]) 3. $UY = UY$ (Reflexive Prop.) 4. $\triangle UXY \cong \triangle UZY$ (AAS Thm. [1, 2, 3]) 5. $XY = ZY$ (Corr. parts of $\cong \triangle$s are =. [4]) 6. $VY = VY$ (Reflexive Prop.) 7. $\triangle XVY \cong$ $\triangle ZVY$ (SAS Post. [2, 5, 6]) 8. $m\angle 1 = m\angle 2$ (Corr. parts of $\cong \triangle$s are =. [7]) **3.** Yes; SSS Post. **5.** Yes; SAS Post. **7.** Yes; ASA Post. **9.** b, d, c, a **11.** *Proof:* 1. $\overline{RT} \perp \overline{US}$; $\overline{TS} \perp \overline{RV}$; $m\angle URS = m\angle VSR$ (Given) 2. $\angle RUS$ and $\angle SVR$ are rt. $\angle$s. (2 $\perp$ lines form 4 rt. $\angle$s. [1]) 3. $m\angle RUS = m\angle SVR$ (All rt. $\angle$s are =. [2]) 4. $RS = SR$ (Reflexive Prop.) 5. $\triangle RUS \cong \triangle SVR$ (AAS Thm. [1, 3, 4]) **17.** $\triangle ADC$, $\triangle BCD$ **19.** $\overline{BD}$; corr. parts of $\cong \triangle$s are =. **21.** SSS Post. **23.** *Proof:* 1. $AF = CD$; $DE = FE$ (Given) 2. AF $+ FE = CD + DE$ (Add. Prop. [1]) 3. $AF + FE =$ AE; $CD + DE = CE$ (Seg. Add. Post.) 4. $AE =$ CE (Substitution Prop. [2, 3]) 5. $m\angle E = m\angle E$ (Reflexive Prop.) 6. $\triangle ADE \cong \triangle CFE$ (SAS Post. [1, 4, 5]) 7. $m\angle A = m\angle C$; $AD = CF$ (Corr. parts of $\cong \triangle$s are =. [6]) 8. $\triangle ADF \cong \triangle CFD$ (SAS Post. [1, 7]) 9. $m\angle AFD = m\angle CDF$ (Corr. parts of $\cong$ $\triangle$s are =. [8]) 10. $\angle EFD$ and $\angle AFD$ are supp. $\angle$s; $\angle EDF$ and $\angle CDF$ are supp. $\angle$s (Supp. Post.) 11. $m\angle EFD = m\angle EDF$ (Supp. of = $\angle$s are =. [9, 10]) **25.** Show that the following parts are =: (1) All 6 pairs of corr. parts; (2) 3 pairs of corr. sides; (3) 2 pairs of corr. sides and their included $\angle$; (4) 2 pairs of corr. $\angle$s and their included side; (5) 2 pairs of corr. $\angle$s and a pair of corr., nonincluded sides. (6) Show that the $\triangle$s are $\cong$ to the same $\triangle$. **26.** *Proof:* 1. $\overrightarrow{AC}$ bisects $\angle BAD$; $\overrightarrow{CA}$ bisects $\angle BCD$. (Given) 2. $m\angle BAC = m\angle DAC$; $m\angle BCA = m\angle DCA$ (Def. of $\angle$ bisector [1]) 3. $AC = AC$ (Reflexive Prop.) 4. $\triangle ABC \cong \triangle ADC$ (ASA Post. [2, 3]) 5. $BC = DC$ (Corr. parts of $\cong$ $\triangle$s are =. [4]) **27.** 2 noncongruent triangles can be drawn with 2 pairs of = corr. sides and a pair of =, nonincluded $\angle$s. (A counterexample is shown on page 201.) **28.** $m\angle 3$; $m\angle 4$ **29.** 35; inductive

Pages 218–219
Written Exercises 1. =; radii of a circle are =. **3.** =; radii of a circle are =. **5.** $\cong$; SSS Post. **28.** $\triangle WZU$, $\triangle YZU$ or $\triangle WZX$, $\triangle YZX$ **29.** $y =$ $-2x - 4$ **30.** Sample answer: You *may* assume (1) U is between Y and W; (2) X, U, and Z are

collinear; (3) $\overline{YW}$ intersects $\overline{XZ}$ at U. You *may not* assume (1) $\overline{YW} \perp \overline{XZ}$; (2) U is midpt. of $\overline{YW}$; (3) $\overline{WZ} \parallel \overline{XY}$.

Pages 222–224
Written Exercises 1. 50; 80 **3.** 100 **5.** 130 **7.** 2 **9.** *Proof:* 1. $m\angle 1 = m\angle 3$ (Given) 2. $m\angle 3 = m\angle 2$ (Vert. $\angle$s are =.) 3. $m\angle 1 =$ $m\angle 3$ (Transitive Prop. [1, 2]) 4. $AB = BC$ (If 2 $\angle$s of a $\triangle$ are =, then the sides opp. those $\angle$s are =. [3]) **11.** *Proof:* 1. $m\angle A = m\angle B$; $\overline{CD}$ is a median of $\triangle ABC$. (Given) 2. $AC = BC$ (If 2 $\angle$s of a $\triangle$ are =, then the sides opp. those $\angle$s are =. [1]) 3. D is midpt. of $\overline{AB}$. (Def. of median [2]) 4. $AD = BD$ (Def. of midpt. [3]) 5. $\triangle ACD \cong$ $\triangle BCD$ (SAS Post. [1, 2, 4]) **13.** *Proof:* 1. $MP =$ NP (Given) 2. $m\angle PMN = m\angle PNM$ (Isos. $\triangle$ Thm. [1]) 3. $\angle 1$ and $\angle PMN$ are supp. $\angle$s; $\angle 3$ and $\angle PNM$ are supp. $\angle$s. (Supplement Post.) 4. $m\angle 1 = m\angle 3$ (Supps. of = $\angle$s are =. [2, 3]) **17.** *Given:* $\triangle ABC$; $AC =$ BC; $\overline{CD}$ is a median. *Prove:* $\overline{CD}$ bisects $\angle ACB$.

19. *Given:* $\triangle ABC$; $AC = BC$; $\overline{CD}$ is a median. (See diagram for Exer. 17.) *Prove:* $\overline{CD}$ is the $\perp$ bisector of $\overline{AB}$. **21.** *Proof:* 1. $\triangle ABC$; $AC = BC$; $\overline{CD}$ is a median. (Given) 2. D is midpt. of $\overline{AB}$. (Def. of median of a $\triangle$ [1]) 3. $AD = BD$ (Def. of midpt. [2]) 4. $CD = CD$ (Reflexive Prop.) 5. $\triangle ACD \cong \triangle BCD$ (SSS Post. [1, 3, 4]) 6. $m\angle ACD = m\angle BCD$ (Corr. parts of $\cong \triangle$s are =. [5]) 7. $\overline{CD}$ bisects $\triangle ACB$. (Def. of $\angle$ bisector [6]) **25.** *Proof:* 1. $\triangle ABC$ and $\triangle DEF$ with rt. $\angle$s at B and E; $AC = DF$; $BC = EF$ (Given) 2. Draw $\overleftrightarrow{DE}$. (Line Post.) 3. Choose G on $\overrightarrow{DE}$ so that $EG = BA$. (Seg. Construction Post.) 4. Draw $\overline{FG}$ (Line Post.) 5. $\angle FEG$ is a rt. $\angle$. (If one $\angle$ of a lin. pr. is a rt. $\angle$, then other $\angle$ is also a rt. $\angle$. [1]) 6. $m\angle B = m\angle FEG$ (All rt. $\angle$s are =. [1, 5]) 7. $\triangle ABC \cong \triangle GEF$ (SAS Post. [1, 3, 6]) 8. $AC =$ GF (Corr. parts of $\cong \triangle$s are =. [7]) 9. $DF = GF$ (Substitution Prop. [1, 8]) 10. $m\angle G = m\angle D$ (Isos. $\triangle$ Thm. [9]) 11. $m\angle FEG = m\angle FED$ (All rt. $\angle$s are =. [1, 5]) 12. $\triangle GEF \cong \triangle DEF$ (AAS Thm. [9, 10, 11]) 13. $\triangle ABC \cong \triangle DEF$ (Congruence of $\triangle$s is transitive. [7, 12])

35. Sometimes **36.** Always **37.** Always **38.** Isosceles; legs: $\overline{MP}$ and $\overline{MN}$; base angles: $\angle N$, $\angle P$; vertex angle: $\angle M$ **39.** $\triangle YZX$

Pages 228–229

Written Exercises **1.** $2 < x < 12$ **3.** $5 < x < 10$ **5.** $\angle U; \angle V$ **7.** Sometimes **9.** Sometimes **11.** $>$ **13.** Yes; yes; no; Since $AH = BH$, $m\angle A = m\angle B$. If $AB < 8$ cm, $m\angle H < m\angle A$. So $m\angle H$ can be 40 when $m\angle A = m\angle B = 70$. If $AB = 8$ cm, $m\angle H = 60$ because $\triangle ABH$ is equilateral. $m\angle H$ cannot be 70, because then $m\angle A = m\angle B = 55$, and then $AB > 8$ cm, which contradicts the given information. **15.** *Proof:* 1. $ST > RS$ (Given) 2. $m\angle SRT > m\angle STR$ (If 2 sides of a $\triangle$ are $\neq$, the $\angle$s opp. them are $\neq$ in the same order. [1]) 3. $m\angle 1 = m\angle 2$; $m\angle 3 = m\angle 4$ (Given) 4. $m\angle STR = m\angle 1 + m\angle 2$; $m\angle SRT = m\angle 3 + m\angle 4$ ($\angle$ Add. Post.) 5. $m\angle STR = m\angle 2 + m\angle 2 = 2(m\angle 2)$; $m\angle SRT = m\angle 3 + m\angle 3 = 2(m\angle 3)$ (Substitution Prop. [3, 4]) 6. $2(m\angle 3) > 2(m\angle 2)$ (Substitution Prop. [2, 5]) 7. $m\angle 3 > m\angle 2$ (Mult. Prop. [6]) 8. $TU > UR$ (If 2 $\angle$s of a $\triangle$ are $\neq$, the sides opp. them are $\neq$ in the same order. [7]) **17.** *Proof:* 1. $m\angle MLJ = m\angle LMJ$; $MN < LN$ (Given) 2. $LJ = MJ$ (If 2 $\angle$s of a $\triangle$ are $=$; then the sides opp. those $\angle$s are $=$. [1]) 3. $NJ = NJ$ (Reflexive Prop.) 4. $m\angle MJN < m\angle LJN$ (If 2 sides of one $\triangle$ are $=$ to 2 sides of another $\triangle$ and the lengths of the third sides are $\neq$, then the measures of the $\angle$s included between the $=$ sides are $\neq$ in the same order. [2, 3]) 5. $\angle MJN$ and $\angle MJK$ are supp. $\angle$s; $\angle LJN$ and $\angle LJK$ are supp. $\angle$s. (Supplement Post.) 6. $m\angle MJN + m\angle MJK = 180$; $m\angle LJN + m\angle LJK = 180$ (Def. of supp. $\angle$s [5]) 7. $m\angle MJN = 180 - m\angle MJK$; $m\angle LJN = 180 - m\angle LJK$ (Subtraction Prop.) 8. $180 - m\angle MJK < 180 - m\angle LJK$ (Substitution Prop. [4, 7]) 9. $m\angle LJK < m\angle MJK$ (Add. Prop. [8]) **20.** 50, 50 **21.** If the hypotenuse and a leg of one rt. $\triangle$ are $=$ to the corr. parts of another rt. $\triangle$, then the $\triangle$s are $\cong$. **22.** altitude **23.** Ruler Post. **24.** dodecagon

Pages 231–233

Written Exercises **1.** $\overline{BC}; \overline{AC}$ **3.** 7 **5.** Yes **7.** 4; 8; 12 **9.** $AP + PC = AC$ and $BP + PD = BD$ by the Seg. Add. Post. $AC < AR + RC$ and $BD < BR + RD$ by the $\triangle$ Inequality Thm. So, $AC + BD < (AR + RC) + (BR + RD)$. By substitution, $(AP + PC) + (BP + PD) < (AR + RC) + (BR + RD)$. **11.** 4

13. *Given:* $\overline{AM}$ is a median of $\triangle ABC$; $\overline{AD}$ is an altitude; M is not D. *Prove:* $AD < AM$

Proof: Since $\overline{AD}$ is an altitude, $\overline{AD} \perp \overline{BC}$ by the def. of altitude. Since M is not D, median $\overline{AM}$ $\not\perp \overline{BC}$ because through a pt. not on a given line, there is exactly one line $\perp$ to the given line. So $AD < AM$ because the $\perp$ seg. from a pt. to a line is the shortest seg. from the pt. to the line. **15.** At the intersection of $\overline{AB}$ and p: any other point on p will yield a sum greater than AB. **19.** $4 < x < 22$ **20.** $\angle C; \angle B$ **21.** 48; 84 **22.** $\angle 3$, $\angle 5$, $\angle 7$ **23.** *Proof:* Either (1) $t \not\perp b$ or (2) $t \perp b$. Assume $t \perp b$. Since $t \perp a$, $a \parallel b$ because in a plane if 2 lines are $\perp$ to the same line, then they are $\parallel$. But this contradicts the given fact that $a \not\parallel b$. Hence, it is false that $t \perp b$. We conclude that $t \not\perp b$.

Chapter 5 Review, Pages 235–236

1. KL, RS; KM, RT; LM, ST **2.** $\angle K$, $\angle R$; $\angle L$, $\angle S$; $\angle M$, $\angle T$ **3.** $\overline{ST}$ **4.** SAS **5.** SSS **6.** $\triangle HJK \cong \triangle MNO$ by ASA Post. **7.** AAS Thm. **8.** SAS Post. **9.** *Proof:* 1. C is midpt. of $\overline{BD}$; $m\angle A = m\angle E$; $m\angle B = m\angle D$ (Given) 2. $BC = DC$ (Def. of midpt. [1]) 3. $\triangle ABC \cong \triangle EDC$ (AAS Thm. [1, 2]) **10.** *Proof:* 1. C is midpt. of $\overline{BD}$; $\overline{AC} \parallel \overline{ED}$; $AC = DE$ (Given) 2. $BC = CD$ (Def. of midpt. [1]) 3. $m\angle ACB = m\angle EDC$ (Lines $\parallel \Rightarrow$ corr. $\angle$s $=$. [1]) 4. $\triangle ABC \cong \triangle ECD$ (SAS Post. [1, 2, 3]) **11.** *Proof:* 1. $\overline{FG} \perp \overline{KF}$; $\overline{JK} \perp \overline{KF}$; $GH = JH$ (Given) 2. $\angle F$ and $\angle K$ are rt. $\angle$s (2 $\perp$ lines form 4 rt. $\angle$s [1]) 3. $m\angle F = m\angle K$ (All rt. $\angle$s are $=$. [2]) 4. $m\angle FHG = m\angle KHJ$ (Vert. $\angle$s are $=$.) 5. $\triangle FGH \cong \triangle KJH$ (AAS Thm. [1, 3, 4]) 6. $FH = KH$ (Corr. parts of $\cong \triangle$s are $=$. [5]) **12.** *Proof:* 1. H is midpt. of $\overline{KF}$ and $\overline{GJ}$. (Given) 2. $FH = KH$; $GH = JH$ (Def. of midpt. [1]) 3. $m\angle FHG = m\angle KHJ$ (Vert. $\angle$s are $=$.) 4. $\triangle FGH \cong \triangle KJH$ (SAS Post. [2, 3]) 5. $m\angle F = m\angle K$ (Corr. parts of $\cong \triangle$s are $=$. [4]) 6. $\overline{FG} \parallel \overline{JK}$ (Alt. int. $\angle$s $= \Rightarrow$ lines $\parallel$. [5]) **13.** $FT = GT = 52$ km. $\angle FTN$ and $\angle GTN$ are rt. $\angle$s, so they are $=$. $NT = NT$. Hence, $\triangle FTN \cong \triangle GTN$ by SAS Post. Then $FT = GT$ by corr. parts, so Fairfield and Grove City are $=$ distances from Tiffin. **14.** *Proof:* 1. $\overline{XY} \perp \overline{VZ}$; $\overline{VW} \perp \overline{XZ}$; $VW = XY$ (Given) 2. $\angle XYZ$ and $\angle VWZ$ are rt. $\angle$s. (2 $\perp$ lines form 4 rt. $\angle$s. [1]) 3. $m\angle XYZ = m\angle VWZ$ (All rt. $\angle$s are $=$. [2]) 4. $m\angle Z = m\angle Z$ (Reflexive Prop.) 5. $\triangle XYZ \cong \triangle VWZ$ (AAS Thm. [1, 3, 4]) **15.** *Proof:* 1. $YT = WT$; $VT = TX$ (Given) 2. $m\angle YTV = m\angle WTX$ (Vert. $\angle$s are $=$.) 3. $\triangle YTV \cong \triangle WTX$ (SAS Post. [1, 2]) 4. $m\angle V = m\angle X$ (Corr. parts of $\cong \triangle$s are

=. [3]) **5.** $m\angle Z = m\angle Z$ (Reflexive Prop.) **6.** YT $+ TX = WT + TV$ (Add. Prop. [1]) **7.** $YT + TX$ $= YX; WT + VT = WV$ (Seg. Add. Post.) **8.** YX $= WV$ (Substitution Prop. [6, 7]) **9.** $\triangle XYZ \cong$ $\triangle VWZ$ (AAS Thm. [4, 5, 8]) **10.** $YZ = WZ$ (Corr. parts of $\cong \triangle$s are =. [9])

16. *Plan for justifying:* Draw $\overline{RT}$ and $\overline{ST}$. $AR = AS$ and $RT = ST$ by construction. Show $\triangle RAT \cong \triangle SAT$ by SSS Post. Use corr. parts to show $m\angle RAT = m\angle SAT$.
Then $\overrightarrow{AT} \perp \overrightarrow{AB}$ because if the $\angle$s in a lin. pr. are =, then the lines containing their sides are $\perp$. So $\angle SAT$ is a rt. $\angle$. $AB = AC$ by construction, so $\triangle ABC$ is an isos. $\triangle$ by *def.*

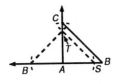

17. *Plan for justifying:* Draw $\overline{AR}$, $\overline{BR}$, $\overline{AC}$, and $\overline{BC}$. $AR = BR$ and $AC = BC$ by construction. Show $\triangle RAC \cong \triangle RBC$ by SSS Post. Then show $m\angle ARD = m\angle BRD$ by corr. parts and show $\triangle ARD \cong \triangle BRD$ by SAS Post. Use corr. parts to show $m\angle ADR = m\angle BDR$. So $\overrightarrow{RD} \perp \overrightarrow{PQ}$ because if the $\angle$s in a lin. pr. are =, then the lines containing their sides are $\perp$. **18.** Never **19.** Sometimes

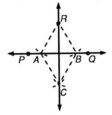

20. Always **21.** 60 **22.** 10 **23.** 10 **24.** *Proof:* 1. $XZ = YZ$ (Given) 2. $m\angle ZXY = m\angle ZYX$ (Isos. $\triangle$ Thm. [1]) 3. $\angle 1$ and $\angle ZXY$ are supp. $\angle$s; $\angle 2$ and $\angle ZYX$ are supp. $\angle$s. (Supp. Post.) 4. $m\angle 1 = m\angle 2$ (Supp. of = $\angle$s are =. [2, 3]) **25.** *Proof:* 1. $m\angle 1 = m\angle 2$ (Given) 2. $\angle 1$ and $\angle ZXY$ are supp. $\angle$s; $\angle 2$ and $\angle ZYX$ are supp. $\angle$s. (Supp. Post.) 3. $m\angle ZXY = m\angle ZYX$ (Supp. of = $\angle$s are =. [1, 2]) 4. $XZ = YZ$ (If 2 $\angle$s of a $\triangle$ are =, then the sides opp. those $\angle$s are =. [3]) **26.** *Proof:* 1. $XZ = YZ; \overline{ZW} \perp \overline{XY}$ (Given) 2. $\angle XWZ$ and $\angle YWZ$ are rt. $\angle$s. (2 $\perp$ lines form 4 rt. $\angle$s [1]) 3. $\triangle XWZ$ and $\triangle YWZ$ are rt. $\triangle$s (Def. of rt. $\triangle$ [2]) 4. $ZW = ZW$ (Reflexive Prop.) 5. $\triangle XWZ \cong$ $\triangle YWZ$ (HL Thm. [1, 3, 4]) 6. $XW = YW$ (Corr. parts of $\cong \triangle$s are =. [5]) 7. W is midpt. of $\overline{XY}$. (Def. of midpt. [6]) 8. $\overline{ZW}$ bisects $\overline{XY}$. (Def. of bisectors of a seg. [7]) **27.** $\angle D; \angle E$ **28.** $\overline{FH}$ **29.** The $\perp$ seg. from a pt. to a line is the shortest seg. from the pt. to the line. **30.** *Proof:* 1. $AD = BC; m\angle CAD < m\angle ACB$ (Given) 2. AC $= AC$ (Reflexive Prop.) 3. $CD < AB$ (Hinge

Thm. [1, 2]) **31.** *Proof:* 1. $AD = BC; AB > CD$ (Given) 2. $AC = AC$ (Reflexive Prop.) 3. $m\angle ACB > m\angle CAD$ (If 2 sides of one $\triangle$ are = to 2 sides of another $\triangle$ and the lengths of the third sides are $\neq$, then the measures of the $\angle$s included between the = sides are $\neq$ in the same order. [1, 2]) **32.** $1 < x < 25$ **33.** $13 < x < 25$

Chapter 6

Pages 241–243
Written Exercises **1.** 18 **3.** 135 **5.** $58\frac{1}{2}$
7. Thm. 6-4 **9.** 7 **11.** 2. Line Post. 3. Reflexive Prop. 4. Opp. sides of a $\square$ are =. [1] 5. $\triangle DAB$ $\cong \triangle BCD$ 6. Def. of $\cong \triangle$s [5] 7. $\triangle ADC \cong$ $\triangle CBA$ 8. Def. of $\cong \triangle$s [7] **13.** $4\sqrt{2}$ **15.** (4, 2) **17.** *Proof:* 1. $\square GRIN; \square GLAD$ (Given) 2. $m\angle G = m\angle I; m\angle G = m\angle A$ (Opp. $\angle$s of a $\square$ are =. [1]) 3. $m\angle I = m\angle A$ (Substitution Prop. [2]) **19.** 20 **21.** *Proof:* 1. $\square ABCD$ (Given) 2. $AB = CD$ (Opp. sides of a $\square$ are =. [1]) 3. $\overleftrightarrow{AB} \parallel \overleftrightarrow{CD}$ (Def. of $\square$ [1]) 4. $m\angle ABD =$ $m\angle CDB; m\angle BAC = m\angle DCA$ (2 lines $\parallel \Rightarrow$ alt. int. $\angle$s =. [3]) 5. $\triangle ABQ \cong \triangle CDQ$ (ASA $\cong$ Post. [2, 4]) 6. $AQ = CQ; BQ = DQ$ (Corres. parts of $\cong \triangle$s are =. [5]) 7. Q is the midpt. of both $\overline{AC}$ and $\overline{BD}$. (Def. of midpt. [6]) 8. $\overline{AC}$ and $\overline{BD}$ bisect each other. (Def. of seg. bisector [7]) **25.** *Proof:* 1. $\triangle MNQ$ is equilateral; $m\angle 1 = m\angle 2 = m\angle N$ (Given) 2. $\triangle MNQ$ is equiangular. (Equilateral $\triangle$ is equiangular. [1]) 3. $m\angle Q = m\angle N$ (Def. of equiangular $\triangle$ [2]) 4. $m\angle Q = m\angle 2; m\angle Q =$ $m\angle 1$ (Substitution Prop. [1, 3]) 5. $\overline{PQ} \parallel \overline{SR}; \overline{QR} \parallel$ $\overline{PS}$ (Corres. $\angle$s = $\Rightarrow$ lines $\parallel$. [4]) 6. PQRS is a $\square$. (Def. of $\square$ [5]) **27.** $PD < PC$; the $\perp$ segment from a pt. to a line is the shortest segment from the pt. to the lines. **28.** 5 **29.** $\overline{SV}$ **30.** $\mathcal{G} \parallel \mathcal{H}$ **31.** If a figure is a pentagon, then it is a convex polygon.

Pages 246–248
Written Exercises **1.** $x = 9$; Thm. 6-7 **3.** $x =$ 50; Thm. 4-4, def. of $\square$ **5.** 1. Given; 2. Alt. int. $\angle$s = $\Rightarrow$ 2 lines $\parallel$. [1] 3. Given 4. $\overline{RS}$; alt. int. $\angle$s = $\Rightarrow$ 2 lines $\parallel$. [3] 5. Def. of $\square$ [2, 4] **9.** *Proof:* 1. $m\angle 1 = m\angle 2$ (Given) 2. $\overleftrightarrow{LM} \parallel \overleftrightarrow{JK}$ (Alt. int. $\angle$s = $\Rightarrow$ lines $\parallel$. [1]) 3. $m\angle MJK =$ $m\angle KLM$ (Given) 4. $MK = MK$ (Reflexive Prop.) 5. $\triangle MKL \cong \triangle KMJ$ (AAS Thm. [1, 3, 4]) 6. $LM =$ JK (Corres. parts of $\cong \triangle$s are =. [5]) 7. JKLM is a $\square$. (If 2 sides of a quad. are $\parallel$ and =, then the quad. is a $\square$. [2, 6]) **11.** $x = 13; y = 6$ **13.** $x =$

6; $y = 3$ **15.** *Proof:* 1. Quadrilateral *ABCD*; *AB* = *CD*; *BC* = *AD* (Given) 2. Draw $\overleftrightarrow{BD}$. (Line Post.) 3. *BD* = *BD* (Reflexive Prop.) 4. △*BCD* ≅ △*DAB* (SSS ≅ Post. [1, 3]) 5. *m*∠1 = *m*∠2 (Corres. parts of ≅ △s are =. [4]) 6. $\overleftrightarrow{CD} \parallel \overleftrightarrow{AB}$ (Alt. int. ∠s = ⇒ lines ∥.) 7. *ABCD* is a ▱ (If 2 sides of a quad. are ∥ and =, then the quad. is a ▱. [1, 6]) **19.** Midpt. of $\overline{AC} = \left(\frac{7}{2}, 3\right)$ = midpt. of $\overline{BD}$; this means *ABCD* is a ▱ because the diags. bisect each other.

23. *Given:* *AB* + *BC* = *k*; *BC* + *CD* = *k*; *CD* + *AD* = *k*; *AD* + *AB* = *k* where *k* is some real number. *Prove:* *ABCD* is a ▱.
Proof: 1. *AB* + *BC* = *k*; *BC* + *CD* = *k*; *CD* + *AD* = *k*; *AD* + *AB* = *k* where *k* is some real number. (Given) 2. *AB* + *BC* = *BC* + *CD*; *BC* + *CD* = *CD* + *DA* (Substitution Prop. [1]) 3. *BC* = *BC*; *CD* = *CD* (Reflexive Prop.) 4. *AB* = *CD*; *BC* = *DA* (Subtraction Prop. [2, 3]) 5. *ABCD* is a ▱. (If both pairs of opp. sides are =, quad. is a ▱. [4]) **25.** Yes; 1) Since the slopes of opp. sides are =, both pairs of opp. sides are ∥. 2) Solving systems of linear equations, the vertices of the quad. are *A*(10, 6), *B*(8, 11), *C*(4, 7), and *D*(6, 2). Then the distance formula gives *AB* = *CD* = $\sqrt{29}$ and *BC* = *AD* = $4\sqrt{2}$. **26.** Opp. sides are ∥; opp. sides are =; opp. ∠s are =; diagonals bisect each other. **27.** *AB* = *CD* = 7; *AD* = *BC* = 11 **28.** No **29.** Division Prop. **30.** *Proof:* 1. *Z* is the midpt. of $\overline{XJ}$ and $\overline{KY}$. (Given) 2. *XZ* = *JZ* and *YZ* = *KZ* (Def. of midpt. [1]) 3. *m*∠*XZY* = *m*∠*KZJ* (Vert. ∠s are =.) 4. △*XYZ* ≅ △*JKZ* (SAS ≅ Post. [2, 4])

Pages 251–253
Written Exercises **1.** *A*, *B*, *L*, *M*, *O* **3.** *A*, *B*, *M*, *O* **5.** *B* **7.** 15 ft. **9.** 18; 168 **11.** 4; 3.25 **13.** Sometimes; = diags. prove only that it is a rect. **15.** Sometimes; the diags. of a ▱ are ⊥ only if the ▱ is a rhombus or a square. **17.** 28; 28 **19.** 100; 80 **21.** *Given:* ▱*ABCD*, *AC* = *BD* *Prove:* *ABCD* is a rect. *Proof:* By hypothesis, *ABCD* is a ▱ with *AC* = *BD*. Since *AD* = *BC* and *AB* = *AB*, △*ABD* ≅ △*BAC* by SSS ≅ Post. Then *m*∠*DAB* = *m*∠*CBA*. Since $\overline{AD} \parallel \overline{BC}$, ∠*DAB* and ∠*CBA* are supp. and *m*∠*DAB* + *m*∠*CBA* = 180. By the Substitution Prop. and Div. Prop., *m*∠*DAB* = *m*∠*CBA* = 90. Therefore, ∠*DAB* and

∠*CBA* are rt. ∠s. Since the opp. ∠s of a ▱ are = and all rt. ∠s are =, ∠*ADC* and ∠*BCD* are rt. ∠s. Then ▱*ABCD* has four rt. ∠s. Therefore △*ABCD* is a rectangle.

23. *Part I: Given:* ▱*ABCD*; $\overline{AC} \perp \overline{BD}$ *Prove:* *ABCD* is a rhombus. *Proof:* By hypothesis, *ABCD* is a ▱ with $\overline{AC} \perp \overline{BD}$. Since 2 ⊥ lines intersect to form 4 rt. ∠s and all rt. ∠s are =, *m*∠*AEB* = *m*∠*CEB*. We know *AE* = *CE* because the diags. of a ▱ bisect each other. Then △*AEB* ≅ △*CEB* (SAS ≅ Post.). Therefore, *AB* = *BC*. Since *ABCD* is a ▱, *AB* = *DC* and *AD* = *BC*. Therefore, by the Substitution Prop., *AB* = *BC* = *CD* = *DA*. So, ▱*ABCD* is a rhombus. *Part II: Given:* *ABCD* is a rhombus. *Prove:* $\overline{AC} \perp \overline{BD}$ *Proof:* By hypothesis, *ABCD* is a rhombus and by the def. of a rhombus, *AB* = *BC*. Since a rhombus is also a ▱, and the diags. of a ▱ bisect each other, *AE* = *EC*. Since *BE* = *BE*, △*ABE* ≅ △*CBE* by SSS ≅ Post. Then *m*∠*AEB* = *m*∠*CEB*. Since ∠*AEB* and ∠*CEB* form a lin. pr., $\overline{AC} \perp \overline{BD}$ (If the ∠s of a lin. pr. are =, then the lines containing their sides are ⊥.) **25.** Rhombus: Since the slope of $\overline{AB}$ = slope of $\overline{DC} = \frac{1}{5}$ and the slope of $\overline{AD}$ = slope $\overline{BC}$ = 5, $\overline{AB} \parallel \overline{DC}$ and $\overline{AD} \parallel \overline{BC}$. By the Dist. Formula *AB* = *BC* = *CD* = *DA* = $\sqrt{26}$. Therefore, *ABCD* is a rhombus by definition. Since the slopes of $\overline{AC}$ and $\overline{BD}$ are neg. reciprocals of each other, $\overline{AC} \perp \overline{BD}$ and *ABCD* is a rhombus by Thm. 6-9. **27.** *RT* = $\frac{21n}{2}$ **29.** By measuring to see that its diags. are = and its opp. sides are = **32.** 1) $\overline{PQ} \parallel \overline{RS}$ and $\overline{PS} \parallel \overline{QR}$; 2) *PQ* = *SR* and *PS* = *QR*; 3) $\overline{PQ} \parallel \overline{RS}$ and *PQ* = *RS*; 4) $\overline{PR}$ and $\overline{QS}$ bisect each other **33.** 21 + *y* **34.** The distance between 2 given ∥ lines is constant. **35.** Yes, by the AAS Theorem **36.** 155; 25

Pages 257–260
Written Exercises **1.** $6\frac{1}{2}$ **3.** 30 **5.** 24 **7.** (10, −11) **9.** Slope of $\overleftrightarrow{XY}$ = slope of $\overleftrightarrow{AC}$ = 0 **11.** 17 **13.** 10.5 **15.** Thm. 6-12 **17.** 60 **19.** 6; 12 **21.** *Proof:* 1. In △*ABC*, *X* and *Y* are midpts. of $\overline{AC}$ and $\overline{BC}$, respectively. (Given) 2. *CX* = *XA*, *CY* = *YB* (Def. of midpt. [1]) 3. Locate *Z* on $\overleftrightarrow{XY}$ so that *YZ* = *XY* (Seg. Construction Post.) 4. *m*∠*CYX* = *m*∠*BYZ* (Vert. ∠s are =.) 5. △*CYX*

$\cong \triangle BYZ$ (SAS $\cong$ Post. [2, 4]) **6.** $m\angle 1 = m\angle 2$ (Corres. parts of $\cong \triangle$s are =. [5]) **7.** $\overline{AX} \parallel \overline{BZ}$ (Alt. int. $\angle$s = $\Rightarrow$ 2 lines $\parallel$. [6]) **8.** $CX = BZ$ (Corres. parts of $\cong \triangle$s are =. [5]) **9.** $AX = BZ$ (Substitution Prop. [2, 8]) **10.** $AXZB$ is a $\square$. (If 2 sides of a quad. are $\parallel$ and =, then the quad. is a $\square$. [7, 9]) **11.** $\overline{XY} \parallel \overline{AB}$ (Def. of $\square$ [10])
12. $XZ = AB$ (Both prs. of opp. sides of a $\square$ are =. [10]) **13.** $XY + YZ = XZ$ (Seg. Add. Post.)
14. $XY + XY = XZ$ or $2(XY) = XZ$ (Substitution Prop. [3, 13]) **15.** $XY = \frac{1}{2}XZ$ (Mult. Prop. [14])
16. $XY = \frac{1}{2}AB$ (Substitution Prop. [12, 15])
23. Draw diag. $\overline{AC}$. In $\triangle ACD$, $\overline{ZY} \parallel \overline{AC}$ and in $\triangle CAB$, $\overline{WX} \parallel \overline{AC}$ by Thm. 6-11. Then $\overline{ZY} \parallel \overline{WX}$ (Two lines $\parallel$ to same line are $\parallel$ to each other). Draw diag. $\overline{BD}$. In $\triangle ABD$, $\overline{ZW} \parallel \overline{BD}$ and in $\triangle CDB$, $\overline{XY} \parallel \overline{BD}$. Therefore, $\overline{ZW} \parallel \overline{XY}$. Thus $WXYZ$ is a $\square$ by the def. of a $\square$. **25.** 6
31. By the Midpoint Formula, the coordinates of D and E are $\left(\frac{x + x_1}{2}, \frac{y + y_1}{2}\right)$ and $\left(\frac{x_1 + x_2}{2}, \frac{y_1 + y_2}{2}\right)$, respectively. Then by the Distance Formula,
$DE = \frac{\sqrt{(x_2 - x_1)^2 + (y_2 - y_1)^2}}{2}$ and
$AC = \sqrt{(x_2 - x_1)^2 + (y_2 - y_1)^2}$. Thus, $DE = \frac{1}{2}AC$. **32.** They are $\perp$; they bisect each other; they bisect the opp. $\angle$s of the rhombus. **33.** Yes; it can be a square. **34.** *Proof:* 1. D is the midpt. of $\overline{MJ}$. (Given) 2. $DM = DJ$ (Def. of midpt. [1]) 3. $m\angle 1 = m\angle 2$ (Given) 4. $\overline{HJ} \parallel \overline{MK}$ (Alt. int. $\angle$s = $\Rightarrow$ lines $\parallel$. [3]) 5. $m\angle HDJ = m\angle KDM$ (Vert. $\angle$s are =.) 6. $\triangle HDJ \cong \triangle KDM$ (ASA $\cong$ Post. [2, 3, 5]) 7. $HJ = MK$ (Corrs. parts of $\cong \triangle$s are =. [6]) 8. $HJKM$ is a $\square$. (If 2 sides of a quad. are both $\parallel$ and =, then the quad. is a $\square$. [4, 7]) **35.** 20
36. 144
Algebra Review 1. $-2x^2 - 18x$ **3.** $-12xy + 6y^2$ **5.** $x^2 + 9x + 14$ **7.** $6x^2 + 26xy + 24y^2$

Pages 264–266
Written Exercises 1. Never **3.** Sometimes
5. Sometimes **7.** $\frac{1}{2}(a + 55)$ **9.** 50 **11.** 4
13. 72 **15.** Yes; $AD = BC = 6$ **17.** *Proof:* By hypothesis, $QRST$ is an isos. trap. and by def. $QT = RS$. $m\angle QTS = m\angle RST$ because each pair of base $\angle$s of an isos. trap. are =. Since $ST = ST$, $\triangle QTS \cong \triangle RST$ by SAS $\cong$ Post. Thus, $QS = RT$ (Corr. parts of $\cong \triangle$s are =.). **19.** 58 **23.** 48 in.
25. 21.5 **27.** $\frac{3\sqrt{29}}{2}$ **29.** *Proof:* 1. Trap. $ABCD$ has

$\overline{AB} \parallel \overline{CD}$ and median $\overline{XY}$. (Given) 2. Draw $\overline{BD}$. (2 pts. determine a line.) 3. Let M be midpt. of $\overline{BD}$. (Seg. has exactly 1 midpt.) 4. Draw $\overline{MX}$ and $\overline{MY}$. (2 pts. determine a line.) 5. X is midpt. of $\overline{AD}$; Y is midpt. of $\overline{BC}$. (Def. of median of trap. [1]) 6. $\overline{MX} \parallel \overline{AB}$; $\overline{MY} \parallel \overline{DC}$; $MX = \frac{1}{2}(AB)$; $MY = \frac{1}{2}(DC)$ (Seg. joining midpts. of 2 sides of $\triangle$ is $\parallel$ to third side and half its length. [3, 5]) 7. $\overline{MY} \parallel \overline{AB}$ (2 lines $\parallel$ to same line are $\parallel$ to each other [1, 6]) 8. $\overline{MY}$ and $\overline{XM}$ lie on the same line: $\overleftrightarrow{XY}$. (Through a pt. not on a given line, there is exactly 1 line $\parallel$ to the given line. [6, 7]) 10. $XY = MX + MY$ (Seg. Add. Post.) 11. $XY = \frac{1}{2}(AB) + \frac{1}{2}(CD) = \frac{1}{2}(AB + CD)$ (Substitution Prop. [6, 10])
31. $DX = CY = \frac{2k + s - t}{4}$ **32.** 9 **33.** 84 **34.** $\square$, rect., rhombus **35.** Sample: $y = 2x + 6$ **36.** SSS $\cong$ Post., SAS $\cong$ Post., ASA $\cong$ Post., AAS Thm., HL Thm.

Pages 270–272
Written Exercises
1. The locus is 2 planes $\parallel$ to the given plane and 10 cm from the given plane.
3. The locus is the pt. of intersection of the diagonals of the square.
5. The locus is the pt. of intersection of the bisectors of the $\angle$s of the $\triangle$.
7. There is no locus that satisfies the conditions.
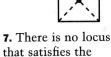
11. In a plane, what is the focus of pts. equidistant from $\parallel$ lines ℓ and k? **13.** What is the locus of pts. equidistant from the vertices of square $WXYZ$? **15.** What is the locus of pts. 3 cm from line ℓ? **25.** The intersection of the bisector of $\angle A$ and the $\perp$ bisector of $\overline{BC}$.
27. Depending on the orientation of the 2 pts., the locus may be (a) 2 pts., (b) no pts., or (c) infinitely many pts. **28.** The median of a trap. is the seg. joining the midpts. of the 2 non-$\parallel$ sides. **29.** They both have = legs and = base $\angle$s. **30.** 12 **32.** $\overline{JM}$

Algebra Review **1.** $4b(3a + b)$ **3.** $(x - 7)(x + 7)$ **5.** $(3x - 4)(2x + 1)$ **7.** $(4a - 3y)(4a + 3y)$

Pages 275–277
Written Exercises **1.** In a plane, the locus of pts. equidistant from 2 given pts. is the ⊥ bisector of the seg. joining the 2 pts. **3.** *Part I*: In a plane, if a point is equidistant from two parallel lines, then it is on a line parallel to the given lines at half the distance between them. *Part II*: If a point is on a line parallel to and half the distance between two parallel lines, then it is equidistant from the given lines. **5.** $\ell \perp \mathcal{K}$ **7.** $n \perp E$ **9.** A point is d cm from a given point if and only if it lies on the circle with radius d and center at the given point. **11.** Line $x = \frac{3}{2}$
13. Line $y = x$, x and y both > 0 **15.** Pts. $(6, -1)$ and $(-4, -1)$
17. *Part I*: Given: P is on $\overrightarrow{BX}$; $\overrightarrow{BX}$ bisects $\angle ABC$; $\overline{PM} \perp \overrightarrow{BA}$; $\overline{PN} \perp \overrightarrow{BC}$; $P \neq B$ Prove: $PM = PN$

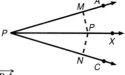

Proof: 1. P is on $\overrightarrow{BX}$, $\overrightarrow{BX}$ bisects $\angle ABC$; $\overline{PM} \perp \overrightarrow{BA}$; $\overline{PN} \perp \overrightarrow{BC}$; $P \neq B$ (Given) 2. $m\angle MBP = m\angle NBP$ (Def. of $\angle$ bisector [1]) 3. $\angle PMB$ and $\angle PNB$ are rt. $\angle$s. (2 ⊥ lines intersect to form 4 rt. $\angle$s. [1]) 4. $m\angle PMB = m\angle PNB$ (All rt. $\angle$s are =. [3]) 5. $BP = BP$ (Reflexive Prop.) 6. $\triangle PMB \cong \triangle PNB$ (AAS Thm. [2, 4, 5]) 7. $PM = PN$ (Corres. parts of $\cong \triangle$s are =. [6]) *Part II*: Given: $\overrightarrow{BX}$ bisects $\angle ABC$; $MP = NP$; $\overline{PM} \perp \overrightarrow{BM}$; $\overline{PN} \perp \overrightarrow{BN}$. Prove: P is on $\overrightarrow{BX}$. Proof: Either P is on $\overrightarrow{BX}$ or P is not on $\overrightarrow{BX}$. Suppose P is not on $\overrightarrow{BX}$. Then $\overrightarrow{BP}$ does not bisect $\angle ABC$ (An angle has exactly 1 bisector.). However, by the HL Thm., $\triangle BPM \cong \triangle BPN$. Thus, $m\angle PBM = m\angle PBN$. And since $m\angle PBM = m\angle PBN$, $\overrightarrow{BP}$ bisects $\angle ABC$. This contradicts the fact that $\overrightarrow{BP}$ does not bisect $\angle ABC$. Therefore, the assumption that P is not on $\overrightarrow{BX}$ is false. We conclude that P is on $\overrightarrow{BX}$. **21.** *Given*: Plane $\mathcal{E} \perp$ line k at P Prove: $\mathcal{E}$ contains all lines ⊥ to k at P. Proof: Either $\mathcal{E}$ contains all lines ⊥ to k at p or $\mathcal{E}$ does not contain all lines ⊥ to k at P. Suppose $\mathcal{E}$ does not contain all lines ⊥ to k at P. Let q be a line, not in $\mathcal{E}$, that is ⊥ to k at P. Let $\mathcal{F}$ be the plane that contains lines k and q (2 intersecting lines determine a plane.); then $\mathcal{F}$ and $\mathcal{E}$ intersect in line ℓ, and ℓ contains P because P is in $\mathcal{E}$ and $\mathcal{F}$. Since ℓ is in $\mathcal{E}$, $\ell \perp k$ at P; thus ℓ and q are 2 lines in $\mathcal{F} \perp$ to k at P. But this contradicts the fact that in a plane, through a given pt. on a given line, there exists exactly 1 line ⊥ to the given line. Therefore, the assumption that $\mathcal{E}$ does not contain all lines ⊥ k at P is false. We conclude that $\mathcal{E}$ contains all lines ⊥ to k at P.

25. $\frac{3\sqrt{5}}{2}$ **26.** 29 **27.** Samples: Ceiling and floor; opposite walls

Chapter 6 Review, Pages 279–280
1. Sample: AB and CD **2.** Sample: $m\angle A$ and $m\angle C$; $m\angle ABD$ and $m\angle BDC$ **3.** Sample: $\angle A$ and $\angle ADC$ **4.** $(4, 1)$ **5.** Thm. 6-6 **6.** Thm. 6-5 **7.** Thm. 6-7 **8.** Def. of $\square$ **9.** Rect. **10.** Rhombus **11.** Square **12.** Rhombus **13.** Square **14.** False **15.** True **16.** True **17.** False **18.** True **19.** 16 **20.** 5.5 **21.** $(10.5, 7)$ **22.** 12.5; 17.5; 35 **23.** 6; 6 **24.** 2.5 **25.** 29 **26.** 13
28. *Proof*: 1. $\overline{XY}$ is the median of isosceles trap. $MNOP$. (Given) 2. $\overline{XY} \parallel \overline{PO}$ (The median of a trap. is $\parallel$ to the bases.) 3. $XYOP$ is a trap. (Def. of trap. [2]) 4. $MP = NO$ (Def. of isos. trap. [1]) 5. X and Y are midpts. of $\overline{MP}$ and $\overline{NO}$, resp. (Def. of median of trap. [1]) 6. $MX = PX$; $NY = OY$ (Def. of midpt. [5]) 7. $MX + XP = MP$; $NY + YO = NO$ (Seg. Add. Post.) 8. $XP + XP = MP$ or $2(XP) = MP$; $YO + YO = NO$ or $2(YO) = NO$ (Substitution Prop. [6, 7]) 9. $2(XP) = 2(YO)$ (Substitution Prop. [4, 8]) 10. $XP = YO$ (Div. Prop. [9]) 11. $XYOP$ is isos. trap. (Def. of isos. trap. [3, 10]) **29.** The locus of pts. is a circle with a radius of r cm and center at the given pt. **30.** The locus of pts. is a cylindrical surface determined by all circles with centers on the given line and with radius k inches, and the plane of each circle is ⊥ to the given line. **31.** The locus of pts. is the seg. joining the midpts. of the other 2 sides of the rect. **32.** *Part I*: If a pt. is on a sphere with a given pt. as the center and a given distance as the radius of the sphere, then the distance from the pt. to the given pt. is the given distance. *Part II*: If a pt. is a given distance from a given pt., then it lies on the sphere with the given pt. as center and the given distance as the radius of the sphere.

33. *Part I: Given:* Sphere with center *P* and radius *r*; *X* is a pt. on the sphere. *Prove:* PX = r *Part II: Given:* Sphere with center *P* and radius *r*; *PX* = *r* *Prove:* X is a pt. on the sphere.

Chapter 7

Pages 289–291

Written Exercises   1. $\frac{8}{14}; \frac{12}{21}; \frac{28}{49}$ **3.** $\frac{5}{1}; \frac{10}{2}; \frac{60}{12}$
5. 3   **7.** $\frac{15}{5} = \frac{9}{3}; \frac{3+9}{9} = \frac{5+15}{15}; \frac{3-9}{9} = \frac{5-15}{15}$
9. 222 mi.   **11.** The third day   **13.** 4 in.; 6 in.;
9 in.   **15.** $3(15) \stackrel{?}{=} 5(9)$, 45 = 45   **17.** $\frac{5}{3} \stackrel{?}{=} \frac{15}{9}; \frac{5}{3} =$
$\frac{5}{3}$ **19.** $\frac{9-15}{15} \stackrel{?}{=} \frac{3-5}{5}; \frac{-6}{15} \stackrel{?}{=} \frac{-2}{5}; \frac{-2}{5} = \frac{-2}{5}$
21. $\frac{5+s}{s}; \frac{4}{4}$(1) was added to $\frac{r}{4}$ and $\frac{s}{s}$(1) was added
to $\frac{5}{s}$.   **23.** x = 2.5   **25.** $\frac{4}{3}$ **27.** 40°; 50°   **29.** 72;
72; 36   **31.** 6 cm; 5 cm   **33.** $\frac{DE}{AB} = \frac{1}{2}; \frac{FE}{BC} = \frac{1}{2};$
$\frac{FD}{AC} = \frac{1}{2}$ **35.** If a point is on the locus, it satisfies
the given conditions and vice versa.   **36.** A line
with equation $y = \frac{1}{2}$ **37.** A line which bisects
the right angle   **38.** Never

Pages 294–296

Written Exercises   1. 20   **3.** $5\frac{1}{3}$ **5.** 6
7. Sometimes   **9.** Never   **11.** Sometimes
13. 4:3   **15.** *Given:* △ABC ~ △DEF *Prove:*
$\frac{\text{Perimeter } \triangle ABC}{\text{Perimeter } \triangle DEF} = \frac{AB}{DE}$ *Plan for Proof:* By
definition of similar polygons, $\frac{AB}{DE} = \frac{BC}{EF} = \frac{CA}{FD}$.
Use the Summation Prop. of Prop. to show that
$\frac{AB + BC + CA}{DE + EF + FD} = \frac{AB}{DE}$.   **17.** ∠W; ∠L   **19.** 70
21. Yes; corresponding angles are equal and the
ratios of lengths of corresponding sides is 1:1.
23. Sample: K(0, −1); L(−4, 3); M(−4, 11); N(−2, 7);
P(6, 9)   **25.** No; corresponding angles are equal,
but lengths of corresponding sides (KF and EL,
and HG and CM) are not proportional.   **27.** x =
11   **28.** 20; 40; 120   **19.** Two lines parallel to *y*
= x + 5: y = x + (5 + 8√2) and
y = x + (5 − 8√2)   **30.** All properties of a
parallelogram; four equal sides; diagonals that
are perpendicular and that bisect pairs of
opposite angles   **31.** 108

Algebra Review   1. 9   **3.** 6   **5.** 60√2   **7.** $\frac{\sqrt{30}}{10}$
9. 5   **11.** 320   **13.** $\frac{\sqrt{15}}{3}$ **15.** $\frac{3\sqrt5}{5}$

Pages 299–300

Written Exercises   1. x = 8   **3.** x = 45   **5.** No
7. 614 cm   **9.** x = 24   **11.** 17 m   **13.** *Proof:*
1. △MNP; MP = NP; $\overline{RT} \perp \overline{PN}$; $\overline{RS} \perp \overline{PM}$
(Given)   2. m∠M = m∠N (Isos. △ Thm. [1])
3. ∠RSM and ∠RTN are rt. ∠s. (2 ⊥ lines form
4 rt. ∠s. [1])   4. m∠RSM = m∠RTN (All rt. ∠s
are =. [3])   5. △MRS ~ △NRT (AA ~ Post. [2,
4])   6. $\frac{RM}{RN} = \frac{RS}{RT}$ (Def. of ~ polygons [5])
7. (RM)(RT) = (RN)(RS) (Multiplication Prop.
[6])   **15.** *Given:* △ABC ~ △DEF *Prove:* △DEF ~
△ABC *Proof:* 1. △ABC ~ △DEF (Given)
2. m∠A = m∠D; m∠B = m∠E (Def. of ~
polygons [1])   3. m∠D = m∠A; m∠E = m∠B
(Symmetric Prop. [2])   4. △DEF ≅ △ABC (AA ~
Post. [3])   **17.** *Proof:* △HJK; ∠J is a rt. ∠; $\overline{JL} \perp$
$\overline{HK}$ (Given   2. ∠JLK is a rt. ∠ (Two ⊥ lines form
4 rt. ∠s. [1])   3. m∠HJK = m∠JLK (All rt. ∠s are
=. [1, 2])   4. m∠K = ∠K (Reflexive Prop.)
5. △HJK ~ △JLK (AA ~ Post. [3, 4])   **18.** m∠F
19. 9.375   **21.** m∠V = m∠X; m∠W = m∠Y;
m∠V + m∠W = 180; m∠W + m∠X = 180;
m∠X + m∠Y = 180; m∠Y + m∠V = 180   **22.** If
the vertex angles of two isosceles triangles are
equal, then the triangles are similar; if two
isosceles triangles are similar, then their vertex
angles are equal; yes; yes

Pages 304–307

Written Exercises   1. 1.2   **3.** 20   **5.** $5\frac{1}{3}$ **7.** 10
9. 30   **11.** No   **13.** No   **15.** No   **17.** Not
similar   **19.** Similar   **21.** AD = 15; AE = 12
23. AC = 3; BD = 4   **25.** x = 12; y = 30; z =
18   **27.** 1,475 ft.   **29.** *Proof:* 1. ▱ABCD; $\overline{EF}$ ∥
$\overline{DC}$; $\overline{GH}$ ∥ $\overline{BC}$ (Given)   2. $\frac{AG}{GB} = \frac{AK}{KC}$, $\frac{AE}{ED} = \frac{AK}{KC}$ (If a
line ∥ to one side of a △ intersects the other 2
sides, then it divides them proportionally. [1])
3. $\frac{AG}{GB} = \frac{AE}{ED}$ (Substitution Prop. [2])   **31.** TR =
2√2   **41.** Yes; the sum of the angle measures of
a triangle is 180, so m∠Y = 69. By the AA
Similarity Postulate, △XYZ ~ △PQR.   **42.** No;
the angles are not necessarily equal.   **43.** the
perpendicular segment from the point to the
line   **44.** ∠S and ∠T; ∠V and ∠U

Pages 312–314

Written Exercises **1.** $x = 6.5$ **3.** $x = 6$
5. Samples: 8, 10, 12; 12, 15, 18; SSS ~ Thm.
7. $x = 10$ **9.** $x = 12$ **11.** Yes; SSS ~ Thm.
13. Yes; SAS or SSS ~ Thm. **15.** 41.5 ft.
19. *Given:* Quadrilateral $ABCD$ with diagonals $\overline{AC}$ and $\overline{BD}$ intersecting at X. *Prove:* $\frac{AX}{CX} = \frac{BX}{DX}$ if and only if $ABCD$ is a parallelogram or a trapezoid. *Proof: Part I:* 1. $ABCD$ is a parallelogram or a trapezoid with diagonals $\overline{AC}$ and $\overline{BD}$ intersecting at X (Given) 2. $\overline{AB} \parallel \overline{DE}$ (Def. parallelogram or trapezoid [1]) 3. $m\angle AXB = m\angle CXD$ (Vertical $\angle$s are =.) 4. $m\angle ABX = m\angle CDX$ (2 lines $\parallel \Rightarrow$ alt. int. $\angle$s =. [2]) 5. $\triangle AXB$ ~ $\triangle CXD$ (AA ~ Post. [3, 4]) 6. $\frac{AX}{CX} = \frac{BX}{DX}$ (Def. ~ polygons [5]) *Part II:* 1. $ABCD$ is a quadrilateral with diagonals $\overline{AC}$ and $\overline{BD}$ intersecting at X; $\frac{AX}{CX} = \frac{BX}{DX}$ (Given) 2. $m\angle AXB = m\angle CXD$ (Vertical $\angle$s are =.) 3. $\triangle AXB$ ~ $\triangle CXD$ (SAS ~ Thm. [1, 2]) 4. $m\angle XBA = m\angle XDC$ (Def. ~ polygons [3]) 5. $\overline{AB} \parallel \overline{DC}$ (Alt. int. $\angle$s = $\Rightarrow$ 2 lines $\parallel$. [4]) 6. $ABCD$ is a parallelogram or a trapezoid. (Def. parallelogram or trapezoid [5]) **20.** $\triangle ABE$, $\triangle ACF$, $\triangle ADG$ **21.** 7.5 **22.** If two angles of one triangle are equal to two angles of another, then the triangles are similar. **23.** No; given $m\angle A + m\angle B = 180$, if $m\angle A \neq m\angle B$, the complements of $\angle A$ and $\angle B$ cannot have the same measure; if $m\angle A = m\angle B$, the complements of $\angle A$ and $\angle B$ would have to have measure 0 and by definition the measure of an angle is between 0 and 180. Yes; given $m\angle A + m\angle B = 90$, if $m\angle A = m\angle B$, the complements of $\angle A$ and $\angle B$ both have measure 45. **24.** Prove that: opposite sides are parallel, opposite sides are equal, opposite angles are equal, diagonals bisect each other, one pair of opposite sides are equal and parallel.

Algebra Review **1.** $x = 3$ or -7 **3.** $x = \frac{3 \pm \sqrt{21}}{2}$ **5.** $x = -2 \pm \sqrt{6}$ **7.** $x = -\frac{2}{3}$ **9.** $x = \pm 9$

Pages 318–320

Written Exercises **1.** $x = 28$ **3.** $x = 7$ **5.** 15
7. 16 **9.** 12 **11.** 24 **13.** 10 **15.** 12 **17.** $x = 36$ **19.** $x = 20$ **21.** AA ~ Post. **23.** AA ~ Post. **25.** SAS ~ Thm. **27.** 71.25 **29.** 15
31. 6 **33.** 4 **39.** *Proof:* 1. $\triangle ABC$; $AC \neq BC$; $\overrightarrow{CE}$ bisects $\angle BCD$. (Given) 2. Draw $\overrightarrow{BG} \parallel \overleftrightarrow{CD}$ intersecting CE at F. (Through a pt. not on a

line, there is exactly one line $\parallel$ to a given line.) 3. $m\angle CFB = m\angle DCF$ (2 lines $\parallel \Rightarrow$ alt. int. $\angle$s =. [2]) 4. $m\angle DCF = m\angle FCB$ (Def. of $\angle$ bisector [1]) 5. $m\angle CFB = m\angle FCB$ (Transitive Prop. [3, 4]) 6. $FB = BC$ (If 2 $\angle$s of a $\triangle$ are =, the sides opposite those $\angle$s are =. [5]) 7. $m\angle E = m\angle E$ (Reflexive Prop.) 8. $m\angle EFB = m\angle ECA$ (2 lines $\parallel \Rightarrow$ corr. $\angle$s =. [2]) 9. $\triangle EFB$ ~ $\triangle ECA$ (AA ~ Post. [7, 8]) 10. $\frac{AE}{EB} = \frac{AC}{FB}$ (Def. of ~ Polygons [9]) 11. $\frac{AE}{EB} = \frac{AC}{BC}$ (Substitution Prop. [6, 10]) **40.** Two $\triangle$s are ~ if: all prs. of corr. $\angle$s are = and lengths of prs. of corr. sides are proportional; 2 prs. of corr. $\angle$s are =; they are $\cong$; they are ~ to the same $\triangle$; lengths of 2 prs. of corr. sides are proportional and the included $\angle$s are =; lengths of all prs. of corr. sides are proportional.
41. $x = 85$ **42.** the parallel lines divide the transversals proportionally **43.** 22
44. Place a corner of the card on the first line and an adjacent corner on the seventh line. Mark the card at the points where the edge of the card intersects the lines between the first and seventh lines.

Pages 323–325

Written Exercises **1.** 6.25 cm **3.** 20 cm
5. 9.6 ft. **7.** 5.4 cm **9.** No; she can see nothing closer than 8 blocks away from the shorter building. **11.** 42.5 m **13.** 3 m **15.** The height at which the braces cross is independent of the distance between the poles. **16.** Angle bisectors, altitudes, medians **17.** $\frac{GE}{DE} = \frac{KG}{KD}$ **18.** $\frac{QR}{TU} = \frac{RP}{UA}$

Chapter 7 Review, Pages 327–328

1. Samples: $\frac{e}{g} = \frac{h}{f}$, $\frac{e}{h} = \frac{g}{f}$, $\frac{e+g}{g} = \frac{h+f}{f}$ **2.** 2,800 mi. **3.** $x = 2$ **4.** $x = 5$ **5.** $x = 7$ **6.** $\angle S$ and $\angle A$; $\angle T$ and $\angle B$; $\angle U$ and $\angle C$; $\angle V$ and $\angle D$ **7.** $\frac{ST}{AB}$, $\frac{TU}{BC}$, $\frac{UV}{CD}$, $\frac{VS}{DA}$ **8.** 16 **9.** *Given:* $\triangle ABD$ ~ $\triangle KED$; $AK = 5$; $KD = 10$ *Prove:* $BD = 3BE$ *Proof:*
1. $\triangle ABD$ ~ $\triangle KED$; $AK = 5$; $KD = 10$ (Given)
2. $\frac{AD}{KD} = \frac{BE}{DE}$ (Def. of ~ polygons [1]) 3. $AD = AK + KD$; $BD = BE + DE$ (Seg. Add. Post.) 4. $AD - KD = AK$; $BD - BE = DE$; $BD - DE = BE$ (Subtraction Prop. [3]) 5. $\frac{AD - KD}{KD} = \frac{BD - DE}{DE}$ (Subtraction Prop. [2]) 6. $\frac{AK}{KD} = \frac{BE}{BD - BE}$

(Substitution Prop. [4, 5]) **7.** $\frac{5}{10} = \frac{1}{2} = \frac{BE}{BD - BE}$
(Substitution Prop. [1, 6]) **8.** $BD - BE = 2BE$
(Mult. Prop. [7]) **9.** $BE = 3BE$ (Add. Prop. [8])
10. No **11.** No **12.** $x = 6$ **13.** $x = 6$ **14.** $x =$
12.5 **15.** *Proof:* 1. $\square ABCD$ (Given) 2. $AB \parallel CD$
(Def. of $\square$ [1]) 3. $m\angle EBO = m\angle CDO$ (2 lines $\parallel$
$\Rightarrow$ alt. int. $\angle$s =. [2]) 4. $m\angle EOB = m\angle COD$
(Vertical $\angle$s re =.) 5. $\triangle BOE \sim \triangle DOC$ (AA $\sim$
Post. [3, 4]) **16.** 18 **17.** 12 **18.** $16\frac{2}{3}$ **19.** 4; 8;
4 **20.** $x = 14$ **21.** $x = 53$ **22.** $x = 1.5$
23. *Proof:* 1. $\frac{AE}{AC} = \frac{AD}{DG}$ (Given) 2. $m\angle A = m\angle A$
(Reflexive Prop.) 3. $\triangle AED \sim \triangle ACB$ (SAS $\sim$
Thm. [1, 2]) 4. $m\angle AED = m\angle ACB$ (Def. of $\sim$
polygon [3]) **24.** 9 **25.** *Proof:* 1. $\triangle CNB \sim$
$\triangle EMA$; $\overrightarrow{NO}$ bisects $\angle CNB$; $\overrightarrow{MD}$ bisects $\angle EMA$
(Given) 2. $m\angle C = m\angle E$; $m\angle CNB = m\angle EMA$
(Def. of $\sim$ polygons [1]) 3. $m\angle CNO = m\angle BNO$;
$m\angle EMD = m\angle AMD$ (Def. of $\angle$ bis. [1])
4. $m\angle CNB = m\angle CNO + m\angle BNO$; $m\angle EMA =$
$m\angle EMD + m\angle AMD$ (Angle Add. Post.)
5. $m\angle CNB = 2(m\angle CNO)$; $m\angle EMA =$
$2(m\angle EMD)$ (Substitution Prop. [3, 4])
6. $2(m\angle CNO) = 2(m\angle EMD)$ (Substitution Prop.
[3, 5]) 7. $m\angle CNO = m\angle EMD$ (Division Prop.
[6]) 8. $\triangle CNO \sim \triangle EMD$ (AA $\sim$ Post. [2, 7])
9. $\frac{NO}{MD} = \frac{CO}{ED}$ (Def. of $\sim$ polygons [8]) 10. $\frac{NO}{CO} =$
$\frac{MD}{CD}$ (Mult. Prop. [9]) **26.** *Proof:* 1. $\triangle PTR \sim$
$\triangle XYZ$; $\overline{TQ} \perp \overline{PR}$; $\overline{YU} \perp \overline{XZ}$; $TS = SR$; $YW =$
WZ (Given) 2. $\overline{TQ}$ is altitude of $\triangle PTR$; $\overline{YU}$ is
altitude of $\triangle XYZ$ (Def. of altitude of $\triangle$ [1])
3. $\overline{PS}$ is median of $\triangle PTR$; $\overline{XW}$ is median of
$\triangle XYZ$ (Def. of median of $\triangle$ [1]) 4. $\frac{TQ}{YV} = \frac{TP}{YX}$ (In
$\sim \triangle$s, the lengths of medians from corr. vertices
are proportional to lengths of corr. sides. [2])
5. $\frac{PS}{XW} = \frac{TP}{YX}$ (In $\sim \triangle$s, the lengths of altitudes
from corr. vertices are proportional to lengths of
corr. sides. [3]) 6. $\frac{TQ}{YV} = \frac{PS}{XW}$ (Substitution Prop.
[4, 5]) **27.** $3,333\frac{1}{3}$ yd. **28.** 20 m

Chapter 8

Pages 334–336
Written Exercises **1.** $6\sqrt{2} \approx 8.48$ **3.** 1,024
5. 10 **7.** $4\sqrt{2} \approx 5.66$ **9.** *Proof:* 1. $\triangle FGH$; $\overline{FG} \perp$
$\overline{GH}$; $\overline{GI} \perp \overline{FH}$; $\overline{FG} \parallel \overline{IJ}$ (Given) 2. $m\angle JIC =$
$m\angle GHF$ (2 lines $\parallel \Rightarrow$ corres. $\angle$s =. [1])
3. $m\angle H = m\angle H$ (Reflexive Prop.) 4. $\triangle IHJ \sim$

$\triangle FHG$ (AA $\sim$ Post. [2, 3]) **5.** $\angle FGH$ is a rt. $\angle$. (2
$\perp$ lines form 4 rt. $\angle$s. [1]) **6.** $\triangle FGH$ is a rt. $\triangle$.
(Def. of rt. $\triangle$ [5]) 7. $\triangle FHG \sim \triangle FGI$ (If altitude
to hypotenuse is drawn in a rt. $\triangle$, the new $\triangle$s
formed are $\sim$ to each other and to the given $\triangle$.
[1, 6]) 8. $\triangle IHJ \sim \triangle FGI$ ($\sim$ of $\triangle$s is transitive. [4,
7]) **13.** $3x$ **15.** $3x + 3$ **17.** $7x$ **19.** *Proof:*
1. $\angle ACB$ is a rt. $\angle$; $WXYZ$ is a square. (Given)
2. $\angle ZWX$ and $\angle YXW$ are rt. $\angle$s. (Def. of square
[1]) 3. $\overline{ZW} \perp \overline{AB}$; $\overline{YX} \perp \overline{AB}$ (Def. of $\perp$ [2])
4. $\angle ZWA$ and $\angle YXB$ are rt. $\angle$s. (Def. of $\perp$ [3])
5. $\triangle ACB$, $\triangle AWZ$ and $\triangle YXB$ are rt. $\triangle$s. (Def. of
rt. $\triangle$ [1, 4]) 6. $\angle XYB$ and $\angle B$ are
complementary. $\angle A$ and $\angle B$ are complementary.
(2 acute $\angle$s of a rt. $\triangle$ are complementary. [5])
7. $m\angle XYB = m\angle A$ (Complements of same $\angle$ are
=. [6]) 8. $m\angle ZWA = m\angle YXB$ (All rt. $\angle$s are =.
[4]) 9. $\triangle AWZ \sim \triangle YXB$ (AA $\sim$ Post. [7, 8])
10. $\frac{AW}{YX} = \frac{WZ}{XB}$ (Corres. sides of $\sim \triangle$s are prop.
[9]) 11. $YX = WX$; $WZ = WX$ (def. of square
[1]) 12. $\frac{AW}{WX} = \frac{WX}{XB}$ (Substitution Prop. [10, 11])
13. $(AW)(XB) = (WX)^2$ (Mult. Prop. [12])
21. 24 **23.** $24\sqrt{35} \approx 141.99$ **25.** 16 **27.** $6\frac{2}{3}$
29. 178.5 m **31.** 12; 6 **36.** Measure $\overline{AC}$ and
$\angle CAT$. Then use $\tan A = \frac{CT}{CA}$ to find CT.

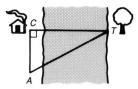

37. Use Todd's height and the angle of
depression to the base of the tree. Then use $\tan$
$\angle DTC = \frac{DC}{CT}$ and solve for CT.

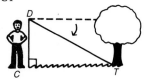

38. 24 **39.** A locus is the set of all points, and
only those points, that satisfy a given condition.
Algebra Review **1.** $x = \pm 7$ **3.** $x = \pm(a + 5)$
5. $x = \pm 13a^2bc^4$ **7.** $x = \pm 8b$ **9.** $x = \pm(a^2 - b^2)$ **11.** $x = \pm(c - 2)$

Pages 340–343

Written Exercises **1.** 50 **3.** $2\sqrt{3} \approx 3.46$
5. $10\sqrt{2} \approx 14.14$ **7.** $18\sqrt{2} \approx 25.46$ **9.** 4
11. 3 **13.** A and G or G and B **15.** 8
21. $\overline{EF} \parallel \overline{GH}$ because they have the same slope,
-3. $\overline{FG} \parallel \overline{HE}$ because they have the same slope,
$\frac{1}{3}$. $EF = FG = GH = HE = \sqrt{10}$ and $EG = HF =$
$2\sqrt{5}$. Since $EF^2 + FG^2 = EG^2$, $FG^2 + GH^2 =$
FH^2, $GH^2 + HE^2 = GE^2$, and $HE^2 + EF^2 = HF^2$,
by Theorem 8-5, $\triangle EFG$, $\triangle FGH$, $\triangle GHE$, and
$\triangle HEF$ are rt. $\triangle$s. Therefore, $\angle E$, $\angle F$, $\angle G$, and
$\angle H$ are rt. $\angle$s. $EFGH$ is a rectangle with equal
sides. Thus, $EFGH$ is a square. **23.** 0.8; 0.8
25. E_4; 2.3; 0 **27.** $\sqrt{277}$ ft. **29.** $6\sqrt{2} \approx 8.49$
31. Use the Pythagorean Theorem or show the
slopes of two sides are negative reciprocals of
each other. **35.** *Proof:* 1. $\angle MAN$ is a rt. $\angle$.
(Given) 2. $\triangle MAL$ and $\triangle MAN$ are rt. $\triangle$s. (Def.
of rt. $\triangle$ [1]) 3. $MA^2 + LA^2 = ML^2$ and $MA^2 +$
$NA^2 = MN^2$ (Pythagorean Thm. [1, 2])
4. $MA^2 = ML^2 - LA^2$ and $MA^2 = MN^2 - NA^2$
(Subtraction Prop. [3]) 5. $ML^2 - LA^2 = MN^2 -$
NA^2 (Substitution Prop. [4]) 6. $NA^2 + ML^2 =$
$MN^2 + AL^2$ (Addition Prop. [5]) **39.** $\triangle RUS$;
$\triangle SUT$ **40.** 6 **41.** 24 ft. **42.** 106
43. parallelogram

Pages 349–350

Written Exercises **1.** 12 **3.** 6 **5.** $18\sqrt{2}$
7. $6\sqrt{2}$ **9.** 18 **11.** $14\sqrt{2}$ **13.** 15; $15\sqrt{2}$; $15\sqrt{2}$
15. 20 **17.** $10 + 10\sqrt{2} + 10\sqrt{3}$ **19.** $30 +$
$6\sqrt{2} + 6\sqrt{3}$ **21.** $2x$; $2x\sqrt{2}$ **23.** $2x\sqrt{6}$; $2x\sqrt{2}$
25. $3\sqrt{21}$; No; $PQ^2 + QR^2 \neq PR^2$ **27.** *Proof:*
1. $\triangle ABC$ is a rt. $\triangle$; $m\angle A = m\angle B = 45$; $AB = c$;
$AC = a$. (Given) 2. $CB = AC$ (If 2 $\angle$s of $\triangle$ are
$=$, sides opp. them are $=$. [1]) 3. $CB = a$
(Transitive Prop. [1, 2]) 4. $a^2 + a^2 = c^2$ or $2a^2 =$
c^2 (Pythagorean Thm. [1, 3]) 5. $c = a\sqrt{2}$
(Algebra) **31.** $\frac{4}{3}\sqrt{3}$ or about 2.31 cm.
33. $4\sqrt{13}$ **34.** $6\sqrt{2}$ **35.** $4\sqrt{5}$ **36.** congruent
37. perpendicular

Pages 352–354

Written Exercises **1.** $7.5\sqrt{3} \approx 12.99$ ft. **3.** 9 ft.
5. $3 + 4\sqrt{3} \approx 9.93$ m **7.** Height = 6 inches;
depth ≈ 10.39 inches **9.** $\sqrt{47.25} \approx 6.9$ ft.
11. Lot A: 96 ft. and 238 ft.; Lot B: 144 ft. and
280 ft. **13.** 16 ft. **15.** $30(\sqrt{3} - 1) \approx 22$ m
17. $4\sqrt{39} \approx 24.98$ **18.** $4\sqrt{3}$ **19.** $9\sqrt{2}$ **20.** No
21. If I am the winner then I receive a trophy. If

I receive a trophy then I am the winner. **22.** A
rectangle is a parallelogram with 4 rt. $\angle$s.

Pages 359–361

Written Exercises **1.** $\frac{3}{4}$ **3.** $\frac{4}{5}$ **5.** $\frac{4}{5}$ **7.** $\tan A$
9. $\cos A$ **11.** $\sin B$ **13.** For $\triangle XYZ$, $(\sin X)^2 +$
$(\cos X)^2 = \left(\frac{15}{25}\right)^2 + \left(\frac{20}{25}\right)^2 = \left(\frac{3}{5}\right)^2 + \left(\frac{4}{5}\right)^2 = \frac{9}{25} = \frac{16}{25} = 1$
and $(\sin Y)^2 + (\cos Y)^2 = \left(\frac{20}{25}\right)^2 + \left(\frac{15}{25}\right)^2 = 1$. For
$\triangle ABC$, $(\sin A)^2 + (\cos A)^2 = \left(\frac{15}{17}\right)^2 + \left(\frac{8}{17}\right)^2 = \frac{225}{289} +$
$\frac{64}{289} = \frac{289}{289} = 1$ and $(\sin B)^2 + (\cos B)^2 = \left(\frac{8}{17}\right)^2 +$
$\left(\frac{15}{17}\right)^2 = 1$. **15.** $\frac{\sqrt{2}}{2}$, $\frac{\sqrt{2}}{2}$, and 1 **17.** 12; 15
19. $\frac{\sqrt{2}}{2}$ **21.** 25 cm **25.** In a right $\triangle ABC$ with
right $\angle C$, $(\tan A)(\tan B) = 1$. *Given:* Rt. $\triangle ABC$
with right $\angle C$ *Prove:* $(\tan A)(\tan B) = 1$ *Proof:*
1. Rt. $\triangle ABC$ with rt. $\angle C$ (Given) 2. $\tan A = \frac{a}{b}$
and $\tan B = \frac{b}{a}$ (Def. of tangent [1]) 3. $(\tan A)(\tan B)$
$= \left(\frac{a}{b}\right)\left(\frac{b}{a}\right) = 1$ (Mult. Prop. [2]) **27.** $4\sqrt{21} \approx 18.33$
ft. **28.** 19 ft. **29.** $32\sqrt{2}$ **30.** 78 **31.** $m\angle PQR$;
$\frac{1}{2}(QR)$

Pages 363–364

Written Exercises **1.** 0.4848 **3.** 0.1564
5. 0.7431 **7.** 9 **9.** 71 **11.** 27 **13.** 16 and 74
15. 13 and 77 **17.** 27.6 **19.** 23.8 m **21.** The
table shows $\sin 1° = \tan 1°$ because the entries
are approximations. *Given:* Rt. $\triangle ABC$ with rt.
$\angle C$ *Prove:* $\tan A > \sin A$ *Proof:* 1. Rt. $\triangle ABC$
with rt. $\angle C$ (Given) 2. $\tan A = \frac{CB}{AC}$ (Def. of
tangent [1]) 3. $\sin A = \frac{CB}{AB}$ (Def. of sine [1])
4. $\overline{AB}$ is the hypotenuse of $\triangle ABC$ (Def. of
hypotenuse of a rt. $\triangle$ [1]) 5. $AB > AC$ ($\perp$
segment from a pt. to a line is the shortest seg.
from the pt. to the line.) 6. $(CB)(AB) > (CB)(AC)$
(Mult. Prop. [5]) 7. $\frac{CB}{AC} > \frac{CB}{AB}$ (Mult. Prop. [6])
8. $\tan A > \sin A$ (Substitution Prop. [2, 3, 7])
23. $\frac{a}{b}$ **24.** $\frac{a}{c}$ **25.** Yes. $2^2 + 4^2 = x^2$ or $x = 2\sqrt{5} \approx$
4.5 ft. Since $2x \approx 9$ ft., a 10-ft. board is long
enough for two diagonal braces.

26.

Pages 366–369

Written Exercises **1.** 57.4 ft. **3.** 364 m
5. 11.3 m **5.** 571.5 ft. **9.** 331 m **11.** 25.7 ft.
13. 31.32 m **15.** *Proof:* 1. Acute $\triangle ABC$ with
sides of lengths a, b, and c (Given) 2. Draw

$\overline{BD} \perp \overline{AC}$ (Through a pt. not on a given line, there is exactly 1 line $\perp$ to the given line.) 3. $\angle BDA$ and $\angle BDC$ are rt. $\angle$s (2 $\perp$ lines form 4 rt. $\angle$s [2]) 4. $\triangle$s BDA and BDC are rt. $\triangle$s (Def. of rt. $\triangle$ [3]) 5. $\sin A = \frac{BD}{c}$ and $\sin C = \frac{BD}{a}$ (Def of sine [3, 4]) 6. $\frac{1}{\sin C} = \frac{a}{BD}$ (Mult. Prop. [5]) 7. $\frac{a}{c}$ $= \frac{\sin A}{\sin C}$ (Mult. Prop. [5, 6]) **19.** 25.7 in.; 81 in. **20.** 0.9135 **21.** 74 **22.** $\frac{3}{5}$ **23.** $5\sqrt{5} \approx 11.18$ **24.** 52.5 miles

Algebra Review **1.** $y = 2x - 1$ **3.** $y = \frac{5}{7}x - \frac{11}{7}$

Chapter 8 Review, Pages 371–372
1. 15 **2.** 8 **3.** 5 **4.** *Proof:* 1. $\overline{CD} \perp \overline{AB}$; $\overline{CD} \parallel$ $\overline{EF}$; $m\angle ACB = 90$ (Given) 2. $m\angle CDB = m\angle EFB$ (2 lines $\parallel \Rightarrow$ corres. $\angle$s =. [1]) 3. $m\angle B = m\angle B$ (Reflexive Prop.) 4. $\triangle CDB \sim \triangle EFB$ (AA Post. [2, 3]) 5. $\angle ACB$ is a rt. $\angle$. (Def. of rt. $\angle$ [1]) 6. $\triangle ACB$ is a rt. $\triangle$. (Def. of rt. $\triangle$ [5]) 7. $\triangle ADC \sim$ $\triangle CDB$ (If alt. is drawn to hypotenuse of rt. $\triangle$, the new $\triangle$s formed are $\sim$ to each other and to the given $\triangle$ [1, 6]) 8. $\triangle ADC \sim \triangle EFB$ ($\sim$ of $\triangle$s is transitive [4, 7]) **5.** 25 **6.** $16\sqrt{5} \approx 35.78$ **7.** $9\sqrt{5} \approx 20.12$ cm **8.** 8 **9.** $12\sqrt{3}$ **10.** $64\sqrt{2}$ cm **11.** $10\sqrt{3}$ cm **12.** 340 ft. **13.** 104 cm **14.** 2 ft. **15.** $\frac{a}{b}$ **16.** $\frac{b}{a}$ **17.** $\frac{b}{c}$ **18.** $\frac{a}{c}$ **19.** $\cos x$ **20.** $\tan Y$ **21.** $\tan X$ **22.** 0.6293 **23.** 0.0872 **24.** 1.2799 **25.** 0.9998 **26.** 0.9998 **27.** 57.2900 **28.** $m\angle A = 68$ **29.** $m\angle A = 28$ **30.** 98 m **31.** 1,099 m **32.** $10°$

Chapter 9

Pages 378–380
Written Exercises **1.** $\overline{OA}$, $\overline{OB}$, $\overline{OC}$ **3.** $\overline{BC}$ **5.** $\overrightarrow{BX}$ **7.** $OX > OA$; $OW < OA$ **9.** Yes; W is in interior of $\odot O$. **11.** $\overline{OT}$ **13.** $\odot S$ **15.** 5 **17.** $3\frac{1}{8}$ **19.** 12 **21.** $\frac{2}{5}$ **23.** $(1, 4)$ **25.** $5\frac{15}{16}$ in. **27.** $(2, 6)$; 4 **29.** $(0, 4)$; 1 **31.** Exterior **33.** 38 inches **35.** 2 pts.; Thm. 9-1 **39.** Tangent at $(-5, 5)$ **40.** 42 ft. **41.** 65 ft. **42.** 0.3640 **43.** 6; $6\sqrt{3} \approx$ 10.39 **44.** 33

Algebra Review **1.** $y = -\frac{1}{2}x$ **3.** $y = -\frac{1}{3}x + \frac{11}{3}$

Pages 383–386
Written Exercises **1.** 2 external **3.** None **5.** *Proof:* 1. $\overline{AB}$ is diameter of $\odot O$; lines ℓ and k are tangent to $\odot O$ at A and B, resp. (Given) 2. $k \perp \overline{OB}$; $\ell \perp \overline{OA}$ (A line tangent to a $\odot$

is $\perp$ to a radius drawn to the pt. of tangency. [1]) 3. $k \perp \overrightarrow{AB}$; $\ell \perp \overrightarrow{AB}$ (Def. of a line $\perp$ to a segment [2]) 4. $k \parallel \ell$ (In a plane, 2 lines $\perp$ to the same line are $\parallel$. [3])
11. 12 **13.** *Proof:* 1. $\overline{QA}$ and $\overline{QB}$ are tangent to $\odot O$ at A and B, respectively. (Given) 2. $QA = OB$ (Segments drawn tangent to a circle from an exterior pt. are =. [1]) 3. $OA = OB$ (Def. of $\odot$ [1]) 4. $QO = QO$ (Reflexive Prop.) 5. $\triangle OAQ \cong$ $\triangle OBQ$ (SSS $\cong$ Post. [2, 3, 4]) 6. $m\angle AQO =$ $m\angle BQO$ (Corres. parts of $\cong \triangle$s are =. [5]) 7. $\overrightarrow{QO}$ bisects $\angle AQB$ (Def. of $\angle$ bisector [6])
15. 6 **17.** 9 **21.** $\frac{9\sqrt{3}}{8} \approx 1.95$ in. **23.** 6 **25.** 4 **27.** 14; 28 **29.** $y = -\frac{2}{5}x + 9$ **31.** *Proof:* 1. $\overrightarrow{UR}$ and $\overrightarrow{ST}$ are common internal tangents of $\odot P$ and $\odot Q$ (Given) 2. $WU = WT$; $WR = WS$ (Tangent segs. drawn from an ext. pt. to pts. on the $\odot$ are =. [1]) 3. $WU + WR = WT + WS$ (Add. Prop. [2]) 4. $WU + WR = UR$ and $WT + WS = ST$ (Seg. Add. Post.) 5. $UR = ST$ (Substitution Prop. [3, 4]) **33.** Diameter **34.** The set of all pts. which are a given distance from a given pt. **35.** 373.21 ft. **36.** $19\frac{1}{5}$ **37.** 4

Algebra Review **1.** $x = 2$; $y = 5$ **3.** $x = -5$; $y = 5$ **5.** $a = -1$; $b = 1$ **7.** No solution

Pages 389–391
Written Exercises **1.** 16 **3.** 9 **5.** Always **7.** Sometimes; If line passes through center of $\odot$ **9.** Always **11.** 21 **13.** 16 **15.** *Proof:* 1. $\odot P$, line ℓ contains pt. P, chord $\overline{AB}$, $\overline{PC} \perp \overline{AB}$ (Given) 2. Draw $\overline{PA}$ and $\overline{PB}$ (2 pts. determine a line.) 3. $PA = PB$ (Def. of $\odot$ [1]) 4. $PC = PC$ (Reflexive Prop.) 5. $\angle PCA$ and $\angle PCB$ are rt. $\angle$s (2 $\perp$ lines form 4 rt. $\angle$s. [1]) 6. $\triangle PCA$ and $\triangle PCB$ are rt. $\triangle$s (Def. of rt. $\triangle$ [5]) 7. $\triangle PCA \cong$ $\triangle PCB$ (HL Thm. [3, 4, 6]) 8. $AC = CB$ (Def. of $\cong \triangle$s [7]) 9. C is the midpt. of $\overline{AB}$ (Def. of midpt. [8]) 10. ℓ bisects $\overline{AB}$ (Def. of seg. bisector [9]) **17.** No; if the chord is a diameter then every line through the center of the $\odot$ will bisect the chord, but not necessarily be $\perp$ to the chord. **19.** 1.5 ft. **21.** $2\sqrt{21} \approx 9.17$ in. **25.** *Given:* $\odot P$ with chord $\overline{AB}$; ℓ is $\perp$ bisector of $\overline{AB}$. *Prove:* ℓ contains P. *Proof:* Either ℓ contains P or ℓ does not contain P. Suppose ℓ does not contain P. Draw $\overrightarrow{PQ} \perp \overline{AB}$. (Through a pt. not on a line, there is exactly 1 line $\perp$ to the given line.) Then $\overrightarrow{PQ}$ is the $\perp$ bisector of $\overline{AB}$. (If a line through the center of a $\odot$ is $\perp$ to a chord,

it bisects the chord.) But this contradicts the given information that ℓ is $\perp$ bisector of $\overline{AB}$ and Thm. 4-10 (In a plane a segment has exactly one $\perp$ bisector.) Therefore the assumption that ℓ does not contain P is false. We conclude that ℓ contains P. **27.** The locus of the midpts. of all chords of a $\odot$ = to a given chord is a circle whose radius is the distance from the center of the given $\odot$ to the given chord. **29.** $2\sqrt{43} \approx$ 13.11 **31.** 1 cm **35.** (2, -1); 5 **38.** *Proof:* 1. $\odot O$ with tangent segs. $\overline{AB}$ and $\overline{AC}$ (Given) 2. $AB = CD$ (Segs. drawn tangent to a $\odot$ from an ext. pt. are =. [1]) 3. $\overline{AB} \perp \overline{BO}$ and $\overline{AC} \perp \overline{CO}$ (A tangent to a $\odot$ is $\perp$ to the radius drawn to the pt. of tangency.) 4. $\angle ABO$ and $\angle ACO$ are rt. $\angle$s (Def. of $\perp$ lines [3]) 5. $m\angle ABO = m\angle ACO$ (All rt. $\angle$s are =. [4]) 6. $OB = OC$ (Def. of $\odot$ [1]) 7. $\triangle ABO \cong \triangle ACO$ (SAS $\cong$ Post. [2, 5, 6]) 8. $m\angle 1 = m\angle 2$ (Corres. parts of $\cong$ $\triangle$s are =. [7]) **39.** M is in the exterior of the $\odot$.

40. Rhombus; square **41.** $11\frac{1}{2}$

Pages 395–398
Written Exercises **1.** Inscribed
3. Circumscribed **5.** She located the circumcenter of the equilateral triangle by constructing the $\perp$ bisectors of the sides. This enabled her to construct the circumcircle. Drawing the segments from the circumcenter to each vertex gave her the smaller $\cong$ $\triangle$s.
7. Always **9.** Sometimes **11.** Always
15. Incenter **17.** Circumcenter **19.** 6.5
21. *Proof:* 1. $\triangle ABC$ is inscribed in $\odot P$; $\overline{PY} \perp \overline{AC}$; $\overline{PX} \perp \overline{AB}$; $XD = EY$ (Given) 2. $PX = PY$ (Def. of a $\odot$ [1]) 3. $PX = PD + DX$; $PY = PE + EY$ (Seg. Add. Post.) 4. $PD + DX = PE + EY$ (Substitution Prop. [2, 3]) 5. $PD = PE$ (Subtraction Prop. [1, 4]) 6. $AB = AC$ (If 2 chords are the same distance from the center of $\odot$, they are =. [5]) 7. $\triangle ABC$ is isosceles. (Def. of isos. $\triangle$ [6]) **23.** 16 **25.** 7 **27.** $10\sqrt{3} \approx 17.32$

29. $\frac{x}{2}$ **31.** 2 **33.** $2\sqrt{3} \approx 3.46$ **35.** (4.75, 1.75)
37. $\left(\frac{5}{2}, \frac{5}{2}\right)$ **39.** $\left(x - \frac{5}{2}\right)^2 + \left(y - \frac{5}{2}\right)^2 = \frac{25}{2} = 12.5$
43. *Given:* Any triangle ABC *Prove:* A circle can be circumscribed about $\triangle ABC$ *Proof:* 1. $\triangle ABC$ is any $\triangle$. (Given) 2. Let P be the pt. of concurrency of the $\perp$ bisectors of the sides so that $PA = PC = PB = r$. (The $\perp$ bisectors of the sides of a $\triangle$ are concurrent in a pt. equidistant from the vertices of the $\triangle$.) 3. The circle with

center P and radius r contains pts. A, B, and C. (Def. of a circle [2]) 4. $\odot P$ circumscribes $\triangle ABC$. (Def. of circumscribe [3]) **47.** Congruent $\odot$s are $\odot$s with = radii. **48.** 4 **50.** $\sqrt{58} \approx 7.62$ **51.** A convex polygon which is both equilateral and also equiangular.

Pages 403–405
Written Exercises **1.** $\frac{1}{6}$ **3.** Sample: $\widehat{BG}$; $\widehat{BC}$
5. 60 **7.** $\widehat{AE}$ **9.** 240 **11.** 360 **13.** 15; $90 \div 6 =$ 15 **15.** Since the blue and red $\triangle$s are all $\cong$, the green triangles can be proved $\cong$ by SSS $\cong$ Post. Two sets of corres. sides of the green $\triangle$s are = because they are corresponding sides of triangles A and B; Thm. 9-10 shows that the third sides of green $\triangle$s are = (They are chords with equal arcs that are measured by = central angles).
17. *Proof:* 1. $m\widehat{AC} = m\widehat{BD}$ (Given) 2. $m\widehat{AB} + m\widehat{BC} = m\widehat{AC}$ and $m\widehat{BC} + m\widehat{CD} = m\widehat{BD}$ (Arc Add. Post.) 3. $m\widehat{AB} + m\widehat{BC} = m\widehat{BC} + m\widehat{CD}$ (Substitution Prop. [1, 2]) 4. $m\widehat{BC} = m\widehat{BC}$ (Reflexive Prop.) 5. $m\widehat{AB} = m\widehat{CD}$ (Subtraction Prop. [3, 4]) **23.** 95 **25.** 80 **27.** Sample: $(x + 3)^2 + (y - 7)^2 = 49$ **29.** 18; 24; 33; 45
31. *Given:* $\overline{AB}$ is a diameter of $\odot P$; $m\widehat{XY} = m\widehat{ZW}$ *Prove:* $XZ = YW$ *Proof:* 1. In $\odot P$, $m\widehat{XY} = m\widehat{ZW}$ (Given) 2. $m\widehat{XY} + m\widehat{YZ} = m\widehat{YZ} + m\widehat{ZW}$ (Add. Prop. [1]) 3. $m\widehat{XZ} = m\widehat{XY} + m\widehat{YZ}$; $m\widehat{YW} = m\widehat{YZ} + m\widehat{ZW}$ (Arc Add. Post.) 4. $m\widehat{XZ} = m\widehat{ZW}$ (Substitution Prop. [2, 3]) 5. $XZ = YW$ (In same or $\cong$ $\odot$s, = minor arcs $\Rightarrow$ = corres. chords. [4]) **35.** 40 **37.** 50 **39.** 7.5 **41.** A polygon whose vertices lie on the $\odot$ **42.** A polygon whose sides are tangent to the $\odot$ **43.** Yes, if $\widehat{DE}$ and $\widehat{XY}$ are minor arcs of the same or $\cong$ $\odot$s **44.** $\triangle XYZ$, $\triangle XWY$, and $\triangle YWZ$ **45.** If $x < 25$, then $x = 19$; false

Pages 409–411
Written Exercises **1.** 32.5 **3.** 68 **5.** 70
7. 180 **9.** 30 **11.** 55 **13.** 35 **15.** *Proof:* 1. $ABCD$ is inscribed in $\odot P$ (Given) 2. $m\angle 1 = m\angle 4$; $m\angle 2 = m\angle 3$ (If 2 inscribed $\angle$s intercept the same arc on a $\odot$, then they are =.) 3. $m\angle 1 + m\angle 2 = m\angle 3 + m\angle 4$ (Add. Prop. [2])
17. *Given* $\angle 1$ is inscribed in semicircle $\widehat{BCA}$ of $\odot P$ *Prove:* $\angle 1$ is a rt. $\angle$.
Proof: 1. $\widehat{BCA}$ is a semicircle of $\odot P$ (Given) 2. $\overline{AB}$ is a diameter of $\odot P$ (Def. of semicircle

(1) 3. $\overarc{BDA}$ is a semicircle (Def. of semicircle
(2) 4. $m\overarc{BDA} = 180$ (Def. of measure of
semicircle) 5. $m\angle 1 = 90$ (The measure of an
inscribed $\angle$ is $\frac{1}{2}$ the measure of its intercepted
arc.) 6. $\angle 1$ is a rt. $\angle$ (Def. of rt. $\angle$ (5)) **19.** Use
the procedure from Exercise 18 to locate a
second diameter. The pt. of intersection of 2
diameters of a $\odot$ is the center of the $\odot$.
21. 120 **23.** 131 **25.** 124 **27.** $AB = 10$; $BC = \sqrt{2^2 + (-4)^2} = \sqrt{20}$; $AC = \sqrt{8^2 + 4^2} = \sqrt{80}$;
$AB^2 = 100$ and $BC^2 + AC^2 = 20 + 80 = 100$
29. A circle with center at midpt. M of $\overline{VP}$,
excluding points V and P
33. *Given:* Quadrilateral $ABCD$ inscribed in $\odot P$
Prove: $\angle A$ and $\angle C$ are supplementary; $\angle B$ and
$\angle C$ are supplementary. *Proof:* 1. Quad. $ABCD$
inscribed in $\odot P$. (Given) 2. $m\angle A = \frac{1}{2}(m\overarc{BCD})$;
$m\angle C = \frac{1}{2}(m\overarc{DAB})$; $m\angle B = \frac{1}{2}(m\overarc{ADC})$; $\angle m\angle D = \frac{1}{2}(m\overarc{ABC})$ (Measure of inscribed $\angle = \frac{1}{2}$ measure
of its intercepted arc.) 3. $m\angle A = \frac{1}{2}(m\overarc{BCD}) = \frac{1}{2}(360 - m\overarc{DAB})$; $m\angle B = \frac{1}{2}(m\overarc{ADC} = \frac{1}{2}(360 - m\overarc{ABC})$ (Def. of measure of a major arc.)
4. $m\angle A + m\angle C = \frac{1}{2}(360 - m\overarc{DAB}) + \frac{1}{2}m\overarc{DAB}) = 180$; $m\angle B + m\angle D = \frac{1}{2}(360 - m\overarc{ABC}) + \frac{1}{2}(m\overarc{ABC}) = 180$ (Substitution Prop. (2, 3)) 5. $\angle A$
and $\angle C$ are supp.; $\angle B$ and $\angle D$ are supp. (Def. of
supp. $\angle$s (4)) **39.** *Proof:* 1. $QRST$ is inscribed
in $\odot P$; $m\angle QRS = m\angle TSR - k$. (Given) 2. $\angle QRS$
is supp. to $\angle QTS$ and $\angle TQR$ is supp. to $\angle TSR$.
(If a quad. is inscribed in a $\odot$, then the opp. $\angle$s
are supp. (1)) 3. $m\angle QRS + m\angle QTS = 180$ and
$m\angle TQR + m\angle TSR = 180$ (Def. supp. $\angle$s (2))
4. $m\angle QRS = 180 - m\angle QTS$ and $m\angle TSR = 180 - m\angle TQR$ (Subtraction Prop. (3)) 5. $180 - m\angle QTS = 180 - m\angle TQR - k$ (Substitution
Prop. (1, 4)) 6. $m\angle TQR = m\angle QTS - k$ (Add.
Prop. (5)) **40.** $\overarc{AB}$; $\overarc{BC}$; $\overarc{CA}$ **41.** $\overarc{ABC}$; $\overarc{ACB}$; $\overarc{BAC}$
42. Inscribed in **43.** 4 **44.** Not necessarily; if j
and k are coplanar, they are parallel; if j and k
are not coplanar, they are skew.

Pages 417–419
Written Exercises **1.** 60 **3.** 110 **5.** 230
7. 100 **9.** 33.5 **11.** 120 **13.** 55 **15.** 8 **17.** 44
19. 10.75 or 14 **21.** 6 or 8 **23.** *Proof:* 1. $\overleftrightarrow{RQ}$
and $\overleftrightarrow{RS}$ are tangent to $\odot U$ (Given) 2. $m\angle R = \frac{1}{2}(m\overarc{STQ} - m\overarc{QS})$ (The measure of an $\angle$ formed

by tangents to a $\odot$ is $=$ to $\frac{1}{2}$ the difference
between the measures of the intercepted arcs.)
3. $m\overarc{STQ} = 360 - m\overarc{QS}$ (Def. of measure of
major arc) 4. $m\overarc{QS} = 360 - m\overarc{STQ}$ (Subtraction
Prop. (3)) 5. $m\angle R = \frac{1}{2}(m\overarc{STQ} - (360 - m\overarc{STQ})) = m\overarc{STQ} - 180$ (Substitution Prop. (2, 3))
6. $m\overarc{STQ} = 180 + m\angle R$ (Add. Prop. (5))
29. *Proof:* 1. In $\odot O$, secant $\overleftrightarrow{AB}$ intersects secant
$\overleftrightarrow{CD}$ at O (Given) 2. Draw $\overline{AD}$ and $\overline{CB}$ (2 pts.
determine a line.) 3. $m\angle C = m\angle A$ (If 2
inscribed $\angle$s intercept the same arc on a $\odot$, then
they are $=$.) 4. $m\angle DOB = m\angle DOB$ (Reflexive
Prop.) 5. $\triangle CBO \sim \triangle ADO$ (AA Post. (3, 4))
6. $\frac{OC}{OA} = \frac{OB}{OD}$ (Corres. sides of $\sim \triangle$s are prop. (5))
7. $(OA)(OB) = (OC)(OD)$ (Mult. Prop. (6)) **31.** 9
33. 18 **35.** 67.4 **37.** 34 **38.** 90 **39.** 100
40. Construct 2 $\perp$ lines, and bisect 1 of the
rt. $\angle$s.

Chapter 9 Review, Pages 423–424
1. tangent **2.** secant **3.** chord **4.** radius
5. diameter **6.** pt. of tangency **7.** False
8. True **9.** (2, −8); 9 **10.** 2 external **11.** 2
external; 2 internal **12.** none **13.** 1 external
14. $\perp$ **15.** $10\sqrt{3} \approx 17.32$ **16.** $12\sqrt{2} \approx 16.97$
17. CD **18.** circles with $=$ radii **19.** Never
20. Always **21.** Sometimes **22.** Always **23.** 30
24. 170 **25.** 20 **26.** 120 **27.** 50 **28.** 190
29. central **30.** Samples: $\overarc{TRS}$; $\overarc{TSQ}$; $\overarc{URS}$ **31.** If
pt. P is on $\overarc{AB}$, then $m\overarc{AP} + m\overarc{PB} = m\overarc{APB}$.
32. 220 **33.** $\angle BEC$ and $\angle BDC$ **34.** $\angle CDE$
35. $\angle AEC$ **36.** 140 **37.** *Proof:* 1. $FG = JK$
(Given) 2. $m\angle F = m\angle J$ (If 2 inscribed $\angle$s
intercept the same arc on the $\odot$, then they are
$=$.) 3. $m\angle FHG = m\angle JHK$ (Vert. $\angle$s are $=$.)
4. $\triangle FGH \cong \triangle JKH$ (AAS Thm. (1, 2, 3))
38. 57.5 **39.** 19 **40.** 44.5 **41.** 120 **42.** 50
43. 45 **44.** 222 **45.** 24

Chapter 10

Pages 432–433
Written Exercises **1.** 75 **3.** 30 sq. in. **5.** 121
sq. ft. **7.** 80 **9.** 4 **11.** 912 tiles **13.** 25 bricks
15. 8 **17.** 45 **19.** 120 m^2 **21.** 8 **23.** 15 ft. by
15 ft. **25.** 15 in. and 5 in. **27.** 42 ft. and 12 ft.
29. 16 **30.** 71 **31.** 212 **32.** The Pythagorean
Theorem **33.** 4

Pages 437–439

Written Exercises **1.** 270 sq. in. **3.** 48
5. $2x^2 - 8x + 8$ **7.** $1.5x^2 + 5x - 12.5$ **9.** 216
11. 4 in. **13.** $2\sqrt{3} \approx 3.46$ sq. yd. **15.** 20
17. No; the side of the $\square$ along the road is
longer than 75 ft. **19.** $\frac{16}{9}\sqrt{3} \approx 3.08$ **21.** $A =$
$40; \; \iota = 36$
25. length: 56 cm; waste: 192 cm^2 **27.** $22\frac{1}{2}$ sq.
ft. **29.** 38.25 sq. ft. **31.** 38.25 sq. ft. **33.** *Proof:*
1. $\triangle GBC$; base $\overline{GB}$ of length b; altitude $\overline{CF}$ of
length h (Given) 2. Through C, draw $\ell \parallel \overline{GB}$.
(Through a pt. not on a given line, there is
exactly one line $\parallel$ to the given line.) 3. On ℓ, on
the B-side of C, locate D such that $CD = GB$.
(Seg. Construction Post.) 4. Draw $\overline{BD}$. (Two pts.
determine a line.) 5. $BGCD$ is a $\square$. (If 2 sides
of quadrilateral are $\parallel$ and $=$, the quadrilateral is
a $\square$. [2, 3]) 6. $m\angle DCB = m\angle GBC$ (2 lines $\parallel \Rightarrow$
alt. int. $\angle$s $=$. [2]) 7. $CB = BC$ (Reflexive Prop.)
8. $\triangle GBC \cong \triangle DCB$ (SAS $\cong$ Post. [3, 6, 7])
9. Area $\triangle GBC =$ area $\triangle DCB$ ($\cong \triangle$s have $=$
areas. [8]) 10. Area $\square BGCD =$ area $\triangle GBC +$
area $\triangle DCB$ (Area Add. Post.) 11. Area
$\square BGCD =$ area $\triangle GBC +$ area $\triangle GBC = 2$(area
$\triangle GBC$) (Substitution Prop. [9, 10]) 12. Area
$\square BGCD = bh$ (Area of a parallelogram [5])
13. $bh = 2$(area $\triangle GBC$) (Substitution Prop. [11,
12]) 14. Area $\triangle GBC = \frac{1}{2}bh$ (Mult. Prop. [13])
37. 14 **39.** 1,800 sq. in. **40.** 324 cm^2
41. 110

Algebra Review **1.** $x = 7$ or -2 **3.** $x =$
$\frac{-5 \pm \sqrt{29}}{2}$ **5.** $x = 2$ or -3 **7.** $x = \frac{3 \pm \sqrt{3}}{3}$ **9.** $x =$
3 or 7

Pages 443–446

Written Exercises **1.** 28 **3.** 24 **5.** $\frac{10}{3}$ **7.** 18
9. $32 - 0.5y^2$ **11.** 22 **13.** Kite; 24 **15.** 70,350
sq. mi. **17.** 84 in. **19.** Multiply the height and
the length of the median. **21.** 48 **23.** $\frac{5x^2\sqrt{3}}{2}$
25. $18\sqrt{3} \approx 31.18$ **27.** $112.5\sqrt{2} \approx 159.1$ sq. ft.
29. 96 **31.** $m\angle RPO = m\angle EPS$ since they are
vert. $\angle$s. Because $\overline{OR} \parallel \overline{VS}$, $\angle$s ORP and SEP are
alt. int. $\angle$s and their measures are $=$. Then,
since $RP = EP$, $\triangle ORP \cong \triangle SEP$ by the ASA Post.
Area $ROVE =$ area $OVEP +$ area $\triangle OPR$ by area
add., and area $ROVE =$ area $OVEP + \triangle SEP$ by
substitution. Finally, area $ROVE =$ area $\triangle VOS$
because area $\triangle VOS =$ area $OVEP +$ area $\triangle SEP$.

33. *Given:* Trap. *ABCD*
with $\overline{AB} \parallel \overline{DC}$; median
$\overline{XY}$, and height h *Prove:*
Area $ABCD = h(XY)$

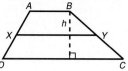

Proof: 1. Trap. *ABCD* with $\overline{AB} \parallel \overline{DC}$ has median
$\overline{XY}$ and height h. (Given) 2. Area $ABCD =$
$\frac{1}{2}h(AB + CD)$ (Area of a trap. [1]) 3. $XY =$
$\frac{1}{2}(AB + CD)$ (Median of a trap. has length $=$ to
half the sum of lengths of bases. [1]) 4. Area
$ABCD = h(XY)$ (Substitution Prop. [2, 3])
35. Texas 285,075 sq. mi. **39.** 30 **41.** 108
42. $9\sqrt{10} \approx 28.46$ **43.** $20\sqrt{10} \approx 63.25$ cm
44. If a creature is a collie, then it has long
hair. **45.** 6

Algebra Review **1.** $y = 2x - 2$ **3.** $y = \frac{2}{3}x + \frac{40}{3}$
5. $y = -3x + 3$

Pages 449–451

Written Exercises **1.** $4:25$ **3.** Ratio of
perimeters is square root of ratio of areas.
5. 2 sq. in. **7.** $12:108 = 1:9$
11. $64x^4:16x^2 = 4x^2:1$; if $x = 2$, $32^2:8^2 =$
$16:1$ **13.** $12:3 = 4:1$ **15.** $441:361$ **17.** $8\sqrt{2} \approx$
11.31 ft. **21.** *Proof:* 1. $\triangle PQR \sim \triangle TUV$;
altitudes $\overline{RS}$ and $\overline{VW}$ (Given) 2. $\frac{\text{Area } \triangle PQR}{\text{Area } \triangle TUV} =$
$\left(\frac{PQ}{TU}\right)^2$ (Areas of $\sim \triangle$s) 3. $\frac{PQ}{TU} = \frac{RS}{VW}$ (In $\sim \triangle$s,
lengths of altitudes from corr. vertices are
proportional to lengths of corr. sides. [1])
4. $\frac{\text{Area } \triangle PQR}{\text{Area } \triangle TUV} = \left(\frac{RS}{VW}\right)^2$ (Substitution Prop. [2, 3])
23. $CG = 4\sqrt{2} \approx 5.66$; $DE = 8\sqrt{2} \approx 11.31$
24. 56 sq. in. **25.** 6.67 cm^2 **26.** $\frac{81\sqrt{3}}{4} \approx$
35.07 m^2 **27.** $(8, 0)$; $r = 7$ **28.** 720

Pages 454–456

Written Exercises **1.** $216\sqrt{3} \approx 374.12$
3. $150\sqrt{3} \approx 259.81$ **5.** Draw ten adjacent 36°
central angles in a circle. Draw the chords for
the angles. **7.** 128 **9.** $\frac{1}{2}$; 4; $\frac{\sqrt{2}}{2}$; 1 **11.** $4.5\sqrt{3}$;
54; 9; $121.5\sqrt{3}$ **13.** $\frac{y\sqrt{3}}{6}$; $3y$; $\frac{y\sqrt{3}}{3}$; $\frac{y^2\sqrt{3}}{4}$
15. 1,920 sq. ft. **17.** Its angles are equal.
19. The angle bisectors in each quadrilateral
intersect. **21.** *Proof:* 1. Reg. poly. has center at
O, side $\overline{AB}$; $\overline{OC} \perp \overline{AB}$ at C. (Given) 2. $\overline{OC}$ is
the apothem. (Def. of apothem [1]) 3. $\overline{OA} = \overline{OB}$
(Radii of the same reg. poly. are $=$. [1])

4. $m\angle OAC = m\angle OBC$ (Isos. $\triangle$ Thm. (3))
5. $\angle OCA$ and $\angle OBC$ are rt. $\angle$s. (Two $\perp$ lines form 4 rt. $\angle$s. (1)) 6. $m\angle OCA = m\angle OCB$ (All rt. $\angle$s are =. (5)) 7. $OC = OC$ (Reflexive Prop.)
8. $\triangle OCA \cong \triangle OCB$ (AAS Thm. (4, 6, 7))
9. $m\angle AOC = m\angle BOC$; $AC = BC$ (Corr. parts of $\cong \triangle$s are =. (8)) 10. $\overrightarrow{OC}$ bisects $\angle AOB$. (Def. of $\angle$ bisector (9)) 11. C is midpt. of $\overline{AB}$. (Def. of midpt. (9)) 12. $\overline{OC}$ bisects $\overline{AB}$. (Def. of bisect (11)) 25. $3\sqrt{3}$ cm 27. $2:3$ 32. $64:9$ 33. 4 cm. 34. 252 35. Proof: 1. $\overline{AB} \parallel \overline{DE}$; $AB = DE$ (Given) 2. $m\angle A = m\angle E$ (Two lines $\parallel \Rightarrow$ alt. int. $\angle$s =. (1)) 3. $m\angle ACB = m\angle ECD$ (Vert. $\angle$s are =.) 4. $\triangle ACB \cong \triangle ECD$ (AAS $\cong$ Thm. (1, 2, 3)) 5. $AC = EC$ (Corr. parts of $\cong \triangle$s are =. (4)) 6. C is midpt. of $\overline{AE}$. (Def. of midpt. (5)) 36. 5

Pages 459–461

Written Exercises 1. $144\pi \approx 452.16$ cm^2
3. $900\pi \approx 2{,}826$ cm^2 5. $0.72\pi \approx 2.26$ m^2
7. 8.60 9. 2; 4 11. 11-inch square; ≈ 8.0 sq. in.
13. $1:4$; $1:16$ 15. $15\pi \approx 47.1$ ft. 17. 7 fans
19. $18\pi \approx 56.52$ 21. $27\pi \approx 84.78$ 23. Given: $\odot A$ with radius a; $\odot B$ with radius b Prove: $\frac{\text{Area } \odot A}{\text{Area } \odot B} = \left(\frac{a}{b}\right)^2$ Proof: 1. $\odot A$ with radius a; $\odot B$ with radius b (Given) 2. Area $\odot A = \pi a^2$; area $\odot B = \pi b^2$ (Area of a $\odot$ (1)) 3. $\frac{\text{Area } \odot A}{\text{Area } \odot B} = \frac{\pi a^2}{\pi b^2}$ (Division Prop. (2)) 4. $\frac{\text{Area } \odot A}{\text{Area } \odot B} = \frac{a^2}{b^2} = \left(\frac{a}{b}\right)^2$ (Multiplication Prop. (3)) 25. 680.33 ft.
27. $100\pi - 192 \approx 122$ sq. in. 29. $9.42x^2$; $6.28\sqrt{3}x \approx 10.88x$ 31. 20π; 100π
35. Draw eight adjacent 45° angles in a circle. Draw the chords for the angles. 36. 48 in.; $96\sqrt{3} \approx 166.28$ sq. in. 37. 324 38. 22 39. 20

Pages 465–467

Written Exercises 1. $10\pi \approx 31.4$ 3. $\frac{10}{3}\pi \approx 10.47$ 5. $\frac{50}{3}\pi \approx 52.33$ 7. $4\pi - 8 \approx 4.56$ 9. 90; $64\pi \approx 200.96$ 11. $228 + 18\pi \approx 284.52$ sq. ft.
13. $56\pi \approx 175.84$ 15. $64\pi - 48\sqrt{3} \approx 117.82$
17. $36\pi - 36 \approx 77.04$ 19. $30\pi + 9\sqrt{3} \approx 109.79$ 21. $\frac{65}{9}\pi \approx 22.68$ 23. $2\pi \approx 6.28$
27. circumference, diameter 28. $12\pi \approx 37.68$; $36\pi \approx 113.04$ 29. 50 30. 6 31. $\odot A$ and $\odot O$ have = radii.

Chapter 10 Review, Pages 469–470

1. 195 2. 12 3. 64 4. 12 5. 49.5 6. $6.25\sqrt{3} \approx 10.83$ 7. 294 8. 90 9. 240 10. 250 11. 350

12. 35 13. $\frac{81}{2}\sqrt{3} \approx 70.15$ 14. 336 15. 144
16. 85 17. 350 18. 337.5 19. 7 20. $7:10$; $49:100$ 21. $7\frac{7}{9}$ 22. $10\sqrt{2} \approx 14.14$ 23. 696
24. $216\sqrt{3} \approx 374.12$ 25. 196 26. 13.8 27. 6; $36\pi \approx 113.04$ 28. $81\pi \approx 254.34$; $18\pi \approx 56.52$
29. $32\pi \approx 100.48$ 30. $40\pi \approx 125.6$ 31. 17; $34\pi \approx 106.76$ 32. $\frac{25}{2}\pi \approx 39.25$ 33. $24\pi - 36\sqrt{3} \approx 13.01$ 34. $\frac{8}{3}\pi \approx 8.37$; $8\pi \approx 25.12$

Chapter 11

Pages 476–477

Written Exercises 1. $e = 15$; $f = 7$; $v = 10$
3. $s = 10$; $f = 12$; $v = 20$ 5. 6 7. 8 9. Given: Prism with bases $PQRSTU$ and $P'Q'R'S'T'U'$ Prove: $\overline{RT} \parallel \overline{R'T'}$ Proof: 1. Prism with bases $PQRSTU$ and $P'Q'R'S'T'U'$ (Given) 2. Draw $\overline{RT}$ and $\overline{R'T'}$. (2 pts. determine a line.) 3. $\overline{RR'} \parallel \overline{TT'}$; $RR' = TT'$ (Lateral edges of a prism are = and $\parallel$. (1, 2)) 4. $RR'T'T$ is a $\square$. (A quad. with 1 pr. opp. sides = and $\parallel$ is a $\square$. (3)) 5. $\overline{RT} \parallel \overline{R'T'}$ (Opp. sides of a $\square$ are $\parallel$. (4)) 11. $20\sqrt{3} \approx 34.64$ cm 15. $\frac{1}{2}m$ 17. $\ell =$ length of edge; $d = \sqrt{e^2 + e^2 + e^2} = \sqrt{3e^2} = e\sqrt{3}$ 19. Proof: 1. Parallelepiped with bases $ABCD$ and $A'B'C'D'$; $\overline{AD} \parallel \overline{B'C'}$ (Given) 2. $ABCD$ is a $\square$; $BB'C'C$ is a $\square$. (Def. parallelepiped (1)) 3. $AD = BC$; $BC = B'C'$ (Opp. sides of $\square$ are =. (2)) 4. $AD = B'C'$ (Transitive Prop. (3)) 5. $ADC'B'$ is a $\square$. (If a pair of opp. sides of a quad. are $\parallel$ and =, then the quad. is a $\square$. (1, 4)) 6. $AB' = DC'$ (Opp. sides of a $\square$ are =. (5)) 23. Proof: 1. Rt. prism with bases $ABCDE$ and $A'B'C'D'E'$; $\overline{MM'} \parallel \overline{DD'}$; $\overline{MM'} \perp$ base $ABCDE$ (Given) 2. Plane of $ABCDE \parallel$ plane of $A'B'C'D'E'$ (Def. of prism (1) 3. $\overline{MM'} \perp$ plane $A'B'C'D'E'$ (If a line is $\perp$ to one of 2 $\parallel$ planes, then it is $\perp$ to the other. (2)) 4. $\overline{MM'} \perp \overline{MD}$; $\overline{MM'} \perp \overline{M'D'}$ (Def. line $\perp$ to a plane (1, 2)) 5. M, D, D', M' are coplanar. (Def. of $\parallel$ lines (1)) 6. $\overline{MM'}, \overline{MD}, \overline{M'D'}$ are coplanar. (Flat Plane Post.) 7. $\overline{MD} \parallel \overline{M'D'}$ (In a plane, 2 lines $\perp$ to same line are $\parallel$. (4, 6)) 8. $MDD'M'$ is a $\square$. (If both prs. opp. sides of a quad. are $\parallel$, then the quad. is a $\square$. (1, 7) 9. $MD = M'D'$ (Opp. sides of a $\square$ are =. (8))
26. $\frac{40\pi}{3} \approx 41.87$ 27. $\frac{4\pi}{3} \approx 4.19$ 28. $7:10$; $49:100$

Pages 480–482

Written Exercises 1. 800 3. 72 cm^2 5. 592
7. 108 9. $4e^2$; $6e^2$ 11. $16x^2$; $24x^2$

13. 1,440 sq. in.; 1,890 sq. in. **15.** 158 m^2
17. 7 in. **19.** 3,360 cm^2 **21.** 780 sq. in.
23. 1,248 + 192$\sqrt{3}$ ≈ 1,580.55;
1,580.55 + 104$\sqrt{3}$ ≈ 1,760.69 **25.** 9:1
26. octagon **27.** $\sqrt{290}$ ≈ 17.03 ft.
29. *Proof:* 1. $m\angle NLM = m\angle OML$; $LN = MO$
(Given) 2. $m\angle M = m\angle M$ (Reflexive Prop.)
3. $\triangle NLM \cong \triangle OML$ (SAS Post. [1, 2]) **30.** 45

Pages 487–489
Written Exercises **1.** 693 **3.** 240 **5.** 7 cm

7. 12 m^3 **9.** 22,500 cm^3 **11.** 122$\frac{2}{3}$ lb.

13. 91,000 g **15.** 4 in. by 4in. by 4 in.
17. 2,916 cu. in. **19.** *Given:* cube with edge e
Prove: Volume of cube = e^3 *Proof:* 1. Cube with
edge e (Given) 2. Cube is a rect. solid. (Def. of
cube) 3. Volume of cube = ℓwh (Vol. of rect.
solid) 4. $\ell = w = h = e$ (Def. of cube [1])
5. Volume of cube = $e \cdot e \cdot e = e^3$ (Substitution
Prop. [3, 4]) **21.** 8 + 16$\sqrt{2}$ ≈ 30.63 sq. ft.
23. right **24.** 820 **25.** Contained in ∥ planes; are
≅ polygonal regions; have = areas; have =
perimeters **26.** sin $Y = \frac{y}{z}$; cos $Y = \frac{x}{z}$; tan $Y = \frac{y}{x}$
27. $\frac{4\sqrt{3}}{9}$ ≈ 0.77
Algebra Review **1.** equal **3.** $y = 4x - 11$
5. $y = \frac{4}{3}x + \frac{7}{3}$

Pages 493–494
Written Exercises **1.** 40π sq. ft.; 52.5π sq. ft.;
50π cu. ft. **3.** 6$a\pi$; 6$a\pi$ + 2$a^2\pi$ **5.** 200π cu. in.
7. 20,400 lb. **9.** 126π; 288π; 567π
11. 3.14 cu. ft. **13.** 2,034.72π cu. in. **15.** 16.12
oz. **17.** 27:8 **19.** Equal **20.** 624 **21.** 460
22. *Given:* $\angle J$ and $\angle K$
form a linear pr.; $\angle Q$
is a complement of
$\angle K$. *Prove:* $m\angle J > 90$
Proof: Either $m\angle J > 90$ or $m\angle J \not> 90$. Assume
$m\angle J \not> 90$. Then $m\angle J \leq 90$. Since $\angle J$ and $\angle K$
form a lin. pr., $m\angle J + m\angle K = 180$ and $m\angle J =$
$180 - m\angle K$. Substituting and simplifying, we
have $180 - m\angle K \leq 90$, or $m\angle K \geq 90$. But this
contradicts the fact that $\angle K$ and $\angle Q$ are
complements, that is, that $m\angle Q + m\angle K = 90$.
Thus our assumption that $m\angle J \not> 90$ must be
false and $m\angle J > 90$ is true.

Pages 499–501
Written Exercises **1.** 60; 96; 48 **3.** 85,000,000
cu. ft. **5.** 384 sq. ft. **7.** 1,728 m^2; 3,024 m^2

9. 8 cm **11.** Yes; the bases of a prism have equal
areas. **13.** Yes; each is half of the same
rectangle. **15.** Exercises 11–14 show that the
volumes of the three pyramids are equal and
their sum equals the volume of the prism.
Therefore, the volume of each pyramid is one
third the volume of the prism. **17.** $\frac{e^3\ell^3}{48}$
19. Trapezoid; 12$\sqrt{13}$ **21.** 224 **23.** 228π ≈
715.92 m^2 **24.** 468π ≈ 1,469.52 m^3 **25.** 1,920
cu. in. **26.** right isosceles **27.** Rectangles;
isosceles trapezoids

Pages 504–505
Written Exercises **1.** 15π; 24π; 12π **3.** 135π;
216π; 324π **5.** 3$\pi\sqrt{17}$; 3π + 3$\pi\sqrt{17}$; 4$\pi\sqrt{3}$
7. 1:3 **9.** 47.38 m^2 **11.** 9.54 ft. **15.** $\frac{64\pi\sqrt{3}}{3}$ ≈
116.02 cu. in. **17.** 2$\pi\sqrt{6}$ ≈ 15.38 cu. in.
18. 224$\sqrt{3}$ ≈ 387.98 m^3 **19.** 144 + 48$\sqrt{34}$ ≈
423.89
21. *Proof:* 1. $m\angle 1 = m\angle 7$ (Given) 2. $m\angle 5 =$
$m\angle 7$ (Vertical angles are =.) 3. $m\angle 1 = m\angle 5$
(Substitution Prop. [1, 2]) 4. $a \parallel b$ (Corr. $\angle$s ⇒
2 lines ∥. [3]) 5. $m\angle 12 = m\angle 16$ (2 lines ∥ ⇒
corr. $\angle$s =. [4]) **22.** 6$\sqrt{5}$ ≈ 13.42

Pages 507–509
Written Exercises **1.** 64π m^2; $\frac{256\pi}{3}$ m^3 **3.** 324π
sq. in.; 972π cu. in. **5.** 3,600π sq. ft.; 36,000π
cu. ft. **7.** 100πt^2; $\frac{500\pi t^3}{3}$ **9.** $r = 27$; $d = 54$; $V =$
26,244π; $C = 54\pi$ **11.** $r = 6$; $d = 12$; $A = 144\pi$;
$C = 12\pi$ **13.** $r = 86$; $d = 172$; $A = 29,584\pi$;
$V = \frac{2,544,224\pi}{3}$ **15.** $A = 484\pi$ ≈ 1,519.76 cm^2;
$V = \frac{5,324}{3}\pi$ ≈ 5,572.45 cm^3 **17.** 379 cm^2
19. 10,717.87 cu. ft. **21.** 251,200 gal.
23. 227.92 m^3 **25.** 2:3 **29.** 221,184 oz. or
13,824 lb. **31.** 6 **32.** 4$\pi\sqrt{65}$ ≈ 101.26 cm^2
33. $\frac{112\pi}{3}$ ≈ 117.23 cm^3 **34.** Volume of a prism =
3 times volume of pyramid **35.** $\frac{1}{2}$

Chapter 11 Review, Pages 511–512
1. 9 **2.** 11 **3.** 42 **4.** 6 **5.** $\sqrt{565}$ ≈ 23.77 in.
6. 12 m^2 **7.** 7,560 sq. in.; 13,320 sq. in.
8. 432 cm^2; 432 + 192$\sqrt{3}$ ≈ 764.55 cm^2
9. 294 cm^2 **10.** 120 cm^2 **11.** 1,728 cu. in.
12. 121.5$\sqrt{3}$ ≈ 210.44 cm^3 **13.** 17,200 cm^3
14. $\frac{45\sqrt{3}}{4}$ ≈ 19.49 m^3 **15.** 24π sq. in.;
56π sq. in.; 48π cu. in. **16.** 140π cm^2;
190π cm^2; 350π cm^3 **17.** 63π sq. ft.;
87.5π sq. ft.; 110.25 cu. ft. **18.** 550 cm^2

19. $100\sqrt{5} \approx 223.61$ sq. in.; $100 + 100\sqrt{5} \approx 323.61$ sq. in.; $\frac{1,000}{3} \approx 333.33$ cu. in.
20. $144\sqrt{3} \approx 249.42$ cm^3; $240\sqrt{3} \approx 415.69$ cm^2; $192\sqrt{5} \approx 429.33$ cm^3 **21.** $108\sqrt{3} \approx 187.06$ cm^2; $144\sqrt{3} \approx 249.42$ cm^2; $144\sqrt{2} \approx 203.65$ cm^3
22. $5\pi\sqrt{61} \approx 122.62$ sq. in.; $5\pi\sqrt{61} + 25\pi \approx 201.12$ sq. in.; $50\pi \approx 157.00$ cu. in.
23. $36\pi\sqrt{481} \approx 2{,}479.16$ cm^2; $36\pi\sqrt{481} + 324\pi \approx 3{,}496.52$ cm^2; $4{,}320\ \pi \approx 13{,}564.80$ cm^3
24. $17\sqrt{145}\pi \approx 642.78$ cm^2; $17\sqrt{145}\pi + 145\pi \approx 1{,}098.08$ cm^2; $580\pi \approx 1{,}821.20$ cm^3 **25.** $h \approx 4.5$ cm **26.** $A = 615.44$ sq. ft.; $V = 1{,}436.03$ cm^3 **27.** 256π m^2; $\frac{2{,}048\pi}{3}$ m^3 **28.** 457.25 cu. in.

Chapter Chapter 12

Pages 517–518
Written Exercises
1.

9. *Proof:* 1. A reflection over ℓ maps P onto P', and Q onto Q'; P and Q are on the same side of ℓ. (Given) 2. Draw $\overline{PP'}$ and $\overline{QQ'}$ intersecting ℓ in M and N, respectively. (Line Post.) 3. Draw $\overline{MQ}$ and $\overline{MQ'}$ (Line Post.) 4. ℓ is the $\perp$ bisector of PP' and QQ'. (Def. of line reflection [1]) 5. $QM = Q'M$; $QN = Q'N$ (In a plane, the locus of pts. equidistant from 2 given pts. is the $\perp$ bisector of the seg. joining the 2 pts. [4]) 6. $MN = MN$ (Reflexive Prop.) 7. $\triangle MNQ \cong \triangle MNQ'$ (SSS Post. [5, 6]) 8. $m\angle MQN = m\angle MQ'N$ (Corr. parts of $\cong \triangle$s are =. [7]) 9. $\overline{PP'} \parallel \overline{QQ'}$ (In a plane, if 2 lines are $\perp$ to the same line, then they are $\parallel$. [4]) 10. $m\angle MQN = m\angle QMP$; $m\angle MQ'N = m\angle Q'MP'$ (Lines $\parallel \Rightarrow$ alt. int. $\angle$s =. [9]) 11. $m\angle QMP = m\angle Q'MP'$ (Substitution Prop. [8, 10]) 12. $PM = PM$ (In a plane, the locus of pts. equidistant from 2 given pts. is the $\perp$ bisector of the seg. joining the 2 pts. [4]) 13. $\triangle PQM \cong \triangle P'Q'M$ (SAS Post. [5, 11, 12]) 14. $PQ = P'Q'$ (Corr. parts of $\cong \triangle$s are =. [13])
13. *Given:* A reflection through O maps P onto P' and Q onto Q'; P, Q, and O are noncollinear. *Prove:* $PQ = P'Q'$ *Proof:* 1. A reflection through O maps P onto P' and Q onto Q'; P, Q, and O are noncollinear. (Given) 2. Draw $\overline{PP'}$, $\overline{QQ'}$, $\overline{PQ}$, and $\overline{P'Q'}$. (Line Post.) 3. O is midpt. of $\overline{PP'}$ and $\overline{QQ'}$. (Def. of pt. reflection [1]) 4. $PO = P'O$;

$QO = Q'O$ (Def. of midpt. [3]) 5. $m\angle POQ = m\angle P'OQ'$ (Vert. $\angle$s are =.) 6. $\triangle POQ \cong m\triangle P'OQ'$ (SAS Post. [4, 5]) 7. $PQ = P'Q'$ (Corr. parts of $\cong \triangle$s are =. [6]) **17.** $(x, -y)$
19. $(6 - x, -y)$ **20.** 324π cm^2 **21.** 972π cm^3
22. 120π cu. units **23.** 2; bases **24.** If the hypotenuse and leg of a rt. $\triangle$ are = to the corr. parts of a 2nd rt. $\triangle$, the $\triangle$s are $\cong$.

Pages 521–522
Written Exercises **1.** D **3.** $\overline{DB}$ **5.** $\triangle DCB$
7. $\overline{CD}$ **9.** $\angle DOA$ **11.** Counterclockwise
13. No; line reflections reverse orientation.
15. By Thm. 12-2 (A pt. reflection is an isometry.) and def. of isometry **17.** $m\angle PQR = m\angle SRQ$ (Ex. 16) and alt. int. $\angle$s = $\Rightarrow$ lines $\parallel$.
19. By Thm. 12-2 (A pt. reflection is an isometry.) and Thm. 12-4 (Isometries map a ray onto a ray.)
27. If $\ell \perp m$, they meet to form a rt. $\angle$. Since isometries preserve $\angle$ meas., ℓ' and m' meet to form a rt. $\angle$. Hence, $\ell' \perp m'$.
29. *Given:* An isometry maps X onto X', Y onto Y', and Z onto Z'. *Prove:* $m\angle XYZ = m\angle X'Y'Z'$ *Proof:* 1. An isometry maps X onto X', Y onto y', and Z onto Z'. (Given) 2. Draw $\overline{XZ}$ and $\overline{X'Z'}$. (Line Post.) 3. $XY = X'Y'$; $XZ = X'Z'$; $YZ = Y'Z'$ (Def. of isometry [1]) 4. $\triangle XYZ \cong \triangle X'Y'Z'$ (SSS Post. [3]) 5. $m\angle XYZ = m\angle X'Y'Z'$ (Corr. parts of $\cong \triangle$s are =. [4]) **32.** A transformation is a one-to-one correspondence between the pts. of a plane and themselves. **33.** An isometry is a transformation that preserves distance.
34. $1{,}774\frac{2}{3}\pi$ m^3 **35.** tangent **36.** $2\sqrt{15}$

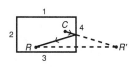

Pages 524–526
Written Exercises
1.

3.

13. $APBP'$ is a rhombus. Since the diagonals of a rhombus are $\perp$ to and bisect each other, P' is the reflection image of P over ℓ for any position of P. **15.** $1{,}080$ m **18.** distance; collinearity; betweenness; $\angle$ measure **19.** orientation
20. Line reflections; pt. reflections; the identity transformation **21.** 40; 140 **22.** $1{,}260$

Pages 529–530

Written Exercises

3. K **5.** $\overline{FK}$ **7.** $\Box GHML$

13. *Given:* A translation maps P onto P' and Q onto Q'. *Prove:* $PQ = P'Q'$

Proof: 1. A translation maps P onto P' and Q onto Q'. (Given) 2. Let ℓ and m be $\parallel$ lines such that this translation is the composite of reflections over ℓ and then m. (Def. of translation [1])3. Let P_1 and Q_1 be the reflection images of P and Q, respectively, over ℓ. (Def. of line reflection) 4. An isometry maps P and Q onto P_1 and Q_1, respectively. (A line reflection is an isometry. [3]) 5. $PQ = P_1Q_1$ (Def. of isometry [4]) 6. P' and Q' are the reflection images of P_1 and Q_1, respectively, over m. (Def. of translation [1, 2, 3]) 7. An isometry maps P_1 and Q_1 onto P' and Q', respectively. (A line reflection is an isometry. [6]) 8. $P_1Q_1 = P'Q'$ (Def. of isometry [7]) 9. $PQ = P'Q'$ (Transitive Prop. [5, 8])

20. A line that intersects a $\odot$ in 2 pts.

Pages 533–534

Written Exercises **1.** D **3.** 120; clockwise **5.** $\angle DEF$ **7.** $\overline{DE}$ **13.–17.** Samples are given.

13. 90° clockwise rotation about G

15. Translation that maps A onto C

17. Half-turn about H

19. *Given:* P' and Q' are the images of P and Q, respectively, under a rotation which is the composite of reflections, first over ℓ and then over m. *Prove:* $PQ = P'Q'$

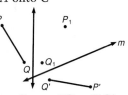

Proof: 1. P' and Q' are the images of P and Q, respectively, under a rotation which is the composite of reflections, first over ℓ, then over m. (Given) 2. Let P_1 and Q_1 be the reflection images of P and Q, respectively, over ℓ. (Def. of line reflection) 3. $PQ = P_1Q_1$ (A line reflection is an isometry. [1]) 4. P' and Q' are the reflection images of P_1 and Q_1, respectively, over m. (Def. of rotation [1]) 5. $P_1Q_1 = P'Q'$ (A line reflection is an isometry.) 6. $PQ = P'Q'$ (Transitive Prop. [3, 5]) **21.** $(y, -x)$ **22.** $\parallel$ **23.** $=$

Pages 537–538

Written Exercises **1.** a. 5; b. No; c. Yes: 72 and 144 in both directions **3.** a. 1; b. No; c. No **5.** a. 5; b. No; c. Yes: 72 and 144 in both

directions **7.** a. 0; b. Yes; c. Yes: 180 in both directions **9.** a. 2; b. Yes; c. Yes: 180 in both directions **11.** a. Infinitely many; b. Yes; c. Yes: 180 in both directions **13.** H, I, M, O, T, U, V, W, X, Y **15.** H, I, N, O, S, X, Z **23.** Not possible **25.** $(-a, b)$ **27.** $(-a, -b)$ **29.** $n - 1$

30. A rotation is the composite of 2 reflections over 2 intersecting lines. **31.** preserve **32.** (2, 8) **33.** $\sqrt{17}$ **34.** *Proof:* Either (1) $\angle 1$ is not an obtuse $\angle$ or (2) $\angle 1$ is an obtuse $\angle$. Suppose $\angle 1$ is an obtuse $\angle$. Then $90 < m\angle 1 < 180$. But this contradicts the given fact that $m\angle 1 = 49$. So it is false that $\angle 1$ is an obtuse $\angle$. We conclude the $\angle 1$ is not an obtuse $\angle$.

Pages 541–542

Written Exercises **1.** L **3.** T **5.** R **7.** L **9.** 120

13. *Given:* $\triangle ABC \cong \triangle A'B'C'$ *Prove:* The isometry that maps $\triangle ABC$ onto $\triangle A'B'C'$ is unique.

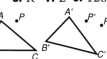

Proof: Either (1) the isometry is unique or (2) there is at least one other distinct isometry that maps $\triangle ABC$ onto $\triangle A'B'C'$. Suppose there is another isometry. Then there is at least one pt. P that is mapped onto P' by the first isometry and onto $P*$ by the second isometry. $AP = A'P'$; and $AP = A'P*$ by the def. of isometry. Thus, $A'P' = A'P*$ by substitution. A' is on the $\perp$ bisector of $\overline{P'P*}$ because in a plane, the locus of pts. equidistant from 2 given pts. is the $\perp$ bisector of the seg. joining the pts. Similarly, $\overline{B'P'} = \overline{B'P*}$ and $\overline{C'P'} = \overline{C'P*}$. So B' and C' are also on the $\perp$ bisector of $\overline{P'P*}$. Thus, A', B', and C' are collinear. But this contradicts the fact that A', B', and C' are vertices of a $\triangle$. Therefore, the assumption that there is another isometry that maps $\triangle ABC$ onto $\triangle A'B'C'$ is false. We conclude that the isometry that maps $\triangle ABC$ onto $\triangle A'B'C'$ is unique. **14.** 2; the lines containing the diagonals **17.** No; the sum of the lengths of any 2 sides > the length of the third side. $8 + 12 \not> 20$ **18.** 3,375 cm³

Page 545

Written Exercises

7. $\frac{1}{3}$ **9.** 4

11. *Given:* A dilation with center C and scale factor k maps A onto A' and B onto B'. *Prove:* $A'B' = k(AB)$

Proof: 1. A dilation with center C and scale factor k maps A onto A' and B onto B'. (Given) 2. $CA' = k(CA)$; $CB' = k(CB)$ (Def. of dilation [1]) 3. $k = \frac{CA'}{CA}$, $k = \frac{CB'}{CB}$ (Division Prop. [2]) 4. $\frac{CA'}{CA} = \frac{CB'}{CB}$ (Substitution Prop. [3]) 5. $m\angle C = m\angle C$ (Reflexive Prop.) 6. $\triangle A'CB' \sim \triangle ACB$ (SAS $\sim$ Thm. [4, 5]) 7. $\frac{A'B'}{AB} = \frac{CA'}{CA}$ (Corr. sides of $\sim \triangle$s are proportional. [6]) 8. $\frac{A'B'}{AB} = k$ (Substitution Prop. [3, 7]) 9. $A'B' = k(AB)$ (Mult. Prop. [8]) **13.** (1) Two $\triangle$s are $\cong$ if and only if there is a correspondence between the vertices such that each pair of corr. sides and each pair of corr. $\angle$s are =. (2) Two $\triangle$s are $\cong$ if and only if there is an isometry that maps one $\triangle$ onto the other. **14.** Yes **16.** The pt. of concurrency of the medians of a $\triangle$ **17.** The distance from the center of a reg. polygon to each side

Pages 547–549
Written Exercises
5.

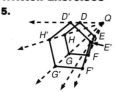

9. 6 **11.** 4 **13.** 55 **19.** Yes **21.** 3
25. *Given:* A', B', and C' are the images of A, B, and C, respectively, under a dilation with center O and scale factor k. *Prove:* $\triangle ABC \sim \triangle A'B'C'$ *Plan for Proof:* Use Thm. 12-11 and the Division Prop. to show $\frac{A'B'}{AB} = \frac{B'C'}{BC} = \frac{A'C'}{AC}$. Then use SSS $\sim$ Thm. to show $\triangle ABC \sim \triangle A'B'C'$. **27.** P; $\frac{2}{3}$ **31.** $\frac{1}{3}$ **32.** When the scale factor > 1; when the scale factor is < 1 **33.** This composite is equivalent to a composite of 3 or less line reflections, by Thm. 12-10. Of those possible, only a single line reflection or a composite of 3 reverse orientation, as does a composite of M of 11 line reflections. **34.** 3 **35.** 120 m

Page 552
Written Exercises
1. 2 **3.** It is the composite of a dilation with $k = 1$ and an isometry, the line reflection. **5.** It is the composite of a dilation with $k = 1$ and an isometry, the translation. **7.** It is the composite of a dilation with $k = 1$ and an isometry, the rotation.

9. Sample: a dilation with center (4, 0) and $k = \frac{1}{2}$, followed by a 90° counterclockwise rotation about the origin **13.** 2 **15.** Let $\odot R_1$ have radius r_1 and $\odot R_2$ have radius r_2. Then a similarity transformation that is the composite of a dilation with $k = \frac{r_2}{r_1}$ followed by an isometry will map $\odot R_1$ onto $\odot R_2$. **17.** No; $\angle$ meas. is not preserved. **18.** Any three: $\angle$ meas., collinearity, betweenness, parallelism, perpendicularity, orientation **19.** $\sim$ **20.** Yes; the center. For $k = 1$, all pts. **21.** 9 **22.** $\triangle NOM$, $\triangle PON$, $\triangle PNM$

Chapter 12 Review, Pages 557–558
1. B **2.** ℓ is the $\perp$ bisector of $\overline{AA'}$. **3.** X **4.** O is the midpt. of $\overline{YY'}$. **5.** When the pt. is on the line of reflection **6.** When the pt. is the half-turn (pt. reflection) **7.** Every pt. is its own image. **8.** $\overleftrightarrow{X'Z'}$ **9.** 32 **10.** Z'; X'; Y' **11.** Draw B', the reflection image of B over $\overline{FG}$. Aim for P, the intersection of $\overline{AB'}$ and $\overline{FG}$. $m\angle 1 = m\angle 2$ because an isometry preserves $\angle$ meas., and $m\angle 2 = m\angle 3$ because vert. $\angle$s are =. So $m\angle 1 = m\angle 3$ and it follows that the puck will travel to B after bouncing off $\overline{FG}$ at P. **12.** G **13.** Q **14.** $\overline{FG}$ **15.** $\overleftrightarrow{GL}$ **16.** $\angle LGH$ **17.** $\angle GMH$ **18.** $\triangle LMH$ **19.** $\square GHML$ **20.** G **21.** $\overline{KL}$ **22.** $\angle BFG$ **23.** $\square LPOK$ **24.** 90, counterclockwise **25.** a. 2; b. 1; c. 5; d. 3; e. 0; f. 6 **26.** a, e, f **27.** a, c, d, e, f **28.** 3 **29.** 1 **30.** 2 **31.** 12 **32.** 12 **33.** Yes, the center C **34.** Yes; if $k = 1$ the dilation is the identity transformation. **35.** $\sim$ **36.** U; $\frac{4}{3}$ **37.** U; $\frac{3}{4}$ **38.** Betweenness, collinearity, $\angle$ measure **39.** Composite of a dilation with center C and $k = \frac{1}{3}$ with a 60° counterclockwise rotation about C

Chapter Chapter 13

Pages 565–566
Written Exercises
7. $AB = 9$; $\left(\frac{9}{2}, 1, 5\right)$ **9.** $EF = \sqrt{94}$; $\left(\frac{7}{2}, \frac{1}{2}, 4\right)$ **11.** $AB = BC = 3\sqrt{10}$ **13.** Since $AB = AC = 6$, $\triangle ABC$ is isos.; since $AB^2 + AC^2 = BC^2$, $\triangle ABC$ is a rt. $\triangle$. **15.** No **17.** $(5 + v, 3 - 2u)$ **19.** Yes; $PQ + PR = QR$ **21.** $RA = \sqrt{b^2 + 0^2} = |b| = ST$; slope of $\overline{RA}$ is 0; slope of $\overline{ST}$ is 0. So, $RA = ST$

and $\overline{RA} \parallel \overline{ST}$. Therefore, $STAR$ is $\square$. (If 2 sides of quad. are = and $\parallel$, then quad. is a $\square$.) **23.** $y_1 + \frac{1}{2}QP = y_1 + \frac{1}{2}(y_2 - y_1) = \frac{1}{2}y_1 + \frac{1}{2}y_2 = \frac{y_1 + y_2}{2}$ **25.** $(12, 0, 0)$; $(0, 4, 0)$; $(0, 0, 6)$ **30.** Faces: 7; Edges: 15 **31.** 53

Pages 571–574
Written Exercises **1.** $y - 3 = 2(x - 2)$; $y = 2x - 1$ **3.** $x = -5$ **5.** $\frac{3}{5}, \frac{10}{3}, -2$ **7.** -3; 1; 3 **9.** $9x + 8y = 32$ **11.** $1x + 0y = 15$ **13.** $r = 5$; $(h, k) = (2, -3)$; yes **15.** Slope of $\overleftrightarrow{PQ}$ = slope of $\overleftrightarrow{RS} = -\frac{1}{4}$. Since slopes are =, the lines are $\parallel$. **17.** By the Distance Formula, $SE = ND = \sqrt{34}$ and $SD = EN = 2\sqrt{34}$. Since both pairs of opp. sides are =, $SEND$ is a $\square$. **19.** $SN = ED = \sqrt{170}$ **21.** $y - 4 = \frac{5}{3}(x + 2)$ **23.** -2 **25.** $(x + 2)^2 + (y - 8)^2 = 25$ **27.** No; $AP = 10$ which is > 7. **29.** AA $\sim$ Post. **31.** $QT = y_2 - y_1$; $PT = x_2 - x_1$; $SU = y_4 - y_3$; $RU = x_4 - x_3$; $\frac{y_2 - y_1}{x_2 - x_1} = \frac{y_4 - y_3}{x_4 - x_3}$ **33.** $y = -5x + 1$; slope of $\overline{EF}$ is -5. **35.** $7x + 6y = 24$; $5x - 18y = -20$; $19x - 6y = 28$ **39.** $2\sqrt{19}$ **40.** $(1, 2, 1)$ **41.** SSS $\sim$ Thm. **42.** 360π; 522π; $1{,}620\pi$ **43.** None
Algebra Review **1.** $x = 0$; $y = -5$; a point **3.** No solution. The lines are $\parallel$.

Pages 578–580
Written Exercises **1.** $F(2k, 0)$; $G(2k, 2k)$ **3.** $C(-2s, 0)$; $F(s, t)$; $G(-s, t)$ **5.** Sample: $A(-a, a)$; $B(a, a)$; $C(a, -a)$; $D(-a, -a)$ **7.** $\overline{RO}$: $((1, \frac{3}{2})$; $\overline{OC}$: $(3, 0)$; $\overline{CK}$: $(\frac{11}{2}, \frac{3}{2})$; $\overline{KR}$: $(\frac{7}{2}, 3)$ **9.** $y = 6(x - 3)$ **11.** Samples: $P(-a, 0)$; $Q(a, 0)$ **13.** $(t - s, u)$
17. Given: $\square ABCD$; $AC = BD$ Prove: $ABCD$ is a rectangle. Proof: Place the coordinate axes on $\square ABCD$ so that $A(0, 0)$, $B(b, 0)$, $C(b + a, d)$, and $D(a, d)$. By the Distance Formula, $AC = \sqrt{(b + a)^2 + d^2}$ and $BD = \sqrt{(b - a)^2 + d^2}$. Since $AC = BD$, $\sqrt{(b + a)^2 + d^2} = \sqrt{(b - a)^2 + d^2}$, or $-a = a$. This is true if and only if $a = 0$. Therefore, $\overline{AD} \perp \overline{AB}$ and $\angle A$ is a rt. $\angle$. Thus, $\angle C$, $\angle D$, and $\angle B$ are also rt. $\angle$s. (Opp. $\angle$s of a $\square$ are =, and int. $\angle$s on same side of transversal are supp.) So $ABCD$ is a rectangle.

27. $\frac{2}{3}$ **28.** $y - 6 = \frac{2}{3}(x - 2)$ or $y - 4 = \frac{2}{3}(x + 1)$ **29.** Yes **30.** 33; 47 **31.** 30; 6

Pages 584–585
Written Exercises **1.** $\vec{c} = \vec{e}$; $\vec{f} = \vec{h}$ **7.** $5\sqrt{2}$; 135 **9.** $3\sqrt{13}$ **11.** 5.8; 121° **13.** 7.6 **15.** No; $\vec{c}$ and $\vec{d}$ have the same magnitude but not opposite directions. **17.** No; $\vec{w}$ and $\vec{v}$ have the same magnitude but not opposite directions. **19.** 240°; $-120°$ **20.** $(a, 0)$; $(-a, 0)$; $(-a, b)$ **21.** $(\frac{7}{2}, \frac{3}{2})$; $(\frac{7}{2}, \frac{3}{2})$ **22.** $y = 2x + 6$ **23.** If a triangle is an acute triangle, then it has no right angle. **24.** *Converse*: If a triangle has no rt. angle, then it is an acute triangle. *Inverse*: If a triangle is not an acute triangle, then it has a right angle. *Contrapositive*: If a triangle has a right angle, then it is not an acute triangle.

Pages 590–592
Written Exercises
7. $(6\sqrt{3}, 6) \approx (10.4, 6)$ **9.** $(0, 5)$ **11.** $(-99.6, 8.7)$ **13.** 7 mph **15.** 250.2 mph; the plane's actual direction is about 2° west of north or its direction angle is about 92°. **19.** When $\vec{a} \parallel \vec{b}$, and $\vec{a}$ and $\vec{b}$ have the same direction, $|\vec{a}| + |\vec{b}| = |\vec{a} + \vec{b}|$. It is also true if $\vec{a}$ or $\vec{b}$ or both are the zero vector. **23.** *Given*: $\vec{a}$ and $\vec{b}$ *Prove*: $\vec{a} + \vec{b} = \vec{b} + \vec{a}$ *Proof*: Since any vector can be translated to any location in a plane, place $\vec{a}$ and $\vec{b}$ in standard position. Let $\vec{a} = (a_1, a_2)$ and $\vec{b} = (b_1, b_2)$, where a_1, a_2, b_1 and b_2 are real numbers. Then by the definition of vector addition, $\vec{a} + \vec{b} = (a_1 + b_1, a_2 + b_2)$ and $\vec{b} + \vec{a} = (b_1 + a_1, b_2 + a_2)$. But since addition of real numbers is commutative, $a_1 + b_1 = b_1 + a_1$, and $a_2 + b_2 = b_2 + a_2$. Thus, $\vec{a} + \vec{b} = \vec{b} + \vec{a}$. **27.** 153 mph; 124° **31.** $\sqrt{17}$; 104 **33.** 684 **34.** 4th line from the top; if 3 or more $\parallel$ lines cut off = segs. on one transversal, then they cut off = segs. on every transversal.

Pages 595–596
Written Exercises
7. $(10, 10\sqrt{3})$ **9.** 20 **11.** $(\frac{5}{2}, 6)$ **13.** 6.5 **15.** (a) $(6, 6)$; (b) $6\sqrt{2} \approx 8.46$; (c) 45° **17.** (a) $(10, 16)$; (b) $2\sqrt{89} \approx 18.87$; (c) 58° **19.** Since $\vec{u} + \vec{v} = (x_1 + x_2, y_1 + y_2)$, $k(\vec{u} + \vec{v}) = (kx_1 + kx_2, ky_1 + ky_2)$. **24.** $(6\sqrt{2}, 6\sqrt{2}) \approx (8.49, 8.49)$ **25.** $\sqrt{53} \approx 7.28$ **26.** 24 in. **27.** *Proof*: 1. $\odot O$; $m\overset{\frown}{AB} = m\overset{\frown}{DC}$

(Given) 2. $AB = DC$ (In a $\odot$, = minor arcs $\Rightarrow$ their chords are =. [1]) 3. $m\angle A = m\angle D$; $m\angle B = m\angle C$ (If 2 inscribed $\angle$s intercept the same arc, then the $\angle$s are =.) 4. $\triangle AEB \cong \triangle DEC$ (ASA $\cong$ Post. [2, 3])

Pages 599–600
Written Exercises

1.

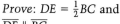

3. No **5.** $x = \vec{b} - \vec{a}$

9. Given: $\triangle ABC$ with D the midpt. of $\overline{AB}$ and E the midpt. of $\overline{AC}$.

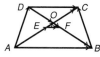

Prove: $DE = \frac{1}{2}BC$ and $\overline{DE} \parallel \overline{BC}$.

Proof: By def. of midpt. $\overrightarrow{DA} = \frac{1}{2}\overrightarrow{BA}$ and $\overrightarrow{AE} = \frac{1}{2}\overrightarrow{AC}$. Then $\overrightarrow{DE} = \overrightarrow{DA} + \overrightarrow{AE} = \frac{1}{2}\overrightarrow{BA} + \frac{1}{2}\overrightarrow{AC} = \frac{1}{2}(\overrightarrow{BA} + \overrightarrow{AC}) = \frac{1}{2}\overrightarrow{BC}$. By def. of = vectors, $\overline{DE} \parallel \overline{BC}$ and $DE = \frac{1}{2}BC$.

13. Given: Trapezoid $ABCD$ with E the midpt. of diagonal $\overline{AC}$ and F the dpt. of diagonal $\overline{DB}$.

Prove: $EF = \frac{1}{2}(AB - DC)$, $\overline{EF} \parallel \overline{DC}$, and $\overline{EF} \parallel \overline{AB}$.

Proof: By def. of vector addition, and substitution: $\overrightarrow{AE} + \overrightarrow{EF} + \overrightarrow{FB} = \overrightarrow{AB}$; $(\overrightarrow{EO} + \overrightarrow{OC}) + \overrightarrow{EF} + (\overrightarrow{DO} + \overrightarrow{OF}) = \overrightarrow{AB}$; $\overrightarrow{EF} + \overrightarrow{EF} + \overrightarrow{OC} + \overrightarrow{DO} = \overrightarrow{AB}$; $2\overrightarrow{EF} + \overrightarrow{DC} = \overrightarrow{AB}$; $2\overrightarrow{EF} = \overrightarrow{AB} - \overrightarrow{DC}$; $\overrightarrow{EF} = \frac{1}{2}(\overrightarrow{AB} - \overrightarrow{DC})$. Therefore, $EF = \frac{1}{2}(AB - DC)$. Since $\overline{DC} \parallel \overline{AB}$, $\overrightarrow{DC} = k\overrightarrow{AB}$ for some real number k and $\overrightarrow{EF} = \frac{1}{2}(\overrightarrow{AB} - k\overrightarrow{AB}) = \frac{1}{2}(1 - k)\overrightarrow{AB}$. Thus $\overline{EF} \parallel \overline{AB}$ and hence $\overline{EF} \parallel \overline{DC}$ also. **14.** Write the statement to be proved in *if . . . then* form; draw and label a diagram; state the Given and the Prove in terms of the diagram; develop a Plan for Proof; write a proof in two-column form or in paragraph form. **15.** All definitions, properties of real numbers, postulates, and theorems in this geometry course **16.** $\frac{1}{2}$ **17.** $\frac{16}{3}$, 16 **18.** No; if two vectors have the same magnitude, they do not necessarily have the same direction.

Pages 604–605
Written Exercises **1.** (a) SAS $\cong$ Post.
(b) (c)

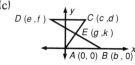

(d) Reflection through E, or a half-turn about E
(e) *Synthetic Method of Proof:* 1. E is the midpt. of $\overline{BD}$ and $\overline{AC}$. (Given) 2. $BE = ED$; $AE = EC$ (Def. of midpt. [1]) 3. $m\angle AEB = m\angle DEC$ (Vert. $\angle$s are =.) 4. $\triangle AEB \cong \triangle CED$ (SAS $\cong$ Post. [2, 3])
Vector Method of Proof: Since E is the midpt. of $\overline{BD}$ and $\overline{AC}$, $BE = ED$ and $CE = EA$. So $\overrightarrow{BE} = \overrightarrow{ED}$ and $\overrightarrow{CE} = \overrightarrow{EA}$. By the def. of vector addition, $\overrightarrow{BA} = \overrightarrow{BE} + \overrightarrow{EA}$ and $\overrightarrow{CD} = \overrightarrow{CE} + \overrightarrow{ED}$. By substitution, $\overrightarrow{BA} = \overrightarrow{ED} + \overrightarrow{CE}$. So $\overrightarrow{BA} = \overrightarrow{CD}$ and $BA = CD$. Therefore, $\triangle AEB \cong \triangle CED$ by the SSS $\cong$ Post. *Coordinate Method of Proof:* Place the coordinate axes on the diagram so that $\overline{AB}$ lies on the x-axis and A is at the origin. Assign coordinates as shown on the diagram. Since E is the midpt. of $\overline{BD}$, $BE = ED$ and $(g, k) = \left(\frac{b + e}{2}, \frac{f}{2}\right)$; and since E is also the midpt. of $\overline{AC}$, $AE = EC$ and $(g, k) = \left(\frac{c}{2}, \frac{d}{2}\right)$. Therefore, $b + e = c$ and $f = d$. Then $DC = \sqrt{(c - e)^2 + (d - f)^2} = \sqrt{b^2 + 0^2} = b = AB$. Thus, the $\triangle$s are $\cong$ by the SSS $\cong$ Post.
Transformation Method of Proof: Since E is the midpt. of $\overline{AC}$ and $\overline{BD}$, under a reflection through E, the image of A is C, the image of B is D, and the image of E is E. Thus, the image of $\triangle ABE$ is $\triangle CDE$. Since a reflection through a pt. is an isometry, $AB = CD$, $AE = CE$, and $BE = DE$. Therefore, the $\triangle$s are $\cong$ by SSS $\cong$ Post.
5. Given: $ABCD$ is $\square$.
Prove: $\overline{AC}$ and $\overline{BD}$ bisect each other.

Synthetic Method: 1. $ABCD$ is a $\square$. (Given) 2. $DC = AB$ (Opp. sides of a $\square$ are =. [1]) 3. $\overline{AB} \parallel \overline{DC}$ (Def. of $\square$ [1]) 4. $m\angle CDB = m\angle ABD$; $m\angle DCA = m\angle BAC$ (Lines $\parallel \Rightarrow$ alt. int. $\angle$s =. [3]) 5. $\triangle DCE \cong \triangle BAE$ (ASA $\cong$ Post. [2, 4]) 6. $AE = EC$; $BE = ED$ (Corres. parts of $\cong \triangle$s are =. [5]) 7. E is the midpt. of $\overline{AC}$ and $\overline{BD}$. (Def. of midpt. [6]) 8. $\overline{AC}$ and $\overline{BD}$ bisect each other. (Def. of segment bisector [7])

Vector Method: See Lesson 13-7, Example 3.

Coordinate Method: Place the coordinate axes so that *A* falls on the origin whose coordinates are (0, 0) and *B* falls on

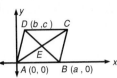

the pos. x-axis with coordinates (*a*, 0). Let the coordinates of *D* be (*b*, *c*). Then *C* has coordinates (*a* + *b*, *c*). The midpt. of $\overline{AC}$ has coordinates $\left(\frac{a+b}{2}, \frac{c}{2}\right)$ and the midpt. of $\overline{BD}$ has coordinates $\left(\frac{a+b}{2}, \frac{c}{2}\right)$. This pt. is common to both segments and *E* is their only intersection pt. $DE = EB = \frac{1}{2}\sqrt{(a-b)^2 + c^2}$. $AE = EC = \frac{1}{2}\sqrt{(a+b)^2 + c^2}$. Therefore, $\overline{AC}$ and $\overline{BD}$ bisect each other.

Transformation Method: Let *E* be the midpt. of $\overline{DB}$. then *DE* = *EB*. Under a reflection through *E*, the image of *D* is *B* and image of *C* is a pt. *C'* on $\overleftrightarrow{CE}$ with *CE* = *EC'*. The image of *E* is *E*. Thus, the image of $\triangle DCE$ is $\triangle BC'E$. Since a reflection is an isometry, $m\angle DCE = m\angle BC'E$. Thus, $\overline{DC} \parallel \overline{BC}$. But $\overline{DC} \parallel \overline{BA}$ by def. of a $\square$. Therefore, *C'* is on $\overleftrightarrow{BA}$ and on $\overleftrightarrow{CE}$. Thus, *C'* = *A*, and *CE* = *EA*. *E* is the midpt. of $\overline{AC}$. So, $\overline{AC}$ and $\overline{BD}$ bisect each other.

9. *Synthetic Method:*

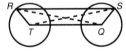

1. $\odot T \cong \odot Q$; $m\angle RTQ = m\angle SQT$ (Given)
   2. *TR* = *QS* (Radii of $\cong \odot$s are =. (1)) 3. Draw $\overline{RQ}$ and $\overline{TS}$. (2 pts. determine a line.) 4. *TQ* = *TQ* (Reflexive Prop.)
5. $\triangle RTQ \cong \triangle SQT$ (SAS $\cong$ Post. (1, 2, 4))
6. $m\angle TRQ = m\angle QST$; *RQ* = *ST* (Corres. parts of $\cong \triangle$s are =. (5)) 7. *RS* = *RS* (Reflexive Prop.)
8. $\triangle RQS \cong \triangle STR$ (SSS $\cong$ Post. (2, 6, 7))
9. $m\angle SRQ = m\angle RST$ (Corres. parts of $\cong \triangle$s are =. (8)) 10. $m\angle TRQ + m\angle SRQ = m\angle QST + m\angle RST$ (Add. Prop. (6, 9)) 11. $m\angle TRQ + m\angle SRQ = m\angle TRS$; $m\angle QST + m\angle RST = m\angle QSR$ (Angle Add. Post.) 12. $m\angle TRS = m\angle QST$ (Substitution Prop. (10, 11))

Transformation Method:
Let ℓ be the $\perp$ bisector of $\overline{TQ}$. Under a reflection over ℓ, the images of *T*, *P*, and *Q* are *Q*, *P*, and *T*, respectively. Since a

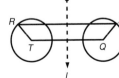

line reflection is an isometry, angle measures and distances are preserved. So the image of $\angle T$ is $\angle Q$ and the image of *R* is *S*. This means that ℓ is the $\perp$ bisector of $\overline{RS}$. Then the image of $\angle R$ is $\angle S$ and $m\angle R = m\angle S$.

Chapter 13 Review, Pages 609–610

1. (1, −1, 4) **2.** *CB* = *CD* = 3; no **3.** (a) 1; (b) Undefined **4.** 0 **5.** (a) $\perp$; (b) $\parallel$ **6.** (a) y − 2 = −3(x + 1) (b) y = −$\frac{3}{4}$x + 4 (c) y − 6 = −2(x + 1) (d) y + 2 = $\frac{2}{3}$(x − 3) (e) y = $\frac{1}{2}$x − 2 **7.** $\frac{3}{5}$; −3 **8.** (a) 3x − 5y = −19 (b) 4x − 3y = 33 (c) x − 2y = 3 **9.** (−2, 3); 11 **10.** (x − 3)^2 + (y + 1)^2 = 81 **11** *G*(0, *c*); *H*(*c*√3, 0) **12.** √3 **13.** $\frac{z}{s}$ **14.** (2s + 2t, 2z) **15.** (s + 2t, z)

16. *Given:* $\square ABCD$ with diags. $\overline{AC}$ and $\overline{BD}$. *Prove:* $\overline{AC}$ and $\overline{BD}$ bisect each other. *Proof:* Place the coordinate plane on

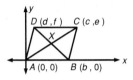

$\square ABCD$ so that *A* coincides with the origin and $\overline{AB}$ lies on the x-axis. Let the coordinates of *A*, *B*, *C*, and *D* be (0, 0), (*b*, 0), (*c*, *e*), and (*d*, *f*), respectively. By def. of $\square$, $\overline{DC} \parallel \overline{AB}$ so the slope of $\overline{DC}$ = the slope of $\overline{AB}$ which = 0 since both are horizontal lines. Then $\frac{e-f}{c-d}$ = 0 and *e* = *f*. Also, $\overline{AD} \parallel \overline{BC}$, so their slopes are =. Thus $\frac{f}{d}$ = $\frac{f}{c-b}$, so *d* = *c* − *b* or *c* = *b* + *d*. Let *X* be the midpt. of $\overline{BD}$. Then *X* has coordinates $\left(\frac{b+d}{2}, \frac{f}{2}\right)$. *Let X' be the* midpt. of $\overline{AC}$. Then *X'* has coordinates $\left(\frac{c}{2}, \frac{e}{2}\right)$ = $\left(\frac{b+d}{2}, \frac{f}{2}\right)$. So *X* = *X'* and the diags. bisect each other. **17.** √29 ≈ 5.39; 22° **18.** 2; 30° **19.** 2; 120° **20.** (7.66, 6.43) **21.** (−7.66, 6.43) **22.** 277.99 mph; 77° **23.** √20 ≈ 4.47; 153°; (−4, 2)

24. *Proof:* Since $\overrightarrow{AC}$ and $\overrightarrow{BD}$ have the same direction and *AC* = *BD*, $\overrightarrow{AC}$ = $\overrightarrow{BD}$. Also, since $\overrightarrow{AF} \parallel \overrightarrow{BE}$ and *AF* = *BE*, $\overrightarrow{AF}$ = $\overrightarrow{BE}$. Then $\overrightarrow{CF}$ = $-\overrightarrow{AC}$ + $\overrightarrow{AF}$ = $-\overrightarrow{BD}$ + $\overrightarrow{AF}$ = $\overrightarrow{DB}$ + $\overrightarrow{BE}$ = $\overrightarrow{DE}$. So $\overrightarrow{CF}$ = $\overrightarrow{DE}$ and $\overline{CF} \parallel \overline{DE}$.

25. *Given:* Equilateral
$\triangle ABC$ with medians
$\overline{AE}$, $\overline{BF}$, and $\overline{CD}$

Prove: $AE = BF = CD$
Synthetic Method: 1. Equilateral $\triangle ABC$ with
medians $\overline{AE}$, $\overline{BF}$, and $\overline{CD}$ (Given) 2. $AB = BC =$
CA (Def. of equilateral $\triangle$ [1]) 3. $\frac{1}{2}AB = \frac{1}{2}BC =$
$\frac{1}{2}CA$ (Mult. Prop. [2]) 4. D, E, and F are midpts.
of $\overline{AB}$, $\overline{BC}$, and $\overline{CA}$, respectively. (Def. of median
[1]) 5. $AD = DB$; $BE = EC$; $CF = FA$ (Def. of
midpt. [4]) 6. $AD + DB = AB$; $BE + EC = BC$;
$CF + FA = CA$ (Seg. Add. Post.) 7. $AD + AD =$
AB; $BE + BE = BC$; $CF + CF = CA$ or $2AD =$
AB; $2BE = BC$; $2CF = CA$ (Substitution Prop. [5,
6]) 8. $AD = \frac{1}{2}AB$; $BE = \frac{1}{2}BC$; $CF = \frac{1}{2}CA$ (Mult.
Prop. [7]) 9. $AD = BE = CF$ (Substitution Prop.
[3, 8]) 10. $\triangle ABC$ is equiangular. (An equilateral
$\triangle$ is equiangular. [1]) 11. $m\angle CAD = m\angle ABE =$
$m\angle BCF$ (Def. of equiangular $\triangle$ [10]) 12. $\triangle CAD$
$\cong \triangle ABE \cong \triangle BCF$ (SAS $\cong$ Post. [2, 9, 10]) 13. $CD =$
$AE = BF$ (Corres. parts of $\cong \triangle$s are =. [12])
Vector Method: By def. of median, D, E, and F
are midpts. By def. of midpt. and vector
addition, $\overrightarrow{CD} = \overrightarrow{CA} + \overrightarrow{AD} = \overrightarrow{CA} + \frac{1}{2}\overrightarrow{AB}$, $\overrightarrow{AE} =$
$\overrightarrow{AB} + \overrightarrow{BE} = \overrightarrow{AB} + \frac{1}{2}\overrightarrow{BC}$, and $\overrightarrow{BF} = \overrightarrow{BC} + \overrightarrow{CF} =$
$\overrightarrow{BC} + \frac{1}{2}\overrightarrow{CA}$. Since $\triangle ABC$ is equilateral, $AB = BC$
$= CA$ and $|\overrightarrow{AB}| = |\overrightarrow{BC}| = |\overrightarrow{CA}|$. And since
the medians of an equilateral $\triangle$ are also
altitudes, $\triangle ABE$, $\triangle BCF$, and $\triangle CAD$ are rt. $\triangle$s.
Therefore, by the Pythagorean Thm,
$|\overrightarrow{CD}|^2 = |\overrightarrow{CA}|^2 + |\frac{1}{2}\overrightarrow{AB}|^2 = |\overrightarrow{CA}|^2 + \frac{1}{4}|\overrightarrow{AB}|^2$,
$|\overrightarrow{AE}|^2 = |\overrightarrow{AB}|^2 + |\frac{1}{2}\overrightarrow{BC}|^2 = |\overrightarrow{CA}|^2 + \frac{1}{4}|\overrightarrow{AB}|^2$, and
$|\overrightarrow{BF}|^2 = |\overrightarrow{BC}|^2 + |\frac{1}{2}\overrightarrow{CA}|^2 = |\overrightarrow{CA}|^2 + \frac{1}{4}|\overrightarrow{AB}|^2$.
Thus, $CD = AE = BF$.

Coordinate Method: Place the coordinate axes so
that D coincides with the origin and $\overline{AB}$ lies on
the x-axis. Since D the midpt. of $\overline{AB}$, $AD = DB$.
Let the coordinates of A and B be $(-2a, 0)$ and
$(2a, 0)$, respectively. Since the medians of an
equilateral $\triangle$ are also altitudes, $\overline{CD} \perp \overline{AB}$ and C
falls on the y-axis. Also, in rt. $\triangle ACD$, $AC = 4a$,
$AD = 2a$, and $CD = 2a\sqrt{3}$. Thus, the
coordinates of C are $(0, 2a\sqrt{3})$. Using the
Midpt. Formula gives $E(a, a\sqrt{3})$ and $F(-a, a\sqrt{3})$.
Then by the Distance Formula,
$AE = \sqrt{(-2a - a)^2 + (0 - a\sqrt{3})^2} = 2a\sqrt{3}$ and
$BF = \sqrt{(-a - 2a)^2 + (a\sqrt{3} - 0)^2} = 2a\sqrt{3}$.
Thus, $CD = AE = BF$.
Transformation Method: In an equilateral $\triangle$,
medians are also altitudes, so $\overline{CD} \perp \overline{AB}$ and
$\overline{AE} \perp \overline{CB}$. Under a reflection over $\overleftrightarrow{CD}$, the
images of C, B, and $\overline{CB}$ are C, A, and $\overline{CA}$.
Similarly, under a reflection over $\overleftrightarrow{AE}$, the images
of A, B, and $\overline{AB}$ are A, C, and $\overline{AC}$. Since a line
reflection preserves distance, collinearity, and
betweenness of points, if E' is the image of E,
then E' is on $\overline{CA}$ with $CE' = CE = \frac{1}{2}CA$. Thus E'
$= F$ since $CF = \frac{1}{2}CA$, and the image of $\overline{AE}$ is $\overline{BF}$.
Therefore, $AE = BF$. Using a similar argument
with the reflection over $\overleftrightarrow{AE}$, $BF = CD$.
Therefore, $AE = BF = CD$.

Additional Answers

CHAPTER 1   Page 3

12.

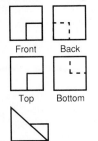

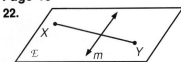

Page 16

22.

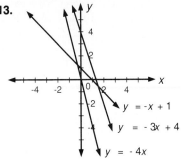

CHAPTER 2   Page 55

2. To investigate the effectiveness of a new drug, a medical researcher will administer it to a sample of people with a particular ailment. If the drug is effective in promoting a cure, it may be tested on a larger sample and ultimately used for the entire population experiencing the ailment.

Pages 63, 64

12.

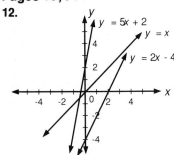

13.

15. a–c.

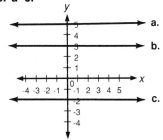

Pages 67–69

1–8. Hypothesis underlined once; conclusion underlined twice.

1. If <u>a student passes the exam</u>, then <u>he will graduate</u>.

2. If <u>a child is in the United States</u>, then <u>he has the right to a quality education</u>.

3. If <u>2 line segments intersect</u>, then <u>they lie in a plane</u>.

4. If <u>2 angles are supplements of the same angle</u>, then <u>they are equal</u>.

5. If <u>a geometric figure is a triangle</u>, then <u>it has three sides</u>.

6. If <u>2 planes intersect</u>, then <u>they intersect in a line</u>.

7. If <u>2 angles are adjacent angles</u>, then <u>they have a common side</u>.

8. If <u>Rover is a collie</u>, then <u>he is a dog</u>.

9.

10.

27. If 2 angles form a linear pair, then they are supplementary angles.

28. Sample:

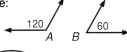

29.

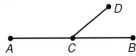

34. If a patient exhibits several distinct symptoms of an illness, then the doctor might draw a conclusion based upon the specific symptoms in forming a diagnosis of the patient's condition.

Page 75

1. Sample:

2. Sample:

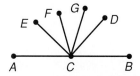

Additional Example 1

By hypothesis, ∠1 and ∠3 are both complementary to ∠2. 2. *p* ⇒ *q*: If two angles are complementary, then the sum of the measures of the angles is 90. (Def. of complementary angles) *p*: ∠1 and ∠3 are both complementary to ∠2. *q*: $m∠1 + m∠2 = 90$; $m∠3 + m∠2 = 90$ 3. *q* ⇒ *r*: For all real numbers *a* and *b*, if *a* = *b*, then *a* or *b* may be replaced by the other in any equation or inequality. (Substitution Prop.) *q*: $m∠1 + m∠2 = 90$; $m∠3 + m∠2 = 90$ *r*: $m∠1 + m∠2 = m∠3 + m∠2$ 4. *r* ⇒ *s*: For all real numbers *a*, *a* = *a*. (Reflexive Prop.) *r*: $m∠1 + m∠2 = m∠3 + m∠2$ *s*: $m∠2 = m∠2$ 5. *s* ⇒ *t*: For all real numbers *a*, *b*, *c* and *d*, if *a* = *b* and *c* = *d*, then *a* − *c* = *b* − *d*. (Subtraction Prop.) *s*: $m∠2 = m∠2$ *t*: $m∠1 + m∠2 − m∠2 = m∠3 + m∠2 − m∠2$, or $m∠1 = m∠3$

---

6. No; the numbers in brackets represent the hypothesis from which the statement is concluded. Step 4 could not be concluded from a subsequent step in the proof.

Page 113

2.

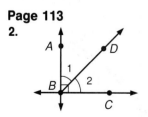

Given: ∠*ABC* is a rt. ∠; $\overrightarrow{BD}$ bisects ∠*ABC*. Prove: $m∠1 = 45$; $m∠2 = 45$

3.

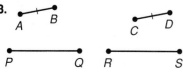

Given: *AB* = *CD*; *PQ* = 2(*AB*); *RS* = 2(*CD*) Prove: *PQ* = *RS*

4.

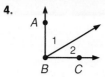

Given: ∠1 is comp. to ∠2; ∠1 is adj. to ∠2. Prove: $\overleftrightarrow{AB} ⊥ \overleftrightarrow{BC}$

Page 120

31. 1. ∠1 is a rt. ∠. (Given) 2. $m∠1 = 90$ (Def. of rt. ∠ [1]) 3. $m∠1 + m∠2 = 180$ (Def. of lin. pr.) 4. $90 + m∠2 = 180$ (Substitution Prop. [2, 3]) 5. $m∠2 = 90$ (Subtraction Prop. [4]) 6. ∠2 is a rt. ∠. (Def. of rt. ∠ [5])

32.

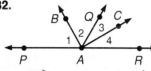

Given: $\overrightarrow{AB}$ bisects ∠*PAQ*; $\overrightarrow{AC}$ bisects ∠*QAR*. Prove: $\overrightarrow{AB} ⊥ \overrightarrow{AC}$ 1. $\overrightarrow{AB}$ bisects ∠*PAQ*. (Given) 2. $m∠1 = m∠2$ (Def. ∠ bisector [1]) 3. $m∠1 + m∠2 = m∠PAQ$ (∠ Add. Post.) 4. $2(m∠2) = m∠PAQ$ (Substitution Prop. [2, 3]) 5. $\overrightarrow{AC}$ bisects ∠*QAR*. (Given) 6. $m∠3 = m∠4$ (Def. ∠ bisector [5]) 7. $m∠3 + m∠4 = m∠QAR$ (∠ Add. Post.) 8. $2(m∠3) = m∠QAR$ (Substitution Prop [6, 7]) 9. $m∠PAQ + m∠QAR = 180$ (Def. of linear pair) 10. $2(m∠2) + 2(m∠3) = 180$ (Substitution Prop. [4, 8, 9]) 11. $m∠2 + m∠3 = 90$ (Division Prop. [10]) 12. $m∠2 + m∠3 = m∠BAC$ (∠ Add. Post.) 13. $m∠BAC = 90$ (Transitive Prop. [11, 12]) 14. $\overrightarrow{AB} ⊥ \overrightarrow{AC}$ (Def. of ⊥ lines [13])

Page 125

12. ∠*ABE* and ∠*CBE* form a lin. pr. Use Thm. 3–10 to show that ∠*ABE* is a rt. ∠, so $m∠ABE = 90$. Then use the ∠ Add. Post. to show that $m∠ABD + m∠DBE = m∠ABE$. Use the Transitive Prop. to show that $m∠ABD + m∠DBE = 90$, so ∠*ABD* and ∠*DBE* are complementary.

---

13. 1. $m∠1 = m∠4$ (Given) 2. $m∠1 = m∠2$ (Vert. ∠s are =.) 3. $m∠4 = m∠2$ (Substitution Prop. [1, 2]) 4. $m∠4 = m∠5$ (Vert. ∠s are =.) 5. $m∠2 = m∠5$ (Substitution Prop. [3, 4]).

14. 1. $m∠2 = m∠3 = m∠4$ (Given) 2. *r* ⊥ *t* (If the ∠s of a lin. pr. are =, then the lines containing their sides are ⊥. [1, 3]). 3. ∠3 is a rt. ∠. (Def. of ⊥ lines [2]) 4. $m∠3 = 90$ (Def. of rt. ∠ [3]) 5. $m∠2 = 90$ (Transitive Prop. [1, 4]) 6. ∠2 is a rt. ∠. (Def. of rt. ∠ [5]) 7. *r* ⊥ *s* (Def. of ⊥ lines [6])

15.

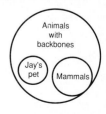

Given: line *m* and pt. *P* not on *m* Prove: *m* and *P* lie in a plane. 1. pts. *A* and *B* on *m* (A line contains at least 2 pts.) 2. pt. *P* not on *m* (Given) 3. *A*, *B* and *P* are noncollinear. (Def. of noncollinear pts. [1, 2]) 4. *m* is the only line that contains both *A* and *B* (2 pts. are contained in exactly one line.) 5. *A*, *B* and *P* are contained in a plane. (3 noncollinear pts. are contained in 1 and only 1 plane.) 6. *m* is contained in the plane. (Flat Plane Post.) 7. *m* and *P* are contained in a plane. (Line Post. [5, 6])

18. They represent the statement(s) where the hypothesis of the reason has been affirmed.

19. If point *P* is between points *A* and *B*, then *AP* + *PB* = *AB*.

20. Not necessarily; the conclusion is based on the converse of the original statement.

1.

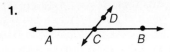

2. Sample:

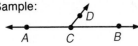

Pages 128–130

1. 1. If necessary, write the statement to be proved in "if . . . then" form.
2. Draw and label an appropriate diagram.
3. State the Given and the Prove in terms of the diagram.
4. Develop a Plan for Proof.
5. Write a two-column proof.

9.

Given: $\angle A$ is acute; $\angle B$ is obtuse.
Prove: $m\angle B > m\angle A$

10.

Given: $\angle A$ and $\angle B$ are complementary. Prove: $\angle A$ and $\angle B$ are acute $\angle$s.

11.

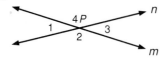

Given: $\angle 1$ is acute; $\angle 1$ and $\angle 2$ are complementary; $\angle 1$ and $\angle 3$ are supplementary. Prove: $m\angle 2 < m\angle 3$

12.

Given: m and n intersecting at P; $\angle 1$ is acute. Prove: $\angle 2$ and $\angle 4$ are obtuse and $\angle 3$ is acute.

13. From the def. of supp. $\angle$s, $m\angle 1 + m\angle 2 = 180$. Use the Substitution Prop. to show that $2(m\angle 1) = 180$ and $2(m\angle 2) = 180$. From the Div. Prop. $m\angle 1 = 90$ and $m\angle 2 = 90$, so $\angle 1$ and $\angle 2$ are rt. $\angle$s.

14. From the def. of midpt., $AM = MB$. Use the Seg. Add. Post. to show that $AM + MB = AB$. Use the Substitution Prop. to show that $2(AM) = AB$. From the Div. Prop. $AM = \frac{1}{2}(AB)$.
15. From the def. of an acute $\angle$, $m\angle A < 90$. From the def. of an obtuse $\angle$, $m\angle B > 90$. Use the Transitive Prop. to show that $m\angle B > m\angle A$.
16. From the def. of comp. $\angle$s, $m\angle A + m\angle B = 90$. Use the Protractor Post. to show that $m\angle A > 0$ and $m\angle B > 0$. From the Subtraction Prop. $m\angle A + m\angle B - m\angle B < 90 - 0$ and $m\angle A - m\angle A + m\angle B < 90 - 0$, or $m\angle A < 90$ and $m\angle B < 90$. From the def. of an acute $\angle$, $\angle A$ and $\angle B$ are acute.
17. From the def. of an acute $\angle$, $0 < m\angle 1 < 90$. From the def. of comp. $\angle$s, $m\angle 1 + m\angle 2 = 90$. Use the Subtraction Prop. to show that $m\angle 2 = 90 - m\angle 1$. From the def. of supp. $\angle$s, $m\angle 1 + m\angle 3 = 180$. Use the Subtraction Prop. to show that $m\angle 3 = 180 - m\angle 1$. Comparison of real numbers shows that $90 < 180$. Then use the Subtraction Prop. to show that $90 - m\angle 1 < 180 - m\angle 1$. Use the Substitution Prop. to show that $m\angle 2 < m\angle 3$.
18. From the def. of an acute $\angle$, $0 < m\angle 1 < 90$. $\angle 1$ and $\angle 2$ form a lin. pr., so they are supp. and $m\angle 1 + m\angle 2 = 180$. Use the Substitution Prop. to show that $90 + m\angle 2 > 180$ and $0 + m\angle 2 < 180$. Then use the Subtraction Prop. to show that $m\angle 2 > 90$ and $m\angle 2 < 180$. The def. of an obtuse $\angle$ shows that $\angle 2$ is obtuse. $\angle 1$ and $\angle 3$ are vert. $\angle$s, and $\angle 2$ and $\angle 4$ are vert. $\angle$s. From Thm. 3–8 $m\angle 1 = m\angle 3$ and $m\angle 2 = m\angle 4$. Then use the Substitution Prop. to show that $0 < m\angle 3 < 90$ and $90 < m\angle 4 < 180$. From the def. of an acute $\angle$, $\angle 3$ is an acute $\angle$ and from the def. of an obtuse $\angle$, $\angle 4$ is an obtuse $\angle$.

19. 1. $m\angle 1 = m\angle 2$ (Given) 2. $\angle 1$ and $\angle 2$ are supplementary. (Given) 3. $m\angle 1 + m\angle 2 = 180$ (Def. supp. $\angle$s [2]) 4. $m\angle 1 + m\angle 1 = 180$, or $2(m\angle 1) = 180$; $m\angle 2 + m\angle 2 = 180$, or $2(m\angle 2) = 180$ (Substitution Prop. [1, 3]); 5. $2 = 2$ (Reflexive Prop.) 6. $m\angle 1 = 90$; $m\angle 2 = 90$ (Div. Prop. [4, 5]); 7. $\angle 1$ and $\angle 2$ are rt. $\angle$s. (Def. of rt. $\angle$ [6])
20. 1. M is the midpt. of $\overline{AB}$. (Given) 2. $AM = MB$ (Def. of midpt. [1]) 3. $AM + MB = AB$ (Seg. Add. Post.) 4. $2(AM) = AB$ (Substitution Prop. [2, 3]) 5. $AM = \frac{1}{2}(AB)$ (Div. Prop. [4])
21. 1. $\angle A$ is acute. (Given) 2. $m\angle A < 90$ (Def. of acute $\angle$ [1]) 3. $\angle B$ is obtuse. (Given) 4. $m\angle B > 90$ (Def. of obtuse $\angle$ [3]) 5. $m\angle B > m\angle A$ (Transitive Prop. [2, 4])
22. 1. $\angle A$ and $\angle B$ are complementary. (Given) 2. $m\angle A + m\angle B = 90$ (Def. of comp. $\angle$s [1]) 3. $m\angle A > 0$; $m\angle B > 0$ (Protractor Post.) 4. $m\angle A < 90$; $m\angle B < 90$ (Subtraction Prop. [2, 3]) 5. $\angle A$ and $\angle B$ are acute. (Def. of acute $\angle$ [3, 4])
23. 1. $\angle 1$ is acute. (Given) 2. $0 < m\angle 1 < 90$ (Def. acute $\angle$ [1]) 3. $\angle 1$ and $\angle 2$ are complementary. (Given) 4. $m\angle 1 + m\angle 2 = 90$ (Def. of comp. $\angle$s) 5. $m\angle 1 = m\angle 1$ (Reflexive Prop.) 6. $m\angle 2 = 90 - m\angle 1$ (Subtraction Prop. [4, 5]) 7. $\angle 1$ and $\angle 3$ are supplementary. (Given) 8. $m\angle 1 + m\angle 3 = 180$ (Def. of supp. $\angle$s [7]) 9. $m\angle 3 = 180 - m\angle 1$ (Subtraction Prop. [5, 8]); 10. $90 < 180$ (Trichotomy Prop.) 11. $90 - m\angle 1 < 180 - m\angle 1$ (Subtraction Prop. [5, 10]) 12. $m\angle 2 < m\angle 3$ (Substitution Prop. [6, 10, 12])
24. 1. $\angle 1$ is acute. (Given) 2. $0 < m\angle 1 < 90$ (Def. of acute $\angle$ [1]) 3. $\angle 1$ and $\angle 2$ are supplementary. ($\angle 1$ and $\angle 2$ form a lin. pr.) 4. $m\angle 1 + m\angle 2 = 180$ (Def. of supp. $\angle$s [3]) 5. $0 + m\angle 2 < 180$; $90 + m\angle 2 > 180$ (Substitution Prop. [2, 4]) 6. $m\angle 2 < 180$; $m\angle 2 > 90$ (Subtrac-

tion Prop. [5]) 7. ∠2 is obtuse. (Def. of obtuse ∠ [6]) 8. m∠1 = m∠3; m∠2 = m∠4 (Vert. ∠s are =.) 9. 0 < m∠3 < 90 (Substitution Prop. [2, 8]) 10. ∠3 is acute. (Def. of acute ∠ [9]) 11. 90 < m∠4 < 180 (Substitution Prop. [6, 8]) 12. ∠4 is obtuse. (Def. of obtuse ∠ [11])

25.

Given: m∠1 = m∠5 Prove: m∠2 = m∠6; m∠3 = m∠7; m∠4 = m∠8
1. m∠1 = m∠5 (Given) 2. ∠1 and ∠2 are supplementary; ∠5 and ∠6 are supplementary (∠1 and ∠2 form a lin. pr. ; ∠5 and ∠6 form a lin. pr.) 3. m∠2 = m∠6 (If ∠s are supp. to = ∠s, then they are =. [1, 2]) 4. m∠1 = m∠3; m∠5 = m∠7 (Vert. ∠s are =.) 5. m∠3 = m∠7 (Transitive Prop. [1, 4]) 6. m∠2 = m∠4; m∠6 = m∠8 (Vert. ∠s are =.) 7. m∠4 = m∠8 (Transitive Prop. [3, 6])

26.

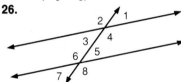

Given: ∠3 and ∠6 are supplementary. Prove: ∠4 and ∠5 are supplementary. 1. ∠3 and ∠6 are supplementary. (Given) 2. ∠3 and ∠4 are supplementary. (∠3 and ∠4 form a lin. pr.) 3. m∠4 = m∠6 (If ∠s are supp. to the same ∠, then they are =. [1, 2]) 4. ∠6 and ∠5 are supplementary. (∠6 and ∠5 form a lin. pr.) 5. m∠6 + m∠5 = 180 (Def. of supp. ∠s [4]) 6. m∠4 + m∠5 = 180 (Substitution Prop. [3, 5]) 7. ∠4 and ∠5 are supplementary. (Def. of supp. ∠s [6])

27. Given: ∠A and ∠B are rt. ∠s. Prove: m∠A = m∠B 1. ∠A and ∠B are rt. ∠s. (Given) 2. m∠A =

90; m∠B = 90 (Def. of rt. ∠[1]) 3. m∠A = m∠B (Substitution Prop. [2])

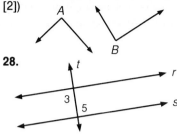

28.

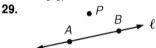

Given: r ⊥ t; m∠3 = m∠5 Prove: s ⊥ t 1. r ⊥ t (Given) 2. ∠3 is a rt. ∠. (Def. of ⊥ lines [1]) 3. m∠3 = 90 (Def. of rt. ∠ [2]) 4. m∠3 = m∠5 (Given) 5. m∠5 = 90 (Transitive Prop. [3, 4]) 6. ∠5 is a rt. ∠. (Def. of rt. ∠ [5]) 7. s ⊥ t (Def. of ⊥ lines [6])

29.

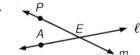

Given: line ℓ and pt. P not on ℓ Prove: ℓ and P lie in a plane. 1. pts. A and B on ℓ (A line contains at least 2 pts.) 2. ℓ is the only line which contains A and B. (2 pts. determine 1 line.) 3. A, B and P are noncollinear. (Def. of noncollinear pts.) 4. A, B and P lie in a plane. (3 noncollinear pts. determine 1 plane.) 5. ℓ and P lie in a plane. (If 2 pts. of a line are contained in a plane, then all pts. on the line are contained in the same plane.)

30.

Given: ℓ and m intersect at E. Prove: ℓ and m lie in a plane. 1. pt. A on ℓ; A ≠ E (A line contains at least 2 pts.) 2. pt. P on m; P ≠ E (A line contains at least 2 pts.) 3. ℓ is the only line which contains A and E. (2 pts. determine 1 line.) 4. P is not on ℓ. (If 2 distinct lines intersect, then their intersection is exactly 1 pt.) 5. A, E and P are noncollinear (Def. of noncollinear pts.) 6. A, E and P lie in a plane. (3

noncollinear pts. determine 1 plane.) 7. ℓ and m lie in a plane. (If 2 pts. of a line are contained in a plane, then all pts. on the line are contained in the same plane.)

---

5. 1. $\overrightarrow{XJ}$ bisects ∠VXY; $\overrightarrow{XK}$ bisects ∠WXZ. (Given) 2. m∠VXJ = m∠JXY (Def. of ∠ bisector [1]); 3. m∠WXK = m∠YXJ (Vert. ∠s are =.) 4. m∠VXJ = m∠WXK (Substitution Prop. [2, 3]
6. 1. M is the midpt. of $\overline{PQ}$. (Given) 2. PM = QM (Def. of midpt. [1]) 3. N is the midpt. of $\overline{PR}$. (Given) 4. PN = RN (Def. of midpt. [3]) 5. QM = RN (Given) 6. PM = PN (Transitive Prop. [2, 4, 5])

CHAPTER 4   Pages 141–143
11.

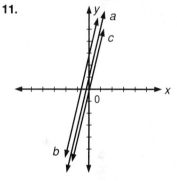

a ∥ b; a ∥ c; (b and c coincident)
12. Proof: 1. m∠1 = m∠3 (Given) 2. $\overleftrightarrow{DE}$ ∥ $\overleftrightarrow{BC}$ (Corres. ∠s = ⇒ lines ∥. [1]) 3. m∠2 = m∠4 (Lines ∥ ⇒ corres. ∠s =. [2])
13. Proof: 1. $\overleftrightarrow{BC}$ ∥ $\overleftrightarrow{DE}$ (Given) 2. m∠1 = m∠3 (Lines ∥ ⇒ corres. ∠s =. [1]) 3. m∠1 = m∠2 (Given) 4. m∠2 = m∠3 (Substitution Prop. [2, 3])
14. Proof: 1. m∠1 = m∠3 (Given) 2. $\overleftrightarrow{DE}$ ∥ $\overleftrightarrow{BC}$ (Corres. ∠s = ⇒ lines ∥. [1]) 3. m∠2 = m∠4 (Lines ∥ ⇒ corres. ∠s =. [2]) 4. m∠1 = m∠2 (Given) 5. m∠3 = m∠4 (Substitution Prop. [1, 3, 4])

30.

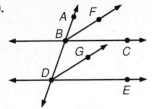

Given: $\overleftrightarrow{BC} \parallel \overleftrightarrow{DE}$; $\overrightarrow{BF}$ bisects $\angle ABC$; $\overrightarrow{DG}$ bisects $\angle BDE$. Prove: $\overrightarrow{BF} \parallel \overrightarrow{DG}$ Proof: 1. $\overleftrightarrow{BC} \parallel \overleftrightarrow{DE}$; $\overrightarrow{BF}$ bisects $\angle ABC$; $\overrightarrow{DG}$ bisects $\angle BDE$ (Given) 2. $m\angle ABC = m\angle BDE$ (Lines $\parallel$ ⇒ corres. $\angle$s are =. [1]) 3. $m\angle ABF = m\angle CBF$; $m\angle BDG = m\angle EDG$ (Def. of $\angle$ bisector [1]) 4. $m\angle ABC = m\angle ABF + m\angle CBF$; $m\angle BDE = m\angle BDG + m\angle EDG$ (Angle Add. Post.) 5. $m\angle ABF + m\angle CBF = m\angle BDG + m\angle EDG$ (Substitution Prop. [2, 4]) 6. $m\angle ABF + m\angle ABF = m\angle BDG + m\angle BDG$, or $2(m\angle ABF) = 2(m\angle BDG)$ (Substitution Prop. [3, 5]) 7. $2 = 2$ (Reflexive Prop.) 8. $m\angle ABF = m\angle BDG$ (Div. Prop. [6, 7]) 9. $\overrightarrow{BF} \parallel \overrightarrow{DG}$ (Corres. $\angle$s = ⇒ lines $\parallel$. [8])

31. (See diagram for Exercise 30.) Given: $\overleftrightarrow{BC}$ and $\overleftrightarrow{DE}$ cut by transversal $\overleftrightarrow{BD}$; $\overrightarrow{BF}$ bisects $\angle ABC$; $\overrightarrow{DG}$ bisects $\angle BDE$; $\overrightarrow{BF} \parallel \overrightarrow{DG}$ Prove: $\overleftrightarrow{BC} \parallel \overleftrightarrow{DE}$ Proof: 1. $\overrightarrow{BF} \parallel \overrightarrow{DG}$; $\overrightarrow{BF}$ bisects $\angle ABC$; $\overrightarrow{DG}$ bisects $\angle BDE$ (Given) 2. $m\angle ABF = m\angle BDG$ (Lines $\parallel$ ⇒ corres. $\angle$s =. [1]) 3. $m\angle ABF = m\angle CBF$; $m\angle BDG = m\angle EDG$ (Def. of $\angle$ bisector [1]) 4. $m\angle ABC = m\angle ABF + m\angle CBF$; $m\angle BDE = m\angle BDG + m\angle EDG$ (Angle Add. Post.) 5. $m\angle ABC = m\angle ABF + m\angle ABF = 2(m\angle ABF)$; $m\angle BDE = m\angle BDG + m\angle BDG = 2(m\angle BDG)$ (Substitution Prop. [3, 4]) 6. $2 = 2$ (Reflexive Prop.) 7. $2(m\angle ABF) = 2(m\angle BDG)$ (Mult. Prop. [2, 6]) 8. $m\angle ABC = m\angle BDE$ (Substitution Prop. [5, 7]) 9. $\overleftrightarrow{BC} \parallel \overleftrightarrow{DE}$ (Corres. $\angle$s = ⇒ lines $\parallel$. [8])

32. Since (x_1, y_1) is on the line whose equation is $y = mx + b$, we can substitute to get $(1) y_1 = mx_1 + b$. Similarly, for (x_2, y_2) we get $(2) y_2 = mx_2 + b$. Solving these equations simultaneously for m by subtracting equation (1) from equation (2) gives $y_2 - y_1 = mx_2 - mx_1$, which simplifies to $\frac{y_2 - y_1}{x_2 - x_1} = m$.

33.

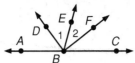

Given: $\angle ABE$ and $\angle EBC$ form a lin. pr.; $\overrightarrow{BD}$ bisects $\angle ABE$; $\overrightarrow{BF}$ bisects $\angle EBC$ Prove: $\overrightarrow{BD} \perp \overrightarrow{BF}$

34. (See diagram for Exercise 33.) Proof: 1. $\angle ABE$ and $\angle EBC$ form a linear pair; $\overrightarrow{BD}$ bisects $\angle ABE$; $\overrightarrow{BF}$ bisects $\angle EBC$. (Given) 2. $\angle ABE$ and $\angle EBC$ are supp. (Supp. Post. [1]) 3. $m\angle ABE + m\angle EBC = 180$ (Def. of supp. $\angle$s [2]) 4. $m\angle ABD = m\angle 1$; $m\angle CBF = m\angle 2$ (Def. of $\angle$ bisector [1]) 5. $m\angle ABE = m\angle ABD + m\angle 1$; $m\angle EBC = m\angle CBF + m\angle 2$ (Angle Add. Post.) 6. $m\angle ABE = m\angle 1 + m\angle 1 = 2(m\angle 1)$; $m\angle EBC = m\angle 2 + m\angle 2 = 2(m\angle 2)$ (Substitution Prop. [4, 5]) 7. $2(m\angle 1) + 2(m\angle 2) = 180$ (Substitution Prop. [3, 6]) 8. $\frac{1}{2} = \frac{1}{2}$ (Reflexive Prop.) 9. $m\angle 1 + m\angle 2 = 90$ (Mult. Prop. [7, 8]) 10. $m\angle 1 + m\angle 2 = m\angle DBF$ (Angle Add. Post.) 11. $m\angle DBF = 90$ (Substitution Prop. [9, 10]) 12. $\angle DBF$ is a rt. $\angle$. (Def. of rt. $\angle$ [11]) 13. $\overrightarrow{BD} \perp \overrightarrow{BF}$ (Def. of $\perp$ lines [12])

35. $m\angle 1 + m\angle 2 = 90$; $m\angle ABC = 90$

36. A postulate is a statement that is assumed to be true.

37. A theorem is a mathematical statement which is proved.

39. Two lines $\parallel$ ⇒ alt. int. $\angle$s =.

40. Two lines $\parallel$ ⇒ int. $\angle$s on the same side of transversal are supp.

Pages 147, 148

23. Proof: 1. $\overleftrightarrow{BC} \parallel \overleftrightarrow{EF}$ (Given) 2. $m\angle 2 = m\angle 4$ (Lines $\parallel$ ⇒ corres. $\angle$s =. [1]) 3. $m\angle 1 + m\angle 4 = 180$ (Given) 4. $m\angle 1 + m\angle 2 = 180$ (Substitution Prop. [2, 3]) 5. $\angle 1$ and $\angle 2$ are supp. $\angle$s. (Def. of supp. [4]) 6. $\overrightarrow{BA} \parallel \overrightarrow{ED}$ (Int. $\angle$s on the same side supp. ⇒ lines $\parallel$. [5])

24. Proof: 1. $\overrightarrow{BC} \parallel \overleftrightarrow{EF}$ (Given) 2. $m\angle 2 = m\angle 4$ (Lines $\parallel$ ⇒ corres. $\angle$s =. [1]) 3. $\overrightarrow{BA} \parallel \overrightarrow{ED}$ (Given) 4. $\angle 1$ and $\angle 2$ are supp. (Lines $\parallel$ ⇒ int. $\angle$s on the same side supp. [3]) 5. $m\angle 1 + m\angle 2 = 180$ (Def. of supp. $\angle$s [4]) 6. $m\angle 1 + m\angle 4 = 180$ (Substitution Prop. [2, 5]) 7. $\angle 1$ and $\angle 4$ are supp. (Def. of supp. $\angle$s [6])

25. Proof: 1. $\overleftrightarrow{HJ} \parallel \overleftrightarrow{ML}$ (Given) 2. $m\angle 7 = m\angle 8$ (Lines $\parallel$ ⇒ corres. $\angle$s =. [1]) 3. $\overleftrightarrow{HG} \parallel \overleftrightarrow{KL}$ (Given) 4. $m\angle 5 = m\angle 7$ (Lines $\parallel$ ⇒ corres. $\angle$s =. [3]) 5. $m\angle 5 = m\angle 8$ (Transitive Prop. [2, 4])

27. $x = 4$; $m\angle 3 = m\angle 5 = 24$

28. $x = 24$; $m\angle 4 = 112$; $m\angle 5 = 68$

29. If $x = 7$, $m\angle 3 = 35$ and $m\angle 6 = 145$; if $x = -7$, $m\angle 3 = 63$ and $m\angle 6 = 117$.

30. Given: Lines ℓ and m with transversal t; $m\angle 3 = m\angle 5$ Prove: $m\angle 4 = m\angle 6$ Proof: 1. Lines ℓ and m with trans. t; $m\angle 3 = m\angle 5$ (Given) 2. $\angle 3$ and $\angle 4$ are supp.; $\angle 5$ and $\angle 6$ are supp. (Supp. Post.) 3. $m\angle 4 = m\angle 6$ (Supps. of = $\angle$s are =. [1, 2])

31. Conjecture (1): If two $\parallel$ lines are cut by a trans., then each pair of alt. ext. $\angle$s are =. Given: $\ell \parallel m$ Prove: $m\angle 1 = m\angle 7$ and $m\angle 2 = m\angle 8$. Proof: 1. $\ell \parallel m$ (Given) 2. $m\angle 1 = m\angle 5$; $m\angle 2 = m\angle 6$ (Lines $\parallel$ ⇒ corres. $\angle$s =. [1]) 3. $m\angle 5 = m\angle 7$; $m\angle 6 = m\angle 8$ (Vert. $\angle$s are =.) 4. $m\angle 1 = m\angle 7$; $m\angle 2 = m\angle 8$ (Transitive Prop. [2, 3])

Conjecture (2): If two lines are cut by a trans. such that a pr. of alt. ext. $\angle$s are =, then the lines are parallel. Given: $m\angle 1 = m\angle 7$ Prove: $\ell \parallel m$ Proof: 1. $m\angle 1 = m\angle 7$ (Given) 2. $m\angle 5 = m\angle 7$ (Vert. $\angle$s are =.) 3. $m\angle 1 = m\angle 5$ (Substitution Prop. [1, 2]) 4. $\ell \parallel m$ (Corres. $\angle$s = ⇒ lines $\parallel$. [3])

32.

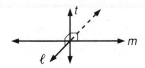

In the diagram, $\ell \perp t$ and $m \perp t$ but $\ell \not\parallel m$ because the lines are not coplanar.

33.

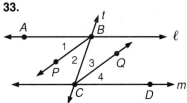

Given: $\ell \parallel m$; $\overrightarrow{BP}$ bisects $\angle ABC$; $\overrightarrow{CQ}$ bisects $\angle BCD$. Prove: $\overrightarrow{BP} \parallel \overrightarrow{CQ}$ Proof: 1. $\ell \parallel m$; $\overrightarrow{BP}$ bisects $\angle ABC$; $\overrightarrow{CQ}$ bisects $\angle BCD$. (Given) 2. $m\angle 1 = m\angle 2$; $m\angle 3 = m\angle 4$ (Def. of $\angle$ bisector [1]) 3. $m\angle ABC = m\angle 1 + m\angle 2$; $m\angle BCD = m\angle 3 + m\angle 4$ (Angle Add. Post.) 4. $m\angle ABC = m\angle 2 + m\angle 2 = 2(m\angle 2)$; $m\angle BCD = m\angle 3 + m\angle 3 = 2(m\angle 3)$ (Substitution Prop. [2, 3]) 5. $m\angle ABC = m\angle BCD$ (Lines $\parallel \Rightarrow$ alt. int. $\angle$s =. [1]) 6. $2(m\angle 2) = 2(m\angle 3)$ (Substitution Prop. [4, 5]) 7. $2 = 2$ (Reflexive Prop.) 8. $m\angle 2 = m\angle 3$ (Div. Prop. [6, 7]) 9. $\overrightarrow{BP} \parallel \overrightarrow{CQ}$ (Alt. int. $\angle$s = $\Rightarrow$ lines $\parallel$. [8])

34. (See the diagram for Exercise 33.) Given: Lines ℓ and m cut by trans. t; $\overrightarrow{BP}$ bisects $\angle ABC$; $\overrightarrow{CQ}$ bisects $\angle BCD$; $\overrightarrow{BP} \parallel \overrightarrow{CQ}$ Prove: $\ell \parallel m$ Proof: 1. ℓ and m cut by trans. t; $\overrightarrow{BP}$ bisects $\angle ABC$; $\overrightarrow{CQ}$ bisects $\angle BCD$; $\overrightarrow{BP} \parallel \overrightarrow{CQ}$ (Given) 2. $m\angle 2 = m\angle 3$ (Lines $\parallel \Rightarrow$ alt. int. $\angle$s =.) 3. $m\angle 1 = m\angle 2$; $m\angle 3 = m\angle 4$ (Def. of $\angle$ bisector [1]) 4. $m\angle 1 + m\angle 2 = m\angle ABC$; $m\angle 3 + m\angle 4 = m\angle BCD$ (Angle Add. Post.) 5. $m\angle ABC = m\angle 2 + m\angle 2 = 2(m\angle 2)$; $m\angle BCD = m\angle 3 + m\angle 3 = 2(m\angle 3)$ (Substitution Prop. [3, 4]) 6. $2 = 2$ (Reflexive Prop.) 7. $2(m\angle 2) = 2(m\angle 3)$ (Mult. Prop. [2, 6]) 8. $m\angle ABC = m\angle BCD$ (Substitution Prop. [5, 7]) 9. $\ell \parallel m$ (Alt. int. $\angle$s = $\Rightarrow$ lines $\parallel$. [8])

41. The solution to a system of linear equations, assuming that the graphs of the equations are two distinct lines and that the lines intersect, is a unique ordered pair of numbers representing the coordinates of the point of intersection of the graphs of the two equations.

42. Sally's assumption is proved false; she may now conclude that her cat Mittens was responsible for the broken vase.

43. If two lines are cut by a trans. such that a pr. of int. $\angle$s on the same side of the trans. are not supp., then the two lines are not $\parallel$; yes.

44. A statement and its contrapositive are logically equivalent; if Thm. 4–5 is true, then its contrapositive is also true.

Page 160

39. (See diagram for Exercise 38.) Converse: If $m\angle QRS = m\angle 1 + m\angle 4$, then $\overleftrightarrow{PQ} \parallel \overleftrightarrow{ST}$. Given: $m\angle QRS = m\angle 1 + m\angle 4$; $\overleftrightarrow{PQ}$, $\overleftrightarrow{ST}$ and R are coplanar. Prove: $\overleftrightarrow{PQ} \parallel \overleftrightarrow{ST}$ Proof: 1. $\overleftrightarrow{PQ}$, $\overleftrightarrow{ST}$ and R are coplanar; $m\angle QRS = m\angle 1 + m\angle 4$ (Given) 2. Draw $\overleftrightarrow{RX} \parallel \overleftrightarrow{ST}$. (Through a pt. not on a given line, there is exactly one line $\parallel$ to the given line.) 3. $m\angle QRS = m\angle 2 + m\angle 3$ (Angle Add. Post.) 4. $m\angle 1 + m\angle 4 = m\angle 2 + m\angle 3$ (Substitution [1, 3]) 5. $m\angle 4 = m\angle 3$ (2 lines $\parallel \Rightarrow$ alt. int. $\angle$s =. [2]) 6. $m\angle 1 = m\angle 2$ (Subtraction Prop. [4, 5]) 7. $\overleftrightarrow{PQ} \parallel \overleftrightarrow{XR}$ (Alt. int. $\angle$s = $\Rightarrow$ lines $\parallel$. [6]) 8. $\overleftrightarrow{PQ} \parallel \overleftrightarrow{ST}$ (In a plane, 2 lines $\parallel$ to the same line are $\parallel$ to each other. [2, 7])

40. Thm. 4–8 would be true; Thm. 4–9 would not be true because in space there are infinitely many lines $\perp$ to the given line through a pt. on the given line; Thm. 4–10 would not be true because in space there are infinitely many lines $\perp$ to and bisecting the given segment.

42.

Given: P and Q on $\overrightarrow{SP}$ Prove: $SP \ne SQ$ Proof: Either $SP = SQ$ or $SP \ne SQ$. Suppose $SP = SQ$. Then there are 2 pts. on ray $\overrightarrow{SP}$ that are the same distance from S. This contradicts the Seg. Const. Post., which states that on any ray, there is exactly one pt. at a given distance from the endpt. of the ray. Thus, the assumption that $SP = SQ$ is false. We conclude $SP \ne SQ$.

44. If 2 $\angle$s are $\ne$, then they are not vert. $\angle$s. [true]

Page 165

31.

32.

33.

34.

35.

Pages 168, 169

1. $\triangle ABC$, $\triangle ABD$, $\triangle ABE$, $\triangle ACD$, $\triangle ACE$, $\triangle ADE$
2. vertices: A, B, C; sides: $\overline{AB}$, $\overline{AC}$, $\overline{BC}$; $\angle$s: $\angle BAC$, $\angle B$, $\angle ACB$
3. $\triangle TRP$
4. $\triangle HEN$
5. $\triangle TRP$
6. $\triangle ABC$
7. $\triangle ABC$
8. $\triangle TRP$

5.

6. none

7.

8.

11. Proof: 1. $\overleftrightarrow{AB} \parallel \overleftrightarrow{CD}$; $\overleftrightarrow{AC} \perp \overleftrightarrow{CD}$ (Given) 2. $\overleftrightarrow{AC} \perp \overleftrightarrow{AB}$ (If a trans. is $\perp$ to one of 2 $\parallel$ lines, it is $\perp$ to the other. [1]) 3. $\angle CAB$ is a rt. $\angle$. (Def. of $\perp$ lines [2]) 4. $\triangle ABC$ is a rt. triangle. (Def. of rt. triangle [3])

12.

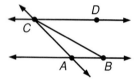

Proof: 1. $\overleftrightarrow{AB} \parallel \overleftrightarrow{CD}$ (Given) 2. $\angle ACD$ and $\angle BAC$ are supp. (2 lines $\parallel \Rightarrow$ int. $\angle$s same side supp. [1]) 3. $m\angle ACD + m\angle CAB = 180$ (Def. of supp. $\angle$s [2]) 4. $m\angle CAB = m\angle CAB$ (Reflexive Prop.) 5. $m\angle ACD = 180 - m\angle CAB$ (Subtraction Prop. [3, 4]) 6. $\angle ACD$ is an acute angle. (Given) 7. $m\angle ACD < 90$ (Def. of acute $\angle$ [6]) 8. $180 - m\angle CAB < 90$ (Substitution Prop. [5, 7]) 9. $180 = 180$ (Reflexive Prop.) 10. $-m\angle CAB < -90$ (Subtraction Prop. [8, 9]) 11. $-1 = -1$ (Reflexive Prop.) 12. $m\angle CAB > 90$ (Mult. Prop. [10, 11]) 13. $\angle CAB$ is an obtuse $\angle$. (Def. of obtuse $\angle$ [12]) 14. $\triangle CAB$ is an obtuse $\triangle$. (Def. of obtuse $\triangle$ [13])

14. Sample:

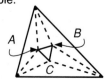

15.

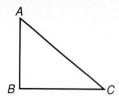

Given: $\triangle ABC$ Prove: $\triangle ABC$ cannot have 2 rt. $\angle$s. Proof: *Either* a $\triangle$ cannot have 2 rt. $\angle$s *or* it can have 2 rt. $\angle$s. *Suppose* $\triangle ABC$ has 2 rt. $\angle$s, $\angle B$ and $\angle C$. Then $\overleftrightarrow{AB} \perp \overleftrightarrow{BC}$ and $\overleftrightarrow{AC} \perp \overleftrightarrow{BC}$. Thus, there are 2 lines through A perpendicular to $\overleftrightarrow{BC}$. *This contradicts* the fact that in a plane, through a pt. not on a given line, there is one and only one line $\perp$ to the given line. *Thus, the assumption* that $\triangle ABC$ has 2 rt. $\angle$s *is false. We conclude* that $\triangle ABC$ cannot have 2 rt. $\angle$s.

26.

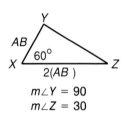

$m\angle Y = 90$
$m\angle Z = 30$

27.

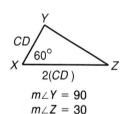

$m\angle Y = 90$
$m\angle Z = 30$

28. If one side of a triangle is twice as long as a second side of the triangle, and the angle between the two sides has a measure of 60, then the $\angle$ opp. the first side has a measure of 90, and the $\angle$ opp. the second side has a measure of 30.

29.

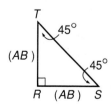

30.

31. If the two legs of a rt. $\triangle$ are $=$, the measure of both acute $\angle$s is 45.

Pages 172–174

13. Proof: 1. $\triangle ABC$ with rt. $\angle$ at B (Given) 2. $m\angle B = 90$ (Def. of rt. $\angle$ [1]) 3. $m\angle CAD > m\angle B$ (The meas. of an ext. $\angle$ of $\triangle$ is greater than either of its remote interior $\angle$s.) 4. $m\angle CAD > 90$ (Substitution Prop. [2, 3]) 5. $\angle CAD$ is obtuse. (Def. of obtuse $\angle$ [4])

14. Proof: 1. $\triangle ABC$ with rt. $\angle$ at B (Given) 2. $m\angle B = 90$ (Def. of rt. $\angle$ [1]) 3. $m\angle DAC = m\angle ACB + m\angle B$ (The meas. of an ext. $\angle$ of a $\triangle =$ sum of meas. of its remote int. $\angle$s.) 4. $m\angle B = m\angle B$ (Reflexive Prop.) 5. $m\angle DAC - m\angle B = m\angle ACB$ (Subtraction Prop. [4, 5]) 6. $m\angle DAC - 90 = m\angle ACB$ (Substitution Prop. [2, 5])

15. Proof: 1. $\triangle ABC$ with rt. $\angle$ at B (Given) 2. $\triangle ABC$ is a rt. triangle. (Def. of rt. triangle [1]) 3. $\angle CAB$ and $\angle C$ are comp. (The acute $\angle$s of a rt. $\triangle$ are comp. [2]) 4. $m\angle CAB + m\angle C = 90$ (Def. of comp. $\angle$s [3]) 5. $m\angle CAB = m\angle C$ (Given) 6. $m\angle CAB + m\angle CAB = 2(m\angle CAB) = 90$ (Substitution Prop. [4, 5]) 7. $2 = 2$ (Reflexive Prop.) 8. $m\angle CAB = 45$ (Div. Prop. [6, 7]) 9. $m\angle C = 45$ (Substitution Prop. [5, 8])

16. Proof: 1. $\triangle ABC$ with rt. $\angle$ at B (Given) 2. $\triangle ABC$ is a rt. triangle. (Def. of rt. triangle [1]) 3. $\angle CAB$ and $\angle C$ are comp. (The acute angles of a rt. $\triangle$ are comp. [2]) 4. $m\angle CAB + m\angle C = 90$ (Def. of comp. $\angle$s [3]) 5. $m\angle CAB = 45$ (Given) 6. $45 + m\angle C = 90$ (Substitution Prop. [4, 5]) 7. $45 = 45$ (Reflexive Prop.) 8. $m\angle C = 45$ (Subtraction Prop. [6, 7]) 9. $m\angle$

CAB = *m*∠*C* (Substitution Prop. [5, 8])
20. *m*∠*BFC* = 51, *m*∠*DCF* = 25, *m*∠*EDF* = 64, *m*∠*AFE* = 31, *m*∠ *ABF* = 40
21.

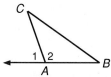

Given: △*ABC* with ext. ∠1 Prove: *m*∠1 = *m*∠*B* + *m*∠*C* Proof: 1. △*ABC* with ext. ∠1 (Given) 2. ∠1 and ∠2 form a linear pair. (Def. of ext. ∠ [1]) 3. ∠1 and ∠2 are supp. (Supp. Post. [2]) 4. *m*∠1 + *m*∠2 = 180 (Def. of supp. ∠s [3]) 5. *m*∠*B* + *m*∠*C* + *m*∠2 = 180 (Sum of meas. of ∠s of △ = 180. [1]) 6. *m*∠1 + *m*∠2 = *m*∠*B* + *m*∠*C* + *m*∠2 (Substitution Prop. [4, 5]) 7. *m*∠2 = *m*∠2 (Reflexive Prop.) 8. *m*∠1 = *m*∠*B* + *m*∠*C* (Add. Prop. [6, 7])
22. (See diagram for Exercise 21.) Given: △*ABC* with ext. ∠1 Prove: *m*∠1 > *m*∠*B*; *m*∠1 > *m*∠*C* Proof: 1. △*ABC* with ext. ∠1 (Given) 2. *m*∠1 = *m*∠*B* + *m*∠*C* (Meas. of ext. ∠ of a △ = sum of meas. of 2 remote int. ∠s. [1]) 3. *m*∠*B* > 0; *m*∠*C* > 0 (Protractor Post.) 4. *m*∠1 > *m*∠*B*; *m*∠1 > *m*∠*C* (Def. of > [2, 3])
23. Proof: 1. ⃡*CD* ⊥ ⃡*AB*; *m*∠*A* = *m*∠*B* (Given) 2. ∠*CDA* and ∠*CDB* are rt. ∠s. (Two ⊥ lines intersect to form 4 rt. ∠s. [1]) 3. *m*∠*CDA* = *m*∠*CDB* (All rt. ∠s are =. [2]) 4. *m*∠*ACD* = *m*∠*BCD* (If 2 ∠s of a △ = 2 ∠s of another △, the third ∠s are =. [1, 3]) 5. ⃗*CD* bisects ∠*ACB* (Def. of ∠ bisector [4])
24. Proof: 1. ⃡*CD* ⊥ ⃡*AB*; ⃗*CD* bisects ∠*ACB*. (Given) 2. ∠*CDA* and ∠*CDB* are rt. ∠s. (Two ⊥ lines intersect to form 4 rt. ∠s. [1]) 3. *m*∠*CDA* = *m*∠*CDB* (All rt. ∠s are =. [2]) 4. *m*∠*ACD* = *m*∠*BCD* (Def. of ∠ bisector [1]) 5. *m*∠*A* = *m*∠*B* (If 2 ∠s of a △ = 2 ∠s of another △, the third ∠s are =. [3, 4])

25.

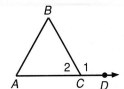

Given: △*ABC* is equiangular with exterior ∠1. Prove: *m*∠1 = 120 Proof: 1. Equiangular △*ABC* with ext. ∠1 (Given) 2. *m*∠*A* = *m*∠*B* = 60 (Each ∠ of equiangular △ has meas. 60. [1]) 3. *m*∠1 = *m*∠*A* + *m*∠*B* (Meas. ext. ∠ = sum of meas. of its two remote int. ∠s. [1]) 4. *m*∠1 = 60 + 60 = 120 (Substitution Prop. [2, 3])
26.

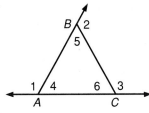

Given: △*ABC* with ext. ∠s ∠1, ∠2, ∠3 Prove: *m*∠1 + *m*∠2 + *m*∠3 = 360 Proof: 1. △*ABC* with ext. ∠s ∠1, ∠2, ∠3. (Given) 2. ∠1 and ∠4 are supp.; ∠2 and ∠5 are supp.; ∠3 and ∠6 are supp. (Supp. Post.) 3. *m*∠1 + *m*∠4 = 180; *m*∠2 + *m*∠5 = 180; *m*∠3 + *m*∠6 = 180 (Def. of supp. ∠s [2]) 4. *m*∠1 + *m*∠2 + *m*∠3 + *m*∠4 + *m*∠5 + *m*∠6 = 540 (Add. Prop. [3]) 5. *m*∠4 + *m*∠5 + *m*∠6 = 180 (Sum of meas. of ∠s of △ = 180.) 6. *m*∠1 + *m*∠2 + *m*∠3 = 360 (Subtraction Prop. [4, 5])
27.

Given: △*ABC* Prove: △*ABC* cannot have two obtuse ∠s. Proof: Either (1) △*ABC* can have two obtuse ∠s or (2) it cannot have two obtuse ∠s. Suppose △*ABC* does have two obtuse ∠s, say ∠*A* and ∠*B*. Then by the def. of an obtuse ∠, *m*∠*A* > 90 and *m*∠*B* > 90, and

by the Add. Prop., *m*∠*A* + *m*∠*B* > 180. Since *m*∠*C* > 0, *m*∠*A* + *m*∠*B* + *m*∠*C* > 180 by the Add. Prop. Thus, the sum of the measures of the angles of △*ABC* is greater than 180. *This contradicts* the fact that the sum of the measures of the angles of any △ is 180. Therefore, *the assumption that* ∠*A* and ∠*B* are both obtuse ∠s *is false. We conclude that* ∠*A* and ∠*B* are not both obtuse ∠s.
28. Proof: 1. *m*∠*SRT* = 30; *m*∠ *TQU* = 25 (Given) 2. *m*∠*SRT* = *m*∠*PRQ* (Vert. ∠s are =.) 3. *m*∠ *PRQ* = 30 (Substitution Prop. [1, 2]) 4. *m*∠*SPU* = *m*∠*TQU* + *m*∠ *PRQ* (Meas. of xt. ∠ of a △ = sum of meas. of its remote int. ∠s.) 5. *m*∠*SPU* = 25 + 30 = 55 (Substitution Prop. [1, 3, 4])
31.

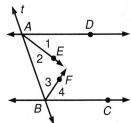

Given: ⃡*AD* ∥ ⃡*BC*; ⃗*AE* bisects ∠*DAB*; ⃗*BF* bisects ∠*ABC*. Prove: Part I: ⃗*AE* and ⃗*BF* intersect. Part II: ⃗*BF* ⊥ ⃗*AE* Part I Proof: *Either* ⃗*AE* and ⃗*BF* intersect *or they do not intersect. Suppose* ⃗*AE* and ⃗*BF* do not intersect. *Then* ⃗*AE* ∥ ⃗*BF* and *m*∠2 + *m*∠3 = 180 (Int. ∠s on same side supp.). Since ⃡*AD* ∥ ⃡*BC*, *m*∠*DAB* + *m*∠*CBA* = 180. Since ⃗*AE* bisects ∠*DAB* and ⃗*BF* bisects ∠*ABC*, the Angle Add. Post. and the def. of angle bisector give (*m*∠1 + *m*∠2) + (*m*∠3 + *m*∠4) = 180, and therefore, 2(*m*∠2) + 2(*m*∠3) = 180. Thus, *m*∠2 + *m*∠3 = 90. *But this contradicts* the fact that if ⃗*AE* ∥ ⃗*BF* then the int. ∠s on same side of the transversal are supplementary. Thus, *the assumption that* ⃗*AE* and ⃗*BF* do not intersect *is false.*

We conclude that $\overrightarrow{AE}$ and $\overrightarrow{BF}$ intersect in a pt. P.

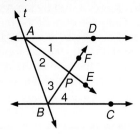

Part II Proof: 1. $\overleftrightarrow{AD} \parallel \overleftrightarrow{BC}$; $\overrightarrow{AE}$ bisects $\angle DAB$; $\overrightarrow{BF}$ bisects $\angle ABC$. (Given) 2. $\overrightarrow{AE}$ and $\overrightarrow{BF}$ intersect at P. (Part I) 3. $m\angle 1 = m\angle 2$; $m\angle 3 = m\angle 4$ (Def. of $\angle$ bisector [1]) 4. $m\angle 1 + m\angle 2 = m\angle DAB$; $m\angle 3 + m\angle 4 = m\angle ABC$ (Angle Add. Post.) 5. $m\angle 2 + m\angle 2 = m\angle DAB$, or $2(m\angle 2) = m\angle DAB$; $m\angle 3 + m\angle 3 = m\angle ABC$, or $2(m\angle 3) = m\angle ABC$ (Substitution Prop. [3, 4]) 6. $\angle DAB$ and $\angle ABC$ are supp. (2 lines $\parallel \Rightarrow$ int. $\angle$s on same side supp. [1]) 7. $m\angle DAB + m\angle ABC = 180$ (Def. of supp. $\angle$s [6]) 8. $2(m\angle 2) + 2(m\angle 3) = 180$ (Substitution Prop. [5, 7]) 9. $m\angle 2 + m\angle 3 = 90$ (Mult. Prop. [8]) 10. $m\angle 2 + m\angle 3 + m\angle APB = 180$ (Sum of meas. of $\angle$s of $\triangle = 180$. [2]) 11. $90 + m\angle APB = 180$ (Substitution Prop. [9, 10]) 12. $m\angle APB = 90$ (Subtraction Prop. [11]) 13. $\angle APB$ is a rt. $\angle$. (Def. of rt. $\angle$ [12]) 14. $\overrightarrow{BF} \perp \overrightarrow{AE}$ (Def. of $\perp$ lines [13])

32. (See diagram for Exercise 31.) Given: $\overrightarrow{AE}$ bisects $\angle DAB$; $\overrightarrow{BF}$ bisects $\angle ABC$; $\overrightarrow{BF} \perp \overrightarrow{AE}$ at P. Prove: $\overleftrightarrow{AD} \parallel \overleftrightarrow{BC}$ Proof: 1. $\overrightarrow{AE}$ bisects $\angle DAB$; $\overrightarrow{BF}$ bisects $\angle ABC$; $\overrightarrow{BF} \perp \overrightarrow{AE}$ at P (Given) 2. $\angle APB$ is a rt. $\angle$. (Def. of $\perp$ lines [1]) 3. $\triangle APB$ is a rt. $\triangle$. (Def. of rt. $\triangle$ [2]) 4. $\angle 2$ and $\angle 3$ are comp. (Acute $\angle$s of a rt. $\triangle$ are comp. [2, 3]) 5. $m\angle 2 + m\angle 3 = 90$ (Def. of comp. $\angle$s [4]) 6. $m\angle 1 + m\angle 2 = m\angle DAB$; $m\angle 3 + m\angle 4 = m\angle ABC$ (Angle Add. Post.) 7. $m\angle 1 = m\angle 2$; $m\angle 3 = m\angle 4$ (Def. of $\angle$ bisector [1]) 8. $m\angle 2 + m\angle 2 = m\angle DAB$, or $2(m\angle 2) = m\angle DAB$; $m\angle 3 + m\angle 3$

$= m\angle ABC$, or $2(m\angle 3) = m\angle ABC$ (Substitution Prop. [6, 7]) 9. $2(m\angle 2) + 2(m\angle 3) = m\angle DAB + m\angle ABC$, or $2(m\angle 2 + m\angle 3) = m\angle DAB + m\angle ABC$ (Add. Prop. [8]) 10. $2(90) = m\angle DAB + m\angle ABC$ or $180 = m\angle DAB + m\angle ABC$ (Substitution Prop. [5, 9]) 11. $\angle DAB$ and $\angle ABC$ are supp. (Def. of supp. [10]) 12. $\overleftrightarrow{AD} \parallel \overleftrightarrow{BC}$ (Int. $\angle$s on same side supp. $\Rightarrow$ 2 lines $\parallel$. [11])

Page 179

4.   **5.**

7.   **8.**

9.   **10.**

11.

Page 183

4. Sample:

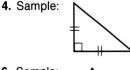

6. Sample:

10. Proof: 1. Quadrilateral $ABCD$ with $\overleftrightarrow{AB} \parallel \overleftrightarrow{DC}$ (Given) 2. $\angle A$ and $\angle D$ are supp.; $\angle B$ and $\angle C$ are supp. (2 lines $\parallel \Rightarrow$ int. $\angle$s on same side supp. [1]) 3. $m\angle A + m\angle D = 180$; $m\angle B + m\angle C = 180$ (Def. of supp. $\angle$s [2]) 4. $m\angle A + m\angle B + m\angle C + m\angle D = 360$ (Add. Prop. [3])

17. Given: $\triangle ABC$ Prove: $\triangle ABC \cong \triangle ABC$

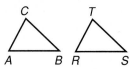

Proof: 1. $\triangle ABC$ (Given) 2. $AB = AB$; $BC = BC$; $AC = AC$; $m\angle A = m\angle A$; $m\angle B = m\angle B$; $m\angle C = m\angle C$ (Reflexive Prop.) 3. $\triangle ABC \cong \triangle ABC$ (Def. of $\cong \triangle$s [2])

18. Given: $\triangle ABC \cong \triangle RST$ Prove: $\triangle RST \cong \triangle ABC$

Proof: 1. $\triangle ABC \cong \triangle RST$ (Given) 2. $AB = RS$; $AC = RT$; $BC = ST$; $m\angle A = m\angle R$; $m\angle B = m\angle S$; $m\angle C = m\angle T$ (Corr. parts of $\cong \triangle$s are $=$. [1]) 3. $RS = AB$; $RT = AC$; $ST = BC$; $m\angle R = m\angle A$; $m\angle S = m\angle B$; $m\angle T = m\angle C$ (Symmetric Prop. [2]) 4. $\triangle RST \cong \triangle ABC$ (Def. of $\cong \triangle$s [3])

19. Given: $\triangle ABC \cong \triangle PQR$; $\triangle PQR \cong \triangle XYZ$ Prove: $\triangle ABC \cong \triangle XYZ$

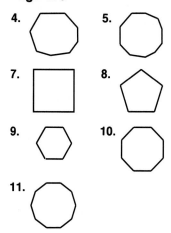

Proof: 1. $\triangle ABC \cong \triangle PQR$; $\triangle PQR \cong \triangle XYZ$ (Given) 2. $AB = PQ$; $PQ = XY$; $AC = PR$; $PR = XZ$; $BC = QR$; $QR = YZ$; $m\angle A = m\angle P$; $m\angle P = m\angle X$; $m\angle B = m\angle Q$; $m\angle Q = m\angle Y$; $m\angle C = m\angle R$; $m\angle R = m\angle Z$ (Corr. parts of $\cong \triangle$s are $=$. [1]) 3. $AB = XY$; $AC = XZ$; $BC = YZ$; $m\angle A = m\angle X$; $m\angle B = m\angle Y$; $m\angle C = m\angle Z$ (Transitive Prop. [2]) 4. $\triangle ABC \cong \triangle XYZ$ (Def. of $\cong \triangle$s [3])

25. Given: $\triangle ABC \cong \triangle DEF$; $\triangle ABC$ is scalene. Prove: $\triangle DEF$ is scalene.

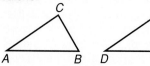

Proof: Either (1) △DEF is scalene or (2) △DEF is not scalene. Suppose △DEF is not scalene. Then at least 2 sides of △DEF are =; say DE = EF. Since △ABC ≅ △DEF and corr. parts of ≅ △s are =, it follows that AB = DE and BC = EF. So, by substitution, AB = BC. But this contradicts the fact that △ABC is scalene. Thus, the assumption that △DEF is not scalene is false. We conclude that △DEF is scalene.

30. Given: $m\angle A = m\angle B$; $\angle A$ and $\angle B$ are complementary. Prove: $m\angle A = 45$; $m\angle B = 45$

Proof: 1. $m\angle A = m\angle B$; $\angle A$ and $\angle B$ are comp. (Given) 2. $m\angle A + m\angle B = 90$ (Def. of comp. ∠s [1]) 3. $m\angle A + m\angle A = 2(m\angle A) = 90$; $m\angle B + m\angle B = 2(m\angle B) = 90$ (Substitution Prop. [1, 2]) 4. $m\angle A = 45$; $m\angle B = 45$ (Division Prop. [3])

32. $MN = PQ = \sqrt{10}$; $LM = PR = \sqrt{10}$; $LN = QR = 2\sqrt{2}$; yes

---

1., 2. Sample:

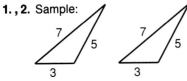

3., 4. Sample:

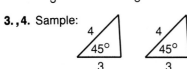

Page 199

27. Proof: 1. $\overline{DC} \perp \mathcal{H}$; △ABC is equilateral. (Given) 2. $AC = BC$ (Def. of equilateral △ [1]) 3. $\overline{DC} \perp \overline{AC}$; $\overline{DC} \perp \overline{BC}$ (Def. of line ⊥ to plane [1]) 4. $\angle ACD$ and $\angle BCD$ are rt. ∠s. (2 ⊥ lines form 4 rt. ∠s. [3]) 5. $m\angle ACD = m\angle BCD$ (All rt. ∠s are =. [4]) 6. $CD = CD$ (Re-

flexive Prop.) 7. △ACD ≅ △BCD (SAS Post. [2, 5, 6])

28. Proof: 1. $\overline{DC} \perp \mathcal{H}$; $m\angle ADC = m\angle BDC$ (Given) 2. $\overline{DC} \perp \overline{AC}$; $\overline{DC} \perp \overline{BC}$ (Def. of line ⊥ to plane [1]) 3. $\angle ACD$ and $\angle BCD$ are rt. ∠s. (2 ⊥ lines form 4 rt. ∠s. [2]) 4. $m\angle ACD = m\angle BCD$ (All rt. ∠s are =. [3]) 5. $CD = CD$ (Reflexive Prop.) 6. △ACD ≅ △BCD (ASA Post. [1, 3, 5])

29. $AB = CB$; $AD = CA$; $BD = BA$; $m\angle BAD = m\angle BCA$; $m\angle ABD = m\angle CBA$; $m\angle BDA = m\angle BAC$

Page 203

11. Proof: 1. $m\angle P = m\angle S$; $m\angle Q = m\angle T$; $QR = TU$ (Given) 2. $m\angle R = m\angle U$ (If 2 ∠s of 1 △ are = to 2 ∠s of another △, then remaining ∠s are =. [1]) 3. △PQR ≅ △STU (ASA Post. [1, 2])

12. Given: △MNP and △RST with $\angle N$ and $\angle S$ rt. ∠s; $MN = RS$; $m\angle P = m\angle T$ Prove: △MNP ≅ △RST

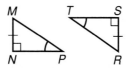

Proof: 1. △MNP and △RST with $\angle N$ and $\angle S$ rt. ∠s; $MN = RS$; $m\angle P = m\angle T$ (Given) 2. $m\angle N = m\angle S$ (All rt. ∠s are =. [1]) 3. △MNP ≅ △RST (AAS Thm. [1, 2])

13. Proof: 1. $\overleftrightarrow{RT}$ bisects $\angle SRW$ and $\angle STW$. (Given) 2. $m\angle SRT = m\angle WRT$; $m\angle STR = m\angle WTR$ (Def. of ∠ bisector [1]) 3. $RT = RT$ (Reflexive Prop.) 4. △RST ≅ △RWT (ASA Post. [2, 3])

14. Proof: 1. $\overline{RS} \perp \overline{ST}$; $\overline{RW} \perp \overline{WT}$; $\overline{ST} \parallel \overline{RW}$ (Given) 2. $\angle RST$ and $\angle TWR$ are rt. ∠s. (2 ⊥ lines form 4 rt. ∠s. [1]) 3. $m\angle RST = m\angle TWR$ (All rt. ∠s are =. [2]) 4. $m\angle RTS = m\angle TRW$ (2 lines ∥ ⇒ alt. int. ∠s =. [3]) 5. $RT = TR$ (Reflexive Prop.) 6. △RST ≅ △TWR (AAS Thm. [3, 4, 5])

15. Proof: 1. $\overline{WT} \parallel \overline{RS}$; $\overline{RW} \parallel \overline{ST}$ (Given) 2. $m\angle RSW = m\angle TWS$; $m\angle$

$RWS = m\angle TSW$ (2 lines ∥ ⇒ alt. int. ∠s =. [1]) 3. $SW = WS$ (Reflexive Prop.) 4. △RSW ≅ △TWS (ASA Post. [2, 3])

16. Proof: 1. $\angle RSQ$ and $\angle QSP$ are rt. ∠s; $PS = RS$ (Given) 2. $m\angle QSP = m\angle RSQ$ (All rt. ∠s are =. [1]) 3. $SQ = SQ$ (Reflexive Prop.) 4. △PSQ ≅ △RSQ (SAS Post. [1, 2, 3])

17. Proof: 1. $m\angle PQS = m\angle PRS$; $\angle QSP$ and $\angle RSP$ are rt. ∠s. (Given) 2. $m\angle QSP = m\angle RSP$ (All rt. ∠s are =. [1]) 3. $PS = PS$ (Reflexive Prop.) 4. △PQS ≅ △PRS (AAS Thm. [1, 2, 3])

18. Locate A and C such that $RA = SC$. Since B is the midpt. of $\overline{RS}$, $RB = SB$. $m\angle R = m\angle S$, because all rt. ∠s are =, and △BRA ≅ △BSC by the SAS Post.

19. For the other end, mark the midpoint, B' of $\overline{R'S'}$. Then, cut $\angle R'B'A'$ and $\angle S'B'C'$ equal to $\angle RBA$ and $\angle SBC$. Since B' is the midpoint of $\overline{R'S'}$, $R'B' = S'B'$. $m\angle R = m\angle S$ because all rt. ∠s are =, and △B'R'A' ≅ △B'S'C by the ASA Post.

Pages 207–209

5. △RSV ≅ △TSV or △RSU ≅ △TSU

6. △RSU ≅ △TSU or △RVU ≅ △TVU

7. △RSU ≅ △TSU

8. △RSV ≅ △TSV or △RVU ≅ △TVU

9. △RSV ≅ △TSV or △RSU ≅ △TSU

10. △RSU ≅ △TSU or △RVU ≅ △TVU

11. Proof: 1. $\overline{AB} \perp \overline{BC}$; $AD = CB$; $m\angle 1 = m\angle 4$ (Given) 2. $CA = AC$ (Reflexive Prop.) 3. △CDA ≅ △ABC (SAS Post. [1, 2]) 4. $\angle B$ is a rt. ∠. (2 ⊥ lines form 4 rt. ∠s. [3]) 5. $m\angle B = 90$ (Def. of rt. ∠ [4]) 6. $m\angle D = m\angle B$ (Corr. parts of ≅ △s are =. [3]) 7. $m\angle D = 90$ (Transitive Prop. [5, 6]) 8. $\angle D$ is a rt. ∠. (Def. of rt. ∠ [7]) 9. $\overline{AD} \perp \overline{DC}$ (Def. of ⊥ lines [8])

12. △WXY ≅ △WZY by SSS Post. $m\angle WYX = m\angle WYZ$ because corr. parts of ≅ △s are =. $\overrightarrow{YW}$ bisects ∠Y by definition.

13. △CED ≅ △CAB by SAS Post. $DE = BA$, $m\angle CED = m\angle CAB$ and $m\angle CDE = m\angle CBA$ because corr. parts of ≅ △s are =.

14. Yes; △PQR ≅ △PSR by SSS Post. $m\angle Q = m\angle S$ because corr. parts of ≅ △s are =.

15. Since ∠C and ∠A are rt. ∠s, $m\angle C = m\angle A$. Also, $m\angle CBP = m\angle ABP'$, and $CB = AB$. So △CBP ≅ △ABP' by ASA Post., and $CP = AP'$ because corr. parts of ≅ △s are =.

16.

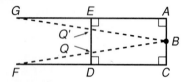

Extend $\overrightarrow{AE}$ and $\overrightarrow{BQ}$ to meet at G; extend $\overrightarrow{CD}$ and $\overrightarrow{BQ}$ to meet at F. Since $m\angle C = m\angle A$, $m\angle ABG$ and $CB = AB$, △CBF ≅ △ABG by ASA Post. Since $CD = AE$ (opp. sides of table) and $CF = AG$ (corr. parts of ≅ △s are =.), it follows that $DF = EG$ by the Subtraction Prop. $m\angle F = m\angle G$ because corr. parts of ≅ △s are =, and $m\angle FDQ = m\angle GEQ'$, so △FDQ ≅ △GEQ' by ASA Post. Hence, $DQ = EQ'$ because corr. parts of ≅ △s are =.

17. Proof: 1. $QR = NS$; $MR = PS$; $m\angle QRM = m\angle NSP$ (Given) 2. $RS = SR$ (Reflexive Prop.) 3. $QR + RS = NS + SR$ (Addition Prop. [1, 2]) 4. $QR + RS = QS$; $NS + SR = NR$ (Seg. Add. Post.) 5. $QS = NR$ (Substitution Prop. [3, 4]) 6. ∠MRN and ∠QRM are supp. ∠s; ∠PSQ and ∠NSP are supp. ∠s. (Supplement Post.) 7. $m\angle MRN = m\angle PSQ$ (Supplements of = ∠s are =. [1, 6]) 8. △MRN ≅ △PSQ (SAS Post. [1, 5, 7]) 9. $m\angle 1 = m\angle 2$ (Corr. parts of ≅ △s are =. [8])

18. Proof: 1. ∠B and ∠D are rt. ∠s; C is the midpt. of $\overline{BD}$; $m\angle A = m\angle E$ (Given) 2. $m\angle B = m\angle D$ (All rt. ∠s are =. [1]) 3. $BC = DC$ (Def. of midpt. [1]) 4. △ABC ≅ △EDC (AAS Thm. [1, 2, 3])

Pages 213, 214

16. Proof: 1. $XU = ZU$; $XY = ZY$ (Given) 2. $UY = UY$ (Reflexive Prop.) 3. △UXY ≅ △UZY (SSS Post. [1, 2]) 4. $m\angle XUY = m\angle ZUY$ (Corr. parts of ≅ △s are =. [3]) 5. $UV = UV$ (Reflexive Prop.) 6. △UVX ≅ △UVZ (SAS Post. [1, 4, 5]) 7. $m\angle UVX = m\angle UVZ$ (Corr. parts of ≅ △s are =. [6]) 8. $\overline{UY} \perp \overline{XZ}$ (If the ∠s in a lin. pr. are =, then the lines containing their sides are ⊥. [7])

18. Proof: 1. $AD = BC$; $m\angle ADC = m\angle BCD$ (Given) 2. $DC = CD$ (Reflexive Prop.) 3. △ADC ≅ △BCD (SAS Post. [1, 2])

23. Proof: 1. $PR = QS$; $SU = RU$ (Given) 2. $PR + RU = QS + SU$ (Add. Prop. [1]) 3. $PR + RU = PU$; $QS + SU = QU$ (Seg. Add. Post.) 4. $PU = QU$ (Substitution Prop. [2, 3]) 5. $m\angle U = m\angle U$ (Reflexive Prop.) 6. △PSU ≅ △QRU (SAS Post. [1, 4, 5]) 7. $m\angle P = m\angle Q$; $PS = QR$ (Corr. parts of ≅ △s are =. [6]) 8. △PSR ≅ △QRS (SAS Post. [1, 7]) 9. $m\angle PRS = m\angle QSR$ (Corr. parts of ≅ △s are =. [8]) 10. ∠URS and ∠PRS are supp. ∠s; ∠USR and ∠QSR are supp. ∠s (Supp. Post.) 11. $m\angle URS = m\angle USR$ (Supp. of = ∠s are =. [9, 10])

24. Proof: 1. $PR = QS$; $m\angle URS = m\angle USR$ (Given) 2. ∠URS and ∠PRS are supp. ∠s; ∠USR and ∠QSR are supp. ∠s. (Supp. Post.) 3. $m\angle PRS = m\angle QSR$ (Supp. of = ∠s are =. [1, 2]) 4. $RS = SR$ (Reflexive Prop.) 5. △PSR ≅ △QRS (SAS Post. [1, 3, 4]) 6. $m\angle P = m\angle Q$; (Corr. parts of ≅ △s are =. [5]) 7. $m\angle U = m\angle U$ (Reflexive Prop.) 8. △PSU ≅ △QRU (AAS

Thm. [6, 7]) 9. $SU = RU$ (Corr. parts of ≅ △s are =. [8])

25. Show that the following parts are =: (1) All 6 pairs of corr. parts; (2) 3 pairs of corr. sides; (3) 2 pairs of corr. sides and their included ∠; (4) 2 pairs of corr. ∠s and their included side; (5) 2 pairs of corr. ∠s and a pair of corr., nonincluded sides. (6) Show that the △s are ≅ to the same △.

26. Proof: 1. $\overrightarrow{AC}$ bisects ∠BAD; $\overrightarrow{CA}$ bisects ∠BCD. (Given) 2. $m\angle BAC = m\angle DAC$; $m\angle BCA = m\angle DCA$ (Def. of ∠ bisector [1]) 3. $AC = AC$ (Reflexive Prop.) 4. △ABC ≅ △ADC (ASA Post. [2, 3]) 5. $BC = DC$ (Corr. parts of ≅ △s are =. [4])

27. 2 noncongruent triangles can be drawn with 2 pairs of = corr. sides and a pair of =, nonincluded ∠s. (A counterexample is shown on page 201.)

11. Proof: 1. $\overline{YZ} \parallel \overline{XW}$; $YZ = XW$ (Given) 2. $m\angle YZX = m\angle WXZ$ (Lines ∥ ⇒ alt. int. ∠s =. [1]) 3. $XZ = ZX$ (Reflexive Prop.) 4. △XYZ ≅ △ZWX (SAS Post. [1, 2, 3])

Pages 223, 224

13. Proof: 1. $MP = NP$ (Given) 2. $m\angle PMN = m\angle PNM$ (Isos. △ Thm. [1]) 3. ∠1 and ∠PMN are supp. ∠s; ∠3 and ∠PNM are supp. ∠s. (Supplement Post.) 4. $m\angle 1 = m\angle 3$ (Supplements of = ∠s are =. [2, 3])

14. Proof: 1. $m\angle A = m\angle B$ (Given) 2. Draw $\overrightarrow{CE}$, the bisector of ∠ACB (∠ Bisector Post.) 3. $m\angle ACD = m\angle BCD$ (Def. of ∠ bisector [2]) 4. $CD = CD$ (Reflexive Prop.) 5. △ACD ≅ △BCD (AAS Thm. [1, 3, 4]) 6. $AC = BC$ (Corr. parts of ≅ △s are =. [5])

15. Given: △ABC is equiangular. Prove: △ABC is equilateral.

Proof: 1. $\triangle ABC$ is equiangular. (Given) 2. $m\angle A = m\angle B = m\angle C$ (Def. of equiangular $\triangle$ [1]) 3. $BC = AC$; $AC = AB$ (If 2 $\angle$s of a $\triangle$ are =, then the sides opp. those $\angle$s are =. [2]) 4. $BC = AC = AB$ (Transitive Prop. [3]) 5. $\triangle ABC$ is equilateral. (Def. of equilateral $\triangle$ [4])

16. Given: $\triangle ABC$ is equilateral. (See diagram for Exer. 15.) Prove: $\triangle ABC$ is equiangular. Proof: 1. $\triangle ABC$ is equilateral. (Given) 2. $AB = AC = BC$ (Def. of equilateral $\triangle$ [1]) 3. $m\angle C = m\angle B$; $m\angle B = m\angle A$ (Isos. $\triangle$ Thm. [2]) 4. $m\angle C = m\angle B = m\angle A$ (Transitive Prop.) 5. $\triangle ABC$ is equiangular. (Def. of equiangular $\triangle$ [4])

17. Given: $\triangle ABC$; $AC = BC$; $\overline{CD}$ is a median. Prove: $\overline{CD}$ bisects $\angle ACB$.

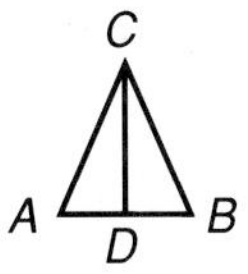

18. Given: $\triangle ABC$; $\overline{CD}$ is an altitude and a median. (See diagram for Exer. 17.) Prove: $\triangle ABC$ is isosceles.

19. Given: $\triangle ABC$; $AC = BC$; CD is a median. (See diagram for Exer. 17.) Prove: $\overline{CD}$ is the $\perp$ bisector of $\overline{AB}$.

21. Proof: 1. $\triangle ABC$; $AC = BC$; $\overline{CD}$ is a median. (Given) 2. D is midpt. of $\overline{AB}$. (Def. of median of a $\triangle$ [1]) 3. $AD = BD$ (Def. of midpt. [2]) 4. $CD = CD$ (Reflexive Prop.) 5. $\triangle ACD \cong \triangle BCD$ (SSS Post. [1, 3, 4]) 6. $m\angle ACD = m\angle BCD$ (Corr. parts of $\cong$ $\triangle$s are =. [5]) 7. $\overline{CD}$ bisects $\angle ACB$. (Def. of $\angle$ bisector [6])

22. Proof: 1. $\triangle ABC$; $\overline{CD}$ is an altitude and a median. (Given) 2. $\overline{CD} \perp \overleftrightarrow{AB}$ (Def. of altitude of a $\triangle$ [1]) 3. $\angle ADC$ and $\angle BDC$ are rt. $\angle$s. (2 $\perp$ lines form 4 rt. $\angle$s. [2]) 4. $m\angle ADC = m\angle BDC$ (All rt. $\angle$s are =. [3]) 5. D is midpt. of $\overline{AB}$. (Def. of median of a $\triangle$ [1]) 6. $AD = BD$ (Def. of midpt. [5]) 7. $CD = CD$ (Reflexive Prop.) 8. $\triangle ACD \cong \triangle BCD$ (SAS Post. [4, 6, 7]) 9. $AC = BC$ (Corr. parts of $\cong$ $\triangle$s are =. [8]) 10. $\triangle ABC$ is isosceles. (Def. of isos. $\triangle$ [9])

23. Proof: 1. $\triangle ABC$; $AC = BC$; CD is a median. (Given) 2. D is midpt. of $\overline{AB}$. (Def. of median of a $\triangle$ [1]) 3. $AD = DB$ (Def. of midpt. [2]) 4. $CD = CD$ (Reflexive Prop.) 5. $\triangle ACD \cong \triangle BCD$ (SSS Post. [1, 3, 4]) 6. $m\angle ADC = m\angle BDC$ (Corr. parts of $\cong$ $\triangle$s are =. [5]) 7. $\overline{CD} \perp \overline{AB}$ (If the $\angle$s in a lin. pr. are =, then the lines containing their sides are $\perp$. [6]) 8. $\overline{CD}$ is $\perp$ bisector of $\overline{AB}$. (Def. of $\perp$ bisector [2, 7])

25. Proof: 1. $\triangle ABC$ and $\triangle DEF$ with rt. $\angle$s at B and E; $AC = DF$; $BC = EF$ (Given) 2. Draw $\overleftrightarrow{DE}$. (Line Post.) 3. Choose G on $\overrightarrow{DE}$ so that $EG = BA$. (Seg. Construction Post.) 4. Draw $\overline{FG}$. (Line Post.) 5. $\angle FEG$ is a rt. $\angle$. (If one $\angle$ of a lin. pr. is a rt. $\angle$, then other $\angle$ is also a rt. $\angle$. [1]) 6. $m\angle B = m\angle FEG$ (All rt. $\angle$s are =. [1, 5]) 7. $\triangle ABC \cong \triangle GEF$ (SAS Post. [1, 3, 6]) 8. $AC = GF$ (Corr. parts of $\cong$ $\triangle$s are =. [7]) 9. $DF = GF$ (Substitution Prop. [1, 8]) 10. $m\angle G = m\angle D$ (Isos. $\triangle$ Thm. [9]) 11. $m\angle FEG = m\angle FED$ (All rt. $\angle$s are =. [1, 5]) 12. $\triangle GEF \cong \triangle DEF$ (AAS Thm. [9, 10, 11]) 13. $\triangle ABC \cong \triangle DEF$ (Congruence of $\triangle$s is transitive. [7, 12])

26. Given: Isos. $\triangle$ with $AC = BC$; $\overline{AD}$ and $\overline{BE}$ are medians. Prove: $AD = BE$

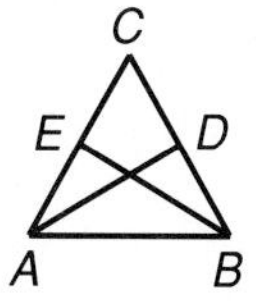

Proof: 1. $AC = BC$; $\overline{AD}$ and $\overline{BE}$ are medians. (Given) 2. D is midpt. of $\overline{BC}$; E is midpt. of $\overline{AC}$. (Def. of median of a $\triangle$ [1]) 3. $BD = DC$; $AE = EC$ (Def. of midpt. [2]) 4. $BC = BD + DC$; $AC = AE + EC$ (Seg. Add. Post.) 5. $BD + DC = AE + EC$ (Substitution Prop. [1, 5]) 6. $2(BD) = 2(AE)$ (Substitution Prop. [3, 5]) 7. $BD = AE$ (Division Prop. [6]) 8. $m\angle ABD = m\angle BAE$ (Isos. $\triangle$ Thm. [1]) 9. $AB = BA$ (Reflexive Prop.) 10. $\triangle ABD \cong \triangle BAE$ (SAS Post. [7, 8, 9]) 11. $AD = BE$ (Corr. parts of $\cong$ $\triangle$s are =. [10])

27. Given: Equiangular $\triangle ABC$ with medians $\overline{AD}$, $\overline{BE}$ and $\overline{CF}$ Prove: $AD = BE = CF$

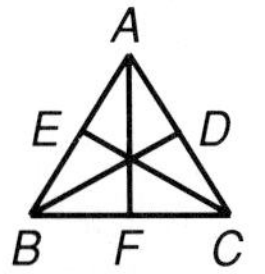

Proof: $\triangle ABC$ is equiangular. (Given) 2. $\triangle ABC$ is equilateral. (An equiangular $\triangle$ is also equilateral. [1]) 3. $AC = BC = AB$ (Def. of equilateral $\triangle$ [2]) 4. $\triangle ABC$ is an isos. $\triangle$. (Def. of isos. $\triangle$ [3]) 5. $\overline{AD}$, $\overline{BE}$ and $\overline{CF}$ are medians. (Given) 6. $AD = BE$; $BE = CF$ (The medians to the = sides of an isos. $\triangle$ are =. [3, 4, 5]) 7. $AD = BE = CF$ (Transitive Prop. [6])

28. Proof: 1. $AC = BC$; $m\angle 1 = m\angle 2$ (Given) 2. $m\angle CAE = m\angle CBE$ (Isos. $\triangle$ Thm. [1]) 3. $m\angle ACE = m\angle BCE$ (If 2 $\angle$s of one $\triangle$ are = to 2 $\angle$s of another $\triangle$, then the remaining $\angle$s are =. [1, 2]) 4. $CD = CD$ (Reflexive Prop.) 5. $\triangle CAD \cong \triangle CBD$ (SAS Post. [1, 3, 4]) 6. $m\angle CAD = m\angle CBD$ (Corr. parts of $\cong$ $\triangle$s are =. [5])

29. Proof: 1. $\overline{AB} \perp \overline{CD}$; $m\angle CAB = m\angle CBA$ (Given) 2. $\angle 1$ and $\angle 2$ are rt. $\angle$s. (2 $\perp$ lines form 4 rt. $\angle$s. [1]) 3. $m\angle 1 = m\angle 2$ (All rt. $\angle$s are =. [2]) 4. $m\angle ACD = m\angle BCD$ (If 2 $\angle$s of one $\triangle$ are = to 2 $\angle$s of another $\triangle$, then the remaining $\angle$s are =. [1, 3]) 5. $AC = BC$ (If 2 $\angle$s of a $\triangle$ are =, then the sides opp. those $\angle$s are =.) 6. $CD = CD$ (Reflexive Prop.) 7. $\triangle ACD \cong \triangle BCD$ (SAS Post. [4, 5, 6]) 8. $AD = BD$ (Corr. parts of $\cong$ $\triangle$s are =. [7]) 9. $m\angle DAB = m\angle DBA$ (Isos. $\triangle$ Thm. [8])

32. Given: Isos. $\triangle ABC$ with $AC = BC$ Prove: $\angle A$ and $\angle B$ are acute.

Proof: 1. $AC = BC$ (Given) 2. $m\angle A = m\angle B$ (Isos. $\triangle$ Thm. [1]) 3. $m\angle A + m\angle B + m\angle C = 180$ (The sum of the measures of the $\angle$s of a $\triangle$ is 180.) 4. $2(m\angle A) + m\angle C = 180$ (Substitution Prop. [2, 3]) 5. $m\angle C > 0$ (Def. of $\angle$ measure) 6. $2(m\angle A) = 2(m\angle A)$ (Reflexive Prop.) 7. $2(m\angle A) + m\angle C > 2(m\angle A)$ (Add. Prop. [5, 6]) 8. $180 > 2(m\angle A)$ (Substitution Prop. [4, 7]) 9. $90 > m\angle A$, or $m\angle A < 90$ (Mult. Prop. [8]) 10. $m\angle B < 90$ (Substitution Prop. [2, 9]) 11. $\angle A$ and $\angle B$ are acute. (Def. of acute $\angle$ [9, 10])

33. See Given and Prove on page 222.

Proof: Either (1) $\triangle ABC \cong \triangle DEF$ or (2) $\triangle ABC \not\cong \triangle DEF$. Suppose $\triangle ABC \not\cong \triangle DEF$. Then $AB \neq DE$ (If $AB = DE$, the $\triangle$s would be $\cong$ by SSS Post.). Choose G on $\overrightarrow{ED}$ so that $GE = AB$, using the Seg. Construction Post. Then $\triangle ABC \cong \triangle GEF$ by SSS Post., and $AC = FG$ by corr. parts. Since $AC = DF$, by substitution $DF = FG$. Applying the Isos. $\triangle$ Thm. to $\triangle DFG$, $m\angle D = m\angle DGF$. But $m\angle DGF > 90$ because it is an exterior $\angle$ of $\triangle GEF$ and the meas. of an exterior $\angle$ is greater than the meas. of either remote interior $\angle$. So, by substitution, $m\angle D > 90$, and $m\angle DGF + m\angle D > 180$. But this contradicts the fact that the sum of the measures of the $\angle$s of a $\triangle$ is 180. The assumption that $\triangle ABC \not\cong \triangle DEF$ is false. We conclude that $\triangle ABC \cong \triangle DEF$.

34. See Given and Prove on page 220 and diag. for Exer. 32. Proof: 1. $AC = BC$ (Given) 2. $BC = AC$ (Symmetric Prop.) 3. $AB = BA$ (Reflexive Prop.) 4. $\triangle ABC \cong \triangle BAC$ (SSS Post. [1, 2, 3]) 5. $m\angle A = m\angle B$ (Corr. parts of $\cong \triangle$s are =. [4])

Challenge

Since $\triangle ADG$ is equilateral, $m\angle GDA = m\angle GAD = m\angle DGA = 60$. Using Addition and Subtraction properties, and the fact that $ABCD$ is a square, we know that $m\angle BAE = m\angle CDE = m\angle GAE = m\angle GDE = 75$. $\triangle EAD$ has = base $\angle$s, so $ED = EA$, and $\triangle DEG \cong \triangle AEG$ by SSS Post. Thus, $m\angle DGE = m\angle AGE = 30$. By SAS Post., $\triangle CDE \cong \triangle GDE$ and $\triangle BAE \cong \triangle GAE$, and $m\angle DCE = m\angle ABE = 30$. Again, by Addition and Subtraction properties, $m\angle ECB = m\angle EBC = 60$, and $\triangle CBE$ is equilateral.

Page 229

18. Proof: 1. $LJ = MJ$; $LK < MK$ (Given) 2. $JK = JK$ (Reflexive Prop.) 3. $m\angle LJK < m\angle MJK$ (If 2 sides of 1 $\triangle$ are = to 2 sides of another $\triangle$ and the lengths of the third sides are $\neq$, then the measures of the $\angle$s included between the = sides are $\neq$ in the same order. [1, 2]) 4. $\angle LJK$ and $\angle LJN$ are supp. $\angle$s; $\angle MJK$ and $\angle MJN$ are supp. $\angle$s. (Supplement Post.) 5. $m\angle LJK + m\angle LJN = 180$; $m\angle MJK + m\angle MJN = 180$ (Def. of supp. $\angle$s [4]) 6. $m\angle LJK = 180 - m\angle LJN$; $m\angle MJK = 180 - m\angle MJN$ (Subtraction Prop. [5]) 7. $180 - m\angle LJN < 180 - m\angle MJN$ (Substitution Prop. [3, 6]) 8. $m\angle MJN < m\angle LJN$ (Add. Prop. [7])

19. Proof: 1. $\triangle ABC$ (Given) 2. Choose D on ray opp. $\overrightarrow{CB}$ so that $AC = DC$. (Seg. Construction Post.) 3. Draw $\overline{AD}$. (Line Post.) 4. $m\angle 1 = m\angle 2$ (Isos. $\triangle$ Thm. [2]) 5. $m\angle BAD = m\angle 1 + m\angle 3$ ($\angle$ Add.

Post.) 6. $m\angle BAD = m\angle 2 + m\angle 3$ (Substitution Prop. [4, 5]) 7. $m\angle 3 > 0$ (Def. of $\angle$ meas.) 8. $m\angle 2 + m\angle 3 > m\angle 2$ (Add. Prop. [7]) 9. $m\angle BAD > m\angle 2$ (Substitution Prop. [6, 8]) 10. $DB > AB$ (If the measures of 2 $\angle$s of a $\triangle$ are $\neq$, then the lengths of the sides opp. those $\angle$s are $\neq$ in the same order. [9]) 11. $DB = DC + CB$ (Seg. Add. Post.) 12. $DB = AC + CB$ (Substitution Prop. [2, 11]) 13. $AC + CB > AB$ (Substitution Prop. [10, 12])

Page 232, 233

14. Given: Plane $\mathcal{H}$ with P not in $\mathcal{H}$; $\overline{PQ} \perp \mathcal{H}$; M is any other pt. in $\mathcal{H}$ other than Q. Prove: $PM > PQ$

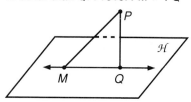

Proof: Using the Line Post., draw $\overrightarrow{MQ}$. Since M and Q are both in $\mathcal{H}$, the Flat Plane Post. ensures that $\overleftrightarrow{MQ}$ is in $\mathcal{H}$. Since $\overline{PQ} \perp \mathcal{H}$, $\overline{PQ} \perp \overleftrightarrow{MQ}$ by the def. of a line $\perp$ to a plane. Since M is not Q, $\overline{PM} \not\perp \overleftrightarrow{MQ}$ because through a pt. not on a given line, there is exactly one line $\perp$ to the given line. So $PM > PQ$ because the $\perp$ seg. from a pt. to a line is the shortest seg. from the pt. to the line.

15. At the intersection of $\overline{AB}$ and p; any other point on p will yield a sum greater than AB.

16. Chicago to Montreal: $383 < d < 1045$; Chicago to Washington: $509 < d < 919$; Montreal to Washington: $126 < d < 536$

17. Given: $AB + BC = AC$ Prove: A, B and C are collinear and B is between A and C.

Proof: Either (1) A, B and C are collinear and B is between A and

C; or (2) *A*, *B* and *C* are collinear and *B* is not between *A* and *C*; or (3) *A*, *B* and *C* are not collinear. Suppose *A*, *B* and *C* are collinear and *B* is not between *A* and *C*. Then either *A* or *C* is between the other 2 pts. If *A* is between *B* and *C*, then, by the Seg. Add. Post., $AB + AC = BC$. So, by the Subtraction Prop., $AC = BC - AB$. It is given that $AB + BC = AC$. By the Transitive Prop., $AB + BC = BC - AB$, and by the Subtraction Prop., $AB = -AB$. Since this is only true if $AB = 0$, this contradicts the Ruler Post. Hence, it is false that *A* is between *B* and *C*. Similarly, if *C* is between *A* and *B*, $AC + BC = AB$, so $AC = AB - BC$. Again, by the Transitive Prop., $AB + BC = AB - BC$, so $BC = -BC$. Since this contradicts the Ruler Post., it is false that *C* is between *A* and *B*. Next, suppose *A*, *B* and *C* are not collinear. Draw *AB*, *AC* and *BC* using the Line Post. to form △*ABC*. By the △ Inequality Thm., $AB + BC > AC$. But this contradicts the Given. So it is false that *A*, *B* and *C* are not collinear. We conclude that the only remaining possibility is true. *A*, *B* and *C* are collinear and *B* is between *A* and *C*.

18. Given: Quadrilateral *ABCD* with diagonals $\overline{AC}$ and $\overline{BD}$ Prove: $AB + BC + CD + AD > AC + BD$ Proof: By the △ Inequality Thm., $AB + BC > AC$, $CD + AD > AC$, $BC + CD > BD$ and $AB + AD > BD$. By properties of inequalities, $AB + BC + CD + AD > 2(AC)$ and $BC + CD + AB + AD > 2(BD)$. So $2(AB + BC + CD + AD) > 2(AC + BD)$. Therefore, $AB + BC + CD + AD > AC + BD$ by the Division Prop.

23. Proof: Either (1) $t \not\perp b$ or (2) $t \perp b$. Assume $t \perp b$. Since $t \perp a$, $a \parallel b$ because in a plane if 2 lines are ⊥ to the same line, then they are ∥. But this contradicts the given fact that $a \not\parallel b$. Hence, it is

false that $t \perp b$. We conclude that $t \not\perp b$.

1.

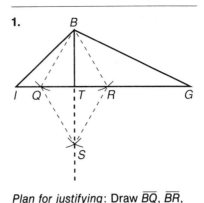

Plan for justifying: Draw $\overline{BQ}$, $\overline{BR}$, $\overline{SQ}$ and $\overline{SR}$. $BQ = BR$ and $SQ = SR$ by construction. Show △*BQS* ≅ △*BRS* by the SSS Post. Show $m\angle QBT = m\angle RBT$ and then △*QBT* ≅ △*RBT* by the SAS Post. Show $m\angle QTB = m\angle RTB$. Then $\overline{BT}$ ⊥ $\overline{IG}$ because if the ∠s in a lin. pr. are =, then the lines containing their sides are ⊥.

3. Proof: 1. $\overline{YX} \perp \overline{ZT}$; $\overline{YZ} \perp \overline{XV}$; $TW = VW$ (Given) 2. ∠*XTW* and ∠*ZVW* are rt. ∠s. (2 ⊥ lines form 4 rt. ∠s. [1]) 3. $m\angle XTW = m\angle ZVW$ (All rt. ∠s are =. [2]) 4. $m\angle TWX = m\angle VWZ$ (Vert. ∠s are =.) 5. △*TWX* ≅ △*VWZ* (ASA Post. [1, 3, 4]) 6. $WX = WZ$ (Corr. parts of ≅ △s are =. [5]) 7. $m\angle WXZ = m\angle WZX$ (Isos. △ Thm. [6])

4. Proof: 1. $XY = ZY$; $XW = ZW$ (Given) 2. $m\angle YXZ = m\angle YZX$; $m\angle TZX = m\angle VXZ$ (Isos. △ Thm. [1]) 3. $XZ = ZX$ (Reflexive Prop.) 4. △*TXZ* ≅ △*VZX* (ASA Post. [2, 3]) 5. $m\angle XTW = m\angle ZVW$ (Corr. parts of ≅ △s are =. [4]) 6. $m\angle TWX = m\angle VWZ$ (Vert. ∠s are =.) 7. △*XTW* ≅ △*ZVW* (AAS Thm. [1, 5, 6])

6. Proof: 1. $MQ = NQ$; $PN = RM$; $PQ > QR$ (Given) 2. $m\angle N > m\angle M$ (If 2 sides of one △ are = to 2 sides of another △ and the lengths of the third sides are ≠, then the measures of the ∠s included between the = sides are ≠ in the same order. [1]) 3. $LM >$

LN (If the measures of 2 ∠s of a △ are ≠, then the lengths of the sides opp. those ∠s are ≠ in the same order. [2])

7. Proof: 1. $MQ = NQ$; $PN = RM$; $LN < LM$ (Given) 2. $m\angle M < m\angle N$ (If the lengths of 2 sides of a △ are ≠, then the measures of the ∠s opp. those sides are ≠ in the same order. [1]) 3. $QR < PQ$ (Hinge Thm. [1, 2])

8. Proof: By the Seg. Add. Post., $WY = WZ + ZY$ and $VX = XZ + ZV$. Since it is given that $WY > VX$, we can substitute to get $WZ + ZY > XZ + ZV$. It is given that $WZ = XZ$, so, by the Subtraction Prop., $ZY > ZV$. It is also given that $VW = XY$, so $m\angle YXZ > m\angle VWZ$ because if 2 sides of one △ are = to 2 sides of another △ and the lengths of the third sides are ≠, then the measures of the ∠s included between the = sides are ≠ in the same order.

9. Proof: $WX = WX$ by the Reflexive Prop. and $VW = XY$ and $m\angle WXY > m\angle VWX$ by the given information. So $WY > VX$ by the Hinge Thm.

Page 236

25. Proof: 1. $m\angle 1 = m\angle 2$ (Given) 2. ∠1 and ∠*ZXY* are supp. ∠s; ∠2 and ∠*ZYX* are supp. ∠s. (Supp. Post.) 3. $m\angle ZXY = m\angle ZYX$ (Supp. of = ∠s are =. [1, 2]) 4. $XZ = YZ$ (If 2 ∠s of a △ are =, then the sides opp. those ∠s are =. [3])

26. Proof: 1. $XZ = YZ$; $\overline{ZW} \perp \overline{XY}$ (Given) 2. ∠*XWZ* and ∠*YWZ* are rt. ∠s. (2 ⊥ lines form 4 rt. ∠s. [1]) 3. △*XWZ* and △*YWZ* are rt. △s. (Def. of rt. △ [2]) 4. $ZW = ZW$ (Reflexive Prop.) 5. △*XWZ* ≅ △*YWZ* (HL Thm. [1, 3, 4]) 6. $XW = YW$ (Corr. parts of ≅ △s are =. [5]) 7. *W* is midpt. of $\overline{XY}$. (Def. of midpt. [6]) 8. $\overline{ZW}$ bisects $\overline{XY}$. (Def. of bisector of a seg. [7])

30. Proof: 1. $AD = BC$; $m\angle CAD < m\angle ACB$ (Given) 2. $AC = AC$ (Re-

flexive Prop.) 3. $CD < AB$ (Hinge Thm. [1, 2])
31. Proof: 1. $AD = BC$; $AB > CD$ (Given) 2. $AC = AC$ (Reflexive Prop.) 3. $m\angle ACB > m\angle CAD$ (If 2 sides of one $\triangle$ are = to 2 sides of another $\triangle$ and the lengths of the third sides are $\neq$, then the measures of the $\angle$s included between the = sides are $\neq$ in the same order. [1, 2])

CHAPTER 6 Pages 246–248

8. Proof: 1. $\overleftrightarrow{JK} \parallel \overleftrightarrow{ML}$; $JX = LX$ (Given) 2. $m\angle 1 = m\angle 2$ (2 lines $\parallel$ $\Rightarrow$ alt. int. $\angle$s =. [1]) 3. $m\angle LXM = m\angle JXK$ (Vert. $\angle$s are =.) 4. $\triangle LXM \cong \triangle JXK$ (AAS Thm. [1, 2, 3]) 5. $JK = ML$ (Corres. parts of $\cong$ $\triangle$s are =. [4]) 6. $JKLM$ is a ▱. (If 2 sides of a quad. are $\parallel$ and =, then the quad. is a ▱. [1, 5])
9. Proof: 1. $m\angle 1 = m\angle 2$ (Given) 2. $\overleftrightarrow{LM} \parallel \overleftrightarrow{JK}$ (Alt. int. $\angle$s = $\Rightarrow$ lines $\parallel$. [1]) 3. $m\angle MJK = m\angle KLM$ (Given) 4. $MK = MK$ (Reflexive Prop.) 5. $\triangle MKL \cong \triangle KMJ$ (AAS Thm. [1, 3, 4]) 6. $LM = JK$ (Corres. parts of $\cong$ $\triangle$s are =. [5]) 7. $JKLM$ is a ▱. (If 2 sides of a quad. are $\parallel$ and =, then the quad. is a ▱. [2, 6])
20. Proof: 1. $AX = CX$; $CY = BY$; $XY = YZ$ (Given) 2. $m\angle BYZ = m\angle CYX$ (Vert. $\angle$s are =.) 3. $\triangle BYZ \cong \triangle CYX$ (SAS $\cong$ Post. [1, 2]) 4. $m\angle YZB = m\angle YXC$; $CX = BZ$ (Corres. parts of $\cong$ $\triangle$s are =. [3]) 5. $\overline{BZ} \parallel \overline{AC}$ (Alt. int. $\angle$s = $\Rightarrow$ lines $\parallel$. [4]) 6. $AX = BZ$ (Transitive Prop. [1, 4]) 7. $ABZX$ is a ▱. (If 2 sides of a quad. are $\parallel$ and =, then the quad. is a ▱. [5, 6])
21.

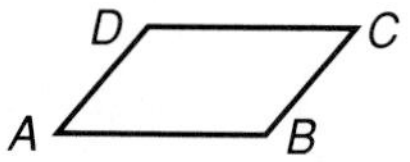

Converse of Theorem 6–2: If both pairs of opp. $\angle$s of a quad. are =, then the quad. is a ▱. Given: $m\angle A = m\angle C$; $m\angle B = m\angle D$ Prove: $ABCD$ is a ▱. Proof: 1. $m\angle A = m\angle C$; $m\angle B = m\angle D$ (Given) 2. $m\angle A + m\angle B = m\angle C + m\angle D = 360$ (The sum of the measures of the $\angle$s of a quad. = 360.) 3. $m\angle A + m\angle B + m\angle A + m\angle B = 360$, or $2(m\angle A) + 2(m\angle B) = 360$ (Substitution Prop. [1, 2]) 4. $m\angle A + m\angle B = 180$ (Div. Prop. [3]) 5. $\angle A$ and $\angle B$ are supp. $\angle$s. (Def. of supp. $\angle$s [4]) 6. $\overleftrightarrow{AD} \parallel \overleftrightarrow{BC}$ (Int. $\angle$s on same side of trans. supp. $\Rightarrow$ 2 lines $\parallel$. [5]) 7. $m\angle A + m\angle D = 180$ (Substitution Prop. [1, 4]) 8. $\angle A$ and $\angle D$ are supp. $\angle$s. (Def. of supp. $\angle$s [7]) 9. $\overleftrightarrow{AB} \parallel \overleftrightarrow{CD}$ (Int. $\angle$s on same side of trans. supp. $\Rightarrow$ 2 lines $\parallel$. [8]) 10. $ABCD$ is a ▱. (Def. of ▱ [6, 9])
22. Proof: 1. $\overleftrightarrow{XW} \perp \overleftrightarrow{AC}$; $\overleftrightarrow{YZ} \perp \overleftrightarrow{AC}$ (Given) 2. $\overleftrightarrow{WX} \parallel \overleftrightarrow{YZ}$ (In a plane, if 2 lines are $\perp$ to the same line, then they are $\parallel$. [1]) 3. $AY = CW$ (Given) 4. $AY = AW + WY$; $CW = CY + YW$ (Seg. Add. Post.) 5. $AW + WY = CY + YW$ (Substitution Prop. [3, 4]) 6. $WY = YW$ (Reflexive Prop.) 7. $AW = CY$ (Subtraction Prop. [5, 6]) 8. $\angle AWX$ and $\angle CYZ$ are rt. $\angle$s. (Def. of $\perp$ lines [1]) 9. $m\angle AWX = m\angle CYZ$ (All rt. $\angle$s are =. [8]) 10. $ABCD$ is a square. (Given) 11. $ABCD$ is a ▱. (Def. of square [10]) 12. $\overleftrightarrow{AB} \parallel \overleftrightarrow{CD}$ (Def. of ▱ [11]) 13. $m\angle XAW = m\angle YCZ$ (Lines $\parallel$ $\Rightarrow$ alt. int. $\angle$s =. [12]) 14. $\triangle AWX \cong \triangle CYZ$ (ASA $\cong$ Post. [7, 9, 13]) 15. $WX = YZ$ (Corres. parts of $\cong$ $\triangle$s are =. [14]) 16. $WXYZ$ is a ▱. (If 2 sides of a quad. are $\parallel$ and =, then the quad. is a ▱. [2, 15])
23.

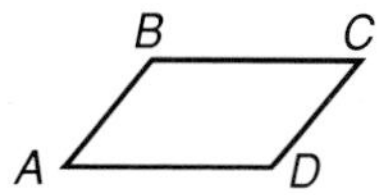

Given: $AB + BC = k$; $BC + CD = k$; $CD + AD = k$; $AD + AB = k$ where k is some real number Prove: $ABCD$ is a ▱. Proof: 1. $AB + BC = k$; $BC + CD = k$; $CD + AD = k$; $AD + AB = k$ where k is some real number. (Given) 2. $AB + BC = BC + CD$; $BC + CD = CD + DA$ (Substitution Prop. [1]) 3. $BC = BC$; $CD = CD$ (Reflexive Prop.) 4. $AB = CD$; $BC = DA$ (Subtraction Prop. [2, 3]) 5. $ABCD$ is a ▱. (If both pairs of opp. sides are =, quad. is a ▱. [4])
24.

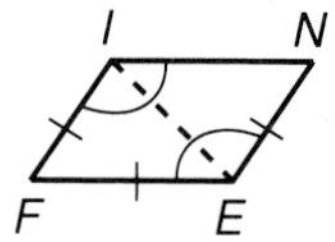

Proof: 1. Quad. $FINE$ has $IF = FE = EN$ and $m\angle FEN = m\angle FIN$. (Given) 2. Draw $\overleftrightarrow{IE}$. (Line Post.) 3. $m\angle FIE = m\angle FEI$ (If 2 sides of a $\triangle$ are =, then the $\angle$s opp. them are =. [1]) 4. $m\angle FIN = m\angle FIE + m\angle NIE$; $m\angle FEN = m\angle FEI + m\angle NEI$ (Angle Add. Post.) 5. $m\angle FIE + m\angle NIE = m\angle FEI + m\angle NEI$ (Substitution Prop. [1, 4]) 6. $m\angle NIE = m\angle NEI$ (Subtraction Prop. [3, 5]) 7. $IN = EN$ (If 2 $\angle$s of a $\triangle$ are =, then the sides opp. them are =. [6]) 8. $FE = IN$ (Substitution Prop. [1, 6]) 9. $FINE$ is a ▱. (If both pairs of opp. sides of a quad. are =, then the quad. is a ▱. [1, 8])
25. Yes. 1) Since the slopes of opp. sides are =, both pairs of opp. sides are $\parallel$. 2) Solving systems of linear equations, the vertices of the quad. are $A(10, 6)$, $B(8, 11)$, $C(4, 7)$ and $D(6, 2)$. Then the Distance Formula gives $AB = CD = \sqrt{29}$ and $BC = AD = 4\sqrt{2}$.
31. rectangle

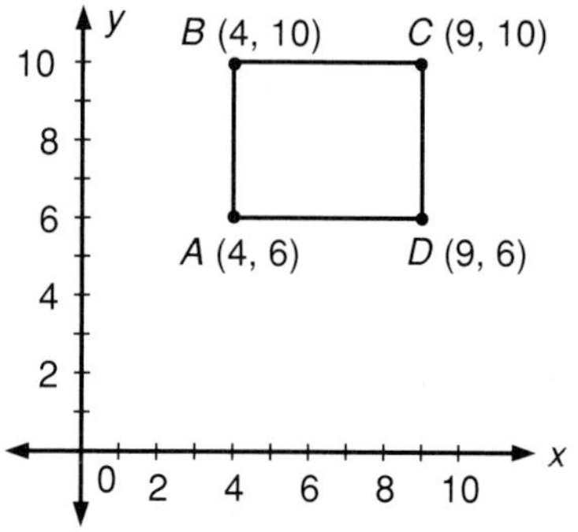

32. square

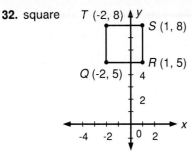

33. rhombus

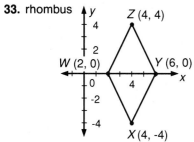

Pages 251–254

2. *Part I:* If the diags. of a ▱ are ⊥ (hypothesis), then it is a rhombus (conclusion). *Part II:* If a ▱ is a rhombus (hypothesis), then its diags. are ⊥ (conclusion).

6. *Part I:* If each diag. of a ▱ bisects the opp. ∠s of the ▱ (hypothesis), then the ▱ is a rhombus (conclusion). *Part II:* If a ▱ is a rhombus (hypothesis), then each diag. bisects a pr. of opp. ∠s (conclusion).

7. If the diags. bisect each other, then the quad. is a ▱; if the diags. of a ▱ are ⊥, then the ▱ is a rhombus.

24.

A B
D C
(with diagonals intersecting at E, angles labeled 1, 2, 5, 6, 7, 8, 3, 4)

Part I: Given: ▱ABCD; $\overline{AC}$ bisects ∠BAD and ∠DCB; $\overline{BD}$ bisects ∠ABC and ∠ADC. Prove: ABCD is a rhombus. Proof: By hypothesis, $\overline{AC}$ bisects ∠BAD and DCB, and $\overline{BD}$ bisects ∠ABC and ∠ADC in ▱ABCD. Since ∠DAC and ∠BCD are opp. ∠s of a ▱ and both ∠s

are bisected, $m∠2 = m∠4$. Then $AB = BC$ because in a △, if 2 ∠s are =, the sides opp. them are =. Since ABCD is a ▱, $AB = DC$ and $AD = BC$. Therefore, by the Substitution Prop., $AB = BC = DC = AD$. Thus, ▱ABCD is a rhombus since it is a ▱ with 4 = sides. *Part II:* Given: ABCD is a rhombus. Prove: $\overline{AC}$ bisects ∠BAD and ∠DCB; $\overline{BD}$ bisects ∠ABC and ∠ADC. Proof: Since ABCD is a rhombus, $AB = CB = DA = DC$. Then $m∠2 = m∠4$, $m∠1 = m∠3$, $m∠5 = m∠7$ and $m∠6 = m∠8$. (In a △, ∠s opp. = sides are =.) Also, $\overline{AB} ∥ \overline{DC}$ and $\overline{AD} ∥ \overline{BC}$ implies that $m∠2 = m∠3$, $m∠5 = m∠8$, $m∠1 = m∠4$ and $m∠6 = m∠7$ since alt. int. ∠s are =. Using the Substitution Prop. gives $m∠1 = m∠2$, $m∠3 = m∠4$, $m∠5 = m∠6$ and $m∠7 = m∠8$. Therefore, $\overline{AC}$ bisects ∠BAD and ∠DCB, and $\overline{BD}$ bisects ∠ABC and ∠ADC by the def. of ∠ bisector.

25. Rhombus. Since the slope of $\overline{AB}$ = slope of $\overline{DC} = \frac{1}{5}$ and the slope of $\overline{AD}$ = slope $\overline{BC} = 5$, $\overline{AB} ∥ \overline{DC}$ and $\overline{AD} ∥ \overline{BC}$. By the Dist. Formula $AB = BC = CD = DA = \sqrt{26}$. Therefore, ABCD is a rhombus by definition. Since the slopes of $\overline{AC}$ and $\overline{BD}$ are neg. reciprocals of each other, $\overline{AC} ⊥ \overline{BD}$ and ABCD is a rhombus by Thm. 6–9.

26. Square. Since the slope of $\overline{EF}$ = slope of $\overline{GH} = 1$ and the slope of $\overline{FG}$ = slope $\overline{EH} = 1$, $\overline{EF} ∥ \overline{GH}$, $\overline{FG} ∥ \overline{EH}$, $\overline{EF} ⊥ \overline{FG}$, $\overline{FG} ⊥ \overline{GH}$, $\overline{GH} ⊥ \overline{HE}$ and $\overline{HE} ⊥ \overline{EF}$. Therefore, ∠E, ∠F, ∠G and ∠H are rt. ∠s and by def. EFGH is a rect. But $EF = FG = GH = EH = 3\sqrt{2}$. Since EFGH is a rect. with 4 = sides, EFGH is a square by def. of a square. Since $\overline{EG}$ is a vert. line and $\overline{FH}$ is a horizontal line, $\overline{EG} ⊥ \overline{FH}$. By Thm. 6–9, EFGH is a rhombus. A rhombus with 4 rt. ∠s is a square.

28. Proof: 1. HELP is a rect. (Given) 2. HELP is a ▱. (Def. of ▱

[1]) 3. $HE = LP$ (Opp. sides of a ▱ are =. [2]) 4. $\overline{OA} ⊥ \overline{LP}$ (Given) 5. $\overline{HE} ∥ \overline{LP}$ (Def. of ▱ [2]) 6. $\overline{OA} ⊥ \overline{HE}$ (In a plane, if a line is ⊥ to one of 2 ∥ lines, then it is ⊥ to the other. [4, 5]) 7. ∠HOA, ∠EOA, ∠PAO and ∠LAO are rt. ∠s. (Def. ⊥ segs. [4, 6]) 8. ∠OHP, ∠HPA, ∠OEL and ∠ALE are rt. ∠s. (Def. of rect. [1]) 9. $\overline{HP} ∥ \overline{EL}$ (Def. of ▱ [2]) 10. $\overline{HP} ⊥ \overline{PL}$; $\overline{EL} ⊥ \overline{PL}$ (Def. ⊥ segs. [8]) 11. $\overline{OA} ∥ \overline{HP}$; $\overline{OA} ∥ \overline{EL}$ (In a plane, if 2 lines are ⊥ to the same line, then they are ∥. [4, 10]) 12. HOAP and EOAL are ▱s. (Def. ▱ [5, 11]) 13. HOAP and EOAL are rects. (Def. of rect. [7, 8, 12]) 14. $PO = HA$ and $OL = EA$ (Diags. of a rect. are =. [13]) 15. △HAE ≅ △POL (SSS ≅ Post. [3, 14])

29. By measuring to see that its diags. are = and its opp. sides are =

30. Proof: Since ABCD is a rect., $AC = BD$. By the Seg. Add. Post. and the Substitution Prop., $AX + XC = BX + XD$. Since ABCD is also a ▱, $\overline{AC}$ and $\overline{BD}$ bisect each other. Thus, $AX = CX$ and $DX = BX$.

Therefore, $XC + XC = BX + BX$
$$2XC = 2BX$$
$$XC = BX$$

By hypothesis, $BC = DX$. Then $BC = BX$ by the Substitution Prop. Therefore, $BC = BX = XC$. △BCX is equilateral. Therefore, △BCX is equiangular and $m∠BXC = 60$.

31.

Given: △ABC is a rt. △ with hypotenuse $\overline{AB}$; $\overline{CM}$ is the median to $\overline{AB}$. Prove: $CM = \left(\frac{1}{2}\right)AB$ Proof: 1. △ABC is a rt. △. (Given) 2. ∠ACB is a rt. ∠. (Def. of rt. △ [1]) 3. Extend $\overrightarrow{CM}$ to pt. X so that $CM = MX$. (Seg. Construction Post.) 4. Draw $\overline{AX}$ and $\overline{BX}$. (Line Post.) 5. $\overline{CM}$ is the median to $\overline{AB}$. (Given) 6. M is the midpt. of $\overline{AB}$. (Def. of

median [4]) 7. *AM = MB* (Def. of midpt. [5]) 8. $\overline{CX}$ and $\overline{AB}$ bisect each other. (Def. of seg. bisector [3, 7]) 9. *AXBC* is a $\square$. (If the diags. of a quad. bisect each other, then the quad. is a $\square$. [8]) 10. $\overline{AC} \parallel \overline{BX}$; $\overline{AX} \parallel \overline{CB}$ (Def. of $\square$ [9]) 11. $\overline{BC} \perp \overline{AC}$ (Def. of $\perp$ segs. [2]) 12. $\overline{AC} \perp \overline{XA}$ (In a plane, if a line is $\perp$ to 1 of 2 $\parallel$ lines, then it is $\perp$ to the other. [10, 11]) 13. $\overline{BX} \perp \overline{XA}$ (In a plane, if a line is $\perp$ to 1 of 2 $\parallel$ lines, then it is $\perp$ to the other. [10, 12]) 14. $\overline{BX} \perp \overline{BC}$ (In a plane, if a line is $\perp$ to 1 of 2 $\parallel$ lines, then it is $\perp$ to the other. [10, 13]) 15. $\angle CAX$, $\angle AXB$ and $\angle XBC$ are rt. $\angle$s. (Def. $\perp$ segs. [12, 13, 14]) 16. *AXBC* is a rect. (Def. of rect. [2, 9, 15]) 17. *CX = AB* (Diags. of a rect. are =. [16]) 18. *CX = CM + MX* (Seg. Add. Post. [3]) 19. *CM + MX = AB* (Substitution Prop. [17, 18]) 20. *CM + CM = AB* or 2*CM = AB* (Substitution Prop. [3, 19]) 21. *CM* = $(\frac{1}{2})AB$ (Multiplication Prop. [20])
32. 1) $\overline{PQ} \parallel \overline{RS}$ and $\overline{PS} \parallel \overline{QR}$; 2) *PQ = SR* and *PS = QR*; 3) $\overline{PQ} \parallel \overline{RS}$ and *PQ = RS*; 4) $\overline{PR}$ and $\overline{QS}$ bisect each other.
34. The distance between 2 given $\parallel$ lines is constant.

```
6.   TO RHOMBUS :DIAG1
        :DIAG2
     CT CG
     PU SETPOS [-1/2*
     :DIAG1 0] PD
     SETPOS [0 1/2*
     :DIAG2] SETPOS
     [1/2*:DIAG1 0]
     SETPOS [0 -1/2*
     :DIAG2] SETPOS
     [-1/2*:DIAG1 0]
     END
```

Page 256

1. SAS $\cong$ Post. (*XY = YZ*; *m*$\angle$*CYX* = *m*$\angle$*BYZ*; *CY = YB*)
2. If a quad. is a $\square$, then both pairs of opp. sides are =.

7. She drew 3 = segs. on a working line and then drew lines through the endpts. of these segs. $\parallel$ to the given line through *B*. By Thm. 6–12, *AP = PQ = QB*.
8. No; the measure of the $\angle$ is irrelevant as long as the segs. are constructed $\parallel$ to the ray through pt. *B*.

Pages 258, 259

23. Draw diag. $\overline{AC}$. In $\triangle ACD$, $\overline{ZY} \parallel \overline{AC}$ and in $\triangle CAB$, $\overline{WX} \parallel \overline{AC}$ by Thm. 6–11. Then $\overline{ZY} \parallel \overline{WX}$ (Two lines $\parallel$ to same line are $\parallel$ to each other). Draw diag. $\overline{BD}$. In $\triangle ABD$, $\overline{ZW} \parallel \overline{BD}$ and in $\triangle CDB$, $\overline{XY} \parallel \overline{BD}$. Therefore, $\overline{ZW} \parallel \overline{XY}$. Thus, *WXYZ* is a $\square$ by the def. of a $\square$.
24. From Exercise 23, *WXYZ* is a $\square$. Using Thm. 6–11, *WX = ZY* = $(\frac{1}{2})AC$ and *WZ = XY* = $(\frac{1}{2})BD$. Since *ABCD* is a rect., *AC = BD* and by the Mult. Prop., $(\frac{1}{2})AC = \frac{1}{2}(BD)$. Therefore, *WZ = ZY = WZ = XY*. Then *WXYZ* is a rhombus by def.
27. Proof: 1. In quad. *HIJK*, *X, Y, Z* and *W* are the midpts. of the sides $\overline{HI}$, $\overline{IJ}$, $\overline{JK}$ and $\overline{KH}$, respectively. (Given) 2. Draw $\overline{KI}$. (Two pts. determine a line.) 3. $\overleftrightarrow{WX} \parallel \overleftrightarrow{KI}$; $\overleftrightarrow{ZY} \parallel \overleftrightarrow{KI}$ (The seg. joining the midpts. of 2 sides of a $\triangle$ is $\parallel$ to the 3rd side. [1, 2]) 4. $\overleftrightarrow{WX} \parallel \overleftrightarrow{ZY}$ (If 2 lines are $\parallel$ to the same line, then they are $\parallel$ to each other. [3])
28. Given: Quad. *HIJK* with *X, Y, Z* and *W*, the midpts. of sides $\overline{HI}$, $\overline{IJ}$, $\overline{JK}$, $\overline{KH}$, respectively Prove: *WXYZ* is a $\square$. Proof: 1. In quad. *HIJK*, *X, Y, Z* and *W* are midpts. of sides $\overline{HI}$, $\overline{IJ}$, $\overline{JK}$ and $\overline{KH}$, respectively. (Given) 2. Draw $\overline{KI}$. (Two pts. determine a line.) 3. $\overleftrightarrow{WX} \parallel \overline{KI}$; $\overleftrightarrow{ZY} \parallel \overline{KI}$; *WX* = $\frac{1}{2}(KI)$; *ZY* = $\frac{1}{2}(KI)$ 4. $\overleftrightarrow{WX} \parallel \overleftrightarrow{ZY}$ (Two lines $\parallel$ to same line are $\parallel$ to each other. [3]) 5. *WX = ZY* (Substitution Prop. [3]) 6. *WXYZ* is a $\square$. (If pair of opp. sides is $\parallel$ and =, quad. is $\square$. [4, 5])

29.

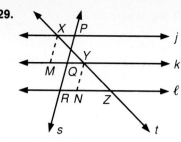

Proof: 1. *j* $\parallel$ *k* $\parallel$ ℓ; *s* and *t* are trans.; *PQ = QR* (Given) 2. Draw $\overline{XM} \parallel$ *s* and $\overline{YN} \parallel$ *s*. (Through a pt. not on a given line, there is exactly 1 line $\parallel$ to the given line.) 3. *MXPQ* and *RQYN* are $\square$s. (Def. of $\square$ [1, 2]) 4. *QR = YN*; *PQ = XM* (Opp. sides of $\square$ are =. [3]) 5. *PQ = YN* (Transitive Prop. [1, 4]) 6. *XM = YN* (Substitution Prop. [4, 5]) 7. *m*$\angle$*XYM = m*$\angle$*YZN* (Lines $\parallel$ $\Rightarrow$ corres. $\angle$s =. [1]) 8. $\overline{XM} \parallel \overline{YN}$ (2 lines $\parallel$ to same line are $\parallel$ to each other. [2]) 9. *m*$\angle$*MXY = m*$\angle$*NYZ* (Lines $\parallel$ $\Rightarrow$ corres. $\angle$s =. [8]) 10. $\triangle MXY \cong \triangle NYZ$ (AAS Thm. [6, 7, 9]) 11. *XY = YZ* (Corres. parts of $\cong$ $\triangle$s are =. [10])
30.

Given: *X* is midpt. of $\overline{AC}$; ℓ contains *X*; $\ell \parallel \overline{BC}$ Prove: ℓ contains the midpt. of $\overline{AB}$. Proof: 1. *X* is midpt. of $\overline{AC}$; ℓ contains *X*; $\ell \parallel \overline{BC}$ (Given) 2. Let *Y* be the midpt. of $\overline{AB}$. (A segment has exactly 1 midpt.) 3. Draw $\overline{XY}$. (2 pts. determine a line.) 4. $\overline{XY} \parallel \overline{BC}$ (Segment joining midpts. of two sides of a $\triangle$ is $\parallel$ to the third side.) 5. *XY* and ℓ are the same line. (Through a pt. *X* not on a given line $\overleftrightarrow{CB}$ there is exactly 1 line $\parallel$ to the given line. [1, 4]) 6. ℓ contains the midpt. of $\overline{AB}$. (Substitution [2, 3, 5])
31. By the Midpoint Formula, the coordinates of *D* and *E* are (($x + x_1$)/2, ($y + y_1$)/2) and (($x_1 + x_2$)/2, ($y_1 + y_2$)/2), respectively. Then by the Distance Formula,

$DE = (\sqrt{(x_2 - x_1)^2 + (y_2 - y_1)^2})/2$ and $AC = \sqrt{(x_2 - x_1)^2 + (y_2 - y_1)^2}$. Thus, $DE = \frac{1}{2}AC$.

32. They are ⊥; they bisect each other; they bisect the opp. ∠s of the rhombus.

34. Proof: 1. D is the midpt. of $\overline{MJ}$. (Given) 2. $DM = DJ$ (Def. of midpt. [1]) 3. $m\angle 1 = m\angle 2$ (Given) 4. $\overline{HJ} \parallel \overline{MK}$ (Alt. int. ∠s = ⇒ lines ∥. [3]) 5. $m\angle HDJ = m\angle KDM$ (Vert. ∠s are =.) 6. $\triangle HDJ \cong \triangle KDM$ (ASA ≅ Post. [2, 3, 5]) 7. $HJ = MK$ (Corres. parts of ≅ △s are =. [6]) 8. $HJKM$ is a ▱. (If 2 sides of a quad. are both ∥ and =, then the quad. is a ▱. [4, 7])

37. The slope of $\overline{AD}$, which is -3, $\neq$ the slope of $\overline{BC}$, which is 3/2.

39. The slope of $\overline{PQ}$, which is 2/3, $\neq$ slope of $\overline{SR}$, which is $-1/3$; $QR = 10$; $PS = 4$; the coordinates of the midpts. are (2, 4) and (2, −3) and the length of the segment joining them is 7.

Pages 263–265

6. Since $\overline{WX} \parallel \overline{ZY}$ and $\overline{ZW}$ is a transversal, $\angle Z$ and $\angle W$ are interior ∠s on the same side of the transversal. 2 lines ∥ ⇒ int. ∠s on same side of trans. supp.

30.

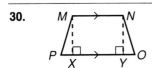

Given: Trap. $MNOP$ with $\overline{MN} \parallel \overline{OP}$ and $m\angle O = m\angle P$ Prove: $MNOP$ is isos. trap. Proof: 1. Trap. $MNOP$ has $\overline{MN} \parallel \overline{OP}$ and $m\angle O = m\angle P$. (Given) 2. Draw $\overline{MX} \perp \overline{PO}$ and $\overline{NY} \perp \overline{PO}$. (Through a pt. not on a given line, there is exactly 1 line ⊥ to the given line.) 3. $\angle MXP$ and $\angle NYO$ are rt. ∠s. (2 ⊥ lines form 4 rt. ∠s. [2]) 4. $m\angle MXP = m\angle NYO$ (All rt. ∠s are =. [3]) 5. $MX = NY$ (Distance between 2 ∥ lines is constant. [1, 2]) 6. $\triangle MXP \cong \triangle NYO$ (AAS Thm. [1, 4, 5]) 7. $MP = NO$ (Corres. parts of ≅ △s are =.

[6]) **8.** $MNOP$ is isos. trap. (Def. of isos. trap. [1, 7])

Pages 270–272

4. The locus is a ray that bisects the ∠, excluding its endpoint.

5. The locus is the 2 pts. at which $\odot B$ intersects the ⊥ bisector of $\overline{AB}$.

6. The locus is a single point on $\overline{PQ}$ where the circles touch.

7. The locus is a sphere with radius 3 cm and center P.

8. There is no locus that satisfies the conditions.

---

10. The locus is a sphere of radius 50 mi. with its center at the television station and all pts. in the interior of the sphere, excluding any pts. which are in the ground.

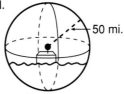

11. In a plane, what is the locus of pts. equidistant from ∥ lines ℓ and k?

12. In a plane, what is the locus of pts. equidistant from the vertices of rect. $ABCD$?

13. What is the locus of pts. equidistant from the vertices of square $WXYZ$?

14. In a plane, what is the locus

of pts. x units from line a?

15. What is the locus of pts. 3 cm from line ℓ?

16. What is the locus of pts. 5 cm from a given plane?

17.

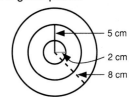

18.

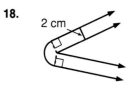

19.

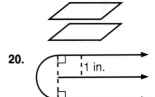

20.

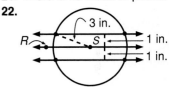

21. There is no locus of points.

22.

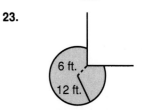

23.

24. at the pt(s). of intersection of the ⊥ bisector of the seg. between the pole and the tree, and a circle with a radius of 20 paces and center at the pole

27. Depending on the orientation of the 2 pts., the locus may be (a) 2 pts., (b) no pts. or (c) infinitely many pts.

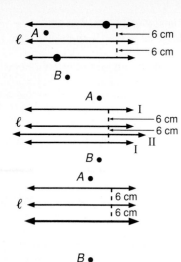

28. The median of a trap. is the seg. joining the midpts. of the 2 non-∥ sides.

29. They both have = legs and = base ∠s.

31.

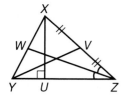

Pages 275–277

2. Proof: *Part I*: 1. ℓ is the ⊥ bisector of $\overline{AB}$; *P* lies on ℓ. (Given) 2. Draw $\overline{PA}$ and $\overline{PB}$. (Two pts. determine a line.) 3. *M* is the midpt. of $\overline{AB}$. (Def. of seg. bisector [1]) 4. *AM* = *BM* (Def. of midpt. [3]) 5. ∠*PMA* and ∠*PMB* are rt. ∠s. (2 ⊥ lines form 4 rt. ∠s. [1]) 6. *m*∠*PMA* = *m*∠*PMB* (All rt. ∠s are =. [5]) 7. *PM* = *PM* (Reflexive Prop.) 8. △*PMA* ≅ △*PMB* (SAS ≅ Post. [4, 6, 7]) 9. *PA* = *PB* (Corres. parts of ≅ △s are =. [8]) *Part II*: 1. *QA* = *QB*; ℓ is the ⊥ bisector of $\overline{AB}$. (Given) 2. *M* is the midpt. of $\overline{AB}$. (Def. of seg. bisector [1]) 3. *AM* = *BM* (Def. of midpt. [2]) 4. *QM* = *QM* (Reflexive Prop.) 5. △*AQM* ≅ △*BQM* (SSS ≅ Post. [1, 3, 4]) 6. *m*∠*QMA* = *m*∠*QMB* (Corres. parts of ≅ △s are =. [5]) 7. $\overline{QM}$ ⊥ $\overline{AB}$ at *M* (If the ∠s of a linear pair are

=, then the lines containing them are ⊥. [6]) 8. *Q* is on ℓ. (In a plane, through a pt. on a given line, there is exactly 1 line ⊥ to the given line. [1, 2, 7])

3. *Part I*: In a plane, if a point is equidistant from two parallel lines, then it is on a line parallel to the given lines at half the distance between them. *Part II*: If a point is on a line parallel to and half the distance between two parallel lines, then it is equidistant from the given lines.

4.

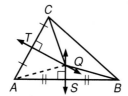

Part I: Given: *a* ∥ *b*; *a* ∥ *k*; *b* ∥ *k*; *P* is equidistant from *a* and *b*; $\overline{QR}$ ⊥ *a*; $\overline{QR}$ ⊥ *b*; $\overline{QR}$ ⊥ *k*; *RS* = *SQ* Prove: *P* is on *k*. *Part II*: Given: *a* ∥ *b*; *k* ∥ *a*; *k* ∥ *b*; *P* is on *k*; $\overline{QR}$ ⊥ *a*; $\overline{QR}$ ⊥ *b*; $\overline{QR}$ ⊥ *k*; *RS* = *SQ* Prove: *P* is equidistant from *a* and *b*.

19.

Given: $\overleftrightarrow{SQ}$ is the ⊥ bisector of $\overline{AB}$; $\overleftrightarrow{TQ}$ is the ⊥ bisector of $\overline{AC}$. Prove: *BQ* = *CQ* Proof: 1. $\overleftrightarrow{SQ}$ is the ⊥ bisector of $\overline{AB}$; $\overleftrightarrow{TQ}$ is the ⊥ bisector of $\overline{AC}$. (Given) 2. Draw $\overline{QA}$. (Two pts. determine a line.) 3. *BQ* = *AQ*; *CQ* = *AQ* (If a pt. is on the ⊥ bisector of a seg., then it is equidistant from the endpts. of that seg. [1]) 4. *BQ* = *CQ* (Substitution Prop. [3])

20. Proof: By hypothesis, ℓ is ⊥ to both *m* and *n*, which lie in plane *ε*. Draw any line in *ε* through *X* and call it *k*. By the Seg. Con-

struction Post., choose pts. *A* and *B* on ℓ so that *AX* = *BX*. Then by the def. of a ⊥ bisector of a seg. *m* and *n* are both ⊥ bisectors of $\overline{AB}$. Choose pt. *C* on *m* and pt. *D* on *n*. Draw $\overline{CD}$ and label its pt. of intersection with *k* pt. *Y*. *AC* = *BC* and *AD* = *BD* because if a pt. lies on the ⊥ bisector of a seg., then it is equidistant from the endpts. of the seg. Since *CD* = *CD*, △*ACD* ≅ △*BCD* by SSS ≅ Post., and then since *m*∠*BCY* = *m*∠*ACY* and *CY* = *CY*, △*ACY* ≅ △*BCY* by SAS ≅ Post. Then *AY* = *BY*, which means that *k* is ⊥ bisector of $\overline{AB}$ in the plane of *A*, *Y* and *B*. (In a plane, a pt. equidistant from the endpts. of a seg. lies on the ⊥ bisector of the seg.) Thus, ℓ ⊥ *k* by def. of ⊥ bisector. Then by the def. of a line ⊥ to a plane, ℓ ⊥ *ε*.

21. Given: Plane *ε* ⊥ line *k* at *P* Prove: *ε* contains all lines ⊥ to *k* at *P*. Proof: Either *ε* contains all lines ⊥ to *k* at *P* or *ε* does not contain all lines ⊥ to *k* at *P*. Suppose *ε* does not contain all lines ⊥ to *k* at *P*. Let *q* be a line, not in *ε*, that is ⊥ to *k* at *P*. Let *ℱ* be the plane that contains lines *k* and *q* (2 intersecting lines determine a plane); then *ℱ* and *ε* intersect in line ℓ, and ℓ contains *P* because *P* is in *ε* and *ℱ*. Since ℓ is in *ε*, ℓ ⊥ *k* at *P*; thus ℓ and *q* are 2 lines in *ℱ* ⊥ to *k* at *P*. But this contradicts the fact that in a plane, through a given pt. on a given line, there exists exactly 1 line ⊥ to the given line. Therefore, the assumption that *ε* does not contain all lines ⊥ *k* at *P* is false. We conclude that *ε* contains all lines ⊥ to *k* at *P*.

22.

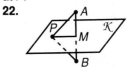

Given: *𝒦* ⊥ $\overline{AB}$ at *M*; *M* is the midpt. of $\overline{AB}$; *P* is equidistant from *A* and *B*. Prove: *P* lies in *𝒦*. Proof:

1. $\mathcal{K} \perp \overline{AB}$ at M; M is the midpt. of $\overline{AB}$; P is equidistant from A and B. (Given) 2. $AM = BM$ (Def. of midpt. [1]) 3. $AP = BP$ (Def. of equidistant [1]) 4. $PM = PM$ (Reflexive Prop.) 5. $\triangle APM \cong \triangle BPM$ (SSS Post. [2, 3, 4]) 6. $m\angle PMA = m\angle PMB$ (Corres. parts of $\cong \triangle$s are =. [5]) 7. $\overline{PM} \perp \overline{AB}$ (If the $\angle$s in a lin. pr. are =, then the lines containing their sides are $\perp$.) 8. $\mathcal{K}$ contains $\overline{PM}$ and P lies in $\mathcal{K}$ (If a plane is $\perp$ to a line at a given pt., then the plane contains all lines $\perp$ to the given line at the given pt.).

23. The locus is 2 lines that are ∥ to the given line and 5 cm from the given line.

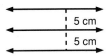

24. The locus is a cylindrical surface determined by all circles with centers on the given line and with radius 5 cm, and the plane of each circle is $\perp$ to the given line.

4. The locus of points is 2 lines ∥ to the given line and 3 in. on either side of the given line.

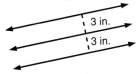

5. If $\mathcal{F}$ is the plane determined by 2 given ∥ lines and line ℓ is the set of pts. in $\mathcal{F}$ equidistant from them, then the locus of points equidistant from the given ∥ lines is plane $\mathcal{E}$ which contains ℓ and is $\perp$ to $\mathcal{F}$.
6. The locus of pts. is a line that is $\perp$ to the plane of the $\triangle$ and contains the pt. of intersection of the bisectors of the $\angle$s of the $\triangle$.
7. The locus of points is a horizontal line represented by the equation $y = 3$.
8. To prove a locus theorem, you must show that: (1) if a pt. is on the locus, then it must satisfy the given condition(s), and (2) if a pt. satisfies the given condition(s), then it is on the locus.

Page 280

31. The locus of pts. is the seg. joining the midpts. of the other 2 sides of the rect.
32. *Part I:* If a pt. is on a sphere with a given pt. as the center and a given distance as the radius of the sphere, then the distance from the pt. to the given pt. is the given distance. *Part II:* If a pt. is a given distance from a given pt., then it lies on the sphere with the given pt. as center and the given distance as the radius of the sphere.

Part I: Given: Sphere with center P and radius r; X is a pt. on the sphere. Prove: $PX = r$ *Part II:* Given: Sphere with center P and radius r; $PX = r$ Prove: X is a pt. on the sphere.

CHAPTER 7   Pages 295, 296

26. Given: Pentagon $ABCDE \sim$ pentagon $VWXYZ$ Prove: $\frac{\text{Perimeter } ABCDE}{\text{Perimeter } VWXYZ} = \frac{AB}{VW}$ Proof: 1. Pentagon $ABCDE \sim$ pentagon $VWXYZ$ (Given) 2. $\frac{AB}{VW} = \frac{BC}{WX} = \frac{CD}{XY} = \frac{DE}{YZ} = \frac{EA}{ZV}$ (Def. of similar polygons [1]) 3. $\frac{AB + BC + CD + DE + EA}{VW + WX + XY + YZ + ZV} = \frac{AB}{VW}$ (Summation Prop. of Prop. [2]) 4. $AB + BC + CD + DE + EA = \text{perimeter } ABCDE$; $VW + WX + XY + YZ + ZV = \text{perimeter } VWXYZ$ (Def. of perimeter) 5. $\frac{\text{Perimeter } ABCDE}{\text{Perimeter } VWXYZ} = \frac{AB}{VW}$ (Substitution Prop. [3, 4])

29. two lines parallel to $y = x + 5$: $y = x + (5 + 8\sqrt{2})$ and $y = x + (5 - 8\sqrt{2})$
30. All properties of a parallelogram; four equal sides; diagonals that are perpendicular and that bisect pairs of opposite angles
32. The ratios are equal.
33. Regardless of size, ratios are equal.
34. If two angles of one triangle are equal to two angles of another, then the triangles are similar.

Pages 298–300

1. No; the measures of corresponding angles are not equal.
2. Yes; the measures of corresponding angles are equal. (AA $\sim$ Post.)
3. No; lengths of only two pairs of corresponding sides are equal.
4. Yes; the measures of corresponding angles are equal. (AA $\sim$ Post.)

13. Proof: 1. $\triangle MNP$; $MP = NP$; $\overline{RT} \perp \overline{PN}$; $\overline{RS} \perp \overline{PM}$ (Given) 2. $m\angle M = m\angle N$ (Isos. $\triangle$ Thm. [1]) 3. $\angle RSM$ and $\angle RTN$ are rt. $\angle$s. (2 $\perp$ lines form 4 rt. $\angle$s. [1]) 4. $m\angle RSM = m\angle RTN$ (All rt. $\angle$s. are =. [3]) 5. $\triangle MRS \sim \triangle NRT$ (AA $\sim$ Post. [2, 4]) 6. $\frac{RM}{RN} = \frac{RS}{RT}$ (Def. of $\sim$ polygons [5]) 7. $(RM)(RT) = (RN)(RS)$ (Multiplication Prop. [6])
14. Proof: 1. $\triangle XYZ$; $m\angle Z = m\angle WXY$ (Given) 2. $m\angle Y = m\angle Y$ (Reflexive Prop.) 3. $\triangle YXW \sim \triangle YZX$ (AA $\sim$ Post. [1, 2]) 4. $\frac{YW}{YX} = \frac{YX}{YZ}$ (Def. of $\sim$ polygons [3]) 5. $(YW)(YZ) = (YX)(YX)$ (Multiplication Prop. [4])
21. $m\angle V = m\angle X$; $m\angle W = m\angle Y$; $m\angle V + m\angle W = 180$; $m\angle W + m\angle X = 180$; $m\angle X + m\angle Y = 180$; $m\angle Y + m\angle V = 180$
22. If the vertex angles of two isosceles triangles are equal, then the triangles are similar; if two isosceles triangles are similar, then their vertex angles are equal; yes; yes

25. If three parallel lines intersect two transversals, then the parallel lines divide the transversals so that lengths of corresponding segments are proportional.

1. Sample:

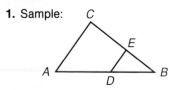

3. If a line parallel to one side of a triangle intersects the other two sides, the lengths of the corresponding segments are proportional.

Page 307

35. Proof: 1. $\square ABCD$; $\overline{TV}$, $\overline{PR}$, $\overline{AC}$ pass through O; $\overline{TP} \perp \overline{AC}$ (Given) 2. $\overline{AD} \parallel \overline{BC}$; $\overline{AB} \parallel \overline{DC}$ (Def. of $\square$ [1]) 3. $m\angle ATO = m\angle CVO$ (2 lines $\parallel \Rightarrow$ alt. int. $\angle$s =. [2]) 4. $m\angle TOA = m\angle VOC$ (Vert. $\angle$s are =.) 5. $\triangle TOA \sim \triangle VOC$ (AA $\sim$ Post. [3, 4]) 6. $m\angle APO = m\angle CRO$ (2 lines $\parallel \Rightarrow$ alt. int. $\angle$s =. [2]) 7. $m\angle AOP = m\angle COR$ (Vert. $\angle$s are =.) 8. $\triangle AOP \sim \triangle COR$ (AA $\sim$ Post. [6, 7]) 9. $\frac{TO}{VO} = \frac{AO}{CO}$; $\frac{AO}{CO} = \frac{PO}{RO}$ (Def. of $\sim$ polygons [5, 8]) 10. $\frac{TO}{VO} = \frac{PO}{RO}$ (Transitive Prop. [9]) 11. $m\angle TOP = m\angle VOR$ (Vert. $\angle$s are =.) 12. $\triangle TOP \sim \triangle VOR$ (SAS $\sim$ Post. [10, 11]) 13. $m\angle TOP = m\angle VRO$ (Def. of $\sim$ polygons [12]) 14. $\overline{TP} \parallel \overline{RV}$ (Alt. int. $\angle$s = $\Rightarrow$ 2 lines $\parallel$. [13]) 15. $\overline{RV} \perp \overline{AC}$ (If a transversal is $\perp$ to one of 2 $\parallel$ lines, then it is $\perp$ to the other. [1, 14])

37.

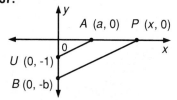

$\frac{a}{x} = \frac{-1}{-b}$, or $-x = a(-b)$. But, $-x = -ab$. So, $a(-b) = -ab$.

38.

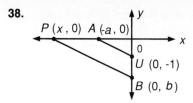

$\frac{-a}{-x} = \frac{-1}{-b}$, or $x = (-a)(-b)$. But, $x = ab$. So, $(-a)(-b) = ab$.

39.

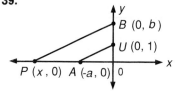

$\frac{-a}{-x} = \frac{1}{b}$, $-x = (-a)b$, or But, $-x = -ab$. So, $(-a)b = -ab$.

40. Proof: 1. Rectangle $ABCD$; $m\angle ABF = m\angle CBE$ (Given) 2. $\angle A$ and $\angle C$ are rt. $\angle$s. (Def. of rectangle [1]) 3. $m\angle A = m\angle C$ (All rt. $\angle$s are =. [2]) 4. $\triangle ABF \sim \triangle CBE$ (AA $\sim$ Post. [1, 3])

41. Yes. The sum of the angle measures of a triangle is 180, so $m\angle Y = 69$. By the AA Similarity Postulate, $\triangle XYZ \sim \triangle PQR$.

42.

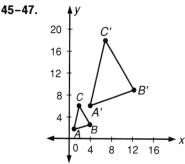

No; the angles are not necessarily equal.

45–47.

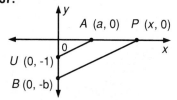

45. They are similar.
46. Side lengths of $\triangle A'B'C'$ are 3 times corresponding side lengths of $\triangle ABC$.
47. $AB = \sqrt{10}$; $BC = \sqrt{13}$; $AC = \sqrt{17}$; $A'B' = 3\sqrt{10}$; $B'C' = 3\sqrt{13}$; $A'C' = 3\sqrt{17}$

48. $\frac{A'B'}{AB} = \frac{3\sqrt{10}}{\sqrt{10}} = \frac{3}{1}$; $\frac{B'C'}{BC} = \frac{3\sqrt{13}}{\sqrt{13}} = \frac{3}{1}$; $\frac{A'C'}{AC} = \frac{3\sqrt{17}}{\sqrt{17}} = \frac{3}{1}$

49. $\triangle A'B'C' \sim \triangle ABC$; side lengths of $\triangle A'B'C'$ are 5 times corresponding side lengths of $\triangle ABC$.

Challenge

The parallel segments divide all the sides of the triangle in the same proportion, so the sixth segment ends at the beginning point. If the segments are started at the midpoint of a side, there will be only three segments.

Pages 313–315

19. Given: Quadrilateral $ABCD$ with diagonals $\overline{AC}$ and $\overline{BD}$ intersecting at X Prove: $\frac{AX}{CX} = \frac{BX}{DX}$ if and only if $ABCD$ is a parallelogram or a trapezoid. Proof: *Part I:* 1. $ABCD$ is a parallelogram or a trapezoid with diagonals $\overline{AC}$ and $\overline{BD}$ intersecting at X; (Given) 2. $\overline{AB} \parallel \overline{DE}$ (Def. of parallelogram or trapezoid [1]) 3. $m\angle AXB = m\angle CXD$ (Vertical $\angle$s are =.) 4. $m\angle ABX = m\angle CDX$ (2 lines $\parallel \Rightarrow$ alt. int. $\angle$s =. [2]) 5. $\triangle AXB \sim \triangle CXD$ (AA $\sim$ Post. [3,4]) 6. $\frac{AX}{CX} = \frac{BX}{DX}$ (Def. of $\sim$ polygons [5]) *Part II:* 1. $ABCD$ is a quadrilateral with diagonals $\overline{AC}$ and $\overline{BD}$ intersecting at X; $\frac{AX}{CX} = \frac{BX}{DX}$ (Given) 2. $m\angle AXB = m\angle CXD$ (Vertical $\angle$s are =.) 3. $\triangle AXB \sim \triangle CXD$ (SAS $\sim$ Thm. [1, 2]) 4. $m\angle XBA = m\angle XDC$ (Def. of $\sim$ polygons [3]) 5. $\overline{AB} \parallel \overline{DC}$ (Alt. int. $\angle$s = $\Rightarrow$ 2 lines $\parallel$. [4]) 6. $ABCD$ is a parallelogram or a trapezoid. (Def. of parallelogram or trapezoid [5])

22. If two angles of one triangle are equal to two angles of another, then the triangles are similar.

23. No; given $m\angle A + m\angle B = 180$, if $m\angle A \neq m\angle B$, the complements of $\angle A$ and $\angle B$ cannot have the same measure; if $m\angle A = m\angle B$, the complements of $\angle A$ and $\angle B$ would have to have measure 0 and by definition, the measure of an angle is between 0 and 180. Yes; given $m\angle A + m\angle B = 90$, if $m\angle A = m\angle B$, the complements of $\angle A$ and $\angle B$ both have measure 45.

24. Prove that: opposite sides are parallel; opposite sides are equal; opposite angles are equal; diagonals bisect each other; one pair of opposite sides are equal and parallel.

28. If two triangles are similar, then the lengths of their altitudes and medians are proportional to the lengths of a pair of corresponding sides.

3. The bisector of an angle in a triangle divides the opposite side into two segments whose lengths are proportional to the lengths of the adjacent sides.

Excursion

7. Proof: 1. $\triangle ABC$ is a golden $\triangle$; $AB = AC$; $BD = BC$ (Given) 2. $m\angle A = m\angle 1 = m\angle 2$ (Exercise 6) 3. $m\angle ABC = m\angle C$ (Isos. $\triangle$ Thm. [1]) 4. $m\angle A + m\angle ABC + m\angle C = 180$ (The sum of the measures of the $\angle$s of a $\triangle$ is 180.) 5. $m\angle 1 + m\angle 2 = m\angle ABC$ (Angle Add. Post.) 6. $m\angle 1 + m\angle 1 = 2(m\angle 1) = m\angle ABC$ (Substitution Prop. [5, Exercise 6]) 7. $m\angle A + 2(m\angle A) + 2(m\angle A) = 5(m\angle A) = 180$ (Substitution [2, 4, 6]) 8. $m\angle A = 36$ (Mult. Prop. [7])

8.

Given: Golden rectangle $ABCD \sim$ golden rectangle $BCEF$ Prove: $\overline{AC} \perp \overline{EB}$ Proof: 1. Golden rectangle $ABCD \sim$ golden rectangle $BCEF$ (Given) 2. $\frac{AB}{BC} = \frac{BC}{EC}$ (Def. of $\sim$ polygons [1]) 3. $\angle ABC$ and $\angle BCE$ are rt. $\angle$s. (Def. of rectangle [1]) 4.

$m\angle ABC = m\angle BCE$ (All rt. $\angle$s are =. [3]) 5. $\triangle ABC \sim \triangle BCE$ (SAS $\sim$ Thm. [2, 4]) 6. $m\angle CAB = m\angle EBC$ (Def. of $\sim$ polygons [5]) 7. $m\angle ACB = m\angle ACB$ (Reflexive Prop.) 8. $m\angle CXB = m\angle ABC$ (If 2 $\angle$s of a $\triangle$ are = to 2 $\angle$s of another $\triangle$, then the 3rd $\angle$s are =. [6, 7]) 9. $m\angle ABC = 90$ (Def. of rt. $\angle$ [3]) 10. $m\angle CXB = 90$ (Substitution Prop. [8, 9]) 11. $\angle CXB$ is a rt. $\angle$. (Def. of rt. $\angle$ [10]) 12. $\overline{AC} \perp \overline{EB}$ (Def. of $\perp$ lines [11])

Page 320

35. Given: $\triangle RST \sim \triangle R'S'T'$; $\overline{TM}$ is the median from $\angle T$; $T'M'$ is the median from $\angle T'$. Prove: $\frac{TM}{T'M'} = \frac{RT}{R'T'}$ Proof: 1. $\triangle RST \sim \triangle R'S'T'$; $RM = MS$; $R'M' = M'S'$ (Given) 2. $RM = MS$; $R'M' = M'S'$ (Definition of median of $\triangle$ [1]) 3. $m\angle R = m\angle R'$ (Def. of $\sim$ polygons [1]) 4. $RS = RM + MS$; $R'S' = R'M' + M'S'$ (Seg. Add. Post.) 5. $RS = RM + RM = 2RM$; $R'S' = R'M' + R'M' = 2R'M'$ (Substitution Prop. [2, 3]) 6. $\frac{RS}{RM} = \frac{2}{1}$; $\frac{R'S'}{R'M'} = \frac{2}{1}$ (Multiplication Prop. [5]) 7. $\frac{RS}{RM} = \frac{R'S'}{R'M'}$ (Substitution Prop. [6]) 8. $\frac{RS}{R'S'} = \frac{RM}{R'M'}$ (Multiplication Prop. [7]) 9. $\frac{RS}{R'S'} = \frac{RT}{R'T'}$ (Def. of $\sim$ polygons [1]) 10. $\frac{RM}{R'M'} = \frac{RT}{R'T'}$ Substitution Prop. [8, 9] 11. $\triangle RMT \sim \triangle R'M'T'$ (SAS $\sim$ Thm. [3, 10]) 12. $\frac{TM}{T'M'} = \frac{RT}{R'T'}$ (Def. of $\sim$ polygons [11])

36. Given: $\triangle ABC$; bisector of $\angle ABC$ intersects $\overline{AC}$ at O. Prove: $\frac{AD}{CD} = \frac{BA}{BC}$ Proof: 1. $\triangle ABC$; bisector of $\angle ABC$ intersects $\overline{AC}$ at D. (Given) 2. Draw $\overline{EC} \parallel \overline{BD}$ with E on $\overrightarrow{AB}$. (Through a pt. not on a given line, there is exactly one line $\parallel$ to the given line.) 3. $m\angle ABD = m\angle E$ (2 lines $\parallel \Rightarrow$ corr. $\angle$s =. [2]) 4. $m\angle DBC = m\angle BCE$ (2 lines $\parallel \Rightarrow$ alt. int. $\angle$s =. [2]) 5. $m\angle ABD = m\angle DBC$ (Def. of $\angle$ bisector [1]) 6. $m\angle E = m\angle BCE$ (Substitution Prop. [3, 4, 5]) 7. $EB = BC$ (If 2 $\angle$s of a $\triangle$ are =, sides opp. are =. [6]) 8. $\frac{AD}{CD} = \frac{BA}{EB}$ (If a line $\parallel$ to one

side of a $\triangle$ intersects the other 2 sides, it divides them proportionally. [2]) 9. $\frac{AD}{CD} = \frac{BA}{BC}$ (Substitution Prop. [7, 8])

37. Proof: 1. $\triangle EFG$; $\overline{HJ} \parallel \overline{FG}$; $\overrightarrow{EK}$ bisects $\angle GEF$. (Given) 2. $\frac{JL}{HL} = \frac{EJ}{EH}$, $\frac{GK}{FK} = \frac{EG}{EF}$ (Bisector of $\angle$ of $\triangle$ divides opp. side into 2 segs. whose lengths are proportional to lengths of adjacent sides. [1]) 3. $\frac{JG}{EJ} = \frac{FH}{EH}$ (If a line $\parallel$ to one side of a $\triangle$ intersects the other 2 sides, then it divides them proportionally. [1]) 4. $\frac{JG + EJ}{EJ} = \frac{FH + EH}{EH}$ (Addition Prop. [3]) 5. $JG + EJ = EG$; $FH + EH = EF$ (Seg. Add. Post.) 6. $\frac{EG}{EJ} = \frac{EF}{EH}$ (Substitution Prop. [4, 5]) 7. $\frac{EG}{EF} = \frac{EJ}{EH}$ (Multiplication Prop. [6]) 8. $\frac{JL}{HL} = \frac{GK}{FK}$ (Substitution Prop. [2, 7])

38. Proof: 1. $\triangle ABC \sim \triangle DEF$; $AJ = JB$; $DK = KE$; $\overline{CG} \perp \overline{AB}$; $\overline{FH} \perp \overline{DE}$ (Given) 2. $\angle CGJ$ and $\angle FHK$ are rt. $\angle$s. (2 $\perp$ lines form 4 rt. $\angle$s. [1]) 3. $m\angle CGJ = m\angle FHK$ (All rt. $\angle$s are =. [2]) 4. $AJ + JB = AB$; $DK + KE = DE$ (Seg. Add. Post.) 5. $AJ + AJ = 2AJ = AB$; $DK + DK = 2DK = DE$ (Substitution Prop. [1, 4]) 6. $\frac{AB}{AJ} = \frac{2}{1}$; $\frac{DE}{DK} = \frac{2}{1}$ (Multiplication Prop. [5]) 7. $\frac{AB}{AJ} = \frac{DE}{DK}$ (Substitution Prop. [6]) 8. $\frac{AB}{DE} = \frac{AJ}{DK}$ (Multiplication Prop. [7]) 9. $\frac{AB}{DE} = \frac{AC}{DF}$; $m\angle A = m\angle D$ (Def. of $\sim$ polygons [1]) 10. $\frac{AC}{DF} = \frac{AJ}{DK}$ (Substitution Prop. [8, 9]) 11. $\triangle AJC \sim \triangle DKF$ (SAS $\sim$ Thm. [9, 10]) 12. $m\angle AJC = m\angle DKF$ (Def. of $\sim$ polygons [11]) 13. $\angle AJC$ and $\angle CJG$ are a lin. pr.; $\angle DKF$ and $\angle HKF$ are a lin. pr. (Def. of lin. pr.) 14. $\angle AJC$ and $\angle CJG$ are supp.; $\angle DKF$ and $\angle HKF$ are supp. (Supp. Post. [13]) 15. $m\angle CJG = m\angle HKF$ (Supps. of = $\angle$s are =. [12, 14]) 16. $\triangle CGJ \sim \triangle FHK$ (AA $\sim$ Post. [3, 15])

39. Proof: 1. $\triangle ABC$; $AC \neq BC$; $\overrightarrow{CE}$ bisects $\angle BCD$. (Given) 2. Draw $\overrightarrow{BG} \parallel \overrightarrow{CD}$ intersecting $\overrightarrow{CE}$ at F. (Through a pt. not on a line, there is exactly one line $\parallel$ to a given line.) 3. $m\angle CFB = m\angle DCF$ (2 lines $\parallel \Rightarrow$ alt. int. $\angle$s =. [2]) 4. $m\angle DCF$

= $m\angle FCB$ (Def. of $\angle$ bisector [1]) 5. $m\angle CFB = m\angle FCB$ (Transitive Prop. [3, 4]) 6. $FB = BC$ (If 2 $\angle$s of a $\triangle$ are =, the sides opposite those $\angle$s are =. [5]) 7. $m\angle E = m\angle E$ (Reflexive Prop.) 8. $m\angle EFB = m\angle ECA$ (2 lines $\parallel \Rightarrow$ corr. $\angle$s =. [2]) 9. $\triangle EFB \sim \triangle ECA$ (AA $\sim$ Post. [7, 8]) 10. $\frac{AE}{EB} = \frac{AC}{FB}$ (Def. of $\sim$ polygons [9]) 11. $\frac{AE}{EB} = \frac{AC}{BC}$ (Substitution Prop. [6, 10])

40. Two $\triangle$s are $\sim$ if: all prs. of corr. $\angle$s are = and lengths of prs. of corr. sides are proportional; 2 prs. of corr. $\angle$s are =; they are $\cong$; they are $\sim$ to the same $\triangle$; lengths of 2 prs. of corr. sides are proportional and the included $\angle$s are =; lengths of all prs. of corr. sides are proportional.

42. The parallel lines divide the transversals proportionally.

44. Place a corner of the card on the first line and an adjacent corner on the seventh line. Mark the card at the points where the edge of the card intersects the lines between the first and seventh lines.

45. Samples:

Choose point C; locate D on $\overline{AC}$ and E on $\overline{CB}$ such that $\frac{CD}{CA} = \frac{CE}{CB}$; measure the above segments and $\overline{DE}$; use SAS $\sim$ Thm. and $\sim$ $\triangle$s.

Choose point E; locate C and D such that $\frac{AE}{DE} = \frac{BE}{CE}$; measure the above segments; use SAS $\sim$ Thm. and $\sim$ $\triangle$s.

Pages 323–324

1. $\triangle ABC \sim \triangle ADE$ by AA $\sim$ Post.

7. $\triangle AOB \sim \triangle DOC$ by SAS $\sim$ Thm.; so $m\angle B = m\angle C$, and the board is parallel to the floor because alt. int. $\angle$s = $\Rightarrow$ 2 lines $\parallel$.
19. Samples:

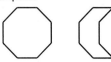

CHAPTER 8   Pages 334, 335

20.

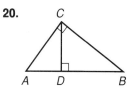

Given: $\triangle ABC$ with right $\angle C$; $\overline{CD} \perp \overline{AB}$ Prove: $\frac{AB}{AC} = \frac{AC}{AD}$ and $\frac{BA}{BC} = \frac{BC}{BD}$
Proof: 1. $\triangle ABC$ with rt. $\angle C$; $\overline{CD} \perp \overline{AB}$ (Given) 2. $\triangle ABC \sim \triangle ACD$ and $\triangle ABC \sim \triangle CBD$ (If altitude is drawn to hypotenuse of rt. $\triangle$, the new $\triangle$s formed are $\sim$ to each other and to the given $\triangle$. [1]) 3. $\frac{AB}{AC} = \frac{AC}{AD}$ and $\frac{BA}{BC} = \frac{BC}{BD}$ (Corres. sides of $\sim$ $\triangle$s are prop. [2])

32. Proof: 1. A rt. $\triangle$ has legs of lengths a and b; altitude to the hypotenuse has length h; altitude divides hypotenuse in segs. of lengths m and n. (Given) 2. $a^2 = m(m + n)$ and $b^2 = n(m + n)$ (If altitude is drawn to hypotenuse of a rt. $\triangle$, length of either leg is geometric mean of lengths of hypotenuse and seg. on hypotenuse adj. to that leg. [1]) 3. $a^2 b^2 = mn(m + n)^2$ (Mult. Prop. [2]) 4. $h^2 = mn$ (Length of altitude to hypotenuse of rt. $\triangle$ is geometric mean of lengths of segs. into which it divides the hypotenuse. [1]) 5. $a^2 b^2 = h^2(m + n)^2$ (Substitution Prop. [3, 4]) 6. $ab = h(m + n)$ (Algebra [5])

33. Proof: 1. A rt. $\triangle$ has legs of lengths a and b; altitude to hypotenuse has length h; altitude divides hypotenuse into segs. of lengths m and n. (Given) 2. $a^2 = m(m + n)$ and $b^2 = n(m + n)$ (If

altitude is drawn to hypotenuse of a rt. $\triangle$, length of either leg is geometric mean of lengths of hypotenuse and seg. on hypotenuse adj. to that leg. [1]) 3. $a^2 + b^2 = m(m + n) + n(m + n)$ (Add. Prop. [2]) 4. $a^2 + b^2 = (m + n)(m + n) = (m + n)^2$ (Algebra)

34. Proof: 1. $\triangle XYZ$; $m\angle YXZ = 2m\angle Z$; $\overline{XF}$ bisects $\angle YXZ$ (Given) 2. $m\angle YXF = m\angle FXZ$ (Def. of $\angle$ bisector [1]) 3. $m\angle YXZ = m\angle YXF + m\angle FXZ$ (Angle Add. Post.) 4. $m\angle YXZ = m\angle YXF + m\angle YXF = 2m\angle YXF$ (Substitution Prop. [2, 3]) 5. $2m\angle Z = 2m\angle YXF$ (Substitution Prop. [1, 4]) 6. $m\angle Z = m\angle YXF$ (Mult. Prop. [5]) 7. $m\angle Y = m\angle Y$ (Reflexive Prop.) 8. $\triangle XYF \sim \triangle ZYX$ (AA $\sim$ Post. [6, 7]) 9. $\frac{XY}{ZY} = \frac{FY}{XY}$ (Corres. sides of $\sim$ $\triangle$s are prop. [8])

35. Proof: 1. $\triangle ABC$ has altitudes $\overline{AY}$, $\overline{BZ}$ and $\overline{CX}$ intersecting at P. (Given) 2. $\overline{CX} \perp \overline{AB}$; $\overline{BZ} \perp \overline{AC}$; $\overline{AY} \perp \overline{BC}$ (Def. of altitude of a $\triangle$ [1]) 3. $\angle AZP$, $\angle CZP$, $\angle CYP$, $\angle BYP$, $\angle BXP$ and $\angle AXP$ are rt. $\angle$s. (2 $\perp$ lines form 4 rt. $\angle$s. [2]) 4. $m\angle AZP = m\angle CZP = m\angle CYP = m\angle BYP = m\angle BXP = m\angle AXP$ (All rt. $\angle$s are =. [3]) 5. $m\angle ZPA = m\angle YPB$; $m\angle XPA = m\angle YPC$; $m\angle XPB = m\angle ZPC$ (Vert. $\angle$s are =.) 6. $\triangle ZPA \sim \triangle YPB$; $\triangle XPA \sim \triangle YPC$; $\triangle XPB \sim \triangle ZPC$ (AA $\sim$ Post. [4, 5]) 7. $\frac{YB}{ZA} = \frac{YP}{ZP}$, $\frac{AX}{CY} = \frac{XP}{YP}$, $\frac{ZC}{XB} = \frac{ZP}{XP}$ (Corres. sides of $\sim$ $\triangle$s are prop. [6]) 8. $\left(\frac{YB}{ZA}\right)\left(\frac{AX}{CY}\right)\left(\frac{ZC}{XB}\right) = \left(\frac{YP}{ZP}\right)\left(\frac{XP}{YP}\right)\left(\frac{ZP}{XP}\right) = 1$ (Mult. Prop. [7]) 9. $\left(\frac{AX}{XB}\right)\left(\frac{BY}{YC}\right)\left(\frac{CZ}{ZA}\right) = 1$ (Commutative Prop. of Mult. [8])

36.

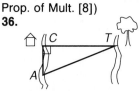

Measure $\overline{AC}$ and $\angle CAT$. Then use $\tan A = \frac{CT}{CA}$ to find CT.

37.

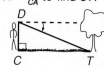

Use Tonya's height and the angle of depression to the base of the tree. Then use tan $\angle DTC = \frac{DC}{CT}$ and solve for CT.

40. Step I: Assume that the opposite of the statement to be proved is true. Step II: Argue to a contradiction of a known fact—a postulate, theorem, definition, algebraic property or given facts. Step III: Conclude that the assumption is false. Step IV: Conclude that the statement to be proved is true.

Pages 342, 343

30. No; $DE = 5\sqrt{2}$, $DF = 5\sqrt{2}$, and $EF = 6\sqrt{2}$, so $(5\sqrt{2})^2 + (5\sqrt{2})^2$ is not equal to $(6\sqrt{2})^2$.
31. Use the Pythagorean Theorem or show the slopes of two sides are negative reciprocals of each other.
33. Proof: 1. In $\triangle ABC$, $BC = a$, $AC = b$ and $AB = c$; $a^2 + b^2 = c^2$ (Given) 2. Draw $\ell \perp m$ through a point F. (Through a point on a line, exactly one $\perp$ can be drawn.) 3. Locate D on ℓ and E on m so that $DF = b$ and $EF = a$. (Seg. Construction Post.) 4. Draw $\overline{DE}$. (2 points determine a line. [3]) 5. Let $DE = f$. (Ruler Post.) 6. $\angle EFD$ is a rt. $\angle$. (2 $\perp$ lines form 4 rt. $\angle$s. [2]) 7. $\triangle EFD$ is a rt. $\triangle$. (Def. of rt. $\triangle$ [6]) 8. $a^2 + b^2 = f^2$ (Pythagorean Thm. [6, 7]) 9. $c^2 = f^2$ (Substitution Prop. [1, 8]) 10. $c = f$ (Algebra [9]) 11. $EF = BC$; $DF = AC$; $AB = DE$ (Substitution Prop. [1, 3, 5]) 12. $\triangle ABC \cong \triangle DEF$ (SSS Post. [11]) 13. $m\angle C = m\angle EFD$ (Corres. parts of $\cong \triangle$s are =. [12]) 14. $m\angle EFD = 90$ (Def. of rt. $\angle$ [6]) 15. $m\angle C = 90$ (Transitive Prop. [13, 14]) 16. $\triangle ABC$ is a rt. $\triangle$. (Def. of a rt. $\triangle$ [15])
34. Proof: 1. $\overline{CD}$ is altitude of $\triangle ABC$. (Given) 2. $\overline{CD} \perp \overline{BA}$ (Def. of altitude) 3. $\angle CDB$ and $\angle CDA$ are rt. $\angle$s. (2 $\perp$ lines form 4 rt. $\angle$s. [2]) 4. $\triangle CDB$ and $\triangle CDA$ are rt. $\triangle$s. (Def. of rt. $\triangle$ [3]) 5. $a^2 = y^2 + (CD)^2$ and $b^2 = x^2 + (CD)^2$

(Pythagorean Thm. [3, 4]) 6. $a^2 - y^2 = (CD)^2$ and $b^2 - x^2 = (CD)^2$ (Subtraction Prop. [5]) 7. $a^2 - y^2 = b^2 - x^2$ (Substitution Prop. [6])
35. Proof: 1. $\angle MAN$ is a rt. $\angle$. (Given) 2. $\triangle MAL$ and $\triangle MAN$ are rt. $\triangle$s. (Def. of rt. $\triangle$ [1]) 3. $MA^2 + LA^2 = ML^2$ and $MA^2 + NA^2 = MN^2$ (Pythagorean Thm. [1, 2]) 4. $MA^2 = ML^2 - LA^2$ and $MA^2 = MN^2 - NA^2$ (Subtraction Prop. [3]) 5. $ML^2 - LA^2 = MN^2 - NA^2$ (Substitution Prop. [4]) 6. $NA^2 + ML^2 = MN^2 + AL^2$ (Addition Prop. [5])
37. Proof: 1. $\angle ACB$ is a rt. $\angle$; $BC = a$; $AC = b$; $AD = n$; $DB = m$; $AB = c$; $\overline{CD} \perp \overline{AB}$ (Given) 2. $\triangle ABC$ is a rt. $\triangle$. (Def. of rt. $\triangle$ [1]) 3. $a^2 + b^2 = c^2$ (Pythagorean Thm. [1, 2, 3]) 4. h is the length of the altitude to $\overline{AB}$ in $\triangle ABC$. (Def. of altitude [1]) 5. $\frac{n}{h} = \frac{h}{m}$ (Length of altitude to hypotenuse of rt. $\triangle$ is the geometric mean of lengths of segments into which it separates the hypotenuse. [1, 2, 3, 5]) 6. $\frac{n}{b} = \frac{b}{c}$ and $\frac{m}{a} = \frac{a}{c}$ (If altitude is drawn to hypotenuse of rt. $\triangle$, length of either leg is geometric mean of lengths of hypotenuse and seg. on hypotenuse adjacent to that leg. [1, 2, 5]) 7. $h^2 = mn$; $b^2 = nc$; $a^2 = mc$ (Mult. Prop. [6, 7]) 8. $a^2b^2 = c^2mn$ (Mult. Prop. [8]) 9. $a^2b^2 = c^2h^2$ (Substitution Prop. [8, 9]) 10. $a^2b^2 = h^2(a^2 + b^2) = h^2a^2 + h^2b^2$ (Substitution Prop. [4, 10]) 11. $\frac{a^2b^2}{a^2b^2h^2} = \frac{h^2a^2}{a^2b^2h^2} + \frac{h^2b^2}{a^2b^2h^2}$, or $\frac{1}{h^2} = \frac{1}{b^2} + \frac{1}{a^2}$ (Mult. Prop. [11])
38.

Q   G   R

y $\,$ $\fbox{}$ $\,$ z

P

x $\,$ w

T   H   S

Given: P is in the interior of rectangle $QRST$. Prove: $x^2 + z^2 = w^2 + y^2$ Proof: 1. P is in the interior of rect. $QRST$. (Given) 2. $QRST$ is a $\square$. (Def. of rect. [1]) 3. $\overline{QR} \parallel \overline{TS}$; $\overline{QT} \parallel \overline{RS}$ (Def. of $\square$ [2]) 4. $\angle QTS$ is a rt. $\angle$. (Def. of rect. [1]) 5. $\overline{QT}$

$\perp \overline{TS}$ (Def. of $\perp$ [4]) 6. Through P, draw $\overleftrightarrow{PH} \perp \overline{TS}$. (Through a point not on a given line, there is exactly 1 line $\perp$ to the given line.) 7. $\overleftrightarrow{PH} \perp \overline{QR}$ at some point, say G. (If a transversal is $\perp$ to one of two $\parallel$ lines, then it is $\perp$ to the other. [3, 6]) 8. $\overline{GH} \parallel \overline{QT}$ (In a plane, 2 lines $\perp$ to same line are $\parallel$. [5, 6]) 9. $\overline{GH} \parallel \overline{RS}$ (2 lines $\parallel$ to same line are $\parallel$ to each other. [3, 8]) 10. $QGHT$ and $GRSH$ are $\square$s. (Def. of $\square$ [3, 8, 9]) 11. $GR = HS$; $QG = TH$ (Opp. sides of a $\square$ are =. [10]) 12. $\overline{PG}$ is an altitude of $\triangle QPR$. $\overline{PH}$ is an altitude of $\triangle TPS$. (Def. of altitude [6, 7]) 13. $x^2 - (TH)^2 = w^2 - (HS)^2$; $z^2 - (GR)^2 = y^2 - (QG)^2$ (Exercise 34 above) 14. $z^2 - (HS)^2 = y^2 - (TH)^2$ (Substitution Prop. [11, 13]) 15. $x^2 - (TH)^2 + z^2 - (HS)^2 = w^2 - (HS)^2 + y^2 - (TH)^2$ (Add. Prop. [13, 14]) 16. $x^2 + z^2 = w^2 + y^2$ (Add. Prop. [15])
46. AB: 18; 16; $16\sqrt{3}$; $4\sqrt{3}$; AD : 6; 16; $8\sqrt{3}$; $2\sqrt{3}$; BD : $6\sqrt{3}$; $16\sqrt{3}$; $9\sqrt{3}$; $8\sqrt{3}$
47. $AD = \frac{1}{2}AB$ and $BD = (\frac{1}{2}AB)\sqrt{2}$.
49. XY : $8\sqrt{2}$; $3\sqrt{2}$; XZ : $10\sqrt{2}$; $12\sqrt{2}$

Challenge

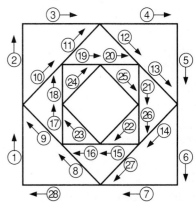

Sum of the lengths of the segments ① to ⑦ and ㉘ is 4 inches. Sum of the lengths of the segments ⑧ to ⑭ and ㉗ is $4(\frac{1}{2}\sqrt{2}) = 2\sqrt{2}$ inches. Sum of the lengths of the segments ⑮ to (21) and (26) is 2 inches. Sum of the lengths of the segments (22) to (25) is $4(\frac{1}{4}\sqrt{2}) = \sqrt{2}$ inches. Total length of the path is $6 + 3\sqrt{2} \approx 10.2$ inches.

Page 350

27. Proof: 1. $\triangle ABC$ is a rt. $\triangle$; $m\angle A = m\angle B = 45$; $AB = C$; $AC = a$. (Given) 2. $CB = AC$ (If 2 $\angle$s of $\triangle$ are $=$, sides opp. them are $=$. [1]) 3. $CB = a$ (Transitive Prop. [1, 2]) 4. $a^2 + a^2 = c^2$ or $2a^2 = c^2$ (Pythagorean Thm. [1, 3]) 5. $c = a\sqrt{2}$ (Algebra)

29. Proof: 1. In rt. $\triangle ABC$, $m\angle A = 60$; $m\angle ABC = 30$; $AC = b$; $AB = c$; $BC = a$ (Given) 2. Draw $\overleftrightarrow{AC}$. (2 pts. determine a line.) 3. Draw $\overrightarrow{BD}$ so that $m\angle CBD = 30$ and D is on $\overrightarrow{AC}$. (Protractor Post.) 4. $m\angle ABC = m\angle ABC + m\angle CBD$ (Angle Add. Post.) 5. $m\angle ABD = 30 + 30 = 60$ (Substitution Prop. [1, 3]) 6. $m\angle A + m\angle ABD + m\angle D = 180$ (Sum of measures of $\angle$s of $\triangle$ is 180.) 7. $60 + 60 + m\angle D = 180$ (Substitution Prop. [1, 5, 6]) 8. $m\angle D = 60$ (Add. Prop. [7]) 9. $m\angle A = m\angle ABD = m\angle D$ (Substitution Prop. [1, 5, 8]) 10. $\triangle ABD$ is equiangular. (Def. of equiangular [9]) 11. $\triangle ABD$ is equilateral. (Equiangular $\triangle$ is equilateral. [10]) 12. $AB = BD$ (Def. of equilateral [11]) 13. $m\angle ABC = m\angle CBD$ (Substitution Prop. [1, 3]) 14. $BC = BC$ (Reflexive Prop.) 15. $\triangle ABC \cong \triangle DBC$ (SAS Post. [12, 13, 14]) 16. $AC = CD$ (Corres. parts of $\cong$ $\triangle$s are $=$. [15]) 17. $AD = AC + CD$ (Seg. Add. Post.) 18. $AD = AC + AC = 2(AC)$ (Substitution Prop. [16, 17]) 19. $AD = 2b$ (Substitution Prop. [1, 18]) 20. $AD = AB$ (Def. of equilateral $\triangle$ [11]) 21. $c = 2b$ (Substitution Prop. [1, 19, 20]) 22. $c^2 = a^2 + b^2$ (Pythagorean Thm. [1]) 23. $(2b)^2 = a^2 + b^2$ (Substitution Prop. [21, 22]) 24. $3b^2 = a^2$ (Algebra) 25. $b\sqrt{3} = a$ (Algebra)

Pages 352, 353

1. (a) $x^2 + RP^2 = PQ^2$ (b) RP and PQ are needed.
2. (a) $x^2 + ZY^2 = XY^2$ (b) ZY and XY are needed; then add $x + ZY$ to find the amount of fencing.
3. (a) $x^2 = UT^2 + TS^2$ (b) UT and TS are needed.
4. (a) $x^2 = AC^2 + BC^2$ (b) AC and BC are needed.
5. (a) $x^2 + CB^2 = AB^2$ (b) CB and AB are needed.
6. (a) $x^2 + OM^2 = OL^2$ (b) OL and OM are needed.

---

8. Place the yardstick as shown in the diagram and mark points A and B. Then measure OA and OB. If $OA^2 + OB^2 = AB^2$, $\triangle AOB$ is a rt. $\triangle$ and $\angle AOB$ is a rt. $\angle$. If $\angle AOB$ is a rt. $\angle$, $\overline{AO} \perp \overline{OB}$.

Page 361

1–4. Sample:

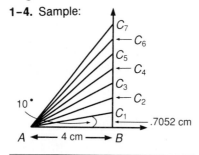

Challenge

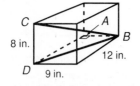

The shortest path is the path of the butterfly, BC. $BC^2 = CD^2 + (DB)^2 = 8^2 + (9^2 + 12^2)$, or $BC = 17$ in.

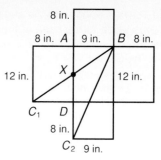

"Open" the cage along the lines where the sides meet. The path of the caterpillar is BC_1. Solving the equation $(BC_1)^2 = 12^2 + 17^2$ for BC_1 gives 20.8 in.

Page 364

21.

The table shows sin 1° = tan 1° because the entries are approximations. Given: Rt. $\triangle ABC$ with rt. $\angle C$ Prove: tan $A >$ sin A Proof:
1. Rt. $\triangle ABC$ with rt. $\angle C$ (Given)
2. tan $A = \frac{CB}{AC}$ (Def. of tangent [1])
3. sin $A = \frac{CB}{AB}$ (Def. of sine [1]) 4. $\overline{AB}$ is the hypotenuse of $\triangle ABC$. (Def. of hypotenuse of a rt. $\triangle$ [1])
5. $AB > AC$ ($\perp$ segment from a pt. to a line is the shortest seg. from the pt. to the line.) 6. $(CB)(AB) > (CB)(AC)$ (Mult. Prop. [5])
7. $\frac{CB}{AC} > \frac{CB}{AB}$ (Mult. Prop. [6]) 8. tan $A >$ sin A (Substitution Prop. [2, 3, 7])

22. *Part I* Given: Rt. $\triangle ABC$ with rt. $\angle C$; $m\angle A > 45$ Prove: sin $A >$ cos A Proof: 1. Rt. $\triangle ABC$ with rt. $\angle C$; $m\angle A > 45$ (Given) 2. $\angle A$ and $\angle B$ are comp. (Acute $\angle$s of a rt. $\triangle$ are comp. [1]) 3. $m\angle A + m\angle B > 45 + m\angle B$ (Add. Prop. [1]) 4. $m\angle A + m\angle B = 90$ (Def. of comp. $\angle$s [2]) 5. $90 > 45 + m\angle B$ (Substitution Prop. [3, 4]) 6. $45 > m\angle B$ (Add. Prop. [5]) 7. $m\angle A > m\angle B$ (Transitive Prop. [1, 6]) 8. $BC > AC$ (If measures of 2 $\angle$s of

△ are ≠, lengths of sides opp. them are ≠ in the same order. [7]) 9. $\frac{BC}{AB} > \frac{AC}{AB}$ (Mult. Prop. [8]) 10. $\overline{AB}$ is the hypotenuse of △ABC. (Def. of hypotenuse [1]) 11. sin $A = \frac{BC}{AB}$ (Def. of sine [1, 10]) 12. cos $A = \frac{AC}{AB}$ (Def. of cosine [1, 10]) 13. sin A > cos A (Substitution Prop. [9, 11, 12]) *Part II* Given: Rt. △ABC with rt. ∠C; m∠A < 45 Prove: sin A < cos A Proof: 1. Rt. △ABC with rt. ∠C; m∠A < 45 (Given) 2. ∠A and ∠B are comp. (Acute ∠s of a rt. △ are comp.). 3. m∠A + m∠B = 90 (Def. of comp. ∠s [2]) 4. m∠A + m∠B < 45 + m∠B (Add. Prop. [1]) 5. 90 < 45 + m∠B (Substitution Prop. [3, 4]) 6. 45 < m∠B (Add. Prop. [5]) 7. m∠A < m∠B (Transitive Prop. [1, 6]) 8. BC < AC (If measures of 2 ∠s of △ are ≠, lengths of sides opp. them are ≠ in the same order. [7]) 9. $\frac{BC}{AB} < \frac{AC}{AB}$ (Mult. Prop. [8]) 10. $\overline{AB}$ is hypotenuse of △ABC. (Def. of hypotenuse [1]) 11. sin $A = \frac{BC}{AB}$ (Def. of sine [1, 10]) 12. cos $A = \frac{AC}{AB}$ (Def. of cosine [1, 10]) 13. sin A < cos A (Substitution Prop. [9, 11, 12])

26.

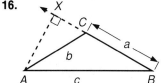

-2 -1 0 1 2 3 4 5 6 7

27. One can be used to prove two triangles congruent and the other can be used to prove two triangles similar. The SAS Postulate says if two sides and the included ∠ of one △ are ≅ to the corres. parts of another △, the the △s are ≅. The SAS Similarity Theorem says if the measure of an angle of one △ equals the measure of an angle of a second △, and if the lengths of the sides including these ∠s are proportional, then the △s are ~.

28. The angles at C are all equal to $\frac{360°}{18}$, or 20°. Since the △s are isosceles △s, the base angles are $\frac{180° - 20°}{2}$, or 80°.

Pages 366–368

2. angle of depression; opp. side and adj. side; tan 52° = $\frac{x}{15}$; x ≈ 19.2

3. angle of depression; opp. side and hypotenuse; sin 35° = $\frac{20}{x}$; x ≈ 34.9

---

15. Proof: 1. Acute △ABC with sides of lengths a, b and c (Given) 2. Draw $\overline{BD} \perp \overline{AC}$. (Through a pt. not on a given line, there is exactly 1 line $\perp$ to the given line.) 3. ∠BDA and ∠BDC are rt. ∠s. (2 $\perp$ lines form 4 rt. ∠s. [2]) 4. △s BDA and BDC are rt. △s (Def. of rt. △ [3]) 5. sin $A = \frac{BD}{c}$ and sin $C = \frac{BD}{a}$ (Def. of sine [3, 4]) 6. $\frac{1}{\sin C} = \frac{a}{BD}$ (Mult. Prop. [5]) 7. $\frac{a}{c} = \frac{\sin A}{\sin C}$ (Mult. Prop. [5, 6])

16.

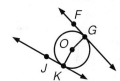

Proof: 1. △ABC with obtuse ∠C and sides of lengths a, b and c (Given) 2. Draw $\overline{AX} \perp \overline{BC}$. (Through a pt. not on a given line, there is exactly 1 line $\perp$ to the given line.) 3. ∠AXC is a rt. ∠. (2 $\perp$ lines form 4 rt. ∠s [2]) 4. △s AXC and AXB are rt. △s. (Def. of rt. △ [3]) 5. $AX^2 + XC^2 = b^2$ and $AX^2 + (XC + a)^2 = c^2$ (Pythagorean Thm. [3, 4]) 6. $AX^2 = b^2 - XC^2$ and $AX^2 = c^2 - (XC^2 + 2a(XC) + a^2)$ (Add. Prop. [5]) 7. $c^2 - XC^2 - 2a(XC) - a^2 = b^2 - XC^2$ (Substitution Prop. [6]) 8. $c^2 = a^2 + b^2 + 2a(XC)$ (Add. Prop. [7]) 9. ∠ACX and ∠C are supp. (Supp. Post.) 10. m∠ACX + m∠C = 180 (Def. of supp. ∠s [9]) 11. m∠ACX = 180 − m∠C (Add. Prop. [10]) 12. cos ∠$ACX = \frac{XC}{b}$ (Def. of cosine [1, 4]) 13. cos (180 − m∠C) = cos (180 − C) = $\frac{XC}{b}$ (Substitution Prop. [11, 12]) 14. b (cos (180 − C)) = XC (Mult. Prop. [13]) 15. $c^2 = a^2 + b^2 + 2ab$ (cos (180 − C)) (Substitution Prop. [8, 14])

17.

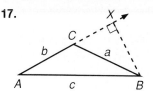

Proof: 1. △ABC with obtuse ∠C and sides of lengths a, b and c (Given) 2. Draw $\overrightarrow{BX} \perp \overrightarrow{AC}$. (Through a pt. not on a given line, there is exactly 1 line $\perp$ to the given line.) 3. ∠AXB is a rt. ∠. (2 $\perp$ lines form 4 rt. ∠s. [2]) 4. △BXC and △BXA are rt. △s. (Def. of rt. △ [3]) 5. sin $A = \frac{XB}{c}$ (Def. of sine [3, 4]) 6. ∠BCX and ∠C are supp. (Supp. Post.) 7. m∠BCX + m∠C = 180 (Def. of supp. ∠s [6]) 8. m∠BCX = 180 − m∠C (Add. Prop. [7]) 9. sin ∠$BCX = \frac{BX}{a}$ (Def. of sine [3, 4]) 10. sin (180 − m∠C) = sin (180 − C) = $\frac{BX}{a}$ (Substitution Prop. [8, 9]) 11. $\frac{1}{\sin (180 - C)} = \frac{a}{BX}$ (Mult. Prop. [10]) 12. $\frac{a}{c} = \frac{\frac{BX}{\sin A}}{\sin (180 - C)}$ (Mult. Prop. [5, 11])

CHAPTER 9   Page 380

45.

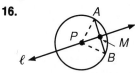

∠OGF and ∠OKJ appear to be rt. ∠s.

Pages 389–391

16.

Given: ⊙P; line ℓ contains P and bisects chord $\overline{AB}$ at M. Prove: $\ell \perp \overline{AB}$ Proof: 1. In ⊙P, ℓ contains P and bisects $\overline{AB}$ at M. (Given) 2. Draw $\overline{PA}$ and $\overline{PB}$. (2 pts. determine a line.) 3. M is the midpt. of $\overline{AB}$. (Def. of bisects [1]) 4. AM = MB (Def. of midpt. [3]) 5. $PA = PB$ (Def. of circle [1]) 6. $PM = PM$

(Reflexive Prop.) 7. △PAM ≅ △PBM (SSS ≅ Post. [4, 5, 6]) 8. m∠PMA = m∠PMB (Corres. parts of ≅ △s are =. [7]) 9. ℓ ⊥ $\overline{AB}$ (If ∠s of a lin. pr. are =, then lines containing their sides are ⊥. [8])

17. No; if the chord is a diameter then every line through the center of the ⊙ will bisect the chord, but not necessarily be ⊥ to the chord.

26. Draw any 2 chords and construct their ⊥ bisectors. The pt. of intersection of these bisectors is the center of the wheel. Measure the distance from the center of the wheel to any pt. on the wheel and double that distance to find the diameter.

27. The locus of the midpts. of all chords of a ⊙ = to a given chord is a circle whose radius is the distance from the center of the given ⊙ to the given chord.

30. ≅ spheres are spheres with = radii.

32. Proof: 1. $\overline{AB}$ is chord of coplanar circles P and Q; $\overleftrightarrow{QP}$ ⊥ $\overline{AB}$ (Given) 2. Draw $\overline{QA}$ and $\overline{PA}$. (2 pts. determine a line.) 3. ∠AXQ and ∠AXP are rt. ∠s. (2 ⊥ lines form 4 rt. ∠s. [1]) 4. m∠AXQ = m∠AXP (All rt. ∠s are =. [3]) 5. QX = XP (Given) 6. AX = AX (Reflexive Prop.) 7. △AXQ ≅ △AXP (SAS ≅ Post. [4, 5, 6]) 8. QA = PA (Corres. parts of ≅ △s are =. [7])

33. Proof: 1. $\overline{AB}$ a chord of coplanar ⊙s P and Q; $\overleftrightarrow{QP}$ ⊥ $\overline{AB}$; QX > PX (Given) 2. ∠AXP and ∠AXQ are rt. ∠s. (2 ⊥ lines form 4 rt. ∠s. [1]) 3. Draw $\overline{QA}$ and $\overline{PA}$. (2 pts. determine a line.) 4. △AXP and △AXQ are rt.△s. (Def. of rt. △s [2]) 5. $(QA)^2 = (QX)^2 + (XA)^2$; $(PA)^2 = (PX)^2 + (XA)^2$ (Pythagorean Thm. [4]) 6. $(QA)^2 - (XA)^2 = (QX)^2$; $(PA)^2 - (XA)^2 = (PX)^2$ (Subtraction Prop. [5]) 7. $(QX)^2 > (PX)^2$ (Mult. Prop. [1]) 8. $(QA)^2 - (XA)^2 > (PA)^2 - (XA)^2$ (Substitution Prop. [6, 7]) 9. $(QA)^2 > (PA)^2$ (Add.

Prop. [8]) 10. QA > PA (Mult. Prop. [9])

34. 125 inches

36.

Given: ⊙P with chords $\overline{AB}$ and $\overline{CD}$; $\overline{PX}$ ⊥ $\overline{AB}$; $\overline{PY}$ ⊥ $\overline{CD}$; AB < CD Prove: PX > PY Proof: 1. ⊙P has chords $\overline{AB}$ and $\overline{CD}$; $\overline{PX}$ ⊥ $\overline{AB}$; $\overline{PY}$ ⊥ $\overline{CD}$; AB < CD (Given) 2. $\overline{PY}$ bisects $\overline{CD}$; $\overline{PX}$ bisects $\overline{AB}$. (If line through center of ⊙ is ⊥ to a chord, it bisects the chord. [1]) 3. Y is midpt. of $\overline{CD}$; X is midpt. of $\overline{AB}$. (Def. of bisects [2]) 4. CY = YD; AX = XB (Def. of midpt. [3]) 5. CD = CY + YD; AB = AX + XB (Seg. Add. Post.) 6. CD = CY + CY = 2(CY); AB = AX + AX = 2(AX) (Substitution Prop.[4, 5]) 7. 2(AX) < 2(CY) (Substitution Prop. [1, 6]) 8. AX < CY (Mult. Prop. [7]) 9. $(AX)^2 < (CY)^2$ (Mult. Prop. [8]) 10. ∠PXA and∠PYC are rt. ∠s. (2 ⊥ lines form 4 rt. ∠s. [1]) 11. Draw $\overline{PA}$ and $\overline{PC}$. (2 pts. determine a line.) 12. PA = PC (Def. of circle [1]) 13. $(PA)^2 = (PC)^2$ (Mult. Prop. [12]) 14. △PXA and △PYC are rt. △s. (Def. of rt. △ [10]) 15. $(PA)^2 = (AX)^2 + (PX)^2$; $(PC)^2 = (CY)^2 + (PY)^2$ (Pythagorean Thm. [14]) 16. $(AX)^2 + (PX)^2 = (CY)^2 + (PY)^2$ (Substitution Prop. [13, 15]) 17. $-(AX)^2 > -(CY)^2$ (Mult. Prop. of Ineq. [9]) 18. $(PX)^2 > (PY)^2$ (Add. Prop. [16, 17]) 19. PX > PY (Mult. Prop. [18])

37.

38. Proof: 1. ⊙O with tangent segs. $\overline{AB}$ and $\overline{AC}$ (Given) 2. AB = CD (Segs. drawn tangent to a ⊙ from an ext. pt. are =. [1]) 3. $\overline{AB}$ ⊥ $\overline{BO}$ and $\overline{AC}$ ⊥ $\overline{CO}$ (A tangent

to a ⊙ is ⊥ to the radius drawn to the pt. of tangency.) 4. ∠ABO and ∠ACO are rt. ∠s. (Def. of ⊥ lines [3]) 5. m∠ABO = m∠ACO (All rt. ∠s are =. [4]) 6. OB = OC (Def. of ⊙ [1]) 7. △ABO ≅ △ACO (SAS ≅ Post. [2, 5, 6]) 8. m∠1 = m∠2 (Corres. parts of ≅ △s are =. [7])

39. M is in the exterior of the ⊙.

40. rhombus; square

42.

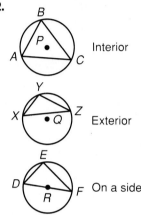

Interior

Exterior

On a side

43. Locate the midpt. of $\overline{LM}$ and label it pt. O. Draw ⊙O with radius OM.

Chapter 9, Lessons 9–4 through 9–7 see *Solution Key*. Chapters 10–13 see *Solution Key*.

▪ *Index*

Italic type indicates that the topic is included in the Teacher's Edition.

Italic type indicates that the topic is included in the Teacher's Edition.

Italic type indicates that the topic is included in the Teacher's Edition.

Italic type indicates that the topic is included in the Teacher's Edition.

Identify extraneous proof
  steps, 77, 112
Order steps in a proof,
  107–112, 119, 133, 202, 212
Supply keying of reasons, 112
Supply missing reasons and
  missing statements, 97–98,
  110–111, 133, *171*, 197–198,
  202, 212, 241, 246
Work backward or forward,
  71–75, 121–125, *129*, 134,
  202, *524, 525*
Write conclusions from given
  statements, 71–75, 79–80,
  118, 134, 165
Write Given and Prove parts of
  proofs, 101–105, *129*, 134,
  143, 223, 575
Write "if . . . then" statements
  from others, 67–68, 82,
  128–129
Write plans for proofs,
  115–120, *129*, 134, 294, 318,
  548
Properties
  of dilations, 546–547
  of isometries, 519–520
  of parallelograms, 239–240
  of proportions, 287–288
  of real numbers, 78
**Property, Transitive, for
  Conditionals,** 76–77
Proportions, 287–288
  fourth proportional, 308
  geometric mean, 332
  summation property of, 288
Proportional lengths
  See Ratio; Proportions.
Protractor, 26
Protractor Postulate, 26
Pyramid, 497–499
  altitude of, 497
  area, lateral, 498
  area, total, 498
  base of, 497
  frustum of, 501
  height of, 497
  lateral faces of, 498
  regular, 497
  slant height of, 497
  vertex, 497
  volume of, 498–499
Pythagorean Theorem, 337–339
  applications of, 351–352

Q

Quadrant, 46
Quadratic equations, 314, 439
Quadrilaterals, 176, 238–241,
  244–246
  See also Kite; Parallelogram;
    Rectangle; Rhombus; Square;
    Trapezoid.
  area of, 430, 434, 441–442
  properties of, 250

R

Radicals, 196
Radius
  of circle, 21, 375
  of regular polygon, 452
  of sphere, 377
Ratio(s), 287
  golden, 315
  in similar polygons, 287–288,
    292–293
  in similar triangles, 297–298,
    302–303, 310–311, 315,
    316–317
  trigonometric, 357–358, 362,
    365–366
Ray(s), 14
  endpoint of, 14
  opposite, 14
  perpendicular, 34
Real-number properties, 78
Reasoning skills, T22,
  See Affirming the hypothesis,
    Conditional statements,
    Deductive reasoning, Indirect
    proof, Inductive reasoning,
    Logic, Strategies for proof,
    Valid arguments.
Rectangle(s), 249–250
  area of, 430–431
  coordinate plane and,
    575–576
Rectangular solid, 474–475
  diagonal of, 474–475
  volume of, 484
Reduction, 544
Reflection(s), 515–517, 554
  applications of, 523
  line of, 515
  rotations and, 531–532
  translation and, 527

Reflection image, 515
Reflexive property, 78
Regular polygon, 176, 185, 421,
  452–453
  apothem of, 452
  area of, 453
  center of, 452
  central angle of, 452
  radius of, 452
Regular polyhedron, 483
Regular prism, 474
Regular pyramid, 497–498
Remote interior angles, 171
Resultant, 586
Reuleaux triangle, 410
Review, Cumulative, 136–137,
  282–285, 426–427, 612–615
Rhombus, 249–250
  area of, 442
Right angle, 32
Right cone, 502–503
Right cylinder, 490–491
Right prism, 474
Right section of prism, 478
Right triangle(s), 166, 330–333
  and altitude, 332–333
  congruence of, 200–201
  hypotenuse of, 166
  isosceles (45-45-90), 347
  legs of, 166
  Pythagorean Theorem,
    337–339, 351–352
  similar, 331–333
  30-60-90, 346
  trigonometric ratios, 357–358,
    362
Rise, 567
Rotation, 531–532
Rotational symmetry, 536
Ruler Postulate, 19
Run, 567

S

SAS Congruence Postulate, 196
SAS Similarity Theorem, 310
Scalar, 593
Scalar multiple, 593–595
Scalar product, 593
Scale, 287
Scale factor, 543
Scalene triangle, 167

Italic type indicates that the topic is included in the Teacher's Edition.

Italic type indicates that the topic is included in the Teacher's Edition.

■ *Acknowledgments* ▬

Unless otherwise acknowledged, all photos are the property of Scott, Foresman and Company. Page positions are as follows: (T) top, (C) center, (B) bottom, (L) left, (R) right.

COVER: © 1989 Images, Louisville, KY
1T: J.Kugler/FPG 1BC: Art Pahlke 2L: Pierre Kopp/West Light 2CL: Camerique/ H. Armstrong Roberts 2CR: Alex Kerstitch/Sea of Cortez Enterprises 2R: David Muench/ H. Armstrong Roberts 4B: Courtesy Douglas Dawson Gallery 5: © 1989 M.C. Escher Heirs/Cordon Art - Baarn - Holland 14: Roger Ressmeyer 32: From GREAT GLASS IN AMERICAN ARCHITECTURE by H. Weber Wilson 41: Cancer Research-Weitman Institute/ Photri, Inc. 52: Erich Lessing/Magnum Photos 71: Dave Walsten 138: Bill Ross/ West Light 149: © 1989 M.C. Escher Heirs/ Cordon Art - Baarn - Holland 153: © 1989 M.C. Escher Heirs/Cordon Art - Baarn - Holland. From the collection of C.V.S. Roosevelt, Washington, D.C. 166: © 1983 Walt Disney Productions 175: Chip Clark 180L: Phil Degginger 180CL: Kristian Hilsen/ Click/Chicago/Tony Stone 180CR: Phil Degginger 180R: Phil Degginger 184: Robert Frerck/Odyssey Productions, Chicago 210L: Dr. E.R. Degginger 210C: Alex Kerstitch/Sea of Cortez Enterprises 210R: Dr. E.R. Degginger 213: John Bryson/The Image Bank 220: James A. Buddenbaum 222: Milt & Joan Mann/ Cameramann International, Ltd. 238: Chuck O'Rear/West Light 242T: Milt & Joan Mann/ Cameramann International, Ltd. 255: Ray R. Hillstrom Jr./Hillstrom Stock Photos 261: Shostal Associates 295B: Robert B. Tolchin 315L: Oxford Scientific Films/ANIMALS ANIMALS 316: Bill Gallery/Stock Boston 321: Robert Frerck/Odyssey Productions, Chicago 337: The British Library 341: Guy Marche/FPG 346: Dr. E.R. Degginger 347: Neil Leiffer 357: Philip Jon Bailey/Stock Boston 366T: H. Armstrong Roberts 367L: Milt & Joan Mann/Cameramann International, Ltd. 367R: Luis Villota/The Stock Market 374: Georg Gerster/COMSTOCK INC. 376: Milt & Joan Mann/Cameramann International, Ltd. 377: Cezus/Click/Chicago/Tony Stone 379C: Photo by J. Barnell/Shostal Associates 399L: Phil Degginger 406TL: From STRING ART: STEP BY STEP by Robert E. Sharpton, Chilton Publishing Co.,

Radnor, PA 406TC: From STRING ART: STEP BY STEP by Robert E. Sharpton, Chilton Publishing Co., Radnor, PA 406TR: From STRING ART: STEP BY STEP by Robert E. Sharpton, Chilton Publishing Co., Radnor, PA 434: Richard A. Blake/Click/ Chicago/Tony Stone 440: Peter J. Menzel/ Stock Boston 453: Craig Aurness/West Light 457: G. Marche/FPG 459T: Luis Villota/ The Stock Market 459B: Photo by J. Barnell/ Shostal Associates 472: Tom Kovacs 484: Reprinted with permission of Frigidaire Company Division of White Consolidated Industries, Inc. 490: Jim Pickerell/Click/ Chicago/Tony Stone 497T: J. Kugler/FPG 503: Camerique/H. Armstrong Roberts 506: Photri, Inc. 507: NASA 508: Robert Frerck/Click/Chicago/Tony Stone 514: © 1989 M.C. Escher Heirs/Cordon Art - Baarn - Holland 525: Courtesy Douglas Dawson Gallery 530: Milt & Joan Mann/Cameramann International, Ltd. 535R: Lab of Arthur M. Siegelman 537TL: Peter Parks/Oxford Scientific Films/ANIMALS ANIMALS 537TCL: Dr. E.R. Degginger/ANIMALS ANIMALS 537TC: Dr. E.R. Degginger/ANIMALS ANIMALS 537TCR: Dr. E.R. Degginger/ANIMALS ANIMALS 537TR: Peter Parks/Oxford Scientific Films/ANIMALS ANIMALS 537CL: Dr. E.R. Degginger 537CR: Phil Degginger 540: © 1989 M.C. Escher Heirs/ Cordon Art - Baarn - Holland 546L: Norman Prince 550: © 1989 M.C.Escher Heirs/ Cordon Art - Baarn - Holland 553: Courtesy Douglas Dawson Gallery 554: © 1989 M.C. Escher Heirs/Cordon Art - Baarn - Holland 560: National Map Collection/Public Archives of Canada

Illustrations and props

65, 68, 83, 87, 400, 403: Julie Abrams 115: Ralph Canaday x, 317, 428: David Cunningham 79, 150, 152, 206, 253, 291, 402, 447, 449, 452, 592: Edward Hughes 75, 361: Jared Lee 268, 269: Jon Rawson 330: George Suyeoka

190: Quilt courtesy of Suzanne Amberg 292: Balalaikas courtesy of Instrument Collection, University of Illinois Russian Folk Orchestra, Urbana-Champaign, Illinois 432: Quilt courtesy of Knit Pickers, Wilmette, Illinois